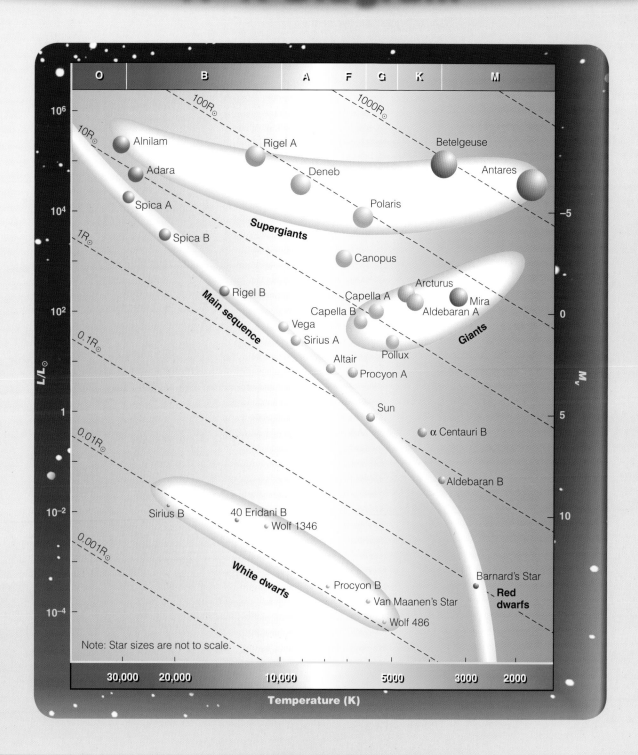

The H–R diagram is the key to understanding stars, their birth, their long lives, and their eventual deaths. Luminosity ($L/L_\odot$) refers to the total amount of energy that a star emits in terms of the sun's luminosity, and the temperature refers to the temperature of its surface. Together, the temperature and luminosity of a star locate it on the H–R diagram and tell astronomers its radius, its family relationships with other stars, and a great deal about its history and fate.

The terrestrial or Earthlike planets lie very close to the sun, and their orbits are hardly visible in a diagram that includes the outer planets.

Mercury, Venus, Earth and its moon, and Mars are small worlds made of rock and metal with little or no atmospheric gases.

The outer worlds of our solar system orbit far from the sun. Jupiter, Saturn, Uranus, and Neptune are Jovian or Jupiter-like planets much bigger than Earth. They contain large amounts of low-density gases.

Pluto is one of a number of small, icy worlds orbiting beyond Neptune. Astronomers have concluded that Pluto is not really a planet and now refer to it as a dwarf planet.

This book is designed to use arrows to alert you to important concepts in diagrams and graphs. Some arrows point things out, but others represent motion, force, or even the flow of light. Look at arrows in the book carefully and use this Flash Reference card to catch all of the arrow clues.

Point at things:

You are here

Force:

Process flow:

Measurement:

Direction:

Radio waves, infrared, photons:

Motion:

Rotation 2-D   *Rotation 3-D*   *Linear*

Light flow:
Updated arrow style

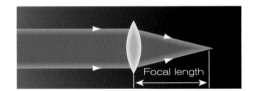

Focal length

The Terrestrial Worlds

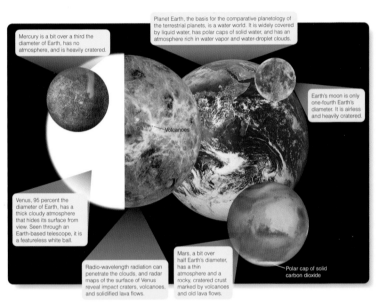

Mercury is a bit over a third the diameter of Earth, has no atmosphere, and is heavily cratered.

Planet Earth, the basis for the comparative planetology of the terrestrial planets, is a water world. It is widely covered by liquid water, has polar caps of solid water, and has an atmosphere rich in water vapor and water-droplet clouds.

Volcanoes

Earth's moon is only one-fourth Earth's diameter. It is airless and heavily cratered.

Venus, 95 percent the diameter of Earth, has a thick cloudy atmosphere that hides its surface from view. Seen through an Earth-based telescope, it is a featureless white ball.

Radio-wavelength radiation can penetrate the clouds, and radar maps of the surface of Venus reveal impact craters, volcanoes, and solidified lava flows.

Mars, a bit over half Earth's diameter, has a thin atmosphere and a rocky, cratered crust marked by volcanoes and old lava flows.

Polar cap of solid carbon dioxide

Planetary Orbits

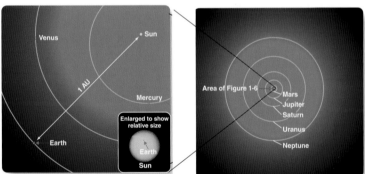

Venus

Sun

1 AU

Mercury

Earth

Enlarged to show relative size

Earth

Sun

Area of Figure 1-6

Mars
Jupiter
Saturn
Uranus
Neptune

The Outer Worlds

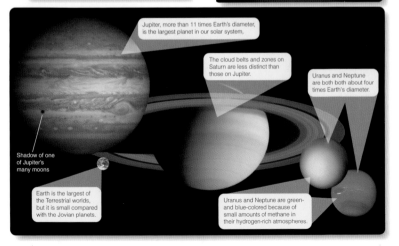

Jupiter, more than 11 times Earth's diameter, is the largest planet in our solar system.

The cloud belts and zones on Saturn are less distinct than those on Jupiter.

Uranus and Neptune are both about four times Earth's diameter.

Shadow of one of Jupiter's many moons

Earth is the largest of the Terrestrial worlds, but it is small compared with the Jovian planets.

Uranus and Neptune are green- and blue-colored because of small amounts of methane in their hydrogen-rich atmospheres.

See page 425 for the terrestrial planets. See page 4 for the two orbital diagrams. See page 494 for the outer worlds.

Foundations
of
Astronomy

About the Authors

Mike Seeds has been a Professor of Physics and Astronomy at Franklin and Marshall College in Lancaster, Pennsylvania, since 1970. In 1989 he received F&M College's Lindback Award for Distinguished Teaching. Mike's love for the history of astronomy led him to create upper-level courses on "Archaeoastronomy" and "Changing Concepts of the Universe." His research interests focus on variable stars and the automation of astronomical telescopes. Mike is coauthor with Dana Backman of *Horizons: Exploring the Universe*, Eleventh Edition (2009), *Astronomy: The Solar System and Beyond*, Sixth Edition (2009), and *Perspectives on Astronomy* (2008), all published by Cengage. He was Senior Consultant for creation of the 20-episode telecourse accompanying the book *Horizons, Exploring the Universe*.

Dana Backman taught in the physics and astronomy department at Franklin and Marshall College in Lancaster, Pennsylvania, from 1991 until 2003. He invented and taught a course titled "Life in the Universe" in F&M's interdisciplinary Foundations program. Dana now teaches introductory astronomy, astrobiology, and cosmology courses in Stanford University's Continuing Studies Program. His research interests focus on infrared observations of planet formation, models of debris disks around nearby stars, and evolution of the solar system's Kuiper belt. Dana is employed by the SETI Institute of Mountain View, California as Director of Outreach for the SOFIA (Stratospheric Observatory for Infrared Astronomy) mission at NASA Ames Research Center. He is coauthor with Mike Seeds of *Horizons: Exploring the Universe*, Eleventh Edition (2009), *Astronomy: The Solar System and Beyond*, Sixth Edition (2009), and *Perspectives on Astronomy* (2008), all published by Cengage.

11

ELEVENTH EDITION

Foundations of Astronomy

Michael A. Seeds

Joseph R. Grundy Observatory
Franklin and Marshall College

Dana E. Backman

SOFIA (Stratospheric Observatory
for Infrared Astronomy)
SETI Institute & NASA Ames
Research Center

 BROOKS/COLE
CENGAGE Learning

Australia • Brazil • Canada •Mexico • Singapore • Spain
United Kingdom •United States

Foundations of Astronomy, Eleventh Edition
Michael A. Seeds, Dana E. Backman

Editor in Chief: Michelle Julet

Acquisitions Editor: Kilean Kennedy

Development Editor: Teri Hyde

Editorial Assistant: Laura Bowen

Senior Media Editor: Rebecca Berardy Schwartz

Marketing Manager: Nicole Mollica

Marketing Coordinator: Kevin Carroll

Marketing Communications Manager: Belinda Krohmer

Associate Content Project Manager: Jill Clark

Senior Art Director: Cate Rickard Barr

Senior Manufacturing Buyer: Diane Gibbons

Senior Rights Account Manager: Bob Kauser

Production Service: Integra Onshore

Text Designer: Liz Harasymczuk Design

Photo Manager: Amanda Groszko

Cover Designer: Irene Morris

Cover Image: NASA

Compositor: Integra Offshore

For product information and technology assistance, contact us at
Cengage Learning Customer & Sales Support, 1-800-354-9706.

For permission to use material from this text or product,
Submit all requests online at **www.cengage.com/permissions.**
Further permissions questions can be emailed to
permissionrequest@cengage.com.

Library of Congress Control Number: 2009935325

ISBN-13: 978-1-4390-5035-4
ISBN-10: 1-4390-5035-X

Brooks/Cole
20 Channel Center Street
Boston, MA 02210
USA

Cengage Learning is a leading provider of customized learning solutions with office locations around the globe, including Singapore, the United Kingdom, Australia, Mexico, Brazil, and Japan. Locate your local office at **international.cengage.com/region**

Cengage Learning products are represented in Canada by Nelson Education, Ltd.

For your course and learning solutions, visit **www.cengage.com.**

Purchase any of our products at your local college store or at our preferred online store **www.ichapters.com.**

Printed in Canada
1 2 3 4 5 6 7 13 12 11 10 09

Dedication

For Emery & Helen Seeds and Edward & Antonette Backman

Part 1   Exploring the Sky

CHAPTER 1   HERE AND NOW   1
CHAPTER 2   THE SKY   11
CHAPTER 3   CYCLES OF THE MOON   31
CHAPTER 4   THE ORIGIN OF MODERN ASTRONOMY   49
CHAPTER 5   GRAVITY   75
CHAPTER 6   LIGHT AND TELESCOPES   98

Part 2   The Stars

CHAPTER 7   ATOMS AND STARLIGHT   122
CHAPTER 8   THE SUN   142
CHAPTER 9   THE FAMILY OF STARS   167
CHAPTER 10   THE INTERSTELLAR MEDIUM   192
CHAPTER 11   THE FORMATION AND STRUCTURE OF STARS   210
CHAPTER 12   STELLAR EVOLUTION   232
CHAPTER 13   THE DEATHS OF STARS   255
CHAPTER 14   NEUTRON STARS AND BLACK HOLES   279

Part 3   The Universe

CHAPTER 15   THE MILKY WAY GALAXY   302
CHAPTER 16   GALAXIES   330
CHAPTER 17   ACTIVE GALAXIES AND SUPERMASSIVE BLACK HOLES   355
CHAPTER 18   MODERN COSMOLOGY   369

Part 4   The Solar System

CHAPTER 19   THE ORIGIN OF THE SOLAR SYSTEM   396
CHAPTER 20   EARTH: THE STANDARD OF COMPARATIVE PLANETOLOGY   424
CHAPTER 21   THE MOON AND MERCURY: COMPARING AIRLESS WORLDS   442
CHAPTER 22   COMPARATIVE PLANETOLOGY OF VENUS AND MARS   464
CHAPTER 23   COMPARATIVE PLANETOLOGY OF JUPITER AND SATURN   493
CHAPTER 24   URANUS, NEPTUNE, AND THE DWARF PLANETS   525
CHAPTER 25   METEORITES, ASTEROIDS, AND COMETS   551

Part 5   Life

CHAPTER 26   ASTROBIOLOGY: LIFE ON OTHER WORLDS   581

Contents

Part 1: Exploring the Sky

Chapter 1 | Here and Now 1

1-1   WHERE ARE YOU? 2

1-2   WHEN IS NOW? 7

1-3   WHY STUDY ASTRONOMY? 7

Chapter 2 | The Sky 11

2-1   THE STARS 12

2-2   THE SKY AND ITS MOTION 16

2-3   THE CYCLES OF THE SUN 20

2-4   ASTRONOMICAL INFLUENCES ON EARTH'S CLIMATE 25

Chapter 3 | Cycles of the Moon 31

3-1   THE CHANGEABLE MOON 32

3-2   LUNAR ECLIPSES 33

3-3   SOLAR ECLIPSES 37

3-4   PREDICTING ECLIPSES 43

Chapter 4 | The Origin of Modern Astronomy 49

4-1   THE ROOTS OF ASTRONOMY 50

4-2   THE COPERNICAN REVOLUTION 58

4-3   PLANETARY MOTION 61

4-4   GALILEO GALILEI 67

4-5   MODERN ASTRONOMY 71

Chapter 5 | Gravity 75

5-1   GALILEO AND NEWTON 76

5-2   ORBITAL MOTION AND TIDES 82

5-3   EINSTEIN AND RELATIVITY 90

Chapter 6 | Light and Telescopes 98

6-1   RADIATION: INFORMATION FROM SPACE 99

6-2   OPTICAL TELESCOPES 101

6-3   SPECIAL INSTRUMENTS 112

6-4   RADIO TELESCOPES 114

6-5   ASTRONOMY FROM SPACE 117

How Do We Know?

1-1   The So-Called Scientific Method 8

2-1   Scientific Models 17

2-2   Pseudoscience 25

2-3   Evidence as the Foundation of Science 27

2-4   Scientific Arguments 28

3-1   Scientific Imagination 38

4-1   Scientific Revolutions 61

4-2   Hypothesis, Theory, and Law 66

5-1   Cause and Effect 80

5-2   Testing a Hypothesis by Prediction 89

6-1   Resolution and Precision 105

Concept Art Portfolios

The Sky Around You 18–19

The Cycle of the Seasons 22–23

The Phases of the Moon 34–35

The Ancient Universe 56–57

Orbiting Earth 84–85

Modern Astronomical Telescopes 110–111

Focus on Fundamentals 1 | Mass 79

Focus on Fundamentals 2 | Energy 86

Part 2: The Stars

Chapter 7 | Atoms and Starlight 122

7-1   ATOMS 123

7-2   THE INTERACTION OF LIGHT AND MATTER 126

7-3   STELLAR SPECTRA 130

Chapter 8 | The Sun 142

8-1   THE SOLAR ATMOSPHERE 143

8-2   NUCLEAR FUSION IN THE SUN 150

8-3   SOLAR ACTIVITY 154

Chapter 9 | The Family of Stars 167

9-1   MEASURING THE DISTANCES TO STARS 168

9-2   APPARENT BRIGHTNESS, INTRINSIC BRIGHTNESS, AND
      LUMINOSITY 170

9-3   THE DIAMETERS OF STARS 173

9-4   THE MASSES OF STARS 178

9-5   A CENSUS OF THE STARS 185

Chapter 10 | The Interstellar Medium 192

10-1   STUDYING THE INTERSTELLAR MEDIUM 193

10-2   COMPONENTS OF THE INTERSTELLAR MEDIUM 202

10-3   THE GAS-STAR-GAS CYCLE 205

**Chapter 11 | The Formation and Structure
             of Stars 210**

11-1   MAKING STARS FROM THE INTERSTELLAR MEDIUM 211

11-2   THE ORION NEBULA: EVIDENCE OF STAR FORMATION 215

11-3   YOUNG STELLAR OBJECTS AND PROTOSTELLAR DISKS 220

11-4   STELLAR STRUCTURE 224

11-5   THE SOURCE OF STELLAR ENERGY 226

11-6   THE PRESSURE-TEMPERATURE THERMOSTAT 228

Chapter 12 | Stellar Evolution 232

12-1   MAIN-SEQUENCE STARS 233

12-2   POST-MAIN-SEQUENCE EVOLUTION 240

12-3   STAR CLUSTERS: EVIDENCE OF EVOLUTION 246

12-4   VARIABLE STARS: EVIDENCE OF EVOLUTION 247

Chapter 13 | The Deaths of Stars 255

13-1   LOWER-MAIN-SEQUENCE STARS 256

13-2   THE EVOLUTION OF BINARY STARS 262

13-3   THE DEATHS OF MASSIVE STARS 266

Chapter 14 | Neutron Stars and Black Holes 279

14-1   NEUTRON STARS 280

14-2   BLACK HOLES 290

14-3   COMPACT OBJECTS WITH DISKS AND JETS 296

How Do We Know?

7-1   **Quantum Mechanics 125**

8-1   **Scientific Confidence 153**

8-2   **Confirmation and Consolidation 160**

9-1   **Chains of Inference 180**

9-2   **Basic Scientific Data 185**

10-1   **Separating Facts from Hypothesis 202**

11-1   **Theories and Proof 215**

12-1   **Mathematical Models 235**

13-1   **Toward Ultimate Causes 259**

14-1   **Checks on Fraud in Science 295**

Concept Art Portfolios

Atomic Spectra 132–133

Sunspots and the Sunspot Cycle 156–157

Magnetic Solar Phenomena 162–163

The Family of Stars 186–187

Three Kinds of Nebulae 194–195

Star Formation in the Orion Nebula 216–217

*Observations of Young Stellar Objects and Protostellar Disks
222–223*

Star Cluster H–R Diagrams 248–249

The Formation of Planetary Nebulae 260–261

The Lighthouse Model of a Pulsar 284–285

Focus on Fundamentals 3 | Temperature, Heat, and
                            Thermal Energy 128

Focus on Fundamentals 4 | Density 137

Focus on Fundamentals 5 | Pressure 203

Celestial Profile 1 | The Sun 144

Part 3: The Universe

Chapter 15 | The Milky Way Galaxy 302
  15-1 THE DISCOVERY OF THE GALAXY   303
  15-2 STRUCTURE OF THE GALAXY   308
  15-3 SPIRAL ARMS AND STAR FORMATION   312
  15-4 THE NUCLEUS   318
  15-5 ORIGIN AND HISTORY OF THE GALAXY   319

Chapter 16 | Galaxies 330
  16-1 THE FAMILY OF GALAXIES   331
  16-2 MEASURING THE PROPERTIES OF GALAXIES   336
  16-3 THE EVOLUTION OF GALAXIES   344

Chapter 17 | Active Galaxies and Supermassive
             Black Holes 355
  17-1 ACTIVE GALACTIC NUCLEI   356
  17-2 SUPERMASSIVE BLACK HOLES   362

Chapter 18 | Modern Cosmology 369
  18-1 INTRODUCTION TO THE UNIVERSE   370
  18-2 THE BIG BANG THEORY   373
  18-3 SPACE AND TIME, MATTER AND ENERGY   380
  18-4 21ST-CENTURY COSMOLOGY   384

How Do We Know?

15-1 Calibration 306
15-2 Nature as Processes 323
16-1 Classification in Science 336
17-1 Statistical Evidence 357
18-1 Reasoning by Analogy 372
18-2 Science: A System of Knowledge 380

Concept Art Portfolios

Sagittarius A*   320–321

Galaxy Classification   334–335

Interacting Galaxies   348–349

Cosmic Jets and Radio Lobes   360–361

Part 4: The Solar System

Chapter 19 | The Origin of the Solar System 396

19-1 THE GREAT CHAIN OF ORIGINS 397

19-2 A SURVEY OF THE SOLAR SYSTEM 401

19-3 THE STORY OF PLANET BUILDING 407

19-4 PLANETS ORBITING OTHER STARS 414

Chapter 20 | Earth: The Standard of Comparative Planetology 424

20-1 A TRAVEL GUIDE TO THE TERRESTRIAL PLANETS 425

20-2 EARTH AS A PLANET 427

20-3 THE SOLID EARTH 429

20-4 EARTH'S ATMOSPHERE 433

Chapter 21 | The Moon and Mercury: Comparing Airless Worlds 442

21-1 THE MOON 443

21-2 MERCURY 455

Chapter 22 | Comparative Planetology of Venus and Mars 464

22-1 VENUS 465

22-2 MARS 476

22-3 THE MOONS OF MARS 489

Chapter 23 | Comparative Planetology of Jupiter and Saturn 493

23-1 A TRAVEL GUIDE TO THE OUTER PLANETS 494

23-2 JUPITER 495

23-3 JUPITER'S FAMILY OF MOONS 503

23-4 SATURN 510

23-5 SATURN'S MOONS 517

Chapter 24 | Uranus, Neptune, and the Dwarf Planets 525

24-1 URANUS 526

24-2 NEPTUNE 539

24-3 THE DWARF PLANETS 544

Chapter 25 | Meteorites, Asteroids, and Comets 551

25-1 METEOROIDS, METEORS, AND METEORITES 552

25-2 ASTEROIDS 559

25-3 COMETS 565

25-4 ASTEROID AND COMET IMPACTS 574

How Do We Know?

19-1 Two Kinds of Theories: Catastrophic and Evolutionary 400

19-2 Scientists: Courteous Skeptics 419

20-1 Understanding Planets: Follow the Energy 426

20-2 Studying an Unseen World 430

21-1 How Hypotheses and Theories Unify the Details 448

22-1 Data Manipulation 469

23-1 Who Pays for Science? 516

24-1 Scientific Discoveries 528

25-1 Selection Effects 555

Concept Art Portfolios

Terrestrial and Jovian Planets 402–403

The Active Earth 434–435

Impact Cratering 446–447

Volcanoes 472–473

Jupiter's Atmosphere 500–501

The Ice Rings of Saturn 514–515

The Rings of Uranus and Neptune 534–535

Observations of Asteroids 560–561

Observations of Comets 568–569

Celestial Profile 2 | Earth 428

Celestial Profile 3 | The Moon 443

Celestial Profile 4 | Mercury 455

Celestial Profile 5 | Venus 465

Celestial Profile 6 | Mars 477

Celestial Profile 7 | Jupiter 496

Celestial Profile 8 | Saturn 511

Celestial Profile 9 | Uranus 529

Celestial Profile 10 | Neptune 540

Part 5: Life

Chapter 26 | Astrobiology: Life on Other
             Worlds   581

  26-1   THE NATURE OF LIFE   582

  26-2   LIFE IN THE UNIVERSE   586

  26-3   INTELLIGENT LIFE IN THE UNIVERSE   595

How Do We Know?

26-1   **The Nature of Scientific Explanation**   583

26-2   **UFOs and Space Aliens**   596

Concept Art Portfolio

DNA: The Code of Life   584–585

AFTERWORD   602

APPENDIX A UNITS AND ASTRONOMICAL DATA   604

APPENDIX B OBSERVING THE SKY   612

GLOSSARY   625

ANSWERS TO EVEN-NUMBERED PROBLEMS   635

INDEX   637

A Note to the Student

From Mike and Dana

We are excited that you are taking an astronomy course and using our book. You are going to see some amazing things, from the icy rings of Saturn to monster black holes. We are proud to be your guides as you explore.

We have developed this book to help you expand your knowledge of astronomy from recognizing the moon and a few stars in the evening sky to a deeper understanding of the extent, power, and diversity of the universe. You will meet worlds where it rains methane, stars so dense their atoms are crushed, colliding galaxies that are ripping each other apart, and a universe that is expanding faster and faster.

Two Goals

This book is designed to help you answer two important questions:

- What are we?
- How do we know?

By the question *What are we?* we mean: How do we fit into the universe and its history? The atoms you are made of had their first birthday in the big bang when the universe began, but those atoms were cooked and remade inside stars, and now they are inside you. Where will they be in a billion years? Astronomy is the only course on campus that can tell you that story, and it is a story that everyone should know.

By the question *How do we know?* we mean: How does science work? What is the evidence, and how do you know it is true? For instance, how can anyone know there was a big bang? In today's world, you need to think carefully about the things so-called experts say. You should demand explanations. Scientists have a special way of knowing based on evidence that makes scientific knowledge much more powerful than just opinion, policy, marketing, or public relations. It is the human race's best understanding of nature. To understand the world around you, you need to understand how science works. Throughout this book, you will find boxed features called *How Do We Know?* They will help you understand how scientists use the methods of science to know what the universe is like.

Expect to Be Astonished

One reason astronomy is exciting is that astronomers discover new things every day. Astronomers expect to be astonished. You can share in the excitement because we have worked hard to include the newest images, the newest discoveries, and the newest insights that will take you, in an introductory course, to the frontier of human knowledge. Huge telescopes in space and on remote mountaintops provide a daily dose of excitement that goes far beyond sensationalism. These new discoveries in astronomy are exciting because they are about us. They tell us more and more about what we are.

As you read this book, notice that it is not organized as lists of facts for you to memorize. That could make even astronomy boring. Rather this book is organized to show you how scientists use evidence and theory to create logical arguments that show how nature works. Look at the list of special features that follows this note. Those features were carefully designed to help you understand astronomy as evidence and theory. Once you see science as evidence and logical arguments, you hold the key to the universe.

Do Not Be Humble

As teachers, our quest is simple. We want you to understand your place in the universe—not just your location in space but your location in the unfolding history of the physical universe. Not only do we want you to know where you are and what you are in the universe; we also want you to understand how scientists know. By the end of this book, we want you to know that the universe is very big but that it is described by a small set of rules and that we humans have found a way to figure out the rules—a method called science.

To appreciate your role in this beautiful universe, you must learn more than just the facts of astronomy. You must understand what we are and how we know. Every page of this book reflects that ideal.

Mike Seeds
mike.seeds@fandm.edu

Dana Backman
dbackman@sofia.usra.edu

Key Content and Pedagogical Changes to the Eleventh Edition

- Every chapter has been reviewed and updated with the latest discoveries and images, such as photos of colliding galaxies and planets orbiting distant stars. You will read about methane lakes on Saturn's moon Titan and the newest understanding of bursts of gamma rays detected coming from the most distant galaxies.

- Some chapters have been reorganized and rewritten to better present their topics. Chapter 10, "The Interstellar Medium," and Chapter 11, "The Formation and Structure of Stars," are completely reorganized to better explain the gas and dust between the stars and how stars form from that material. Chapter 17, "Active Galaxies and Supermassive Black Holes," is newly redesigned to include the latest understanding of these peculiar objects.

- Chapter 4, "The Origin of Modern Astronomy," has been reorganized to better tell the story of the development of scientific thought at the end of the Renaissance. Chapter 15, "The Milky Way Galaxy," has been reorganized to better convey the roles each part of the galaxy have played in its history and evolution. Chapter 26, "Astrobiology" Life on Other Worlds," has a new subsection on "extremophiles," life that thrives on Earth in extreme environments.

- Guideposts for all of the chapters have been rewritten and shortened to open each chapter with a short list of questions that will help you focus your reading on the main objectives of the chapter.

- Throughout the book, the newest images have been included to keep you up to date with the rapid advances in modern astronomy.

Special Features

- **What Are We?** essays are placed at the end of each chapter to help you understand your own role in the astronomy you have just learned.

- **How Do We Know?** commentaries appear in every chapter and will help you see how science works. They will point out where scientists use statistical evidence, why they think with analogies, and how they build confidence in theories.

- **Special two-page art spreads** provide an opportunity for you to create your own understanding and share in the satisfaction that scientists feel as they uncover the secrets of nature.

- **Guided discovery figures** illustrate important ideas visually and guide you to understand relationships and contrasts interactively.

- **Focus on Fundamentals** will help you understand five concepts from physics that are critical to understanding modern astronomy.

- **Guideposts** on the opening page of each chapter help you see the organization of the book by focusing on a small number of questions to be answered as you read the chapter.

- **Scientific Arguments** at the end of many text sections are carefully designed questions to help you review and synthesize concepts from the section. A short answer follows to show how scientists construct scientific arguments from observations, evidence, theories, and natural laws that lead to a conclusion. A further question then gives you a chance to construct your own scientific argument on a related issue.

- **End-of-Chapter Review Questions** are designed to help you review and test your understanding of the material.

- **End-of-Chapter Discussion Questions** go beyond the text and invite you to think critically and creatively about scientific questions. You can think about these questions yourself or discuss them in class.

- **Virtual Astronomy Laboratories.** These online labs give you an exciting, interactive way to learn, putting some of astronomy's most useful instruments into your hands— precise telescope controls to measure angular size, a photometer to measure light intensity, and a spectrograph to measure Doppler-shifted spectral lines.

- **TheSky Student Edition CD-ROM** turns a personal computer into a powerful personal planetarium. Loaded with data on 118,000 stars and 13,000 deep-sky objects with images, it allows you to view the universe at any point in time from 4000 years ago to 8000 years in the future, to see the sky in motion, to view constellations, to print star charts, and much more.

New for Instructors

- WebTutor™ to jump-start your course with customizable and rich, text-specific content, which includes:
- Integration with your Blackboard®, ANGEL, or WebCT learning management systems
- Interactive and gradable study materials, which include Reading Questions, Active Figures, Guidepost Questions, Problems from the textbook, and Ranking Task Exercises
- Instructor supplements, which include PowerPoint® lectures, digital images from the text, and Test Bank content
- Interactive eBook
- Videos and Animations

Acknowledgments

Over the years we have had the guidance of a great many people who care about astronomy and teaching. We would like to thank all of the students and teachers who have contributed their insights and suggestions. Their comments have been very helpful in shaping this book.

We would especially like to thank the reviewers whose careful analysis and thoughtful suggestions have been invaluable in completing this new edition.

Many observatories, research institutes, laboratories, and individual astronomers have supplied figures and diagrams for this edition. They are listed next to each figure, and we would like to thank them specifically for their generosity.

Special thanks go to Kathryn Coolidge, who has reviewed chapters word by word and been a tremendous help with issues of organization, presentation, and writing. Jamie Backman also has been a careful reader, contributing many insights to the way the contents of the book should be organized and presented.

We are happy to acknowledge the use of images and data from a number of important programs. In preparing materials for this book we used NASA's Sky View facility located at NASA Goddard Space Flight Center. We have used atlas images and mosaics obtained as part of the Two Micron All Sky Survey (2MASS), a joint project of the University of Massachusetts and the Infrared Processing and Analysis Center/California Institute of Technology, funded by the National Aeronautics and Space Administration and the National Science Foundation. A number of solar images are used by the courtesy of the SOHO consortium, a project of international cooperation between ESA and NASA.

It is always a pleasure to work with the Cengage Learning team. Special thanks go to all of the people who have contributed to this project including Jill Clark, Cate Barr, Nicole Mollica, Belinda Krohmer, and Rebecca Berardy Schwartz.

We have enjoyed working on production with Margaret Pinette of Heckman & Pinette, and we appreciate her understanding and goodwill. We would especially like to thank editors Kilean Kennedy and Teri Hyde for their help and guidance throughout this project.

Most of all, we would like to thank our families for putting up with "the books." They know all too well that textbooks are made of time.

Mike Seeds
Dana Backman

Reviewers

Romeel Dave, University of Arizona
C. Renee James, Sam Houston State University
Dan Lester, University of Texas
Mark Showalter, SETI Institute
Gerald Cecil, University of North Carolina
William Keel, University of Alabama
Alexander G. Tielens, Leiden Observatory

1 | Here and Now

Visual wavelength image

Guidepost

As you study astronomy, you will learn about yourself. You are a planet walker, and this chapter will give you a preview of what that means. The planet you live on whirls around a star that drifts through a universe filled with other stars and galaxies. You owe it to yourself to know where you are in the universe because that is the first step to knowing what you are.

In this chapter, you will meet three essential questions about astronomy:

Where are you in the universe?

How does human history fit into the time scale of the universe?

Why should you study astronomy?

As you study astronomy, you will see how science gives you a way to know how nature works. In this chapter, you can begin thinking about science in a general way. Later chapters will give you more specific insights into how scientists work and think and know about nature.

This chapter is a jumping-off place for your exploration of deep space and deep time. The next chapter continues your journey by looking at the night sky as seen from Earth.

These clouds of gas are so far away that their light takes 7200 years to reach Earth. They are a small part of a larger cloud that has formed a cluster of stars. More stars are probably forming in the darkest, densest parts of the cloud. (NASA, ESA, and The Hubble Heritage Team, STScI/AURA)

> *The longest journey begins*
> *with a single step.*
>
> — LAO TSE

1-1 Where Are You?

To FIND YOUR PLACE among the stars, you can take a cosmic zoom, a ride out through the universe to preview the kinds of objects you are about to study.

You can begin with something familiar. ■ Figure 1-1 shows a region about 50 feet across occupied by a human being, a sidewalk, and a few trees—all objects whose size you can understand. Each successive picture in this cosmic zoom will show you a region of the universe that is 100 times wider than the preceding picture. That is, each step will widen your **field of view**, the region you can see in the image, by a factor of 100.

Widening your field of view by a factor of 100 allows you to see an area 1 mile in diameter (■ Figure 1-2). People, trees, and sidewalks have become too small to see, but now you see a college campus and surrounding streets and houses. The dimensions of houses and streets are familiar. This is still the world you know.

Before leaving this familiar territory, you should make a change in the units you use to measure sizes. All scientists, including astronomers, use the metric system of units because it is well understood worldwide and, more important, because it simplifies

■ **Figure 1-2**

This box ■ represents the relative size of the previous frame. (USGS)

■ **Figure 1-1**

Michael A. Seeds

calculations. If you are not already familiar with the metric system, or if you need a review, study Appendix A before reading on.

The photo in Figure 1-2 is 1 mile across, which equals about 1.6 kilometers. You can see that a kilometer (abbreviated km) is a bit under two-thirds of a mile—a short walk across a neighborhood. But when you expand your field of view by a factor of 100, the neighborhood you saw in the previous photo vanishes (■ Figure 1-3). Now your field of view is 160 km wide, and you see cities and towns as patches of gray. Wilmington, Delaware, is visible at the lower right. At this scale, you can see some of the natural features of Earth's surface. The Allegheny Mountains of southern Pennsylvania cross the image in the upper left, and the Susquehanna River flows southeast into Chesapeake Bay. What look like white bumps are a few puffs of clouds.

Figure 1-3 is an infrared photograph in which healthy green leaves and crops show up as red. Human eyes are sensitive to only a narrow range of colors. As you explore the universe, you will learn to use a wide range of other "colors," from X-rays to radio waves, to reveal sights invisible to unaided human eyes. You will learn much more about infrared, X-rays, and radio energy in later chapters.

At the next step in your journey, you can see your entire planet, which is nearly 13,000 km in diameter (■ Figure 1-4). At any particular moment, half of Earth's surface is exposed to sunlight, and half is in darkness. As Earth rotates on its axis, it carries you through sunlight and then through darkness, producing the cycle of day and night. The blurriness you see at the extreme right of the photo is the boundary between day and night—the sunset line. This is a good example of how a photo can give you

■ Figure 1-3

NASA

visual clues to understanding a concept. Special questions called "Learning to Look" at the end of each chapter give you a chance to use your own imagination to connect images with theories about astronomical objects.

Enlarge your field of view by a factor of 100, and you see a region 1,600,000 km wide (■ Figure 1-5). Earth is the small blue dot in the center, and the moon, whose diameter is only one-fourth that of Earth, is an even smaller dot along its orbit 380,000 km away.

These numbers are so large that it is inconvenient to write them out. Astronomy is sometimes known as the science of big numbers, and soon you will be using numbers much larger than these to discuss the universe. Rather than writing out these numbers as in the previous paragraph, it is more convenient to write them in **scientific notation**. This is nothing more than a simple way to write very big or very small numbers without using lots of zeros. In scientific notation, 380,000 becomes 3.8×10^5. If you are not familiar with scientific notation, read the section on powers of 10 notation in Appendix A. The universe is too big to discuss without using scientific notation.

When you once again enlarge your field of view by a factor of 100, Earth, the moon, and the moon's orbit all lie in the small red box at lower left of ■ Figure 1-6. Now you can see the sun and two other planets that are part of our solar system. Our **solar system** consists of the sun, its family of planets, and some smaller bodies, such as moons and comets.

Earth, Venus, and Mercury are **planets**, small, spherical, nonluminous bodies that orbit a star and shine by reflected light. Venus is about the size of Earth, and Mercury is just over a third of Earth's diameter. On the diagram, they are both too small to be seen as anything but tiny dots. The sun is a **star**, a self-luminous

■ Figure 1-4

NASA

■ Figure 1-5

NASA

■ **Figure 1-6**

NOAO

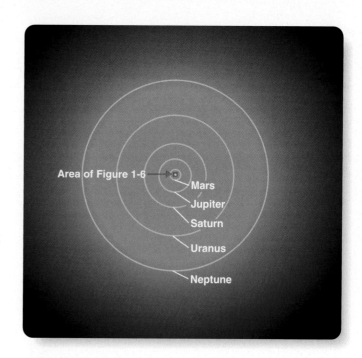

■ **Figure 1-7**

ball of hot gas that generates its own energy. Even though the sun is 109 times larger in diameter than Earth (inset), it too is nothing more than a dot in this diagram.

This diagram represents an area with a diameter of 1.6×10^8 km. One way astronomers simplify calculations using large numbers is to define larger units of measurement. For example, the average distance from Earth to the sun is a unit of distance called the **astronomical unit (AU)**, which is equal to 1.5×10^8 km. Using that, you can express the average distance from Venus to the sun as about 0.72 AU and the average distance from Mercury to the sun as about 0.39 AU.

These distances are averages because the orbits of the planets are not perfect circles. This is particularly apparent in the case of Mercury. Its orbit carries it as close to the sun as 0.307 AU and as far away as 0.467 AU. You can see the variation in the distance from Mercury to the sun in Figure 1-6. Earth's orbit is more circular, and its distance from the sun varies by only a few percent.

Enlarge your field of view again, and you can see the entire solar system (■ Figure 1-7). The sun, Mercury, Venus, and Earth lie so close together that you cannot see them separately at this scale, and they are lost in the red square at the center of this diagram. You can see only the brighter, more widely separated objects such as Mars, the next planet outward. Mars is only 1.5 AU from the sun, but Jupiter, Saturn, Uranus, and Neptune are farther from the sun and so are easier to place in this diagram. They are cold worlds far from the sun's warmth. Light from the sun

reaches Earth in only 8 minutes, but it takes over 4 hours to reach Neptune.

You can remember the order of the plants from the sun outward by remembering a simple sentence: *My Very Educated Mother Just Served Us Noodles*. The first letter of each word reminds you of a planet: Mercury, Venus, Earth, Mars, Jupiter, Saturn, Uranus, Neptune.

When you again enlarge your field of view by a factor of 100, the solar system vanishes (■ Figure 1-8). The sun is only a point of light, and all the planets and their orbits are now crowded into the small red square at the center. The planets are too small and too faint to be visible so near the brilliance of the sun.

Nor are any stars visible except for the sun. The sun is a fairly typical star, and it seems to be located in a fairly average neighborhood in the universe. Although there are many billions of stars like the sun, none are close enough to be visible in this diagram, which shows a region only 11,000 AU in diameter. Stars in the sun's neighborhood are typically separated by distances about 30 times larger than that.

In ■ Figure 1-9, your field of view has expanded to a diameter of a bit over 1 million AU. The sun is at the center, and at this scale you can see a few of the nearest stars. These stars are so distant that it is not convenient to give their distances in astronomical units. To express distances so large, astronomers define a new unit of distance, the light-year. One **light-year (ly)** is the distance that light travels in one year, roughly 10^{13} km or 63,000 AU. It is a **Common Misconception** that a light-

■ Figure 1-8

year is a unit of time, and you can sometimes hear the term misused in science fiction movies and TV shows. The next time you hear someone say, "It will take me light-years to finish my history paper," you could tell the person that a light-year is a distance, not a time. The diameter of your field of view in Figure 1-9 is 17 ly.

Another **Common Misconception** is that stars look like disks when seen through a telescope. Although stars are roughly the same size as the sun, they are so far away that astronomers cannot see them as anything but points of light. Even the closest star to the sun—Alpha Centauri, only 4.2 ly from Earth—looks like a point of light through even the biggest telescopes on Earth. Furthermore, planets that circle other stars are much too small, too faint, and too close to the glare of their star to be easily visible. Astronomers have used indirect methods to detect over 300 planets orbiting other stars, but very few have been photographed directly.

Figure 1-9 follows the astronomical custom of making the sizes of the dots represent not the sizes of the stars but their brightness. This is how star images are recorded on photographs. Bright stars make larger spots on a photograph than faint stars, so the size of a star image in a photograph tells you not how big the star is but only how bright it looks.

In ■ Figure 1-10, you expand your field of view by another factor of 100, and the sun and its neighboring stars vanish into the background of thousands of other stars. The field of view is now 1700 ly in diameter. Of course, no one has ever journeyed thousands of light-years from Earth to look back and photograph the solar neighborhood, so this is a representative photograph of the sky. The sun is a relatively faint star that would not be easily located in a photo at this scale.

If you again expand your field of view by a factor of 100, you see our galaxy, a disk of stars about 80,000 ly in diameter (■ Figure 1-11). A **galaxy** is a great cloud of stars, gas, and dust

■ Figure 1-9

■ Figure 1-10

NOAO

■ Figure 1-11

© Mark Garlick/space-art.com

Milky Way Galaxy →

■ Figure 1-12

held together by the combined gravity of all of its matter. Galaxies range from 1500 to over 300,000 ly in diameter, and some contain over 100 billion stars. In the night sky, you can see our galaxy as a great, cloudy wheel of stars ringing the sky. This band of stars is known as the **Milky Way**, and our galaxy is called the **Milky Way Galaxy**.

How does anyone know what our galaxy looks like if no one can leave it and look back? Astronomers use evidence to guide their explanations as they imagine what the Milky Way looks like. Artists can then use those scientific descriptions to create a painting. Many images in this book are artists' renderings of objects and events that are too big or too dim to see clearly, emit energy your eyes cannot detect, or happen too slowly or too rapidly for humans to sense. These images are not just guesses; they are scientifically based illustrations guided by the best information astronomers can gather. As you explore, notice how astronomers use the methods of science to imagine, understand, and depict cosmic events.

The artist's conception of the Milky Way reproduced in Figure 1-11 shows that our galaxy, like many others, has graceful **spiral arms** winding outward through its disk. In a later chapter, you will learn that the spiral arms are places where stars are formed from clouds of gas and dust. Our own sun was born in one of these spiral arms; and, if you could see the sun in this picture, it would be in the disk of the galaxy about two-thirds of the way out from the center.

Ours is a fairly large galaxy. Only a century ago astronomers thought it was the entire universe—an island cloud of stars in an otherwise empty vastness. Now they know that our galaxy is not unique; it is only one of many billions of galaxies scattered throughout the universe.

You can see a few of these other galaxies when you expand your field of view by another factor of 100 (■ Figure 1-12). Our galaxy appears as a tiny luminous speck surrounded by other specks in a region 17 million light-years in diameter. Each speck represents a galaxy. Notice that our galaxy is part of a cluster of a few dozen galaxies. Galaxies are commonly grouped together in such clusters. Some galaxies have beautiful spiral patterns like our own galaxy, but others do not. Some are strangely distorted. In a later chapter, you will learn what produces these differences among the galaxies.

Now is a chance for you to correct another **Common Misconception**. People often say "galaxy" when they mean "solar system," and they sometimes confuse both terms with "universe." Your cosmic zoom has shown you the difference. The solar system is the sun and its planets. Our galaxy contains our solar system plus billions of other stars and whatever planets orbit around them, in other words, billions of planetary systems. The universe includes everything: all of the galaxies, stars, and planets, including our own galaxy and a very small part of it, our solar system.

If you expand your field of view one more time, you can see that clusters of galaxies are connected in a vast network (■ Figure 1-13). Clusters are grouped into superclusters—clusters of clusters—and the superclusters are linked to form long filaments and walls outlining nearly empty voids. These filaments and walls appear to be the largest structures in the universe. Were you to expand your field of view another time, you would probably see a uniform fog of filaments and walls. When you puzzle over the origin of these structures, you are at the frontier of human knowledge.

Figure 1-13

(Based on data from M. Seldner, B. L. Siebers, E. J. Groth, and P. J. E. Peebles, *Astronomical Journal 82* [1977].)

1-2 When Is Now?

Now that you have an idea where you are in space, you need to know where you are in time. The stars shined for billions of years before the first human looked up and wondered what they were. To get a sense of your place in time, all you need is a long red ribbon.

Imagine stretching a ribbon from goal line to goal line down the center of a football field, as shown on the inside front cover of this book. Imagine that one end of the ribbon is *today* and that the other end represents the beginning of the universe—the moment of beginning that astronomers call the *big bang*. In a later chapter, "Modern Cosmology," you will learn all about the big bang and see evidence that the universe is about 14 billion years old. Your long red ribbon represents 14 billion years, the entire history of the universe.

Imagine beginning at the goal line labeled *Big Bang* and replaying the entire history of the universe as you walk along your ribbon toward the goal line labeled *Today*. Observations tell astronomers that the big bang filled the entire universe with hot, glowing gas, but as the gas cooled and dimmed the universe went dark. All that happened along the first half inch of the ribbon. There was no light for the first 400 million years, until gravity was able to pull some of the gas together to form the first stars. That seems like a lot of years, but if you stick a little flag beside

the ribbon to mark the birth of the first stars, it would be not quite 3 yards from the goal line where the universe began.

You have to walk only about 5 yards along the ribbon before galaxies formed in large numbers. Our home galaxy would be one of those taking shape. By the time you cross the 50-yard line, the universe is full of galaxies, but the sun and Earth have not formed yet. You need to walk past the 50-yard line down to the 35-yard line before you can finally stick a flag beside the ribbon to mark the formation of the sun and planets—our solar system.

You can carry your flags a few yards farther to the 29-yard line to mark the appearance of the first life on Earth–microscopic creatures in the oceans—and you have to walk all the way to the 3-yard line before you can mark the emergence of life on land. Your dinosaur flag goes just inside the 2-yard line. Dinosaurs go extinct as you pass the one-half-yard line.

What about people? You can put a little flag for the first humanlike creatures only about an inch—four million years–from the goal line labeled *Today*. Civilization, the building of cities, began about 10,000 years ago, so you have to try to fit that flag in only 0.0026 inch from the goal line. That's half the thickness of a sheet of paper. Compare the history of human civilization with the history of the universe. Every war you have ever heard of, every person whose name is recorded, every structure ever built from Stonehenge to the building you are in right now fits into that 0.0026 inch.

Humanity is very new to the universe. Our civilization on Earth has existed for only a flicker of an eyeblink in the history of the universe. As you will discover in the chapters that follow, only in the last hundred years or so have astronomers begun to understand where we are in space and in time.

1-3 Why Study Astronomy?

Your exploration of the universe will help you answer two fundamental questions:

What are we?
How do we know?

The question, "What are we?" is the first organizing theme of this book. Astronomy is important to you because it will tell you what you are. Notice that the question is not "*Who* are we?" If you want to know who we are, you may want to talk to a sociologist, theologian, paleontologist, artist, or poet. "*What* are we?" is a fundamentally different question.

As you study astronomy, you will learn how you fit into the history of the universe. You will learn that the atoms in your body had their first birthday in the big bang when the universe began. Those atoms have been cooked and remade inside generations of stars, and now, after billions of years, they are inside you. Where will they be in another billion years? This is a story

The So-Called Scientific Method

How do scientists learn about nature? You have probably heard of the scientific method as the process by which scientists form hypotheses and test them against evidence gathered by experiment or observation. Scientists use the scientific method all the time, and it is critically important, but they rarely think of it at all, and they certainly don't think of it as a numbered list of steps. It is such an ingrained way of thinking and understanding nature that it is almost invisible to the people who use it most.

Scientists try to form hypotheses that explain how nature works. If a hypothesis is contradicted by evidence from experiments or observations, it must be revised or discarded. If a hypothesis is confirmed, it must be tested further. In that very general way, the scientific method is a way of testing and refining ideas to better describe how nature works.

For example, Gregor Mendel (1822–1884) was an Austrian abbot who liked plants. He formed a hypothesis that offspring usually inherit traits from their parents not as a

smooth blend, as most scientists of the time believed, but in discrete units according to strict mathematical rules. Mendel cultivated and tested over 28,000 pea plants, noting which produced smooth peas and which produced wrinkled peas and how that trait was inherited by successive generations. His study of pea plants confirmed his hypothesis and allowed the development of a series of laws of inheritance. Although the importance of his work was not recognized in his lifetime, Mendel is now called the "father of modern genetics."

The scientific method is not a simple, mechanical way of grinding facts into understanding. It is, in fact, a combination of many ways of analyzing information, finding relationships, and creating new ideas. A scientist needs insight and ingenuity to form and test a good hypothesis. Scientists use the scientific method almost automatically, forming, testing, revising, and discarding hypotheses almost minute by minute as they discuss a new idea. Sometimes, however,

Whether peas are wrinkled or smooth is an inherited trait (Inspirestock/jupiterimages).

a scientist will spend years studying a single promising hypothesis. The so-called scientific method is a way of thinking and a way of knowing about nature. The "How Do We Know?" essays in the chapters that follow will introduce you to some of those methods.

everyone should know, and astronomy is the only course on campus that can tell you that story.

Every chapter in this book ends with a short segment titled "What Are We?" This summary shows how the astronomy in the chapter relates to your role in the story of the universe.

The question, "How do we know?" is the second organizing theme of this book. It is a question you should ask yourself whenever you encounter statements made by so-called experts in any field. Should you swallow a diet supplement recommended by a TV star? Should you vote for a candidate who warns of a climate crisis? To understand the world around you and to make wise decisions for yourself, for your family, and for your nation, you need to understand how science works.

You can use astronomy as a case study in science. In every chapter of this book, you will find short essays titled "How Do We Know?" They are designed to help you think not about *what* is known but about *how* it is known. To do that, they will explain different aspects of scientific reasoning and in that way help you understand how scientists know about the natural world.

Over the last four centuries, scientists have developed a way to understand nature that has been called the **scientific method (How Do We Know? 1-1)**. You will see this process applied over and over as you read about exploding stars, colliding galaxies, and alien planets. The universe is very big, but it is described by a small set of rules, and we humans have found a way to figure out the rules—a method called *science*.

Astronomy will give you perspective on what it means to be here on Earth. This chapter has helped you locate yourself in space and time. Once you realize how vast our universe is, Earth seems quite small. People on the other side of the world seem like neighbors. And, in the entire history of the universe, the human story is only the blink of an eye. This may seem humbling at first, but you can be proud of how much we humans have understood in such a short time.

Not only does astronomy locate you in space and time, it places you in the physical processes that govern the universe. Gravity and atoms work together to make stars, light the universe, generate energy, and create the chemical elements in your body. The chapters that follow will show how you fit into that cosmic process.

Although you are very small and your kind have existed in the universe for only a short time, you are an important part of something very large and very beautiful.

Study and Review

Summary

► You surveyed the universe by taking a cosmic zoom in which each **field of view (p. 2)** was 100 times wider than the previous field of view.

► Astronomers use the metric system because it simplifies calculations and use **scientific notation (p. 3)** for very large or very small numbers.

► You live on a **planet (p. 3)**, Earth, which orbits our **star (p. 3)**, the sun, once a year. As Earth rotates once a day, you see the sun rise and set.

► The moon is only one-fourth the diameter of Earth, but the sun is 109 times larger in diameter than Earth—a typical size for a star.

► The **solar system (p. 3)** includes the sun at the center, all of the planets that orbit around it—Mercury, Venus, Earth, Mars, Jupiter, Saturn, Uranus, and Neptune—plus the moons of the planets, plus other objects bound to the sun by its gravity.

► The **astronomical unit (AU) (p. 4)** is the average distance from Earth to the sun. Mars, for example, orbits 1.5 AU from the sun. The **light-year (ly) (p. 4)** is the distance light can travel in one year. The nearest star is 4.2 ly from the sun.

► Many stars seem to have planets, but such small, distant worlds are difficult to detect. Only a few hundred have been found so far, but planets seem to be common, so you can probably trust that there are lots of planets in the universe, including some like Earth.

► The **Milky Way (p. 6)**, the hazy band of light that encircles the sky, is the **Milky Way Galaxy (p. 6)** seen from inside. The sun is just one out of the billions of stars that fill the Milky Way Galaxy.

► **Galaxies (p. 5)** contain many billions of stars. Our galaxy is about 80,000 ly in diameter and contains over 100 billion stars.

► Some galaxies, including our own, have graceful **spiral arms (p. 6)** bright with stars, but some galaxies are plain clouds of stars.

► Our galaxy is just one of billions of galaxies that fill the universe in great clusters, clouds, filaments, and walls—the largest structures in the universe.

► The universe began about 14 billion years ago in an event called the big bang, which filled the universe with hot gas.

► The hot gas cooled, the first galaxies began to form, and stars began to shine only about 400 million years after the big bang.

► The sun and planets of our solar system formed about 4.6 billion years ago.

► Life began in Earth's oceans soon after Earth formed but did not emerge onto land until only 400 million years ago. Dinosaurs evolved not long ago and went extinct only 65 million years ago.

► Humanlike creatures developed on Earth only about 4 million years ago, and human civilizations developed only about 10,000 years ago.

► Although astronomy seems to be about stars and planets, it describes the universe in which you live, so it is really about you. Astronomy helps you answer the question, "What are we?"

► As you study astronomy, you should ask "How do we know?" and that will help you understand how science gives us a way to understand nature.

► In its simplest outline, science follows the **scientific method (p. 8)**, in which scientists expect statements to be supported by evidence compared with hypotheses. In fact, science is a complex and powerful way to think about nature.

Review Questions

1. What is the largest dimension of which you have personal knowledge? Have you run a mile? Hiked 10 miles? Run a marathon?
2. What is the difference between our solar system, our galaxy, and the universe?
3. Why are light-years more convenient than miles, kilometers, or astronomical units for measuring certain distances?
4. Why is it difficult to detect planets orbiting other stars?
5. What does the size of the star image in a photograph tell you?
6. What is the difference between the Milky Way and the Milky Way Galaxy?
7. What are the largest known structures in the universe?
8. How does astronomy help answer the question, "What are we?"
9. **How Do We Know?** How does the scientific method give scientists a way to know about nature?

Discussion Questions

1. Do you think you have a right to know the astronomy described in this chapter? Do you think you have a duty to know it? Can you think of ways this knowledge helps you enjoy a richer life and be a better citizen?

2. How is a statement in a political campaign speech different from a statement in a scientific discussion? Find examples in newspapers, magazines, and this book.

Problems

1. The diameter of Earth is 7928 miles. What is its diameter in inches? In yards? If the diameter of Earth is expressed as 12,756 km, what is its diameter in meters? In centimeters? Give your answers in scientific notation.

2. If a mile equals 1.609 km and the moon is 2160 miles in diameter, what is its diameter in kilometers?

3. One astronomical unit is about 1.5×10^8 km. Explain why this is the same as 150×10^6 km.

4. Venus orbits 0.72 AU from the sun. What is that distance in kilometers?

5. Light from the sun takes 8 minutes to reach Earth. How long does it take to reach Mars?

6. The sun is almost 400 times farther from Earth than is the moon. How long does light from the moon take to reach Earth?

7. If the speed of light is 3×10^5 km/s, how many kilometers are in a light-year? How many meters?

8. How long does it take light to cross the diameter of our Milky Way Galaxy?

9. The nearest galaxy to our own is about 2 million light-years away. How many meters is that?

10. How many galaxies like our own would it take, laid edge to edge, to reach the nearest galaxy? (*Hint*: See Problem 9.)

Learning to Look

1. In Figure 1-4, the division between daylight and darkness is at the right on the globe of Earth. How do you know this is the sunset line and not the sunrise line?

2. Look at Figure 1-6. How can you tell that Mercury does not follow a circular orbit?

3. Of the objects listed here, which would be contained inside the object shown in the photograph at the right? Which would contain the object in the photo?

   stars

   planets

   galaxy clusters

   filaments

   spiral arms

Bill Schoening/NOAO/AURA/NSF

4. In the photograph shown here, which stars are brightest, and which are faintest? How can you tell? Why can't you tell which stars in this photograph are biggest or which have planets?

NOAO

2 | The Sky

Guidepost

The previous chapter took you on a cosmic zoom through space and time. That quick preview only sets the stage for the drama to come. Now it is time to look closely at the sky and answer four essential questions:

— **How do astronomers refer to stars and compare their brightness?**

— **How does the sky appear to move as Earth rotates?**

— **What causes the seasons?**

— **How can astronomical cycles affect Earth's climate?**

As you study the sky and its motions, you will be learning to think of Earth as a planet rotating on its axis. The next chapter will introduce you to some of the most dramatic cycles in the sky.

The sky above mountain-top observatories far from city lights is the same sky you see from your window. The stars above you are other suns scattered through the universe.
(Kris Koenig/Coast Learning Systems)

The Southern Cross I saw every night abeam. The sun every morning came up astern; every evening it went down ahead. I wished for no other compass to guide me, for these were true.

— CAPTAIN JOSHUA SLOCUM
SAILING ALONE AROUND THE WORLD

THE NIGHT SKY is the rest of the universe as seen from our planet. When you look up at the stars, you are looking out through a layer of air only a little more than a hundred kilometers deep. Beyond that, space is nearly empty, and the stars are scattered light-years apart.

As you read this chapter, keep in mind that you live on a planet in the midst of these scattered stars. Because Earth turns on its axis once a day, the sky appears to revolve around you in a daily cycle. Not only does the sun rise in the eastern part of the sky and set in the western part, but so do the stars.

2-1 The Stars

ON A DARK NIGHT far from city lights, you can see a few thousand stars. The ancients organized what they saw by naming stars and groups of stars. Some of those names survive today.

Constellations

All around the world, ancient cultures celebrated heroes, gods, and mythical beasts by giving their names to groups of stars—**constellations** (■ Figure 2-1). You should not be surprised that the star patterns do not look like the creatures they represent any more than Columbus, Ohio, looks like Christopher Columbus. The constellations simply celebrate the most important mythical figures in each culture. The oldest constellations named by Western cultures originated in Assyria over 3000 years ago, and others were added by Babylonian and Greek astronomers during the classical age. Of these ancient constellations, 48 are still in use.

Different cultures grouped stars and named constellations differently. The constellation you know as Orion was known as Al Jabar, the giant, to the ancient Syrians, as the White Tiger to the Chinese, and as Prajapati in the Form of a Stag in India. The Pawnee Indians knew the constellation Scorpius as two

groupings. The long tail of the scorpion was the Snake, and the two bright stars at the tip of the scorpion's tail were the Two Swimming Ducks.

Many ancient cultures, including the Greeks, northern Asians, and Native Americans, associated the stars of the Big Dipper with a bear. The concept of the celestial bear may have crossed the land bridge into North America with the first Americans roughly 12,000 years ago. The names of some of the constellations you see in the sky may be among the oldest surviving traces of human culture.

To the ancients, a constellation was a loose grouping of stars. Many of the fainter stars were not included in any constellation, and the stars of the southern sky not visible to the ancient astronomers of northern latitudes were not grouped into constellations. Constellation boundaries, when they were defined at all, were only approximate (■ Figure 2-2a), so a star like Alpheratz could be thought of as part of Pegasus or part of Andromeda. To correct these gaps and ambiguities, astronomers have added 40 modern constellations, and in 1928 the International Astronomical Union established 88 official constellations with clearly defined boundaries (Figure 2-2b). Consequently, a constellation now represents not a group of stars but an area of the sky, and any star within the region belongs to one and only one constellation. Alpheratz belongs to Andromeda.

■ **Figure 2-1**

The constellations are an ancient heritage handed down for thousands of years as celebrations of great heroes and mythical creatures. Here Sagittarius and Scorpius hang above the southern horizon.

■ **Figure 2-2**

(a) In antiquity, constellation boundaries were poorly defined, as shown on this map by the curving dotted lines that separate Pegasus from Andromeda. (From Duncan Bradford, *Wonders of the Heavens,* Boston: John B. Russell, 1837.) (b) Modern constellation boundaries are precisely defined by international agreement.

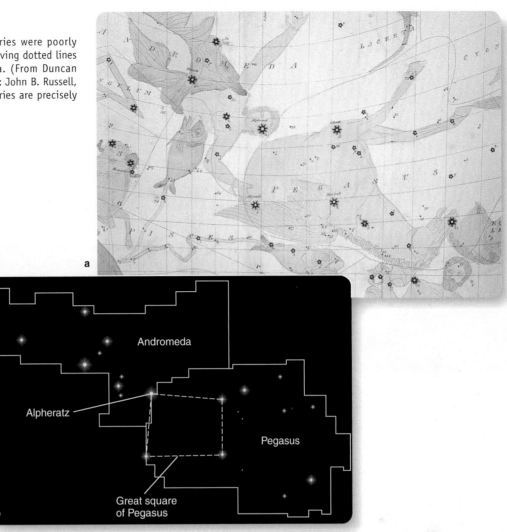

In addition to the 88 official constellations, the sky contains a number of less formally defined groupings called **asterisms.** The Big Dipper, for example, is a well-known asterism that is part of the constellation Ursa Major (the Great Bear). Another asterism is the Great Square of Pegasus (Figure 2-2b), which includes three stars from Pegasus plus Alpheratz from Andromeda. The star charts at the end of this book will introduce you to the brighter constellations and asterisms.

Although constellations and asterisms are groups of stars that appear close together in the sky, it is important to remember that most are made up of stars that are not physically associated with one another. Some stars may be many times farther away than others and moving through space in different directions. The only thing they have in common is that they happen to lie in approximately the same direction from Earth (■ Figure 2-3).

The Names of the Stars

In addition to naming groups of stars, ancient astronomers gave individual names to the brightest individual stars. Modern astronomers still use many of those ancient names. Although the constellation names came from Greek translated into Latin—the language of science until the 19th century—most star names come from ancient Arabic, though much altered by the passing centuries. The name of Betelgeuse, the bright orange star in Orion, for example, comes from the Arabic *yad al jawza,* meaning "shoulder of Jawza [Orion]." Names such as Sirius (the Scorched One) and Aldebaran (the Follower of the Pleiades) are beautiful additions to the mythology of the sky.

Naming individual stars is not very helpful because you can see thousands of them. How many names could you remember? Also, a simple name gives you no clues to the location of the star in the sky or to its brightness. A more useful way to identify stars is to assign letters to the bright stars in a constellation in approximate order of brightness. Astronomers use the Greek alphabet for this purpose. Thus, the brightest star in a constellation is usually designated alpha, the second brightest beta, and so on. Often the name of the Greek letter is spelled out, as in "alpha," but sometimes the actual Greek letter is used, especially in charts. You will find the Greek alphabet in Appendix A. For many constellations, the letters follow the order of brightness, but some constellations, by tradition, mistake, or the personal preferences of early chart makers, are exceptions (■ Figure 2-4).

To identify a star by its Greek-letter designation, you would give the Greek letter followed by the possessive (genitive) form of the constellation name; for example, the brightest star in the constellation Canis Major is alpha Canis Majoris, which can also be written α Canis Majoris. This both identifies the star and the constellation and gives a clue to the relative brightness of the star. Compare this with the ancient name for this star, Sirius, which tells you nothing about location or brightness.

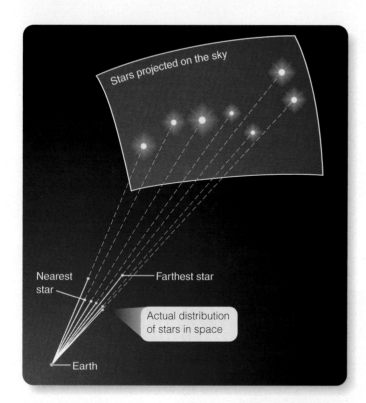

■ Figure 2-3

You see the Big Dipper in the sky because you are looking through a group of stars scattered through space at different distances from Earth. You see them as if they were projected on a screen, and they form the shape of the Dipper.

Favorite Stars

It is fun to know the names of the brighter stars, but they are more than points of light in the sky. They are glowing spheres of gas much like the sun, each with its unique characteristics. ■ Figure 2-5 identifies eight bright stars that you can adopt as Favorite Stars. As you study astronomy you will discover their peculiar personalities and enjoy finding them in the evening sky. You will learn, for example, that Betelgeuse is not just an orange point of light but is an aging, cool star over 800 times larger than the sun. As you learn more in later chapters, you may want to add more Favorite Stars to your list.

You can use the star charts at the end of this book to help you locate these Favorite Stars. You can see Polaris

year-round, but Sirius, Betelgeuse, Rigel, and Aldebaran are in the winter sky. Spica is a summer star, and Vega is visible evenings in later summer and fall. Alpha Centauri, only 4 ly away, is the nearest star to the sun, and you will have to travel as far south as southern Florida to glimpse it above the southern horizon.

The Brightness of Stars

Besides naming individual stars, astronomers need a way to describe their brightness. Astronomers measure the brightness of stars using the **magnitude scale,** a system that first appeared in the writings of the ancient astronomer Claudius Ptolemy about AD 140. The system probably originated even earlier, and most astronomers attribute it to the Greek astronomer Hipparchus (about 190–120 BC). Hipparchus compiled the first known star catalog, and he may have used the magnitude system in that catalog. Almost 300 years later, Ptolemy used the magnitude system in his own catalog, and successive generations of astronomers have continued to use the system.

The ancient astronomers divided the stars into six classes. The brightest were called first-magnitude stars and those that

■ Figure 2-4

Stars in a constellation can be identified by Greek letters and by names derived from Arabic. The spikes on the star images in the photograph were produced by the optics in the camera. (William Hartmann)

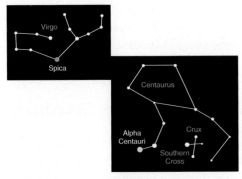

Sirius	Brightest star in the sky	Winter
Betelgeuse	Bright red star in Orion	Winter
Rigel	Bright blue star in Orion	Winter
Aldebaran	Red eye of Taurus the Bull	Winter
Polaris	The North Star	Year round
Vega	Bright star overhead	Summer
Spica	Bright southern star	Summer
Alpha Centauri	Nearest star to the sun	Spring, far south

■ **Figure 2-5**

Favorite Stars: Locate these bright stars in the sky and learn why they are interesting.

were fainter, second-magnitude. The scale continued downward to sixth-magnitude stars, the faintest visible to the human eye. Thus, the larger the magnitude number, the fainter the star. This makes sense if you think of the bright stars as first-class stars and the faintest visible stars as sixth-class stars.

Ancient astronomers could only estimate magnitudes, but modern astronomers can measure the brightness of stars to high precision, so they have made adjustments to the scale of magnitudes. Instead of saying that the star known by the charming name Chort (Theta Leonis) is third magnitude, they can say its magnitude is 3.34. Accurate measurements show that some stars are actually brighter than magnitude 1.0. For example, Favorite Star Vega (alpha Lyrae) is so bright that its magnitude, 0.04, is

■ **Figure 2-6**

The scale of apparent visual magnitudes extends into negative numbers to represent the brightest objects and to positive numbers larger than 6 to represent objects fainter than the human eye can see.

almost zero. A few are so bright the modern magnitude scale must extend into negative numbers (■ Figure 2-6). On this scale, our Favorite Star Sirius, the brightest star in the sky, has a magnitude of –1.47. Modern astronomers have had to extend the faint end of the magnitude scale as well. The faintest stars you can see with your unaided eyes are about sixth magnitude, but if you use a telescope, you will see stars much fainter. Astronomers must use magnitude numbers larger than 6 to describe these faint stars.

These numbers are known as **apparent visual magnitudes** (m_V), and they describe how the stars look to human eyes observing from Earth. Although some stars emit large amounts of infrared or ultraviolet light, human eyes can't see those types of radiation, and they are not included in the apparent visual magnitude. The subscript "V" stands for "visual" and reminds you that only visible light is included. Apparent visual magnitude also does not take into account the distance to the stars. Very distant stars look fainter, and nearby stars look brighter. Apparent visual magnitude ignores the effect of distance and tells you only how bright the star looks as seen from Earth.

Magnitude and Intensity

Your interpretation of brightness is quite subjective, depending on both the physiology of human eyes and the psychology of perception. To be accurate you should refer to **flux**—a measure of the light energy from a star that hits one square meter in one second. Such measurements precisely define the intensity of starlight, and a simple relationship connects apparent visual magnitudes and intensity.

Astronomers use a simple formula to convert between magnitudes and intensities. If two stars have intensities I_A and I_B, then the ratio of their intensities is I_A/I_B. To make today's measurements agree with ancient catalogs, astronomers have defined the modern magnitude scale so that two stars that differ by five magnitudes have an intensity ratio of exactly 100. Then two stars that differ by one magnitude must have an intensity ratio that equals the fifth root of 100, $5\sqrt{100}$, which equals about 2.512—that is, the light of one star must be 2.512 times more intense.

This allows you to compare the brightness of two stars. If they differ by two magnitudes. they will have an intensity ratio of 2.512×2.512, or about 6.3. If they differ by three magnitudes, they will have an intensity ratio of $2.512 \times 2.512 \times 2.512$, which is 2.512^3 or about 6.3, and so on (■Table 2-1).

For example, suppose one star is third magnitude, and another star is ninth magnitude. What is the intensity ratio? In this case, the magnitude difference is six magnitudes, and the table shows the intensity ratio is 250. Therefore light from one star is 250 times more intense than light from the other star.

A table is convenient, but for more precision you can express the relationship as a simple formula. The intensity ratio I_A/I_B is equal to 2.512 raised to the power of the magnitude difference $m_B - m_A$:

$$\frac{I_A}{I_B} = (2.512)^{(m_B - m_A)}$$

If, for example, the magnitude difference is 6.32 magnitudes, then the intensity ratio must be $2.512^{6.32}$. A pocket calculator tells you the answer: 337. One of the stars is 337 times brighter than the other.

On the other hand, when you know the intensity ratio of two stars and want to find their magnitude difference, it is convenient to rearrange the formula above and write it as

$$m_B - m_A = 2.5 \log\left(\frac{I_A}{I_B}\right)$$

For example, the light from Sirius is 24.2 times more intense than light from Polaris. The magnitude difference is 2.5 log(24.2). Your pocket calculator tells you the logarithm of 24.2 is 1.38, so the magnitude difference is 2.5×1.38, which equals 3.4 magnitudes. Sirius is 3.4 magnitudes brighter than Polaris.

The modern magnitude system has some big advantages. It compresses a tremendous range of intensity into a small range of magnitudes, as you can see in Table 2-1. More important, it

allows modern astronomers to measure and report the brightness of stars to high precision while still making comparisons to observations of apparent visual magnitude that go back to the time of Hipparchus.

2-2 The Sky and Its Motion

THE SKY ABOVE seems to be a great blue dome in the daytime and a sparkling ceiling at night. It was this ceiling that the first astronomers observed long ago as they tried to understand the night sky.

The Celestial Sphere

Ancient astronomers believed the sky was a great sphere surrounding Earth with the stars stuck on the inside like thumbtacks in a ceiling. Modern astronomers know that the stars are scattered through space at different distances, but it is still convenient to think of the sky as a great starry sphere enclosing Earth.

The Concept Art Portfolio **The Sky Around You** on pages 18–19 takes you on an illustrated tour of the sky. Throughout this book, these two-page art spreads introduce new concepts and new terms through photos and diagrams. These concepts and new terms are not discussed elsewhere, so examine the art spreads carefully. Notice that The Sky Around You introduces you to three important principles and 16 new terms that will help you understand the sky:

1 The sky appears to rotate westward around Earth each day, but that is a consequence of the eastward rotation of Earth. That rotation produces day and night. Notice how reference points on the *celestial sphere* such as the *zenith, nadir, horizon, celestial equator,* and the *north celestial pole* and *south celestial pole* define the four directions, *north point, south point, east point,* and *west point.*

2 Astronomers measure *angular distance* across the sky as angles and express them as degrees, *arc minutes,* and *arc seconds.* The same units are used to measure the *angular diameter* of an object.

3 What you can see of the sky depends on where you are on Earth. If you lived in Australia, you would see many constellations and asterisms invisible from North America, but you would never see the Big Dipper. How many *circumpolar constellations* you see depends on where you are. Remember your Favorite Star Alpha Centauri? It is in the southern sky and isn't visible from most of the United States. You could just glimpse it above the southern horizon if you were in Miami, Florida, but you could see it easily from Australia.

Pay special attention to the new terms on pages 18–19. You need to know these terms to describe the sky and its motions, but don't fall into the trap of just memorizing new terms. The goal of

■ Table 2-1 | Magnitude and Intensity

Magnitude Difference	Approximate Intensity Ratio
0	1
1	2.5
2	6.3
3	16
4	40
5	100
6	250
7	630
8	1600
9	4000
10	10,000
⋮	⋮
15	1,000,000
20	100,000,000
25	10,000,000,000
⋮	⋮

Scientific Models

How can a scientific model be useful if it isn't entirely true? A scientific model is a carefully devised conception of how something works, a framework that helps scientists think about some aspect of nature, just as the celestial sphere helps astronomers think about the motions of the sky.

Chemists, for example, use colored balls to represent atoms and sticks to represent the bonds between them, kind of like Tinkertoys. Using these molecular models, chemists can see the three-dimensional shape of molecules and understand how the atoms interconnect. The molecular model of DNA proposed by Watson and Crick in 1953 led to our modern understanding of the mechanisms of genetics. You have probably seen elaborate ball-and-stick models of DNA, but does the molecule really look like Tinkertoys? No, but the model is both simple enough and accurate enough to help scientists think about their theories.

A scientific model is not a statement of truth; it does not have to be precisely true to be useful. In an idealized model, some complex aspects of nature can be simplified or omitted. The ball-and-stick model of a molecule doesn't show the relative strength of the chemical bonds, for instance. A model gives scientists a way to think about some aspect of nature but need not be true in every detail.

When you use a scientific model, it is important to remember the limitations of that model. If you begin to think of a model as true, it can be misleading instead of helpful. The celestial sphere, for instance, can help you think about the sky, but you must remember that it is only a model. The universe is much larger and much more interesting than this ancient scientific model of the heavens.

Balls represent atoms and rods represent chemical bonds in this model of a DNA molecule. (Digital Vision/Getty Images)

science is to understand nature, not to memorize definitions. Study the diagrams and see how the geometry of the celestial sphere and its motions produce the sky you see above you.

The celestial sphere is an example of a **scientific model,** a common feature of scientific thought (**How Do We Know? 2-1**). Notice that a scientific model does not have to be true to be useful. You will encounter many scientific models in the chapters that follow, and you will discover that some of the most useful models are highly simplified descriptions of the true facts.

This is a good time to eliminate a couple of **Common Misconceptions.** Lots of people, without thinking about it much, assume that the stars are not in the sky during the daytime. The stars are actually there day and night; they are just invisible during the day because the sky is lit up by sunlight. Also, many people insist that Favorite Star Polaris is the brightest star in the sky. It is actually the 51st visually brightest star. You now know that Polaris is important because of its position, not because of its brightness.

In addition to causing the obvious daily motion of the sky, Earth's rotation conceals a very slow celestial motion that can be detected only over centuries.

Precession

Over 2000 years ago, Hipparchus compared a few of his star positions with those recorded nearly two centuries earlier and realized that the celestial poles and equator were slowly moving across the sky. Later astronomers understood that this motion is caused by the top-like motion of Earth.

If you have ever played with a gyroscope or top, you have seen how the spinning mass resists any sudden change in the direction of its axis of rotation. The more massive the top and the more rapidly it spins, the more it resists your efforts to twist it out of position. But you probably recall that even the most rapidly spinning top slowly swings its axis around in a circle... The weight of the top tends to make it tip over, and this combines with its rapid rotation to make its axis sweep out the shape of a cone in a motion called **precession** (■ Figure 2-7a). In later chapters, you will learn that many celestial bodies precess.

Earth spins like a giant top, but it does not spin upright in its orbit; it is tipped 23.5° from vertical. Earth's large mass and rapid rotation keep its axis of rotation pointed toward a spot near the star Polaris, and the axis would not wander if it were not for precession.

The Sky Around You

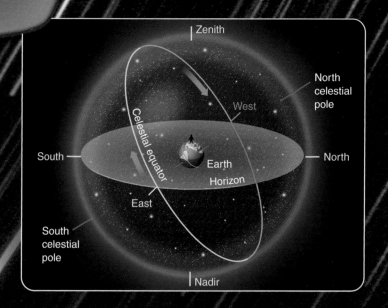

1 The eastward rotation of Earth causes the sun, moon, and stars to move westward in the sky as if the **celestial sphere** were rotating westward around Earth. From any location on Earth you see only half of the celestial sphere, the half above the **horizon.** The **zenith** marks the top of the sky above your head, and the **nadir** marks the bottom of the sky directly under your feet. The drawing at right shows the view for an observer in North America. An observer in South America would have a dramatically different horizon, zenith, and nadir.

The apparent pivot points are the **north celestial pole** and the **south celestial pole** located directly above Earth's north and south poles. Halfway between the celestial poles lies the **celestial equator.** Earth's rotation defines the directions you use every day. The **north point** and **south point** are the points on the horizon closest to the celestial poles. The **east point** and the **west point** lie halfway between the north and south points. The celestial equator always touches the horizon at the east and west points.

AURA/NOAO/NSF

1a This time exposure of about 30 minutes shows stars as streaks, called star trails, rising behind an observatory dome. The camera was facing northeast to take this photo. The motion you see in the sky depends on which direction you look, as shown at right. Looking north, you see the Favorite Star Polaris, the North Star, located near the north celestial pole. As the sky appears to rotate westward, Polaris hardly moves,

Astronomers measure distance across the sky as angles.

Angular distance

North celestial pole

Zenith

Latitude 90°

Zenith

North celestial pole

W

S — — N

Latitude 60°   E

2 Astronomers might say, "The star was only 2 degrees from the moon." Of course, the stars are much farther away than the moon, but when you think of the celestial sphere, you can measure distances *on the sky* as **angular distances** in degrees, minutes of arc, and seconds of arc. An **arc minute** is 1/60th of a degree, and an **arc second** is 1/60th of a minute of arc. Then the **angular diameter** of an object is the angular distance from one edge to the other. The sun and moon are each about half a degree in diameter, and the bowl of the Big Dipper is about 10° wide. In order to distinguish these units from the similarly named units of time, astronomers refer to small angles in arc minutes or arc seconds. The word *arc* indicates that the numbers refer to angles and not time.

Zenith

North celestial pole

W

L

S — — N

Latitude 30°   E

3 What you see in the sky depends on your latitude as shown at right. Imagine that you begin a journey in the ice and snow at Earth's North Pole with the north celestial pole directly overhead. As you walk southward, the celestial pole moves toward the horizon, and you can see farther into the southern sky. The angular distance from the horizon to the north celestial pole always equals your latitude (L)—the basis for celestial navigation. As you cross Earth's equator, the celestial equator would pass through your zenith, and the north celestial pole would sink below your northern horizon.

Zenith

North celestial pole

W

S — — N

Latitude 0°   E

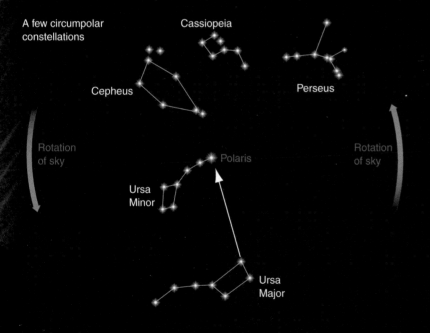

A few circumpolar constellations

Cassiopeia

Cepheus

Perseus

Rotation of sky

Rotation of sky

Polaris

Ursa Minor

Ursa Major

South celestial pole

Zenith

W

S — — N

Latitude −30°   E

3a **Circumpolar constellations** are those that never rise or set. From mid-northern latitudes, as shown at left, you see a number of familiar constellations circling Polaris and never dipping below the horizon. As the sky rotates, the pointer stars at the front of the Big Dipper always point toward Polaris. Circumpolar constellations near the south celestial pole never rise as seen from mid-northern latitudes. From a high latitude such as Norway, you would have more circumpolar constellations, and from Quito, Ecuador, located on Earth's equator, you would have no circumpolar constellations at all.

Because of its rotation, Earth has a slight bulge around its middle, and the gravity of the sun and moon pull on this bulge, tending to twist Earth's axis "upright" relative to its orbit. If Earth were a perfect sphere, it would not get twisted. Notice that gravity tends to make the top fall over, but it tends to twist Earth upright in its orbit. In both cases, the twisting of the axis of rotation combines with the rotation of the object and causes precession. Earth's axis precesses, taking about 26,000 years for one cycle (Figure 2-7b).

Because the locations of the celestial poles and equator are defined by Earth's rotational axis, precession slowly moves these reference marks. You would notice no change at all from night to night or year to year, but precise measurements can reveal the slow precession of the celestial poles and the resulting change in orientation of the celestial equator.

Over centuries, precession has dramatic effects. Egyptian records show that 4800 years ago the north celestial pole was near the star Thuban (alpha Draconis). The pole is now approaching Polaris and will be closest to it in about the year 2100. In about 12,000 years, the pole will have moved to within 5° of Vega (alpha Lyrae). Next time you glance at Favorite Star Vega, remind yourself that it will someday be a very impressive north star. Figure 2-7c shows the path followed by the north celestial pole.

2-3) The Cycles of the Sun

EARTH'S ROTATION ON ITS AXIS causes the cycle of day and night, but it is its motion around the sun in its orbit that defines the year. Notice an important distinction. **Rotation** is the turning of a body on its axis, but **revolution** means the motion of a body around a point outside the body. Consequently, astronomers are careful to say Earth rotates once a day on its axis and revolves once a year around the sun.

Because day and night are caused by the rotation of Earth, your time of day depends on your location on Earth. You can see this if you watch live international news. It may be lunchtime where you are, but for a newscaster in the Middle East, it can already be dark. In ■ Figure 2-8, you can see that four people in different places on Earth have different times of day.

The Annual Motion of the Sun

Even in the daytime, the sky is filled with stars, but the glare of sunlight fills Earth's atmosphere with scattered light, and you can see only the brilliant sun. If the sun were fainter, you would be able to see it rise in the morning in front of the stars. During the day, you would see the sun and the stars moving westward, and the sun would eventually set in front of the same stars. If you watched carefully as the day passed, you would notice that the sun was creeping slowly eastward against the background of stars.

■ Figure 2-7

Precession. (a) A spinning top precesses in a conical motion around the perpendicular to the floor because its weight tends to make it fall over. (b) Earth precesses around the perpendicular to its orbit because the gravity of the sun and moon acting on Earth's equatorial bulge tend to twist it upright. (c) Precession causes the north celestial pole to move slowly among the stars, completing a circle in 26,000 years.

■ Figure 2-8

Looking down on Earth from above the North Pole shows how the time of day or night depends on your location on Earth.

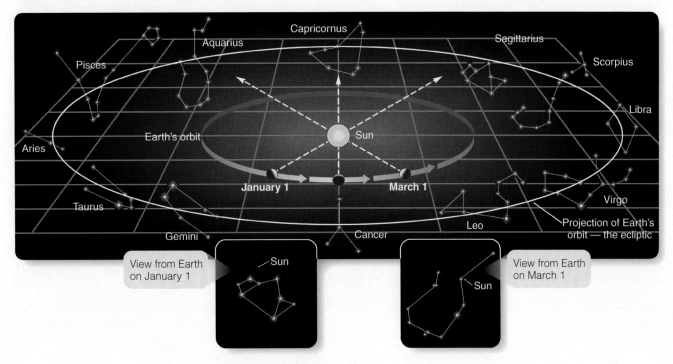

■ Figure 2-9

Earth's orbit is a nearly perfect circle, but it is shown in an inclined view in this diagram and consequently looks oval. Earth's motion around the sun makes the sun appear to move against the background of the stars. Earth's circular orbit is thus projected on the sky as the circular path of the sun, the ecliptic. If you could see the stars in the daytime, you would notice the sun crossing in front of the distant constellations as Earth moves along its orbit.

It would move a distance roughly equal to its own diameter between sunrise and sunset. This motion is caused by the motion of Earth in its nearly circular orbit around the sun.

For example, in January, you would see the sun in front of the constellation Sagittarius (■ Figure 2-9). As Earth moves along its circular orbit, the sun appears to move eastward among the stars. By March, you would see it in front of Aquarius.

Although people often say the sun is "in Sagittarius" or "in Aquarius," it isn't really correct to say the sun is "in" a constellation. The sun is only 1 AU away, and the stars visible in the sky are at least a million times more distant. Nevertheless, in March of each year, the sun crosses in front of the stars that make up Aquarius, and people conventionally use the expression, "The sun is in Aquarius."

The apparent path of the sun against the background of stars is called the **ecliptic.** If the sky were a great screen, the ecliptic would be the shadow cast by Earth's orbit. That is why the ecliptic is often called the projection of Earth's orbit on the sky.

Earth circles the sun in 365.25 days and, consequently, the sun appears to circle the sky in the same period. That means the sun, traveling 360° around the ecliptic in 365.25 days, travels about 1° eastward in 24 hours, about twice its angular diameter. You don't notice this apparent motion of the sun because you can't see the stars in the daytime, but it does have an important consequence that you do notice—the seasons.

The Seasons

Earth would not experience seasons if it rotated upright in its orbit, but because its axis of rotation is tipped 23.4° from the perpendicular to its orbit, it has seasons. Study **The Cycle of the Seasons** on pages 22–23 and notice two important principles and six new terms:

1 Because Earth's axis of rotation is inclined 23.4°, the sun moves into the northern sky in the spring and into the southern sky in the fall. That causes the cycle of the seasons. Notice how the *vernal equinox,* the *summer solstice,* the *autumnal equinox,* and the *winter solstice* mark the beginning of the seasons. Further, notice the very minor effects of Earth's slightly elliptical orbit as it travels from *perihelion* to *aphelion.*

2 Earth goes through a cycle of seasons because of changes in the amount of solar energy that Earth's northern and southern hemispheres receive at different times of the year. Because of circulation patterns in Earth's atmosphere, the northern and southern hemispheres are mostly isolated from each other and exchange little heat. When one hemisphere receives more solar energy than the other, it grows rapidly warmer.

Notice that the seasons in Earth's southern hemisphere are reversed with respect to those in the northern hemisphere. Australia and other lands in the southern hemisphere experience

The Cycle of the Seasons

1 You can use the celestial sphere to help you think about the seasons. The celestial equator is the projection of Earth's equator on the sky, and the ecliptic is the projection of Earth's orbit on the sky. Because Earth is tipped in its orbit, the ecliptic and equator are inclined to each other by 23.5° as shown at right. As the sun moves eastward around the sky, it spends half the year in the southern half of the sky and half the year in the northern half. That causes the seasons.

The sun crosses the celestial equator going northward at the point called the **vernal equinox**. The sun is at its farthest north at the point called the **summer solstice**. It crosses the celestial equator going southward at the **autumnal equinox** and reaches its most southern point at the **winter solstice**.

North celestial pole

Celestial equator

Autumnal equinox

Winter solstice

Ecliptic

Vernal equinox

23.5°

Summer solstice

South celestial pole

1a The seasons are defined by the dates when the sun crosses these four points, as shown in the table at the right. *Equinox* comes from the word for "equal"; the day of an equinox has equal amounts of daylight and darkness. *Solstice* comes from the words meaning "sun" and "stationary." *Vernal* comes from the word for "green." The "green" equinox marks the beginning of spring.

Event	Date*	Season
Vernal equinox	March 20	Spring begins
Summer solstice	June 22	Summer begins
Autumnal equinox	September 22	Autumn begins
Winter solstice	December 22	Winter begins

* Give or take a day due to leap year and other factors.

1b On the day of the summer solstice in late June, Earth's northern hemisphere is inclined toward the sun, and sunlight shines almost straight down at northern latitudes. At southern latitudes, sunlight strikes the ground at an angle and spreads out. North America has warm weather, and South America has cool weather.

Earth's axis of rotation points toward Polaris, and, like a top, the spinning Earth holds its axis fixed as it orbits the sun. On one side of the sun, Earth's northern hemisphere leans toward the sun; on the other side of its orbit, it leans away. However, the direction of the axis of rotation does not change.

23.5°

To Polaris

40° N latitude

Equator

40° S latitude

Sunlight nearly direct on northern latitudes

To sun →

Sunlight spread out on southern latitudes

Earth at summer solstice

Summer solstice light

1c Light striking the ground at a steep angle spreads out less than light striking the ground at a shallow angle. Light from the summer solstice sun strikes northern latitudes from nearly overhead and is concentrated.

Winter solstice light

Light from the winter solstice sun strikes northern latitudes at a much shallower angle and spreads out. The same amount of energy is spread over a larger area, so the ground receives less energy from the winter sun.

2 The two causes of the seasons are shown at right for someone in the northern hemisphere. First, the noon summer sun is higher in the sky and the winter sun is lower, as shown by the longer winter shadows. Thus winter sunlight is more spread out. Second, the summer sun rises in the northeast and sets in the northwest, spending more than 12 hours in the sky. The winter sun rises in the southeast and sets in the southwest, spending less than 12 hours in the sky. Both of these effects mean that northern latitudes receive more energy from the summer sun, and summer days are warmer than winter days.

At summer solstice

At winter solstice

Earth at winter solstice

1d On the day of the winter solstice in late December, Earth's northern hemisphere is inclined away from the sun, and sunlight strikes the ground at an angle and spreads out. At southern latitudes, sunlight shines almost straight down and does not spread out. North America has cool weather and South America has warm weather.

Earth's orbit is only very slightly elliptical. About January 3, Earth is at **perihelion,** its closest point to the sun, when it is only 1.7 percent closer than average. About July 5, Earth is at **aphelion,** its most distant point from the sun, when it is only 1.7 percent farther than average. This small variation does not significantly affect the seasons.

winter from June 22 to September 22, and summer from December 22 to March 20.

Now you can set your friends straight if they mention two of the most **Common Misconceptions** about the seasons. First, the seasons don't occur because Earth moves closer to or farther from the sun. If that were the cause, both of Earth's hemispheres would experience winter at the same time, and that's not what happens. Earth's orbit is nearly circular. Earth is only 1.7 percent closer to the sun in January and 1.7 percent farther away in July, and that small variation isn't enough to cause the seasons. Rather, the seasons arise because Earth's axis is not perpendicular to its orbit.

Here's a second **Common Misconception:** It is not easier to stand a raw egg on end on the day of the vernal equinox. Have you heard that one? Radio and TV personalities love to talk about it, but it just isn't true. It is one of the silliest misconceptions in science. You can stand a raw egg on end any day of the year if you have steady hands. (*Hint:* It helps to shake the egg really hard to break the yoke inside so it can settle to the bottom.)

In ancient times, the cycle of the seasons, especially the solstices and equinoxes, were celebrated with rituals and festivals. Shakespeare's play *A Midsummer Night's Dream* describes the enchantment of the summer solstice night. (In Shakespeare's time, the equinoxes and solstices were taken to mark the midpoints of the seasons.) Many North American Indians marked the summer solstice with ceremonies and dances. Early church officials placed Christmas day in late December to coincide with an earlier pagan celebration of the winter solstice.

The Motion of the Planets

The planets of our solar system produce no visible light of their own; they are visible only by reflected sunlight. Mercury, Venus, Mars, Jupiter, and Saturn are all easily visible to the unaided eye and look like stars, but Uranus is usually too faint to be seen, and Neptune is never bright enough.

All of the planets of the solar system, including Earth, move in nearly circular orbits around the sun. If you were looking down on the solar system from the north celestial pole, you would see the planets moving in the same counterclockwise direction around their orbits, with the planets farthest from the sun moving the slowest. Seen from Earth, the outer planets move slowly eastward* along the ecliptic. In fact, the word *planet* comes from the Greek word meaning "wanderer." Mars moves completely around the ecliptic in slightly less than 2 years, but Saturn, being farther from the sun, takes nearly 30 years.

Mercury and Venus also stay near the ecliptic, but they move differently from the other planets. They have orbits inside Earth's orbit, and that means they are never seen far from the sun in the sky. Observed from Earth, they move eastward away from the sun and then back toward the sun, crossing the near part of their

---
*You will discover occasional exceptions to this eastward motion in Chapter 4.

orbit. They continue moving westward away from the sun and then move back crossing the far part of their orbit before they move out east of the sun again. To find one of these planets, you need to look above the western horizon just after sunset or above the eastern horizon just before sunrise. Venus is easier to locate because it is brighter and because its larger orbit carries it higher above the horizon than does Mercury's (■ Figure 2-10). Mercury's orbit is so small that it can never get farther than 28° from the sun. Consequently, it is hard to see against the sun's glare and is often hidden in the clouds and haze near the horizon.

By tradition, any planet visible in the evening sky is called an **evening star,** even though planets are not stars. Similarly, any planet visible in the sky shortly before sunrise is called a **morning star.** Perhaps the most beautiful is Venus, which can become as bright as magnitude –4.7. As Venus moves around its orbit, it can dominate the western sky each evening for many weeks, but eventually its orbit carries it back toward the sun, and it is lost in the haze near the horizon. In a few weeks, it reappears in the dawn sky, a brilliant morning star.

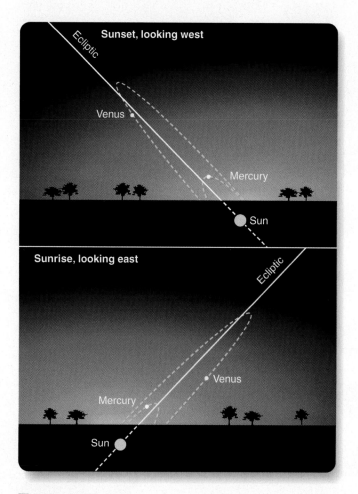

■ **Figure 2-10**

Mercury and Venus follow orbits that keep them near the sun, and they are visible only soon after sunset or before sunrise when the brilliance of the sun is hidden below the horizon. Venus takes 584 days to move from the morning sky to the evening sky and back again, but Mercury zips around in only 116 days.

Pseudoscience

What is the difference between a science and a pseudoscience? Astronomers have a low opinion of beliefs such as astrology, mostly because they are groundless but also because they *pretend* to be a science. They are pseudosciences, from the Greek *pseudo,* meaning false.

A **pseudoscience** is a set of beliefs that appear to be based on scientific ideas but that fail to obey the most basic rules of science. For example, in the 1970s a claim was made that pyramidal shapes focus cosmic forces on anything underneath and might even have healing properties. For example, it was claimed that a pyramid made of paper, plastic, or other materials would preserve fruit, sharpen razor blades, and do other miraculous things. Many books promoted the idea of the special power of pyramids, and this idea led to a popular fad.

A key characteristic of science is that its claims can be tested and verified. In this case, simple experiments showed that any shape, not just a pyramid, protects a piece of fruit from airborne spores and allows it to dry

without rotting. Likewise, any shape allows oxidation to improve the cutting edge of a razor blade. Because experimental evidence contradicted the claim and because supporters of the theory declined to abandon or revise their claims, you can recognize pyramid power as a pseudoscience. Disregard of contradictory evidence and alternate theories is a sure sign of a pseudoscience.

Pseudoscientific claims can be self-fulfilling. For example, some believers in pyramid power slept under pyramidal tents to improve their rest. There is no logical mechanism by which such a tent could affect a sleeper, but because people wanted and expected the claim to be true they reported that they slept more soundly. Vague claims based on personal testimony that cannot be tested are another sign of a pseudoscience.

Astrology is another pseudoscience. It has been tested over and over for centuries, and it doesn't work. Nevertheless, many people believe in astrology despite contradictory evidence.

Astrology may be the oldest pseudoscience.

Many pseudosciences appeal to our need to understand and control the world around us. Some such claims involve medical cures, ranging from using magnetic bracelets and crystals to focus mystical power to astonishingly expensive, illegal, and dangerous treatments for cancer. Logic is a stranger to pseudoscience, but human fears and needs are not.

The cycles of the sky are so impressive that it is not surprising that people have strong feelings about them. Ancient peoples saw the motion of the sun around the ecliptic as a powerful influence on their daily lives, and the motion of the planets along the ecliptic seemed similarly meaningful. The ancient superstition of astrology is based on the cycles of the sun and planets around the sky. You have probably heard of the **zodiac,** a band around the sky extending 9 degrees above and below the ecliptic. The signs of the zodiac take their names from the 12 principal constellations along the ecliptic. A **horoscope** is just a diagram showing the location of the sun, moon, and planets around the ecliptic and their position above or below the horizon for a given date and time. Centuries ago, astrology was an important part of astronomy, but the two are now almost exact opposites—astronomy is a science that depends on evidence, and astrology is a superstition that survives in spite of evidence (**How Do We Know? 2-2**). The signs of the zodiac are no longer important in astronomy.

2-4 Astronomical Influences on Earth's Climate

THE SEASONS ARE PRODUCED by the annual motion of Earth around the sun, but subtle changes in that motion can have dramatic affects on climate. You don't notice these changes during your lifetime; but, over thousands of years, they can bury continents under glaciers.

Earth has gone through ice ages when the worldwide climate was cooler and dryer and thick layers of ice covered polar regions, extending partway to the equator. Between ice ages, Earth is warmer and there are no ice sheets even at the poles. Scientists have found evidence of at least four ice ages in Earth's past. One occurred 2.5 billion years ago, but the other three that have been identified have all occurred in the last billion years. There were probably others, but evidence of early ice ages is usually erased by more recent ice sheets. The lengths of ice ages range from a few tens of millions of years to a few hundred million years. The most recent ice age began only about 3 million years ago and is still going on. You are living during one of the periodic episodes during an ice age when Earth grows slightly warmer and the glaciers melt back and do not extend as far from the poles. The current warm period began about 12,000 years ago.

Ice ages seem to occur with a period of roughly 250 million years, and glaciers advance and melt back during ice ages in a complicated pattern that involves cycles of about 40,000 years and 100,000 years. (These cycles have no connection with global warming, which can produce changes in Earth's climate over just a few decades. Global warming is discussed in Chapter 20.) Evidence shows that these slow cycles of the ice ages have an astronomical origin.

The Hypothesis

Sometimes a theory or hypothesis is proposed long before scientists can find the critical evidence to test it. That happened in 1920 when the Yugoslavian meteorologist Milutin Milankovitch proposed what became known as the **Milankovitch hypothesis**—that small changes in Earth's orbit, precession, and inclination affect Earth's climate and can cause ice ages. You should examine each of these motions separately.

First, Earth's orbit is only very slightly elliptical, but astronomers know that, because of gravitational interactions with the other planets, the elliptical shape varies slightly over a period of about 100,000 years. As you learned earlier in this chapter, Earth's orbit at present carries it 1.7 percent closer than average to the sun during northern hemisphere winters and 1.7 percent farther away in northern hemisphere summers. This makes northern winters very slightly warmer, and that is critical—most of the landmass where ice can accumulate is in the northern hemisphere. When Earth's orbit becomes more elliptical, northern summers might be too cool to melt all of the snow and ice from the previous winter. That would make glaciers grow larger.

A second factor is also at work. Precession causes Earth's axis to sweep around a cone with a period of about 26,000 years, and that gradually changes the points in Earth's orbit where a given hemisphere experiences the seasons. Northern hemisphere summers now occur when Earth is 1.7 percent farther from the sun, but in 13,000 years northern summers will occur on the other side of Earth's orbit where Earth is 1.7 percent closer to the sun. Northern summers will be warmer, which could melt all of the previous winter's snow and ice and prevent the growth of glaciers.

The third factor is the inclination of Earth's equator to its orbit, currently at 23.4°. Because of gravitational tugs of the moon, sun, and even the other planets, this angle varies from 22° to 24°, with a period of roughly 41,000 years. When the inclination is greater, seasons are more severe.

In 1920, Milankovitch proposed that these three factors cycle against each other to produce complex periodic variations in Earth's climate and the advance and retreat of glaciers (■ Figure 2-11a). No evidence was available to test the theory in 1920, however, and scientists treated it with skepticism. Many thought it was laughable.

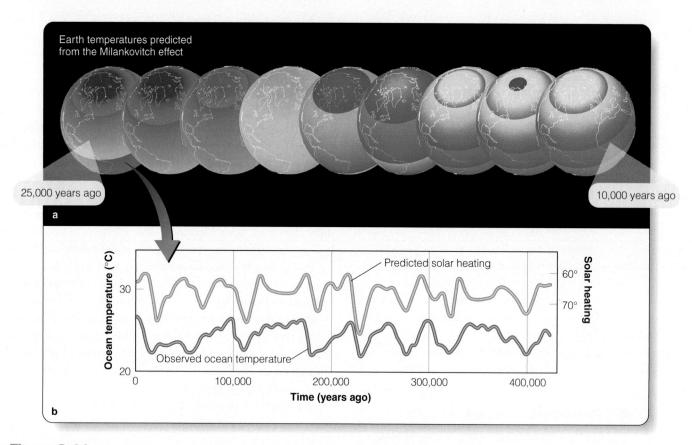

■ Figure 2-11

(a) Mathematical models of the Milankovitch effect can be used to predict temperatures on Earth over time. In these Earth globes, cool temperatures are represented by violet and blue and warm temperatures by yellow and red. These globes show the warming that occurred beginning 25,000 years ago, which ended the last ice age about 12,000 years ago. (Courtesy Arizona State University, Computer Science and Geography Departments) (b) Over the last 400,000 years, changes in ocean temperatures measured from fossils found in sediment layers from the seabed approximately match calculated changes in solar heating. (Adapted from Cesare Emiliani)

Evidence as the Foundation of Science

Why is evidence critical in science? From colliding galaxies to the inner workings of atoms, scientists love to speculate and devise theories, but all scientific knowledge is ultimately based on evidence from observations and experiments. Evidence is reality, and scientists constantly check their ideas against reality.

When you think of evidence, you probably think of criminal investigations in which detectives collect fingerprints and eyewitness accounts. In court, that evidence is used to try to understand the crime, but there is a key difference in how lawyers and scientists use evidence. A defense attorney can call a witness and intentionally fail to ask a question that would reveal evidence harmful to the defendant. In contrast, the scientist must be objective and not ignore any known evidence.

The attorney is presenting only one side of the case, but the scientist is searching for the truth. In a sense, the scientist must deal with the evidence as both the prosecution and the defense.

It is a characteristic of scientific knowledge that it is supported by evidence. A scientific statement is more than an opinion or a speculation because it has been tested objectively against reality.

As you read about any science, look for the evidence in the form of observations and experiments. Every theory or conclusion should have supporting evidence. If you can find and understand the evidence, the science will make sense. All scientists, from astronomers to zoologists, demand evidence. You should, too.

Fingerprints are evidence to past events.
(Dorling Kindersly/Getty Images)

The Evidence

By the middle 1970s, Earth scientists were able to collect the data that Milankovitch had lacked. Oceanographers drilled deep into the seafloor to collect long cores of sediment. In the laboratory, geologists could take samples from different depths in the cores and determine the age of the samples and the temperature of the oceans when they were deposited on the seafloor. From this, scientists constructed a history of ocean temperatures that convincingly matched the predictions of the Milankovitch hypothesis (Figure 2-11b).

The evidence seemed very strong, and by the 1980s the Milankovitch hypothesis was widely considered the leading hypothesis. But science follows a mostly unstated set of rules that holds that a hypothesis must be tested over and over against all available evidence (**How Do We Know? 2-3**). In 1988, scientists discovered contradictory evidence.

For 500,000 years rainwater has collected in a deep crack in Nevada called Devil's Hole. That water has deposited the mineral calcite in layer on layer on the walls of the crack. It isn't easy to get to, and scientists had to dive with scuba gear to drill out samples of the calcite, but it was worth the effort. Back in the laboratory, they could determine the age of each layer in their core samples and the temperature of the rainwater that had formed the calcite in each layer. That gave them a history of temperatures at Devil's Hole that spanned many thousands of years, and the results were a surprise. The evidence seemed to show that Earth had begun warming up thousands of years too early for the last ice age to have been caused by the Milankovitch cycles.

These contradictory findings are irritating because we humans naturally prefer certainty, but such circumstances are common in science. The disagreement between the ocean floor samples and the Devil's Hole samples triggered a scramble to understand the problem. Were the age determinations of one or the other set of samples wrong? Were the calculations of ancient temperatures wrong? Or were scientists misunderstanding the significance of the evidence?

In 1997, a new study of the ages of the samples confirmed that those from the ocean floor are correctly dated. But the same study found that the ages of the Devil's Hole samples are also correct. Evidently the temperatures at Devil's Hole record local climate changes in the region that became the southwestern United States. The ocean floor samples record global climate changes, and they fit well with the Milankovitch hypothesis. This has given scientists renewed confidence in the Milankovitch hypothesis, and although it is widely accepted today, it is still being tested whenever scientists can find more evidence.

As you review this section, notice that it is a **scientific argument,** a careful presentation of theory and evidence in a logical discussion. **How Do We Know? 2-4** expands on the ways

Scientific Arguments

How is a scientific argument different from an advertisement? Advertisements sometimes sound scientific, but they are fundamentally different from scientific arguments. An advertisement is designed to convince you to buy a product. "Our shampoo promises 85 percent shinier hair." The statement may sound like science, but it isn't a complete, honest discussion. "Shinier than what?" you might ask. An advertiser's only goal is a sale.

Scientists construct arguments because they want to test their own ideas and give an accurate explanation of some aspect of nature. For example, in the 1960s, biologist E. O. Wilson presented a scientific argument to show that ants communicate by smells. The argument included a description of his careful observations and the ingenious experiments he had conducted to test his theory. He also considered other evidence and other theories

for ant communication. Scientists can include any evidence or theory that supports their claim, but they must observe one fundamental rule of science: They must be totally honest—they must include all of the evidence and all of the theories.

Scientists publish their work in scientific arguments, but they also think in scientific arguments. If, in thinking through his argument, Wilson had found a contradiction, he would have known he was on the wrong track. That is why scientific arguments must be complete and honest. Scientists who ignore inconvenient evidence or brush aside other theories are only fooling themselves.

A good scientific argument gives you all the information you need to decide for yourself whether the argument is correct. Wilson's study of ant communication is now widely

Scientists have discovered that ants communicate with a large vocabulary of smells.
(Eye of Science/Photo Researchers, Inc.)

understood and is being applied to other fields such as pest control and telecommunications networks.

scientists organize their ideas in logical arguments. Throughout this book, many chapter sections end with short reviews entitled "Scientific Argument." These feature a review question, which is then analyzed in a scientific argument. A second question gives you a chance to build your own scientific argument on a related topic. You can use these "Scientific Argument" features to review chapter material, but also to practice thinking like a scientist.

SCIENTIFIC ARGUMENT

Why was it critical in testing the Milankovitch hypothesis to determine the ages of ocean sediment?
Ocean floors accumulate sediment year after year in thin layers. Scientists can drill into the ocean floor and collect cores of those sediment layers, and from chemical tests they can find the temperature of the seawater when each layer was deposited. Those observations of temperature could be used as reality checks for the climate temperatures predicted by the Milankovitch theory, but that meant the ages of the sediment layers had to be determined correctly. When a conflict arose with evidence from Devil's Hole in Nevada, the age determinations of the samples were carefully reexamined and found to be correct.

After reviewing all of the evidence, scientists concluded that the ocean core samples do indeed support the Milankovitch hypothesis. Now construct your own argument. **What might the temperatures recorded at Devil's Hole represent?**

What Are We?
Along for the Ride

Human civilization is spread over the surface of planet Earth like a thin coat of paint. Great cities of skyscrapers and tangles of superhighways may seem impressive, but if you use your astronomical perspective, you can see that we humans are confined to the surface of our world.

The rotation of Earth creates a cycle of day and night that controls everything from TV schedules to the chemical workings of our brains. We wake and sleep within that 24-hour cycle of light and dark. Furthermore, Earth's orbital motion around the sun, combined with the inclination of its axis, creates a yearly cycle of seasons, and we humans, along with every other living thing on Earth, have evolved to survive within those extremes of temperature. We protect ourselves from the largest extremes and have spread over most of Earth, hunting, gathering, and growing crops within the cycle of the seasons.

In recent times, we have begun to understand that conditions on Earth's surface are not entirely stable. Slow changes in its motions produce a cycle of ice ages with irregular pulses of glaciation. All of recorded history, including all of the cities and superhighways that paint our globe, has occurred since the last glacial retreat only 12,000 years ago, so we humans have no recorded experience of Earth's harshest climate. We have never experienced our planet's icy personality. We are along for the ride and enjoying Earth's good times.

Summary

▶ Astronomers divide the sky into 88 **constellations (p. 12)**. Although the constellations originated in Greek and Middle Eastern mythology, the names are Latin. Even the modern constellations, added to fill in the spaces between the ancient figures, have Latin names. Named groups of stars that are not constellations are called **asterisms (p. 13)**.

▶ The names of stars usually come from ancient Arabic, though modern astronomers often refer to a star by its constellation and a Greek letter assigned according to its brightness within the constellation.

▶ Astronomers refer to the brightness of stars using the **magnitude scale (p. 14)**. First-magnitude stars are brighter than second-magnitude stars, which are brighter than third-magnitude stars, and so on. The magnitude you see when you look at a star in the sky is its **apparent visual magnitude, m_v (p. 15)**, which includes only types of light visible to the human eye and does not take into account the star's distance from Earth.

▶ **Flux (p. 15)** is a measure of light energy related to intensity. The magnitude of a star is related directly to the flux of light received on Earth and so to its intensity.

▶ The **celestial sphere (p. 18)** is a **scientific model (p. 17)** of the sky, to which the stars appear to be attached. Because Earth rotates eastward, the celestial sphere appears to rotate westward on its axis.

▶ The **north** and **south celestial poles (p. 18)** are the pivots on which the sky appears to rotate, and they define the four directions around the **horizon (p. 18)**: the **north, south, east,** and **west points (p. 18)**. The point directly over head is the **zenith (p. 18)**, and the point on the sky directly underfoot is the **nadir (p. 18)**.

▶ The **celestial equator (p. 17)**, an imaginary line around the sky above Earth's equator, divides the sky into northern and southern halves.

▶ Astronomers often refer to distances "on" the sky as if the stars, sun, moon, and planets were equivalent to spots painted on a plaster ceiling. These **angular distances (p. 19)**, measured in degrees, **arc minutes (p. 19)**, and **arc seconds (p. 19)**, are unrelated to the true distance between the objects in light-years. The angular distance across an object is its **angular diameter (p. 19)**.

▶ What you see of the celestial sphere depends on your latitude. Much of the southern hemisphere of the sky is not visible from northern latitudes. To see that part of the sky, you would have to travel southward over Earth's surface. **Circumpolar constellations (p. 19)** are those close enough to a celestial pole that they do not rise or set.

▶ The angular distance from the horizon to the north celestial pole always equals your latitude. This is the basis for celestial navigation.

▶ **Precession (p. 17)** is caused by the gravitational forces of the moon and sun acting on the equatorial bulge of the spinning Earth and causing its axis to sweep around in a conical motion like the motion of a top's axis. Earth's axis of rotation precesses with a period of 26,000 years, and consequently the celestial poles and celestial equator move slowly against the background of the stars.

▶ The **rotation (p. 20)** of Earth on its axis produces the cycle of day and night, and the **revolution (p. 20)** of Earth around the sun produces the cycle of the year.

▶ Because Earth orbits the sun, the sun appears to move eastward along the **ecliptic (p. 21)** through the constellations completing a circuit of the sky in a year. Because the ecliptic is tipped 23.4° to the celestial equator, the sun spends half the year in the northern celestial hemisphere and half in the southern celestial hemisphere.

▶ In each hemisphere's summer, the sun is above the horizon longer and shines more directly down on the ground. Both effects cause warmer weather in that hemisphere and leave Earth's other hemisphere cooler. In each hemisphere's winter, the sun is above the sky fewer hours than in summer and shines less directly, so the winter hemisphere has colder weather, and the opposite hemisphere has summer. Consequently the seasons are reversed in Earth's southern hemisphere relative to the northern hemisphere.

▶ The beginning of spring, summer, winter, and fall are marked by the **vernal equinox (p. 22)**, the **summer solstice (p. 22)**, the **autumnal equinox (p. 22)**, and the **winter solstice (p. 22)**.

▶ Earth is slightly closer to the sun at **perihelion (p. 23)** in January and slightly farther away from the sun at **aphelion (p. 23)** in July. This has almost no effect on the seasons.

▶ The planets move generally eastward along the ecliptic, and all but Uranus and Neptune are visible to the unaided eye looking like stars. Mercury and Venus never wander far from the sun and are sometimes visible in the evening sky after sunset or in the dawn sky before sunrise.

▶ Planets visible in the sky at sunset are traditionally called **evening stars (p. 24)**, and planets visible in the dawn sky are called **morning stars (p. 24)** even though they are not actually stars.

▶ The locations of the sun and planets along the **zodiac (p. 25)** are diagramed in a **horoscope (p. 25)**, which is the bases for the ancient **pseudoscience (p. 25)** known as astrology.

▶ According to the **Milankovitch hypothesis (p. 26)**, changes in the shape of Earth's orbit, in its precession, and in its axial tilt can alter the planet's heat balance and cause the cycle of ice ages. Evidence found in seafloor samples support the hypothesis, and it is widely accepted today.

▶ Scientists routinely test their own ideas by organizing theory and evidence into a **scientific argument (p. 27)**.

Review Questions

1. Why are most modern constellations composed of faint stars or located in the southern sky?

2. How does the Greek-letter designation of a star give you clues to its location and brightness?

3. From your knowledge of stars names and constellations, which of the following stars in each pair is the brighter? Explain your answers.
   a. Alpha Ursae Majoris; Epsilon Ursae Majoris
   b. Epsilon Scorpii; Alpha Pegasus
   c. Alpha Telescopium; Alpha Orionis

4. How did the magnitude system originate in a classification of stars by brightness?

5. What does the word *apparent* mean in *apparent visual magnitude?*

6. What does the word *visual* mean in *apparent visual magnitude?*

7. In what ways is the celestial sphere a scientific model?

8. If Earth did not rotate, could you define the celestial poles and celestial equator?

9. Where would you go on Earth if you wanted to be able to see both the north celestial pole and the south celestial pole at the same time?

10. Why does the number of circumpolar constellations depend on the latitude of the observer?

11. Explain two reasons why winter days are colder than summer days.

12. How do the seasons in Earth's southern hemisphere differ from those in the northern hemisphere?

13. Why should the eccentricity of Earth's orbit make winter in Earth's northern hemisphere different from winter in Earth's southern hemisphere?

14. **How Do We Know?** How can a scientific model be useful if it isn't a correct description of nature?

15. **How Do We Know?** In what way is astrology a pseudoscience?

16. **How Do We Know?** How is evidence a distinguishing characteristic of science?

17. **How Do We Know?** Why must a scientific argument dealing with some aspect of nature include all of the evidence?

Discussion Questions

1. All cultures on Earth named constellations. Why do you suppose this was such a common practice?

2. If you were lost at sea, you could find your approximate latitude by measuring the altitude of Polaris. But Polaris isn't exactly at the celestial pole. What else would you need to know to measure your latitude more accurately?

3. Do planets orbiting other stars have ecliptics? Could they have seasons?

Problems

1. Star A has a magnitude of 2.5; Star B, 5.5; and Star C, 9.5. Which is brightest? Which are visible to the unaided eye? Which pair of stars has an intensity ratio of 16?

2. If one star is 6.3 times brighter than another star, how many magnitudes brighter is it?

3. If light from one star is 40 times more intense than light from another star, what is their difference in magnitudes?

4. If two stars differ by 7 magnitudes, what is their intensity ratio?

5. If two stars differ by 8.6 magnitudes, what is their intensity ratio?

6. If star A is magnitude 4 and star B is magnitude 9.6, which is brighter and by what factor?

7. By what factor is the sun brighter than the full moon? (*Hint:* See Figure 2-6.)

8. What is the angular distance from the north celestial pole to the point on the sky called the summer solstice? To the winter solstice?

9. If you are at a latitude of 35 degrees north of Earth's equator, what is the angular distance from the northern horizon up to the north celestial pole? From the southern horizon down to the south celestial pole?

Learning to Look

1. Find Sagittarius and Scorpius in the photograph that opens this chapter.

2. The stamp below shows the constellation Orion. Explain why this looks odd to residents of the northern hemisphere.

3. Imagine that the diagram below is a photograph taken in mid-September. Use the star charts at the back of this book to decide about what time of night the photo would have been taken.

Cycles of the Moon

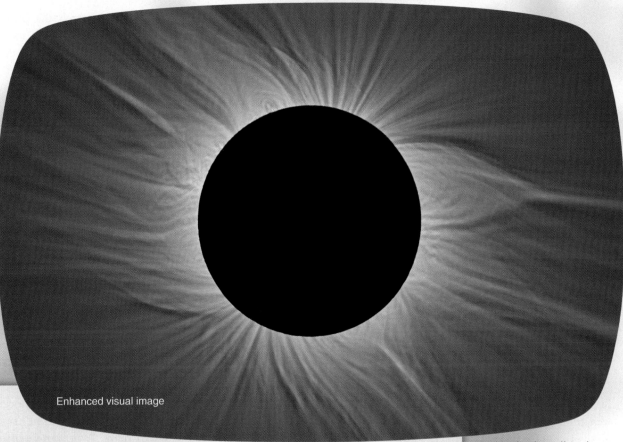

Enhanced visual image

■ Guidepost

In the previous chapter, you studied the cycle of day and night and the cycle of the seasons. Now you are ready to study the brightest object in the night sky. The moon moves rapidly against the background of stars, changing its shape and occasionally producing spectacular events called eclipses. This chapter will help you answer four essential questions about Earth's satellite:

— **Why does the moon go through phases?**

— **What causes a lunar eclipse?**

— **What causes a solar eclipse?**

— **How can eclipses be predicted?**

Understanding the phases of the moon and eclipses will exercise your scientific imagination and help you enjoy the sight of the moon crossing the sky.

Once you have a 21st-century understanding of your world and its motion, you will be ready to read the next chapter, in which you will see how Renaissance astronomers analyzed what they saw in the sky, used their imaginations, and came to a revolutionary conclusion—that Earth is a planet.

A total solar eclipse is a lunar phenomenon. It occurs when the moon crosses in front of the sun and hides its brilliant surface. Then you can see the sun's extended atmosphere. (© F. Espenak, www.MrEclipse.com)

Even a man who is pure in heart and says his prayers by night

May become a wolf when the wolfbane blooms and the moon shines full and bright.

— PROVERB FROM OLD WOLFMAN MOVIES

DID ANYONE EVER WARN YOU, "Don't stare at the moon—you'll go crazy"? For centuries, the superstitious have associated the moon with insanity. The word *lunatic* comes from a time when even doctors thought that the insane were "moonstruck." Of course, the moon does not cause madness, but it is so bright and moves so rapidly along the ecliptic that people *expect* it to affect them. It is, in fact, one of the most beautiful and dramatic objects in the sky.

3-1 The Changeable Moon

STARTING THIS EVENING, begin looking for the moon in the sky. As you watch for the moon on successive evenings, you will see it following its orbit around Earth and cycling through its phases as it has done for billions of years.

The Motion of the Moon

Just as the planets revolve counterclockwise around the sun as seen from the direction of the celestial north pole, the moon revolves counterclockwise around Earth. Because the moon's orbit is tipped a little over 5 degrees from the plane of Earth's orbit, the moon's path takes it slightly north and then slightly south, but it is always somewhere near the ecliptic.

The moon moves rapidly against the background of the constellations. If you watch the moon for just an hour, you can see it move eastward by slightly more than its angular diameter. In the previous chapter, you learned that the moon is about 0.5° in angular diameter, and it moves eastward a bit more than 0.5° per hour. In 24 hours, it moves 13°. Thus, each night you see the moon about 13° eastward of its location the night before.

As the moon orbits around Earth, its shape changes from night to night in a month-long cycle.

The Cycle of Phases

The changing shape of the moon as it revolves around Earth is one of the most easily observed phenomena in astronomy. Study **The Phases of the Moon** on pages 34–35 and notice three important points and two new terms:

1 The moon always keeps the same side facing Earth. "The man in the moon" is produced by the familiar features on the moon's near side, but you never see the far side of the moon.

2 The changing shape of the moon as it passes through its cycle of phases is produced by sunlight illuminating different parts of the side of the moon you can see.

3 Notice the difference between the orbital period of the moon around Earth (*sidereal period*) and the length of the lunar phase cycle (*synodic period*). That difference is a good illustration of how your view from Earth is produced by the combined motions of Earth and other heavenly bodies, such as the sun and moon.

You can figure out where the moon will be in the sky by making a moon-phase dial from the middle diagram on page 34. Cover the lower half of the moon's orbit with a sheet of paper and align the edge of the paper to pass through the word "Full" at the left and the word "New" at the right. Push a pin through the edge of the paper at Earth's North Pole to make a pivot and, under the word "Full," write on the paper "Eastern Horizon." Under the word "New," write "Western Horizon." The paper now represents the horizon you see when you stand facing south. You can set your moon-phase dial for a given time by rotating the diagram behind the horizon-paper. For example, set the dial to sunset by turning the diagram until the human figure labeled "sunset" is standing at the top of the Earth globe; the dial shows, for example, that the full moon at sunset would be at the eastern horizon.

The phases of the moon are dramatic, and they have attracted a number of peculiar ideas. You have probably heard a number of **Common Misconceptions** about the moon. Sometimes people are surprised to see the moon in the daytime sky, and they think something has gone wrong! No, the gibbous moon is often visible in the daytime, although quarter moons and especially crescent moons can also be in the daytime sky but are harder to see when the sun is above the horizon. You may hear people mention "the dark side of the moon," but you will be able to assure them that this is a misconception; there is no permanently dark side. Any location on the moon is sunlit for two weeks and is in darkness for two weeks as the moon rotates in sunlight. Finally, you have probably heard one of the strangest misconceptions about the moon: that people tend to act up at full moon. Actual statistical studies of records from schools, prisons, hospitals, and so on, show that it isn't true. There are always a few people who misbehave; the moon has nothing to do with it.

For billions of years, the man in the moon has looked down on Earth. Ancient civilizations saw the same cycle of phases that you see (■ Figure 3-1), and even the dinosaurs may have noticed the changing phases of the moon. Occasionally, however, the moon displays more complicated moods when it turns copper-red in a lunar eclipse.

■ Figure 3-1

In this sequence of lunar phases, the moon cycles through its phases from crescent to full to crescent. You see the same face of the moon, the same mountains, craters, and plains, but the changing direction of sunlight produces the lunar phases.

3-2 Lunar Eclipses

IN CULTURES ALL AROUND THE WORLD, the sky is a symbol of order and power, and the moon is the regular counter of the passing days. So it is not surprising that people are startled and sometimes worried when they see the moon grow dark and angry-red. Such events are neither mysterious nor frightening once you understand how they arise. To begin, you can think about Earth's shadow.

Earth's Shadow

The orbit of the moon is tipped only a few degrees from the plane of Earth's orbit around the sun, and Earth's shadow points directly away from the sun also in the plane of Earth's orbit. A **lunar eclipse** can occur at full moon if the moon's path carries it through the shadow of Earth. That is unusual because most full moons pass north or south of Earth's shadow and there is no eclipse. If the moon enters Earth's shadow, sunlight is cut off, and the moon grows dim.

The shadow consists of two parts (■ Figure 3-2). The **umbra** is the region of total shadow. If you were drifting in your spacesuit

in the umbra of Earth's shadow, the sun would be completely hidden behind Earth, and you would not be able to see any part of the sun's bright disk. If you drifted into the **penumbra,** however, you would see part of the sun peeking around the edge of Earth, so you would be in partial shadow. In the penumbra, sunlight is dimmed but not extinguished.

The umbra of Earth's shadow is over three times longer than the distance to the moon and points directly away from the sun. A giant screen placed in the shadow at the average distance of the moon would reveal a dark umbral shadow about 2.5 times the diameter of the moon. The faint outer edges of the penumbra would mark a circle about 4.6 times the diameter of the moon. Consequently, when the moon's orbit carries it through the umbra, it has plenty of room to become completely immersed in shadow.

Total Lunar Eclipses

Once or twice a year, the orbit of the moon carries it through the umbra of Earth's shadow; and, if no part of the moon remains outside the umbra in the partial sunlight of the penumbra, you

■ Figure 3-2

The shadows cast by a map tack resemble the shadows of Earth and the moon. The umbra is the region of total shadow; the penumbra is the region of partial shadow.

The Phases of the Moon

1 As the moon orbits Earth, it rotates to keep the same side facing Earth as shown at right. Consequently you always see the same features on the moon, and you never see the far side of the moon. A mountain on the moon that points at Earth will always point at Earth as the moon revolves and rotates.

(Not to scale)

First quarter

Waxing gibbous

Waxing crescent

Sunset

North Pole

Midnight ← → Noon

Earth's rotation

Sunrise

New

Full

Waning crescent

Waning gibbous

Third quarter

Sunlight

2 As seen at left, sunlight always illuminates half of the moon. Because you see different amounts of this sunlit side, you see the moon cycle through phases. At the phase called "new moon," sunlight illuminates the far side of the moon, and the side you see is in darkness. At new moon you see no moon at all. At full moon, the side you see is fully lit, and the far side is in darkness. How much you see depends on where the moon is in its orbit.

Notice that there is no such thing as the "dark side of the moon." All parts of the moon experience day and night in a month-long cycle.

In the diagram at the left, you see that the new moon is close to the sun in the sky, and the full moon is opposite the sun. The time of day depends on the observer's location on Earth.

2a The first 2 weeks of the cycle of the moon are shown below by its position at sunset on 14 successive evenings. As the moon grows fatter from new to full, it is said to wax.

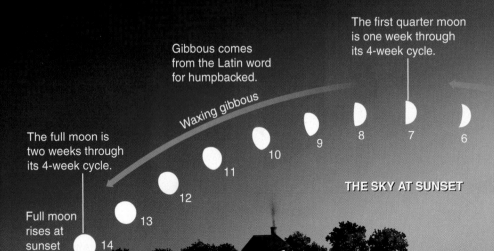

The first quarter moon is one week through its 4-week cycle.

Gibbous comes from the Latin word for humpbacked.

Waxing gibbous

Waxing crescent

The full moon is two weeks through its 4-week cycle.

Full moon rises at sunset

THE SKY AT SUNSET

Days since new moon

New moon is invisible near the sun

14 13 12 11 10 9 8 7 6 5 4 3 2 1

3 The moon orbits eastward around Earth in 27.32 days, its **sidereal period.** This is how long the moon takes to circle the sky once and return to the same position among the stars.

A complete cycle of lunar phases takes 29.53 days, the moon's **synodic period.** (Synodic comes from the Greek words for "together" and "path.")

To see why the synodic period is longer than the sidereal period, study the star charts at the right.

Although you think of the lunar cycle as being about 4 weeks long, it is actually 1.53 days longer than 4 weeks. The calendar divides the year into 30-day periods called months (literally "moonths") in recognition of the 29.53 day synodic cycle of the moon.

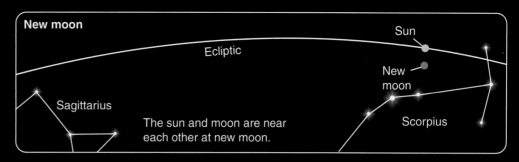

New moon

Ecliptic

Sun

New moon

Sagittarius

Scorpius

The sun and moon are near each other at new moon.

One sidereal period after new moon

Ecliptic

Sun

Sagittarius

Moon

Scorpius

One sidereal period after new moon, the moon has returned to the same place among the stars, but the sun has moved on along the ecliptic.

One synodic period after new moon

Sun

Ecliptic

New moon

Sagittarius

Scorpius

One synodic period after new moon, the moon has caught up with the sun and is again at new moon.

You can use the diagram on the opposite page to determine when the moon rises and sets at different phases.

TIMES OF MOONRISE AND MOONSET

Phase	Moonrise	Moonset
New	Dawn	Sunset
First quarter	Noon	Midnight
Full	Sunset	Dawn
Third quarter	Midnight	Noon

2b The last two weeks of the cycle of the moon are shown below by its position at sunrise on 14 successive mornings. As the moon shrinks from full to new, it is said to wane.

The third quarter moon is 3 weeks through its 4-week cycle.

Waning crescent

Waning gibbous

New moon is invisible near the sun

27 26 25 24 23 22 21 20 19 18 17 16 15 14

THE SKY AT SUNRISE

Full moon sets at sunrise

East　　　　**South**　　　　**West**

During a total lunar eclipse, the moon takes a number of hours to move through Earth's shadow.

A cross section of Earth's shadow shows the umbra and penumbra.

Motion of moon

Visual

Sunlight scattered from Earth's atmosphere bathes the totally eclipsed moon in a coppery glow.

Orbit of moon

To sun   Umbra   Penumbra   (Not to scale)

■ **Figure 3-3**

In this diagram of a total lunar eclipse, the moon passes from right to left through Earth's shadow. A multiple-exposure photograph shows the moon passing through the umbra of Earth's shadow. A longer exposure was used to record the moon while it was totally eclipsed. The moon's path appears curved in the photo because of photographic effects. (© 1982 Dr. Jack B. Marling)

see a **total lunar eclipse** (■ Figure 3-3). As you watch the eclipse begin, the moon first moves into the penumbra and dims slightly; the deeper it moves into the penumbra, the more it dims. Eventually, the moon reaches the umbra, and you see the umbral shadow first darken part, then all, of the moon.

When the moon is totally eclipsed, it does not disappear completely. Although it receives no direct sunlight, the moon in the umbra does receive some sunlight that is refracted (bent) through Earth's atmosphere. If you were on the moon during **totality,** you would not see any part of the sun because it would be entirely hidden behind Earth. However, you would see Earth's atmosphere illuminated from behind by the sun. The red glow from this ring of "sunsets" and "sunrises" illuminates the moon during totality and makes it glow coppery red, as shown in ■ Figure 3-4.

How dim the totally eclipsed moon becomes depends on a number of things. If Earth's atmosphere is especially cloudy in the regions that would bend light into the umbra, the moon will be darker than usual. An unusual amount of dust in Earth's atmosphere (from volcanic eruptions, for instance) also causes a dark eclipse. Also, total lunar eclipses tend to be darkest when the moon's orbit carries it through the center of the umbra.

The exact timing of a lunar eclipse depends on where the moon crosses Earth's shadow. If it crosses through the center of the umbra, the eclipse will have maximum length. For such an eclipse, the moon spends about an hour crossing the penumbra and then another hour entering the darker umbra. Totality can last as long as 1 hour 45 minutes, followed by the emergence of the moon into the penumbra, plus another hour as it emerges into full sunlight. A total lunar eclipse can take nearly six hours from start to finish.

Partial and Penumbral Lunar Eclipses

Because the moon's orbit is inclined by a bit over 5° to the plane of Earth's orbit, the moon does not always pass through the center of the umbra. If the moon passes a bit too far north or south, it may only partially enter the umbra, and you see a **partial lunar eclipse.** The part of the moon that

Visual

■ **Figure 3-4**

During a total lunar eclipse, the moon turns coppery red. In this photo, the moon is darkest toward the lower right, the direction toward the center of the umbra. The edge of the moon at upper left is brighter because it is near the edge of the umbra. (Celestron International)

■ Table 3-1 | Total and Partial Eclipses of the Moon, 2010 to 2017*

Year	Time** of Mid-eclipse (GMT)	Length of Totality (Hr: Min)	Length of Eclipse† (Hr: Min)
2010 June 26	11:40	Partial	2:42
2010 Dec. 21	8:18	1:12	3:28
2011 June 15	20:13	1:40	3:38
2011 Dec. 10	14:33	0:50	3:32
2012 June 4	11:03	Partial	2:08
2013 April 25	20:10	Partial	0:28
2014 April 15	7:48	1:18	3:34
2014 Oct. 8	10:55	0:58	3:18
2015 April 4	12:02	Partial	3:28
2015 Sept. 28	2:48	72	3:30
2017 Aug. 7	18:22	Partial	1:54

*There are no total or partial lunar eclipses during 2016.

**Times are Greenwich Mean Time. Subtract 5 hours for Eastern Standard Time, 6 hours for Central Standard Time, 7 hours for Mountain Standard Time, and 8 hours for Pacific Standard Time. From your time zone, lunar eclipses that occur between sunset and sunrise will be visible, and those at midnight will be best placed.

†Does not include penumbral phase.

remains in the penumbra receives some direct sunlight, and the glare is usually great enough to prevent your seeing the faint coppery glow of the part of the moon in the umbra. Partial eclipses are interesting, but they are not as beautiful as a total lunar eclipse.

If the orbit of the moon carries it far enough north or south of the umbra, the moon may pass through only the penumbra and never reach the umbra. Such **penumbral lunar eclipses** are not dramatic at all. In the partial shadow of the penumbra, the moon is only partially dimmed. Most people glancing at a penumbral eclipse would not notice any difference from a full moon.

Total, partial, or penumbral, lunar eclipses are interesting events in the night sky and are not difficult to observe. When the full moon passes through Earth's shadow, the eclipse is visible from anywhere on Earth's dark side. Consult ■ Table 3-1 to find the next lunar eclipse visible in your part of the world.

SCIENTIFIC ARGUMENT

What would a total lunar eclipse look like if Earth had no atmosphere?

As a way to test and improve their understanding, scientists often experiment with their ideas by changing one thing and trying to imagine what would happen. In this case, the absence of an atmosphere around Earth would mean that no sunlight would be bent toward the eclipsed moon, and it would not glow red. It would be very dark in the sky during totality.

Now change a different parameter. **What would a lunar eclipse look like if the moon and Earth were the same diameter?**

3-3 Solar Eclipses

FOR MILLENNIA, cultures worldwide have understood that the sun is the source of life, so you can imagine the panic people felt at the fearsome sight of the sun gradually disappearing in the middle of the day. Many imagined that the sun was being devoured by a monster (■ Figure 3-5). Modern scientists must

■ Figure 3-5

(a) A 12th-century Mayan symbol believed to represent a solar eclipse. The black-and-white sun symbol hangs from a rectangular sky symbol, and a voracious serpent approaches from below. (b) The Chinese representation of a solar eclipse shows a monster usually described as a dragon flying in front of the sun. (From the collection of Yerkes Observatory) (c) This wall carving from the ruins of a temple in Vijayanagaara in southern India symbolizes a solar eclipse as two snakes approach the disk of the sun. (T. Scott Smith)

Scientific Imagination

How do scientists produce theories to test? Good scientists are invariably creative people with strong imaginations who can look at raw data about some invisible aspect of nature such as an atom and construct mental pictures as diverse as a plum pudding or a solar system. These scientists share the same human impulse to understand nature that drove ancient cultures to imagine eclipses as serpents devouring the sun.

As the 20th century began, physicists were busy trying to imagine what an atom was like. No one can see an atom, but English physicist J. J. Thomson used what he knew from his experiments and his powerful imagination to create an image of what an atom might be like. He suggested that an atom was a ball of positively charged material with negatively charged electrons distributed throughout like plums in a plum pudding.

The key difference between using a plum pudding to represent the atom and a hungry serpent to represent an eclipse is that the plum pudding model was based on experimental data and could be tested against new evidence. As it turned out, Thomson's student, Ernest Rutherford, performed ingenious new experiments and showed that atoms can't be made like plum puddings. Rather, he imagined an atom as a tiny positively charged nucleus surrounded by negatively charged electrons much like a tiny solar system with planets circling the sun. Later experiments confirmed that Rutherford's description of atoms is closer to reality, and it has become a universally recognized symbol for atomic energy.

Ancient cultures pictured the sun being devoured by a serpent. Thomson, Rutherford, and scientists like them used their scientific imaginations to visualize natural processes and

A model image of the atom as electrons orbiting a small nucleus has become the symbol for atomic energy.

then test and refine their ideas with new experiments and observations. The critical difference is that scientific imagination is continually tested against reality and is revised when necessary.

---

use their imaginations to visualize how nature works, but with a key difference; they test their ideas against reality (**How Do We Know? 3-1**). You can take comfort that today's astronomers explain solar eclipses without imagining celestial monsters.

A **solar eclipse** occurs when the moon moves between Earth and the sun. If the moon covers the disk of the sun completely, you see a spectacular **total solar eclipse** (■Figure 3-6). If, from your location, the moon covers only part of the sun, you see a less dramatic **partial solar eclipse.** During a solar eclipse, people in one place on Earth may see a total eclipse while people only a few hundred kilometers away see a partial eclipse.

The geometry of a solar eclipse is quite different from that of a lunar eclipse. You can begin by considering how big the sun and moon look in the sky.

The Angular Diameter of the Sun and Moon

Solar eclipses are spectacular because Earth's moon happens to have nearly the same angular diameter as the sun, so it can cover the sun's disk almost exactly. You learned about angular diameter in Chapter 2; now you need to think carefully about how the size and distance of an object like the moon determine its angular diameter.

Visual wavelength images

■ Figure 3-6

Solar eclipses are dramatic. In June 2001, an automatic camera in southern Africa snapped pictures every 5 minutes as the afternoon sun sank lower in the sky. From upper right to lower left, you can see the moon crossing the disk of the sun. A longer exposure was needed to record the total phase of the eclipse. (©2001 F. Espenak)

Linear diameter is simply the distance between an object's opposite sides. You use linear diameter when you order a 16-inch pizza—the pizza is 16 inches across. The linear diameter of the moon is 3476 km.

The angular diameter of an object is the angle formed by lines extending toward you from opposite edges of the object and meeting at your eye (■ Figure 3-7). Clearly, the farther away an object is, the smaller its angular diameter.

To find the angular diameter of the moon, you need to use the **small-angle formula.** It gives you a way to figure out the angular diameter of any object, whether it is a pizza or the moon. In the small-angle formula, you should always express angular diameter in arc seconds and always use the same units for distance and linear diameter:

$$\frac{\text{angular diameter}}{206{,}265} = \frac{\text{linear diameter}}{\text{distance}}$$

You can use this formula* to find any one of these three quantities if you know the other two; in this case, you are interested in finding the angular diameter of the moon.

The moon has a linear diameter of 3476 km and a distance from Earth of about 384,000 km. Because the moon's linear diameter and distance are both given in the same units, kilometers, you can put them directly into the small-angle formula:

$$\frac{\text{angular diameter}}{206{,}265} = \frac{3476 \text{ km}}{384{,}000 \text{ km}}$$

To solve for angular diameter, multiply both sides by 206,265. You will find that the angular diameter of the moon is 1870 arc seconds. If you divide by 60, you get 31 arc minutes, or, dividing by 60 again, about 0.5°. The moon's orbit is slightly elliptical, so the moon can sometimes look a bit larger or smaller, but its angular diameter is always close to 0.5°. It is a **Common Misconception** that the moon is larger when it is on the horizon. Certainly the rising full moon looks big when you see it on the horizon, but that is an optical illusion. In reality, the moon is the same size on the horizon as when it is high overhead.

Now repeat this small-angle calculation to find the angular diameter of the sun. The sun is 1.39×10^6 km in linear diameter and 1.50×10^8 km from Earth. If you put these numbers into the small-angle formula, you will discover that the sun has an angular diameter of 1900 arc seconds, which is 32 arc minutes, or about 0.5°. Earth's orbit is slightly elliptical, and consequently the sun can sometimes look slightly larger or smaller in the sky, but it, like the moon, is always close to 0.5° in angular diameter.

By fantastic good luck, you live on a planet with a moon that is almost exactly the same angular diameter as your sun. Thanks to that coincidence, when the moon passes in front of the sun, it is almost exactly the right size to cover the sun's brilliant surface but leave the sun's atmosphere visible.

---

*The number 206,265 is the number of arc seconds in a radian. When you divide by 206,265, you convert the angle from arc seconds to radians.

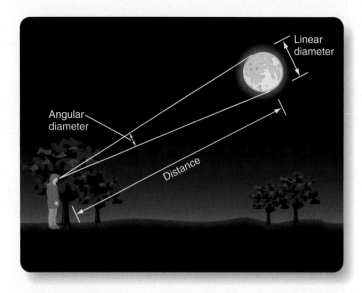

■ **Figure 3-7**

The angular diameter of an object is related to both its linear diameter and its distance.

The Moon's Shadow

To see a solar eclipse, you have to be in the moon's shadow. Like Earth's shadow, the moon's shadow consists of a central umbra of total shadow and a penumbra of partial shadow. The moon's umbral shadow produces a spot of darkness about 270 km (170 mi) in diameter on Earth's surface. (The exact size of the umbral shadow depends on the location of the moon in its elliptical orbit and the angle at which the shadow strikes Earth.) Because of the orbital motion of the moon and the rotation of Earth, the moon's shadow rushes across Earth at speeds of at least 1700 km/h (1060 mph) sweeping out a **path of totality** (■ Figure 3-8). People lucky enough to be in the path of totality will see a total eclipse of the sun when the umbral spot sweeps over them. Observers just outside the path of totality will see a partial solar eclipse as the penumbral shadow sweeps over their location. Those living even farther from the path of totality will see no eclipse.

Sometimes the moon's umbral shadow is not long enough to reach Earth, and, seen from Earth's surface, the disk of the moon is not big enough to cover the sun. The orbit of the moon is slightly elliptical, and its distance from Earth varies. When it is at **apogee,** its farthest point from Earth, its angular diameter is about 6 percent smaller than average, and when it is at **perigee,** its closest point to Earth, its angular diameter is 6 percent larger than average. Another factor is Earth's slightly elliptical orbit around the sun. When Earth is closest to the sun in January, the sun looks 1.7 percent larger in angular diameter; and, when Earth is at its farthest point in July, the sun looks 1.7 percent smaller. If the moon crosses in front of the sun when the moon's disk is smaller in angular diameter than the sun's, it produces an **annular eclipse,** a solar eclipse in which a ring (or annulus) of light is visible around the disk of the moon (■ Figure 3-9). An annular eclipse swept across the United States on May 10, 1994.

b Visual

■ **Figure 3-8**

(a) The umbra of the moon's shadow sweeps from west to east across Earth, and observers in the path of totality see a total solar eclipse. Those outside the umbra but inside the penumbra see a partial eclipse. (b) Eight photos made by a weather satellite have been combined to show the moon's shadow moving across Mexico, Central America, and Brazil. (NASA GOES images courtesy of MrEclipse.com)

■ **Figure 3-9**

Because the angular diameter of the moon and the sun vary slightly, the disk of the moon is sometimes too small to cover the disk of the sun. This means the umbra of the moon does not reach Earth, and the eclipse is annular. From Earth, you see an annular eclipse because the moon's angular diameter is smaller than the angular diameter of the sun. In the photograph of the annular eclipse of 1994, the dark disk of the moon is almost exactly centered on the bright disk of the sun. (Daniel Good)

■ Table 3-2 | Total and Annular Eclipses of the Sun, 2010 to 2019*

Date	Total/ Annular (T/A)	Time of Mid-eclipse** (GMT)	Maximum Length of Total or Annular Phase (Min:Sec)	Area of Visibility
2010 Jan. 15	A	7^h	11:10	Africa, Indian Ocean
2010 July 11	T	20^h	5:20	Pacific, South America
2012 May 20	A	23^h	5:46	Japan, North Pacific, western USA
2012 Nov. 13	T	22^h	4:02	Australia, South Pacific
2013 May 10	A	0^h	6:04	Australia, Pacific
2013 Nov. 3	AT	13^h	1:40	Atlantic, Africa
2015 March 20	T	10^h	2:47	North Atlantic, Arctic
2016 March 9	T	2^h	4:10	Borneo, Pacific
2016 Sept. 1	A	9^h	3:06	Atlantic, Africa, Indian Ocean
2017 Feb. 26	A	15^h	1:22	S. Pacific, S. America, Africa
2017 Aug. 21	T	18^h	2:40	Pacific, USA, Atlantic
2019 July 2	T	19^h	4:32	Pacific, South America
2019 Dec. 26	A	5^h	3:40	Southeast Asia, Pacific

The next major total solar eclipse visible from the United States will occur on August 21, 2017, when the path of totality will cross the United States from Oregon to South Carolina.

*There are no total or partial solar eclipses in 2011, 2014, or 2018.

**Times are Greenwich Mean Time. Subtract 5 hours for Eastern Standard time, 6 hours for Central Standard Time, 7 hours for Mountain Standard Time, and 8 hours for Pacific Standard Time.

^{h} hours.

Total solar eclipses are rare as seen from any one place. If you stay in one location, you will see a total solar eclipse about once in 360 years. Some people are eclipse chasers. They plan years in advance and travel halfway around the world to place themselves in the path of totality. ■ Table 3-2 shows the date and location of solar eclipses over the next few years.

Features of Solar Eclipses

A solar eclipse begins when you first see the edge of the moon encroaching on the sun. This is the moment when the edge of the penumbra sweeps over your location.

During the partial phases of a solar eclipse, the moon gradually covers the bright disk of the sun (■ Figure 3-10). Totality begins as the last sliver of the sun's bright surface disappears behind the moon. This is the moment when the edge of the umbra sweeps over your location. So long as any of the sun is visible, the countryside is bright; but, as the last of the sun disappears, dark falls in a few seconds. Automatic streetlights come on, car drivers switch on their headlights, and birds go to roost. The darkness of totality depends on a number of factors, including the weather at the observing site, but it is usually dark enough to make it difficult to read the settings on cameras.

The totally eclipsed sun is a spectacular sight. With the moon covering the bright surface of the sun, called the **photosphere,*** you can see the sun's faint outer atmosphere, the **corona,** glowing with a pale, white light so faint you can safely look at it directly. The corona is made of hot, low-density gas that is given a wispy appearance by the solar magnetic field, as shown in the last frame of Figure 3-10. Also visible just above the photosphere is a thin layer of bright gas called the **chromosphere.** The chromosphere is often marked by eruptions on the solar surface, called **prominences** (■ Figure 3-11a), that glow with a clear, pink color due to the high temperature of the gases involved. The small-angle formula reveals that a large prominence is about 3.5 times the diameter of Earth.

Totality during a solar eclipse cannot last longer than 7.5 minutes under any circumstances, and the average is only 2 to 3 minutes. Totality ends when the sun's bright surface reappears at the trailing edge of the moon. Daylight returns quickly, and the corona and chromosphere vanish. This corresponds to the moment when the trailing edge of the moon's umbra sweeps over the observer.

Just as totality begins or ends, a small part of the photosphere can peek through a valley at the edge of the lunar disk. Although it is intensely bright, such a small part of the photosphere does not completely drown out the fainter corona, which forms a silvery ring of light with the brilliant spot of photosphere gleaming like a diamond (■ Figure 3-11b). This **diamond ring effect** is one of the most spectacular of astronomical sights, but it is not visible during every solar eclipse. Its occurrence depends on the exact orientation and motion of the moon.

Observing an Eclipse

Not too many years ago, astronomers traveled great distances to forbidding places to get their instruments into the path of totality so they could study the faint outer corona that is visible only during the few minutes of a total solar eclipse. Now, many of those observations can be made every day by solar telescopes in

---
*The photosphere, corona, chromosphere, and prominences will be discussed in detail in Chapter 8. Here the terms are used as the names of features you see during a total solar eclipse.

A Total Solar Eclipse

The moon moving from the right just begins to cross in front of the sun.

The disk of the moon gradually covers the disk of the sun.

Sunlight begins to dim as more of the sun's disk is covered.

During totality, pink prominences are often visible.

A longer-exposure photograph during totality shows the fainter corona.

■ **Figure 3-10**

This sequence of photos shows the first half of a total solar eclipse. (Daniel Good)

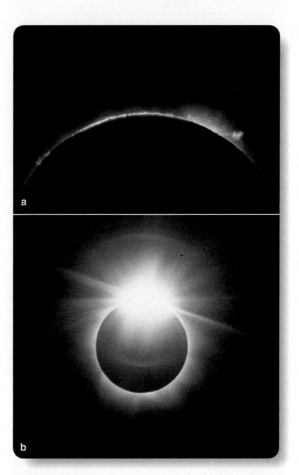

■ **Figure 3-11**

(a) During a total solar eclipse, the moon covers the photosphere, and the ruby-red chromosphere and prominences are visible. Only the lower corona is visible in this image. (©2005 by Fred Espenak) (b) The diamond ring effect can sometimes occur momentarily at the beginning or end of totality if a small segment of the photosphere peeks out through a valley at the edge of the lunar disk. (National Optical Astronomy Observatory)

space, but eclipse enthusiasts still journey to exotic places for the thrill of seeing a total solar eclipse.

No matter how thrilling a solar eclipse is, you must be cautious when viewing it. During the partial phase, part of the sun remains visible, so it is hazardous to look at the eclipse without protection.

Dense filters and exposed film do not necessarily provide protection because some filters do not block the invisible heat radiation (infrared) that can burn the retina of your eyes. Dangers like these have led officials to warn the public not to look at solar eclipses at all and have even frightened some people into locking themselves and their children into windowless rooms. It is a **Common Misconception** that sunlight is somehow more dangerous during an eclipse. In fact, it is always dangerous to look at the sun. The danger posed by an eclipse is that people are tempted to ignore common sense and look at the sun directly, which can burn their eyes.

The safest and simplest way to observe the partial phases of a solar eclipse is to use pinhole projection. Poke a small pinhole in a sheet of cardboard. Hold the sheet with the hole in sunlight and allow light to pass through the hole and onto a second sheet of cardboard (■ Figure 3-12). On a day when there is no eclipse, the result is a small, round spot of light that is an image of the sun. During the partial phases of a solar eclipse, the image will show the dark silhouette of the moon obscuring part of the sun. Pinhole

Sunlight

Pinhole

Image of partially
eclipsed sun

■ **Figure 3-12**

A safe way to view the partial phases of a solar eclipse. Use a pinhole in a card to project an image of the sun on a second card. The greater the distance between the cards, the larger (and fainter) the image will be.

images of the partially eclipsed sun can also be seen in the shadows of trees as sunlight peeks through the tiny openings between the leaves and branches. This can produce an eerie effect just before totality as the remaining sliver of sun produces thin crescents of light on the ground under trees. Once totality begins, it is safe to look directly. The totally eclipsed sun is fainter than the full moon.

SCIENTIFIC ARGUMENT

If you were on Earth watching a total solar eclipse, what would astronauts on the moon see when they looked at Earth?
Building this argument requires that you change your point of view and imagine seeing the eclipse from a new location. Scientists commonly imagine seeing events from multiple points of view as a way to develop and test their understanding. Astronauts on the moon could see Earth only if they were on the side that faces Earth. Because solar eclipses always happen at new moon, the near side of the moon would be in darkness, and the far side of the moon would be in full sunlight. The astronauts on the near side of the moon would be standing in darkness, and they would be looking at the fully illuminated side of Earth. They would see Earth at full phase. The moon's shadow would be crossing Earth; and, if the astronauts looked closely, they might be able to see the spot of darkness where the moon's umbral shadow touched Earth. It would take hours for the shadow to cross Earth.

Standing on the moon and watching the moon's umbral shadow sweep across Earth would be a cold, tedious assignment. Perhaps you can imagine a more interesting assignment for the astronauts. **What would astronauts on the moon see while people on Earth were seeing a total lunar eclipse?**

A CHINESE STORY TELLS of two astronomers, Hsi and Ho, who were too drunk to predict the solar eclipse of October 22, 2137 BC. Or perhaps they failed to conduct the proper ceremonies to scare away the dragon that, according to Chinese tradition, was snacking on the sun's disk. When the emperor recovered from the terror of the eclipse, he had the two astronomers beheaded.

Making exact eclipse predictions requires a computer and proper software, but some ancient astronomers could make educated guesses as to which full moons and which new moons might result in eclipses. There are three good reasons to reproduce their methods. First, it is an important chapter in the history of science. Second, it will illustrate how apparently complex phenomena can be analyzed in terms of cycles. Third, eclipse prediction will exercise your scientific imagination and help you visualize Earth, the moon, and the sun as objects moving through space.

Conditions for an Eclipse

You can predict eclipses by thinking about the motion of the sun and moon in the sky. Imagine that you can look up into the sky from your home on Earth and see the sun moving along the ecliptic and the moon moving along its orbit. Because the orbit of the moon is tipped slightly over 5 degrees to the plane of Earth's orbit, you see the moon follow a path tipped by the same angle to the ecliptic. Each month, the moon crosses the ecliptic at two points called **nodes.** It crosses at one node going southward, and two weeks later it crosses at the other node going northward.

Eclipses can only occur when the sun is near one of the nodes of the moon's orbit. Only then can the new moon cross in front of the sun and produce a solar eclipse, as shown in ■ Figure 3-13a. Most new moons pass too far north or too far south of the sun to cause an eclipse. When the sun is near one node, Earth's shadow points near the other node, and a full moon can enter the shadow and be eclipsed. A lunar eclipse doesn't happen at every full moon because most full moons pass too far north or too far south of the ecliptic and miss Earth's shadow. You can see a partial lunar eclipse illustrated in ■ Figure 3-13b.

So, there are two conditions for an eclipse: The sun must be near a node, and the moon must be crossing either the same node (solar eclipse) or the other node (lunar eclipse). That means, of course, that solar eclipses can occur only when the moon is new, and lunar eclipses can occur only when the moon is full.

Now you know the ancient secret of predicting eclipses. An eclipse can occur only in a period called an **eclipse season,** during which the sun is close to a node in the moon's orbit. For solar eclipses, an eclipse season is about 32 days long. Any new moon during this period will produce a solar eclipse. For lunar eclipses, the eclipse season is a bit shorter, about 22 days. Any full moon in this period will encounter Earth's shadow and be eclipsed.

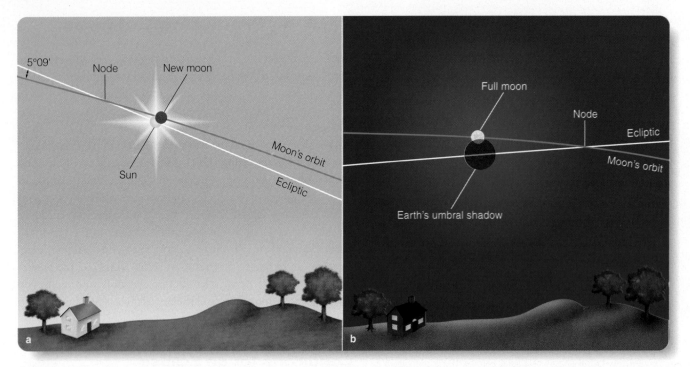

■ Figure 3-13

Eclipses can occur only when the sun is near one of the nodes of the moon's orbit. (a) A solar eclipse occurs when the moon meets the sun near a node. (b) A lunar eclipse occurs when the sun and moon are near opposite nodes. Partial eclipses are shown here for clarity.

This makes eclipse prediction easy. All you have to do is keep track of where the moon crosses the ecliptic (where the nodes of its orbit are). This system works fairly well, and ancient astronomers such as the Maya may have used such a system. You could have been a very successful ancient Mayan astronomer with what you know about eclipse seasons, but you can do even better if you change your point of view.

The View from Space

Change your point of view and imagine that you are looking at the orbits of Earth and the moon from a point far away in space. You can imagine the moon's orbit tipped at an angle to Earth's orbit. As Earth orbits the sun, the moon's orbit remains fixed in direction. The nodes of the moon's orbit are the points where it passes through the plane of Earth's orbit; an eclipse season occurs each time the line connecting these nodes, the **line of nodes,** points toward the sun. Look at ■ Figure 3-14a and notice that the line of nodes does not point at the sun in the example at lower left, and no eclipses are possible; the shadows miss. At lower right, the line of nodes points toward the sun, and the shadows produce eclipses.

The shadows of Earth and moon are long and thin, as shown in ■ Figure 3-14b. That is why it is so easy for them to miss their mark at new moon or full moon and fail to produce an eclipse. Only during an eclipse season do the long, skinny shadows produce eclipses.

If you watched for years from your point of view in space, you would see the orbit of the moon precess like a hubcap

spinning on the ground. This precession is caused mostly by the gravitational influence of the sun, and it makes the line of nodes rotate once every 18.6 years. People back on Earth see the nodes slipping westward along the ecliptic 19.4° per year. Consequently, the sun does not need a full year to go from a node all the way around the ecliptic and back to that same node. Because the node is moving westward to meet the sun, it will cross the node after only 346.6 days (an **eclipse year**). This means that, according to our calendar, the eclipse seasons begin about 19 days earlier every year (■ Figure 3-15). If you see an eclipse in late December one year, you will see eclipses in early December the next year, and so on.

Once you see a few eclipses, you know when the eclipse seasons are occurring, and you can predict next year's eclipse seasons by subtracting 19 days. New moons and full moons near those dates are candidates for causing eclipses.

The cyclic pattern of eclipses shown in Figure 3-15 gives you another way to predict eclipses. Eclipses follow a pattern, and if you were an ancient astronomer and understood the pattern, you could predict eclipses without ever knowing what the moon was or how an orbit works.

The Saros Cycle

Ancient astronomers could predict eclipses in an approximate way using eclipse seasons, but they could have been much more accurate if they had recognized that eclipses occur following certain patterns. The most important of these is the **saros cycle**

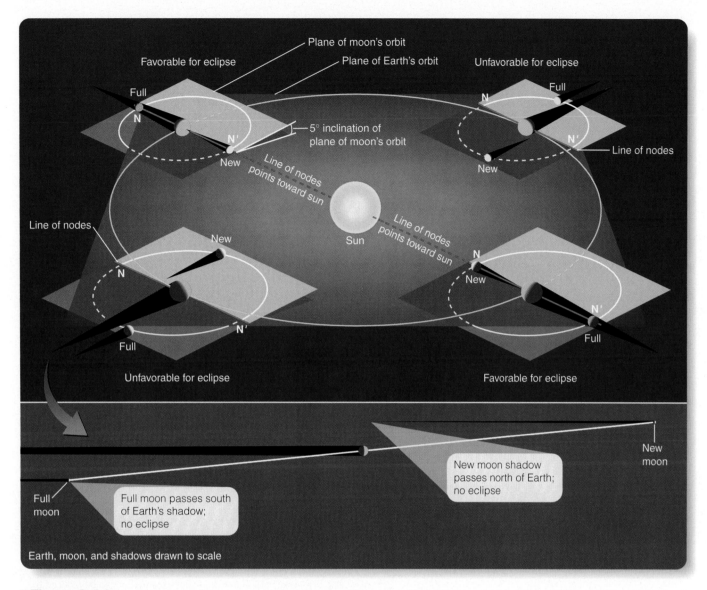

■ Figure 3-14

The moon's orbit is tipped a bit over 5° to Earth's orbit. The nodes N and N' are the points where the moon passes through the plane of Earth's orbit. If the line of nodes does not point at the sun, the long narrow shadows miss, and there are no eclipses at new moon and full moon. At those parts of Earth's orbit where the line of nodes points toward the sun, eclipses are possible at new moon and full moon.

(sometimes referred to simply as the saros). After one saros cycle of 18 years $11\frac{1}{3}$ days, the pattern of eclipses repeats. In fact, *saros* comes from a Greek word that means "repetition."

One saros contains 6585.321 days, which is equal to 223 lunar months. Therefore, after one saros cycle, the moon is back to the same phase it had when the cycle began. But one saros is also equal to 19 eclipse years. After one saros cycle, the sun has returned to the same place it occupied with respect to the nodes of the moon's orbit when the cycle began. If an eclipse occurs on a given day, then 18 years $11\frac{1}{3}$ days later the sun, the moon, and the nodes of the moon's orbit return to nearly the same relationship, and the eclipse occurs all over again.

Although the eclipse repeats almost exactly, it is not visible from the same place on Earth. The saros cycle is one-third of a day longer than 18 years 11 days. When the eclipse happens again, Earth will have rotated one-third of a turn farther east, and the eclipse will occur one-third of the way westward around Earth (■ Figure 3-16). That means that after three saros cycles—a period of 54 years 1 month—the same eclipse occurs in the same part of Earth.

One of the most famous predictors of eclipses was the Greek philosopher Thales of Miletus (about 640–546 BC), who supposedly learned of the saros cycle from the Chaldeans. No one knows which eclipse Thales predicted, but some scholars suspect the eclipse of May 28, 585 BC. In any case, the eclipse occurred at the height of a battle between the Lydians and the Medes, and the mysterious darkness in midafternoon so startled the two armies that they concluded a truce.

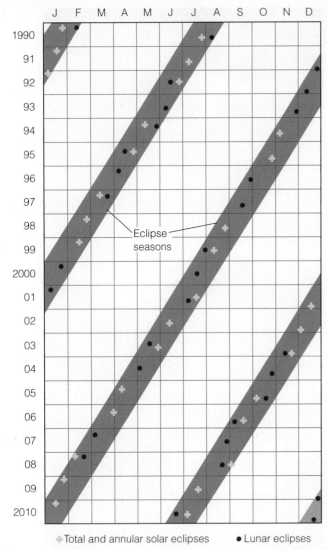

Figure 3-15

A calendar of eclipse seasons. Each year the eclipse seasons begin about 19 days earlier. Any new moon or full moon that occurs during an eclipse season results in an eclipse. Only total and annular eclipses are shown here.

➕ Total and annular solar eclipses   ● Lunar eclipses

Although there are historical reasons to doubt that Thales actually predicted the eclipse, the important point is that he could have done it. If he had had records of past eclipses of the sun visible from the area, he could have discovered that they tended to recur with a period of 54 years 1 month (three saros cycles). Indeed, he could have predicted the eclipse without ever understanding what the sun and moon were or how they moved.

Figure 3-16

The saros cycle at work. The total solar eclipse of March 7, 1970, recurred after 18 years $11\frac{1}{3}$ days over the Pacific Ocean. After another interval of 18 years $11\frac{1}{3}$ days, the same eclipse was visible from Asia and Africa. After a similar interval, the eclipse will again be visible from the United States.

SCIENTIFIC ARGUMENT

Why can't two successive full moons be totally eclipsed?
Most people suppose that eclipses occur at random or in some pattern so complex you need a big computer to make predictions. In fact, like many natural events, eclipse prediction can be reduced to a series of simple steps.

A lunar eclipse can happen only when the sun is near one node and the moon crosses Earth's shadow at the other node. A lunar eclipse season is only 22 days long, and any full moon in that time will be eclipsed. However, the moon takes 29.5 days to go from one full moon to the next. If one full moon is totally eclipsed, the next full moon 29.5 days later will occur long after the end of the eclipse season, and there can be no second eclipse.

Now use your knowledge of the cycles of the sun and moon to revise your argument. **How can the sun be eclipsed by two successive new moons?**

The moon is a companion in our daily lives, in our history, and in our mythology. It makes a dramatic sight as it moves through the sky, cycling through a sequence of phases that has repeated for billions of years. The moon has been humanity's timekeeper. Moses, Jesus, and Muhammad saw the same moon that you see. The moon is part of our human heritage, and famous paintings, poems, plays, and music celebrate the beauty of the moon.

Eclipses of the sun and moon have frightened and fascinated for millennia, and some of humanity's earliest efforts to understand nature were focused on counting the phases of the moon and predicting eclipses. Some astronomers have found evidence that Stonehenge could have been used for eclipse prediction, and the ancient Maya in Central America left behind elaborate tables that allowed them to predict eclipses.

Our lives are ruled by the moon as it divides our year into months, and its cycle from new to first quarter to full to third quarter and back to full divides the month into four weeks. In a Native American story, Coyote gambles with the sun to see if the sun will return after the winter solstice to warm Earth. The moon keeps score. The moon is a symbol of regularity, reliability, and dependability. It is the scorekeeper counting out our weeks and months.

Study and Review

Summary

▶ The moon orbits eastward around Earth once a month and rotates on its axis so as to keep the same side facing Earth throughout the month.

▶ Because you see the moon by reflected sunlight, its shape appears to change as it orbits Earth and sunlight illuminates different amounts of the side facing Earth.

▶ The lunar phases wax from new moon to first quarter to full moon and wane from full moon to third quarter to new moon.

▶ A complete cycle of lunar phases takes 29.53 days, which is known as the moon's **synodic period (p. 35)**. The **sidereal period (p. 35)** of the moon—its orbital period with respect to the stars—is a bit over two days shorter.

▶ If a full moon passes through Earth's shadow, sunlight is cut off, and the moon darkens in a **lunar eclipse (p. 33)**. If the moon fully enters the dark **umbra (p. 33)** of Earth's shadow, the eclipse is a **total lunar eclipse (p. 36)**; but if it only grazes the umbra, the eclipse is a **partial lunar eclipse (p. 36)**. If the moon enters the partial shadow of the **penumbra (p. 33)** but not the umbra, the eclipse is a **penumbral lunar eclipse (p. 37)**.

▶ During **totality (p. 36)**, the eclipsed moon looks copper-red because of sunlight refracted through Earth's atmosphere.

▶ The **small-angle formula (p. 39)** allows you to calculate an object's angular diameter from its linear diameter and distance. The angular diameter of the sun and moon is about 0.5 degrees.

▶ A **solar eclipse (p. 38)** occurs if a new moon passes between the sun and Earth and the moon's shadow sweeps over Earth's surface along the **path of totality (p. 39)**. Observers inside the path of totality see a **total solar eclipse (p. 38)**, and those just outside the path of totality see a **partial solar eclipse (p. 38)**.

▶ When the moon is near **perigee (p. 39)**, the closest point in its orbit, its angular diameter is large enough to cover the sun's photosphere and produce a total eclipse. But if the moon is near **apogee (p. 39)**, the farthest point in its orbit, it looks too small and can't entirely cover the photosphere. A solar eclipse occurring then would be an **annular eclipse (p. 39)**.

▶ During a total eclipse of the sun, the bright **photosphere (p. 41)** of the sun is covered, and the fainter **corona (p. 41)**, **chromosphere (p. 41)**, and **prominences (p. 41)** become visible.

▶ Sometimes at the beginning or end of the total phase of a total solar eclipse, a small piece of the sun's photosphere can peek out through a valley at the edge of the moon and produce a **diamond ring effect (p. 41)**.

▶ Looking at the sun is dangerous and can burn the retinas of your eyes. The safest way to observe the partial phases of a solar eclipse is by pinhole projection. Only during totality, when the photosphere is completely hidden, is it safe to look at the sun directly.

▶ Solar eclipses must occur at new moon, and lunar eclipses must occur at full moon. Because the moon's orbit is tipped a few degrees from the plane of Earth's orbit, most new moons cross north or south of the sun, and there are no solar eclipses in those months. Similarly, most full moons cross north or south of Earth's shadow, and there are no lunar eclipses in those months.

▶ The moon's orbit crosses the ecliptic at two locations called **nodes (p. 43)**, and eclipses can occur only when the sun is crossing a node. During these periods, called **eclipse seasons (p. 43)**, a new moon will cause a solar eclipse, and a full moon can cause a lunar eclipse. An eclipse season occurs each time the **line of nodes (p. 44)** points toward the sun. Knowing when the eclipse seasons occur would allow you to guess which new moons and full moons could cause eclipses.

▶ Because the orbit of the moon precesses, the nodes slip westward along the ecliptic, and it takes the sun only about 347 days to go from a node around the ecliptic and back to the same node. This is called an **eclipse year (p. 44)**.

▶ Because the nodes of the moon's orbit move westward, eclipse seasons begin about 19 days earlier each year.

▶ Eclipses follow a pattern called the **saros cycle (p. 44)**. After one saros of 18 years $11\frac{1}{3}$ days, the pattern of eclipses repeats. Some ancient astronomers knew of the saros cycle and used it to predict eclipses.

Review Questions

1. Which lunar phases would be visible in the sky at dawn? At midnight?

2. If you looked back at Earth from the moon, what phase would Earth have when the moon was full? New? A first-quarter moon? A waxing crescent?

3. If a planet has a moon, must that moon go through the same phases that Earth's moon displays?

4. Could a solar-powered spacecraft generate any electricity while passing through Earth's umbral shadow? Through Earth's penumbral shadow?

5. If a lunar eclipse occurred at midnight, where in the sky would you look to see it?

6. Why do solar eclipses happen only at new moon? Why not every new moon?

7. Why isn't the corona visible during partial or annular solar eclipses?

8. Why can't the moon be eclipsed when it is halfway between the nodes of its orbit?

9. Why aren't solar eclipses separated by one saros cycle visible from the same location on Earth?

10. How could Thales of Miletus have predicted the date of a solar eclipse without observing the location of the moon in the sky?

11. **How Do We Know?** Some people think science is like a grinder that cranks data into theories. What would you tell them about the need for scientists to be creative and imaginative?

Discussion Questions

1. How would eclipses be different if the moon's orbit were not tipped with respect to the plane of Earth's orbit?

2. Are there other planets in our solar system from whose surface you could see a "lunar" (moon) eclipse? A total solar eclipse? Which ones and why?

Problems

1. Identify the phases of the moon if on March 20 the moon is located at the point on the ecliptic called (a) the vernal equinox, (b) the autumnal equinox, (c) the summer solstice, (d) the winter solstice.

2. Identify the phases of the moon if at sunset the moon is (a) near the eastern horizon, (b) high in the southern sky, (c) in the southeastern sky, (d) in the southwestern sky.

3. About how many days must elapse between first-quarter moon and third-quarter moon?

4. If on March 1 the full moon is near the Favorite Star Spica, when will the moon next be full? When will it next be near Spica?

5. How many times larger than the moon is the diameter of Earth's umbral shadow at the moon's distance? (*Hint:* See the photo in Figure 3-3.)

6. Use the small-angle formula to calculate the angular diameter of Earth as seen from the moon.

7. During solar eclipses, large solar prominences are often seen extending 5 arc minutes from the edge of the sun's disk. How far is this in kilometers? In Earth diameters?

8. If a solar eclipse occurs on October 3: (a) Why can't there be a lunar eclipse on October 13? (b) Why can't there be a solar eclipse on December 28?

9. A total eclipse of the sun was visible from Canada on July 10, 1972. When did eclipse occur next with the same sun-moon-Earth geometry? From what part of Earth was it total?

10. When will the eclipse described in Problem 9 next be total as seen from Canada?

11. When will the eclipse seasons occur during the current year? What eclipse(s) will occur?

Learning to Look

1. Use the photos in Figure 3-1 as evidence to show that the moon always keeps the same side facing Earth.

2. Draw the umbral and penumbral shadows onto the diagram in the middle of page 34. Use the diagram to explain why lunar eclipses can occur only at full moon and solar eclipses can occur only at new moon.

3. Can you detect the saros cycle in Figure 3-15?

4. The stamp at right shows a crescent moon. Explain why the moon could never look this way.

5. The photo at right shows the annular eclipse of May 30, 1984. How is it different from the annular eclipse shown in Figure 3-9?

4 | The Origin of Modern Astronomy

Guidepost

The preceding chapters gave you a modern view of Earth. You can now imagine how Earth, the moon, and the sun move through space and how that produces the sights you see in the sky. But how did humanity first realize that we live on a planet moving through space? That required the revolutionary overthrow of an ancient and honored theory of Earth's place.

By the 16th century, many astronomers were uncomfortable with the ancient theory that Earth sat at the center of a spherical universe. In this chapter, you will discover how a Polish astronomer named Nicolaus Copernicus changed the old theory, how a German astronomer named Johannes Kepler discovered the laws of planetary motion, and how the Italian Galileo Galilei changed the way we know about nature. Here you will find answers to four essential questions:

— **How did classical philosophers describe Earth's place in the universe?**

— **How did Copernicus revise that ancient theory?**

— **How did astronomers discover the laws of planetary motion?**

— **Why was Galileo condemned by the Inquisition?**

This chapter is not just about the history of astronomy. As they struggled to understand Earth and the heavens, the astronomers of the Renaissance invented a new way of understanding nature—a way of thinking that is now called science.

How you would burst out laughing, my dear Kepler, if you would hear what the greatest philosopher of the Gymnasium told the Grand Duke about me...

— FROM A LETTER BY GALILEO GALILEI

ABOUT FOUR CENTURIES AGO, Galileo was condemned by the Inquisition for his part in a huge controversy over the nature of the universe, a controversy that focused on two problems. The place of the Earth was the most acrimonious issue; was it the center of the universe or was the sun at the center? A related issue was the nature of planetary motion. Ancient astronomers could see the sun, moon, and planets moving along the ecliptic, but they couldn't describe those motions precisely. To solve the first problem of the place of the Earth, astronomers also had to solve the second problem of planetary motion.

4-1 The Roots of Astronomy

ASTRONOMY HAS ITS ORIGIN in a noble human trait, curiosity. Just as modern children ask their parents what the stars are and why the moon changes, so did ancient humans ask themselves those same questions. Their answers, often couched in mythical or religious terms, reveal great reverence for the order of the heavens.

Archaeoastronomy

Most of the history of astronomy is lost forever. You can't go to a library or search the Internet to find out what the first astronomers thought about their world because they left no written record. The study of the astronomy of ancient peoples has been called **archaeoastronomy,** and it clearly shows that trying to understand the heavens is part of human nature.

Perhaps the best-known example of archaeoastronomy is also a huge tourist attraction. Stonehenge, standing on Salisbury Plain in southern England, was built in stages from about 3000 BC to about 1800 BC, a period extending from the late Stone Age into the Bronze Age. Though the public is most familiar with the monument's massive stones, they were added late in its history. In its first stages, Stonehenge consisted of a circular ditch slightly larger in diameter than the length of a football field, with a concentric bank just inside the ditch and a long avenue leading away toward the northeast. A massive stone, the Heelstone, stood then, as it does now, outside the ditch in the opening of the avenue.

As early as AD 1740, the English scholar W. Stukely suggested that the avenue pointed toward the rising sun at the summer solstice, but few historians accepted that it was intentional. Nevertheless, seen from the center of the monument, the summer solstice sun does rise behind the Heelstone. More recently, astronomers have recognized other significant astronomical alignments at Stonehenge. For example, sight lines point toward the most northerly and most southerly risings of the moon (■ Figure 4-1).

The significance of these alignments has been debated. Some have claimed that the Stone Age people who built Stonehenge were using it as a device to predict lunar eclipses. After studying eclipse prediction in the previous chapter, you understand that predicting eclipses is easier than most people assume, so perhaps it was used in that way, but the truth may never be known. The builders of Stonehenge had no written language and left no records of their intentions. Nevertheless, the presence of solar and lunar alignments at Stonehenge and at many other Stone Age monuments dotting England and continental Europe shows that so-called primitive peoples were paying close attention to the sky. The roots of astronomy lie not in sophisticated science and logic but in human curiosity and wonder.

Astronomical alignments in sacred structures are common all around the world. For example, many tombs are oriented toward the rising sun, and Newgrange, a 5000-year-old passage-grave in Ireland (■ Figure 4-2), faces southeast so that, at dawn on the day of the winter solstice, light from the rising sun shines into its long passageway and illuminates the central chamber. No one today knows what the alignment meant to the builders of Newgrange, and many experts doubt that it was actually intended to be a tomb. Whatever its original purpose, Newgrange is clearly a sacred site linked by its alignment to the order and power of the sky.

Building astronomical alignments into structures gives them meaning by connecting them with the heavens. Navajo Indians of the American southwest, for example, have for centuries built their hogans with the door facing east so they can greet the rising sun each morning with prayers and offerings.

Some alignments may have served calendrical purposes. The 2000-year-old Temple of Isis in Dendera, Egypt, was build to align with the rising point of the bright star Sirius. The first appearance of this star in the dawn twilight marked the flooding of the Nile, so it was an important calendrical indicator. The link between Sirius and the Nile was described in Egyptian mythology; the goddess Isis was associated with the star Sirius, and her husband, Osiris, was linked to the constellation you know as Orion and also to the Nile, the source of Egypt's agricultural fertility.

An intriguing American site in New Mexico known as the Sun Dagger unfortunately has no surviving mythology to tell its

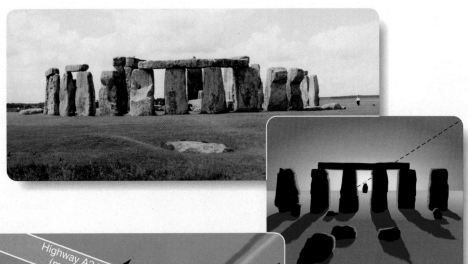

Sunrise on the morning of the summer solstice

■ **Figure 4-1**

The central horseshoe of upright stones is only the most obvious part of Stonehenge. The best-known astronomical alignment at Stonehenge is the summer solstice sun rising over the Heelstone. Although a number of astronomical alignments have been found at Stonehenge, experts debate their significance.
(Photo: Jamie Backman)

N / E

Highway A344 (modern)

Most northerly moonset

Summer solstice sunrise

Most northerly moonrise

Summer solstice sunrise

Most southerly moonrise at winter solstice

Most northerly moonset

Winter solstice sunset

Summer solstice sunrise

Winter solstice sunrise

Most southerly moonrise

Winter solstice sunset

Most southerly moonrise

Ditch
Bank
● Stone
○ Aubrey Hole

■ **Figure 4-2**

Newgrange was built on a small hill in Ireland about 3200 BC. A long passageway extends from the entryway back to the center of the mound, and sunlight shines down the passageway into the central chamber at dawn on the day of the winter solstice. Other passage graves have similar alignments, but their purpose is unknown.
(Newgrange: Benelux Press/Index Stock Imagery)

High on Fajada Butte, the Sun Dagger is off limits to visitors.

The spiral pattern is the size of a dinner plate.

■ **Figure 4-3**

In the ancient Native American settlement known as Chaco Canyon, New Mexico, sunlight shines between two slabs of stone high on the side of 440-foot-high Fajada Butte to form a dagger of light on the cliff face. About noon on the day of the summer solstice, the dagger of light slices through the center of a spiral pecked into the sandstone.
(NPS Chaco Culture National Historic Park)

story. At noon on the day of the summer solstice, a narrow dagger of sunlight shines across the center of a spiral carved on a cliff face high above the desert floor (■ Figure 4-3). The purpose of the Sun Dagger is open to debate, but similar examples have been found throughout the American Southwest. It may have been more a symbolic and ceremonial marker than a precise calendrical indicator. In any case, it is just one of the many astronomical alignments that ancient people built into their structures to link themselves with the sky.

Some scholars are examining not ancient structures but small artifacts made thousands of years ago. Scratches on certain bone and stone implements follow a pattern that may record the phases of the moon (■ Figure 4-4). Some scientists contend that humanity's first attempts at writing were stimulated by a desire to record and predict lunar phases.

Archaeoastronomy is uncovering the earliest roots of astronomy and simultaneously revealing some of the first human efforts at systematic inquiry. The most important lesson of archaeoastronomy is that humans don't have to be technologically sophisticated to admire and study the universe. Efforts to understand the sky have been part of human cultures for a long time.

Although the methods of archaeoastronomy can show how ancient people observed the sky, their thoughts about their universe are in many cases lost. Many cultures had no written language. In other cases, the written record has been lost. Dozens, perhaps hundreds, of beautiful Mayan manuscripts, for instance, were burned by Spanish missionaries who believed that the books were the work of Satan. Only four of these books have survived, and all four contain astronomical references. One contains sophisticated tables that allowed the Maya to predict the motion of Venus and eclipses of the moon. No one will ever know what was burnt.

The fate of the Mayan books illustrates one reason why histories of astronomy usually begin with the Greeks. Some of their writing has survived, and from it you can discover what they thought about the shape and motion of the heavens.

The Astronomy of Greece

Greek astronomy was derived from Babylon and Egypt, but the Greek philosophers took a new approach. Rather than relying on religion and astrology, the Greeks proposed a rational universe whose secrets could be understood through logic and reason. Before you begin your study of the history of

■ **Figure 4-4**

A fragment of a 27,000-year-old mammoth tusk found at Gontzi in Ukraine contains scribe marks on its edge, simplified in this drawing. These markings have been interpreted as a record of four cycles of lunar phases. Although controversial, such finds suggest that some of the first human attempts at recording events in written form were stimulated by astronomical phenomena.

astronomical thought from the classical Greek era through the Renaissance, you should remember the point made in Chapter 1 that the terms *solar system, galaxy,* and *universe* have very different meanings. You know now that our solar system, consisting of Earth, the moon, the sun, Earth's sibling planets, their moons, and so on, is your very local neighborhood, much smaller than the Milky Way Galaxy, which in turn is tiny compared with the observable universe. However, from ancient times up through Copernicus's day, it was thought that the whole universe, everything that exists, did not extend much beyond the farthest planet of our solar system. Asking back then whether Earth or the sun is the center of the solar system was the same question as asking whether Earth or the sun is the center of the universe. As you read this chapter, but only this chapter, you can pretend to have the old-fashioned view in which "solar system" and "universe" meant much the same thing.

This new Greek attitude toward studying the heavens with logic and reason was a first step toward modern science, and it was made possible by two early Greek philosophers. Thales of Miletus (c. 624–547 BC) lived and worked in what is now Turkey. He taught that the universe is rational and that the human mind can understand why the universe works the way it does. This view contrasts sharply with that of earlier cultures, which believed that the ultimate causes of things are mysteries beyond human understanding. To Thales and his followers, the mysteries of the universe were mysteries only because they were unknown, not because they were unknowable.

The other philosopher who made the new scientific attitude possible was Pythagoras (c. 570–500 BC). He and his students noticed that many things in nature seem to be governed by geometrical or mathematical relations. Musical pitch, for example, is related in a regular way to the lengths of plucked strings. This led Pythagoras to propose that all nature was underlain by musical principles, by which he meant mathematics. One result of this philosophy was the later belief that the harmony of the celestial movements produced actual music, the music of the spheres. But, at a deeper level, the teachings of Pythagoras made Greek astronomers look at the universe in a new way. Thales said that the universe could be understood, and Pythagoras said that the underlying rules were mathematical.

In trying to understand the universe, Greek astronomers did something that Babylonian astronomers had never done— they tried to describe the universe using geometrical forms. Anaximander (c. 611–546 BC) described a universe made up of wheels filled with fire: The sun and moon were holes in the wheels through which the flames could be seen. Philolaus (fifth century BC) argued that Earth moved in a circular path around a central fire (not the sun), which was always hidden behind a counter-Earth located between the fire and Earth. This, by the way, was the first theory to suppose that Earth is in motion.

The great philosopher Plato (428–347 BC) was not an astronomer, but his teachings influenced astronomy for 2000 years. Plato argued that the reality humans see is only a distorted shadow of a perfect, ideal form. If human observations are distorted, then observation can be misleading, and the best path to truth, said Plato, is through pure thought on the ideal forms that underlie nature.

Plato argued that the most perfect geometrical form was the sphere, and therefore, he said, the perfect heavens must be made up of spheres rotating at constant rates and carrying objects around in circles. Consequently, later astronomers tried to describe the motions of the heavens by imagining multiple rotating spheres. This became known as the principle of **uniform circular motion.**

Eudoxus of Cnidus (409–356 BC), a student of Plato, applied this principle when he devised a system of 27 nested spheres that rotated at different rates about different axes to produce a mathematical description of the motions of the universe (■ Figure 4-5).

At the time of the Greek philosophers, it was common to refer to systems such as that of Eudoxus as descriptions of the world, where the word *world* included not only Earth but all of the heavenly spheres. The reality of these spheres was open to debate. Some thought of the spheres as nothing more than mathematical ideas that described motion in the world model, while others began to think of the spheres as real objects made of perfect celestial material. Aristotle, for example, seems to have thought of the spheres as real.

■ **Figure 4-5**

The spheres of Eudoxus explain the motions in the heavens by means of nested spheres rotating about various axes at different rates. Earth is located at the center. In this illustration, only four of the 27 spheres are shown.

Aristotle and the Nature of Earth

Aristotle (384–322 BC), another of Plato's students, made his own unique contributions to philosophy, history, politics, ethics, poetry, drama, and other subjects (■ Figure 4-6). Because of his sensitivity and insight, he became the greatest authority of antiquity, and his astronomical model was accepted with minor variations for almost 2000 years.

Much of what Aristotle wrote about scientific subjects was wrong, but that is not surprising. The scientific method, with its insistence on evidence and hypothesis, had not yet been invented. Aristotle, like other philosophers of his time, attempted to understand his world by reasoning logically and carefully from first principles. A first principle is something that is held to be obviously true. The perfection of the heavens, meaning that the heavens had to be composed of rotating perfect spheres, was, for Aristotle, a first principle. Once a principle is recognized as true, whatever can be logically derived from it must also be true.

Aristotle believed that the universe was divided into two parts: Earth, imperfect and changeable; and the heavens, perfect and unchanging. Like most of his predecessors, he believed that Earth was the center of the universe, so his model is called a **geocentric universe.** The heavens surrounded Earth, and he added to the model proposed by Eudoxus to bring the total to 55 crystalline spheres turning at different rates and at different angles to carry the sun, moon, and planets across the sky. The lowest sphere, that of the moon, marked the boundary between the changeable imperfect region of Earth and the unchanging perfection of the celestial realm above the moon.

Because he believed Earth to be immobile, Aristotle had to make this entire nest of spheres whirl westward around Earth every 24 hours to produce day and night. The spheres also had to move more slowly with respect to one another to produce the motions of the sun, moon, and planets against the background of the stars. Because his model was geocentric, he taught that Earth

■ **Figure 4-6**

Aristotle, honored on this Greek stamp, wrote on such a wide variety of subjects and with such deep insight that he became the great authority on all matters of learning. His opinions on the nature of Earth and the sky were widely accepted for almost two millennia.

could be the only center of motion, meaning that all of the whirling spheres had to be centered on Earth.

About a century after Aristotle, the Alexandrian philosopher Aristarchus proposed that Earth rotated on its axis and revolved around the sun. This theory is, of course, generally correct, but most of the writings of Aristarchus were lost, and his theory was not well known. Later astronomers rejected any suggestion that Earth could move, because it conflicted with the teachings of the great philosopher Aristotle.

Aristotle had taught that Earth had to be a sphere because it always casts a round shadow during lunar eclipses, but he could only estimate its size. About 200 BC, Eratosthenes, working in the great library in the Egyptian city of Alexandria, found a way to measure Earth's radius. He learned from travelers that the city of Syene (Aswan) in southern Egypt contained a well into which sunlight shone vertically on the day of the summer solstice. This told him that the sun was at the zenith at Syene; but, on that same day in Alexandria, he noted that the sun was 1/50 of the circumference of the sky (about 7°) south of the zenith.

Because sunlight comes from such a great distance, its rays arrive at Earth traveling almost parallel. That allowed Eratosthenes to use simple geometry to conclude that the distance from Alexandria to Syene was 1/50 of Earth's circumference (■ Figure 4-7).

To find Earth's circumference, Eratosthenes had to learn the distance from Alexandria to Syene. Travelers told him it took 50 days to cover the distance, and he knew that a camel can travel about 100 stadia per day. That meant the total distance was about 5000 stadia. If 5000 stadia is 1/50 of Earth's circumference, then Earth must be 250,000 stadia in circumference, and, dividing by 2π, Eratosthenes found Earth's radius to be 40,000 stadia.

How accurate was Eratosthenes? The stadium (singular of *stadia*) had different lengths in ancient times. If you assume 6 stadia to the kilometer, then Eratosthenes's result was too big by only 4 percent. If he used the Olympic stadium, his result was 14 percent too big. In any case, this was a much better measurement of Earth's radius than Aristotle's estimate, which was much too small, about 40 percent of the true radius.

You might think this is just a disagreement between two ancient philosophers, but it is related to a **Common Misconception.** Christopher Columbus did not have to convince Queen Isabella that the world was round. At the time of Columbus, all educated people knew that the world was round and not flat, but they weren't sure how big it was. Columbus, like many others, adopted Aristotle's diameter for Earth, so he thought Earth was small enough that he could sail west and reach Japan and the Spice Islands of the East Indies. If he had accepted Eratosthenes' diameter, Columbus would never have risked the voyage. He and his crew were lucky that America was in the way; if there had been open ocean all the way to Japan, they would have starved to death long before they reached land.

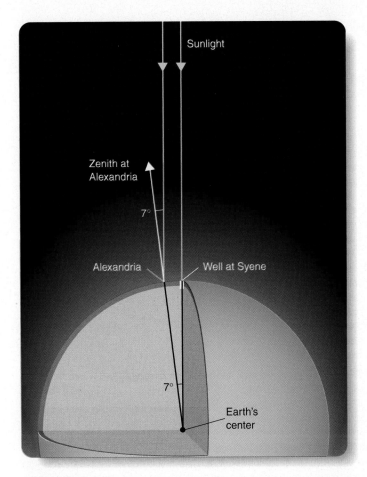

■ Figure 4-7

On the day of the summer solstice, sunlight fell to the bottom of a well at Syene, but the sun was about $\frac{1}{50}$ of a circle (7°) south of the zenith at Alexandria. From this, Eratosthenes was able to calculate Earth's radius.

Aristotle, Aristarchus, and Eratosthenes were philosophers, but the next person you will meet was a real astronomer who observed the sky in detail. Little is known about Hipparchus, who lived during the second century BC, about two centuries after Aristotle. He is usually credited with the invention of trigonometry, the creation of the first star catalog, and the discovery of precession (Chapter 2). Hipparchus also described the motion of the sun, moon, and planets as following circular paths with Earth near, but not at, their centers. These off-center circles are now known as **eccentrics.** Hipparchus recognized that he could reproduce this motion in a model where the celestial bodies traveled around a small circle that followed a larger circle around Earth. The compounded circular motion that he devised became the key element in the masterpiece of the last great astronomer of classical times, Claudius Ptolemy.

The Ptolemaic Universe

Claudius Ptolemaeus was one of the great astronomer-mathematicians of antiquity. His nationality and birth date are unknown, but around AD 140 he lived and worked in the Greek settlement at Alexandria in what is now Egypt. He ensured the continued acceptance of Aristotle's universe by transforming it into a sophisticated mathematical model.

When you read **The Ancient Universe** on pages 56–57, notice three important ideas and five new terms that show how first principles influenced early descriptions of the universe and it motions:

1 Ancient philosophers and astronomers accepted as first principles that the heavens were geocentric with Earth located at the center and sun, moon, and planets moving in uniform circular motion. It seemed clear to them that Earth was not moving because they saw no *parallax* in the positions of the stars.

2 The observed motion of the planets, the evidence, did not fit the theory very well. The *retrograde motion* of the planets was very difficult to explain using geocentrism and uniform circular motion.

3 Ptolemy attempted to explain the motion of the planets by devising a small circle, an *epicycle,* that rotated along the edge of a larger circle, and the *deferent,* which enclosed a slightly off-center Earth. An *equant* was a point from which the center of an epicycle appeared to move at a constant rate. That meant the speed of the planets would vary slightly as viewed from Earth.

Ptolemy lived roughly five centuries after Aristotle, and although Ptolemy based his work on the Aristotelian universe, he was interested in a different problem—the motion of the planets. He was a brilliant mathematician, and he was mainly interested in creating a mathematical description of the motions he saw in the heavens. For him, first principles took second place to mathematical precision.

Aristotle's universe, as embodied in the mathematics of Ptolemy, dominated ancient astronomy, but it was wrong. The planets don't follow circles at uniform speeds. At first, the Ptolemaic system predicted the positions of the planets well; but, as centuries passed, errors accumulated. If your watch gains only one second a year, it will keep time well for many years, but the error will gradually become noticeable. So, too, did the errors in the Ptolemaic system gradually accumulate as the centuries passed, but, because of the deep respect people had for the writings of Aristotle, the Ptolemaic system was not abandoned. Islamic and later European astronomers tried to update the system, computing new constants and adjusting epicycles. In the middle of the 13th century, a team of astronomers supported by King Alfonso X of Castile studied the *Almagest* for 10 years. Although they did not revise the theory very much, they simplified the calculation of the positions of the planets using the Ptolemaic system and published the result as *The Alfonsine Tables,* the last great attempt to make the Ptolemaic system of practical use.

The Ancient Universe

1 For 2000 years, the minds of astronomers were shackled by a pair of ideas. The Greek philosopher Plato argued that the heavens were perfect. Because the only perfect geometrical shape is a sphere, which carries a point on its surface around in a circle, and because the only perfect motion is uniform motion, Plato concluded that all motion in the heavens must be made up of combinations of circles turning at uniform rates. This idea was called uniform circular motion.

Plato's student Aristotle argued that Earth was imperfect and lay at the center of the universe. Such a model is known as a geocentric universe. His model contained 55 spheres turning at different rates and at different angles to carry the seven known planets (the moon, Mercury, Venus, the sun, Mars, Jupiter, and Saturn) across the sky.

Aristotle was known as the greatest philosopher in the ancient world, and for 2000 years his authority chained the minds of astronomers with uniform circular motion and geocentrism. See the model at right.

From *Cosmographica*
by Peter Apian (1539).

Seen by left eye

Seen by right eye

1a Ancient astronomers believed that Earth did not move because they saw no **parallax,** the apparent motion of an object because of the motion of the observer. To demonstrate parallax, close one eye and cover a distant object with your thumb held at arm's length. Switch eyes, and your thumb appears to shift position as shown at left. If Earth moves, ancient astronomers reasoned, you should see the sky from different locations at different times of the year, and you should see parallax distorting the shapes of the constellations. They saw no parallax, so they concluded Earth could not move. Actually, the parallax of the stars is too small to see with the unaided eye.

2 Planetary motion was a big problem for ancient astronomers. In fact, the word *planet* comes from the Greek word for "wanderer," referring to the eastward motion of the planets against the background of the fixed stars. The planets did not, however, move at a constant rate, and they could occasionally stop and move westward for a few months before resuming their eastward motion. This backward motion is called **retrograde motion.**

Every 2.14 years, Mars passes through a retrograde loop. Two successive loops are shown here. Each loop occurs farther east along the ecliptic and has its own shape.

Gemini

March 10, 2010

Cancer

West

Leo

Dec. 18, 2009

Position of Mars
at 5 day intervals

April 17, 2012

Ecliptic

Regulus

2a Simple uniform circular motion centered on Earth could not explain retrograde motion, so ancient astronomers combined uniformly rotating circles much like gears in a machine to try to reproduce the motion of the planets.

3   Uniformly rotating circles were key elements of ancient astronomy. Claudius Ptolemy created a mathematical model of the Aristotelian universe in which the planet followed a small circle called the **epicycle** that slid around a larger circle called the **deferent.** By adjusting the size and rate of rotation of the circles, he could approximate the retrograde motion of a planet. See illustration at right.

To adjust the speed of the planet, Ptolemy supposed that Earth was slightly off center and that the center of the epicycle moved such that it appeared to move at a constant rate as seen from the point called the **equant.**

To further adjust his model, Ptolemy added small epicycles (not shown here) riding on top of larger epicycles, producing a highly complex model.

3a   Ptolemy's great book *Mathematical Syntaxis* (c. AD 140) contained the details of his model. Islamic astronomers preserved and studied the book through the Middle Ages, and they called it *Al Magisti* (The Greatest). When the book was found and translated from Arabic to Latin in the 12th century, it became known as *Almagest*.

3b   The Ptolemaic model of the universe shown below was geocentric and based on uniform circular motion. Note that Mercury and Venus were treated differently from the rest of the planets. The centers of the epicycles of Mercury and Venus had to remain on the Earth–Sun line as the sun circled Earth through the year.

Equants and smaller epicycles are not shown here. Some versions contained nearly 100 epicycles as generations of astronomers tried to fine-tune the model to better reproduce the motion of the planets.

Notice that this modern illustration shows rings around Saturn and sunlight illuminating the globes of the planets, features that could not be known before the invention of the telescope.

4-2 The Copernican Revolution

YOU WOULD NOT HAVE EXPECTED NICOLAUS COPERNICUS to trigger a revolution in astronomy and science. He was born in 1473 to a merchant family in Poland. Orphaned at the age of 10, he was raised by his uncle, an important bishop, who sent him to the University of Cracow and then to the best universities in Italy. There he studied law and medicine before pursuing a life-long career as an important administrator in the Church. Nevertheless, he had a passion for astronomy (■ Figure 4-8).

The Copernican Model

If you had sat beside Copernicus in his astronomy classes, you would have studied the Ptolemaic universe. The central location of Earth was widely accepted, and everyone knew that the heavens moved in uniform circular motion. For most scholars, questioning these principles was not an option because, over the course of centuries, Aristotle's proposed geometry had become

■ **Figure 4-8**

Nicolaus Copernicus (1473–1543) pursued a lifetime career in the Church, but he was also a talented mathematician and astronomer. His work triggered a revolution in human thought. These stamps were issued in 1973 to mark the 500th anniversary of his birth.

linked with Christian teachings. According to the Aristotelian universe, the most perfect region was in the heavens and the most imperfect at Earth's center. This classical geocentric universe matched the commonly held Christian geometry of heaven and hell, so anyone who criticized the Ptolemaic model was not only questioning Aristotle's geometry but also indirectly challenging belief in heaven and hell.

For this reason, Copernicus probably found it difficult at first to consider alternatives to the Ptolemaic universe. Throughout his life, he was associated with the Catholic Church, which had adopted many of Aristotle's ideas. His uncle was an important bishop in Poland, and, through his uncle's influence, Copernicus was appointed a canon at the cathedral in Frauenberg at the unusually young age of 24. (A canon was not a priest but a Church administrator.) This gave Copernicus an income, although he continued his studies at the universities in Italy. When he left the universities, he joined his uncle and served as his secretary and personal physician until his uncle died in 1512. At that point, Copernicus moved into quarters adjoining the cathedral in Frauenburg, where he served as canon for the rest of his life.

His close connection with the Church notwithstanding, Copernicus began to consider an alternative to the Ptolemaic universe, probably while he was still at university. Sometime before 1514, he wrote an essay proposing a model of a **heliocentric universe** in which the sun, not Earth, was the center of that universe. To explain the daily and annual cycles of the sky, he proposed that Earth rotates on its axis and revolves around the sun. He distributed this commentary in handwritten form, without a title, and in some cases anonymously, to friends and astronomical correspondents. He may have been cautious out of modesty, or out of respect for the Church, or out of fear that his revolutionary ideas would be attacked unfairly. After all, the place of Earth was a controversial theological subject. Although this early essay discusses every major aspect of his later work, it did not include observations and calculations. His ideas needed supporting evidence, so he began gathering observations and making detailed calculations to be published as a book that would demonstrate the truth of his revolutionary idea.

De Revolutionibus

Copernicus worked on his book *De Revolutionibus Orbium Coelestium (The Revolutions of the Celestial Spheres)* over a period of many years and was essentially finished by about 1529; yet he hesitated to publish it even though other astronomers already knew of his theories. Even Church officials, concerned about the reform of the calendar, sought his advice and looked forward to the publication of his book.

One reason he hesitated was that he knew that the idea of a heliocentric universe would be highly controversial. This was a time of rebellion in the Church—Martin Luther (1483–1546) was speaking harshly about fundamental Church teachings, and others, both scholars and scoundrels, were questioning the Church's authority. Even matters as abstract as astronomy could stir controversy. Remember, too, that Earth's place in astronomical theory was linked to the geometry of heaven and hell, so moving Earth from its central place was a controversial and perhaps heretical idea.

Another reason Copernicus may have hesitated to publish was that his work was incomplete. His model could not accurately predict planetary positions, so he continued to refine it. Finally in 1540 he allowed the visiting astronomer Joachim Rheticus (1514–1576) to publish an account of the Copernican universe in Rheticus's book *Prima Narratio (First Narrative)*. In 1542, Copernicus sent the manuscript for *De Revolutionibus* off to be printed. He died in the spring of 1543 before the printing was completed.

The most important idea in the book was the location of the sun at the center of the universe. That single innovation had an astonishing consequence—the retrograde motion of the planets was immediately explained in a straightforward way without the large epicycles that Ptolemy had used.

In the Copernican system, Earth moves faster along its orbit than the planets that lie farther from the sun. Consequently, Earth periodically overtakes and passes these planets. To visualize this, imagine that you are in a race car, driving rapidly along the inside lane of a circular racetrack. As you pass slower cars driving in the outer lanes, they fall behind, and if you did not realize you were moving, it would look as if the cars in the outer lanes occasionally slowed to a stop and then backed up for a short interval. ■ Figure 4-9 shows how the same thing happens as Earth passes a planet such as Mars. Although Mars moves steadily along its orbit, as seen from Earth it appears to slow to a stop and move westward (retrograde) as Earth passes it. This happens to any planet whose orbit lies outside Earth's orbit, so the ancient astronomers saw Mars, Jupiter, and Saturn occasionally move retrograde along the ecliptic. Because the planetary orbits do not lie in precisely the same plane, a planet does not resume its eastward motion in precisely the same path it followed earlier. Consequently, it describes a loop whose shape depends on the angle between the orbital planes.

Copernicus could explain retrograde motion without epicycles, and that was impressive. The Copernican system was elegant and simple compared with the whirling epicycles and off-center equants of the Ptolemaic system. You can see Copernicus's own diagram for his heliocentric system in ■ Figure 4-10a. However, *De Revolutionibus* failed in one critical way—the Copernican model could not predict the positions of the planets any more accurately than the Ptolemaic system could. To understand why it failed, you must understand Copernicus and his world.

Copernicus proposed a revolutionary idea when he made the planetary system heliocentric, but he was a classical astronomer with tremendous respect for the old concept of uniform circular

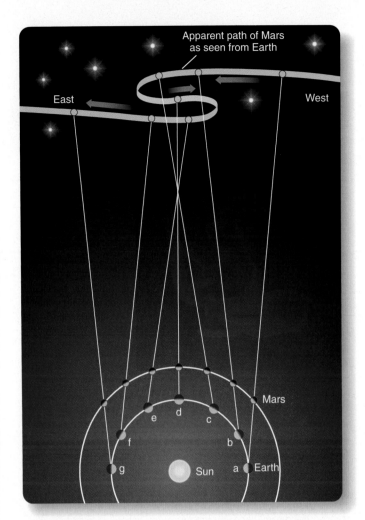

■ **Figure 4-9**

The Copernican explanation of retrograde motion. As Earth overtakes Mars (a–c), Mars appears to slow its eastward motion. As Earth passes Mars (d), Mars appears to move westward. As Earth draws ahead of Mars (e–g), Mars resumes its eastward motion against the background stars. The positions of Earth and Mars are shown at equal intervals of one month.

motion. In fact, Copernicus objected strongly to Ptolemy's use of the equant. It seemed arbitrary to Copernicus, an obvious violation of the elegance of Aristotle's philosophy of the heavens. Copernicus called equants "monstrous" because they undermined both geocentrism and uniform circular motion. In devising his model, Copernicus demonstrated a strong belief in uniform circular motion.

Although he did not need epicycles to explain retrograde motion, Copernicus quickly discovered that the sun, moon, and planets suffered other small variations in their motions that he could not explain using uniform circular motion centered on the sun. Today astronomers recognize those variations as the result of planets following elliptical orbits, but because Copernicus held firmly to uniform circular motion, he had to introduce small epicycles to try to reproduce these minor variations in the motions of the sun, moon, and planets.

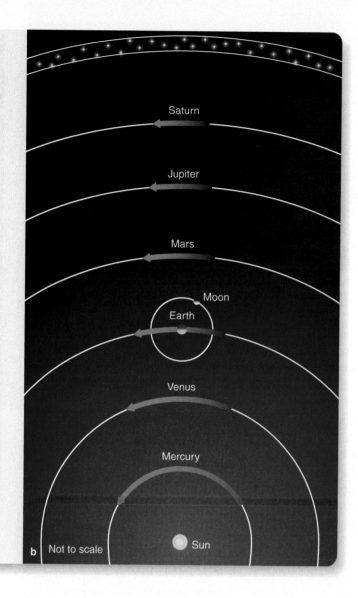

■ **Figure 4-10**

(a) The Copernican universe as reproduced in *De Revolutionibus*. Earth and all the known planets revolve in separate circular orbits about the sun (Sol) at the center. The outermost sphere carries the immobile stars of the celestial sphere. Notice the orbit of the moon around Earth (Terra). (Yerkes Observatory) (b) The model was elegant not only in its arrangement of the planets but also in their motions. Orbital speed (blue arrows) decreased from Mercury, the fastest, to Saturn, the slowest. Compare the elegance of this model with the complexity of the Ptolemaic model on page 57.

Because Copernicus imposed uniform circular motion on his model, it could not accurately predict the motions of the planets. *The Prutenic Tables* (1551) were based on the Copernican model, and they were not significantly more accurate than the 13th-century *Alfonsine Tables* that were based on Ptolemy's model. Both could be in error by as much as 2°, which is four times the angular diameter of the full moon.

The Copernican *model* is inaccurate. It includes uniform circular motion and consequently does not precisely describe the motions of the planets. But the Copernican *hypothesis* that the universe is heliocentric is correct, considering how little astronomers of the time knew of other stars and galaxies. The planets circle the sun, not Earth, so the universe that Copernicus knew was heliocentric.

Although astronomers throughout Europe read and admired *De Revolutionibus*, they did not immediately accept the Copernican hypothesis. The mathematics was elegant, and the astronomical observations and calculations were of tremendous value; but few astronomers believed, at first, that the sun actually was the center of the planetary system and that Earth moved. How the Copernican hypothesis was gradually recognized as correct has been called the Copernican Revolution because it was

Scientific Revolutions

How do scientific revolutions occur? You might think from what you know of the scientific method that science grinds forward steadily as new theories are tested against evidence and accepted or rejected. In fact, science sometimes leaps forward in scientific revolutions. The Copernican Revolution is often cited as the perfect example; in a few decades, astronomers rejected the 2000-year-old geocentric model and adopted the helio-centric model. Why does that happen? It's all because scientists are human.

The American philosopher of science Thomas Kuhn has referred to a commonly accepted set of scientific ideas and assumptions as a scientific **paradigm**. The pre-Copernican astronomers shared a geocentric paradigm that included uniform circular motion, geocentrism, and the perfection of the heavens. Although they were intelligent, they were prisoners of that paradigm. A scientific paradigm is powerful because it shapes your perceptions. It determines what you judge to be important questions and what you judge to be significant evidence. Consequently, the ancient astronomers could not recognize how their geocentric paradigms limited what they understood.

You will see here how the work of Copernicus, Galileo, and Kepler overthrew the geocentric paradigm. Scientific revolutions occur when the deficiencies of the old paradigm build up until finally a scientist has the insight to think "outside the box." Pointing out the failings of the old ideas and proposing a new paradigm with supporting evidence is like poking a hole in a dam; suddenly the pressure is released, and the old paradigm is swept away.

Scientific revolutions are exciting because they give you a dramatic new understanding of nature, but they are also times of conflict as new insights sweep away old ideas.

The ancients believed the stars were attached to a starry sphere. (NOAO and Nigel Sharp)

not just the adoption of a new idea but a total change in the way astronomers, and, in fact, all of humanity, thought about the place of the Earth (**How Do We Know? 4-1**).

There are probably a number of reasons why the Copernican hypothesis gradually won support, including the revolutionary temper of the times, but the most important factor may have been the elegance of the idea. Placing the sun at the center of the universe produced a symmetry among the motions of the planets that is pleasing to the eye as well as to the intellect (Figure 4-10b). In the Ptolemaic model, Mercury and Venus were treated differently from the rest of the planets; their epicycles had to remain centered on the Earth–sun line. In the Copernican model, all of the planets were treated the same. They all followed orbits that circled the sun at the center. Furthermore, their speed depended in an orderly way on their distance from the sun, with those closest moving fastest.

The most astonishing consequence of the Copernican hypothesis was not what it said about the sun but what it said about Earth. By placing the sun at the center, Copernicus made Earth into a planet, moving along an orbit like the other planets. By making Earth a planet, Copernicus revolutionized humanity's view of its place in the universe and triggered a controversy that would eventually bring the astronomer Galileo Galilei before the Inquisition. This controversy over the apparent conflict between scientific knowledge and philosophical and theological ideals continues even today.

SCIENTIFIC ARGUMENT

Why would you say the Copernican hypothesis was correct but the model was inaccurate?
To build this argument, you must distinguish carefully between a hypothesis and a model. The Copernican hypothesis was that the sun and not Earth was the center of the universe. Given the limited knowledge of the Renaissance astronomers about distant stars and galaxies, that hypothesis was correct.

The Copernican model, however, included not only the helio-centric hypothesis but also uniform circular motion. The model is inaccurate because the planets don't really follow circular orbits, and the small epicycles that Copernicus added to his model never quite reproduced the motions of the planets.

Now build a new argument. The Copernican hypothesis won converts because it is elegant and can explain retrograde motion. **How does its explanation of retrograde motion work, and how is it more elegant than the Ptolemaic explanation?**

4-3 Planetary Motion

THE COPERNICAN HYPOTHESIS solved the problem of the place of Earth, but it didn't explain planetary motion. If planets don't move in uniform circular motion, how do they move? The puzzle of planetary motion was solved during the century following the death of Copernicus through the work of two men. One compiled the observations, and the other did the analysis.

Tycho Brahe

Tycho Brahe (1546–1601) was not a churchman like Copernicus but rather a nobleman from an important family, educated at the finest universities. He was well known for his vanity and his lordly manners, and by all accounts he was a proud and haughty nobleman. Tycho's disposition was not improved by a dueling injury from his university days. His nose was badly disfigured, and for the rest of his life he wore false noses made of gold and silver, stuck on with wax (■ Figure 4-11).

Although Tycho officially studied law at the university, his real passions were mathematics and astronomy, and early in his university days he began measuring the positions of the planets in the sky. In 1563, Jupiter and Saturn passed very near each other in the sky, nearly merging into a single point on the night of August 24. Tycho found that the *Alfonsine Tables* were a full month in error and that the *Prutenic Tables* were in error by a number of days.

In 1572, a "new star" (now called Tycho's supernova) appeared in the sky, shining more brightly than Venus, and Tycho carefully measured its position. According to classical astronomy, the new star represented a change in the heavens and therefore had to lie below the sphere of the moon. To Tycho, who still believed in a geocentric universe, that meant that the new star should show parallax, meaning that it would appear slightly too far east as it rose and slightly too far west as it set (■ Figure 4-12). But Tycho saw no parallax in the position of the new star, so he concluded that it must lie above the sphere of the moon and was probably on the starry sphere itself. This contradicted Aristotle's conception of the starry sphere as perfect and unchanging.

No one before Tycho could have made this discovery because no one had ever measured the positions of celestial objects so accurately. Tycho had great confidence in the precision of his measurements, and he had studied astronomy thoroughly, so when he failed to detect parallax for the new star, he knew it was important evidence against the Ptolemaic theory. He announced his discovery in a small book, *De Stella Nova (The New Star),* published in 1573.

The book attracted the attention of astronomers throughout Europe, and soon Tycho's family introduced him to the court of the Danish King Frederik II, where he was offered funds to build an observatory on the island of Hveen just off the Danish coast. To support his observatory, Tycho was given a steady income as lord of a coastal district from which he collected rents. (He was not a popular landlord.) On Hveen, Tycho constructed

■ Figure 4-11

Tycho Brahe (1546–1601) was, during his lifetime, the most famous astronomer in the world. Proud of his noble rank, he wears the elephant medal awarded him by the king of Denmark. His artificial nose is suggested in this engraving. Tycho Brahe's model of the universe retained the first principles of classical astronomy; it was geocentric with the sun and moon revolving around Earth, but the planets revolved around the sun. All motion was along circular paths.

■ Figure 4-12

(a) A fan hanging below a ceiling displays parallax when seen from the side. (b) According to Aristotle, the new star of 1572 should have been located below the sphere of the moon; consequently, reasoned Tycho, it should display parallax and be seen east of its average position as it was rising and west of its average position when it was setting. Because he did not detect this daily parallax, he concluded that the new star of 1572 had to lie on the celestial sphere.

a luxurious home with six towers especially equipped for astronomy and populated it with servants, assistants, and a dwarf to act as jester. Soon Hveen was an international center of astronomical study.

Tycho Brahe's Legacy

Tycho made no direct contribution to astronomical theory. Because he could measure no parallax for the stars, he concluded that Earth had to be stationary, thus rejecting the Copernican hypothesis. However, he also rejected the Ptolemaic model because of its inaccuracy. Instead he devised a complex model in which Earth was the immobile center of the universe around which the sun and moon moved. The other planets circled the sun (Figure 4-11). The model thus incorporated part of the Copernican model, but in it Earth—not the sun—was stationary. In this way, Tycho preserved the central immobile Earth. Although Tycho's model was very popular at first, the Copernican model replaced it within a century. The true value of Tycho's work was observational. Because he was able to devise new and better instruments, he was able to make highly accurate observations of the position of the stars, sun, moon, and planets. Tycho had no telescopes—they were not invented until the next century—so his observations were made by the unaided eye peering along sight-lines. He and his assistants made precise observations for 20 years at Hveen.

Unhappily for Tycho, King Fredrik II died in 1588, and his young son took the throne. Suddenly, Tycho's temper, vanity, and noble presumptions threw him out of favor. In 1596, taking most of his instruments and books of observations, he went to Prague, the capital of Bohemia, and became imperial mathematician to the Holy Roman Emperor Rudolph II. His goal was to revise the *Alfonsine Tables* and publish the result as a monument to his new patron. It would be called the *Rudolphine Tables*.

Tycho did not intend to base the *Rudolphine Tables* on the Ptolemaic system but rather on his own Tyconic system, proving once and for all the validity of his hypothesis. To assist him, he hired a few mathematicians and astronomers, including one Johannes Kepler. Then, in November 1601, Tycho collapsed at a nobleman's home. Before he died, 11 days later, he asked Rudolph II to make Kepler imperial mathematician. The newcomer became Tycho's replacement (though at one-sixth Tycho's salary).

Kepler: An Astronomer of Humble Origins

No one could have been more different from Tycho Brahe than Johannes Kepler (■ Figure 4-13). Kepler was born in 1571 to a poor family in a region that is now part of southwest Germany. His father was unreliable and shiftless, principally employed as a mercenary soldier fighting for whoever paid enough. He was often absent for long periods and finally failed to return from a military

■ **Figure 4-13**

Johannes Kepler (1571–1630) was Tycho Brahe's successor. This diagram, based on one drawn by Kepler, shows how he believed the sizes of the celestial spheres carrying the outer three planets—Saturn, Jupiter, and Mars—are determined by spacers (blue) consisting of two of the five regular solids. Inside the sphere of Mars, the remaining regular solids separate the spheres of the Earth, Venus, and Mercury (not shown in this drawing). The sun lay at the very center of this Copernican universe based on geometrical spacers.

expedition. Kepler's mother was apparently an unpleasant and unpopular woman. She was accused of witchcraft in later years, and Kepler had to defend her in a trial that dragged on for three years. She was finally acquitted, but died the following year.

In spite of family disadvantages and chronic poor health, Kepler did well in school, winning promotion to a Latin school and eventually a scholarship to the university at Tübingen, where he studied to become a Lutheran pastor. During his last year of study, Kepler accepted a job in Graz teaching mathematics and astronomy, a job he resented because he knew little about the subjects. Evidently he was not a good teacher—he had few students his first year and none at all his second. His superiors put him to work teaching a few introductory courses and preparing an annual alma-nac that contained astronomical, astrological, and weather predic-tions. Through good luck, in 1595 some of his weather predictions were fulfilled, and he gained a reputation as an astrologer and seer. Even in later life he earned money from his almanacs.

While still a college student, Kepler had become a believer in the Copernican hypothesis, and at Graz he used his extensive spare time to study astronomy. By 1596, the same year Tycho arrived in Prague, Kepler was sure he had solved the mystery of the universe. That year he published a book called *The Forerunner of Dissertations on the Universe, Containing the Mystery of the Universe.* The book, like nearly all scientific works of that age, was written in Latin and is now known as *Mysterium Cosmographicum.*

By modern standards, the book contains almost nothing of value. It begins with a long appreciation of Copernicanism and then goes on to speculate on the reasons for the spacing of the planetary orbits. Kepler assumed that the heavens could be described by only the most perfect of shapes. Therefore he felt that he had found the underlying architecture of the universe in the sphere plus the five regular solids.* In Kepler's model, the five regular solids became spacers for the orbits of the six planets which were repre-sented by nested spheres (Figure 4-13). In fact, Kepler concluded that there could be only six planets (Mercury, Venus, Earth, Mars, Jupiter, and Saturn) because there were only five regular solids to act as spacers between their spheres. He provided astrological, numero-logical, and even musical arguments for his theory.

The second half of the book is no better than the first, but it has one virtue—as Kepler tried to fit the five solids to the plan-etary orbits, he demonstrated that he was a talented mathemati-cian and that he was well versed in astronomy. He sent copies of his book to Tycho on Hveen and to Galileo in Rome.

Joining Tycho

Life was unsettled for Kepler because of the persecution of Protestants in the region, so when Tycho Brahe invited him to Prague in 1600, Kepler went readily, eager to work with the famous

Danish astronomer. Tycho's sudden death in 1601 left Kepler, the new imperial mathematician, in a position to use the observations from Hveen to analyze the motions of the planets and complete *The Rudolphine Tables.* Tycho's family, recognizing that Kepler was a Copernican and guessing that he would not follow the Tychonic system in completing *The Rudolphine Tables,* sued to recover the instruments and books of observations. The legal wrangle went on for years. Tycho's family did get back the instruments Tycho had brought to Prague, but Kepler had the books, and he kept them.

Whether Kepler had any legal right to Tycho's records is debatable, but he put them to good use. He began by studying the motion of Mars, trying to deduce from the observations how the planet moved. By 1606, he had solved the mystery, this time correctly. The orbit of Mars is an ellipse and not a circle, he real-ized, and with that he abandoned the 2000-year-old belief in the circular motion of the planets. But even this insight was not enough to explain the observations. The planets do not move at uniform speeds along their elliptical orbits. Kepler's analysis showed that they move faster when close to the sun and slower when farther away. With those two brilliant discoveries, Kepler abandoned uniform circular motion and finally solved the puzzle of planetary motion. He published his results in 1609 in a book called *Astronomia Nova (New Astronomy).*

In spite of the abdication of Rudolph II in 1611, Kepler continued his astronomical studies. He wrote about a supernova that appeared in 1604 (now known as Kepler's supernova) and about comets, and he wrote a textbook about Copernican astron-omy. In 1619, he published *Harmonice Mundi (The Harmony of the World),* in which he returned to the cosmic mysteries of *Mysterium Cosmographicum.* The only thing of note in *Harmonice Mundi* is his discovery that the radii of the planetary orbits are related to the planets' orbital periods. That and his two previous discoveries are so important that they have become known as the three most fundamental rules of orbital motion.

Kepler's Three Laws of Planetary Motion

Although Kepler dabbled in the philosophical arguments of his day, he was at heart a mathematician, and his triumph was his explanation of the motion of the planets. The key to his solution was the ellipse.

An **ellipse** is a figure that can be drawn around two points, called the *foci,* in such a way that the distance from one focus to any point on the ellipse and back to the other focus equals a constant. This makes it easy to draw ellipses using two thumbtacks and a loop of string. Press the thumbtacks into a board, loop the string about the tacks, and place a pencil in the loop. If you keep the string taut as you move the pencil, it traces out an ellipse (■ Figure 4-14).

The geometry of an ellipse is described by two simple num-bers. The **semimajor axis, *a,*** is half of the longest diameter, as you can see in Figure 4-14. The **eccentricity, *e,*** of an ellipse is half the distance between the foci divided by the semimajor axis.

---

*The five regular solids, also known as the Platonic solids, are the tetrahedron, cube, octahedron, dodecahedron, and icosahedron. They were considered perfect because the faces and the angles between the faces are the same at every corner.

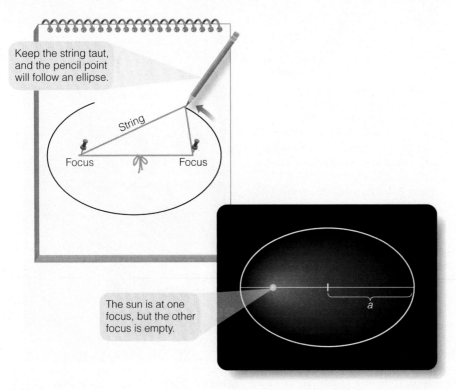

Keep the string taut, and the pencil point will follow an ellipse.

String

Focus   Focus

The sun is at one focus, but the other focus is empty.

a

■ Figure 4-14

The geometry of elliptical orbits: Drawing an ellipse with two tacks and a loop of string is easy. The semimajor axis, *a*, is half of the longest diameter. The sun lies at one of the foci of the elliptical orbit of a planet.

The eccentricity of an ellipse tells you its shape; if *e* is nearly equal to one, the ellipse is very elongated. If *e* is closer to zero, the ellipse is more circular. To draw a circle with the string and tacks shown Figure 4-14, you would have to move the two thumbtacks together because a circle is really just an ellipse with eccentricity equal to zero. Try fiddling with real thumbtacks and string, and you'll be surprised how easy it is to draw graceful, smooth ellipses with various eccentricities.

Ellipses are a prominent part of Kepler's three fundamental rules of planetary motion. Those rules have been tested and confirmed so many times that astronomers now refer to them as natural laws (**How Do We Know? 4-2**). They are commonly called Kepler's laws of planetary motion (**■ Table 4-1**).

> **■ Table 4-1 | Kepler's Laws of Planetary Motion**
>
> I. The orbits of the planets are ellipses with the sun at one focus.
> II. A line from a planet to the sun sweeps over equal areas in equal intervals of time.
> III. A planet's orbital period squared is proportional to its average distance from the sun cubed:
> $$P^2_{yr} = a^3_{AU}$$

Kepler's first law says that the orbits of the planets around the sun are ellipses with the sun at one focus. Thanks to the precision of Tycho's observations and the sophistication of Kepler's mathematics, Kepler was able to recognize the elliptical shape of the orbits even though they are nearly circular. Mercury has the most elliptical orbit, but even it deviates only slightly from a circle (**■ Figure 4-15**).

Kepler's second law says that an imaginary line drawn from the planet to the sun always sweeps over equal areas in equal intervals of time. This means that when the planet is closer to the sun and the line connecting it to the sun is shorter, the planet moves more rapidly, and the line sweeps over the same area that is swept over when the planet is farther from the sun. You can see how the planet in Figure 4-15 would move from point *A* to point *B* in one month, sweeping over the area shown. But when the planet is farther from the sun, one month's motion would be shorter, from *A'* to *B'*, and the area swept out would be the same.

Kepler's third law relates a planet's orbital period to its average distance from the sun. The orbital period, *P*, is the time a planet takes to travel around the sun once. Its average distance from the sun turns out to equal the semimajor axis of its orbit, *a*. Kepler's third law says that a planet's orbital period squared is proportional to the semimajor axis of its orbit cubed. Measuring *P* in years and *a* in astronomical units, you can summarize the third law as

$$P^2_y = a^3_{AU}$$

For example, Jupiter's average distance from the sun is roughly 5.2 AU. The semimajor axis cubed is about 140, so the period must be the square root of 140, which equals just under 12 years.

Notice that Kepler's three laws are empirical. That is, they describe a phenomenon without explaining why it occurs. Kepler derived the laws from Tycho's extensive observations, not from any first principle, fundamental assumption, or theory. In fact, Kepler never knew what held the planets in their orbits or why they continued to move around the sun.

The Rudolphine Tables

Kepler continued his mathematical work on *The Rudolphine Tables,* and at last, in 1627, it was ready. He financed the printing himself, dedicating the book to the memory of Tycho Brahe. In fact, Tycho's name appears in larger type on the title page than Kepler's own. This is surprising because the tables were not based on the Tyconic system but on the heliocentric model of Copernicus and the elliptical orbits of Kepler. The reason for

Hypothesis, Theory, and Law

Why is a theory much more than just a guess? Scientists study nature by devising and testing new hypotheses and then developing the successful ideas into theories and laws that describe how nature works. A good example is the connection between sour milk and the spread of disease.

A scientist's first step in solving a natural mystery is to propose a reasonable explanation based on what is known so far. This proposal, called a **hypothesis**, is a single assertion or statement that must be tested through observation and experimentation. From the time of Aristotle philosophers believed that food spoils as a result of the spontaneous generation of life—for example, mold growing out of drying bread. French chemist Louis Pasteur (1822–1895) hypothesized that microorganisms were not spontaneously generated but were carried through the air. To test his hypothesis he sealed an uncontaminated nutrient broth in glass completely protecting it from the microorganisms on dust particles in the air. No mold grew, effectively disproving spontaneous generation. Although others had argued against spontaneous generation before Pasteur, it was Pasteur's meticulous testing of his hypothesis through experimentation that finally convinced the scientific community.

A **theory** generalizes the specific results of well-confirmed hypotheses to give a broader description of nature, which can be applied to a wide variety of circumstances. For instance, Pasteur's specific hypothesis about mold growing in broth contributed to a broader theory that disease is caused by microorganisms transmitted from sick people to well people. This theory, called the germ theory of disease, is a cornerstone of modern medicine. It is a **Common Misconception** that the word "theory" means a tentative idea, a guess. As you have just learned, scientists actually use the word "theory" to mean an idea that is widely applicable and confirmed by abundant evidence.

Sometimes, when a theory has been refined, tested, and confirmed so often that scientists have great confidence in it, it is called a **natural law.** Natural laws are the most fundamental principles of scientific knowledge. Kepler's laws of planetary motion are good examples.

Confidence is the key. In general, scientists have more confidence in a theory than in a hypothesis and the most confidence in a natural law. However, there is no precise distinction among a hypothesis, a theory, and a law, and use of these terms is sometimes a matter of tradition. For instance, some textbooks refer to the Copernican "theory" of heliocentrism, but it had not been well tested when Copernicus proposed it, and it is more rightly called the Copernican hypothesis. At the other extreme, Darwin's "theory" of evolution,

A fossil of a 500-million-year-old trilobite: Darwin's theory of evolution has been tested many times and is universally accepted in the life sciences, but by custom it is called Darwin's theory and not Darwin's law.
(From the collection of John Coolidge III)

containing many hypotheses that have been tested and confirmed over and over for nearly 150 years, might more correctly be called a natural law.

Kepler's evident deference was Tycho's family, still powerful and still intent on protecting Tycho's reputation. They even demanded a share of the profits and the right to censor the book before publication, though they changed nothing but a few words on the title page and added an elaborate dedication to the emperor.

The Rudolphine Tables was Kepler's masterpiece. It could predict the positions of the planets 10 to 100 times more accurately than previous tables. Kepler's tables were the precise model of planetary motion that Copernicus had sought but failed to find. The accuracy of *The Rudolphine Tables* was strong evidence that both Kepler's laws of planetary motion and the Copernican hypothesis for the place of Earth were correct. Copernicus would have been pleased.

Kepler died in 1630. He had solved the problem of planetary motion, and his *Rudolphine Tables* demonstrated his solution. Although he did not understand why the planets moved or

why they followed ellipses, insights that had to wait half a century for Isaac Newton, Kepler's three laws worked. In science the only test of a theory is, "Does it describe reality?" Kepler's laws have been used for almost four centuries as a true description of orbital motion.

SCIENTIFIC ARGUMENT

How was Kepler's model with regular solids based on first principles? How were his three laws based on evidence?
When he was younger, Kepler accepted Plato's argument for the perfection of the heavens. Furthermore, Kepler argued that the five regular solids were perfect geometrical figures and should be part of the perfect heavens along with spheres. He then arranged the five regular solids to produce the approximate spacing among the spheres that carried the planets in the Copernican model. Kepler's model was thus based on a first principle—the perfection of the heavens.

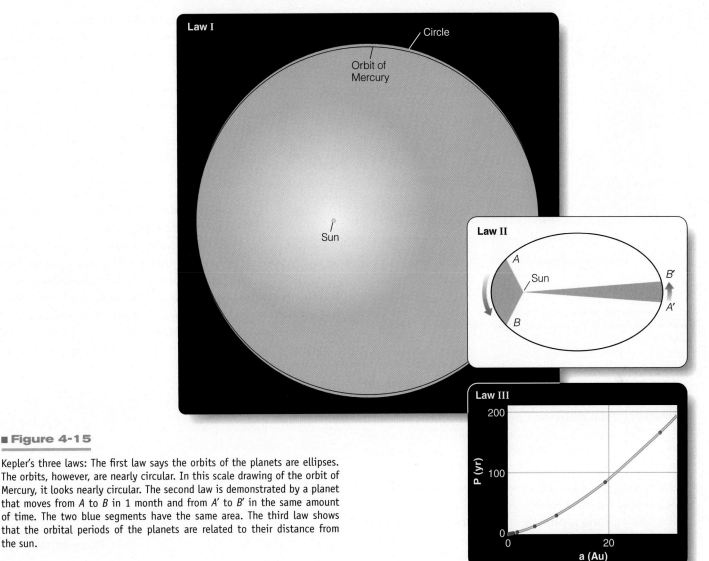

Law I

Circle

Orbit of Mercury

Sun

Law II

A

Sun

B′

A′

B

Law III

200

P (yr)

100

0

0   20

a (Au)

■ **Figure 4-15**

Kepler's three laws: The first law says the orbits of the planets are ellipses. The orbits, however, are nearly circular. In this scale drawing of the orbit of Mercury, it looks nearly circular. The second law is demonstrated by a planet that moves from *A* to *B* in 1 month and from *A′* to *B′* in the same amount of time. The two blue segments have the same area. The third law shows that the orbital periods of the planets are related to their distance from the sun.

Much later, Kepler derived his three laws of motion from the observations made by Tycho Brahe during 20 years on Hveen. The observations were the evidence, and they gave Kepler a reality check each time he tried a new calculation. He chose ellipses because they fit the data and not because he thought ellipses had any special significance.

The Copernican model was a poor predictor of planetary motion, but *The Rudolphine Tables* was much more accurate. **What first principle did Copernicus follow that was abandoned when Kepler looked at the evidence?**

4-4 Galileo Galilei

MOST PEOPLE THINK they know two facts about Galileo, but both facts are wrong; they are **Common Misconceptions,** so you have probably heard them. Galileo did not invent the telescope, and he was not condemned by the Inquisition for believing that Earth moved around the sun. Then why is Galileo so famous? Why did the Vatican reopen his case in 1979, almost 400 years after his trial? As you learn about Galileo, you will discover that his trial concerned not just the place of Earth and the motion of the planets but also a new and powerful method of understanding nature, a method called science.

Telescopic Observations

Galileo Galilei (■ Figure 4-16) was born in 1564 in Pisa, a city in what is now Italy, and he studied medicine at the university there. His true love, however, was mathematics, and, although he had to leave school early for financial reasons, he returned only four years later as a professor of mathematics. Three years after that he became professor of mathematics at the university at Padua, where he remained for 18 years.

■ Figure 4-16

Galileo, remembered as the great defender of Copernicanism, also made important discoveries in the physics of motion. He was honored here on an Italian 2000-lira note.

During this time, Galileo seems to have adopted the Copernican model, although he admitted in a 1597 letter to Kepler that he did not support Copernicanism publicly. At that time, the Copernican hypothesis was not officially considered heretical, but it was hotly debated among astronomers, and Galileo, living in a region controlled by the Church, cautiously avoided trouble. It was the telescope that finally drove Galileo to publicly defend the heliocentric model.

The telescope was apparently invented around 1608 by lens makers in Holland. Galileo, hearing descriptions in the fall of 1609, was able to build telescopes in his workshop. In fact, Galileo was not the first person to look at the sky through a telescope, but he was the first person to apply telescopic observations to the theoretical problem of the day—the place of Earth.

What Galileo saw through his telescopes was so amazing that he rushed a small book into print. *Sidereus Nuncius (The Sidereal Messenger)* reported three major discoveries. First, the moon was not perfect. It had mountains and valleys on its surface, and Galileo even used some of the mountains' shadows to calculate their height. Aristotle's philosophy held that the moon was perfect, but Galileo showed that it was not only imperfect but was a world with features like Earth's.

The second discovery reported in the book was that the Milky Way was made up of myriad stars too faint to see with the unaided eye. While intriguing, this could not match Galileo's third discovery. Galileo's telescope revealed four new "planets" circling Jupiter, objects known today as the **Galilean moons** of Jupiter (■ Figure 4-17).

The moons of Jupiter were strong evidence for the Copernican model. Critics of Copernicus had said Earth could not move because the moon would be left behind, but Galileo's discovery showed that Jupiter, which everyone agreed was moving, was able to keep its satellites. That suggested that Earth, too, could move and keep its moon. Aristotle's philosophy also included the belief that all heavenly motion was centered on Earth. Galileo's observations showed that Jupiter's moons revolve around Jupiter, suggesting that there could be other centers of motion besides Earth.

Some time after *Sidereus Nuncius* was published, Galileo noticed something else that made Jupiter's moons even stronger evidence for the Copernican model. When he measured the orbital periods of the four moons, he found that the innermost moon had the shortest period and that the moons farther from Jupiter had proportionally longer periods. Jupiter's moons made up a harmonious system ruled by Jupiter, just as the planets in the Copernican universe were a harmonious system ruled by the sun.

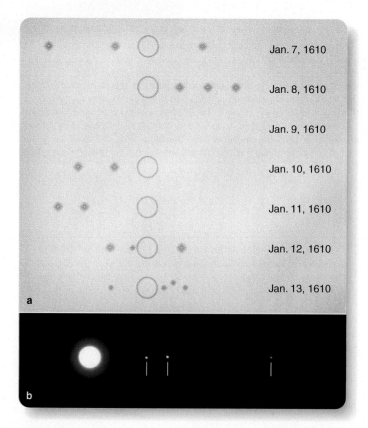

■ Figure 4-17

(a) On the night of January 7, 1610, Galileo saw three small "stars" near the bright disk of Jupiter and sketched them in his notebook. On subsequent nights (excepting January 9, which was cloudy), he saw that the stars were actually four moons orbiting Jupiter. (b) This photo taken through a modern telescope shows the overexposed disk of Jupiter and three of the four Galilean moons. (Grundy Observatory)

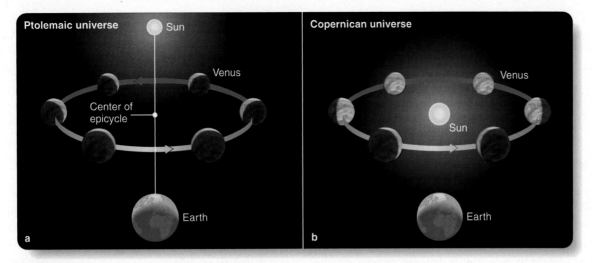

■ Figure 4-18

(a) If Venus moved in an epicycle centered on the Earth–sun line (see page 57), it would always appear as a crescent.
(b) Galileo's telescope showed that Venus goes through a full set of phases, proving that it must orbit the sun.

(See Figure 4-10b.) The similarity isn't proof, but Galileo saw it as an argument that the solar system could be sun centered rather than Earth centered.

In the years following publication of *Sidereus Nuncius,* Galileo made two additional discoveries. When he observed the sun, he discovered sunspots, raising the suspicion that the sun was less than perfect. Further, by noting the movement of the spots, he concluded that the sun was a sphere and that it rotated on its axis.

His most dramatic discovery came when he observed Venus. Galileo saw that it was going through phases like those of the moon. In the Ptolemaic model, Venus moves around an epicycle centered on a line between Earth and the sun. That means it would always be seen as a crescent (■ Figure 4-18a). But Galileo saw Venus go through a complete set of phases, which proved that it did indeed revolve around the sun (Figure 4-18b). There is no way the Ptolemaic model could produce those phases. This was the strongest evidence that came from Galileo's telescope; but, when controversy erupted, it focused more on the perfection of the sun and moon and the motion of the satellites of Jupiter.

Sidereus Nuncius was very popular and made Galileo famous. He became chief mathematician and philosopher to the Grand Duke of Tuscany in Florence. In 1611, Galileo visited Rome and was treated with great respect. He had long, friendly discussions with the powerful Cardinal Barberini, but he also made enemies. Personally, Galileo was outspoken, forceful, and sometimes tactless. He enjoyed debate, but most of all he enjoyed being right. In lectures, debates, and letters he offended important people who questioned his telescopic discoveries.

By 1616, Galileo was the center of a storm of controversy. Some critics said he was wrong, and others said he was lying. Some refused to look through a telescope lest it mislead them,

■ Figure 4-19

Galileo's telescope made him famous, and he demonstrated his telescope and discussed his observations with powerful people. Some thought the telescope was the work of the devil and would deceive anyone who looked. In any case, Galileo's discoveries produced intense and, in some cases, angry debate. (Yerkes Observatory)

and others looked and claimed to see nothing (hardly surprising, given the awkwardness of those first telescopes) (■ Figure 4-19). Pope Paul V decided to end the disruption, so when Galileo visited Rome in 1616 Cardinal Bellarmine interviewed him privately and ordered him to cease debate. There is some controversy today about the nature of Galileo's instructions, but he did not pursue astronomy for some years after the interview. Books relevant to Copernicanism were banned in all Catholic lands, although *De Revolutionibus,* recognized as an important and useful book in astronomy, was only suspended pending revision. Everyone who owned a copy of the book was required to cross out certain statements and add handwritten corrections stating that Earth's motion and the central location of the sun were only theories and not facts.

Dialogo and Trial

In 1621 Pope Paul V died, and his successor, Pope Gregory XV, died in 1623. The next pope was Galileo's friend Cardinal Barberini, who took the name Urban VIII. Galileo rushed to Rome hoping to have the prohibition of 1616 lifted; and, although the new pope did not revoke the orders, he did apparently encourage Galileo. Soon after returning home, Galileo began to write his great defense of Copernicanism, finally completing it at the end of 1629. After some delay, the book was approved by both the local censor in Florence and the head censor of the Vatican in Rome. It was printed in February 1632.

Called *Dialogo Sopra i Due Massimi del Mondo (Dialogue Concerning the Two Chief World Systems),* it confronts the ancient astronomy of Aristotle and Ptolemy with the Copernican model and with telescopic observations as evidence. Galileo wrote the book in the form of a debate among three friends. Salviati, a swift-tongued defender of Copernicus, dominates the book; Sagredo is intelligent but largely uninformed. Simplicio, the dismal defender of Ptolemy, makes all the old arguments and sometimes doesn't seem very bright.

The publication of *Dialogo* created a storm of controversy, and it was sold out by August 1632, when the Inquisition ordered sales stopped. The book was a clear defense of Copernicus, and, probably unintentionally, Galileo exposed the pope's authority to ridicule. Urban VIII was fond of arguing that, as God was omnipotent, He could construct the universe in any form while making it appear to humans to have a different form, and thus its true nature could not be deduced by mere observation. Galileo placed the pope's argument in the mouth of Simplicio, and Galileo's enemies showed the passage to the pope as an example of Galileo's disrespect. The pope thereupon ordered Galileo to face the Inquisition.

Galileo was interrogated by the Inquisition four times and was threatened with torture. He must have thought often of Giordano Bruno, a philospher, poet, and Dominican monk, who was tried, condemned, and burned at the stake in Rome in 1600. One of Bruno's offenses had been Copernicanism. However, Galileo's trial did not center on his belief in Copernicanism. *Dialogo* had been approved by two censors. Rather, the trial centered on the instructions given Galileo in 1616. From his file in the Vatican, his accusers produced a record of the meeting between Galileo and Cardinal Bellarmine

that included the statement that Galileo was "not to hold, teach, or defend in any way" the principles of Copernicus. Some historians believe that this document, which was signed neither by Galileo nor by Bellarmine nor by a legal secretary, was a forgery. Others suspect it may be a draft that was never used. It is quite possible that Galileo's actual instructions were much less restrictive; but, in any case, Bellarmine was dead and could not testify at Galileo's trial.

The Inquisition condemned Galileo not for heresy but for disobeying the orders given him in 1616. On June 22, 1633, at the age of 70, kneeling before the Inquisition, Galileo read a recantation admitting his errors. Tradition has it that as he rose he whispered *"E pur si muove"* ("Still it moves"), referring to Earth.

Although he was sentenced to life imprisonment, he was, perhaps through the intervention of the pope, confined at his villa for the next ten years. He died there on January 8, 1642, 99 years after the death of Copernicus.

Galileo was not condemned for heresy, nor was the Inquisition interested when he tried to defend Copernicanism. He was tried and condemned on a charge you might call a technicality. Nevertheless, in his recantation he was forced to abandon all belief in heliocentrism. His trial has been held up as an example of the suppression of free speech and free inquiry and as a famous attempt to deny reality. Some of the world's greatest authors, including Bertolt Brecht, have written about Galileo's trial. That is why Pope John Paul II created a commission in 1979 to reexamine the case against Galileo.

To understand the trial, you must recognize that it was the result of a conflict between two ways of understanding the universe. Since the Middle Ages, biblical scholars had taught that the only path to true understanding was through religious faith. St. Augustine (AD 354–430) wrote *"Credo ut intelligame,"* which can be translated as "Believe in order to understand." Galileo and other scientists of the Renaissance, however, used their own observations as evidence to try to understand nature. When their observations contradicted Scripture, they assumed that it was their observations that truly represented reality. Galileo paraphrased Cardinal Baronius in saying, "The Bible tells us how to go to heaven, not how the heavens go." The trial of Galileo was not really about the place of Earth in the universe. It was not about Copernicanism. It wasn't even about the instructions Galileo received in 1616. It was, in a larger sense, about the birth of modern science as a rational way to understand the universe (■ Figure 4-20).

The commission appointed by John Paul II in 1979, reporting its conclusions in October 1992, said of Galileo's inquisitors, "This subjective error of judgment, so clear to us today, led them to a disciplinary measure from which Galileo 'had much to suffer.'" Galileo was not found innocent in 1992 so much as the Inquisition was forgiven for having charged him in the first place.

Although he did not invent it, Galileo will always be associated with the telescope because it was the source of the observational evidence he used to try to understand the universe. By depending on observation of reality instead of first principles of philosophy and theology, Galileo led the way to the invention of modern science as a way to know about the natural world.

SCIENTIFIC ARGUMENT

How were Galileo's observations of the moons of Jupiter evidence against the Ptolemaic model?

Scientific arguments are based on evidence, and reasoning from evidence was Galileo's fundamental way of knowing about the heavens. Galileo presented his arguments in the form of evidence and conclusions, and the moons of Jupiter were key evidence. Ptolemaic astronomers argued that Earth could not move or it would lose its moon, but even in the Ptolemaic universe Jupiter moved, and the telescope showed that it had moons and kept them. Evidently, Earth could move and not leave its moon behind. Furthermore, moons circling Jupiter did not fit the classical belief that all motion was centered on Earth. Obviously there could be other centers of motion. Finally, the orbital periods of the moons were related to their distance from Jupiter, just as the orbital periods of the planets were, in the Copernican system, related to their distance from the sun. This similarity suggested that the sun rules its harmonious family of planets just as Jupiter rules its harmonious family of moons.

Of all of Galileo's telescopic observations, the moons of Jupiter caused the most debate, but the craters on the moon and the phases of Venus were also critical evidence. Build an argument to discuss that evidence. **How did craters on the moon and the phases of Venus argue against the Ptolemaic model?**

4-5 Modern Astronomy

THE SCIENCE KNOWN AS MODERN ASTRONOMY began during the 99 years between the deaths of Copernicus and Galileo (1543 to 1642). It was an age of transition that marked the change from the Ptolemaic model of the universe to the Copernican model with the attendant controversy over the place of the Earth. But that same period also marked a transition in the nature of astronomy in particular and of science in general, a transition illustrated in the solution of the puzzle of planetary motion. The puzzle was not solved by philosophical arguments about the perfection of the heavens or by debate over the meaning of scripture. It was solved by precise observation and careful computation, techniques that are the foundation of modern science.

The discoveries made by Kepler and Galileo found acceptance in the 1600s because the world was in transition. Astronomy was not the only thing changing during this period. The Renaissance is commonly taken to be the period between 1300 and 1600, and these 99 years of astronomical history lie at the culmination of the reawakening of learning in all fields (■ Figure 4-21). Ships were sailing to new lands and encountering new cultures. The world was open to new ideas and new observations. Martin Luther reformed the Christian religion, and other philosophers and scholars rethought their areas of human knowledge. Had Copernicus not published his hypothesis, someone else would have suggested that the universe is heliocentric. History was ready to shed the Ptolemaic system.

This period marks the beginning of the modern scientific method. Beginning with Copernicus, scientists such as Tycho, Kepler, and Galileo depended more and more on evidence, observation, and measurement rather than on first principles. This, too, is coupled to the Renaissance and its advances in metalworking and lens making. At the time of Copernicus, no astronomer had looked through a telescope, because one could not be made. By 1642, not only telescopes but also other sensitive measuring instruments had transformed science into something new and precise. As you can imagine, scientists were excited by these discoveries, and they founded scientific societies that increased the exchange of observations and hypotheses and stimulated more and better work. The most important advance, however, was the application of mathematics to scientific questions. Kepler's work demonstrated the power of mathematical analysis; and, as the quality of these numerical techniques improved, the progress of science accelerated. This story of the birth of modern astronomy is actually the story of the birth of modern science as well.

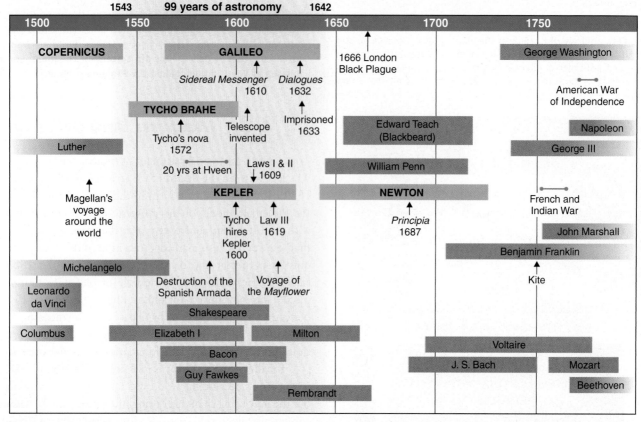

■ Figure 4-21

The 99 years between the death of Copernicus in 1543 and the death of Galileo in 1642 marked the transition from the ancient astronomy of Ptolemy and Aristotle to the revolutionary theory of Copernicus and, simultaneously, the invention of science as a way of understanding nature.

What Are We? Participants

The scientific revolution began when Copernicus made humanity part of the universe. Before Copernicus, people thought of Earth as a special place different from any of the objects in the sky; but, in trying to explain the motions in the sky, Copernicus made Earth one of the planets. Galileo and those who brought him to trial understood the significance of making Earth a planet. It made Earth and humanity part of the universe, part of nature.

Kepler showed that the planets move according to simple rules. We are not in a special place ruled by mysterious planetary forces. Earth, the sun, and all of humanity are part of a universe whose motions can be described by a few fundamental laws. If simple laws describe the motions of the planets, then the universe is not ruled by mysterious influences as in astrology or the whims of the gods atop Mount Olympus. And if the universe can be described by simple rules, then it is open to scientific study.

Before Copernicus, people felt they were special because they thought they were at the center of the universe. Copernicus, Kepler, and Galileo showed that we are not at the center but are part of an elegant and complex universe. Astronomy tells us that we are special because we can study the universe and eventually understand what we are. But it also tells us that we are not just observers of nature; we are participants.

Summary

▶ **Archaeoastronomy (p. 50)** is the study of the astronomy of ancient peoples. Many cultures around the world observed the sky and marked important alignments. Structures such as Stonehenge, Newgrange, and the Sun Dagger have astronomical alignments. In most cases, ancient cultures, having no written language, left no detailed records of their astronomical beliefs.

▶ Greek astronomy, derived in part from Babylon and Egypt, is better known because written documents have survived.

▶ Classical philosophers accepted as a first principle that Earth was the unmoving center of the universe. Another first principle was that the heavens were perfect, so philosophers such as Plato argued that, because the sphere was the most perfect geometrical form, the heavens must be made up of spheres in uniform rotation. This led to the belief in **uniform circular motion (p. 53)**.

▶ Many astronomers argued that Earth could not be moving because they could see no **parallax (p. 56)** in the positions of the stars.

▶ Aristotle's estimate for the size of Earth was only about one-third of its true size. Eratosthenes used the well at Syene to measure the diameter of Earth and got an accurate estimate.

▶ The **geocentric universe (p. 54)** became part of the teachings of the great philosopher Aristotle, who argued that the sun, moon, and stars were carried around Earth on rotating crystalline spheres.

▶ Hipparchus, who lived about two centuries after Aristotle, devised a model in which the sun, moon, and planets revolved in circles called **eccentrics (p. 55)** with Earth near but not precisely at their centers.

▶ **Retrograde motion (p. 56)**, the occasional westward (backward) motion of the planets, was difficult for astronomers to explain.

▶ About AD 140, Aritotle's model was given mathematical form in Claudius Ptolemy's book *Almagest*. Ptolemy preserved the principles of geocentrism and uniform circular motion, but he added **epicycles (p. 57)**, **deferents (p. 57)**, and **equants (p. 57)**. Ptolemy's epicycles could approximate retrograde motion, but the Ptolemaic model was not very accurate, and it had to be revised a number of times as centuries passed.

▶ Copernicus devised a **heliocentric universe (p. 58)**. He preserved the principle of uniform circular motion, but he argued that Earth rotates on its axis and revolves around the sun once a year. His theory was controversial because it contradicted Church teaching. He published his theory in his book *De Revolutionibus* in 1543, the same year he died.

▶ A **hypothesis (p. 66)** is a specific statement about nature that needs further testing, but a **theory (p. 66)** is usually a general description of some aspect of nature that has been tested. Some theories are very well understood and widely accepted. A **natural law (p. 66)** is a fundamental principle in which scientists have great confidence.

▶ Because Copernicus kept uniform circular motion as part of his theory, his model did not predict the motions of the plants well, but it did offer a simple explanation of retrograde motion without using big epicycles.

▶ One reason the Copernican model won converts was that it was more elegant. Venus and Mercury were treated the same as all the other planets, and the velocity of each planet was related to its distance from the sun.

▶ The shift from the geocentric **paradigm (p. 61)** to the heliocentric paradigm is an example of a scientific revolution.

▶ Although Tycho Brahe developed his own model in which the sun and moon circled Earth and the planets circled the sun, his great contribution was to compile detailed observations of the positions of the sun, moon, and planets over a period of 20 years, observations that were later used by Kepler.

▶ Kepler inherited Tycho's books of observations in 1601 and used them to discover three laws of planetary motion. He found that the planets follow **ellipses (p. 64)** with the sun at one focus, that they move faster when near the sun, and that a planet's orbital period squared is proportional to the **semimajor axis, a (p. 64)**, of its orbit cubed.

▶ The **eccentricity, e (p. 64)**, of an orbit is a measure of its departure from a perfect circle. A circle is an ellipse with an eccentricity of zero.

▶ Kepler's final book, *The Rudolphine Tables* (1627), combined heliocentrism with elliptical orbits and predicted the positions of the planets well.

▶ Galileo used the newly invented telescope to observe the heavens, and he recognized the significance of what he saw there. His discoveries of the phases of Venus, the satellites of Jupiter now known as the **Galilean moons (p. 68)**, the mountains of Earth's moon, and other phenomena helped undermine the Ptolemaic universe.

▶ Galileo based his analysis on observational evidence. In 1633, he was condemned by the Inquisition for disobeying instructions not to hold, teach, or defend Copernicanism.

▶ Historians of science view Galileo's trial as a conflict between two ways of knowing about nature, reasoning from first principles and depending on evidence.

▶ The 99 years from the death of Copernicus to the death of Galileo marked the birth of modern science. From that time on, science depended on evidence to test theories and relied on the mathematical analytic methods first demonstrated by Kepler.

Review Questions

1. What evidence is there that early human cultures observed astronomical phenomena?

2. Why did Plato propose that all heavenly motion was uniform and circular?

3. In Ptolemy's model, how do the epicycles of Mercury and Venus differ from those of Mars, Jupiter, and Saturn?

4. Why did Copernicus have to keep small epicycles in his model?

5. When Tycho observed the new star of 1572, he could detect no parallax. Why did that result undermine belief in the Ptolemaic system?

6. Does Tycho's model of the universe explain the phases of Venus that Galileo observed? Why or why not?

7. How do the first two of Kepler's three laws overthrow one of the basic beliefs of classical astronomy?

8. How did *The Alfonsine Tables, The Prutenic Tables,* and *The Rudolphine Tables* differ?

9. Explain how each of Galileo's telescopic discoveries contradicted the Ptolemaic theory.

10. Galileo was condemned, but Kepler, also a Copernican, was not. Why not?

11. **How Do We Know?** What is a paradigm, and how it is related to a scientific revolution?

12. **How Do We Know?** How would you describe the difference between a hypothesis, a theory, and a law?

Discussion Questions

1. Historian of science Thomas Kuhn has said that *De Revolutionibus* was a revolution-making book but not a revolutionary book. How was it an old-fashioned, classical book?

2. Why might Tycho Brahe have hesitated to hire Kepler? Why do you suppose he appointed Kepler his scientific heir?

3. How does the modern controversy over creationism and evolution reflect two ways of knowing about the physical world?

Problems

1. Draw and label a diagram of the eastern horizon from northeast to southeast and label the rising point of the sun at the solstices and equinoxes. (See page 19 and Figure 4-1.)

2. If you lived on Mars, which planets would exhibit retrograde motion? Which would never be visible as crescent phases?

3. If a planet has an average distance from the sun of 4 AU, what is its orbital period?

4. If a space probe is sent into an orbit around the sun that brings it as close as 0.5 AU and as far away as 5.5 AU, what will be its orbital period?

5. Neptune orbits the sun with a period of 164.8 years. What is its average distance from the sun?

6. Galileo's telescope showed him that Venus has a large angular diameter (61 arc seconds) when it is a crescent and a small angular diameter (10 arc seconds) when it is nearly full. Use the small-angle formula to find the ratio of its maximum distance to its minimum distance. Is this ratio compatible with the Ptolemaic universe shown on page 57?

7. Galileo's telescopes were not of high quality by modern standards. He was able to see the moons of Jupiter, but he never reported seeing features on Mars. Use the small-angle formula to find the angular diameter of Mars when it is closest to Earth. How does that compare with the maximum angular diameter of Jupiter?

Learning to Look

1. Study Figure 4-11 and describe the phases that Venus would have displayed to Galileo's telescope if the Tychonic universe had been correct.

2. What three astronomical objects are represented here? What are the two rings?

3. Use the figure below to explain how the Ptolemaic model treated some planets differently from the rest. How did the Copernican model treat all of the planets the same?

5 | Gravity

⎯ Guidepost

If only Renaissance astronomers had understood gravity, they wouldn't have had so much trouble describing the motion of the planets, but that insight didn't appear until three decades after the trial of Galileo. Isaac Newton started from the work of Galileo and devised a way to explain motion and gravity that allowed astronomers to understand orbits and tides. Later, in the early 20th century, Albert Einstein found an even better way to describe gravity.

This chapter is about gravity, the master of the universe. Here you will find answers to five essential questions:

⎯ **What happens when an object falls?**

⎯ **How did Newton discover gravity?**

⎯ **How does gravity explain orbital motion?**

⎯ **How does gravity explain tides?**

⎯ **How did Einstein better describe motion and gravity?**

Gravity rules. The moon orbiting Earth, matter falling into black holes, and the overall structure of the universe are dominated by gravity. As you study gravity, you will see science in action.

Nature and Nature's laws lay hid in night: God said, "Let Newton be!" and all was light.

— ALEXANDER POPE

ISN'T IT WEIRD that Isaac Newton is said to have "discovered" gravity in the late 17th century—as if people didn't have gravity before that, as if they floated around holding onto tree branches? Of course, everyone experienced gravity without noticing it. Newton's insight was to see gravity as a force that both makes things fall, and keeps moons and planets in their orbits, and that realization changed the way people thought about nature (■ Figure 5-1).

5-1 Galileo and Newton

ISAAC NEWTON WAS BORN in Woolsthorpe, England, on December 25, 1642, and on January 4, 1643. This was not a biological anomaly but a calendrical quirk. Most of Europe, following the lead of the Catholic countries, had adopted the Gregorian calendar, but Protestant England continued to use the Julian calendar. So December 25 in England was January 4 in Europe. If you use the English date, then Newton was born in the same year that Galileo Galilei died.

Newton became one of the greatest scientists who ever lived, but even he admitted the debt he owed to those who had studied nature before him. He said, "If I have seen farther than other men, it is because I stood on the shoulders of giants." In the previous chapter, you learned about Galileo as the defender of Copernicanism who made the first use of an astronomical telescope, but he also was the first scientist who carefully studied the motions of falling bodies. That was the key information that led Newton to understand gravity.

Galileo and Motion

Galileo (■ Figure 5-2) began studying the motion of freely moving bodies even before he built his first telescope. After the Inquisition condemned and imprisoned him in 1633, he continued his study of motion. He seems to have realized that he would

■ Figure 5-1

Space stations and astronauts, as well as planets, moons, stars, and galaxies, follow paths called orbits that are described by three simple laws of motion and a theory of gravity first understood by Isaac Newton (1642–1727). Newtonian physics is adequate to send astronauts to the moon and to analyze the rotation of the largest galaxies. (NASA)

Although Galileo is often associated with the telescope, as on this Italian stamp, he also made systematic studies of the motion of falling bodies and made discoveries that led to the law of inertia.

have to understand motion before he could truly understand the Copernican system.

In addition to writing about a geocentric universe, Aristotle also wrote about the nature of motion, and those ideas still held sway in Galileo's time. Aristotle said that the world is made up of four classical elements: earth, water, air, and fire, each located in its proper place. The proper place for earth (meaning soil and rock) is the center of the universe, and the proper place of water is just above earth. Air and then fire form higher layers, and above them lies the realm of the planets and stars. (You can see the four layers of the classical elements in the diagram at the top of page 56.) The four elements were believed to have a natural tendency to move toward their proper place in the cosmos. Things made up mostly of air or fire—smoke, for instance—tend to move upward. Things composed mostly of earth and water—wood, rock, flesh, bone, and so on—tend to move downward. According to Aristotle, objects fall downward because they are moving toward their proper place.*

Aristotle called these motions **natural motions** to distinguish them from the **violent motions** that are produced when, for instance, you push on an object and make it move other than toward its proper place. According to Aristotle, such motions stop as soon as the force is removed. To explain how an arrow could continue to move upward even after it had left the bowstring, he said currents in the air around the arrow carried it forward even though the bowstring was no longer pushing it.

In Galileo's time and for the two preceding millennia, scholars had tended to resolve problems by referring to authority. To analyze the flight of a cannonball, for instance, they would turn to the writings of Aristotle and other classical philosophers and try to deduce what those philosophers would have said on the subject. This generated a great deal of discussion but little real progress. Galileo broke with this tradition when he conducted his own experiments.

---

*This is one reason why Aristotle had to have a geocentric universe. If Earth's center had not also been the center of the cosmos, his explanation of gravity would not have worked.

He began by studying the motions of falling bodies, but he quickly discovered that the velocities were so great and the times so short that he could not measure them accurately. Consequently, he began using polished bronze balls rolling down gently sloping inclines. In that instance, the velocities are lower, and the times are longer. Using an ingenious water clock, he was able to measure the time the balls took to roll given distances down the incline, and he correctly recognized that these times are proportional to the times he would have measured using falling bodies.

Galileo found that falling bodies do not fall at constant rates, as Aristotle had said, but are accelerated. That is, they move faster with each passing second. Near Earth's surface, a falling object will have a velocity of 9.8 m/s (32 ft/s) at the end of 1 second, 19.6 m/s (64 ft/s) after 2 seconds, 29.4 m/s (96 ft/s) after 3 seconds, and so on. Each passing second adds 9.8 m/s (32 ft/s) to the object's velocity (■ Figure 5-3). In modern terms, this steady increase in the velocity of a falling body by 9.8 m/s each second (usually written 9.8 m/s²) is called the **acceleration of gravity** at Earth's surface.

Galileo also discovered that the acceleration does not depend on the weight of the object. This, too, is contrary to the teachings of Aristotle, who believed that heavy objects, containing more earth and water, fell with higher velocity. Galileo found that the acceleration of a falling body is the same whether it is heavy or light. According to some accounts, he demonstrated this by dropping balls of iron and wood from the top of the Leaning Tower of Pisa to show that they would fall together and hit the ground at the same time (■ Figure 5-4a). In fact, he probably didn't perform this experiment. It would not have been conclusive anyway because of air resistance. More than 300 years later, Apollo 15 astronaut David Scott, standing on the airless moon, demonstrated the truth of Galileo's discovery by simultaneously dropping a feather and a steel geologist's hammer. They fell at the same rate and hit the lunar surface at the same time (Figure 5-4b).

Having described natural motion, Galileo turned his attention to violent motion—that is, motion directed other than toward an object's proper place in the cosmos. Aristotle said that such motion must be sustained by a cause. We would say "a cause" today. Galileo pointed out that an object rolling down an incline is accelerated and that an object rolling up the same incline is decelerated. If the incline were perfectly horizontal and frictionless, he reasoned, there could be no acceleration or deceleration to change the object's velocity, and, in the absence of friction, the object would continue to move forever. In his own words, "any velocity once imparted to a moving body will be rigidly maintained as long as the external causes of acceleration or retardation are removed." Motion need not be sustained by a cause, said Galileo. Once begun, motion continues until something changes it. In fact, Galileo's statement is a perfectly valid summary of the law of inertia, which became Newton's first law of motion.

■ Figure 5-3

Galileo found that a falling object is accelerated downward. Each second, its velocity increases by 9.8 m/s (32 ft/s).

1 s
9.8 m/s

2 s
19.6 m/s

3 s
29.4 m/s

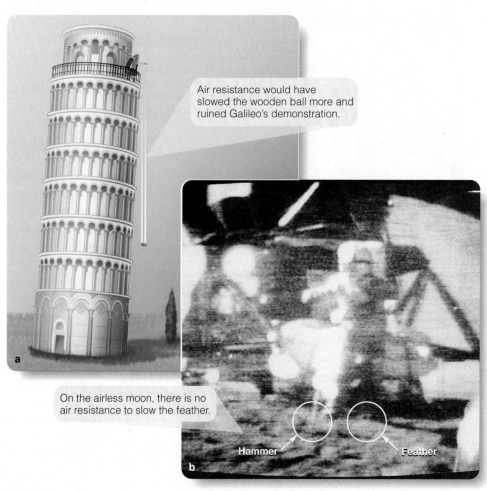

Air resistance would have slowed the wooden ball more and ruined Galileo's demonstration.

On the airless moon, there is no air resistance to slow the feather.

Hammer

Feather

■ Figure 5-4

(a) According to tradition, Galileo demonstrated that the acceleration of a falling body is independent of its weight by dropping balls of iron and wood from the Leaning Tower of Pisa. In fact, air resistance would have confused the result. (b) In a historic television broadcast from the moon on August 2, 1971, David Scott dropped a hammer and a feather at the same instant. They fell with the same acceleration and hit the surface together. (NASA)

Galileo published his work on motion in 1638, two years after he had become entirely blind and only four years before his death. The book was called *Mathematical Discourses and Demonstrations Concerning Two New Sciences, Relating to Mechanics and to Local Motion*. It is known today as *Two New Sciences*.

The book is a brilliant achievement for a number of reasons. To understand motion, Galileo had to abandon the authority of the ancients, devise his own experiments, and draw his own conclusions. In a sense, this was the first example of experimental science. But Galileo also had to generalize his experiments to discover how nature worked. Though his apparatus was finite and his results skewed by friction, he was able to imagine an infinite, frictionless plane on which a body moves at constant velocity. In his workshop, the law of inertia was obscure, but in his imagination it was clear and precise.

Newton and the Laws of Motion

From the work of Galileo, Kepler, and other early scientists, Isaac Newton was able to deduce three laws of motion (■ Table 5-1) that describe any moving object, from an automobile driving along a highway to galaxies colliding with each other. Those laws led Newton to an understanding of gravity.

Mass

One of the most fundamental parameters in science is **mass**, a measure of the amount of matter in an object. A bowling ball, for example, contains a large amount of matter and so is more massive than a child's rubber ball of the same size.

Mass is not the same as weight. Your weight is the force that Earth's gravity exerts on the mass of your body. Because gravity pulls you downward, you press against the bathroom scale, and you can measure your weight. Floating in space, you would have no weight at all; a bathroom scale would be useless. But your body would still contain the same amount of matter, so you would still have the same mass you do on Earth.

Sports analogies illustrate the importance of mass in dramatic ways. A bowling ball, for example, must be massive to have a large effect on the pins it strikes. Imagine trying to knock down all the pins with a balloon instead of a bowling ball. In space, where the bowling ball would be weightless, a bowling ball would still have more effect on the pins than a balloon would. On the other hand, runners want track shoes that have low mass so that they are easy to move. Imagine trying to run a 100-meter dash wearing track shoes that were as massive as bowling balls. It would be difficult to accelerate away from the starting blocks. Finally, think of the shot put. It takes muscle because the shot is massive, not because it is heavy. Imagine throwing the shot in space where it would have no weight. It would still be massive, and it would take great effort to start it moving.

Mass is a unique measure of the amount of material in an object. Using the metric system (Appendix A), mass is measured in kilograms.

100 kg

Mass is not the same as weight.

MASS | ENERGY | TEMPERATURE AND HEAT | DENSITY | PRESSURE

■ Table 5-1	Newton's Three Laws of Motion

I. A body continues at rest or in uniform motion in a straight line unless acted on by some force.
II. The acceleration of a body is inversely proportional to its mass, directly proportional to the force, and in the same direction as the force.
III. To every action, there is an equal and opposite reaction.

Newton's first law of motion is really a restatement of Galileo's law of inertia. An object continues at rest or in uniform motion in a straight line unless acted on by some force. Astronauts drifting in space will travel at constant rates in straight lines forever if no forces act on them (■ Figure 5-5a).

Newton's first law also explains why a projectile continues to move after all forces have been removed—for instance, how an arrow continues to move after leaving the bowstring. The object continues to move because it has momentum. You can think of an object's **momentum** as a measure of its amount of motion.

An object's momentum is equal to its velocity times its mass. A paper clip tossed across a room has low velocity and therefore little momentum, and you could easily catch it in your hand. But the same paper clip fired at the speed of a rifle bullet would have tremendous momentum, and you would not dare try to catch it. Momentum also depends on the mass of an object (**Focus on**

Fundamentals 1). Now imagine that, instead of tossing a paper clip, someone tosses you a bowling ball. A bowling ball contains much more mass than a paper clip and therefore has much greater momentum, even though it is moving at the same velocity.

Newton's second law of motion is about forces. Where Galileo spoke only of accelerations, Newton saw that an acceleration is the result of a force acting on a mass (Figure 5-5b). Newton's second law is commonly written as

$$F = ma$$

As always, you must define terms carefully when you look at an equation. An **acceleration** is a change in velocity, and a **velocity** is a directed speed. Most people use the words *speed* and *velocity* interchangeably, but they mean two different things. Speed is a rate of motion and does not have any direction associated with it, but velocity does. If you drive a car in a circle at 55 mph, your speed is constant, but your velocity is changing because your direction of motion is changing. An object experiences an acceleration if its speed changes or if its direction of motion changes. Every automobile has three accelerators—the gas pedal, the brake pedal, and the steering wheel. All three change the car's velocity.

In a way, the second law is just common sense; you experience its consequences every day. The acceleration of a body is proportional to the force applied to it. If you push gently against a grocery cart, you expect a small acceleration. The second law of motion also says that the acceleration depends on the mass of the body. If your grocery cart is filled with bricks and you push it gently, you expect

Cause and Effect

Why is the principle of cause and effect so important to scientists? One of the most often used and least often stated principles of science is cause and effect. Modern scientists all believe that events have causes, but ancient philosophers such as Aristotle argued that objects moved because of tendencies. They said that earth and water, and objects made mostly of earth and water, had a natural tendency to move toward the center of the universe. This natural motion had no cause but was inherent in the nature of the objects. Newton's second law of motion *(F = ma)* was the first clear statement of the principle of cause and effect. If an object (of mass *m*) changes its motion (*a* in the equation), then it must be acted on by a force (*F* in the equation). Any effect *(a)* must be the result of a cause *(F)*.

The principle of cause and effect goes far beyond motion. It gives scientists confidence that every effect has a cause. The struggle

against disease is an example. Cholera is a horrible disease that can kill its victims in hours. Long ago it was probably blamed on bad magic or the will of the gods, and only two centuries ago it was blamed on "bad air." When an epidemic of cholera struck England in 1854, Dr. John Snow carefully mapped cases in London showing that the victims had drunk water from a small number of wells contaminated by sewage. In 1876, the German Dr. Robert Koch traced cholera to an even more specific cause when he identified the microscopic bacillus that causes the disease. Step by step, scientists tracked down the cause of cholera.

If the universe did not depend on cause and effect, then you could never expect to understand how nature works. Newton's second law of motion was arguably the first clear statement that the behavior of the universe depends rationally on causes.

Cause and effect: Why did this star explode in 1992? There must have been a cause. (ESA/STScI and NASA)

very little result. If it is full of inflated balloons, however, it will move easily in response to a gentle push. Finally, the second law says that the resulting acceleration is in the direction of the force. This is also what you would expect. If you push on a cart that is not moving, you expect it to begin moving in the direction you push.

The second law of motion is important because it establishes a precise relationship between cause and effect (**How Do We Know? 5-1**). Objects do not just move. They accelerate due to the action of a force. Moving objects do not just stop. They decelerate due to a force. And moving objects don't just change direction for no reason. Any change in direction is a change in

velocity and requires the presence of a force. Aristotle said that objects move because they have a tendency to move. Newton said that objects move due to a specific cause, a force.

Newton's third law of motion specifies that for every action there is an equal and opposite reaction. In other words, forces must occur in pairs directed in opposite directions. For example, if you stand on a skateboard and jump forward, the skateboard will shoot away backward. As you jump, your feet must exert a force against the skateboard, which accelerates it toward the rear. But forces must occur in pairs, so the skateboard must exert an equal but opposite force on your feet, and that is what accelerates your body forward (Figure 5-5c).

■ **Figure 5-5**

Newton's three laws of motion.

Mutual Gravitation

Once Newton understood the three laws of motion, he was able to consider the force that causes objects to fall. The first and second laws tell you that falling bodies accelerate downward because some force must be pulling downward on them. Newton realized that some force has to act on the moon. The moon follows a curved path around Earth, and motion along a curved path is accelerated motion. The second law of motion says that an acceleration requires a force, so a force must be making the moon follow that curved path.

Newton wondered if the force that holds the moon in its orbit could be the same force that causes apples to fall—gravity. He was aware that gravity extends at least as high as the tops of mountains, but he did not know if it could extend all the way to the moon. He believed that it could, but he thought it would be weaker at greater distances, and he guessed that its strength would decrease as the square of the distance increased.

This relationship, the **inverse square law,** was familiar to Newton from his work on optics, where it applied to the intensity of light. A screen set up 1 meter from a candle flame receives a certain amount of light on each square meter. However, if that screen is moved to a distance of 2 meters, the light that originally illuminated 1 square meter must now cover 4 square meters (■ Figure 5-6). Consequently, the intensity of the light is inversely proportional to the square of the distance to the screen.

Newton made a second assumption that enabled him to predict the strength of Earth's gravity at the distance of the moon. Not only did he assume that the strength of gravity follows the inverse square law, but he also assumed that the critical distance is the distance from Earth's center, not the distance from Earth's surface. Because the moon is about 60 Earth radii away, Earth's gravity at the distance of the moon should be about 60^2 times less than at Earth's surface. Instead of being 9.8 m/s^2 at Earth's surface, it should be about 0.0027 m/s^2 at the distance of the moon.

Now, Newton wondered, was this enough acceleration to keep the moon in orbit? He knew the moon's distance and its orbital period, so he could calculate the actual acceleration needed to keep it in its curved path. The answer turned out to be 0.0027 m/s^2, as his inverse-square-law calculations predicted. The moon is held in its orbit by gravity, and gravity obeys the inverse square law.

Newton's third law says that forces always occur in pairs, so if Earth pulls on the moon, then the moon must pull on Earth. This is called mutual gravitation and is a general property of the universe. The sun, the planets, and all their moons must also attract each other by mutual gravitation. In fact, every particle of mass in the universe must attract every other particle, which is why Newtonian gravity is often called universal mutual gravitation.

Clearly the force of gravity depends on mass. Your body is made of matter, and you have your own personal gravitational field. But your gravity is weak and does not attract personal satellites orbiting around you. Larger masses have stronger gravity. From an analysis of the third law of motion, Newton realized that the mass that resists acceleration in the first law is identical to the mass associated with causing gravity. Newton performed precise experiments with pendulums and confirmed this equivalence between the mass that resists acceleration and the mass that produces gravity.

From this, combined with the inverse square law, he was able to write the famous formula for the gravitational force between two masses, *M* and *m:*

$$F = -\frac{GMm}{r^2}$$

The constant *G* is the gravitational constant; it is the constant that connects mass to gravity. In the equation, *r* is the distance between the masses. The negative sign means that the force is attractive, pulling the masses together and making *r* decrease. In plain English, Newton's law of gravitation says: The force of gravity between two masses *M* and *m* is proportional to the product of the masses and inversely proportional to the square of the distance between them.

Newton's description of gravity was a difficult idea for physicists of his time to accept because it is an example of action at a distance. Earth and moon exert forces on each other even though there is no physical connection between them. Modern scientists resolve this problem by referring to gravity as a **field.** Earth's presence produces a gravitational field directed toward Earth's center. The strength of the field decreases according to the inverse square law. Any particle of mass in that field experiences a force that depends on the mass of the particle and the strength of the field

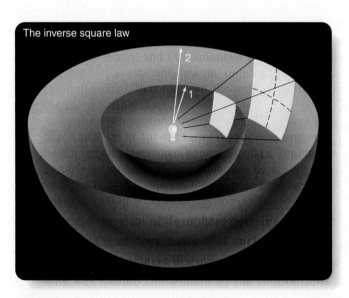

The inverse square law

■ **Figure 5-6**

As light radiates away from a source, it spreads out and becomes less intense. Here the light falling on one square meter on the inner sphere must cover four square meters on a sphere twice as big. This shows how the intensity of light is inversely proportional to the square of the distance.

at the particle's location. The resulting force is directed toward the center of the field.

The field is an elegant way to describe gravity, but it still does not say what gravity is. Later in this chapter, when you learn about Einstein's theory of curved space-time, you will get a better idea of what gravity really is.

SCIENTIFIC ARGUMENT

What do the words universal and mutual mean when you say "universal mutual gravitation"?
Scientists often build arguments that proceed step by step, and this is a good example. Newton argued that the force that makes an apple accelerate downward is the same as the force that accelerates the moon and holds it in its orbit. The third law of motion says that forces always occur in pairs, so if Earth attracts the moon, then the moon must attract Earth. That is, gravitation is *mutual* between any two objects.

Furthermore, if Earth's gravity attracts the apple and the moon, then it must attract the sun, and the third law says that the sun must attract Earth. But if the sun attracts Earth, then it must also attract the other planets and even distant stars, which, in turn, must attract the sun and each other. Step by step, Newton's third law of motion leads to the conclusion that gravitation must apply to all masses in the universe. That is, gravitation must be *universal*.

Aristotle explained gravity in a totally different way. **Why couldn't Aristotle's explanation of a falling apple on Earth account for a hammer falling on the surface of the moon?**

5-2 Orbital Motion and Tides

ORBITAL MOTION AND TIDES are two different kinds of gravitational phenomena. As you think about the orbital motion of the moon and planets, you need to think about how gravity pulls on an object. When you think about tides, you must think about how gravity pulls on different parts of an object. Analyzing these two kinds of phenomena will give you a deeper insight into how gravity works.

Orbits

Newton was the first person to realize that objects in orbit are falling. You can explore Newton's insight by analyzing the motion of objects orbiting Earth. Carefully read **Orbiting Earth** on pages 84–85 and notice three important concepts and six new terms.

1 An object orbiting Earth is actually falling (being accelerated) toward Earth's center. The object continuously misses Earth because of its orbital velocity. To follow a circular orbit, the object must move at *circular velocity*, and at the

right distance from Earth it could be a very useful *geosynchronous satellite.*

2 Notice that objects orbiting each other actually revolve around their *center of mass.*

3 Finally, notice the difference between *closed orbits* and *open orbits.* If you want to leave Earth never to return, you must accelerate your spaceship at least to *escape velocity, V_e,* so it will follow an open orbit.

Orbital Velocity

If you were about to ride a rocket into orbit, you would have to answer a critical question: "How fast must I go to stay in orbit?" An object's circular velocity is the lateral velocity it must have to remain in a circular orbit. If you assume that the mass of your spaceship is small compared with the mass of Earth, then the circular velocity is:

$$V_c = \sqrt{\frac{GM}{r}}$$

In this formula, M is the mass of the central body (Earth in this case) in kilograms, r is the radius of the orbit in meters, and G is the gravitational constant, 6.67×10^{-11} m^3/s^{2}kg. This formula is all you need to calculate how fast an object must travel to stay in a circular orbit.

For example, how fast does the moon travel in its orbit? Earth's mass is 5.97×10^{24} kg, and the radius of the moon's orbit is 3.84×10^8 m. Then the moon's velocity is:

$$V_c = \sqrt{\frac{6.67 \times 10^{-11} \times 5.98 \times 10^{24}}{3.84 \times 10^8}} = \sqrt{\frac{39.9 \times 10^{13}}{3.84 \times 10^8}}$$

$$= \sqrt{1.04 \times 10^6} = 1020 \text{ m/s} = 1.02 \text{ km/s}$$

This calculation shows that the moon travels 1.02 km along its orbit each second. That is the circular velocity at the distance of the moon.

A satellite just above Earth's atmosphere is only about 200 km above Earth's surface, or 6578 km from Earth's center, so Earth's gravity is much stronger, and the satellite must travel much faster to stay in a circular orbit. You can use the formula above to find that the circular velocity just above Earth's atmosphere is about 7780 m/s, or 7.7 km/s. This is about 17,400 miles per hour, which shows why putting satellites into Earth orbit takes such large rockets. Not only must the rocket lift the satellite above Earth's atmosphere, but the rocket's trajectory must then curve over and accelerate the satellite horizontally to circular velocity.

A **Common Misconception** holds that there is no gravity in space. You can see that space is filled with gravitational forces from Earth, the sun, and all other objects in the universe. An astronaut who appears weightless in space is actually falling along a path at the urging of the combined gravitational fields in the rest of the universe. Just above Earth's atmosphere, the orbital motion of the astronaut is dominated by Earth's gravity.

Calculating Escape Velocity

If you launch a rocket upward, it will consume its fuel in a few moments and reach its maximum speed. From that point on, it will coast upward. How fast must a rocket travel to coast away from Earth and escape? Of course, no matter how far it travels, it can never escape from Earth's gravity. The effects of Earth's gravity extend to infinity. It is possible, however, for a rocket to travel so fast initially that gravity can never slow it to a stop. Then the rocket could leave Earth.

Escape velocity is the velocity required to escape from the surface of an astronomical body. Here you are interested in escaping from Earth or a planet; in later chapters you will consider the escape velocity from stars, galaxies, and even black holes.

The escape velocity, V_e, is given by a simple formula:

$$V_e = \sqrt{\frac{2GM}{r}}$$

Again, G is the gravitational constant 6.67×10^{-11} m^3/s^{2}kg, M is the mass of the astronomical body in kilograms, and r is its radius in meters. (Notice that this formula is very similar to the formula for circular velocity; in fact the escape velocity formula is $\sqrt{2}$ times the circular velocity formula.)

You can find the escape velocity from Earth by again using its mass, 5.97×10^{24} kg, and plugging in its radius, 6.38×10^6 m. Then the escape velocity is:

$$V_e = \sqrt{\frac{2 \times 6.67 \times 10^{-11} \times 5.97 \times 10^{24}}{6.38 \times 10^6}} = \sqrt{\frac{7.96 \times 10^{14}}{6.38 \times 10^6}}$$

$$= \sqrt{1.25 \times 10^8} = 11{,}200 \text{ m/s} = 11.2 \text{ km/s}$$

This is equal to about 24,600 miles per hour.

Notice from the formula that the escape velocity from a body depends on both its mass and radius. A massive body might have a low escape velocity if it has a very large radius. You will meet such objects when you consider giant stars. On the other hand, a rather low-mass body could have a very large escape velocity if it had a very small radius, a condition you will meet when you study black holes.

Once Newton understood gravity and motion, he could do what Kepler had failed to do—he could explain why the planets obey Kepler's laws of planetary motion.

Kepler's Laws Reexamined

Now that you understand Newton's laws, gravity, and orbital motion, you can look at Kepler's laws of planetary motion in a new and more sophisticated way.

Kepler's first law says that the orbits of the planets are ellipses with the sun at one focus. The orbits of the planets are ellipses because gravity follows the inverse square law. In one of his most famous mathematical proofs, Newton showed that if a planet moves in a closed orbit under the influence of an attractive force that follows the inverse square law, then the planet must follow an elliptical path.

Even though Kepler correctly identified the shape of the planets' orbits, he still wondered why the planets keep moving along these orbits, and now you know the answer. They move because there is nothing to slow them down. Newton's first law says that a body in motion stays in motion unless acted on by some force. In the absence of friction, the planets must continue to move.

Kepler's second law says that a planet moves faster when it is near the sun and slower when it is farther away. Once again, Newton's discoveries explain why. Imagine you are in an elliptical orbit around the sun. After you round the most distant part of the ellipse, aphelion, you begin to move back closer to the sun, and the sun's gravity pulls you slightly forward in your orbit. You pick up speed as you fall closer to the sun, so, of course, you go faster as you approach the sun. After you round the closest point to the sun, perihelion, you begin to move away from the sun, and the sun's gravity pulls slightly backward on you, slowing you down as you climb away from the sun. If you were in a circular orbit, the sun's gravity would always pull perpendicular to your motion, and you would not speed up or slow down. So Kepler's second law makes sense when you analyze it in terms of forces and motions.

Physicists think of Kepler's second law in a more elegant way. Earlier you saw that a body moving on a frictionless surface will continue to move in a straight line until it is acted on by some force; that is, the object has momentum. In a similar way, an object set rotating on a frictionless surface will continue rotating until something acts to speed it up or slow it down. Such an object has **angular momentum,** a measure of the rotation of the body about some point. A planet circling the sun in an orbit has a given amount of angular momentum; and, with no outside influences to alter its motion, it must conserve its angular momentum. That is, its angular momentum must remain constant. Mathematically, a planet's angular momentum is the product of its mass, velocity, and distance from the sun. This explains why a planet must speed up as it comes closer to the sun along an elliptical orbit. Because its angular momentum is conserved, as its distance from the sun decreases, its velocity must increase. Conversely, the planet's velocity must decrease as its distance from the sun increases.

The conservation of angular momentum is actually a common human experience. Skaters spinning slowly can draw their arms and legs closer to their axis of rotation and, through conservation of angular momentum, spin faster (■ Figure 5-7). To slow their rotation, they can extend their arms again. Similarly, divers can spin rapidly in the tuck position and then slow their rotation by stretching into the extended position.

Kepler's third law says that a planet's orbital period depends on its distance from the sun. That law is also explained by a conservation law, but in this case it is the law of conservation of

Orbiting Earth

1 You can understand orbital motion by thinking of a cannonball falling around Earth in a circular path. Imagine a cannon on a high mountain aimed horizontally as shown at right. A little gunpowder gives the cannonball a low velocity, and it doesn't travel very far before falling to Earth. More gunpowder gives the cannonball a higher velocity, and it travels farther. With enough gunpowder, the cannonball travels so fast it never strikes the ground. Earth's gravity pulls it toward Earth's center, but Earth's surface curves away from it at the same rate it falls. It is in orbit. The velocity needed to stay in a circular orbit is called the **circular velocity**. Just above Earth's atmosphere, circular velocity is 7780 m/s or about 17,400 miles per hour, and the orbital period is about 90 minutes.

A satellite above Earth's atmosphere feels no friction and will fall around Earth indefinitely.

North Pole

Earth satellites eventually fall back to Earth if they orbit too low and experience friction with the upper atmosphere.

1a A **geosynchronous satellite** orbits eastward with the rotation of Earth and remains above a fixed spot — ideal for communications and weather satellites.

A Geosynchronous Satellite

At a distance of 42,250 km (26,260 miles) from Earth's center, a satellite orbits with a period of 24 hours.

The satellite orbits eastward, and Earth rotates eastward under the moving satellite.

The satellite remains fixed above a spot on Earth's equator.

1b According to Newton's first law of motion, the moon should follow a straight line and leave Earth forever. Because it follows a curve, Newton knew that some force must continuously accelerate it toward Earth — gravity. Each second the moon moves 1020 m (3350 ft) eastward and falls about 1.6 mm (about 1/16 inch) toward Earth. The combination of these motions produces the moon's curved orbit. The moon is falling.

Straight line motion of the moon

Motion toward Earth

Curved path of moon's orbit

Earth

1c Astronauts in orbit around Earth feel weightless, but they are not "beyond Earth's gravity," to use a term from old science fiction movies. Like the moon, the astronauts are accelerated toward Earth by Earth's gravity, but they travel fast enough along their orbits that they continually "miss the Earth." They are literally falling around Earth. Inside or outside a spacecraft, astronauts feel weightless because they and their spacecraft are falling at the same rate. Rather than saying they are weightless, you should more accurately say they are in free fall.

NASA

2 To be precise you should not say that an object orbits Earth. Rather the two objects orbit each other. Gravitation is mutual, and if Earth pulls on the moon, the moon pulls on Earth. The two bodies revolve around their common **center of mass**, the balance point of the system.

2a Two bodies of different mass balance at the center of mass, which is located closer to the more massive object. As the two objects orbit each other, they revolve around their common center of mass as shown at right. The center of mass of the Earth–moon system lies only 4708 km (2926 miles) from the center of Earth — inside the Earth. As the moon orbits the center of mass on one side, the Earth swings around the center of mass on the opposite side.

Center of mass

3 **Closed orbits** return the orbiting object to its starting point. The moon and artificial satellites orbit Earth in closed orbits. Below, the cannonball could follow an elliptical or a circular closed orbit. If the cannonball travels as fast as **escape velocity**, the velocity needed to leave a body, it will enter an open orbit. An **open orbit** does not return the cannonball to Earth. It will escape.

Hyberbola

A cannonball with a velocity greater than escape velocity will follow a hyperbola and escape from Earth.

Parabola

A cannonball with escape velocity will follow a parabola and escape.

North Pole

Ellipse

Circle

3a As described by Kepler's second law, an object in an elliptical orbit has its lowest velocity when it is farthest from Earth (apogee), and its highest velocity when it is closest to Earth (perigee). Perigee must be above Earth's atmosphere, or friction will rob the satellite of energy and it will eventually fall back to Earth.

Energy

Physicists define **energy** as the ability to do work, but you might paraphrase that definition as the ability to produce a change. A moving body has energy called **kinetic energy.** A planet moving along its orbit, a cement truck rolling down the highway, and a golf ball sailing down the fairway all have the ability to produce a change. Imagine colliding with any of these objects!

Energy need not be represented by motion. Sunlight falling on a green plant, on photographic film, or on unprotected skin can produce chemical changes, and thus light is a form of energy. Batteries and gasoline are examples of chemical energy, and uranium fuel rods contain nuclear energy. A tank of hot water contains thermal energy.

Potential energy is the energy an object has because of its position in a gravitational field. A bowling ball on a shelf above your desk has potential energy. It is only potential, however, and doesn't produce any changes until the bowling ball descends onto your desk. The higher the shelf, the more potential energy the ball has.

Energy constantly flows through nature and produces changes. Sunlight (energy) is absorbed by ocean plants and stored as sugars and starches (energy). When the plant dies, it and other ocean life are buried and become oil (energy), which gets pumped to the surface and burned in automobile engines to produce motion (energy).

Aristotle believed that all change originated in the motion of the starry sphere and flowed down to Earth. Modern science has found a more sophisticated description of the continual change you see around you. In a way, science is the study of the way energy flows through the world and produces change. Energy is the pulse of the natural world.

Using the metric system (Appendix A), energy is expressed in **joules** (abbreviated **J**).

One joule is about as much energy as that given up when an apple falls from a table to the floor.

Energy is the ability to cause change.

MASS | ENERGY | TEMPERATURE AND HEAT | DENSITY | PRESSURE

---

energy (**Focus on Fundamentals 2**). A planet orbiting the sun has a specific amount of energy that depends only on its average distance from the sun. That energy can be divided between energy of motion and energy stored in the gravitational attraction between the planet and the sun. The energy of motion depends on how fast the planet moves, and the stored energy depends on the size of its orbit. The relation between these two kinds of energy is determined by Newton's laws. That means there has to be a fixed relationship between the rate at which a planet moves around its orbit and the size of the orbit—between its orbital period P and the orbit's semimajor axis a. You can even derive Kepler's third law from Newton's laws of motion as shown in the next section.

Newton's Version of Kepler's Third Law

The equation for circular velocity is actually a version of Kepler's third law, as you can prove with three lines of simple algebra. The result is one of the most useful formulas in astronomy.

The equation for circular velocity, as you have seen, is:

$$V_c = \sqrt{\frac{GM}{r}}$$

The orbital velocity of a planet is simply the circumference of its orbit divided by the orbital period:

$$V = \frac{2\pi r}{P}$$

If you substitute this for V in the first equation and solve for P^2, you will get:

$$P^2 = \frac{(4\pi^2)}{(GM)} r^3$$

■ **Figure 5-7**

Skaters demonstrate conservation of angular momentum when they spin faster by drawing their arms and legs closer to their axis of rotation.

Here M is just the total mass of the system in kilograms. For a planet orbiting the sun, you can use the mass of the sun for M, because the mass of the planet is negligible compared to the mass of the sun. (In a later chapter, you will apply this formula to two stars orbiting each other, and then the mass M will be the sum of the two masses.) For a circular orbit, r equals the semimajor axis a, so this formula is a general version of Kepler's third law, $P^2 = a^3$. In Kepler's version, you used astronomical units (AU) and years, but in Newton's version of the formula, you should use units of meters, seconds, and kilograms. G, of course, is the gravitational constant.

This is a powerful formula. Astronomers use it to calculate the masses of bodies by observing orbital motion. If, for example, you observed a moon orbiting a planet and you could measure the size of the moon's orbit, r, and its orbital period, P, you could use this formula to solve for M, the total mass of the planet plus the moon. There is no other way to find masses of objects in the universe, and, in later chapters, you will see this formula used over and over to find the masses of stars, galaxies, and planets.

This discussion is a good illustration of the power of Newton's work. By carefully defining motion and gravity and by giving them mathematical expression, Newton was able to derive new truths, among them Newton's version of Kepler's third law. His work transformed the mysterious wanderings of the planets into understandable motions that follow simple rules. In fact, his discovery of gravity explained something else that had mystified philosophers for millennia—the ebb and flow of the oceans.

Tides and Tidal Forces

Newton understood that gravity is mutual—Earth attracts the moon, and the moon attracts Earth—and that means the moon's gravity can explain the ocean tides.

Tides are caused by small differences in gravitational forces. For example, Earth's gravity attracts your body downward with a force equal to your weight. The moon is less massive and more distant, so it attracts your body with a force that is a tiny percent of your weight. You don't notice that little force, but Earth's oceans respond dramatically.

The side of Earth that faces the moon is about 4000 miles closer to the moon than is the center of Earth. Consequently, the moon's gravity, tiny though it is at the distance of Earth, is just a bit stronger when it acts on the near side of Earth than on the center. It pulls on the oceans on the near side of Earth a bit more strongly than on Earth's center, and the oceans respond by flowing into a bulge of water on the side of Earth facing the moon. There is also a bulge on the side of Earth that faces away from the moon because the moon pulls more strongly on Earth's center than on the far side. Thus the moon pulls Earth away from the oceans, which flow into a bulge away from the moon as shown at the top of ■ Figure 5-8.

You might wonder: If Earth and moon accelerate toward each other, why don't they smash together? The answer is that they would collide in about two weeks except that they are orbiting around their common center of mass. The ocean tides are caused by the accelerations Earth and its oceans feel as they orbit around that center of mass.

A **Common Misconception** holds that the moon's effect on tides means that the moon has an affinity for water—including the water in your body—and, according to some people, that's how the moon affects you. That's not true. If the moon's gravity affected only water, then there would be only one tidal bulge, the one facing the moon. As you know, the moon's gravity acts on the rock of Earth as well as on water, and that produces the tidal bulge in the oceans on the far side of Earth. In fact, small tidal bulges occur in the rocky bulk of Earth as it is deformed by the moon's gravity, and although you don't notice it, as Earth rotates, its mountains and plains rise and fall by a few centimeters. The moon has no special affinity for water, and, because your body is so much smaller than Earth, any tides the moon raises in your body are immeasurably small. Ocean tides are large because oceans are large.

You can see dramatic evidence of tides if you watch the ocean shore for a few hours. As Earth rotates on its axis, the tidal bulges remain fixed with respect to the moon. As the turning Earth carries you and your beach into a tidal bulge, the ocean water deepens, and the tide crawls up the sand. The tide does not so much "come in" as you are carried into the tidal bulge. Later, when Earth's rotation carries you out of the bulge, the ocean becomes shallower, and the tide falls. Because there are two bulges on opposite sides of Earth, the tides rise and fall twice a day on an ideal coast.

In reality, the tidal cycle at any given location can be quite complex because it is affected by the latitude of the site, shape of the shore, winds, and so on. Tides in the Bay of Fundy (New Brunswick, Canada), for example, occur twice a day and can exceed 40 feet. In contrast, the northern coast of the Gulf of Mexico has only one tidal cycle a day of roughly 1 foot.

Gravity is universal, so the sun also produces tides on Earth. The sun is roughly 27 million times more massive than the moon, but it lies almost 400 times farther from Earth. Tides on Earth caused by the sun are less than half as high as those caused by the moon. Twice a month, at new moon and at full moon, the moon and sun produce tidal bulges that add together and produce extreme tidal changes; high tide is exceptionally high, and low tide is exceptionally low. Such tides are called **spring tides.** Here the word *spring* does not refer to the season of the year but to the rapid welling up of water. At first- and third-quarter moons, the sun and moon pull at right angles to each other, and the sun's tides cancel out some of the moon's tides. These less-extreme tides are called **neap tides,** and they do not rise very high or fall very low. The word *neap* comes from an obscure Old English word, *nep*, that seems to have meant "lacking power to advance." Spring tides and neap tides are illustrated in Figure 5-8.

Galileo tried to understand tides, but it was not until Newton described gravity that astronomers could analyze tidal

Lunar gravity acting on Earth and its oceans

North Pole

The moon's gravity pulls more on the near side of Earth than on the far side.

Tidal bulge   North Pole

Subtracting off the force on Earth reveals the small outward forces that produce tidal bulges.

Friction with ocean beds slows Earth and drags its tidal bulges slightly ahead (exaggerated here).

Gravitational force of tidal bulges

Earth's rotation

Moon

Gravity of tidal bulges pulls the moon forward and alters its orbit.

■ **Figure 5-8**

Tides are produced by small differences in the gravitational force exerted on different parts of an object. The side of Earth nearest the moon feels a larger force than the side farthest away. Relative to Earth's center, small forces are left over, and they cause the tides. Both the moon and sun produce tides on Earth. Tides can alter both an object's rotation and its orbital motion.

Spring tides occur when tides caused by the sun and moon add together.

Spring tides are extreme.

Full moon   New moon   To sun

Neap tides are mild.   First quarter

Neap tides occur when tides caused by the sun and moon partially cancel out.

To sun

Third quarter   Diagrams not to scale

forces and recognize their surprising effects. For example, the moving water in tidal bulges experiences friction with the ocean beds and resistance as it runs into continents, and that slows Earth's rotation and makes the length of a day grow by 0.0023 second per century. Thin layers of silt laid down millions of years ago where rivers empty into the oceans record tidal cycles as well as daily, monthly, and annual cycles. Those confirm that only 620 million years ago Earth's day was less than 22 hours long. Tidal forces can also affect orbital motion. Earth rotates eastward, and friction with the ocean beds drags the tidal bulges slightly eastward out of a direct Earth–moon line. These tidal bulges are massive, and their gravitational field pulls the moon forward in its orbit, as shown at the bottom of Figure 5-8. As a result, the

moon's orbit is growing larger by about 3.8 cm a year, an effect that astronomers can measure by bouncing laser beams off reflectors left on the lunar surface by the Apollo astronauts.

Earth's gravitation exerts tidal forces on the moon, and although there are no bodies of water on the moon, friction within the flexing rock has slowed the moon's rotation to the point that it now keeps the same face toward Earth.

Newton's gravitation is much more than just the force that makes apples fall. In later chapters, you will see how tides can pull gas away from stars, rip galaxies apart, and melt the interiors of small moons orbiting near massive planets. Tidal forces produce some of the most surprising and dramatic processes in the universe.

Astronomy After Newton

Newton published his work in 1687 in a book called *Philosophiae Naturalis Principia Mathematica (Mathematical Principles of Natural Philosophy)*, now known simply as *Principia* (pronounced *Prin-KIP-ee-uh*) (■ Figure 5-9). It is one of the most important books ever written. *Principia* changed astronomy, changed science, and changed the way people think about nature.

Testing a Hypothesis by Prediction

How are the predictions of a hypothesis useful in science? (Note the careful use of language here, to distinguish a tentative hypothesis from a theory that is well confirmed.) Scientific hypotheses face in two directions. They look back into the past and explain phenomena previously observed. For example, Newton's laws of motion and gravity explained observations of the movements of the planets made over many centuries. But hypotheses also look forward in that they make predictions about what you should find as you explore further. For example, Newton's laws allowed astronomers to calculate the orbits of comets, predict their return, and eventually understand their origin.

Scientific predictions are important in two ways. First, if a prediction of a hypothesis is confirmed, scientists gain confidence that the hypothesis is a true description of nature. But predictions are important for a second reason. They can point the way to unexplored avenues of knowledge.

Particle physics is a field in which predictions have played a key role in directing research. In the early 1970s, physicists proposed a hypothesis about the fundamental forces and particles in atoms called the Standard Model. This hypothesis explained what scientists had already observed in experiments, but it also predicted the existence of particles that hadn't yet been observed. To test the hypothesis, scientists focused their efforts on building more and more powerful particle accelerators in the hopes of detecting the predicted particles.

A number of these particles have since been discovered, and they do match the characteristics predicted by the Standard Model, further confirming the hypothesis. One predicted particle, the Higgs boson, has not yet been found, as of this writing, but an even larger accelerator may allow its detection. Will the Higgs boson be found, or will someone come up with a better hypothesis? This is only one of many cliff-hangers in modern science.

You learned in an earlier chapter that a hypothesis that has passed many tests and made successful predictions can "graduate" to

Physicists build huge accelerators to search for sub-atomic particles predicted by their theories. (Brookhaven National Laboratory)

being considered a theory. As you read about any scientific hypothesis or theory, think about both what it can explain and what it can predict.

Principia changed astronomy by ushering in a new age. No longer did people have to appeal to the whim of the gods to explain things in the heavens. No longer did they speculate on why the planets wander across the sky. After *Principia* astronomers understood that the motions of the heavenly bodies are governed by simple, universal rules that describe the motions of everything from orbiting planets to falling apples. Suddenly the universe was understandable in simple terms, and astronomers could accurately predict future planetary motions (**How Do We Know? 5-2**).

Principia also changed science in general. The works of Copernicus and Kepler had been mathematical, but no book before had so clearly demonstrated the power of mathematics as a language of precision. Newton's arguments in *Principia* were so powerful an illustration of the quantitative study of nature that scientists around the world adopted mathematics as their most powerful tool.

Also, *Principia* changed the way people thought about nature. Newton showed that the rules that govern the universe are simple.

Particles move according to three rules of motion and attract each other with a force called gravity. These motions are predictable, and that makes the universe a vast machine based on a few simple rules. It is complex only in that it contains a vast number

■ Figure 5-9

Newton, working from the discoveries of Galileo and Kepler, derived three laws of motion and the principle of mutual gravitation. He and some of his discoveries were honored on this old English pound note. Notice the diagram of orbital motion in the background and the open copy of *Principia* in Newton's hands.

of particles. In Newton's view, if he knew the location and motion of every particle in the universe, he could, in principle, derive the past and future of the universe in every detail. This mechanical determinism has been undermined by modern quantum mechanics, but it dominated science for more than two centuries during which scientists thought of nature as a beautiful clockwork that would be perfectly predictable if they knew how all the gears meshed.

Most of all, Newton's work broke the last bonds between science and formal philosophy. Newton did not speculate on the good or evil of gravity. He did not debate its meaning. Not more than a hundred years before, scientists would have argued over the "reality" of gravity. Newton didn't care for these debates. He wrote, "It is enough that gravity exists and suffices to explain the phenomena of the heavens."

Newton's laws dominated astronomy for two centuries. Then, early in the 20th century, Albert Einstein proposed a new way to describe gravity. The new theory did not replace Newton's laws but rather showed that they were only approximately correct and could be seriously in error under special circumstances. Einstein's theories further extend the scientific understanding of the nature of gravity. Just as Newton had stood on the shoulders of Galileo, Einstein stood on the shoulders of Newton.

■ **Figure 5-10**

Einstein has become a symbol of the brilliant scientist. His fame began when he was a young man and thought deeply about the nature of motion. That led him to revolutionary insights into the meaning of space and time and a new understanding of gravity.

SCIENTIFIC ARGUMENT

How do Newton's laws of motion explain the orbital motion of the moon?

The key here is to build your argument step by step. If Earth and the moon did not attract each other, the moon would move in a straight line in accord with Newton's first law of motion and vanish into deep space. Instead, gravity pulls the moon toward Earth's center, and the moon accelerates toward Earth. This acceleration is just enough to pull the moon away from its straight-line motion and cause it to follow a curve around Earth. In fact, it is correct to say that the moon is falling, but because of its lateral motion it continuously misses Earth.

Every orbiting object is falling toward the center of its orbit but is also moving laterally fast enough to compensate for the inward motion, and it follows a curved orbit. That is an elegant argument, but it raises a question: **How can astronauts float inside spacecraft in a "weightless" state? Why might "free fall" be a more accurate term?**

5-3) Einstein and Relativity

IN THE EARLY YEARS OF THE LAST CENTURY, Albert Einstein (1879–1955) (■ Figure 5-10) began thinking about how motion and gravity interact. He soon gained international fame by showing that Newton's laws of motion and gravity were only partially correct. The revised theory became known as the theory of relativity. As you will see, there are really two theories of relativity.

Special Relativity

Einstein began by thinking about how moving observers see events around them. His analysis led him to the first postulate of relativity, also known as the principle of relativity:

> **First postulate** (the principle of relativity): Observers can never detect their *uniform* motion except relative to other objects.

You may have experienced the first postulate while sitting on a train in a station. You suddenly notice that the train on the next track has begun to creep out of the station. However, after several moments you realize that it is your own train that is moving and that the other train is still motionless on its track. You can't tell which train is moving until you look at external objects such as the station platform.

Consider another example. Suppose you are floating in a spaceship in interstellar space, and another spaceship comes coasting by (■ Figure 5-11a). You might conclude that it is moving and you are not, but someone in the other ship might be equally sure that you are moving and it is not. Of course, you could just look out a window and compare the motion of your spaceship with a nearby star, but that just expands the problem. Which is moving, your spaceship or the star? The principle of relativity says that there is no experiment you can perform to decide which ship is moving and which is not. This means that there is no such thing as absolute rest—all motion is relative.

Because neither you nor the people in the other spaceship could perform any experiment to detect your absolute motion through space, the laws of physics must have the same form in both spaceships. Otherwise, experiments would produce different results in the two ships, and you could decide who was moving. So, a more general way of stating the first postulate refers to these laws of physics:

> **First postulate** (alternate version): The laws of physics are the same for all observers, no matter what their motion, so long as they are not *accelerated*.

■ Figure 5-11

(a) The principle of relativity says that observers can never detect their uniform motion, except relative to other objects. Thus, neither of these travelers can decide who is moving and who is not. (b) If the velocity of light depended on the motion of the observer through space, then these travelers could perform measurements inside their spaceships to discover who was moving. If the principle of relativity is correct, then the velocity of light must be a constant when measured by any observer.

The word *accelerated* is important. If either spaceship were to fire its rockets, then its velocity would change. The crew of that ship would know it because they would feel the acceleration pressing them into their couches. Accelerated motion, therefore, is different—the pilots of the spaceships can always tell which ship is accelerating and which is not. The postulates of relativity discussed here apply only to the special case of observers in *uniform* motion, which means *unaccelerated* motion. That is why the theory is called the **special theory of relativity.**

The first postulate led Einstein to the conclusion that the speed of light must be constant for all observers. No matter how you are moving, your measurement of the speed of light has to give the same result (Figure 5-11b). This became the second postulate of special relativity:

Second postulate: The speed of light is constant and will be the same for all observers independent of their motion relative to the light source.

Remember, this is required by the first postulate; if the speed of light were not constant, then the pilots of the spaceships could measure the speed of light inside their spaceships and decide who was moving.

Once Einstein had accepted the basic postulates of relativity, he was led to some startling discoveries. Newton's laws of motion and gravity worked well as long as distances were small and velocities were low. But when Einstein began to think about very large distances or very high velocities, he realized that Newton's laws were no longer adequate to describe what happens. Instead, the postulates led Einstein to derive a more accurate description of nature now known as the special theory of relativity. It predicts some peculiar effects. For example, special relativity shows that the observed mass of a moving particle depends on its velocity. The higher the velocity, the greater the mass of the particle. This is not significant at low velocities, but it becomes very important as the velocity approaches the speed of light. Such increases in mass are actually observed whenever physicists accelerate atomic particles to high velocities (■ Figure 5-12).

This discovery led to yet another insight. The relativistic equations that describe the energy of a moving particle predict

The observed mass of moving electrons depends on their velocity. As the ratio of their velocity to the velocity of light, v/c, gets larger, the mass of the electrons in terms of their mass at rest, m/m_0, increases. Such relativistic effects are quite evident in particle accelerators, which accelerate atomic particles to very high velocities.

that the energy of a motionless particle is not zero. Rather, its energy at rest is $m_0 c^2$. This is of course the famous equation:

$$E = m_0 c^2$$

The constant c is the speed of light, and m_0 is the mass of the particle when it is at rest. This simple formula shows that mass and energy are related, and you will see in later chapters how nature can convert one into the other inside stars.

For example, suppose that you convert 1 kg of matter into energy. The speed of light is 3×10^8 m/s, so your result is 9×10^{16} joules (J) (approximately equal to a 20-megaton nuclear bomb). Recall that a joule is a unit of energy roughly equivalent to the energy given up when an apple falls from a table to the floor. This simple calculation shows that the energy equivalent of even a small mass is very large.

Other relativistic effects include the slowing of moving clocks and the shrinkage of lengths measured in the direction of motion. A detailed discussion of the major consequences of the special theory of relativity is beyond

the scope of this book, but you can have confidence that these strange effects have been confirmed many times in experiments. Einstein's work is called the special *theory* of relativity because it meets the scientific definition of a *theory*: it is very well understood, has been checked many times in many ways, and is widely applicable.

The General Theory of Relativity

In 1916, Einstein published a more general version of the theory of relativity that dealt with accelerated as well as uniform motion. This **general theory of relativity** contained a new description of gravity.

Einstein began by thinking about observers in accelerated motion. Imagine an observer sitting in a windowless spaceship. Such an observer cannot distinguish between the force of gravity and the inertial forces produced by the acceleration of the spaceship (■ Figure 5-13). This led Einstein to conclude that gravity

■ **Figure 5-13**

(a) An observer in a closed spaceship on the surface of a planet feels gravity. (b) In space, with the rockets smoothly firing and accelerating the spaceship, the observer feels inertial forces that are equivalent to gravitational forces.

and acceleration are related, a conclusion now known as the equivalence principle:

> **Equivalence principle:** Observers cannot distinguish locally between inertial forces due to acceleration and uniform gravitational forces due to the presence of a massive body.

This should not surprise you. Earlier in this chapter you read that Newton concluded that the mass that resists acceleration is the same as the mass that exerts gravitational forces. He even performed an elegant experiment with pendulums to test the equivalence of the mass related to motion and the mass related to gravity.

The importance of the general theory of relativity lies in its description of gravity. Einstein concluded that gravity, inertia, and acceleration are all associated with the way space is related to time in what is now referred to as space-time. This relation is often referred to as curvature, and a one-line description of general relativity explains a gravitational field as a curved region of space-time:

> **Gravity according to general relativity:** Mass tells space-time how to curve, and the curvature of space-time (gravity) tells mass how to accelerate.

So, you feel gravity because Earth's mass causes a curvature of space-time. The mass of your body responds to that curvature by accelerating toward Earth's center, and that presses you downward in your chair. According to general relativity, all masses cause curvature, and the larger the mass, the more severe the curvature. That's gravity.

Confirmation of the Curvature of Space-Time

Einstein's general theory of relativity has been confirmed by a number of experiments, but two are worth mentioning here because they were among the first tests of the theory. One involves Mercury's orbit, and the other involves eclipses of the sun.

Johannes Kepler understood that the orbit of Mercury is elliptical, but it wasn't until 1859 that astronomers discovered that the long axis of its orbit sweeps around the sun in a motion that is an example of precession (■ Figure 5-14). The total observed precession is a little over 1.5° per century. This precession is produced by the gravitation of Venus, Earth, and the other planets and by the precession of Earth's axis. However, when astronomers take all known effects into account and use Newton's description of gravity to account for the gravitational influence of all of the planets, they are left with a small excess. Mercury's orbit is advancing 43 seconds of arc per century faster than Newton's laws predict.

This is a tiny effect. Each time Mercury returns to perihelion, its closest point to the sun, it is about 29 km (18 mi) past the position predicted by Newton's laws. This is such a small

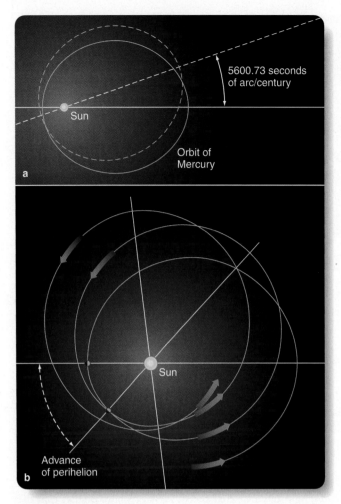

■ Figure 5-14

(a) Mercury's orbit precesses 43.11 arc seconds per century faster than predicted by Newton's laws. (b) Even when you ignore the influences of the other planets, Mercury's orbit is not a perfect ellipse. Curved space-time near the sun distorts the orbit from an ellipse into a rosette. The advance of Mercury's perihelion is exaggerated about a million times in this figure.

distance compared with the planet's diameter of 4850 km that it could never have been detected had it not been cumulative. Each orbit, Mercury gains 29 km, and in a century it gains over 12,000 km—more than twice its own diameter. This tiny effect, called the advance of perihelion of Mercury's orbit, accumulated into a serious discrepancy in the Newtonian description of the universe.

The advance of perihelion of Mercury's orbit was one of the first problems to which Einstein applied the principles of general relativity. First he calculated how much the sun's mass curves space-time in the region of Mercury's orbit, and then he calculated how Mercury moves through the space-time. The theory predicted that the curved space-time should cause Mercury's orbit to advance by 43.03 seconds of arc per century, well within the observational accuracy of the excess (Figure 5-14b).

When his theory matched observations, Einstein was so excited he could not return to work for three days. He would be

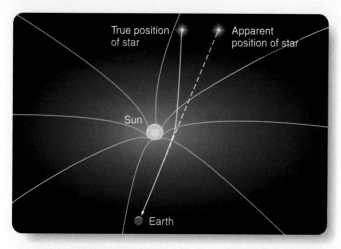

Like a depression in a putting green, the curved space-time near the sun deflects light from distant stars and makes them appear to lie slightly farther from the sun than their true positions.

■ **Figure 5-16**

(a) Schematic drawing of the deflection of starlight by the sun's gravity. Dots show the true positions of the stars as photographed months before the eclipse. Lines point toward the positions of the stars during the eclipse. (b) Actual data from the eclipse of 1922. Random uncertainties of observation cause some scatter in the data, but in general the stars appear to move away from the sun by 1.77 arc seconds at the edge of the sun's disk. The deflection of stars is magnified by a factor of 2300 in both (a) and (b).

even happier with modern studies that have shown that Mercury, Venus, Earth, and even Icarus, an asteroid that comes close to the sun, have orbits observed to be slipping forward due to the curvature of space-time near the sun. This same effect has been detected in pairs of stars that orbit each other.

A second test of general relativity was directly related to the motion of light through the curved space-time near the sun. Because light has a limited speed, Newton's laws predict that the gravity of an object should slightly bend the paths of light beams passing nearby. The equations of general relativity indicated that light would have an extra deflection caused by curved space-time, just as a rolling golf ball is deflected by undulations in a putting green. Einstein predicted that starlight grazing the sun's surface would be deflected by 1.75 arc seconds, twice the deflection that Newton's law of gravity would predict (■ Figure 5-15). Starlight passing near the sun is normally lost in the sun's glare, but during a total solar eclipse stars beyond the sun can be seen. As soon as Einstein published his theory, astronomers rushed to observe such stars and test the curvature of space-time.

The first solar eclipse following Einstein's announcement in 1916 occurred on June 8, 1918. It was cloudy at some observing sites, and results from other sites were inconclusive. The next occurred on May 29, 1919, only months after the end of World War I, and was visible from Africa and South America. British teams went to both Brazil and Príncipe, an island off the coast of Africa. Months before the eclipse, they photographed the part of the sky where the sun would be located during the eclipse and measured the positions of the stars on the photographic plates. Then, during the eclipse, they photographed the same star field with the eclipsed sun located in the middle. After measuring the plates, they found slight changes in the positions of the stars. During the eclipse, the positions of the stars on the plates were shifted outward, away from the sun (■ Figure 5-16). If a star had been located at the edge of the solar disk, it would have been shifted outward by about 1.8 arc seconds. This represents good agreement with the theory's prediction.

Because the angles are so small, this is a very delicate observation, and it has been repeated at many total solar eclipses since 1919, with similar results. The most accurate results were obtained in 1973 when a Texas–Princeton team measured a deflection of 1.66 ± 0.18 arc seconds—good agreement with Einstein's theory.

The general theory of relativity is critically important in modern astronomy. You will meet the theory again in the discussions of black holes, distant galaxies, and the big bang universe. Einstein revolutionized modern physics by providing an explanation of gravity based on the geometry of curved space-time. Galileo's inertia and Newton's mutual gravitation are shown to be not just descriptive rules but fundamental properties of space and time.

SCIENTIFIC ARGUMENT

What does the equivalence principle tell you?

The equivalence principle says that there is no observation you can make inside a closed spaceship to distinguish between uniform acceleration and gravitation. Of course, you could open a window and look outside, but then you would no longer be in a closed spaceship. As long as you make no outside observations, you can't tell whether your spaceship is firing its rockets and accelerating through space or resting on the surface of a planet where gravity gives you weight.

Einstein took the equivalence principle to mean that gravity and acceleration through space-time are somehow related. The general theory of relativity gives that relationship mathematical form and shows that gravity is really a distortion in space-time that physicists refer to as curvature. Consequently, you can say "mass tells space-time how to curve, and space-time tells mass how to accelerate." The equivalence principle led Einstein to an explanation for gravity.

Einstein began his work by thinking carefully about common things such as what you feel when you are moving uniformly or accelerating. This led him to deep insights now called postulates. Special relativity sprang from two postulates. **Why does the second postulate have to be true if the first postulate is true?**

What Are We? Falling

Everything in the universe is falling. The moon is falling around Earth. Earth is falling along its orbit around the sun, and the sun and every other star in our galaxy are falling along their orbits around the center of our galaxy. Stars in other galaxies are falling around the center of those galaxies, and every galaxy in the universe is falling as it feels the gravitational tugs of every bit of matter that exists.

Newton's explanation of gravity as a force between two unconnected masses was action at a distance, and it offended many of the scientists of his time. They thought Newton's gravity seemed like magic. Einstein explained that gravity is a curvature of space-time and that every mass accelerates according to the curvature it feels around it. That's not action at a distance, and it can give you a new insight into how the universe works.

The mass of every atom in the universe contributes to the curvature, creating a universe filled with three-dimensional hills and valleys of curved space-time. You and your world, your sun, your galaxy, and every other object in the universe are falling through space guided by the curvature of space-time.

Study and Review

Summary

- Aristotle argued that the universe was composed of four elements: earth at the center, with water, air, and fire in layers above. **Natural motion (p. 77)** occurred when a displaced object returned to its natural place. **Violent motion (p. 77)** was motion other than natural motion and had to be sustained by a force.

- Galileo found that a falling object is accelerated; that is, it falls faster and faster with each passing second. The rate at which it accelerates, termed the **acceleration of gravity (p. 77)**, is 9.8 m/s² (32 ft/s²) at Earth's surface and does not depend on the weight of the object, contrary to what Aristotle said.

- According to tradition, Galileo demonstrated this by dropping balls of iron and wood from the Leaning Tower of Pisa to show that they would fall together. Air resistance would have ruined the experiment, but a feather and a hammer dropped on the airless moon by an astronaut did fall together.

- Galileo stated the law of inertia: In the absence of friction, a moving body on a horizontal plane will continue moving forever.

- The first of Newton's three laws of motion was based on Galileo's law of inertia: A body continues at rest or in uniform motion in a straight line unless it is acted on by some force.

- **Momentum (p. 79)** is the tendency of a moving body to continue moving.

- **Mass (p. 79)** is the amount of matter in a body.

- Newton's second law says that an **acceleration (p. 79)** (a change in velocity) must be caused by a force. A **velocity (p. 79)** is a directed speed, so a change in speed or direction is an acceleration.

- Newton's third law says that forces occur in pairs acting in opposite directions.

- Newton realized that the curved path of the moon meant that it was being accelerated toward Earth and away from a straight-line path. That required the presence of a force—gravity.

▶ From his mathematical analysis, Newton was able to show that the force of gravity between two masses is proportional to the product of their masses and obeys the **inverse square law (p. 81)**. That is, the force of gravity is inversely proportional to the square of the distance between the two objects.

▶ To explain how gravity can act at a distance, scientists describe it as a **field (p. 81)**.

▶ An object in space near Earth would move along a straight line and quickly leave Earth were it not for Earth's gravity accelerating the object toward Earth's center and forcing it to follow a curved path, an orbit. Objects in orbit around Earth are falling (being accelerated) toward Earth's center. If there is no friction, the object will fall around its orbit forever.

▶ An object in a **closed orbit (p. 85)** follows an elliptical path. A circle is just a special case of an ellipse with zero eccentricity. To follow a circular orbit, an object must orbit with **circular velocity (p. 84)**. At a certain distance from Earth, a **geosynchronous satellite (p. 84)** stays above a spot on Earth's equator as Earth rotates.

▶ If a body's velocity equals or exceeds the **escape velocity, V_e (p. 85)**, it will follow a parabola or hyperbola. These orbits are termed **open orbits (p. 85)** because the object never returns to its starting place.

▶ Two objects in orbit around each other actually orbit their common **center of mass (p. 85)**.

▶ Newton's laws explain Kepler's three laws of planetary motion. The planets follow elliptical orbits because gravity obeys the inverse square law. The planets move faster when closer to the sun and slower when farther away because they conserve **angular momentum (p. 83)**. A planet's orbital period squared is proportional to its orbital radius cubed because the moving planet conserves energy.

▶ **Energy (p. 86)** refers to the ability to produce a change. **Kinetic energy (p. 86)** is an object's energy of motion, and **potential energy (p. 86)** is the energy an object has because of its position in a gravitational field. The unit of energy is the **joule (J) (p. 86)**.

▶ Tides are caused by differences in the force of gravity acting on different parts of a body. Tides on Earth occur because the moon's gravity pulls more strongly on the near side of Earth than on the center of Earth, and more strongly on the center of Earth than on the far side of Earth. As a result, there are two tidal bulges on Earth caused by the moon's gravity, one toward the moon on Earth's near side and one away from the moon on Earth's far side.

▶ Tides produced by the moon combine with tides produced by the sun to cause extreme tides (called **spring tides) (p. 87)** at new and full moons. The moon and sun work against each other to produce smallest tides (**neap tides) (p. 87)** at quarter moons.

▶ Friction from tides can slow the rotation of a rotating world, and the gravitational pull of tidal bulges can make orbits change slowly.

▶ Einstein published two theories that extended Newton's laws of motion and gravity, the special theory of relativity and the general theory of relativity.

▶ **Special theory of relativity (p. 91)** says that uniform (unaccelerated) motion is relative. Observers cannot detect their uniform motion through space except relative to outside objects. This is known as the first postulate. This leads to the second postulate: The speed of light is a constant for all observers.

▶ A consequence of special relativity is that mass and energy are related.

▶ The **general theory of relativity (p. 92)** says that a gravitational field is a curvature of space-time caused by the presence of a mass. For example, Earth's mass curves space-time, and the mass of your body responds to that curvature by accelerating toward Earth's center.

▶ The curvature of space-time was confirmed by the slow advance in perihelion (precession) of the orbit of Mercury, and by the deflection of starlight passing near the sun observed during a 1919 total solar eclipse.

Review Questions

1. Why wouldn't Aristotle's explanation of gravity work if Earth is not the center of the universe?
2. According to the principles of Aristotle, what part of the motion of a baseball pitched across the home plate is natural motion? What part is violent motion?
3. If you drop a feather and a steel hammer at the same moment, they should hit the ground at the same instant. Why doesn't this work on Earth, and why does it work on the moon?
4. What is the difference between mass and weight? Between speed and velocity?
5. Why did Newton conclude that some force had to pull the moon toward Earth?
6. Why did Newton conclude that gravity has to be mutual and universal?
7. How does the concept of a field explain action at a distance? Name another kind of field also associated with action at a distance.
8. Why can't a spacecraft go "beyond Earth's gravity?"
9. What is the center of mass of the Earth–moon system? Where is it?
10. How do planets orbiting the sun, and skaters doing a spin, both conserve angular momentum?
11. Why is the period of an open orbit undefined?
12. How does the first postulate of special relativity imply the second?
13. When you ride a fast elevator upward, you feel slightly heavier as the trip begins and slightly lighter as the trip ends. How is this phenomenon related to the equivalence principle?
14. From your knowledge of general relativity, would you expect radio waves from distant galaxies to be deflected as they pass near the sun? Why or why not?
15. **How Do We Know?** Why would science be impossible if some natural events happened without causes?
16. **How Do We Know?** Why is it important that a theory make testable predictions?

Discussion Questions

1. How did Galileo idealize his inclines to conclude that an object in motion stays in motion until it is acted on by some force?
2. Give an example from everyday life to illustrate each of Newton's laws.
3. People who lived before Newton may not have believed in cause and effect as strongly as you do. How do you suppose that affected how they saw their daily lives?

Problems

1. Compared with the strength of Earth's gravity at its surface, how much weaker is gravity at a distance of 10 Earth radii from Earth's center? At 20 Earth radii?
2. Compare the force of lunar gravity on the surface of the moon with the force of Earth's gravity at Earth's surface.
3. If a small lead ball falls from a high tower on Earth, what will be its velocity after 2 seconds? After 4 seconds?
4. What is the circular velocity of an Earth satellite 1000 km above Earth's surface? (*Hint:* Earth's radius is 6380 km.)
5. What is the circular velocity of an Earth satellite 36,000 km above Earth's surface? What is its orbital period? (*Hint:* Earth's radius is 6380 km.)
6. What is the orbital period of an imaginary satellite orbiting just above Earth's surface? Ignore friction with the atmosphere.
7. Repeat the previous problem for Mercury, Venus, the moon, and Mars. (*Hint:* Find the masses and radii of each of these objects in the Appendix A tables.)

8. Describe the orbit followed by the slowest cannonball on page 84 on the assumption that the cannonball could pass freely through Earth. (Newton got this problem wrong the first time he tried to solve it.)

9. If you visited an asteroid 30 km in radius with a mass of 4.0×10^{17} kg, what would be the circular velocity at its surface? A major league fastball travels about 90 mph. Could a good pitcher throw a baseball into orbit around the asteroid?

10. What is the orbital period of a satellite orbiting just above the surface of the asteroid in Problem 9?

11. What would be the escape velocity at the surface of the asteroid in Problem 9? Could a major league pitcher throw a baseball off of the asteroid?

Learning to Look

1. Why can the object shown below be bolted in place and used 24 hours a day without adjustment?

Larry Mulvehill/The Image Works

2. Why is it a little bit misleading to say that this astronaut is weightless?

NASA/JSC

Guidepost

In the early chapters of this book, you looked at the sky the way ancient astronomers did, with the unaided eye. In the last chapter, you got a glimpse through Galileo's telescope, and it revealed amazing things about the moon, Jupiter, and Venus. Now it is time to examine the instruments of the modern astronomer.

You can begin by studying telescopes that gather and focus visible light, so you need to be sure you understand what light is and how it behaves. But you will quickly meet telescopes that gather invisible forms of radiation such as X-rays and radio waves. Astronomers cannot overlook any clues, so they must use all forms of light. This chapter will help you answer five essential questions:

What is light?

How do telescopes work, and how are they limited?

What kind of instruments do astronomers use to record and analyze light?

Why do astronomers use radio telescopes?

Why must some telescopes go into space?

Astronomy is almost entirely an observational science. Astronomers cannot visit distant galaxies and far-off worlds, so they must observe using astronomical telescopes. Twenty chapters remain in your exploration, and every one will discuss information gathered by telescopes.

The strongest thing that's given us to see with's
A telescope. Someone in every town
Seems to me owes it to the town to keep one.

—ROBERT FROST, "THE STAR-SPLITTER"

STARLIGHT IS GOING TO WASTE. Every night it falls on trees, oceans, and parking lots, and it is all wasted. To an astronomer, nothing is so precious as starlight. It is the only strong link to the universe, so the astronomer's quest is to gather as much of it as possible and extract from it the secrets of the heavens.

The telescope is the symbol of the astronomer because it gathers and concentrates light for analysis. Most of the interesting objects in the sky are faint, so astronomers are driven to build huge telescopes to gather the maximum amount of light (■ Figure 6-1). Some telescopes collect radio waves or X-rays, and some go into space, but they all gather information about our universe.

In the quotation that opens this chapter, Robert Frost suggests that someone in every town should own a telescope. Astronomy is more than technology and scientific analysis. It helps tell us what we are, and every town should have a telescope to keep us looking upward.

■ Figure 6-1

Astronomical telescopes are often very large to gather large amounts of starlight. The Southern Gemini telescope stands over 19 m (60 ft) high when pointed straight up, and its main mirror, shown at lower left, is 8.1 m (26.5 ft) in diameter—larger than some classrooms. The sides of the telescope dome open to allow quick equalization of inside and outside temperatures at sunset. (Gemini Observatory/Aura)

6-1) Radiation: Information from Space

JUST AS A BOOK ON BAKING BREAD might begin with a discussion of flour, this chapter on telescopes begins with a discussion of light—not just visible light, but the entire range of radiation from the sky.

Light as a Wave and a Particle

When you admire the colors of a rainbow, you are seeing light behave as a wave. But when you use a digital camera to take a picture of the same rainbow, the light hitting the camera's detector acts like a particle. Light is peculiar in that it is both wave and particle, and how it acts depends on how you observe it.

Light is a form of **electromagnetic radiation** and carries energy through space as electric and magnetic waves. We use the word *light* to refer to electromagnetic radiation that we can see, but visible light is only a small part of a larger range that includes X-rays and radio waves. Electromagnetic radiation travels through space at 300,000 km/s (186,000 mi/s). This is commonly referred to as the speed of light, *c*, but it is in fact the speed of all electromagnetic radiation.

Some people flinch at the word *radiation*, but that reflects a **Common Misconception**. *Radiation* refers to anything that radiates from a source. High-energy particles emitted from radioactive atoms are called radiation, and you have learned to be a little bit concerned when you see this word. But light, like all electromagnetic radiation, spreads outward from a source, so you can correctly refer to light as a form of radiation.

Electromagnetic radiation can act as a wave phenomenon—that is, it is associated with a periodically repeating disturbance, a wave. You are familiar with waves in water: If you disturb a pool of water, waves spread across the surface. Imagine that you use a meter stick to measure the distance between the successive peaks of a wave. This distance is the **wavelength,** usually represented by the Greek letter lambda (λ).

Wavelength is related to **frequency,** the number of waves that pass a stationary point in 1 second (■ Figure 6-2). Wavelength and frequency are related, and you can calculate the wavelength by dividing the speed of light by the frequency.

$$\lambda = \frac{c}{f}$$

When you tune in your favorite FM station at, say, 89.5 on the dial, which means 89.5 MHz (million cycles per second), you are adjusting your radio to detect radio waves with a wavelength of 3.35 m. Note that the higher the frequency, the shorter the wavelength.

Sound is another example of a wave, in that case a mechanical disturbance that travels through air from source to ear. Sound requires a medium; so, on the moon, where there is no air, there can be no sound. In contrast, light is made up of electric and magnetic fields that can travel through empty space. Unlike sound,

■ **Figure 6-2**

All electromagnetic waves travel at the speed of light. The wavelength is the distance between successive peaks. The frequency of the wave is the number of peaks that pass you in one second.

light does not require a medium, and so it can travel through a perfect vacuum. There is no sound on the moon, but there is plenty of sunlight. There is a **Common Misconception** that radio waves are related to sound. Actually, radio waves are a type of light, electromagnetic radiation that your radio converts into sound so you can listen. Radio communication works just fine between astronauts standing on the moon.

Although electromagnetic radiation can behave as a wave, it can also behave as a flood of particles. A particle of electromagnetic radiation is called a **photon,** and you can think of a photon as a bundle of waves.

The amount of energy a photon carries depends inversely on its wavelength. That is, shorter-wavelength photons carry more energy, and longer-wavelength photons carry less. A simple formula expresses this relationship:

$$E = \frac{hc}{\lambda}$$

Here h is Planck's constant (6.63×10^{-34} joule s), c is the speed of light (3.00×10^8 m/s), and λ is the wavelength in meters. This book will not use this formula for calculations; the important point is the inverse relationship between the energy E and the wavelength λ. As λ gets smaller, E gets larger. A photon of long wavelength carries a very small amount of energy, but a photon with a very short wavelength can carry much more energy.

The Electromagnetic Spectrum

A **spectrum** is an array of electromagnetic radiation displayed in order of wavelength. You are most familiar with the spectrum of visible light, which you see in rainbows. The colors of the visible spectrum differ in wavelength, with red having the longest wavelength and violet the shortest. The visible spectrum is shown at the top of ■ Figure 6-3.

The average wavelength of visible light is about 0.0005 mm. You could put roughly 50 light waves end to end across the

thickness of a sheet of household plastic wrap. It is awkward to describe such short distances in millimeters, so scientists give the wavelength of light using **nanometer (nm)** units, equal to one-billionth of a meter (10^{-9} m). Another unit that astronomers commonly use is called the **angstrom (Å)** (named after the Swedish astronomer Anders Jonas Ångström). One angstrom is 10^{-10} m, one-tenth of a nanometer. The wavelength of visible light ranges from about 400 to 700 nm (4000 to 7000 Å). Just as you sense the wavelength of sound as pitch, you sense the wavelength of light as color. Light near the short-wavelength end of the visible spectrum (400 nm) looks violet to your eyes, and light near the long-wavelength end (700 nm) looks red.

Figure 6-3 shows that the visible spectrum makes up only a small part of the entire electromagnetic spectrum. Beyond the red end of the visible spectrum lies **infrared radiation,** where wavelengths range from 700 nm to about 1 mm. Your eyes are not sensitive to this radiation, but your skin senses it as heat. A "heat lamp" warms you by giving off infrared radiation.

Beyond the infrared part of the electromagnetic spectrum lie radio waves. The radio radiation used for AM radio transmissions has wavelengths of a few kilometers down to a few hundred meters, while FM, television, military, government, cell phone, and ham radio transmissions have wavelengths that range down to a few centimeters. Microwave transmission, used for radar and some long-distance telephone communications as well as for cooking food in a microwave oven, has wavelengths from a few centimeters down to about 1 mm.

The boundaries between the sections of the spectrum are not sharply defined. Long-wavelength infrared radiation blends smoothly into the shortest microwave radio waves. Similarly, there is no natural division between the short-wavelength infrared and the long-wavelength part of the visible spectrum.

Now look at the other end of the electromagnetic spectrum in Figure 6-3 and notice that electromagnetic waves shorter than violet are called **ultraviolet.** Electromagnetic waves that are even shorter are called X-rays, and the shortest are gamma rays. Again, the boundaries between these wavelength ranges are defined only by conventional usage, not by natural divisions.

Recall the formula for the energy of a photon. Extremely short-wavelength photons such as X-rays and gamma rays have high energies and can be dangerous. Even ultraviolet photons have enough energy to do you harm. Small doses of ultraviolet produce a suntan, and larger doses cause sunburn and skin cancers. Contrast this to the lower-energy infrared photons. Individually they have too little energy to affect skin pigment, a fact that explains why you can't get a tan from a heat lamp. Only by concentrating many low-energy photons in a small area, as in a microwave oven, can you transfer significant amounts of energy.

Astronomers are interested in electromagnetic radiation from space because it carries clues to the nature of stars, planets, and other celestial objects. Earth's atmosphere is opaque to most electromagnetic radiation, as shown in the graph at the bottom

■ Figure 6-3

The spectrum of visible light, extending from red to violet, is only part of the electromagnetic spectrum. Most radiation is absorbed in Earth's atmosphere, and only radiation in the visual window and the radio window can reach Earth's surface.

of Figure 6-3. Gamma rays, X-rays, and some radio waves are absorbed high in Earth's atmosphere, and a layer of ozone (O_3) at altitudes of about 15–30 km absorbs ultraviolet radiation. Water vapor in the lower atmosphere absorbs the longer-wavelength infrared radiation. Only visible light, some shorter-wavelength infrared, and some radio waves reach Earth's surface through two wavelength regions called **atmospheric windows.** Obviously, if you wish to study the sky from Earth's surface, you must look out through one of these windows.

SCIENTIFIC ARGUMENT

What would you see if your eyes were sensitive only to X-rays?
Sometimes the best way to understand a concept is to build a scientific argument and change one factor so you must imagine a totally new situation. In this case, you might at first expect to be able to see through walls, but remember that your eyes detect only light that already exists. There are almost no X-rays bouncing around at Earth's surface, so if you had X-ray eyes, you would be in the dark and would be unable to see anything. Even when you looked up at the sky, you would see nothing, because Earth's atmosphere is not transparent to X-rays. If Superman can see through walls, it is not because his eyes can detect X-rays.

But now imagine a slightly different situation and modify your argument. **Would you be in the dark if your eyes were sensitive only to radio wavelengths?**

6-2 Optical Telescopes

EARTH HAS TWO ATMOSPHERIC WINDOWS, so there are two main types of ground-based telescopes—optical telescopes and radio telescopes. You can start with optical telescopes, which gather light and focus it into sharp images. This requires sophisticated optical and mechanical designs, and it leads astronomers to build gigantic telescopes on the tops of high mountains.

Two Kinds of Optical Telescopes

Optical telescopes can focus light into an image by using either a lens or a mirror, as shown in ■ Figure 6-4. In a **refracting telescope,** the **primary** (or **objective**) **lens** bends (refracts) the light as it passes through the glass and brings it to a focus to form a small inverted image. In a **reflecting telescope,** the **primary**

You can trace rays of light from the top and bottom of a candle as they are refracted by a lens or reflected from a mirror to form an image. The focal length is the distance from the lens or mirror to the point where parallel rays of light come to a focus.

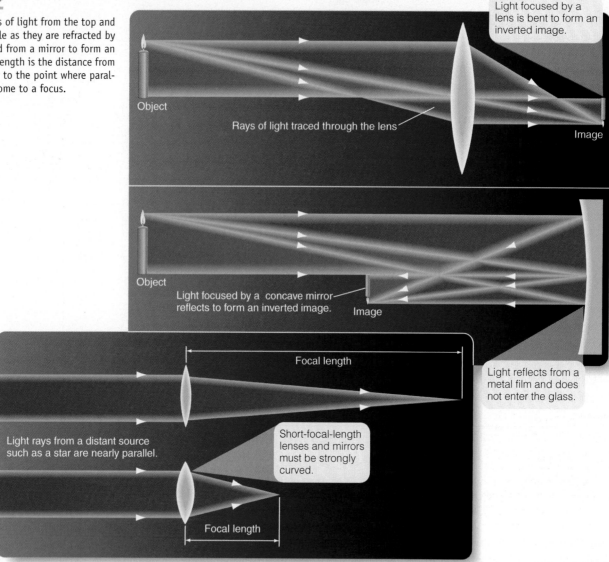

Light focused by a lens is bent to form an inverted image.

Object

Rays of light traced through the lens

Image

Object

Light focused by a concave mirror reflects to form an inverted image.

Image

Light reflects from a metal film and does not enter the glass.

Focal length

Light rays from a distant source such as a star are nearly parallel.

Short-focal-length lenses and mirrors must be strongly curved.

Focal length

(or **objective**) **mirror**—a concave piece of glass with a reflective surface—forms an image by reflecting the light. In either case, the **focal length** is the distance from the lens or mirror to the image of a distant light source such as a star. Short-focal-length lenses and mirrors must be strongly curved, and long-focal-length lenses and mirrors are less strongly curved. Grinding the proper shape on a lens or mirror is a delicate, time-consuming, and expensive process.

The image formed by the primary lens or primary mirror of a telescope is small, inverted, and difficult to view directly. Astronomers use a small lens called the **eyepiece** to magnify the image and make it convenient to view (■ Figure 6-5).

Refracting telescopes suffer from a serious optical distortion that limits their usefulness. When light is refracted through glass, shorter wavelengths bend more than longer wavelengths, so blue light, for example, having shorter wavelengths, comes to a focus closer to the lens than does red light (■ Figure 6-6a). That means

if you focus the eyepiece on the blue image, the other colors are out of focus, and you see a colored blur around the image. If you focus on the red image, all the other colors blur. This color separation is called **chromatic aberration.** Telescope designers can grind a telescope lens of two components made of different kinds of glass and so bring two different wavelengths to the same focus (Figure 6-6b). This does improve the image, but these **achromatic lenses** are not totally free of chromatic aberration. Even though two colors have been brought together, the other wavelengths still blur. Telescopes made with achromatic lenses were popular until the end of the 19th century.

The primary lens of a refracting telescope is more expensive than a mirror of the same size. The lens must be achromatic, so it must be made of two different kinds of glass with four precisely ground surfaces. Also, the glass must be pure and flawless because the light passes through it. The largest refracting telescope in the world was completed in 1897 at Yerkes Observatory in Wisconsin.

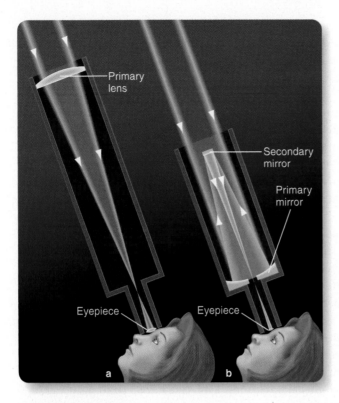

■ Figure 6-5

(a) A refracting telescope uses a primary lens to focus starlight into an image that is magnified by a lens called an eyepiece. The primary lens has a long focal length, and the eyepiece has a short focal length. (b) A reflecting telescope uses a primary mirror to focus the light by reflection. A small secondary mirror reflects the starlight back down through a hole in the middle of the primary mirror to the eyepiece.

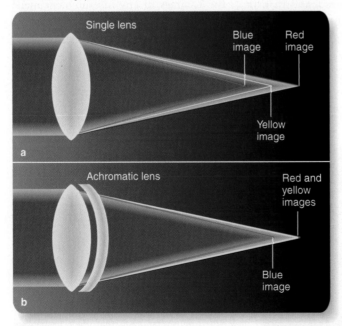

■ Figure 6-6

(a) A normal lens suffers from chromatic aberration because short wavelengths bend more than long wavelengths. (b) An achromatic lens, made in two pieces of two different kinds of glass, can bring any two colors to the same focus, but other colors remain slightly out of focus.

Its lens is 1 m (40 in.) in diameter and weighs half a ton. Larger refracting telescopes are prohibitively expensive.

The primary mirrors of reflecting telescopes are much less expensive because the light reflects off the front surface of the mirror. This means that only the front surface needs to be ground to precise shape. This front surface is coated with a highly reflective surface of an aluminum alloy, and the light reflects from this front surface without entering the glass. Consequently, the glass of the mirror need not be perfectly transparent, and the mirror can be supported over its back surface to reduce sagging. Most important, reflecting telescopes do not suffer from chromatic aberration because the light is reflected before it enters the glass. For these reasons, every large astronomical telescope built since the beginning of the 20th century has been a reflecting telescope.

The Powers of a Telescope

Astronomers build large telescopes because a telescope can aid your eyes in three ways—the three powers of a telescope—and the two most important of these powers depends on the diameter of the telescope.

Nearly all of the interesting objects in the sky are faint sources of light, so astronomers need telescopes that can gather large amounts of light to produce bright images. **Light-gathering power** refers to the ability of a telescope to collect light. Catching light in a telescope is like catching rain in a bucket—the bigger the bucket, the more rain it catches (■ Figure 6-7). Light-gathering power is proportional to the area of the telescope

■ Figure 6-7

Gathering light is like catching rain in a bucket. A large-diameter telescope gathers more light and has a brighter image than a smaller telescope of the same focal length.

objective. A lens or mirror with a large area gathers a large amount of light. The area of a circular lens or mirror is πr^2, or, written in terms of the diameter, the area is $\pi(D/2)^2$. To compare the relative light-gathering powers *(LGP)* of two telescopes *A* and *B,* you can calculate the ratio of the areas of their objectives, which reduces to the ratio of their diameters *(D)* squared.

$$\frac{LGP_A}{LGP_B} = \left(\frac{D_A}{D_B}\right)^2$$

For example, suppose you compared a telescope 24 cm in diameter with a telescope 4 cm in diameter. The ratio of the diameters is 24/4, or 6, but the larger telescope does not gather six times as much light. Light-gathering power increases as the ratio of diameters squared, so it gathers 36 times more light than the smaller telescope. This example shows the importance of diameter in astronomical telescopes. Even a small increase in diameter produces a large increase in light-gathering power and allows astronomers to study much fainter objects.

The second power, **resolving power,** refers to the ability of the telescope to reveal fine detail. Because light acts as a wave, it produces a small **diffraction fringe** around every point of light in the image, and you cannot see any detail smaller than the fringe (■ Figure 6-8). Astronomers can't eliminate diffraction fringes, but the larger a telescope is in diameter, the smaller the diffraction fringes are. That means the larger the telescope, the better its resolving power.

If you consider only optical telescopes, you can estimate the resolving power by calculating the angular distance between two stars that are just barely visible through the telescope as two separate images. Astronomers say the two images are "resolved," meaning they are separated from each other. The resolving power, α, in arc seconds, equals 11.6 divided by the diameter of the telescope in centimeters:

$$\alpha = \frac{11.6}{D}$$

For example, the resolving power of a 25.0 cm telescope is 11.6 divided by 25.0, or 0.46 arc seconds. No matter how perfect the telescope optics, this is the smallest detail you can see through that telescope.

This calculation gives you the best possible resolving power of a telescope of diameter *D*, but the actual resolution can be limited by two other factors—lens quality and atmospheric conditions. A telescope must contain high-quality optics to achieve its full potential resolving power. Even a large telescope reveals little detail if its optics are marred with imperfections. Also, when you look through a telescope, you are looking up through miles of turbulent air in Earth's atmosphere, which makes the image dance and blur, a condition called **seeing.** A related phenomenon is the twinkling of stars. The twinkles are caused by turbulence in Earth's atmosphere, and a star near the horizon, where you look through more air, will twinkle and blur more than a star overhead.

On a night when the atmosphere is unsteady, the images are blurred, and the seeing is bad (■ Figure 6-9). Even under good seeing conditions, the detail visible through a large telescope is limited, not by its diffraction fringes but by the air through which the telescope must look. A telescope performs better on a high mountaintop where the air is thin and steady, but even there Earth's atmosphere limits the detail the best telescopes can reveal to about 0.5 arc seconds. You will learn later in this chapter about telescopes that orbit above Earth's atmosphere and are not limited by seeing.

Seeing and diffraction limit the amount of information in an image, and that limits the accuracy of any measurement made based on that image. Have you ever tried to magnify a newspaper photo to distinguish some detail? Newspaper photos are made up of tiny dots of ink, and no detail smaller than a single dot will be visible no matter how much you magnify the photo. In an astronomical image, the resolution is often limited by seeing. You can't see a detail in the image that is smaller than the resolution.

a   b

■ **Figure 6-8**

(a) Stars are so far away that their images are points, but the wave nature of light surrounds each star image with diffraction fringes (much magnified in this computer model). (b) Two stars close to each other have overlapping diffraction fringes and become impossible to detect separately. (Computer model by M. A. Seeds)

Resolution and Precision

What limits the detail you can see in an image? All images have limited resolution. You see this on your computer screen because images there are made up of picture elements, pixels. If your screen has large pixels, the resolution is low, and you can't see much detail. In an astronomical image, the size of a picture element is set by seeing and by diffraction in the telescope. You can't see detail smaller than that resolution limit.

This limitation on the detail in an image is related to the limited precision of any measurement. Imagine a zoologist trying to measure the length of a live snake by holding it along a meter stick. The wriggling snake is hard to hold, so it is hard to measure accurately. Also, meter sticks are usually not marked finer than millimeters. Both factors limit the precision of the measurement. If the zoologist said the snake was 43.28932 cm long, you might be suspicious. The resolution of the measurement technique does not justify the accuracy implied by all those digits.

Whenever you make a measurement you should ask yourself how accurate that measurement can be. The accuracy of the measurement is limited by the resolution of the measurement technique, just as the amount of detail in a photograph is limited by its resolution. If you photographed a star, you would not be able to see details on its surface for the same reason the zoologist can't measure the snake to high precision.

A high-resolution image of Mars reveals details such as mountains, craters, and the southern polar cap. (NASA)

That's why stars look like fuzzy points of light no matter how big your telescope. All measurements have some built-in uncertainty (**How Do We Know? 6-1**), and scientists must learn to work within those limitations.

Visual-wavelength image

■ **Figure 6-9**

The left half of this photograph of a galaxy is from an image recorded on a night of poor seeing. Small details are blurred. The right half of the photo is from an image recorded on a night when Earth's atmosphere above the telescope was steady and the seeing was better. Much more detail is visible under good seeing conditions. (Courtesy William Keel)

It is a **Common Misconception** that the purpose of an astronomical telescope is to magnify the image. In fact, the **magnifying power** of a telescope, its ability to make the image bigger, is the least important of the three powers. Because the amount of detail you can see is limited by the seeing conditions and the resolving power, very high magnification does not necessarily show more detail. You can change the magnification by changing the eyepiece, but you cannot alter the telescope's light-gathering power or resolving power without changing the diameter of the objective lens or mirror, and that would be so expensive that you might as well build a whole new telescope.

You can calculate the magnification of a telescope by dividing the focal length of the objective by the focal length of the eyepiece:

$$M = \frac{F_o}{F_e}$$

For example, if a telescope has an objective with a focal length of 80 cm and you use an eyepiece whose focal length is 0.5 cm, the magnification is 80/0.5, or 160 times.

Notice that the two most important powers of the telescope, light-gathering power and resolving power, depend on the diameter of the telescope. This explains why astronomers refer to telescopes by diameter and not by magnification. Astronomers will refer to a telescope as an 8-meter telescope or a 10-meter telescope, but they would never identify a research telescope as being a 200-power telescope.

The quest for light-gathering power and high resolution explains why nearly all major observatories are located far from big cities and usually on high mountains. Astronomers avoid cities because **light pollution,** the brightening of the night sky by light scattered from artificial outdoor lighting, can make it impossible to see faint objects (■ Figure 6-10a). In fact, many residents of cities are unfamiliar with the beauty of the night sky because they can see only the brightest stars. Even far from cities, nature's own light pollution, the moon, is sometimes so bright it drowns out fainter objects, and astronomers are often unable to observe on the nights near full moon. On such nights, faint objects cannot be detected even with the largest telescopes on high mountains.

Astronomers prefer to place their telescopes on carefully selected high mountains for a number of reasons. The air there is thin, very dry, and more transparent, especially in the infrared. For the best seeing, astronomers select mountains where the air flows smoothly and is not turbulent. Building an observatory on top of a high mountain far from civilization is difficult and expensive, as you can imagine from the photo in Figure 6-10b, but the dark sky and steady seeing make it worth the effort.

Buying a Telescope

Thinking about how to shop for a new telescope will not only help you if you decide to buy one but will also illustrate some important points about astronomical telescopes.

Assuming you have a fixed budget, you should buy the highest-quality optics and the largest-diameter telescope you can afford. You can't make the atmosphere less turbulent, but you can choose good optics. If you buy a telescope from a toy store and it has plastic lenses, you shouldn't expect to see very much. Also, you want to maximize the light-gathering power of your telescope, so you want to purchase the largest-diameter telescope you can afford. Given a fixed budget, that means you should buy a reflecting telescope rather than a refracting telescope. Not only will you get more diameter per dollar, but your telescope will not suffer from chromatic aberration.

You can safely ignore magnification. Department stores and camera shops may advertise telescopes by quoting their magnification, but it is not an important number. What you can see is determined by light-gathering power, optical quality, and Earth's atmosphere. You can change the magnification simply by changing eyepieces.

Other things being equal, you should choose a telescope with a solid mounting that will hold the telescope steady and allow you to point it at objects easily. Computer-controlled

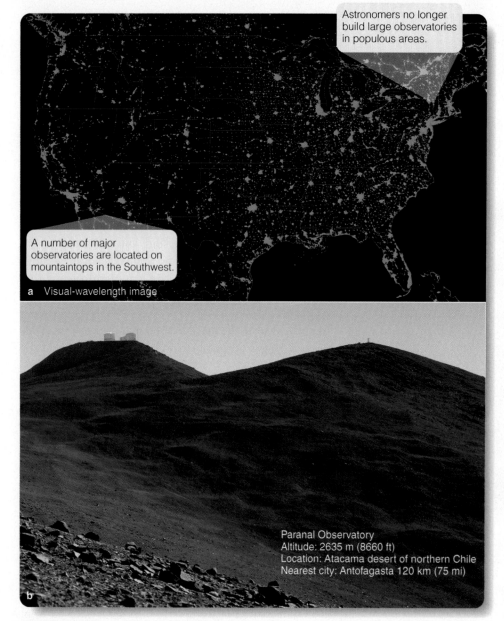

Astronomers no longer build large observatories in populous areas.

A number of major observatories are located on mountaintops in the Southwest.

a   Visual-wavelength image

Paranal Observatory
Altitude: 2635 m (8660 ft)
Location: Atacama desert of northern Chile
Nearest city: Antofagasta 120 km (75 mi)

b

■ **Figure 6-10**

(a) This satellite view of the continental United States at night shows the light pollution and energy waste produced by outdoor lighting. Observatories cannot be located near large cities. (NASA) (b) The domes of four giant telescopes are visible at upper left at Paranal Observatory, built by the European Southern Observatory. The Atacama Desert is believed to be the driest place on Earth. (ESO) pointing systems are available for a price on many small telescopes. A good telescope on a poor mounting is almost useless.

You might be buying a telescope to put in your backyard, but you must think about the same issues astronomers consider when they design giant telescopes to go on mountaintops.

Observing Beyond the Ends of the Visible Spectrum

Telescopes in mountain-top observatories usually observe at visual wavelengths, but important observations also can be made from Earth at some infrared and ultraviolet wavelengths.

Beyond the red end of the visible spectrum, some infrared radiation leaks through the atmosphere in narrow, partially open atmospheric windows ranging from wavelengths of 1200 nm to about 20,000 nm. Infrared astronomers usually measure wavelength in micrometers (10^{-6} meters), so they refer to this wavelength range as 1.2 to 30 micrometers (or microns for short). Even in this range, much of the radiation from celestial sources is absorbed by water vapor, carbon dioxide, and ozone molecules. Nevertheless, some infrared observations can be made from mountaintops where the air is thin and dry. For example, a number of important infrared telescopes observe from the 4200-m (13,800-ft) summit of Mauna Kea in Hawaii. At this altitude, the telescopes are above much of the water vapor in Earth's atmosphere (■ Figure 6-11).

Infrared telescopes have flown to high altitudes under balloons and in airplanes to get above absorption by water vapor. NASA is now testing the Stratospheric Observatory for Infrared Astronomy (SOFIA), a Boeing 747SP that will carry a 2.5-m telescope, control systems, and a team of astronomers, technicians, and educators into the dry fringes of the atmosphere. Once at that altitude, they can open a door above the telescope and make infrared observations for hours as the plane flies a precisely calculated path. You can see the door in the photo in Figure 6-11.

To reduce internal noise, the light-sensitive detectors in astronomical telescopes are cooled to very low temperatures, usually with liquid nitrogen, as shown in Figure 6-11. This is especially necessary for a telescope observing at infrared wavelengths. Infrared radiation is emitted by heated objects, and if the telescope is warm it will emit many times more infrared radiation than that coming from a distant object. Imagine trying to look for something at night through binoculars that are themselves glowing.

Beyond the other end of the visible spectrum, astronomers can observe in the near-ultraviolet at wavelengths of about 290 to 400 nm. Your eyes don't detect this radiation, but it can be recorded by specialized detectors. Wavelengths shorter than about 290 nm, the far-ultraviolet, are completely absorbed by the ozone layer extending from about 15 km to 30 km above Earth's surface. No mountaintop is that high, and no airplane can fly to such an altitude. To observe in the far-ultraviolet or beyond at X-ray or gamma-ray wavelengths, telescopes must be in space above the atmosphere.

Infrared astronomers can often observe with the dome lights on. Their instruments are not usually sensitive to visible light.

SOFIA will fly at roughly 12 km (over 40,000 ft) to get above most of Earth's atmosphere.

Adding liquid nitrogen to the camera on a telescope is a familiar task for astronomers.

■ Figure 6-11

Comet Hale–Bopp hangs in the sky over the 3-meter NASA Infrared Telescope Facility (IRAF) atop Mauna Kea. The air at high altitudes is so dry that it is transparent to shorter infrared photons. SOFIA will fly at altitudes up to 14 km (45,000 feet) where it will be able to observe infrared wavelengths that cannot be observed from mountaintops. Most astronomical CCD cameras must be cooled to low temperatures, and this is especially true for infrared cameras. (IRTF: William Keel; SOFIA: NASA; Camera: Kris Koenig/Coast Learning Systems)

New-Generation Telescopes

For most of the 20th century, astronomers faced a serious limitation on the size of astronomical telescopes. Traditional telescope mirrors were made thick to avoid sagging that would distort the reflecting surface, but those thick mirrors were heavy. The 5-m (200-in.) mirror on Mount Palomar weighs 14.5 tons. These traditional telescopes were big, heavy, and expensive.

Today's astronomers have solved these problems in a number of ways. Read **Modern Astronomical Telescopes** on pages 110–111 and notice three important points about telescope design and ten new terms that describe astronomical telescopes and their operation:

1 Traditional telescopes use large, solid, heavy mirrors to focus starlight to a *prime focus*, or, by using a *secondary mirror,* to a *Cassegrain focus.* Some small telescopes have a *Newtonian focus* or a *Schmidt-Cassegrain focus.*

2 Telescopes must have a *sidereal drive* to follow the stars, and an *equatorial mounting* with easy motion around a *polar axis* is the traditional way to provide that motion. Today, astronomers can build simpler, lighter-weight telescopes on *alt-azimuth mountings* that depend on computers to move the telescope so that it follows the westward motion of the stars as Earth rotates.

3 *Active optics,* computer control of the shape of telescope mirrors, allows the use of thin, lightweight mirrors—either "floppy" mirrors or segmented mirrors. Reducing the weight of the mirror reduces the weight of the rest of the telescope and makes it stronger and less expensive. Also, thin mirrors cool faster at nightfall and produce better images.

High-speed computers have allowed astronomers to build new, giant telescopes with unique designs. A few are shown in ■ Figure 6-12. The European Southern Observatory has built the Very Large Telescope (VLT) high in the remote Andes Mountains of northern Chile. The VLT actually consists of four telescopes, each with a computer-controlled mirror 8.2 m in diameter and only 17.5 cm (6.9 in.) thick. The four telescopes can work singly or can combine their light to work as one large telescope. Italian and American astronomers have built the Large Binocular Telescope, which carries a pair of 8.4-m mirrors on a single mounting. The Gran Telescopio Canarias, located atop a volcanic peak in the Canary Islands, carries a segmented mirror 10.4 meters in diameter and holds, for the moment, the record as the largest single telescope in the world

Other giant telescopes are being planned with segmented mirrors or with multiple mirrors (■ Figure 6-13). The Giant Magellan Telescope will carry seven thin mirrors, each 8.4 meters in diameter, on a single mounting. It will be located in the Chilean Andes and is planned to have the light-gathering power of a 22-m telescope. The Thirty Meter Telescope, now under development by American astronomers, will have a mirror 30 meters in diameter, composed of 492 hexagonal segments. The European Extremely Large Telescope is being planned by an international team. It will carry 906 segments, making up a mirror 42 meters in diameter. Other very large telescopes are being proposed with completion dates of 2016 or later.

Large Binocular Telescope

The mirrors in the VLT telescopes are each 8.2 m in diameter.

Only 6 of the mirror segments have been installed in this photo.

■ **Figure 6-12**

The four telescopes of the VLT are housed in separate domes at Paranal Observatory in Chile (Figure 6-10). The Large Binocular Telescope (LBT) carries two 8.4-m mirrors that combine their light. The entire building rotates as the telescope moves. The Gran Telescopio Canarias contains 36 hexagonal mirror segments in its 10.4-m primary mirror. (VLT: ESO; LBT: Large Binocular Telescope Project and European Industrial Engineer; GMT: ESO; GTC: Gara Mora, IAC)

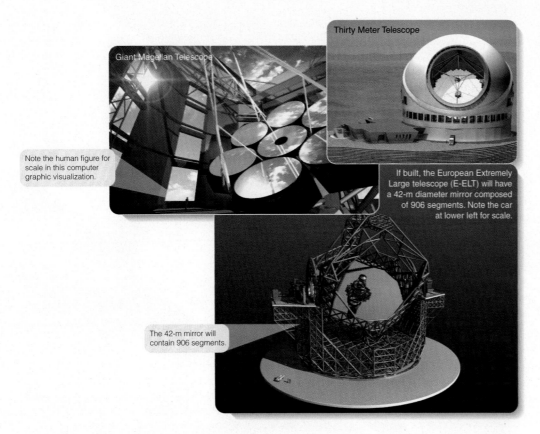

Giant Magellan Telescope

Note the human figure for scale in this computer graphic visualization.

Thirty Meter Telescope

If built, the European Extremely Large telescope (E-ELT) will have a 42-m diameter mirror composed of 906 segments. Note the car at lower left for scale.

The 42-m mirror will contain 906 segments.

■ **Figure 6-13**

The proposed Giant Magellan Telescope will have the resolving power of a telescope 24.5 meters in diameter when it is finished in about 2016. The Thirty Meter Telescope (TMT) is planned to occupy a specially designed dome. Like nearly all of the newest large telescopes, the European Extremely Large Telescope will be on an alt-azimuth mounting. (GMT: ESO; TMT: TMT: Thirty-Meter Telescope; E-ELT: ESO)

Adaptive Optics

Not too many years ago, astronomers thought it was pointless to build more large telescopes on Earth's surface because of seeing distortion caused by the atmosphere. In the 1990s, computers became fast enough to allow astronomers to correct for some of that distortion, and that has made the new generation of giant telescopes possible.

Adaptive optics uses high-speed computers to monitor the distortion produced by turbulence in Earth's atmosphere and then correct the telescope image to sharpen a fuzzy blob into a crisp picture. The resolution of the image is still limited by diffraction in the telescope, but removing much of the seeing distortion produces a dramatic improvement in the detail visible (■ Figure 6-14). Don't confuse adaptive optics with the slower-speed active optics that controls the overall shape of a telescope mirror.

To monitor the distortion in an image, adaptive optics systems must look at a fairly bright star in the field of view, and there isn't always such a star properly located near a target object such as a faint galaxy. In that case, astronomers can point a laser at a spot in the sky very close to their target object, and where the laser excites gas in Earth's upper atmosphere, it produces a glowing

Modern computers have revolutionized telescope design and operation. Nearly all large telescopes are operated by astronomers and technicians working at computers in a control room, and some telescopes can be operated by astronomers thousands of miles from the observatory. Some telescopes are fully automated and observe without direct human supervision. This has made possible huge surveys of the sky in which millions of objects are observed. The Sloan Digital Sky Survey, for example, mapped the sky, measuring the position and brightness of 100 million stars and galaxies at a number of wavelengths. The Two-Micron All Sky Survey (2MASS) has mapped the entire sky at three wavelengths in the infrared. Other surveys are being made at other wavelengths. Astronomers will study those data banks for decades to come.

Adaptive Optics

Off

On

■ **Figure 6-14**

In these images of the center of our galaxy, the adaptive optics system was turned off for the left image and on for the right image. Not only are the images of stars sharper, but because the light is focused into smaller images, fainter stars are visible. The laser beam shown leaving one of the Keck Telescopes produces an artificial star in the field of view, and the adaptive optics system uses the laser-produced point of light to reduce seeing distortion in the entire image. (left, CFHT; right, Paul Hirst)

Modern Astronomical Telescopes

1 The traditional telescopes described on this page are limited by complexity, weight, and Earth's atmosphere. Modern solutions are shown on the opposite page.

In larger telescopes the light can be focused to a **prime focus** position high in the telescope tube as shown at the right. Although it is a good place to image faint objects, the prime focus is inconvenient for large instruments. A **secondary mirror** can reflect the light through a hole in the primary mirror to a **Cassegrain focus.** This focal arrangement may be the most common form of astronomical telescope.

Secondary mirror

With the secondary mirror removed, the light converges at the prime focus. In large telescopes, astronomers can ride inside the prime-focus cage, although most observations are now made by instruments connected to computers in a separate control room.

Traditional mirrors are thick to prevent the optical surface from sagging and distorting the image as the telescope is moved around the sky. Large mirrors can weigh many tons and are expensive to make and difficult to support. Also, they cool slowly at nightfall. Expansion and contraction in the cooling mirror causes distortion in the images.

The Cassegrain focus is convenient and has room for large instruments.

1a Smaller telescopes are often found with a **Newtonian focus,** the arrangement that Isaac Newton used in his first reflecting telescope. The Newtonian focus is inconvenient for large telescopes as shown at right.

Newtonian focus

Thin correcting lens

Schmidt-Cassegrain telescope

1b Many small telescopes such as the one on your left use a **Schmidt-Cassegrain focus.** A thin correcting plate improves the image but is too slightly curved to introduce serious chromatic aberration

1c Shown below, the 4-meter Mayall Telescope at Kitt Peak National Observatory in Arizona can be used at either the prime focus or the Cassegrain focus. Note the human figure at lower right.

Prime focus cage

Secondary mirror

Primary mirror (inside)

Cassegrain focus

Astronomer

Equatorial mounting

To north celestial pole

Westward rotation about polar axis follows stars.

Polar axis

To north celestial pole

Eastward rotation of Earth

North Pole

Alt-azimuth mounting

Computer control of motion about both axes follows stars.

To north celestial pole

To north celestial pole

Eastward rotation of Earth

North Pole

2 Telescope mountings must contain a **sidereal drive** to move smoothly westward and counter the eastward rotation of Earth. The traditional **equatorial mounting** (far left) has a **polar axis** parallel to Earth's axis, but the modern **alt-azimuth mounting** (near left) moves like a cannon — up and down and left to right. Such mountings are simpler to build but need computer control to follow the stars.

3 Unlike traditional thick mirrors, thin mirrors, sometimes called floppy mirrors as shown at right, weigh less and require less massive support structures. Also, they cool rapidly at nightfall and there is less distortion from uneven expansion and contraction.

Floppy mirror

Computer-controlled thrusters   Support structure

3a Grinding a large mirror may remove tons of glass and take months, but new techniques speed the process. Some large mirrors are cast in a rotating oven that causes the molten glass to flow to form a concave upper surface. Grinding and polishing such a preformed mirror is much less time consuming.

3b Mirrors made of segments are economical because the segments can be made separately. The resulting mirror weighs less and cools rapidly. See image at right.

Segmented mirror

Computer-controlled thrusters   Support structure

3c Both floppy mirrors and segmented mirrors sag under their own weight. Their optical shape must be controlled by computer-driven thrusters under the mirror in what is called **active optics.**

Keck I telescope mirror segments

3d The two Keck telescopes, each 10 meters in diameter, are located atop the volcano Mauna Kea in Hawaii. The two mirrors are composed of hexagonal mirror segments as shown at right.

artificial star in the field of view. The adaptive optics system can use the artificial star to correct the image of the fainter target.

Today astronomers are planning huge optical telescopes composed of segmented mirrors tens of meters in diameter. Those telescopes would be almost useless without adaptive optics.

Interferometry

One of the reasons astronomers build big telescopes is to increase resolving power, and astronomers have been able to achieve very high resolution by connecting multiple telescopes together to work as if they were a single telescope. This method of synthesizing a larger telescope is known as **interferometry** (■ Figure 6-15). One expert said, "We combine the light from separate telescopes and fool the waves into thinking they were collected by one big 'scope." The images from such a virtual telescope are not limited by the diffraction fringes of the individual small telescopes but rather by the diffraction fringes of the much larger virtual telescope.

In an interferometer, the light from the separate telescopes must be combined as if it had been collected by a single large mirror. That means that a network of small, high-precision mirrors must bring the light beams together, and the path that each light beam travels must be controlled so that it does not vary more than a small fraction of the wavelength. Turbulence in Earth's atmosphere constantly distorts the light, and high-speed computers must continuously adjust the light paths. Recall that

the wavelength of light is very short, roughly 0.0005 mm, so building optical interferometers is one of the most difficult technical problems that astronomers face. Infrared- and radio-wavelength interferometers are slightly easier to build because the wavelengths are longer. In fact, as you will discover later in this chapter, the first astronomical interferometers were built by radio astronomers.

The VLT shown in Figure 6-12 consists of four 8.2-m telescopes that can operate separately but can also be linked together through underground tunnels with three 1.8-m telescopes on the same mountaintop. The resulting optical interferometer provides the resolution (but, of course, not the light gathering power) of a telescope 200 meters in diameter. Other telescopes, such as the two Keck 10-m telescopes, can work as interferometers. The CHARA array on Mt. Wilson combines six 1-meter telescopes to create the resolving power equivalent of a telescope one-fifth of a mile in diameter. The Large Binocular Telescope shown in Figure 6-12 can be used as an interferometer.

Although turbulence in Earth's atmosphere can be partially averaged out in an interferometer, plans are being made to put interferometers in space to avoid atmospheric turbulence altogether. The Space Interferometry Mission, for example, will work at visual wavelengths and study everything from the cores of erupting galaxies to planets orbiting nearby stars.

Simulated large-diameter telescope

Beams combined to produce final image

Precision optical paths in tunnels

■ **Figure 6-15**

In an astronomical interferometer, smaller telescopes can combine their light through specially designed optical tunnels to simulate a larger telescope with a resolution set by the separation of the smaller telescopes.

6-3) Special Instruments

JUST LOOKING THROUGH A TELESCOPE doesn't tell you much. A star looks like a point of light. A planet looks like a little disk. A galaxy looks like a hazy patch. To use an astronomical telescope to learn about the universe, you must be able to analyze the light the telescope gathers. Special instruments attached to the telescope make that possible.

Imaging Systems

The original imaging device in astronomy was the photographic plate. It could record images of faint objects in long time exposures and could be stored for later analysis. But photographic plates have been almost entirely replaced by electronic imaging systems.

Most modern astronomers use **charge-coupled devices (CCDs)** to record images. A CCD is a specialized computer chip containing millions of microscopic light detectors arranged in an array about the size of a postage stamp. Although CCDs for astronomy are extremely sensitive and therefore expensive, less sophisticated CCDs are used in video and digital cameras. Not only can CCD chips replace photographic plates, but they have some dramatic advantages. They can detect both bright and faint objects in a single exposure, are much more sensitive than photographic plates, and can be read directly into computer memory for later analysis.

You can easily sharpen and enhance images from your digital camera because the image from a CCD is stored as numbers in computer memory. Astronomers can also manipulate images to bring out otherwise invisible details. Astronomers can produce **false-color images** in which different colors represent different levels of intensity and are not related to the true colors of the object. Or they can use false colors to represent different wavelengths not otherwise visible to the human eye, as in ■ Figure 6-16. False-color images are so useful they are commonly used in many other fields, such as medicine and meteorology.

In the past, measurements of intensity and color were made using specialized light meters attached to a telescope or on photographic plates. Today, nearly all such measurements are made more easily and more accurately with CCD images.

The Spectrograph

To analyze light in detail, astronomers need to spread the light out according to wavelength to form a spectrum, a task performed by a **spectrograph.** You can understand how this instrument works if you imagine reproducing an experiment performed by Isaac Newton in 1666. Newton bored a small hole in the window shutter of his bedroom to admit a thin beam of sunlight. When he placed a prism in the beam, it spread the light into a beautiful spectrum that splashed across his bedroom wall. From this and related experiments Newton concluded that white light is made of a mixture of all the colors.

Light passing through a prism is bent at an angle that depends on its wavelength. Violet (short wavelength) bends most, red (long wavelength) least, so the white light is spread into a spectrum (■ Figure 6-17). You could build a simple spectrograph using a prism to spread the light and a lens to guide the light into a camera.

Nearly all modern spectrographs use a grating in place of a prism. A **grating** is a piece of glass with thousands of microscopic

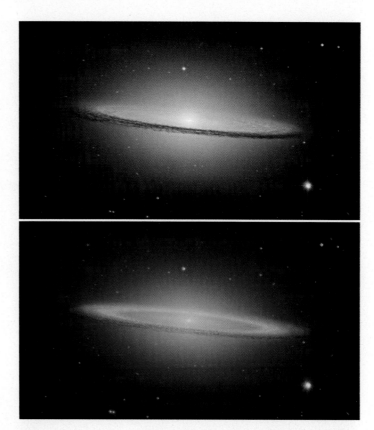

■ **Figure 6-16**

(a) The Sombrero Galaxy is 29 million light-years from Earth and contains many billions of stars. This visual wavelength image shows the clouds of dust in its disk. (NASA, Hubble Heritage Team; STScI/AURA) (b) This infrared image is reproduced in false color to show different wavelengths of infrared emission. Red represents the longest wavelengths and blue the shortest. (NASA/ JPL-Caltech, Hubble Heritage Team; STScI/AURA)

parallel grooves scribed onto its surface. Different wavelengths of light reflect from the grating at slightly different angles, so white light is spread into a spectrum. You have probably noticed this effect when you look at the closely spaced lines etched onto a compact disk; as you tip the disk, different colors flash across its surface. You could build a modern spectrograph by using a high-quality grating to spread light into a spectrum and a CCD camera to record the spectrum.

The spectrum of an astronomical object can contain hundreds of **spectral lines**—dark or bright lines that cross the spectrum at specific wavelengths. The sun's spectrum, for instance, contains hundreds of dark spectral lines produced by the atoms in the sun's hot gases. To measure the precise wavelengths of individual lines and identify the atoms that produced them, astronomers use a **comparison spectrum** as a calibration. Special bulbs built into the spectrograph produce bright lines given off by such atoms as thorium, argon, or neon. The wavelengths of these spectral lines have been measured to high precision in the laboratory, so astronomers can use spectra of these light sources as guides to measure wavelengths and identify spectral lines in the spectrum of a star, galaxy, or planet.

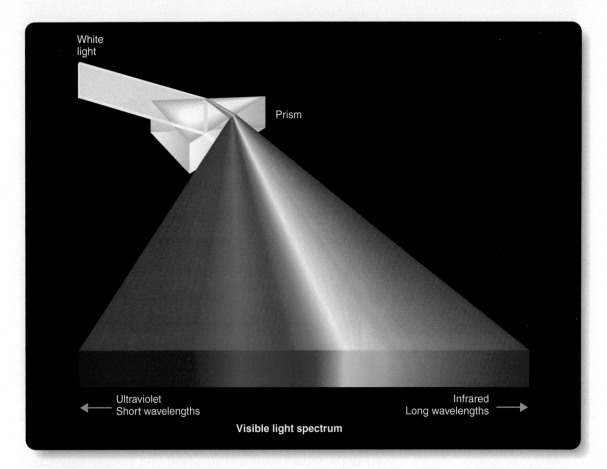

White
light

Prism

Ultraviolet
Short wavelengths

Infrared
Long wavelengths

Visible light spectrum

■ **Figure 6-17**

A prism bends light by an angle that depends on the wavelength of the light. Short wavelengths bend most and long wavelengths least. Thus, white light passing through a prism is spread into a spectrum.

Because astronomers understand how light interacts with matter, a spectrum carries a tremendous amount of information, and that makes a spectrograph the astronomer's most powerful instrument. In the next chapter, you will learn more about the information astronomers can extract from a spectrum. An astronomer once remarked, "We don't know anything about an object till we get a spectrum," and that is only a slight exaggeration.

6-4 Radio Telescopes

CELESTIAL OBJECTS such as clouds of gas and erupting stars emit radio energy, and astronomers on Earth can study such objects by observing at wavelengths in the radio window where Earth's atmosphere is transparent to radio waves (see Figure 6-3). You might think an erupting star would produce a strong radio signal, but the signals arriving on Earth are astonishingly weak—a million to a billion times weaker than the signal from an FM radio station. Detecting such weak signals calls for highly sensitive equipment.

The Operation of a Radio Telescope

A radio telescope usually consists of four parts: a dish reflector, an antenna, an amplifier, and a recorder (■ Figure 6-18). These components, working together, make it possible for astronomers to detect radio radiation from celestial objects.

The dish reflector of a radio telescope, like the mirror of a reflecting telescope, collects and focuses radiation. Because radio waves are much longer than light waves, the dish need not be as smooth as a mirror; wire mesh will reflect all but the shortest wavelength radio waves.

Though a radio telescope's dish may be many meters in diameter, the antenna may be as small as your hand. Like the antenna on a TV set, its only function is to absorb the radio energy collected by the dish. Because the radio energy from celestial objects is so weak, it must be strongly amplified before it can be measured and its strength is recorded in computer memory.

Radio telescopes do not produce images. A single observation with a radio telescope measures the amount of radio energy coming from a specific point on the sky. So the radio telescope

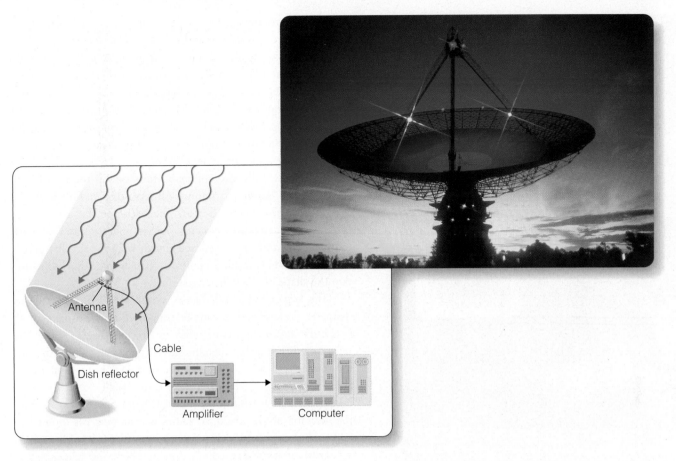

In most radio telescopes, a dish reflector concentrates the radio signal on the antenna. The signal is then amplified and recorded. For all but the shortest radio waves, wire mesh is an adequate reflector.

must be scanned over an object to produce a map of the radio intensity at different points. Such radio maps are usually represented using contours to mark areas of similar radio intensity, much like a weather map where contours filled with color indicate areas of precipitation (■ Figure 6-19).

Limitations of a Radio Telescope

A radio astronomer works under three handicaps: poor resolution, low intensity, and interference. Recall that the resolving power of an optical telescope depends on the diameter of the objective lens or mirror. It also depends on the wavelength of the radiation because, at very long wavelengths like those of radio waves, the diffraction fringes are very large. That means a radio map can't show fine detail. As with an optical telescope, there is no way to improve the resolving power without building a bigger telescope. Consequently, radio telescopes generally have large diameters to minimize the diffraction fringes.

Even so, the resolving power of a radio telescope is not good. A dish 30 m in diameter receiving radiation with a wavelength of 21 cm has a resolving power of about 0.5°. Such a radio telescope would be unable to detect any details in the sky smaller than the

moon. Fortunately, radio astronomers can combine two or more radio telescopes to form a **radio interferometer** capable of much higher resolution. Just as in the case of optical interferometers, the radio astronomer combines signals from two or more widely separated dishes and "fools the waves" into behaving as if they were collected by a much bigger radio telescope.

Radio interferometers can be quite large. The Very Large Array (VLA) consists of 27 dish antennas spread in a Y-shape across the New Mexico desert (■ Figure 6-20). In combination, they have the resolving power of a radio telescope 36 km (22 mi) in diameter. The VLA can resolve details smaller than 1 arc second. Eight new dish antennas being added across New Mexico will give the VLA ten times better resolving power. Another large radio interferometer, the Very Long Baseline Array (VLBA), consists of matched radio dishes spread from Hawaii to the Virgin Islands and has an effective diameter almost as large as Earth. The Allen Telescope Array being built in California will eventually include 350 separate radio dishes. Radio astronomers are now planning the Square Kilometer Array, which will contain a huge number of radio dishes totaling a square kilometer of collecting area and spread to a diameter of at least 6000 kilometers. These

Radio energy map
Red strongest
Violet weakest

■ **Figure 6-19**

(a) A typical weather map uses contours with added color to show which areas are likely to receive precipitation. (b) A false-color-image radio map of Tycho's supernova remnant, the expanding shell of gas produced by the explosion of a star in 1572. The radio contour map has been color-coded to show intensity. (Courtesy NRAO)

giant radio interferometers depend on state-of-the-art, high-speed computers to combine signals and create radio maps.

The second handicap radio astronomers face is the low intensity of the radio signals. You learned earlier that the energy of a photon depends on its wavelength. Photons of radio energy have such long wavelengths that their individual energies are quite low. To get detectable signals focused on the antenna, the radio astronomer must build large collecting areas either as single large dishes or arrays of smaller dishes.

The largest fully steerable radio telescope in the world is at the National Radio Astronomy Observatory in Green Bank, West Virginia (■ Figure 6-21a). The telescope has a reflecting surface 100 meters in diameter, big enough to hold an entire football field, and can be pointed anywhere in the sky. Its surface consists of 2004 computer-controlled panels that adjust to maintain the shape of the reflecting surface.

The largest radio dish in the world is 300 m (1000 ft) in diameter. So large a dish can't be supported in the usual way, so it is built into a mountain valley in Arecibo, Puerto Rico. The reflecting dish is a thin metallic surface supported above the valley floor by cables attached near the rim, and the antenna hangs above the dish on cables from three towers built on three mountain peaks that surround the valley (Figure 6-21b). By moving the antenna above the dish, radio astronomers can point the telescope at any object that passes within 20 degrees of the zenith as Earth rotates. Since completion in 1963, the telescope has been an international center of radio astronomy research.

The third handicap the radio astronomer faces is interference. A radio telescope is an extremely sensitive radio receiver listening to faint radio signals. Such weak signals are easily drowned out by interference that includes everything from poorly designed transmitters in Earth satellites to automobiles with faulty ignition systems. A few narrow radio bands in the electromagnetic spectrum are reserved for radio astronomy, but even those are often contaminated by radio noise. To avoid interference, radio astronomers locate their telescopes as far from civilization as possible. Hidden deep in mountain valleys, they are able to listen to the sky protected from human-made radio noise.

■ **Figure 6-20**

(a) The Very Large Array uses 27 radio dishes, which can be moved to different positions along a Y-shaped set of tracks across the New Mexico desert. They are shown here in the most compact arrangement. Signals from the dishes are combined to create very-high-resolution radio maps of celestial objects. (NRAO) (b) The proposed Square Kilometer Array will have a concentration of detectors and radio dishes near its center with more dishes scattered up to 3000 km away. (Xilostudios/SKA Program Development Office)

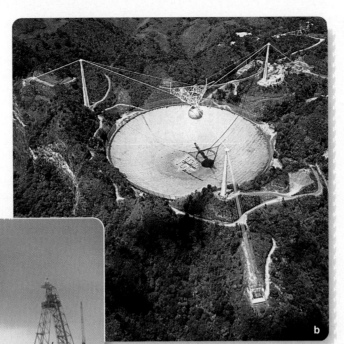

■ **Figure 6-21**

(a) The largest steerable radio telescope in the world is the GBT located in Green Bank, West Virginia. With a diameter of 100 m, it stands higher than the Statue of Liberty. (Mike Bailey: NRAO/AUII) (b) The 300-m (1000-ft) radio telescope in Arecibo, Puerto Rico, hangs from cables over a mountain valley. The Arecibo Observatory is part of the National Astronomy and Ionosphere Foundation operated by Cornell University and the National Science Foundation. (David Parker/Science Photo Library)

unhindered, giving radio astronomers an unobscured view. (The same is also true, to a large extent, of infrared radiation.)

Finally, radio telescopes are important because they can detect objects that are more luminous at radio wavelengths than at visible wavelengths. This includes, for example, intensely hot gas orbiting black holes. Some of the most violent events in the universe are detectable at radio wavelengths.

Advantages of a Radio Telescope

Building large radio telescopes in isolated locations is expensive, but three factors make it all worthwhile. First, and most important, a radio telescope can reveal where clouds of cool hydrogen and other atoms and molecules are located. These clouds are important because, for one thing, they are the places where stars are born. Although cool clouds of gas are completely invisible to normal telescopes because they produce no visible light of their own and reflect too little to be detected in photographs, some gas atoms and molecules do emit radio photons. Cool hydrogen, for example, emits radio energy at the specific wavelength of 21 cm. (You will see how the hydrogen produces this radiation when you learn about the gas clouds in space in Chapter 10.) Other gas molecules emit radio energy with their own characteristic wavelengths. The only way astronomers can detect these clouds is with a radio telescope.

Another reason radio telescopes are important is related to dust in space. Astronomers observing at visual wavelengths can't see through the dusty clouds in space. Light waves are so short that they are scattered by the tiny dust grains and never get through the dust to reach optical telescopes on Earth. However, radio signals have wavelengths much longer than the diameters of dust grains, so radio waves from far across the galaxy pass

6-5 Astronomy from Space

YOU HAVE LEARNED about the observations that ground-based telescopes can make through the two atmospheric windows in the visible and radio parts of the electromagnetic spectrum. Most of the rest of the electromagnetic radiation—infrared, ultraviolet, X-ray, and gamma ray—never reaches Earth's surface; it is absorbed high in Earth's atmosphere. To observe at these wavelengths, telescopes must go above the atmosphere.

The Hubble Space Telescope

Named after Edwin Hubble, the astronomer who discovered the expansion of the universe, the Hubble Space Telescope is the most successful telescope ever to orbit Earth (■ Figure 6-22). It was launched in 1990 and contains a 2.4-m (95-in.) mirror with which it can observe visible, near-ultraviolet, and near-infrared light. It is controlled from a research center on Earth and observes continuously. Nevertheless, the telescope has time to complete only a fraction of the projects proposed by astronomers from around the world.

Most of the observations Hubble makes are at visual wavelengths, so its greatest advantage in being above Earth's

The Hubble Space Telescope orbits Earth only 569 km (353 mi) above the surface. Here it is looking to the upper left. The James Webb Space Telescope, planned to replace Hubble, will be over six times larger in collecting area. It will not have a tube but will observe from behind a sun screen. The infrared Spitzer Space Telescope orbits the sun slightly more slowly than Earth and gradually falls behind as it uses up its liquid helium coolant. (NASA/JPL-Caltech)

atmosphere is the lack of seeing distortion. It can detect fine detail, and, because it concentrates light into sharp images, it can see faint objects.

The telescope is as big as a large bus and has been visited a number of times by the space shuttle so that astronauts can maintain its equipment and install new cameras and spectrographs. Astronomers hope that it will last until it is replaced by the James Webb Space Telescope expected to launch no sooner than 2013. The Webb telescope will carry a cluster of beryllium segments that will open to form a 6.5-m (256-in.) mirror once in space.

Infrared Astronomy from Orbit

Telescopes that observe in the far-infrared must be protected from heat and must get above Earth's absorbing atmosphere. They have limited lifetimes because they must carry coolant to chill their optics. The Infrared Astronomical Satellite (IRAS) was a joint project of the United Kingdom, the United States, and the Netherlands. IRAS was launched in January of 1983 and carried liquid helium coolant to keep its telescope cold. It made 250,000 observations and, for example, discovered disks of dust around stars where planets are now thought to have formed. Its coolant ran out after 300 days of observation.

The most sophisticated of the infrared telescopes put in orbit, the Spitzer Space Telescope, like IRAS, is cooled to –269°C (–452°F). Launched in 2003, it observes from behind a

sunscreen. In fact, it could not observe from Earth orbit because Earth is such a strong source of infrared radiation, so the telescope was sent into an orbit around the sun that will carry it slowly away from Earth as its coolant is used up. Named after theoretical physicist Lyman Spitzer Jr. who originally suggested that space telescopes would be useful, it has made important discoveries concerning star formation, planets orbiting other stars, distant galaxies, and more.

High-Energy Astrophysics

High-energy astrophysics refers to the use of X-ray and gamma-ray observations of the sky. Making such observations is difficult but can reveal the secrets of processes such as the explosive deaths of massive stars and eruptions of supermassive black holes.

The first astronomical satellite, Ariel 1, was launched by British astronomers in 1962 and made solar observations in the ultraviolet and X-ray part of the spectrum. Since then many space telescopes have made high-energy observations from orbit. Some of these satellites have been general-purpose telescopes that can observe many different kinds of objects. ROSAT, for example, was an X-ray observatory developed by an international consortium of European astronomers. Some space telescopes are designed to study a single problem or a single object. The Japanese satellite Hinode, for example, studies the sun continuously at visual, ultraviolet, and X-ray wavelengths.

Figure 6-23

From space, the Chandra X-Ray Observatory recorded an X-ray image of galaxy M101. It is superimposed here on a visual wavelength image from the Hubble Space Telescope and an infrared image from the Spitzer Space Telescope. Blue shows hot gas around newborn stars, while red shows cool, dusty clouds of gas. (X-ray: NASA/CSC/JHU/K. Kuntz et al.; Optical: NASA/ESA/STScI/JHU/K. Kuntz et al.; IR: NASA/JPL-Caltech/STScI/K. Gordon)

The largest X-ray telescope to date, the Chandra X-ray Observatory, was launched in 1999. Chandra orbits a third of the way to the moon and is named for the late Indian-American Nobel laureate Subrahmanyan Chandrasekhar, who was a pioneer in many branches of theoretical astronomy. Focusing X-rays is difficult because they penetrate into most mirrors, so astronomers devised cylindrical mirrors in which the X-rays reflect from the polished inside of the cylinders and form images on special detectors. The telescope has made important discoveries about everything from star formation to monster black holes in distant galaxies (■ Figure 6-23) that will be described in later chapters.

One of the first gamma-ray observatories was the Compton Gamma Ray Observatory, launched in 1991. It mapped the entire sky at gamma-ray wavelengths. The European INTEGRAL satellite was launched in 2002 and has been very productive in the study of violent eruptions of stars and black holes. The GLAST (Gamma-Ray Large Area Space Telescope), launched in 2008, is capable of mapping large areas of the sky to high sensitivity.

Modern astronomy has come to depend on observations that cover the entire electromagnetic spectrum. More orbiting space telescopes are planned that will be more versatile and more sensitive.

Cosmic Rays

All of the radiation you have read about in this chapter has been electromagnetic radiation, but there is another form of energy raining down from space, and scientists aren't sure where it comes from. **Cosmic rays** are subatomic particles traveling through space at tremendous velocities. Almost no cosmic rays reach the ground, but they do smash gas atoms in the upper atmosphere, and fragments of those atoms shower down on you day and night over your entire life. These secondary cosmic rays are passing through you as you read this sentence.

Some cosmic-ray research can be done from high mountains or high-flying aircraft; but, to study cosmic rays in detail, detectors must go into space. A number of cosmic-ray detectors have been carried into orbit, but this area of astronomical research is just beginning to bear fruit.

Astronomers can't be sure what produces cosmic rays. Because they are atomic particles with electric charges, they are deflected by the magnetic fields spread through our galaxy, and that means astronomers can't tell where their original sources are located. The space between the stars is a glowing fog of cosmic rays. Some lower-energy cosmic rays come from the sun, and observations show that at least some high-energy cosmic rays are produced by the violent explosions of dying stars and by supermassive black holes at the centers of galaxies.

At present, cosmic rays largely remain an exciting mystery. You will meet them again in future chapters.

What Are We? Curious

Telescopes are creations of curiosity. You look through a telescope to see more and to understand more. The unaided eye is a limited detector, and the history of astronomy is the history of bigger and better telescopes gathering more and more light to search for fainter and more distant objects.

The old saying, "Curiosity killed the cat," is an insult to the cat and to curiosity. We humans are curious, and curiosity is a noble trait—the mark of an active, inquiring mind. At the limits of human curiosity lies the fundamental question, "What are we?" Telescopes extend and amplify our senses, but they also extend and amplify our curiosity about the universe around us.

When people find out how something works, they say their curiosity is *satisfied.*

Curiosity is an appetite like hunger or thirst, but it is an appetite for understanding. As astronomy expands our horizons and we learn how distant stars and galaxies work, we feel satisfaction because we are learning about ourselves. We are beginning to understand what we are.

Summary

- Light is the visible form of **electromagnetic radiation (p. 99)**, an electric and magnetic disturbance that transports energy at the speed of light. The electromagnetic **spectrum (p. 100)** includes gamma rays, X-rays, ultraviolet radiation, visible light, infrared radiation, and radio waves.

- You can think of a particle of light, a **photon (p. 100)**, as a bundle of waves that sometimes acts as a particle and sometimes acts as a wave.

- The energy a photon carries depends on its **wavelength (p. 99)**. The wavelength of visible light, usually measured in **nanometers (p. 100)** (10^{-9} m) or **angstroms (p. 100)** (10^{-10} m), ranges from 400 nm to 700 nm (4000 to 7000 Å). Radio and **infrared radiation (p. 100)** have longer wavelengths and carry less energy. X-ray, gamma-ray, and **ultraviolet** radiation **(p. 100)** have shorter wavelengths and more energy.

- **Frequency (p. 99)** is the number of waves that pass a stationary point in 1 second. Wavelength equals the speed of light divided by the frequency.

- Earth's atmosphere is fully transparent in only two **atmospheric windows (p. 101)**—visible light and radio.

- Astronomical telescopes use a **primary lens (p. 101)** or **mirror (pp. 101–102)** (also called an **objective lens** or **mirror [pp. 101–102]**) to gather light and focus it into a small image, which can be magnified by an **eyepiece (p. 102)**. Short-**focal-length (p. 102)** lenses and mirrors must be more strongly curved and are more expensive to grind to shape.

- A **refracting telescope (p. 101)** uses a lens to bend the light and focus it into an image. Because of **chromatic aberration (p. 102)**, refracting telescopes cannot bring all colors to the same focus, resulting in color fringes around the images. An **achromatic lens (p. 102)** partially corrects for this, but such lenses are expensive and cannot be made much larger than about 1 m in diameter.

- **Reflecting telescopes (p. 101)** use a mirror to focus the light and are less expensive than refracting telescopes of the same diameter. Also, reflecting telescopes do not suffer from chromatic aberration. Most large telescopes are reflectors.

- **Light-gathering power (p. 103)** refers to the ability of a telescope to produce bright images. **Resolving power (p. 104)** refers to the ability of a telescope to resolve fine detail. **Diffraction fringes (p. 104)** in the image limit the detail visible. **Magnifying power (p. 105)**, the ability to make an object look bigger, is less important because it can be changed by changing the eyepiece.

- Astronomers build observatories on remote, high mountains for two reasons. Turbulence in Earth's atmosphere blurs the image of an astronomical telescope, a phenomenon that astronomers refer to as **seeing (p. 104)**. Atop a mountain, the air is steady, and the seeing is better. Observatories are located far from cities to avoid **light pollution (p. 106)**.

- In a reflecting telescope, light first comes to a focus at the **prime focus (p. 110)**, but **secondary mirrors (p. 110)** can direct light to other focus locations such as a **Cassegrain focus (p. 110)** or a **Newtonian focus (p. 110)**. The **Schmidt-Cassegrain focus (p. 110)** is popular for small telescopes.

- Because Earth rotates, telescopes must have a **sidereal drive (p. 111)** to follow the stars. An **equatorial mounting (p. 111)** with a **polar axis (p. 111)** makes this possible, but **alt-azimuth mountings (p. 111)** are becoming more popular.

- Very large telescopes can be built with **active optics (p. 111)**, maintaining the shape of floppy mirrors that are thin or in segments.

Such thin mirrors weigh less, are easier to support, and cool faster at nightfall.

- High-speed **adaptive optics (p. 109)** can monitor distortions caused by turbulence in Earth's atmosphere and partially cancel out the blurring caused by seeing.

- **Interferometry (p. 112)** refers to connecting two or more separate telescopes together to act as a single large telescope that has a resolution equivalent to that of a telescope as large in diameter as the separation between the telescopes.

- For many decades astronomers used photographic plates to record images at the telescope, but modern electronic systems such as **charge-coupled devices (CCDs) (p. 113)** have replaced photographic plates in most applications.

- Astronomical images in digital form can be computer enhanced and reproduced as **false-color images (p. 113)** to bring out subtle details.

- **Spectrographs (p. 113)** using prisms or a **grating (p. 113)** spread starlight out according to wavelength to form a spectrum revealing hundreds of **spectral lines (p. 113)** produced by atoms in the object being studied. A **comparison spectrum (p. 113)** containing lines of known wavelength allows astronomers to measure wavelengths in spectra of astronomical objects.

- Astronomers use radio telescopes for three reasons: They can detect cool hydrogen and other atoms and molecules in space; they can see through dust clouds that block visible light; and they can detect certain objects invisible at other wavelengths.

- Most radio telescopes contain a dish reflector, an antenna, an amplifier, and a data recorder. Such a telescope can record the intensity of the radio energy coming from a spot on the sky. Scans of small regions are used to produce radio maps.

- Because of the long wavelength, radio telescopes have very poor resolution, and astronomers often link separate radio telescopes together to form a **radio interferometer (p. 115)** capable of resolving much finer detail.

- Earth's atmosphere absorbs gamma rays, X-rays, ultraviolet, and far-infrared. To observe at these wavelengths, telescopes must be located in space.

- Earth's atmosphere distorts and blurs images. Telescopes in orbit are above this seeing distortion and are limited only by diffraction in their optics.

- **Cosmic rays (p. 119)** are not electromagnetic radiation; they are subatomic particles such as electrons and protons traveling at nearly the speed of light. They can best be studied from above Earth's atmosphere.

Review Questions

1. Why would you not plot sound waves in the electromagnetic spectrum?

2. If you had limited funds to build a large telescope, which type would you choose, a refractor or a reflector? Why?

3. Why do nocturnal animals usually have large pupils in their eyes? How is that related to astronomical telescopes?

4. Why do optical astronomers often put their telescopes at the tops of mountains, while radio astronomers sometimes put their telescopes in deep valleys?

5. Optical and radio astronomers both try to build large telescopes but for different reasons. How do these goals differ?

6. What are the advantages of making a telescope mirror thin? What problems does this cause?

7. Small telescopes are often advertised as "200 power" or "magnifies 200 times." As someone knowledgeable about astronomical telescopes, how would you improve such advertisements?

8. Not too many years ago an astronomer said, "Some people think I should give up photographic plates." Why might she change to something else?

9. What purpose do the colors in a false-color image or false-color radio map serve?

10. How is chromatic aberration related to a prism spectrograph?

11. Why would radio astronomers build identical radio telescopes in many different places around the world?

12. Why do radio telescopes have poor resolving power?

13. Why must telescopes observing in the far-infrared be cooled to low temperatures?

14. What might you detect with an X-ray telescope that you could not detect with an infrared telescope?

15. The moon has no atmosphere at all. What advantages would you have if you built an observatory on the lunar surface?

16. **How Do We Know?** How is the resolution of an astronomical image related to the precision of a measurement?

Discussion Questions

1. Why does the wavelength response of the human eye match so well the visual window of Earth's atmosphere?

2. Most people like beautiful sunsets with brightly glowing clouds, bright moonlit nights, and twinkling stars. Astronomers don't. Why?

Problems

1. The thickness of the plastic in plastic bags is about 0.001 mm. How many wavelengths of red light is this?

2. What is the wavelength of radio waves transmitted by a radio station with a frequency of 100 million cycles per second?

3. Compare the light-gathering powers of one of the 10-m Keck telescopes and a 0.5-m telescope.

4. How does the light-gathering power of one of the Keck telescopes compare with that of the human eye? (*Hint:* Assume that the pupil of your eye can open to about 0.8 cm.)

5. What is the resolving power of a 25-cm telescope? What do two stars 1.5 arc seconds apart look like through this telescope?

6. Most of Galileo's telescopes were only about 2 cm in diameter. Should he have been able to resolve the two stars mentioned in Problem 5?

7. How does the resolving power of a 5-m telescope compare with that of the Hubble Space Telescope? Why does the HST outperform a 5-m telescope?

8. If you build a telescope with a focal length of 1.3 m, what focal length should the eyepiece have to give a magnification of 100 times?

9. Astronauts observing from a space station need a telescope with a light-gathering power 15,000 times that of the human eye, capable of resolving detail as small as 0.1 arc seconds and having a magnifying power of 250. Design a telescope to meet their needs. Could you test your design by observing stars from Earth?

10. A spy satellite orbiting 400 km above Earth is supposedly capable of counting individual people in a crowd. Roughly what minimum-diameter telescope must the satellite carry? (*Hint:* Use the small-angle formula.)

Learning to Look

1. The two images at the right show a star before and after an adaptive optics system was switched on. What causes the distortion in the first image, and how does adaptive optics correct the image?

ESO

2. The star images in the photo at the right are tiny disks, but the diameter of these disks is not related to the diameter of the stars. Explain why the telescope can't resolve the diameter of the stars.

NASA, ESA and G. Meylan

3. The X-ray image at right shows the remains of an exploded star. Explain why images recorded by telescopes in space are often displayed in false color rather than in the "colors" received by the telescope.

NASA/CXC/PSU/S. Park

7 | Atoms and Starlight

Clouds of gas 170,000 light-years away glow in this false-color image. Red represents sulfur atoms, green hydrogen, and blue oxygen. Clues hidden in the starlight tell a story of star birth and star death. (NASA, ESA, and M. Livio, STScI)

Guidepost

In the last chapter, you read how telescopes gather starlight and how spectrographs spread out the light into spectra. Now you are ready to see what all the fuss is about. Here you will find answers to four essential questions:

— **What is an atom?**

— **How do atoms interact with light?**

— **What kinds of spectra do you see when you look at celestial objects?**

— **What can you learn from a star's spectrum?**

This chapter marks a change in the way you will look at nature. Up to this point, you have been thinking about what you can see with your eyes alone or aided by telescopes. In this chapter, you will begin using modern astrophysics to search out secrets that lie beyond what you can see.

The analysis of spectra is a powerful technique, and in the chapters that follow, you will use spectra to study stars, galaxies, and planets.

Awake! for Morning in the Bowl of Night

Has flung the Stone that puts the Stars to Flight:

And Lo! the Hunter of the East has caught

The Sultan's Turret in a Noose of Light.

— *THE RUBÁIYÁT OF OMAR KHAYYÁM*, TRANS. EDWARD FITZGERALD

THE UNIVERSE IS FILLED with fabulously beautiful clouds of glowing gas illuminated by brilliant stars, but they are all hopelessly beyond reach. No laboratory jar on Earth holds a sample labeled "star stuff," and no space probe has ever visited the inside of a star. The stars are far away, and the only information you can obtain about them comes hidden in starlight (■ Figure 7-1).

Earthbound humans knew almost nothing about stars until the early 19th century, when the German optician Joseph von Fraunhofer studied the solar spectrum and found it interrupted by some 600 dark lines representing colors that are missing from the sunlight Earth receives. When scientists realized that those spectral lines are related to the presence of various atoms in the

sun's atmosphere, and found that the spectra of other stars have similar patterns of lines, a window finally opened to a scientific understanding of the sun and stars. In this chapter you will look through that window, seeing how the sun and other stars produce light, and how atoms interact with light to cause spectral lines. Once you understand that, you will know how astronomers determine the chemical composition of stars, as well as measure motions of gas at their surfaces and in their atmospheres.

7-1 Atoms

STARS ARE GREAT BALLS OF HOT GAS, and the atoms in that gas leave their marks on the light the stars emit. By understanding what atoms are and how they interact with light, you can decode the spectra of the stars and learn their secrets.

A Model Atom

To think about atoms and how they interact with light, you need a working model of an atom. In Chapter 2, you used a model of the sky, the celestial sphere. In this chapter, you will begin your study of atoms by creating a model of an atom. Remember that a model can have practical value without being true. The stars are not actually attached to a sphere surrounding Earth, but to navigate a ship or point a telescope, it is useful to pretend they are. The electrons in an atom are not actually little beads orbiting the nucleus the way planets orbit the sun, but for some purposes it is useful to picture them as such.

Your model atom contains a positively charged **nucleus** at the center, which consists of two kinds of particles: **Protons** carry a positive electrical charge, and **neutrons** have no charge. This means the nucleus has a net positive charge.

The nucleus of this model atom is surrounded by a cloud of orbiting **electrons,** low-mass particles with negative charges. Normally the number of electrons equals the number of protons, and the positive and negative charges balance to produce a neutral atom. Protons and neutrons have masses about 1840 times greater than that of an electron, so most of the mass of an atom lies in the nucleus. Even so, a single atom is not a massive object. A hydrogen atom, for example, has a mass of only 1.67×10^{-27} kg, about a trillionth of a trillionth of a gram.

An atom is mostly empty space. To see this, imagine constructing a simple scale model of a hydrogen atom. Its nucleus is a single proton with a diameter of about 0.0000016 nm, or 1.6×10^{-15} m. If you multiply this by one trillion (10^{12}), you can represent the nucleus of your model atom with something about 0.16 cm in diameter—a grape seed would do. The region of a hydrogen atom that contains the electron has a diameter of about 0.4 nm, or 4×10^{-10} m. Multiplying by a trillion increases the diameter to about 400 m, or about 4.5 football fields laid end to end (■ Figure 7-2). When you imagine a grape seed in the middle

Visual-wavelength image

■ **Figure 7-1**

What's going on here? The sky is filled with beautiful and mysterious objects that lie far beyond your reach—in the case of the nebula NGC 6751, about 6500 ly beyond your reach. The only way to understand such objects is by analyzing their light. Such an analysis reveals that this object is a dying star surrounded by the expanding shell of gas it ejected a few thousand years ago. You will learn more about this phenomenon in a later chapter. (NASA Hubble Heritage Team/STScI/AURA)

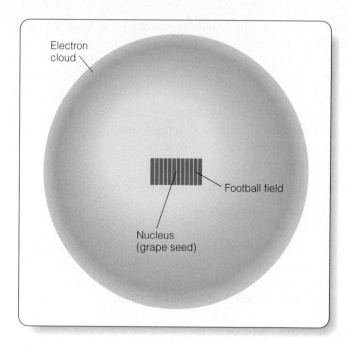

■ Figure 7-2

Magnifying a hydrogen atom by 10^{12} makes the nucleus the size of a grape seed and the diameter of the electron cloud about 4.5 times larger than a football field.

of a sphere 4.5 football fields in diameter, you can see that an atom is mostly empty space.

Now you can consider a **Common Misconception.** Most people, without thinking about it much, imagine that matter is solid, but you have seen that atoms are mostly empty space. The chair you sit on, the floor you walk on, are mostly not there. When you study the deaths of stars in a later chapter, you will see what happens to a star when most of the empty space gets squeezed out of its atoms.

Different Kinds of Atoms

There are over a hundred chemical elements. The number of protons in the nucleus of an atom identifies which element it is. For example, a carbon atom has six protons in its nucleus. An atom with one more proton than this is nitrogen, and an atom with one fewer proton is boron.

Although an atom of a given element always has the same number of protons in its nucleus, the number of neutrons is less restricted. For instance, if you added a neutron to a carbon nucleus, it would still be carbon, but it would be slightly heavier. Atoms that have the same number of protons but a different number of neutrons are **isotopes.** Carbon has two stable isotopes. One contains six protons and six neutrons for a total of 12 particles and is thus called carbon-12. Carbon-13 has six protons and seven neutrons in its nucleus.

The number of electrons in an atom of a given element can vary. Protons and neutrons are bound tightly into the nucleus, but the electrons are held loosely in the electron cloud. Running

a comb through your hair creates a static charge by removing a few electrons from their atoms. An atom that has lost or gained one or more electrons is said to be **ionized** and is called an **ion.** A neutral carbon atom has six electrons that balance the positive charge of the six protons in its nucleus. If you ionize the atom by removing one or more electrons, the atom is left with a net positive charge. Under some circumstances, an atom may capture one or more extra electrons, giving it more negative charges than positive. Such a negatively charged atom is also considered an ion.

Atoms that collide may form bonds with each other by exchanging or sharing electrons. Two or more atoms bonded together form a **molecule.** Atoms do collide in stars, but the high temperatures cause violent collisions that are unfavorable for chemical bonding. Only in the coolest stars are the collisions gentle enough to permit the formation of chemical bonds. You will see later that the presence of molecules such as titanium oxide (TiO) in a star is a clue that the star is very cool. In later chapters, you will see that molecules also can form in cool gas clouds in space and in the atmospheres of planets.

Electron Shells

So far you have been thinking of the cloud of the whirling electrons in a general way, but now it is time to be more specific about how the electrons behave within the cloud.

Electrons are bound to the atom by the attraction between their negative charge and the positive charge on the nucleus. This attraction is known as the **Coulomb force,** after the French physicist Charles-Augustin de Coulomb (1736–1806). To ionize an atom, you need a certain amount of energy to pull an electron completely away from the nucleus. This energy is the electron's **binding energy,** the energy that holds it to the atom.

The size of an electron's orbit is related to the energy that binds it to the atom. If an electron orbits close to the nucleus, it is tightly bound, and a large amount of energy is needed to pull it away. Consequently, its binding energy is large. An electron orbiting farther from the nucleus is held more loosely, and less energy is needed to pull it away. That means it has less binding energy.

Nature permits atoms only certain amounts (quanta) of binding energy, and the laws that describe how atoms behave are called the laws of **quantum mechanics (How Do We Know? 7-1).** Much of this discussion of atoms is based on the laws of quantum mechanics.

Because atoms can have only certain amounts of binding energy, your model atom can have orbits only of certain sizes, called **permitted orbits.** These are like steps in a staircase: You can stand on the number-one step or the number-two step, but not on the number-one-and-one-quarter step–there isn't one. The electron can occupy any permitted orbit, but there are no orbits in between.

Quantum Mechanics

How can you understand nature if it depends on the atomic world you cannot see? You can see objects such as stars, planets, aircraft carriers, and hummingbirds, but you can't see individual atoms. As scientists apply the principle of cause and effect, they study the natural effects they can see and work backward to find the causes. Invariably that quest for causes leads back to the invisible world of atoms.

Quantum mechanics is the set of rules that describe how atoms and subatomic particles behave. On the atomic scale, particles behave in ways that seem unfamiliar. One of the principles of quantum mechanics specifies that you cannot know simultaneously the exact location and motion of a particle. This is why physicists prefer to go one step beyond the simple atomic model that has electrons following orbits and instead describe the electrons in an atom as if they were a cloud of negative charge. That's a better model.

This raises some serious questions about reality. Is an electron really a particle at all? If you can't know simultaneously the position and motion of a specific particle, how can you know how it will react to a collision with a photon or another particle? The answer is that you can't know, and that seems to violate the principle of cause and effect.

Many of the phenomena you can see depend on the behavior of huge numbers of atoms, and quantum mechanical uncertainties average out. Nevertheless, the ultimate causes that scientists seek lie at the level of atoms, and modern physicists are trying to understand the nature of the particles that make up atoms. That is one of the most exciting frontiers of science.

The world you see, including these neon signs, is animated by the properties of atoms and subatomic particles. (Jeff Greenberg/PhotoEdit)

The arrangement of permitted orbits depends primarily on the charge of the nucleus, which in turn depends on the number of protons. Consequently, each kind of element has its own pattern of permitted orbits (■ Figure 7-3). Isotopes of the same elements have nearly the same pattern because they have the same number of protons. However, ionized atoms have orbital patterns that differ from their un-ionized forms. Thus, the arrangement of permitted orbits differs for every kind of atom and ion.

Hydrogen nuclei have one positive charge; the electron orbits are not tightly bound.

Only the innermost orbits are shown.

Boron nuclei have 5 positive charges; the electron orbits are more tightly bound.

Hydrogen

Helium

Boron

■ Figure 7-3

The electron in an atom may occupy only certain permitted orbits. Because different elements have different charges on their nuclei, the elements have different, unique patterns of permitted orbits.

SCIENTIFIC ARGUMENT

How many hydrogen atoms would it take to cross the head of a pin?

This is not a frivolous question. In answering it, you will discover how small atoms really are, and you will see how powerful physics and mathematics can be as a way to understand nature. Many scientific arguments are convincing because they have the precision of mathematics. To begin, assume that the head of a pin is about 1 mm in diameter. That is 0.001 m. The size of a hydrogen atom is represented by the diameter of the electron cloud, roughly 0.4 nm. Because 1 nm equals 10^{-9} m, you can multiply and discover that 0.4 nm equals 4×10^{-10} m. To find out how many atoms would stretch 0.001 m, you can divide the diameter of the pinhead by the diameter of an atom. That is, divide 0.001 m by 4×10^{-10} m, and you get 2.5×10^{6}. It would take 2.5 million hydrogen atoms lined up side by side to cross the head of a pin.

Now you can see how tiny an atom is and also how powerful a bit of physics and mathematics can be. It reveals a view of nature beyond the capability of your eyes. Now build an argument using another bit of arithmetic. **How many hydrogen atoms would you need to add up to the mass of a paper clip (1 g)?**

7-2) The Interaction of Light and Matter

IF LIGHT DID NOT INTERACT WITH MATTER, you would not be able to see these words. In fact, you would not exist, because, among other problems, photosynthesis would be impossible, so there would be no grass, wheat, bread, beef, cheeseburgers, or any other kind of food. The interaction of light and matter makes life possible, and it also makes it possible for you to understand the universe.

You have already been considering a model hydrogen atom. Now you can use that model as you begin your study of light and matter. Hydrogen is both simple and common. Roughly 90 percent of all atoms in the universe are hydrogen.

The Excitation of Atoms

Each electron orbit in an atom represents a specific amount of binding energy, so physicists commonly refer to the orbits as **energy levels.** Using this terminology, you can say that an electron in its smallest and most tightly bound orbit is in its lowest permitted energy level, which is called the atom's **ground state.** You could move the electron from one energy level to another by supplying enough energy to make up the difference between the two energy levels. It would be like moving a flowerpot from a low shelf to a high shelf; the greater the distance between the shelves, the more energy you would need to raise the pot. The amount of energy needed to move the electron is the energy difference between the two energy levels.

If you move an electron from a low energy level to a higher energy level, the atom becomes an **excited atom.** That is, you have added energy to the atom by moving its electron outward from the nucleus. An atom can become excited by collision. If two atoms collide, one or both may have electrons knocked into a higher energy level. This happens very commonly in hot gas, where atoms move rapidly and collide often.

Another way an atom can become excited is to absorb a photon. As you learned in the previous chapter, a photon is a bundle of electromagnetic waves with a specific energy. Only a photon with exactly the right amount of energy can move the electron from one level to another. If the photon has too much or too little energy, the atom cannot absorb it. Because the energy of a photon depends on its wavelength, only photons of certain wavelengths can be absorbed by a given kind of atom. ■ Figure 7-4 shows the lowest four energy levels of the hydrogen atom, along with three photons the atom could absorb. The longest-wavelength photon has only enough energy to excite the electron to the second energy level, but the shorter-wavelength photons can excite the electron to higher levels. Because the hydrogen atom has many more energy levels than shown in Figure 7-4, it can absorb photons of many different wavelengths.

Atoms, like humans, cannot exist in an excited state forever. An excited atom is unstable and must eventually (usually within 10^{-6} to 10^{-9} second) give up the energy it has absorbed and return its electron to a lower energy level. Thus the electron in an excited atom tends to tumble down to its lowest energy level, its ground state.

When an electron drops from a higher to a lower energy level, it moves from a loosely bound level to one that is more tightly bound. The atom then has a surplus of energy—the energy difference between the levels—that it can emit as a photon with a wavelength corresponding to that amount of energy (Chapter 6). Study the sequence of events shown in ■ Figure 7-5 to see how an atom can absorb and emit photons. Because each type of atom or ion has a unique set of energy levels, each type absorbs and

■ **Figure 7-4**

A hydrogen atom can absorb only those photons that move the atom's electron to one of the higher-energy orbits. Here three different photons are shown along with the change they would produce if they were absorbed.

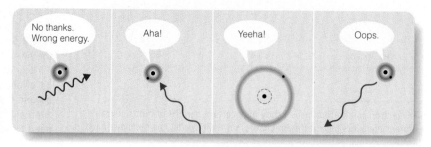

■ **Figure 7-5**

An atom can absorb a photon only if the photon has the correct amount of energy. The excited atom is unstable and within a fraction of a second returns to a lower energy level, re-radiating the photon in a random direction.

emits photons with a unique set of wavelengths. As a result, you can identify the elements in a gas by studying the characteristic wavelengths of light that are absorbed or emitted.

The process of excitation and emission is a common sight in urban areas at night. A neon sign glows when atoms of neon gas in a glass tube are excited by electricity flowing through the tube. As the electrons in the electric current flow through the gas, they collide with the neon atoms and excite them. Almost immediately after a neon atom is excited, its electron drops back to a lower energy level, emitting the surplus energy as a photon of a certain wavelength. The photons emitted by excited neon blend to produce a reddish-orange glow. Signs of other colors, generically called "neon signs," contain other gases or mixtures of gases instead of pure neon. Whenever you look at a neon sign, you are seeing atoms absorbing and emitting energy in the form of photons with specific colors determined by the structure of electron orbits in those atoms.

Neon signs are simple, but stars are complex. The colors of stars are not determined by the gases they contain. In the next section, you will discover why some stars are red and some are blue, and that will give you a new insight into how light interacts with matter.

Radiation from a Heated Object

If you look closely at the stars in the constellation Orion, you will notice that they are not all the same color (see Figure 2-4). One of your Favorite Stars, Betelgeuse, in the upper left corner of Orion, is quite red; another Favorite Star, Rigel, in the lower right corner, is blue. These differences in color arise from differences in temperature.

The starlight that you see comes from gases that make up the visible surface of the star, its photosphere. (Recall that you met the photosphere of the sun in Chapter 3.) Layers of gas deeper inside the star also emit light, but that light is reabsorbed before it can reach the surface. The gas above the photosphere is too thin to emit much light. The photosphere is the visible surface of a star because it is dense enough to emit lots of light but transparent enough to allow that light to escape.

Stars produce their light for the same reason heated horseshoes glow in a blacksmith's forge—because they are hot. If a horseshoe is not too hot, it glows ruddy red, but as it heats up it grows brighter and yellower. Yellow-hot is hotter than red-hot but not as hot as white-hot.

The light from stars and from glowing horseshoes is produced by the acceleration of charged particles. Usually the accelerated particles are electrons because they are the least massive charged particles, and they are on the outsides of atoms, so they are the easiest to get moving. An electron is surrounded by an electric field; and, if you disturb an electron, the change in its electric field spreads outward at the speed of light as electromagnetic radiation. You learned in Chapter 5 that "acceleration" means any change in motion. Whenever you change the motion of an electron or other charged particle, you generate electromagnetic waves. If you run a comb through your hair, you disturb electrons in both hair and comb, producing static electricity. That produces electromagnetic radiation, which you can hear as snaps and crackles if you are standing near an AM radio. Stars don't comb their hair, of course, but they are hot, and they are made up of ionized gases, so there are plenty of electrons zipping around.

The molecules and atoms in any object are in constant motion, and in a hot object they are more agitated than in a cool object. You can refer to this agitation as **thermal energy.** If you touch an object that contains lots of thermal energy, it will feel hot as the thermal energy flows into your fingers. The flow of thermal energy is called **heat.** In contrast, **temperature** refers to the average speed of the particles. Hot cheese and hot green beans can have the same temperature, but the cheese can contain more thermal energy and can burn your tongue. Thus, *heat* refers to the flow of thermal energy, and *temperature* refers to the intensity of the agitation among the particles (**Focus on Fundamentals 3**).

When astronomers refer to the temperature of a star, they are talking about the temperature of the gases in the photosphere, and they express those temperatures on the **Kelvin temperature scale.** On this scale, zero degrees Kelvin (written 0 K) is **absolute zero** (–459.7°F), the temperature at which an object contains no thermal energy that can be extracted. Water freezes at 273 K and boils at 373 K. The Kelvin temperature scale is useful in astronomy because it is based on absolute zero and consequently is related directly to the motion of the particles in an object.

Now you can understand why a hot object glows, or to put it another way, why a hot object emits photon bundles of electromagnetic energy. The hotter an object is, the more motion there is among its particles. The agitated particles, including electrons, collide with each other, and when electrons accelerate—change their motion–part of the energy is carried away as electromagnetic radiation. The radiation emitted by a heated object is called **blackbody radiation,** a name translated from a German term that refers to the way a perfectly opaque object would behave. A perfectly opaque object would be both a perfect emitter and a perfect absorber of radiation. At room temperature, such a perfect absorber and emitter would look black, but at higher temperatures it would glow at wavelengths visible to a human eye. In astronomy and physics you will see the term *blackbody* referring to objects that glow brightly.

Blackbody radiation is quite common. In fact, it is responsible for the light emitted by an incandescent light bulb. Electricity flowing through the filament of the bulb heats it to high temperature, and it glows. You can also recognize the light emitted by a heated horseshoe as blackbody radiation. Many objects in the sky, including the sun and stars, primarily emit blackbody radiation because they are mostly opaque.

Focus on Fundamentals ③

Temperature, Heat, and Thermal Energy

One of the most **Common Misconceptions** in science involves temperature. People often say "temperature" when they really mean "heat," and sometimes they say "heat" when they mean something entirely different. This is a fundamental idea, so you need to understand the difference.

Even in an object that is solid, the atoms and molecules are continuously jiggling around bumping into each other. When something is hot, the particles are moving rapidly. Temperature is a measure of the average motion of the particles. (Mathematically, temperature is proportional to the square of the average velocity.) If you have your temperature taken, it will probably be 37.0°C (98.6°F), an indication that the atoms and molecules in your body are moving about at a normal pace. If you measure the temperature of a baby, the thermometer should register the same temperature, showing that the atoms and molecules in the baby's body are moving at

the same average velocity as the atoms and molecules in your body.

The total energy of all of the moving particles in a body is called thermal energy. You have much more mass than the baby, so you must contain more thermal energy even though you have the same temperature. The thermal energy in your body and in the baby's body has the same intensity (temperature) but different amounts. People often confuse temperature and thermal energy, so you must be careful to distinguish between them. Temperature is like an intensity, and thermal energy is a total amount.

Many people say "heat" when they should say "thermal energy." Heat is the thermal energy that moves from a hot object to a cool object. If two objects have the same temperature, you and the infant for example, there is no transfer of thermal energy and no heat.

When you hear someone say "heat," check to see if he or she doesn't really mean thermal energy. You may have burned yourself on

What's the difference between temperature and heat?

cheese pizza, but you probably haven't burned yourself on green beans. At the same temperature, cheese holds more thermal energy than green beans. It isn't the temperature that burns your tongue, but the flow of thermal energy, and that's heat.

| MASS | ENERGY | **TEMPERATURE AND HEAT** | DENSITY | PRESSURE |

Hot objects emit blackbody radiation, but so do cold objects. Ice cubes are cold, but their temperature is higher than absolute zero, so they contain some thermal energy and must emit some blackbody radiation. The coldest gas drifting in space has a temperature only a few degrees above absolute zero, but it too emits blackbody radiation.

Two features of blackbody radiation are important. First, the hotter an object is, the more blackbody radiation it emits. Hot objects emit more radiation because their agitated particles collide more often and more violently with electrons. That's why a glowing coal from a fire emits more total energy than an ice cube of the same size.

The second feature is the relationship between the temperature of the object and the wavelengths of the photons it emits. The wavelength of the photon emitted when a particle collides with an electron depends on the violence of the collision. Only a violent collision can produce a short-wavelength (high-energy) photon. The electrons in an object have a distribution of speeds; a few travel very fast, and a few travel very slowly, but most travel at intermediate speeds. The hotter the object is, the faster, on average, the electrons travel. Because high-velocity electrons are rare, extremely violent collisions don't occur very often, and

short-wavelength photons are rare. Similarly, most collisions are not extremely gentle, so long-wavelength (low-energy) photons are also rare. Consequently, blackbody radiation is made up of photons with a distribution of wavelengths with medium wavelengths most common. The **wavelength of maximum intensity** (λ_{max}) is the wavelength at which the object emits the most intense radiation and occurs at some intermediate wavelength. (Make special note that λ_{max} does not refer to the maximum wavelength but to the wavelength of maximum.)

■ Figure 7-6 shows the intensity of radiation versus wavelength for three objects of different temperatures. The curves are high in the middle and low at either end because the objects emit most intensely at intermediate wavelengths. The total area under each curve is proportional to the total energy emitted, and you can see that the hotter object emits more total energy than the cooler objects. Look closely at the curves, and you will see that the wavelength of maximum intensity depends on temperature. The hotter an object is, the shorter will be the wavelength of its maximum emitted intensity. The figure shows how temperature determines the color of a glowing blackbody. The hotter object emits more blue light than red and thus looks blue, and the cooler object emits more red than blue and consequently looks

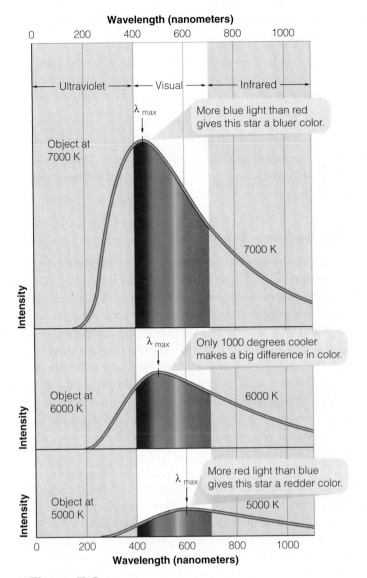

Wavelength (nanometers)

Ultraviolet — Visual — Infrared

More blue light than red gives this star a bluer color.

Object at 7000 K

λ_{max}

7000 K

Only 1000 degrees cooler makes a big difference in color.

λ_{max}

Object at 6000 K

6000 K

More red light than blue gives this star a redder color.

λ_{max}

Object at 5000 K

5000 K

Wavelength (nanometers)

Intensity

■ **Figure 7-6**

Graphs of blackbody radiation intensity versus wavelength from three objects at different temperatures demonstrate that a hot body radiates more total energy and that the wavelength of maximum intensity is shorter for hotter objects. The hotter object here would look blue to your eyes, while the cooler object would look red.

red. Now you can understand why two of your Favorite Stars, Betelgeuse and Rigel, have such different colors. Betelgeuse is cool and looks red, but Rigel is hot and looks blue.

Cool objects don't glow at visible wavelengths but still produce blackbody radiation. For example, the human body has a temperature of 310 K and emits blackbody radiation mostly in the infrared part of the spectrum. Infrared security cameras can detect burglars by the radiation they emit, and mosquitoes can track you down in total darkness by homing in on your infrared radiation. Although you emit lots of infrared radiation, you rarely emit higher-energy photons; and you almost never emit an

X-ray or gamma-ray photon. Your wavelength of maximum intensity lies in the infrared part of the spectrum.

Two Radiation Laws

The two features of blackbody radiation that you have just considered can be given precise mathematical form, and they have proven so dependable that they are known as laws. One law is related to energy and one to color.

As you saw in the previous section, a hot object emits more blackbody radiation than a cool object. That is, it emits more energy. Recall from Chapter 5 that energy is expressed in units called joules (J); 1 joule is about the energy of an apple falling from a table to the floor. The total radiation given off by 1 square meter of the surface of the object in joules per second equals a constant number, represented by σ times the temperature raised to the fourth power.* This relationship is called the Stefan–Boltzmann law:

$$E = \sigma T^4 \ (J/s/m^2)$$

How does this help you understand stars? Suppose a star the same size as the sun had a surface temperature that was twice as hot as the sun's surface. Then each square meter of that star would radiate not twice as much energy, but 2^4, or 16, times as much energy. From this law you can see that a small difference in temperature can produce a very large difference in the amount of energy a star's surface emits.

The second radiation law is related to the color of stars. In the previous section, you saw that hot stars look blue and cool stars look red. Wien's law written for conventional intensity units tells you that the wavelength at which a star radiates the most energy, its wavelength of maximum intensity (λ_{max}), depends only on the star's temperature:

$$\lambda_{max} = 2.90 \times 10^6/T$$

That is, the wavelength of maximum radiation in nanometers equals 2.9 million divided by the temperature on the Kelvin scale.

This law is a powerful tool in astronomy, because it relates the temperature of a star to its wavelength of maximum intensity. For example, you might find a star emitting light with a maximum intensity at a wavelength of 1000 nm—in the near-infrared. Then the surface temperature of the star must be 2900 K. Later you will meet stars much hotter than the sun; such stars radiate most of their energy at very short wavelengths. The hottest stars, for instance, radiate most of their energy in the ultraviolet.

---

*For the sake of completeness, you can note that the constant σ equals 5.67 × 10^{-8} J/(s m² K⁴) (units of joules per second per square meter per degree Kelvin to the fourth power).

7-3 Stellar Spectra

SCIENCE IS A WAY OF UNDERSTANDING NATURE, and the spectrum of a star can tell you a great deal about the star's temperature, motion, and composition. In later chapters, you will use spectra to study many more astronomical objects such as galaxies and planets, but you can begin by looking at the spectra of stars, including that of the sun.

The Formation of a Spectrum

The spectrum of a star is formed as light passes outward through the gases near its surface. Read **Atomic Spectra** on pages 132–133 and notice that it describes three important properties of spectra and defines 12 new terms that will help you discuss astronomical spectra:

1 There are three kinds of spectra: (i) *continuous spectra;* (ii) *absorption* or *dark-line spectra,* which contain *absorption lines;* and (iii) *emission* or *bright-line spectra,* which contain *emission lines.* These spectra are described by *Kirchhoff's laws.* When you see one of these types of spectra, you can recognize the kind of matter that emitted the light.

2 Photons are emitted or absorbed when an electron in an atom makes a *transition* from one energy level to another. The wavelengths of the photons depend on the energy difference between the two levels. Hydrogen atoms can produce many spectral lines in series such as the *Lyman, Balmer,* and *Paschen* series. Only three lines in the Balmer series are visible to human eyes. The emitted photons coming from a hot cloud of hydrogen gas have the same wavelengths as the photons absorbed by hydrogen atoms in the gases of a star.

3 Most modern astronomy books display spectra as graphs of intensity versus wavelength. Be sure you recognize the connection between the dark absorption lines and the dips in the graphed spectrum.

Whatever kind of celestial object's spectrum astronomers look at, the most common spectral lines are the Balmer lines of hydrogen. In the next section, you will see how Balmer lines can tell you the temperature of a star's surface.

The Balmer Thermometer

You can use the Balmer absorption lines as a thermometer to find the temperatures of stars. From the discussion of blackbody radiation, you already know how to estimate temperature using color, but the Balmer lines give you much greater accuracy.

Recall that astronomers use the Kelvin temperature scale when referring to stellar temperatures. These temperatures range from about 40,000 K to about 2500 K and refer to the temperature of the star's surface. Compare these extremes with the surface temperature of the sun, about 5800 K. The centers of stars are much hotter—millions of degrees—but the colors and spectra of stars tell you only about the surface because that's where the light comes from.

The Balmer thermometer works because the strength of the Balmer lines depends on the temperature of the star's surface layers. Both hot and cool stars have weak Balmer lines, but medium-temperature stars have strong Balmer lines.

The Balmer absorption lines are produced only by atoms with electrons in the second energy level. If a star is cool, there are few violent collisions between atoms to excite the electrons, so the electrons of most atoms are in the ground state, not the second level. Electrons in the ground state can't absorb photons in the Balmer series. As a result, you should expect to find weak Balmer absorption lines in the spectra of cool stars.

In the surface layers of hot stars, on the other hand, there are many violent collisions between atoms. These collisions can excite electrons to high energy levels or ionize some atoms by knocking electrons out of the atoms. Consequently, there are few hydrogen atoms with their electrons in the second orbit to form Balmer absorption lines. Hot stars, like cool stars, have weak Balmer absorption lines.

In stars of an intermediate temperature, roughly 10,000 K, the collisions are just right to excite large numbers of electrons into the second energy level. Hydrogen gas at that temperature absorbs Balmer wavelength photons very well and produces strong Balmer lines.

Theoretical calculations can predict exactly how strong the Balmer lines should be for stars of various temperatures. Such calculations are the key to finding temperatures from stellar

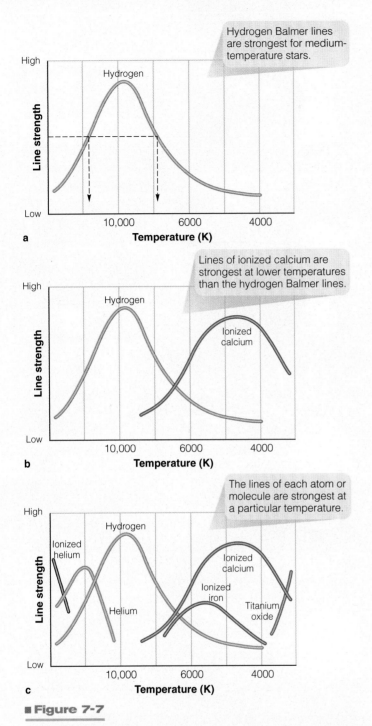

Hydrogen Balmer lines are strongest for medium-temperature stars.

a

Lines of ionized calcium are strongest at lower temperatures than the hydrogen Balmer lines.

b

The lines of each atom or molecule are strongest at a particular temperature.

c

■ **Figure 7-7**

The strength of spectral lines can tell you the temperature of a star. (a) Balmer hydrogen lines alone are not enough because they give two answers. Balmer lines of a certain strength could be produced by a hotter star or a cooler star. (b) Adding another atom to the diagram helps, and (c) adding many atoms and molecules to the diagram creates a precise aid to find the temperatures of stars.

spectra. The curve in ■ Figure 7-7a shows the strength of the Balmer lines for various stellar temperatures. But you can see from the graph that a star with Balmer lines of a certain strength might have either of two temperatures, one high and one low. How do you know which is right? You must examine other spectral lines to choose the correct temperature.

Temperature has a similar effect on the spectral lines of other elements, but the temperature at which the lines reach their maximum strength differs for each element (Figure 7-7b). If you add a number of chemical elements to your graph, you will have a powerful aid for finding the stars' temperatures (Figure 7-7c).

Now you can determine a star's temperature by comparing the strengths of its spectral lines with your graph. For instance, if you found medium-strength Balmer lines and strong helium lines in a star's spectrum, you could conclude that it had a temperature of about 20,000 K. But if the star had weak hydrogen lines and strong lines of ionized iron, you would assign it a temperature of about 5800 K, similar to that of the sun.

The spectra of stars cooler than about 3500 K contain dark bands produced by molecules such as titanium oxide (TiO). Because of their structure, molecules can absorb photons at many wavelengths, producing numerous, closely spaced spectral lines that blend together to form bands. These molecular bands appear in the spectra of only the coolest stars because, as mentioned before, molecules in cool stars are not subject to the violent collisions that would break them apart in hotter stars.

Spectral Classification

You have seen that the strengths of a star's various spectral lines depend on its surface temperature. From this you can conclude that all stars of a given temperature should have similar spectra. If you learn to recognize the pattern of spectral lines produced by a 6000 K star, for instance, you need not use Figure 7-7c every time you see that kind of spectrum. You can save time by classifying stellar spectra rather than analyzing each one individually.

The first widely used classification system was devised by astronomers at Harvard during the 1890s and 1900s. One of the astronomers, Annie J. Cannon, personally inspected and classified the spectra of over 250,000 stars. The spectra were first classified into groups labeled A through Q, but some groups were later dropped, merged with others, or reordered. The final classification includes the seven major **spectral classes,** or **types,** still used today: O, B, A, F, G, K, M.*

This sequence of spectral types, called the **spectral sequence,** is important because it is a temperature sequence. The O stars are the hottest, and the temperature decreases along the sequence to the M stars, the coolest. For increased precision, astronomers divide each spectral class into ten subclasses. For example, spectral class A consists of the subclasses A0, A1, A2, ... A8, A9. Next come F0, F1, F2, and so on. This finer division gives a star's temperature to an accuracy of about 5 percent. The sun, for example, is not just a

---

*Generations of astronomy students have remembered the spectral sequence using the mnemonic "Oh, Be A Fine Girl (Guy), Kiss Me." More recent suggestions from students include "Oh Boy, An F Grade Kills Me" and "Only Bad Astronomers Forget Generally Known Mnemonics."

Atomic Spectra

1 To understand how to analyze a spectrum, begin with a simple incandescent lightbulb. The hot filament emits blackbody radiation, which forms a **continuous spectrum.**

An **absorption spectrum** results when radiation passes through a cool gas. In this case you can imagine that the lightbulb is surrounded by a cool cloud of gas. Atoms in the gas absorb photons of certain wavelengths, which are missing from the spectrum, and you see their positions as dark **absorption lines.** Such spectra are sometimes called **dark-line spectra.**

An **emission spectrum** is produced by photons emitted by an excited gas. You could see **emission lines** by turning your telescope aside so that photons from the bright bulb did not enter the telescope. The photons you would see would be those emitted by the excited atoms near the bulb. Such spectra are also called **bright-line spectra.**

Telescope   Spectrograph

Continuous spectrum

Gas atoms

Absorption spectrum

Emission spectrum

1a The spectrum of a star is an absorption spectrum. The denser layers of the photosphere emit blackbody radiation. Gases in the atmosphere of the star absorb their specific wavelengths and form dark absorption lines in the spectrum.

Absorption spectrum

GUSTAV ROBERT KIRCHHOFF

1824
1887

30

DEUTSCHE BUNDESPOST BERLIN

KIRCHHOFF'S LAWS

Law I: **The Continuous Spectrum**

A solid, liquid, or dense gas excited to emit light will radiate at all wavelengths and thus produce a continuous spectrum.

Law II: **The Emission Spectrum**

A low-density gas excited to emit light will do so at specific wavelengths and thus produce an emission spectrum.

Law III: **The Absorption Spectrum**

If light comprising a continuous spectrum passes through a cool, low-density gas, the result will be an absorption spectrum.

1b In 1859, long before scientists understood atoms and energy levels, the German scientist Gustav Kirchhoff formulated three rules, now known as **Kirchhoff's laws,** that describe the three types of spectra.

2 The electron orbits in the hydrogen atom are shown here as energy levels. When an electron makes a **transition** from one orbit to another, it changes the energy stored in the atom. In this diagram, arrows pointed inward represent transitions that result in the emission of a photon. If the arrows pointed outward, they would represent transitions that result from the absorption of a photon. Long arrows represent large amounts of energy and correspondingly short-wavelength photons.

2a Transitions in the hydrogen atom can be grouped into series—the **Lyman series**, **Balmer series**, **Paschen series**, and the like. Transitions and the resulting spectral lines are identified by Greek letters. Only the first few transitions in the first three series are shown at left.

954.6 nm
1005.0 nm
1093.8 nm
1281.8 nm
1875.1 nm

388.9 nm
397.0 nm
410.2 nm
434.0 nm
486.1 nm
656.3 nm

93.8 nm
95.0 nm
97.2 nm
102.6 nm
121.5 nm

Paschen series (IR)

H_ε

Balmer series (Visible-UV)

H_β
H_α

Lyman series (UV)

Nucleus

2b In this drawing (right) of the hydrogen spectrum, emission lines in the infrared and ultraviolet are shown as gray. Only the first three lines of the Balmer series are visible to human eyes.

2c Excited clouds of gas in space emit light at all of the Balmer wavelengths, but you see only the red, blue, and violet photons blending to create the pink color typical of ionized hydrogen.

The shorter-wavelength lines in each series blend together.

Visual-wavelength image

AURA/NOAO/NSF

3 Modern astronomers rarely work with spectra as bands of light. Spectra are usually recorded digitally, so it is easy to represent them as graphs of intensity versus wavelength. Here the artwork above the graph suggests the appearance of a stellar spectrum. The graph below reveals details not otherwise visible and allows comparison of relative intensities. Notice that dark absorption lines in the spectrum appear as dips in the curve of intensity.

Intensity

H_γ
H_β
H_α

500
600
700

Wavelength (nm)

2000 nm

1500 nm

Infrared

Paschen lines

1000 nm

500 nm

Visible

H_α

H_β

H_γ

Balmer lines

100 nm

Ultraviolet

Lyman lines

Spectral Class	Approximate Temperature (K)	Hydrogen Balmer Lines	Other Spectral Features	Naked-Eye Example
O	40,000	Weak	Ionized helium	Meissa (O8)
B	20,000	Medium	Neutral helium	Achernar (B3)
A	10,000	Strong	Ionized calcium weak	Sirius (A1)
F	7500	Medium	Ionized calcium weak	Canopus (F0)
G	5500	Weak	Ionized calcium medium	Sun (G2)
K	4500	Very weak	Ionized calcium strong	Arcturus (K2)
M	3000	Very weak	TiO strong	Betelgeuse (M2)

G star, but a G2 star. ■ Table 7-1 breaks down some of the information contained in Figure 7-7c and presents it in tabular form according to spectral class. For example, if a star has weak Balmer lines and lines of ionized helium, it must be an O star.

Thirteen stellar spectra are arranged in ■ Figure 7-8 from the hottest at the top to the coolest at the bottom. You can easily see how the strength of spectral lines depends on temperature.

The Balmer lines are strongest in A stars, where the temperature is moderate but still high enough to excite the electrons in hydrogen atoms to the second energy level, where they can absorb Balmer wavelength photons. In the hotter stars (O and B), the Balmer lines are weaker because the higher temperature excites the electrons to energy levels above the second or ionizes the atoms. The Balmer lines in cooler stars (F through M) are also

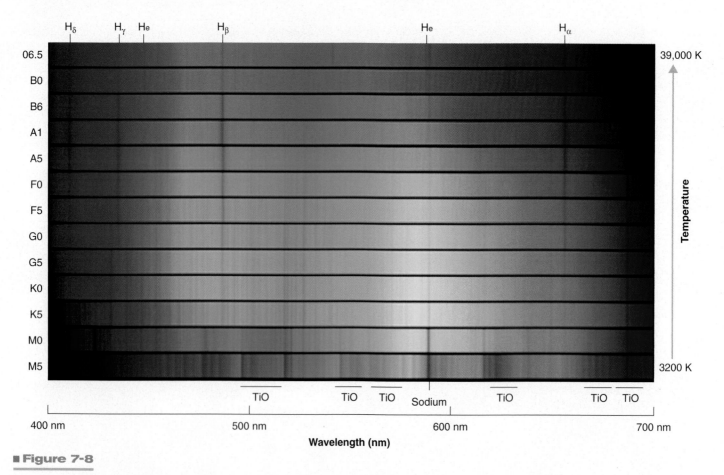

■ **Figure 7-8**

These spectra show stars ranging from hot O stars at the top to cool M stars at the bottom. The Balmer lines of hydrogen are strongest at spectral type A0, but the two closely spaced lines of sodium in the yellow are strongest for very cool stars. Helium lines appear only in the spectra of the hottest stars. Notice that the helium line visible in the top spectrum has nearly but not exactly the same wavelength as the sodium lines visible in cooler stars. Bands produced by the molecule titanium oxide are strong in the spectra of the coolest stars. (AURA/NOAO/NSF) weaker but for a different reason. The lower temperature cannot excite many electrons to the second energy level, so few hydrogen atoms are capable of absorbing Balmer wavelength photons.

Although these spectra are attractive, astronomers rarely work with spectra as color images. Rather, they display spectra as graphs of intensity versus wavelength that show dark absorption lines as dips in the graph (■ Figure 7-9). Such graphs allow more detailed analysis than photographs. Notice, for example, that the overall curves are segments of blackbody curves with spectral lines superimposed. The wavelength of maximum intensity is in the infrared for the coolest stars and in the ultraviolet for the hottest stars. Look carefully at these graphs, and you can see that helium is visible only in the spectra of the hottest classes and titanium oxide bands only in the coolest. Two lines of ionized calcium increase in strength from A to K and then decrease from K through M. Because the strengths of these spectral lines depend on temperature, it requires only a few moments to study a star's spectrum and determine its temperature.

Now you can learn something new about your Favorite Stars. Sirius, brilliant in the winter sky, is an A1 star; and Vega, bright overhead in the summer sky, is an A0 star. They have nearly the same temperature and color, and both have strong Balmer lines in their spectra. The bright red star in Orion is Betelgeuse, a cool M2 star, but blue-white Rigel is a hot B8 star. Polaris, the North Star, is an F8 star a bit hotter than our sun, and Alpha Centauri, the closest star to the sun, is a G2 star just like the sun.

The study of spectral types is a century old, but astronomers continue to discover new types. The **L dwarfs,** found in 1998, are cooler and fainter than M stars, and are understood to be objects smaller than stars but larger than planets called "brown dwarfs" that you will learn about in a later chapter. The spectra of M stars contain bands produced by metal oxides such as titanium oxide (TiO), but L dwarf spectra contain bands produced by molecules such as iron hydride (FeH). The **T dwarfs,** discovered in 2000, are an even cooler and fainter type of brown dwarf than L dwarfs. Their spectra show absorption by methane (CH_4) and water vapor (■ Figure 7-10). The development of giant telescopes and highly sensitive infrared cameras and spectrographs is allowing astronomers to find and study these cool objects.

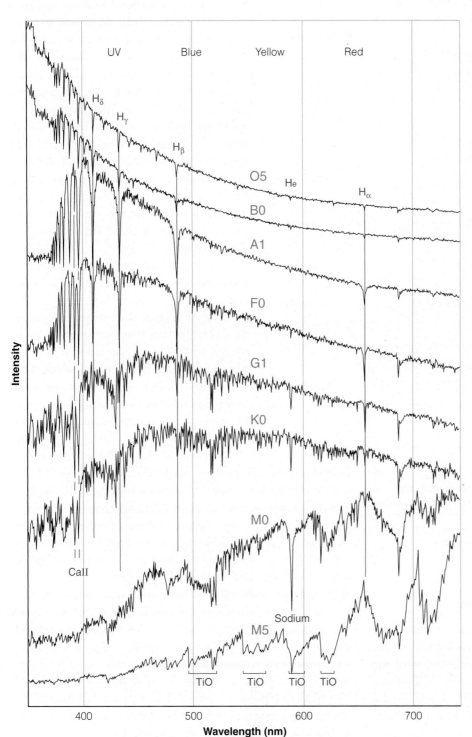

■ Figure 7-9

Modern digital spectra are often represented as graphs of intensity versus wavelength with dark absorption lines appearing as sharp dips in the curves. The hottest stars are at the top and the coolest at the bottom. Hydrogen Balmer lines are strongest at about A0, while lines of ionized calcium (Ca II) are strong in K stars. Titanium oxide (TiO) bands are strongest in the coolest stars. Compare these spectra with Figures 7-7c and 7-8. (Courtesy NOAO, G. Jacoby, D. Hunter, and C. Christian)

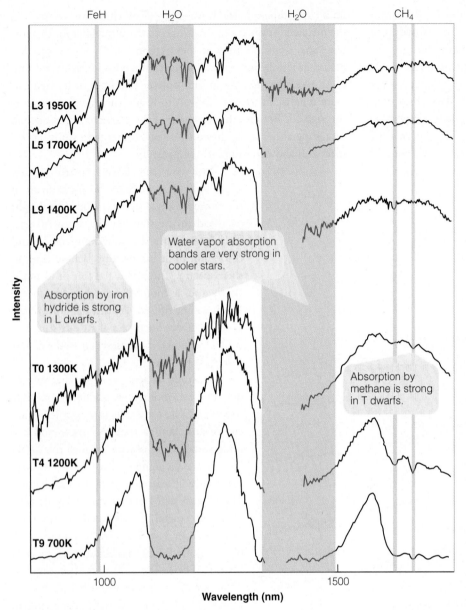

FeH H$_2$O H$_2$O CH$_4$

L3 1950K

L5 1700K

L9 1400K

Water vapor absorption bands are very strong in cooler stars.

Absorption by iron hydride is strong in L dwarfs.

T0 1300K

Absorption by methane is strong in T dwarfs.

T4 1200K

T9 700K

Intensity

1000   1500
Wavelength (nm)

■ **Figure 7-10**

These six infrared spectra show the dramatic differences between L dwarfs and T dwarfs. Spectra of M stars show titanium oxide bands (TiO), but L and T dwarfs are so cool that TiO molecules do not form. Other molecules, such as iron hydride (FeH), water (H$_2$O), and methane (CH$_4$), can form in these very cool objects. (Adapted from Thomas R. Geballe, Gemini Observatory, from a graph that originally appeared in *Sky and Telescope Magazine*, February 2005, p. 37.)

The Composition of the Stars

It seems as though it should be easy to learn the composition of the sun and stars just by looking at their spectra, but this is actually a difficult problem that wasn't well understood until the 1920s. The story is worth telling, not only because it illustrates the temperature dependence of stellar spectral types, it is also the story of an important American astronomer who waited decades to get proper credit for her work.

As a child in England, Cecilia Payne (1900–1979) excelled in classics, languages, mathematics, and literature, but her first love was astronomy. After finishing Newnham College in Cambridge, she left England, sensing that there were few opportunities there for a woman in science. In 1922, Payne arrived at Harvard, where she eventually earned her Ph.D. (although her degree was awarded by Radcliffe because Harvard did not then admit women).

In her thesis, Payne attempted to relate the strength of the absorption lines in stellar spectra to the physical conditions in the atmospheres of the stars. This was not easy; a given spectral line can be weak because the atom is rare or because the temperature is either too high or too low for it to absorb efficiently. If you see sodium lines in a star's spectrum, you can be sure that the star contains sodium atoms, but if you see no sodium lines, you must consider the possibility that sodium is present but the star is too hot or too cool for that type of atom to produce detectable spectral lines.

Density is another factor. If a gas is dense, the atoms are packed tighter together, collide more often, distort the electron orbits, and thereby change the strength of spectral lines (**Focus on Fundamentals 4**). If the gas is low density, the atoms collide less often and the spectral lines are less affected.

Payne's problem was to untangle these factors and find both the true temperatures of the stars and the true abundance of the atoms in their atmospheres. Solving this puzzle required some of the most recent advances in atomic physics and quantum mechanics. About the time Payne left Cambridge University, Indian physicist Meghnad Saha published his work on the ionization of atoms. Drawing from such theoretical work, Payne's calculations showed that over 90 percent of the atoms in stars (including the sun) must be hydrogen and most of the rest are helium (■ Table 7-2). The heavier atoms like calcium, sodium, and iron seem more abundant only because they are better at absorbing photons at the temperatures of stars.

At the time, astronomers found it hard to believe Payne's abundances of hydrogen and helium. They especially found such a high abundance of helium unacceptable. After all, hydrogen lines are at least visible in most stellar spectra, but helium lines are almost invisible in the spectra of all but the hottest stars. Nearly all astronomers assumed that the stars had roughly the same composition as Earth's surface; that is, they believed that the stars were composed mainly of heavier atoms such as carbon,

Density

You are about as dense as an average star. What does that mean? As you study astronomy, you will use the term *density* often, so you should be sure to understand this fundamental concept. **Density** is a measure of the amount of matter in a given volume. Density is expressed as mass per volume, such as grams per cubic centimeter. The density of water, for example, is about 1 g/cm³, and you are almost as dense as water.

To get a feel for density, imagine holding a brick in one hand and a similar-sized block of Styrofoam in the other hand. You can easily tell that the brick contains more matter than the Styrofoam block, even though both are the same size. The brick weighs more than the Styrofoam, but it isn't really the weight that you should consider. Rather, you should think about the mass of the two objects. In space, where they have no weight, the brick and the Styrofoam would still have mass, and

you could tell just by moving them around that the brick contains more mass than the Styrofoam. For example, imagine tapping each object gently with your hand. The massive brick would be easy to distinguish from the low-mass Styrofoam block, even in weightlessness.

Density is a fundamental concept in science because it is a general property of materials. Metals tend to be dense; lead, for example, has a density of about 7 g/cm³. Rock, in contrast, has a density of 3 to 4 g/cm³. Water and ice have densities of about 1 g/cm³. If you knew that a small moon orbiting Saturn had a density of 1.5 g/cm³, you could immediately draw some conclusions about what kinds of materials the little moon might be made of—ice and a little rock, but not much metal. The density of an object is a basic clue to its composition.

Astronomical bodies can have dramatically different densities. The gas clouds between

A brick would be dense even in space where it had no weight.

the stars can have very low densities, but the same kind of gas in a star can have a much higher density. The sun, for example, has an average density of about 1 g/cm³, about the same as your body. As you study astronomical objects, pay special attention to their densities.

MASS | ENERGY | TEMPERATURE AND HEAT | DENSITY | PRESSURE

■ Table 7-2	**The Most Abundant Elements in the Sun**	
Element	Percentage by Number of Atoms	Percentage by Mass
Hydrogen	91.0	70.9
Helium	8.9	27.4
Carbon	0.03	0.3
Nitrogen	0.008	0.1
Oxygen	0.07	0.8
Neon	0.01	0.2
Magnesium	0.003	0.06
Silicon	0.003	0.07
Sulfur	0.002	0.04
Iron	0.003	0.1

Payne worked for many years as a staff astronomer at the Harvard College Observatory with no formal position on the faculty. She married Russian astronomer Sergei Gaposchkin in 1934 and was afterward known as Cecilia Payne-Gaposchkin. In 1956, Harvard accepted women to its faculty, and Payne-Gaposchkin was appointed a full professor and made chair of the Harvard astronomy department. By that time, the importance of her research 30 years earlier had come to be widely recognized.

Cecilia Payne-Gaposchkin's work on the chemical composition of the stars illustrates the importance of fully understanding the interaction between light and matter. It was her detailed understanding of the physics that led her to the correct composition. As you turn your attention to other information that can be derived from stellar spectra, you will again discover the importance of understanding light.

silicon, iron, and aluminum. Even the most eminent astronomers dismissed Payne's result as illusory. Faced with this pressure and realizing that as a female scientist in the 1920s she faced an uphill battle, Payne could not press her discovery.

By 1929, astronomers generally understood the importance of temperature on measurements of composition derived from stellar spectra. At that point, they recognized that stars are mostly hydrogen and helium, but Payne received no credit.

The Doppler Effect

Surprisingly, one of the pieces of information hidden in a spectrum is the velocity of the light source. Astronomers can measure the wavelengths of the lines in a star's spectrum and find the velocity of the star. The **Doppler effect** is the apparent change in the wavelength of radiation caused by the motion of the source.

When astronomers talk about the Doppler effect, they are talking about a shift in the wavelength of electromagnetic radiation. But the Doppler shift can occur in any form of wave phenomena, including sound waves, so you probably hear the Doppler effect every day without noticing.

The pitch of a sound is determined by its wavelength. Sounds with long wavelengths have low pitches, and sounds with short wavelengths have higher pitches. You hear a Doppler shift every time a car or truck passes you and the pitch of its engine noise drops. Its sound is shifted to shorter wavelengths and higher pitches while it is approaching and is shifted to longer wavelengths and lower pitches after it passes.

To see why the sound waves are shifted in wavelength, consider a fire truck approaching you with a bell clanging once a second. When the bell clangs, the sound travels ahead of the truck to reach your ears. One second later, the bell clangs again, but, during that one second, the fire truck has moved closer to you, so the bell is closer at its second clang. Now the sound has a shorter distance to travel and reaches your ears a little sooner than it would have if the fire truck were not approaching. If you timed the clangs, you would find that you heard them slightly less than one second apart. After the fire truck passes you and is moving away, you hear the clangs sounding slightly more than one second apart because now each successive clang of the bell occurs farther from you and the sound travels farther to reach your ears.

■ Figure 7-11a shows a fire truck moving toward one observer and away from another observer. The position of the bell at each clang is shown by a small black bell. The sound of the clangs spreading outward is represented by black circles. You can see how the clangs are squeezed together ahead of the fire truck and stretched apart behind. If the fire truck has a siren instead of a bell, the sound coming from the siren will be a wave with a series of compressions and un-compressions. If the truck and siren are moving toward an observer, the compressions and un-compressions of the siren's sound wave will arrive more often—at a higher frequency—than if the truck were not moving, and the observer will hear the siren at a higher pitch than the same siren when it is stationary.

Now you can substitute a source of light for the clanging bell or wailing siren (Figure 7-11b). Imagine the light source emitting waves continuously as it approaches you. Each time the source emits the peak of a wave, it will be slightly closer to you than when it emitted the peak of the previous wave. From your vantage point, the successive peaks of the wave will seem closer together in the same way that the clangs of the bell seemed closer together. The light will appear to have a shorter wavelength, making it slightly bluer. Because the light is shifted slightly toward the blue end of the spectrum, this is called a **blueshift.** After the light source has passed you and is moving away, the peaks of successive waves seem farther apart, so the light has a longer wavelength and is redder. This is a **redshift.** The shifts are

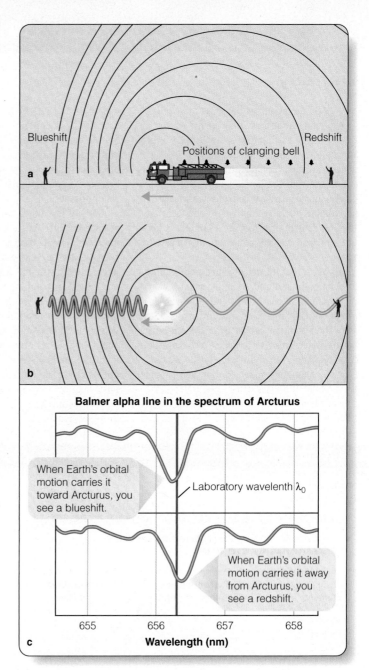

■ Figure 7-11

The Doppler effect. (a) The clanging bell on a moving fire truck produces sounds that move outward (black circles). An observer ahead of the truck hears the clangs closer together, while an observer behind the truck hears them farther apart. Similarly, the sound waves from a siren on an approaching truck will be received more often, and thus be heard with a higher tone, than a stationary truck, and the siren will have a lower tone if it is going away. (b) A moving source of light emits waves that move outward (black circles). An observer toward whom the light source is moving observes a shorter wavelength (a blueshift), and an observer for whom the light source is moving away observes a longer wavelength (a redshift). (c) Absorption lines in the spectrum of the bright star Arcturus are shifted to the blue in winter, when Earth's orbital motion carries it toward the star, and to the red in summer when Earth moves away from the star.

much too small to change the color of a star, but they are easily detected in spectra.

The terms *redshift* and *blueshift* are used to refer to any range of wavelengths. The light does not actually have to be red or blue, and the terms apply equally to wavelengths in other parts of the electromagnetic spectrum such as X-rays and radio waves. *Red* and *blue* refer to the direction of the shift, not to actual color.

The amount of change in wavelength, and thus the magnitude of the Doppler shift, depends on the velocity of the source. A moving car has a smaller Doppler shift than a jet plane, and a slow-moving star has a smaller Doppler shift than one that is moving more quickly. You can measure the velocity of a star by measuring the size of its Doppler shift. If a star is moving toward Earth, it has a blue shift and each of its spectral lines is shifted very slightly toward shorter wavelengths. If it is receding from Earth, it has a red shift. The next section will show how astronomers can convert Doppler shifts into velocities.

When you think about the Doppler effect, it is important to understand two things. Earth itself moves, so a measurement of a Doppler shift really measures the relative motion between Earth and the star. Figure 7-11c shows the Doppler effect in two spectra of the star Arcturus. Lines in the top spectrum are slightly blueshifted because the spectrum was recorded when Earth, in the course of its orbit, was moving toward Arcturus. Lines in the bottom spectrum are redshifted because it was recorded six months later, when Earth was moving away from Arcturus. To find the true motion of Arcturus, astronomers must subtract the motion of Earth.

The second point to remember is that the Doppler shift is sensitive only to the part of the velocity directed away from you or toward you—the **radial velocity** (*V_r*) (■ Figure 7-12a). You cannot use the Doppler effect to detect any part of the velocity that is perpendicular to your line of sight. A star moving to the left, for example, would have no blueshift or redshift because its distance from Earth would not be decreasing or increasing. This is why police using radar guns park right next to the highway (Figure 7-12b). They want to measure your full velocity as you drive past, not just part of your velocity.

Calculating the Doppler Velocity

It is easy to calculate the radial velocity of an object from its Doppler shift. The formula is a simple proportion relating the

■ **Figure 7-12**

(a) From Earth, astronomers can use the Doppler effect to measure the radial velocity *(V_r)* of a star, but they cannot measure its true velocity, *V*, through space. (b) Police radar can measure only the radial part of your velocity *(V_r)* as you drive down the highway, not your true velocity along the pavement *(V)*. That is why police using radar should never park far from the highway. This police car is poorly placed to make a good measurement.

radial velocity V_r divided by the speed of light c, to the change in wavelength, λ, divided by the un-shifted wavelength, λ_0:

$$\frac{V_r}{c} = \frac{\Delta\lambda}{\lambda_0}$$

For example, suppose you observed a line in a star's spectrum with a wavelength of 600.1 nm. Laboratory measurements show that the line should have a wavelength of 600 nm. That is, its un-shifted wavelength is 600 nm. What is the star's radial velocity? First note that the change in wavelength is 0.1 nm:

$$\frac{V_r}{c} = \frac{0.1}{600} = 0.000167$$

Multiplying by the speed of light, 3.00×10^5 km/s, gives the radial velocity, 50 km/s. Because the wavelength is shifted to the red (lengthened), the star must be receding.

Do you suppose chickens ever look at the sky and wonder what the stars are? Probably not. Chickens are very good at the chicken business, but they are not known for big brains and deep thought. Humans, in contrast, have highly evolved, sophisticated brains and are extremely curious. In fact, curiosity may be the most reliable characteristic of intelligence, and curiosity about the stars is a natural extension of our continual attempts to understand the world around us.

For early astronomers like Copernicus and Kepler, the stars were just points of light. There seemed to be no way to learn anything about them. Galileo's telescope revealed surprising details about the planets; but, even viewed through a large telescope, the stars are just points of light. Even when later astronomers began to assume that the stars were other suns, the stars seemed forever beyond human knowledge.

As you have seen, the key is understanding how light interacts with matter. In the last 150 years or so, scientists have discovered how atoms and light interact to form spectra, and astronomers have applied those discoveries to the ultimate object of human curiosity—the stars.

Chickens may never wonder what the stars are, or even wonder what chickens are, but humans are curious animals, and we do wonder about the stars and about ourselves. Our yearning to understand the stars is just part of our quest to understand what we are.

Study and Review

Summary

- An atom consists of a **nucleus (p. 123)** surrounded by a cloud of **electrons (p. 123)**. The nucleus is made up of positively charged **protons (p. 123)** and uncharged **neutrons (p. 123)**.

- The number of protons in an atom determines which element it is. Atoms of the same element (that is, having the same number of protons) with different numbers of neutrons are called **isotopes (p. 124)**.

- A neutral atom is surrounded by a number of negatively charged electrons equal to the number of protons in the nucleus. An atom that has lost or gained an electron is said to be **ionized (p. 124)** and is called an **ion (p. 124)**.

- Two or more atoms joined together form a **molecule (p. 124)**.

- The electrons in an atom are attracted to the nucleus by the **Coulomb force (p. 124)**. As described by **quantum mechanics (p. 124)**, the **binding energy (p. 124)** that holds electrons in an atom is limited to certain energies, and that means the electrons may occupy only certain **permitted orbits (p. 124)**.

- The size of an electron's orbit depends on its energy, so the orbits can be thought of as **energy levels (p. 126)** with the lowest possible energy level known as the **ground state (p. 126)**.

- An **excited atom (p. 126)** is one in which an electron is raised to a higher orbit by a collision between atoms or the absorption of a photon of the proper energy.

- The agitation among the atoms and molecules of an object is called **thermal energy (p. 127)**, and the flow of thermal energy is **heat (p. 127)**. In contrast, **temperature (p. 127)** refers to the intensity of the agitation and can be expressed on the **Kelvin temperature scale (p. 127)**, which gives temperature above **absolute zero (p. 127)**.

- Collisions among the particles in a body accelerate electrons and cause the emission of **blackbody radiation (p. 127)**. The hotter an object is, the more it radiates and the shorter is its **wavelength of maximum intensity**, λ_{max} **(p. 128)**. This allows astronomers to estimate the temperatures of stars from their colors.

- **Density (p. 137)** is a measure of the amount of matter in a given volume.

- **Kirchhoff's laws (p. 132)** explain that a hot solid, liquid, or dense gas emits electromagnetic radiation at all wavelengths and produces a **continuous spectrum (p. 132)**. An excited low-density gas produces an **emission (bright-line) spectrum (p. 132)** containing **emission lines (p. 132)**. A light source viewed through a low-density gas produces an **absorption (dark-line) spectrum (p. 132)** containing **absorption lines (p. 132)**.

- An atom can emit or absorb a photon when an electron makes a **transition (p. 133)** between orbits.

- Because orbits of only certain energy differences are permitted in an atom, photons of only certain wavelengths can be absorbed or emitted. Each kind of atom has its own characteristic set of spectral lines. The hydrogen atom has the **Lyman (p. 133)** series of lines in the ultraviolet, the **Balmer series (p. 133)** partially in the visible, and the **Paschen series (p. 133)** (plus others) in the infrared.

- The strength of spectral lines depends on the temperature of the star. For example, in cool stars, the Balmer lines are weak because atoms are not excited out of the ground state. In hot stars, the Balmer lines are weak because atoms are excited to higher orbits or are ionized. Only at medium temperatures are the Balmer lines strong.

- A star's **spectral class** (or **type**) **(p. 131)** is determined by the absorption lines in its spectrum. The resulting **spectral sequence (p. 131)**, OBAFGKM, is important because it is a temperature sequence. By classifying a star, the astronomer learns the temperature of the star's surface.

▶ Long after the spectral sequence was created, astronomers found the **L dwarfs (p. 135)** and **T dwarfs (p. 135)** at temperatures even cooler than the M stars.

▶ A spectrum can tell you the chemical composition of the stars. The presence of spectral lines of a certain element shows that that element must be present in the star, but you must proceed with care. Lines of a certain element may be weak or absent if the star is too hot or too cool even if that element is present in the star's atmosphere.

▶ The **Doppler effect (p. 137)** can provide clues to the motions of the stars. When a star is approaching, you observe slightly shorter wavelengths, a **blueshift (p. 138)**, and when it is receding, you observe slightly longer wavelengths, a **redshift (p. 138)**. This Doppler effect reveals a star's **radial velocity, V_r (p. 139)**, that part of its velocity directed toward or away from Earth.

Review Questions

1. Why might you say that atoms are mostly empty space?
2. What is the difference between an isotope and an ion?
3. Why is the binding energy of an electron related to the size of its orbit?
4. Explain why ionized calcium can form absorption lines, but ionized hydrogen cannot.
5. Describe two ways an atom can become excited.
6. Why do different atoms have different lines in their spectra?
7. Why does the amount of blackbody radiation emitted depend on the temperature of the object?
8. Why do hot stars look bluer than cool stars?
9. What kind of spectrum does a neon sign produce?
10. Why are Balmer lines strong in the spectra of medium-temperature stars and weak in the spectra of hot and cool stars?
11. Why are titanium oxide features visible in the spectra of only the coolest stars?
12. Explain the similarities among Table 7-1, Figure 7-7c, Figure 7-8, and Figure 7-9.
13. Explain why the presence of spectral lines of a given element in the solar spectrum tells you that element is present in the sun, but the absence of the lines would not necessarily mean the element is absent from the sun.
14. Why does the Doppler effect detect only radial velocity?
15. How can the Doppler effect explain shifts in both light and sound?
16. **How Do We Know?** How is the world you see around you determined by a world you cannot see?

Discussion Questions

1. In what ways is the model of an atom a scientific model? In what ways is it incorrect?
2. Can you think of classification systems used to simplify what would otherwise be complex measurements? Consider foods, movies, cars, grades, and clothes.

Problems

1. Human body temperature is about 310 K (3.10×10^2 K, or 98.6°F). At what wavelength do humans radiate the most energy? What kind of radiation do we emit?

2. If a star has a surface temperature of 20,000 K (2.00×10^4 K), at what wavelength will it radiate the most energy?

3. Infrared observations of a star show that it is most intense at a wavelength of 2000 nm (2.00×10^3 nm). What is the temperature of the star's surface?

4. If you double the temperature of a blackbody, by what factor will the total energy radiated per second per square meter increase?

5. If one star has a temperature of 6000 K and another star has a temperature of 7000 K, how much more energy per second will the hotter star radiate from each square meter of its surface?

6. Electron orbit transition A produces light with a wavelength of 500 nm. Transition B involves twice as much energy as A. What wavelength light does it produce?

7. Determine the temperatures of the following stars based on their spectra. Use Figure 7-7c.
    a. medium-strength Balmer lines, strong helium lines
    b. medium-strength Balmer lines, weak ionized-calcium lines
    c. strong TiO bands
    d. very weak Balmer lines, strong ionized-calcium lines

8. To which spectral classes do the stars in Problem 7 belong?

9. In a laboratory, the Balmer beta line has a wavelength of 486.1 nm. If the line appears in a star's spectrum at 486.3 nm, what is the star's radial velocity? Is it approaching or receding?

10. The highest-velocity stars an astronomer might observe have velocities of about 400 km/s (4.00×10^2 km/s). What change in wavelength would this cause in the Balmer gamma line? (*Hint:* Wavelengths are given on page 133.)

Learning to Look

1. Consider Figure 7-3. When an electron in a hydrogen atom moves from the third orbit to the second orbit, the atom emits a Balmer-alpha photon in the red part of the spectrum. In what part of the spectrum would you look to find the photon emitted when an electron in a helium atom makes the same transition?

2. Where should the police car in Figure 7-12 have parked to make a good measurement?

3. The nebula shown below contains mostly hydrogen excited to emit photons. What kind of spectrum would you expect this nebula to produce?

T. Rector, University of Alaska, and WTYN/NURO/AURA/NSF

4. If the nebula in the image here crosses in front of the star, and the nebula and star have different radial velocities, what might the spectrum of the star look like?

8 | The Sun

Far UV image

This far-ultraviolet image of the sun made from space has been enhanced and rendered in false color to reveal complex structure on the surface and clouds of gas trapped in arched magnetic fields above the surface. (NASA/TRACE)

▬ Guidepost

The sun is the source of light and warmth in our solar system, so it is a natural object of human curiosity. It is also the one star that is most clearly visible from Earth. The interaction of light and matter, which you studied in Chapter 7, can reveal the secrets of the sun and introduce you to the stars.

In this chapter, you will discover how the analysis of the solar spectrum can paint a detailed picture of the sun's atmosphere and how basic physics has solved the mystery of the sun's core. Here you will answer four essential questions:

— **What do you see when you look at the sun?**

— **How does the sun make its energy?**

— **What are the dark sunspots?**

— **Why does the sun go through a cycle of activity?**

Although this chapter is confined to the center of the solar system, it introduces you to a star and leads your thoughts onward among the stars and galaxies that fill the universe.

All cannot live on the piazza, but everyone may enjoy the sun.

— ITALIAN PROVERB

A WIT ONCE REMARKED that solar astronomers would know a lot more about the sun if it were farther away. The sun is so close that Earth's astronomers can see swirling currents of gas and arched bridges of magnetic force. The details seem overwhelming. But the sun is just an average star; and, in a sense, it is a simple object. It is made up almost entirely of the gases hydrogen and helium confined by its own gravity in a sphere 109 times Earth's diameter (**Celestial Profile 1**). The gases of the sun's surface are hot and radiate the light and heat that make life possible on Earth. That solar atmosphere is where you can begin your exploration.

8-1 The Solar Atmosphere

THE SUN'S ATMOSPHERE is made up of three layers. The visible surface is the *photosphere*, and above that are the *chromosphere* and the corona. (You first met these terms in Chapter 3 when you learned about solar eclipses.)

When you look at the sun you see a hot, glowing surface with a temperature of about 5800 K. At that temperature, every square millimeter of the sun's surface must be radiating more energy than a 60-watt light bulb. With all that energy radiating into space, the sun's surface would cool rapidly if energy did not flow up from the interior to keep the surface hot, so simple logic tells you that energy in the form of heat is flowing outward from the sun's interior. Not until the 1930s did astronomers understand that the sun makes its energy by nuclear reactions at the center. Those nuclear reactions are discussed in detail later in this chapter.

For now, you can consider the sun's atmosphere in its quiescent, average state. Later you can add the details of its continuous activity as heat flows up from the sun's interior and makes the outer layers churn like a pot of boiling soup.

The Photosphere

The visible surface of the sun looks like a smooth layer of gas marked only by a few dark **sunspots** that come and go over a few weeks. Although the photosphere seems to be a distinct surface, it is not solid. In fact, the sun is gaseous from its outer atmosphere right down to its center. The photosphere is the thin layer of gas from which Earth receives most of the sun's light. It is less than 500 km deep, and if the sun magically shrank to the size of a bowling ball, the photosphere would be no thicker than a layer of tissue paper wrapped around the ball (■ Figure 8-1).

a Chromosphere

Photosphere

Corona

b Visual-wavelength image

■ **Figure 8-1**

(a) A cross section at the edge of the sun shows the relative thickness of the photosphere and chromosphere. Earth is shown for scale. On this scale, the disk of the sun would be more than 1.5 m (5 ft) in diameter. The corona extends from the top of the chromosphere to great height above the photosphere. (b) This photograph, made during a total solar eclipse, shows only the inner part of the corona. (Daniel Good)

The photosphere is the layer in the sun's atmosphere that is dense enough to emit plenty of light but not so dense that the light can't escape. Below the photosphere, the gas is denser and hotter and therefore radiates plenty of light, but that light cannot escape from the sun because it is blocked by the outer layers of gas. So you cannot detect light from these deeper layers. Above the photosphere, the gas is less dense and so is unable to radiate much light.

Although the photosphere appears to be substantial, it is really a very-low-density gas. Even in its deepest and densest layers, the photosphere is less than 1/3000 as dense as the air you breathe. To find gases as dense as the air at Earth's surface, you would have to descend about 70,000 km below the photosphere, about 10 percent of the way to the sun's center. With fantastically efficient insulation, you could fly a spaceship right through the photosphere.

The spectrum of the sun is an absorption spectrum, and that can tell you a great deal about the photosphere. You know from Kirchhoff's third law that an absorption spectrum is produced when the source of a continuous spectrum is viewed through a gas. The deeper layers of the photosphere are dense enough to produce a continuous spectrum, but atoms in the photosphere absorb photons of specific wavelengths, producing absorption lines of hydrogen, helium, and other elements.

In good photographs, the photosphere has a mottled appearance because it is made up of dark-edged regions called granules. The overall pattern is called **granulation** (■ Figure 8-2a). Each granule is about the size of Texas and lasts for only 10 to 20 minutes before fading, shrinking, and being replaced by a new

a **Visual-wavelength image**

Granule

Sinking gas

Rising gas

b

■ **Figure 8-2**

(a) This ultra-high-resolution image of the photosphere shows granulation. The largest granules here are about the size of Texas. (b) This model explains granulation as the tops of rising convection currents just below the photosphere. Heat flows upward as rising currents of hot gas and downward as sinking currents of cool gas. The rising currents heat the solar surface in small regions seen from Earth as granules.

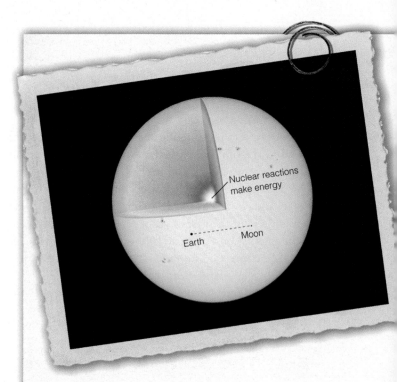

Nuclear reactions make energy

Earth   Moon

This visible image of the sun shows a few sunspots and is cut away to show the location of energy generation at the sun's center. The Earth–moon system is shown for scale. (Daniel Good)

Celestial Profile 1: The Sun
From Earth:

Average distance from Earth	1.000 AU (1.496×10^8 km)
Maximum distance from Earth	1.017 AU (1.521×10^8 km)
Minimum distance from Earth	0.983 AU (1.471×10^8 km)
Average angular diameter	0.53° (32 arc minutes)
Period of rotation	25.4 days at equator
Apparent visual magnitude	−26.74

Characteristics:

Radius	6.96×10^5 km
Mass	1.99×10^{30} kg
Average density	1.41 g/cm³
Escape velocity at surface	618 km/s
Luminosity	3.83×10^{26} J/s
Surface temperature	5800 K
Central temperature	15×10^6 K
Spectral type	G2 V
Absolute visual magnitude	4.83

Personality Profile:

In Greek mythology, the sun was carried across the sky in a golden chariot pulled by powerful horses and guided by the sun god Helios. When Phaeton, the son of Helios, drove the chariot one day, he lost control of the horses, and Earth was nearly set ablaze before Zeus smote Phaeton from the sky. Even in classical times, people understood that life on Earth depends critically on the sun.

granule. Spectra of granules show that the centers are a few hundred degrees hotter than the edges, and Doppler shifts reveal that the centers are rising and the edges are sinking at speeds of about 0.4 km/s.

From this evidence, astronomers recognize granulation as the surface effects of convection just below the photosphere. **Convection** occurs when hot fluid rises and cool fluid sinks, as when, for example, a convection current of hot gas rises above a candle flame. You can watch convection in a liquid by adding a bit of cool non-dairy creamer to an unstirred cup of hot coffee. The cool creamer sinks, warms, expands, rises, cools, contracts, sinks again, and so on, creating small regions on the surface of the coffee that mark the tops of convection currents. Viewed from above, these regions look much like solar granules.

In the sun, rising currents of hot gas heat small regions of the photosphere, which, being slightly hotter, emit more blackbody radiation and look brighter. The cool sinking gas of the edges emits less light and thus looks darker (Figure 8-2b). The presence of granulation is clear evidence that energy is flowing upward through the photosphere.

Spectroscopic studies of the solar surface have revealed another less obvious kind of granulation. **Supergranules** are regions a little over twice Earth's diameter that include about 300 granules each. These supergranules are regions of very slowly rising currents that last a day or two. They appear to be produced by larger gas currents that lie deeper under the photosphere.

The edge, or **limb,** of the solar disk is dimmer than the center (see the figure in Celestial Profile 1). This **limb darkening** is caused by the absorption of light in the photosphere. When you look at the center of the solar disk, you are looking directly down into the sun, and you see deep, hot, bright layers in the photosphere. In contrast, when you look near the limb of the solar disk, you are looking at a steep angle to the surface and cannot see as deeply. The photons you see come from shallower, cooler, dimmer layers in the photosphere. Limb darkening proves that the temperature in the photosphere increases with depth, yet another confirmation that energy is flowing up from below.

The Chromosphere

Above the photosphere lies the chromosphere. Solar astronomers define the lower edge of the chromosphere as lying just above the visible surface of the sun, with its upper regions blending gradually with the corona. You can think of the chromosphere as an irregular layer with a depth on average less than Earth's diameter (see Figure 8-1). Because the chromosphere is roughly 1000 times fainter than the photosphere, you can see it with your unaided eyes only during a total solar eclipse when the moon covers the brilliant photosphere. Then, the chromosphere

flashes into view as a thin line of pink just above the photosphere. The word *chromosphere* comes from the Greek word *chroma*, meaning "color." The pink color is produced by the combined light of three bright emission lines—the red, blue, and violet Balmer lines of hydrogen.

Astronomers know a great deal about the chromosphere from its spectrum. The chromosphere produces an emission spectrum, and Kirchhoff's second law tells you it must be an excited, low-density gas. The chromosphere is about 10^8 times less dense than the air you breathe.

Spectra reveal that atoms in the lower chromosphere are ionized, and atoms in the higher layers of the chromosphere are even more highly ionized. That is, they have lost more electrons. Hydrogen atoms contain only one electron, but atoms like calcium and iron contain many more, and at high enough temperatures they can lose a number of electrons and become highly ionized. From the ionization state of the gas, astronomers can find the temperature in different parts of the chromosphere. Just above the photosphere the temperature falls to a minimum of about 4500 K and then rises rapidly (■ Figure 8-3) to the extremely high temperatures of the corona. The upper chromosphere is hot enough to emit X-rays and can be studied by X-ray telescopes in space.

Solar astronomers can take advantage of some elegant physics to study the chromosphere. The gases of the chromosphere are transparent to nearly all visible light, but atoms in the gas are very good at absorbing photons of specific wavelengths. This produces certain dark absorption lines in the spectrum of the photosphere. A photon at one of those wavelengths is very

■ **Figure 8-3**

The chromosphere. If you could place thermometers in the sun's atmosphere, you would discover that the temperature increases from 5800 K at the photosphere to 1,000,000 K at the top of the chromosphere.

■ **Figure 8-4**

H_α filtergrams reveal complex structure in the chromosphere that cannot be seen at visual wavelengths, including spicules springing from the edges of supergranules over twice the diameter of Earth. Seen at the edge of the solar disk, spicules look like a burning prairie, but they are not at all related to burning. Compare with Figure 8-1. (BBSO; © 1971 NOAO/NSO; Hinode)

Spicules

H_α image

H_α image

Visual-wavelength image

Diameter of the Earth (8000 miles)

unlikely to escape from deeper layers. A **filtergram** is an image of the sun made using light in one of those dark absorption lines. Those photons can only have escaped from higher in the sun's atmosphere. In this way, filtergrams reveal detail in the upper layers of the chromosphere. Another way to study these high, hot layers of gas is to record solar images in the far-ultraviolet or in the X-ray part of the spectrum.

■ Figure 8-4 shows a filtergram made at the wavelength of the H_α Balmer line. This image shows complex structure in the chromosphere. **Spicules** are flamelike jets of gas extending upward into the chromosphere and lasting 5 to 15 minutes. Seen at the limb of the sun's disk, these spicules blend together and look like flames covering a burning prairie (Figure 8-1), but they are not flames at all. Spectra show that spicules are cooler gas from the lower chromosphere extending upward into hotter regions. Images at the center of the solar disk show that spicules spring up around the edge of supergranules like weeds around flagstones (Figure 8-4).

The Solar Corona

The outermost part of the sun's atmosphere is called the corona, after the Greek word for crown. The corona is so dim that, like the chromosphere, it is not visible in Earth's daytime sky because of the glare of scattered light from the sun's brilliant photosphere. During a total solar eclipse, the innermost parts of the corona are

visible to the unaided eye, as shown in Figure 8-1b. Observations made with specialized telescopes called **coronagraphs** can block the light of the photosphere and record the corona out beyond 20 solar radii, almost 10 percent of the way to Earth. Such images reveal streamers in the corona that follow magnetic lines of force in the sun's magnetic field (■ Figure 8-5).

The spectrum of the corona can tell you a great deal about the coronal gases and simultaneously illustrate how astronomers analyze a spectrum. Some of the light from the outer corona produces a spectrum with absorption lines that are the same as the photosphere's spectrum. This light is just sunlight reflected from dust particles in the corona. In contrast, some of the light from the corona produces a continuous spectrum that lacks absorption lines, and that happens when sunlight from the photosphere is scattered off free electrons in the ionized coronal gas. Because the coronal gas has a temperature over 1 million K and the electrons travel very fast, the reflected photons suffer large, random Doppler shifts that smear out absorption lines to produce a continuous spectrum.

Superimposed on the corona's continuous spectrum are emission lines of highly ionized gases. In the lower corona, the atoms are not as highly ionized as they are at higher altitudes, and this tells you that the temperature of the corona rises with altitude. Just above the chromosphere, the temperature is about 500,000 K, but in the outer corona the temperature can be 2 million K or more.

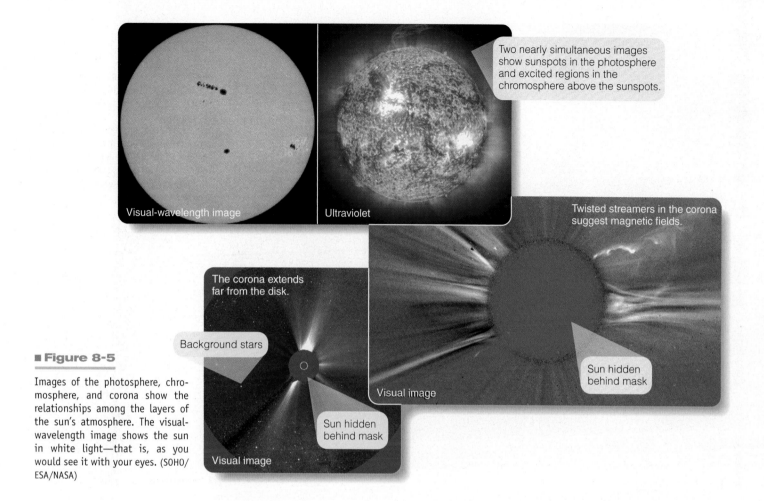

The two nearly simultaneous images show sunspots in the photosphere and excited regions in the chromosphere above the sunspots.

Visual-wavelength image

Ultraviolet

Twisted streamers in the corona suggest magnetic fields.

The corona extends far from the disk.

Background stars

Sun hidden behind mask

Visual image

Sun hidden behind mask

Visual image

■ **Figure 8-5**

Images of the photosphere, chromosphere, and corona show the relationships among the layers of the sun's atmosphere. The visual-wavelength image shows the sun in white light—that is, as you would see it with your eyes. (SOHO/ESA/NASA)

The corona is exceedingly hot gas. In fact, as you learned earlier, the gas in the corona and upper chromosphere is so hot it can emit X-rays. Nevertheless, the coronal gas is not very bright. Its density is very low, only 10^6 atoms/cm^3 in its lower regions. That is about 10^{12} times less dense than the air you breathe. In its outer layers the corona contains only 1 to 10 atoms/cm^3, fewer than in the best vacuum in laboratories on Earth. Because of its low density, the hot gas does not emit much radiation.

Astronomers have wondered for years how the corona and chromosphere can be so hot. Heat flows from hot regions to cool regions, never from cool to hot. So how can the heat from the photosphere, with a temperature of only 5800 K, flow out into the much hotter chromosphere and corona? Observations made by the SOHO satellite have mapped a **magnetic carpet** of looped magnetic fields extending up through the photosphere (■ Figure 8-6). Remember that the gas of the chromosphere and corona has a very low density, so it can't resist movement of the magnetic fields. Turbulence below the photosphere seems to flick the magnetic loops back and forth and whip the gas about, heating the gas. Furthermore, observations with the Hinode spacecraft have revealed magnetic waves generated by turbulence below the photosphere traveling up into the chromosphere and

corona and heating the gas. Because the gas in the corona has such a low density, it doesn't take much energy flowing outward as agitation in the magnetic fields to heat the corona to high temperature.

Ionized, low-density gas cannot cross magnetic fields, so where the sun's field loops back to the surface, the gas is trapped. However, some of the magnetic fields lead outward into space, and there the gas flows away from the sun in a breeze called the **solar wind.** Like an extension of the corona, the low-density gases of the solar wind blow past Earth at 300 to 800 km/s with gusts as high as 1000 km/s. Earth is bathed in the corona's hot breath.

Because of the solar wind, the sun is slowly losing mass, but this is only a minor loss for an object as massive as the sun. The sun loses about 10^7 tons per second, but that is only 10^{-14} of a solar mass per year. Later in life, the sun, like many other stars, will lose mass rapidly in a more powerful wind. You will see in future chapters how this affects the evolution of stars.

Do other stars have chromospheres, coronae, and stellar winds like the sun? Stars are so far away they never look like more than points of light, but ultraviolet and X-ray observations suggest that the answer is yes. The spectra of many stars contain emission lines in the far-ultraviolet that could have formed only

■ **Figure 8-6**

Flying through the magnetic carpet. This computer model shows an extreme-ultraviolet image of a section of the sun's lower corona (green) with black and white areas marking regions of opposite magnetic polarity. A mathematical model has drawn lines to show how the areas are linked by loops of magnetic force. The largest loops here could encircle Earth. (Stanford-Lockheed Institute for Space Research, Palo Alto, CA, and NASA GSFC)

in the low-density, high-temperature gases of a chromosphere and corona. Also, many stars are sources of X-rays, which appear to have been produced by the high-temperature gas in their chromospheres and coronae. This observational evidence gives astronomers good reason to believe that the sun, for all its complexity, is a typical star.

The layers of the solar atmosphere are all that astronomers can observe directly, but there are phenomena in those layers that reveal what it's like inside the sun—your next destination.

Below the Photosphere

Almost no light emerges from below the photosphere, so you can't see into the solar interior. However, solar astronomers can study naturally occurring vibrations in the sun to explore its depths in a process called **helioseismology.** Random convective movements of gas in the sun constantly produce vibrations—rumbles that would be much too low to hear with human ears even if your ears could survive a visit to the sun's atmosphere. Some of these vibrations resonate in the sun like sound waves in organ pipes. A vibration with a period of 5 minutes is strongest, but the periods range from 3 to 20 minutes. These are very, very low-pitched sounds!

Astronomers can detect these vibrations by observing Doppler shifts in the solar surface. As a vibrational wave travels down into the sun, the increasing density and temperature curve its path, and it returns to the surface, where it makes the photosphere heave up and down by small amounts—roughly plus or minus 15 km. Many of these vibrations occurring simultaneously cover the surface of the sun with a pattern of rising and falling regions that can be mapped using the Doppler effect (■ Figure 8-7). By observing these motions, astronomers can determine which vibrations resonate and become stronger and which become weaker. Short-wavelength waves penetrate less deeply and travel shorter distances than longer-wavelength waves, so the different wavelength vibrations explore different layers in the sun. Just as geologists can study Earth's interior by analyzing vibrations from earthquakes, so solar astronomers can use helioseismology to explore the sun's interior.

You can better understand how helioseismology works if you think of a duck pond. If you stood at the shore of a duck pond and looked down at the water, you would see ripples arriving from all parts of the pond. Because every duck on the pond contributes to the ripples, you could, in principle, study the ripples near the shore and draw a map showing the position and velocity

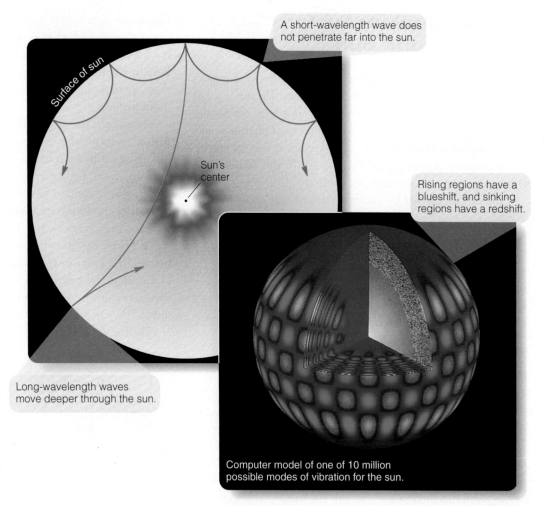

A short-wavelength wave does not penetrate far into the sun.

Surface of sun

Sun's center

Rising regions have a blueshift, and sinking regions have a redshift.

Long-wavelength waves move deeper through the sun.

Computer model of one of 10 million possible modes of vibration for the sun.

■ **Figure 8-7**

Helioseismology: The sun can vibrate in millions of different patterns or modes, and each mode corresponds to a different wavelength vibration penetrating to a different level. By measuring Doppler shifts as the surface moves gently up and down, astronomers can map the inside of the sun. (AURA/NOAO/NSF)

of every duck on the pond. Of course, it would be difficult to untangle the different ripples, so you would need lots of data and a big computer. Nevertheless, all of the information would be there, lapping at the shore.

Helioseismology demands huge amounts of data, so astronomers have used a network of telescopes around the world operated by the Global Oscillation Network Group (GONG). The network can observe the sun continuously for weeks at a time as Earth rotates. The sun never sets on GONG. The SOHO satellite in space can observe solar oscillations continuously and can detect motions as slow as 1 mm/s (0.002 mph). Solar astronomers can then use high-speed computers to separate the different patterns on the solar surface and measure the strength of the waves at many different wavelengths.

Helioseismology has allowed astronomers to map the temperature, density, and rate of rotation inside the sun. They have been able to map great currents of gas flowing below the photosphere and the development of sunspots before they become visible in the photosphere. Helioseismology can even locate sunspots on the back side of the sun, sunspots that are not yet visible from Earth.

SCIENTIFIC ARGUMENT

What evidence leads astronomers to conclude that temperature increases with height in the chromosphere and corona?
Scientific arguments usually involve evidence, and in astronomy that means observations. Solar astronomers can observe the spectrum of the chromosphere, and they find that atoms there are more highly ionized (have lost more electrons) than atoms in the photosphere. Atoms in the corona are even more highly ionized. That must mean the chromosphere and corona are hotter than the photosphere.

Evidence is the key to understanding how science works. Now it is time to build a new argument. **What evidence leads astronomers to conclude that other stars have chromospheres and coronae like those of the sun?**

8-2 Nuclear Fusion in the Sun

LIKE SOAP BUBBLES, stars are structures balanced between opposing forces that individually would destroy them. The sun is a ball of hot gas held together by its own gravity. If it were not for the sun's gravity, the hot, high-pressure gas in the sun's interior would explode outward. Likewise, if the sun were not so hot, its gravity would compress it into a small dense body. In this section, you will discover how the sun generates its heat.

The sun is powered by nuclear reactions that occur near its center.* The energy keeps the interior hot and keeps the gas totally ionized. That is, the electrons are not attached to atomic nuclei, so the gas is an atomic soup of rapidly moving particles colliding with each other at high velocities. Nuclear reactions inside stars involve atomic nuclei, not whole atoms.

How exactly can the nucleus of an atom yield energy? The answer lies in the force that holds the nuclei together.

Nuclear Binding Energy

The sun generates its energy by breaking and reconnecting the bonds between the particles *inside* atomic nuclei. This is quite different from the way you would generate energy by burning wood in a fireplace. The process of burning wood extracts energy by breaking and rearranging chemical bonds among atoms in the wood. Chemical bonds are formed by the electrons in atoms, and you saw in Chapter 7 that the electrons are bound to the atoms by the electromagnetic force. So the chemical energy released when these bonds are broken and rearranged originates in the electromagnetic force.

There are only four forces in nature: the force of gravity, the electromagnetic force, the **weak force,** and the **strong force.** The weak force is involved in the radioactive decay of certain kinds of nuclear particles, and the strong force binds together atomic nuclei. The weak force and the strong force are both much stronger than either gravity or the electromagnetic force, but they are short-range forces that are effective only within the nuclei of atoms. Nuclear reactions break and reform the bonds that hold atomic nuclei together, so nuclear energy comes from the strong force. (In a later chapter you will learn that physicists have discovered the electromagnetic force and the weak force are actually different aspects of one force, and they have a goal of eventually finding a way to "unify" all four forces, including gravity, within one general mathematical description).

There are two ways to generate energy from atomic nuclei. Nuclear power plants on Earth generate energy through **nuclear fission** reactions that split uranium nuclei into less massive fragments. A uranium nucleus contains a total of 235 protons and neutrons, and when it decays, it splits into a range of possible fragments, each containing roughly half as many particles. Because the fragments that are produced are more tightly bound than the uranium nuclei, binding energy is released during uranium fission.

Stars don't use nuclear fission. They make energy in **nuclear fusion** reactions that combine light nuclei into heavier nuclei. The most common reaction inside stars, the one that occurs in the sun, fuses hydrogen nuclei (single protons) into helium nuclei, which contain two protons and two neutrons. Because the nuclei produced are more tightly bound than the original nuclei, energy is released.

■ Figure 8-8 shows how tightly different atomic nuclei are bound. The lower in the diagram, the more tightly the particles in a nucleus are held. Notice that both fusion and fission reactions move downward in the diagram toward more tightly bound nuclei. They both produce energy by releasing binding energy of atomic nuclei.

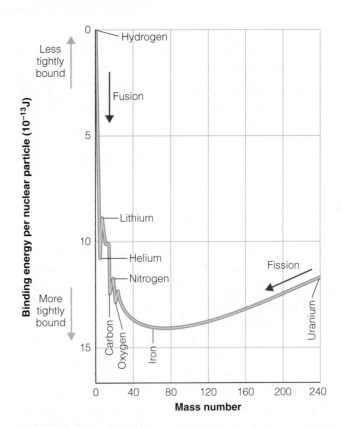

■ **Figure 8-8**

The red line in this graph shows the binding energy per particle, the energy that holds particles inside an atomic nucleus. The horizontal axis shows the atomic mass number of each element, the number of protons and neutrons in the nucleus. Both fission and fusion nuclear reactions move downward in the diagram (arrows), meaning the nucleus produced by a reaction is more tightly bound than the nuclei that went into the reaction. Iron has the most tightly bound nucleus, so no nuclear reactions can begin with iron and release energy.

---

*Astronomers sometimes use unhelpful words when they talk about nuclear reactions inside stars. They may use words like *burn* or *ignite*. What goes on inside stars is not related to simple burning but is comprised of nuclear reactions.

Hydrogen Fusion

The sun fuses together four hydrogen nuclei to make one helium nucleus. Because one helium nucleus has 0.7 percent less mass than four hydrogen nuclei, it seems that some mass vanishes in the process. To see this, subtract the mass of a helium nucleus from the mass of four hydrogen nuclei:

$$
\begin{aligned}
4 \text{ hydrogen nuclei} &= 6.693 \times 10^{-27} \text{ kg} \\
-1 \text{ helium nucleus} &= 6.645 \times 10^{-27} \text{ kg} \\
\hline
\text{Difference in mass} &= 0.048 \times 10^{-27} \text{ kg}
\end{aligned}
$$

This small amount of mass does not actually disappear but is converted to energy according to Einstein's famous equation:

$$
\begin{aligned}
E &= mc^2 \\
&= (0.048 \times 10^{-27} \text{ kg}) \times (3.0 \times 10^8 \text{ m/s})^2 \\
&= 0.43 \times 10^{-11} \text{ J}
\end{aligned}
$$

You can symbolize the fusion reactions in the sun with a simple nuclear reaction:

$$4 \, ^1\text{H} \rightarrow \, ^4\text{He} + \text{energy}$$

In this equation, ^1H represents a proton, the nucleus of a hydrogen atom, and ^4He represents the nucleus of a helium atom. The superscripts indicate the approximate weight of the nuclei (the number of protons plus the number of neutrons). The actual steps in the process are more complicated than this convenient summary suggests. Instead of waiting for four hydrogen nuclei to collide simultaneously, a highly unlikely event, the process normally proceeds step by step in a chain of reactions—the proton–proton chain.

The **proton–proton chain** is a series of three nuclear reactions that builds a helium nucleus by adding together protons. This process can only happen at temperatures above about 4 million K, and is efficient above 10 million K. The sun makes over 90 percent of its energy in this way.

The three steps in the proton–proton chain entail these reactions:

$$
\begin{aligned}
^1\text{H} + \, ^1\text{H} &\rightarrow \, ^2\text{H} + e^+ + \nu \\
^2\text{H} + \, ^1\text{H} &\rightarrow \, ^3\text{He} + \gamma \\
^3\text{He} + \, ^3\text{He} &\rightarrow \, ^4\text{He} + \, ^1\text{H} + \, ^1\text{H}
\end{aligned}
$$

In the first reaction, two hydrogen nuclei (two protons) combine and emit a particle called a **positron,** e^+ (a positively charged electron), and a **neutrino,** ν (a subatomic particle having an extremely low mass and a velocity nearly equal to the velocity of light). The emission of the positively charged positron results from the conversion of one of the protons into a neutron, and that forms a heavy hydrogen nucleus called **deuterium,** which contains a proton and a neutron. In the second reaction, the heavy hydrogen nucleus absorbs another proton and, with the emission of a gamma ray, γ, becomes a lightweight helium nucleus. Finally, two lightweight helium nuclei combine to form a nucleus of normal helium and two hydrogen nuclei. Because the last reaction needs two ^3He nuclei, the first and second reactions must occur twice (■ Figure 8-9). The net result of this chain reaction is the transformation of four hydrogen nuclei into one helium nucleus plus energy.

The energy appears in the form of gamma rays, positrons, neutrinos and the energy of motion of all the particles. The gamma rays are photons that are absorbed by the surrounding gas before they can travel more than a fraction of a millimeter. This heats the gas. The positrons produced in the first reaction combine with free electrons, and both particles vanish, converting their mass into gamma rays, which are absorbed and also help keep the gas hot. In addition, when fusion produces new nuclei, they fly apart at high velocity and collide with other particles. This energy of motion helps raise the temperature of the gas. The neutrinos, on the other hand, don't heat the gas. Neutrinos are particles that almost never interact with other particles. The average neutrino could pass unhindered through a lead wall a light-year thick. Consequently, the neutrinos do not warm the gas but race out of the sun at nearly the speed of light, carrying away roughly 2 percent of the energy produced.

■ **Figure 8-9**

The proton–proton chain combines four protons (at far left) to produce one helium nucleus (at right). Energy is produced mostly as gamma rays and as positrons, which combine with electrons and convert their mass into energy. Neutrinos escape, carrying away about 2 percent of the energy produced.

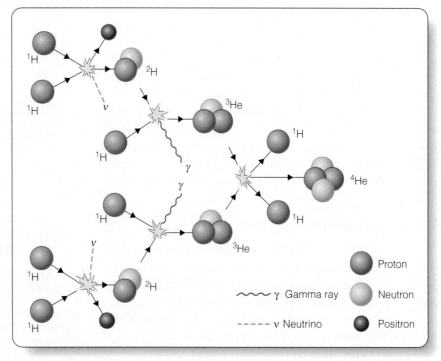

Creating one helium nucleus makes only a small amount of energy, hardly enough to raise a housefly one-thousandth of an inch. Because one reaction produces such a small amount of energy, it is obvious that many reactions are necessary to supply the energy needs of a star. The sun, for example, completes 10^{38} reactions per second, transforming 5 million tons of matter into energy every second. It might sound as if the sun is losing mass at a furious rate, but in its entire 10-billion-year lifetime, the sun will convert less than 0.07 percent of its mass into energy.

It is a **Common Misconception** that nuclear fusion in the sun is tremendously powerful. After all, the fusion of a milligram of hydrogen (roughly the mass of a match head) produces as much energy as burning 30 gallons of gasoline. However, at any one time, only a tiny fraction of the hydrogen atoms are fusing into helium, and the nuclear reactions in the sun are spread through a large volume in its core. Any single gram of matter produces only a little energy. A person of normal mass eating a normal diet produces about 4000 times more heat per gram than the matter in the core of the sun. Gram for gram, you are a much better heat producer than the sun. The sun produces a lot of energy because it contains a lot of grams of matter in its core.

Fusion reactions can occur only when the nuclei of two atoms get very close to each other. Because atomic nuclei carry positive charges, they repel each other with an electrostatic force called the Coulomb force. Physicists commonly refer to this repulsion between nuclei as the **Coulomb barrier.** To overcome this barrier and get close together, atomic nuclei must collide violently. Sufficiently violent collisions are rare unless the gas is very hot, in which case the nuclei move at high enough speeds. (Remember, an object's temperature is related to the speed with which its particles move.)

Nevertheless, the fusion of two protons is a highly unlikely process. If you could follow a single proton in the sun's core, you would see it encountering and bouncing off other protons millions of times a second, but you would have to follow it around for roughly a billion years before it happened to penetrate the Coulomb barrier and combine with another proton.

Because of the dependence of nuclear reactions on particle collisions, the reactions in the sun take place only near the center, where the gas is hot and dense. A high temperature ensures that collisions between nuclei are violent, and a high density ensures that there are enough collisions, and thus enough reactions, to make energy at the sun's rate.

Energy Transport in the Sun

Now you are ready to follow the energy from the core of the sun to the surface. You will learn in a later chapter that astronomers have computed models indicating that the temperature at the center of the sun is about 15 million K. Compared with that, the sun's surface is very cool, only about 5800 K, so energy must flow from the high temperature core outward to the cooler surface where it is radiated into space.

Because the core is so hot, the photons bouncing around there are gamma rays. Each time a gamma ray encounters an electron, it is deflected or scattered in a random direction, and, as it bounces around, it slowly drifts outward toward the surface. That carries energy outward in the form of radiation, so astronomers refer to the inner parts of the sun as a **radiative zone.**

To examine this process, imagine picking a single gamma ray and following it to the surface. As your gamma ray is scattered over and over by the hot gas, it drifts outward into cooler layers, where the cooler gas tends to emit photons of longer wavelength. Your gamma ray will eventually be absorbed by the gas and reemitted as two X-rays. Now you must follow those two X-rays as they bounce around, and soon you will see them drifting outward into even cooler gas, where they will become a number of longer-wavelength photons.

The packet of energy you have been following, now represented by many photons, eventually reaches the outer layers of the sun, where the gas is so cool that it is not very transparent to radiation. There, energy backs up like water behind a dam, and the gas begins to churn in convection. Hot blobs of gas rise, and cool blobs sink. In this region, known as a **convective zone,** your packet of energy is carried outward not as photons but as circulating gas (■ Figure 8-10). Rising hot gas carries energy outward, of course, but sinking cool gas is a necessary part of the cycle that results in the net transport of energy outward.

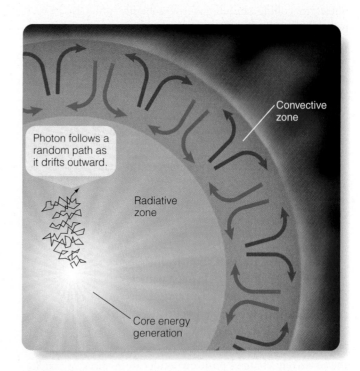

■ Figure 8-10

A cross-section of the sun. Near the center, nuclear fusion reactions generate high temperatures. Energy flows outward through the radiative zone as photons are randomly deflected over and over by electrons. In the cooler, more opaque outer layers, the energy is carried by rising convection currents of hot gas (red arrows) and sinking currents of cooler gas (blue arrows).

Scientific Confidence

How can scientists be certain of something?
Sometimes scientists stick so firmly to their ideas in the face of contradictory claims that it sounds as if they are stubbornly refusing to consider alternatives. To see why they do this, consider the perpetual motion machine, a device that supposedly runs continuously with no source of energy. If you could invest in a real perpetual motion machine, you could sell cars that would run without any fuel. That's good mileage.

For centuries people have claimed to have invented perpetual motion machines, and for just as long scientists have been dismissing these claims as impossible. The problem with a perpetual motion machine is that it violates the law of conservation of energy, and scientists are not willing to accept that the law could be wrong. In fact, the Royal Academy of Sciences in Paris was so sure that a perpetual motion machine was impossible, and so tired of debunking hoaxes, that in 1775 they issued a formal statement refusing to deal with them. The U.S. Patent Office is so skeptical that they won't even consider granting a patent for one without seeing a working model first. Why do scientists seem so stubborn and close-minded on this issue?

Why isn't one person's belief in perpetual motion just as valid as another person's belief

in the law of conservation of energy? In fact, the two positions are not equally valid. The confidence physicists have in their law is not a belief or even an opinion; it is an understanding founded on the fact that the law has been tested uncountable times and has never failed. The law is a fundamental truth about nature and can be used to understand what is possible and what is impossible. In contrast, no one has ever successfully demonstrated a perpetual motion machine.

When the first observations of solar neutrinos detected fewer than were predicted, some scientists speculated that astronomers misunderstood how the sun makes its energy or that they misunderstood the internal structure of the sun. But many astronomers stubbornly refused to reject their model because the nuclear physics of the proton–proton chain is well understood, and models of the sun's structure have been tested successfully many times. The confidence astronomers felt in their understanding of the sun was an example of scientific certainty, and that confidence in basic natural laws prevented them from abandoning decades of work in the face of a single contradictory observation.

For centuries, people have tried to design a perpetual motion machine, but not a single one has ever worked. Scientists understand why.

What seems to be stubbornness among scientists is really their confidence in basic principles that have been tested over and over. Those principles are the keel that keeps the ship of science from rocking before every little breeze. Without even looking at that perpetual motion machine, your physicist friends can warn you not to invest.

It can take a million years for the energy from a single gamma ray to work its way outward first as radiation and then as convection. When the energy finally reaches the photosphere, it is radiated into space as about 1800 photons of visible light.

It is time to ask the critical question that lies at the heart of science. What is the evidence to support this theoretical explanation of how the sun makes its energy?

Counting Solar Neutrinos

Nuclear reactions in the sun's core produce floods of neutrinos that rush out of the sun and off into space. Over 10^{12} solar neutrinos flow through your body every second, but you never feel them because you are almost perfectly transparent to neutrinos. If you could detect these neutrinos, you could probe the sun's interior. You can't focus neutrinos with a lens or mirror, and they zip right through detectors used to count other atomic particles, but neutrinos of certain energies can trigger the radioactive decay of certain atoms. That gives astronomers a way to count solar neutrinos.

In the 1960s, chemist Raymond Davis Jr. devised a way to count neutrinos produced by hydrogen fusion in the sun. He buried a 100,000-gallon tank of cleaning fluid (perchloroethylene, C_2Cl_4) in the bottom of a South Dakota gold mine where cosmic rays could not reach it (■ Figure 8-11a) and counted the number of times a neutrino triggered a chlorine atom into becoming an argon atom. He expected to detect one neutrino a day, but he actually counted one-third as many as expected, only one every three days.

The Davis neutrino experiment created a huge controversy. Were scientists wrong about nuclear fusion in the sun? Did they misunderstand how neutrinos behave? Was the detector not working properly? Because astronomers had great confidence in their understanding of the solar interior, they didn't abandon their theories immediately (**How Do We Know? 8-1**). It took over 30 years, but eventually physicists were able to build better detectors, and they discovered that neutrinos oscillate among three different types, which physicists call flavors. Nuclear reactions in

■ Figure 8-11

(a) The Davis solar neutrino experiment used cleaning fluid and could detect only one of the three flavors of neutrinos. (Brookhaven National Laboratory) (b) The Sudbury Neutrino Observatory is a 12-meter-diameter globe containing water rich in deuterium (heavy hydrogen) in place of ordinary hydrogen. Buried 2100 m (6800 ft) deep in an Ontario mine, it can detect all three flavors of neutrinos and confirms that neutrinos oscillate. (Photo courtesy of SNO)

the sun produce only one flavor, and the Davis experiment was designed to detect (taste) that flavor. But during the 8-minute journey from the sun's core to Earth, the neutrinos oscillated so much that they were evenly distributed among the three different flavors by the time they arrived at Earth. That's why the Davis experiment detected only one-third of the number predicted.

The missing neutrinos have been detected by more sophisticated detectors (Figure 8-11b). In 2007, scientists announced that a supersensitive experiment in a tunnel under the Italian Alps had detected 50 neutrinos a day coming from the sun. The neutrinos have lower energies that those caught by the Davis experiment and are produced by a side reaction that produces beryllium-7. The number of neutrinos detected matches the prediction of models of nuclear fusion in the sun.

The center of the sun seems forever beyond human experience, but counting solar neutrinos provides evidence to confirm the theories. The sun makes its energy through nuclear fusion.

SCIENTIFIC ARGUMENT

Why does nuclear fusion require that the gas be very hot?
This argument has to include the basic physics of atoms and thermal energy. Inside a star, the gas is so hot it is ionized, which means the electrons have been stripped off the atoms leaving bare, positively charged nuclei. In the case of hydrogen, the nuclei are single protons. These atomic nuclei repel each other because of their positive charges, so they must collide with each other at high velocity if they are to overcome that repulsion and get close enough together to fuse. If the atoms in a gas are moving rapidly, then the gas must have a high temperature, so nuclear fusion requires that the gas be very hot. If the gas is cooler than about 4 million K, hydrogen can't fuse because the protons don't collide violently enough to overcome the repulsion of their positive charges.

It is easy to see why nuclear fusion in the sun requires high temperature, but now expand your argument. **Why does it require high density?**

8-3 Solar Activity

THE SUN IS NOT QUIET. It is home to slowly changing spots larger than Earth and vast eruptions that dwarf human imagination. All of these seemingly different forms of solar activity have one thing in common—magnetic fields. The weather on the sun is magnetic.

Observing the Sun

Solar activity is often visible with even a small telescope, but you should be very careful if you try to observe the sun. Sunlight is intense, and when it enters your eye it is absorbed and converted into thermal energy. The infrared radiation in sunlight is especially dangerous because your eyes can't detect it. You don't sense how intense the infrared is, but it is converted to thermal energy in your eyes and can burn and scar your retinas.

(a) Looking through a telescope at the sun is dangerous, but you can always view the sun safely with a small telescope by projecting its image on a white screen. (b) If you sketch the location and structure of sunspots on successive days, you will see the rotation of the sun and gradual changes in the size and structure of sunspots, just as Galileo did in 1610.

It is not safe to look directly at the sun, and it is even more dangerous to look at the sun through any optical instrument such as a telescope, binoculars, or even the viewfinder of a camera. The light-gathering power of such an optical system concentrates the sunlight and can cause severe injury. Never look at the sun with any optical instrument unless you are certain it is safe. ■ Figure 8-12a shows a safe way to observe the sun with a small telescope.

In the early 17th century, Galileo observed the sun and saw spots on its surface; day by day he saw the spots moving across the sun's disk. He rightly concluded that the sun was a sphere and was rotating. If you repeated his observations, you would probably also detect sunspots, a view that would look something like Figure 8-12b.

Sunspots

The dark sunspots that you see at visible wavelengths only hint at the complex processes that go on in the sun's atmosphere. To explore those processes, you must analyze images and spectra at a wide range of wavelengths.

Study **Sunspots and the Sunspot Cycle** on pages 156–157 and notice five important points and four new terms:

1 Sunspots are cool spots on the sun's surface caused by strong magnetic fields.

2 Sunspots follow an 11-year cycle, becoming more numerous, reaching a maximum, and then becoming much less numerous. The *Maunder butterfly diagram* shows how the location of sunspots changes during a cycle.

3 The *Zeeman effect* gives astronomers a way to measure the strength of magnetic fields on the sun and provide evidence that sunspots contain strong magnetic fields.

4 The intensity of the sunspot cycle can vary from cycle to cycle and appears to have almost faded away during the *Maunder minimum* in the late 17th century. That seems to have affected Earth's climate.

5 The evidence is clear that sunspots are part of *active regions* dominated by magnetic fields that involve all layers of the sun's atmosphere.

The sunspot groups are merely the visible traces of magnetically active regions. But what causes this magnetic activity? The answer is linked to the growth and decay cycle of the sun's overall magnetic field.

Sunspots and the Sunspot Cycle

1 The dark spots that appear on the sun are only the visible traces of complex regions of activity. Observations over many years and at a range of wavelengths tell you that sunspots are clearly linked to the sun's magnetic field.

Spectra show that sunspots are cooler than the photosphere with a temperature of about 4200 K. The photosphere has a temperature of about 5800 K. Because the total amount of energy radiated by a surface depends on its temperature raised to the fourth power, sunspots look dark in comparison. Actually, a sunspot emits quite a bit of radiation. If the sun were removed and only an average-size sunspot were left behind, it would be brighter than the full moon.

Visual wavelength image

Umbra

Penumbra

A typical sunspot is about twice the size of Earth, but there is a wide range of sizes. They appear, last a few weeks to as long as 2 months, and then shrink away. Usually, sunspots occur in pairs or complex groups.

Earth to scale

NASA

Sunspots are not shadows, but astronomers refer to the dark core of a sunspot as its umbra and the outer, lighter region as the penumbra.

Hinode JAXA/NASA

Streamers above a sunspot suggest a magnetic field.

Hinode JAXA/NASA

2 The number of spots visible on the sun varies in a cycle with a period of 11 years. At maximum, there are often over 100 spots visible. At minimum, there are very few.

Sunspot minimum

Sunspot maximum

2a Early in the cycle, spots appear at high latitudes north and south of the sun's equator. Later in the cycle, the spots appear closer to the sun's equator. If you plot the latitude of sunspots versus time, the graph looks like butterfly wings, as shown in this **Maunder butterfly diagram,** named after E. Walter Maunder of Greenwich Observatory.

3 Astronomers can measure magnetic fields on the sun using the **Zeeman effect** as shown below. When an atom is in a magnetic field, the electron orbits are altered, and the atom is able to absorb a number of different wavelength photons even though it was originally limited to a single wavelength. In the spectrum, you see single lines split into multiple components, with the separation between the components proportional to the strength of the magnetic field.

Sunspot groups

Magnetic fields around sunspot groups

Ultraviolet filtergram

Magnetic image

Simultaneous images

J. Harvey/NSO and HAO/NCAR

Slit allows light from sunspot to enter spectrograph.

AURA/NOAO/NSF

Visual

Spectral line split by Zeeman effect

3a Images of the sun above show that sunspots contain magnetic fields a few thousand times stronger than Earth's. The strong fields are believed to inhibit gas motion below the photosphere; consequently, convection is reduced below the sunspot, and the surface there is cooler. Heat prevented from emerging through the sunspot is deflected and emerges around the sunspot, which can be detected in ultraviolet and infrared images.

4 Historical records show that there were very few sunspots from about 1645 to 1715, a phenomenon known as the **Maunder minimum.** This coincides with a period called the "little ice age," a period of unusually cool weather in Europe and North America from about 1500 to about 1850, as shown in the graph at left. Other such periods of cooler climate are known. The evidence suggests that there is a link between solar activity and the amount of solar energy Earth receives. This link has been confirmed by measurements made by spacecraft above Earth's atmosphere.

Chart: **Number of sunspots** vs **Year** (1650 to 2000)
- Maunder minimum few spots colder winters
- Winter severity in London and Paris
- Warmer winters
- ↑ Warm / ↓ Cold

Magnetic fields can reveal themselves by their shape. For example, iron filings sprinkled over a bar magnet reveal an arched shape.

M. Seeds

5 Observations at nonvisible wavelengths reveal that the chromosphere and corona above sunspots are violently disturbed in what astronomers call **active regions.** Spectrographic observations show that active regions contain powerful magnetic fields. Arched structures above an active region are evidence of gas trapped in magnetic fields.

Far-UV image

The complexity of an active region becomes visible at short wavelengths.

Visual-wavelength image

Simultaneous images

Far-UV image

NASA/TRACE

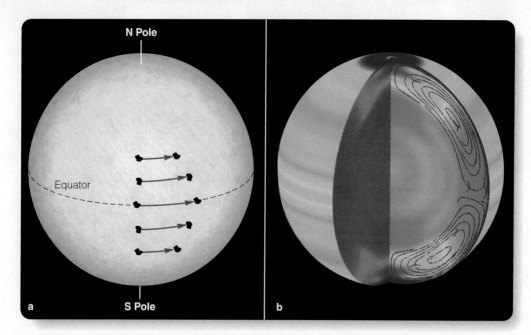

(a) In general, the photosphere of the sun rotates faster at the equator than at higher latitudes. If you started five sunspots in a row, they would not stay lined up as the sun rotates. (b) Detailed analysis of the sun's rotation from helioseismology reveals regions of slow rotation (blue) and rapid rotation (red). Such studies show that the interior of the sun rotates differentially and that currents similar to the trade winds in Earth's atmosphere flow through the sun. (NASA/SOI)

The Sun's Magnetic Cycle

The sun's magnetic field is powered by the energy flowing outward through the moving currents of gas. The gas is highly ionized, so it is a very good conductor of electricity. When an electrical conductor rotates and is stirred by convection, it can convert some of the energy flowing outward as convection into a magnetic field. This process is called the **dynamo effect,** and it is understood also to operate in Earth's core and produce Earth's magnetic field. Helioseismologists have found evidence that the dynamo effect generates the sun's magnetic field at the bottom of the convection zone deep under the photosphere.

The sun's magnetic field cannot be as stable as Earth's. The sun does not rotate as a rigid body. It is a gas from its outermost layers down to its center, so some parts of the sun can rotate faster than other parts. The equatorial region of the photosphere rotates faster than do regions at higher latitudes (■ Figure 8-13a). At the equator, the photosphere rotates once every 25 days, but at latitude 45° one rotation takes 27.8 days. Helioseismology can map the rotation throughout the interior (Figure 8-13b) and has found that different levels in the sun rotate with different periods. This phenomenon is called **differential rotation,** and it is clearly linked with the magnetic cycle.

Although the magnetic cycle is not fully understood, the **Babcock model** (named for its inventor) explains the magnetic cycle as a progressive tangling of the solar magnetic field. Because the electrons in an ionized gas are free to move, the gas is a very good conductor of electricity, so any magnetic field in the gas is "frozen" into it. If the gas moves, the magnetic field must move with it. Differential rotation drags the magnetic field along and wraps it around the sun like a long string caught on a turning

hubcap. Rising and sinking gas currents twist the field into rope-like tubes, which tend to float upward. The model predicts that sunspot pairs occur where these magnetic tubes burst through the sun's surface (■ Figure 8-14).

Sunspots tend to occur in groups or pairs, and the magnetic field around the pair resembles that around a bar magnet with one end magnetic north and the other end magnetic south, just as you would expect if a magnetic tube emerged through one sunspot in a pair and reentered through the other. At any one time, sunspot pairs south of the sun's equator have reversed polarity compared with those north of the sun's equator. ■ Figure 8-15 illustrates this by showing sunspot pairs south of the sun's equator moving with magnetic south poles leading, and sunspots north of the sun's equator moving with magnetic north poles leading. At the end of an 11-year sunspot cycle, the new spots appear with reversed magnetic polarity.

The Babcock model accounts for the reversal of the sun's magnetic field from cycle to cycle. As the magnetic field becomes tangled, adjacent regions of the sun are dominated by magnetic fields that point in different directions. After about 11 years of tangling, the field becomes so complex that adjacent regions of the sun begin changing their magnetic field to agree with neighboring regions. The entire field quickly rearranges itself into a simpler pattern, and differential rotation begins winding it up to start a new cycle. But the newly organized field is reversed, and the next sunspot cycle begins with magnetic north replaced by magnetic south. Consequently, the complete magnetic cycle is 22 years long, and the sunspot cycle is 11 years long.

This magnetic cycle also explains the Maunder butterfly diagram. As a sunspot cycle begins, the twisted tubes of magnetic force first begin to float upward and produce sunspot pairs at

The Solar Magnetic Cycle

Magnetic field line

Sun

For simplicity, a single line of the solar magnetic field is shown.

Differential rotation drags the equatorial part of the magnetic field ahead.

As the sun rotates, the magnetic field is eventually dragged all the way around.

Differential rotation wraps the sun in many turns of its magnetic field.

Where loops of tangled magnetic field rise through the surface, sunspots occur.

Bipolar sunspot pair

■ **Figure 8-14**

The Babcock model of the solar magnetic cycle explains the sunspot cycle as a consequence of the sun's differential rotation gradually winding up the magnetic field near the base of the sun's outer, convective layer.

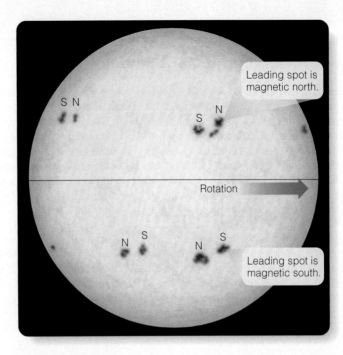

Leading spot is magnetic north.

Rotation

Leading spot is magnetic south.

■ **Figure 8-15**

In sunspot groups, here simplified into pairs of major spots, the leading spot and the trailing spot have opposite magnetic polarity. Spot pairs in the southern hemisphere have reversed polarity from those in the northern hemisphere.

higher latitudes on the sun. Consequently the first sunspots in a cycle appear farther north and south of the equator. Later in the cycle, when the field is more tightly wound, the tubes of magnetic force arch up through the surface closer to the equator. As a result, the later sunspot pairs in a cycle appear closer to the equator.

Notice the power of a scientific model. The Babcock model may in fact be incorrect in some details, but it provides a framework around which to organize descriptions of complex solar activity. Even though the model of the sky in Chapter 2 and the model of the atom in Chapter 7 are only partially correct, they served as organizing themes to guide your thinking. Similarly, although the precise details of the solar magnetic cycle are not yet understood, the Babcock model gives you a general picture of the behavior of the sun's magnetic field (**How Do We Know? 8-2**).

Spots and Magnetic Cycles of Other Stars

The sun seems to be a representative star, so you should expect other stars to have similar cycles of starspots and magnetic fields. This is a difficult topic, because, except for the sun, the stars are so far away that no surface detail is visible. Some stars, however, vary in brightness in ways that suggest they are mottled by dark spots. As these stars rotate, their total brightnesses change slightly, depending on the number of spots on the side facing Earth. High-precision spectroscopic analysis has even allowed astronomers to map the locations of spots on the surfaces of

Confirmation and Consolidation

What do scientists do all day? The scientific method is sometimes portrayed as a kind of assembly line where scientists crank out new hypotheses and then test them through observation. In reality, scientists don't often generate entirely new hypotheses. It is rare that an astronomer makes an observation that disproves a long-held theory and triggers a revolution in science. Then what is the daily grind of science really about?

Many observations and experiments confirm already-tested hypotheses. The biologist knows that all worker bees in a hive are sisters because they are all female, and they all had the same mother, the queen bee. A biologist can study the DNA from many workers and confirm that hypothesis. By repeatedly confirming a hypothesis, scientists build confidence in the hypothesis and may be able to extend it. Do all of the workers in a hive have the same father, or did the queen mate with more than one male drone?

Another aspect of routine science is consolidation, the linking of a hypothesis to other well-studied phenomena. A biologist can study yellow jacket wasps from a single nest and discover that the wasps, too, are sisters. There must be a queen wasp who lays all of the eggs in a nest. But in a few nests, the scientist may find two sets of unrelated sister workers. Those nests must contain two queens sharing the nest for convenience and protection. From his study of wasps, the biologist consolidates what he knows about bees with what others have learned about wasps and reveals something new: That bees and wasps have evolved in similar ways for similar reasons.

Confirmation and consolidation allow scientists to build confidence in their

A yellow jacket is a wasp from a nest containing a queen wasp. (Michael Dunham/Getty Images)

understanding and extend it to explain more about nature.

---

certain stars (■ Figure 8-16a). Such results confirm that the sunspots you see on our sun are not unusual.

Certain features found in stellar spectra are associated with magnetic fields. Regions of strong magnetic fields on the solar surface emit strongly at the central wavelengths of the two strongest lines of ionized calcium. This calcium emission appears in the spectra of other sun-like stars and suggests that these stars, too, have strong magnetic fields on their surfaces. In some cases, the strength of this calcium emission varies over periods of days or weeks and suggests that the stars have active regions and are rotating with periods similar to that of the sun. These stars presumably have sunspots ("starspots") as well.

In 1966, astronomers began a long-term project that monitored the strengths of these calcium emission features in the spectra of 91 stars with temperatures ranging from 1000 K hotter than the sun to 3000 K cooler, considered most likely to have sun-like magnetic activity on their surfaces. The observations show that the strength of the calcium emission varies over periods of years. The calcium emission averaged over the sun's disk varies with the sunspot cycle, and similar periodic variations can be seen in the spectra of some of the stars studied (Figure 8-16b). The star 107 Piscium, for example, appears to have a starspot cycle lasting nine years. At least one star, tau Bootis, has been observed to reverse its magnetic field. This kind of evidence suggests that stars like the sun have similar magnetic cycles, and that the sun is normal in this respect.

Chromospheric and Coronal Activity

The solar magnetic fields extend high into the chromosphere and corona, where they produce beautiful and powerful phenomena. Study **Magnetic Solar Phenomena** on pages 162–163 and notice three important points and seven new terms:

1 All solar activity is magnetic. The arched shapes of *prominences* are produced by magnetic fields, and *filaments* are prominences seen from above.

2 Tremendous energy can be stored in arches of magnetic field, and when two arches encounter each other a *reconnection* can release powerful eruptions called *flares*. Although these eruptions occur far from Earth, they can affect us in dramatic ways, and *coronal mass ejections (CMEs)* can trigger communications blackouts and *auroras*.

3 In some regions of the solar surface, the magnetic field does not loop back. High-energy gas from these *coronal holes* flows outward and produces much of the solar wind.

You may have heard the **Common Misconception** that an auroral display in the night sky is caused by sunlight reflecting off of the ice and snow at Earth's North Pole. It is fun to think of polar bears standing on sunlit slabs of ice, but that doesn't cause auroras. You know that auroras are produced by gases in Earth's upper atmosphere excited to glowing by energy from the solar wind.

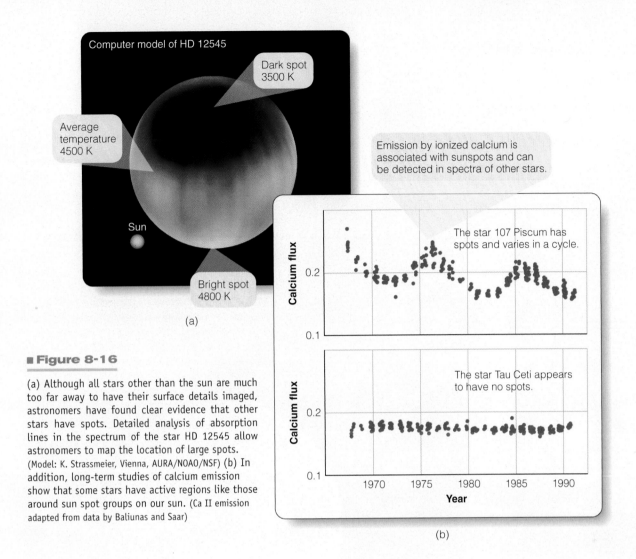

Computer model of HD 12545

Dark spot
3500 K

Average
temperature
4500 K

Sun

Bright spot
4800 K

(a)

Emission by ionized calcium is
associated with sunspots and can
be detected in spectra of other stars.

The star 107 Piscum has
spots and varies in a cycle.

Calcium flux

0.2

0.1

The star Tau Ceti appears
to have no spots.

Calcium flux

0.2

0.1

1970   1975   1980   1985   1990
Year

(b)

■ **Figure 8-16**

(a) Although all stars other than the sun are much too far away to have their surface details imaged, astronomers have found clear evidence that other stars have spots. Detailed analysis of absorption lines in the spectrum of the star HD 12545 allow astronomers to map the location of large spots. (Model: K. Strassmeier, Vienna, AURA/NOAO/NSF) (b) In addition, long-term studies of calcium emission show that some stars have active regions like those around sun spot groups on our sun. (Ca II emission adapted from data by Baliunas and Saar)

The Solar Constant

Even a small change in the sun's energy output could produce dramatic changes in Earth's climate. The continued existence of the human species depends on the constancy of the sun, but we humans know very little about the variation of the sun's energy output.

The energy production of the sun can be monitored by adding up all of the energy falling on 1 square meter of Earth's surface during 1 second. Of course, some correction for the absorption of Earth's atmosphere is necessary, and you must count all wavelengths from X-rays to radio waves. The result, which is called the **solar constant,** amounts to about 1360 joules per square meter per second. Is the sun really constant? A change in the solar constant of only 1 percent could change Earth's average temperature by about 1°C (roughly 2°F). This may not seem like much, but during the last ice age Earth's average temperature was only about 5°C cooler than it is now.

Some of the best measurements of the solar constant were made by instruments aboard the Solar Maximum Mission satellite. These have shown variations in the energy received from the sun of about 0.1 percent that lasted for days or weeks. Superimposed on that random variation is a long-term decrease of about 0.018 percent per year that has been confirmed by observations made by sounding rockets, balloons, and satellites. This long-term decrease may be related to a cycle of activity on the sun with a period longer than the 22-year magnetic cycle.

Small, random fluctuations will not affect Earth's climate, but a long-term decrease over a decade or more could cause worldwide cooling. History contains some evidence that the solar constant may have varied in the past. As you saw on page 157, the "Little Ice Age" was a period of unusually cool weather in Europe and America that lasted from about 1500 to 1850.* The average temperature worldwide was about 1°C cooler than it is now. This period of cool weather corresponded to the Maunder minimum, a period of reduced solar activity—few sunspots, no auroral displays, and no solar coronas visible during solar eclipses.

---

*Ironically, the Maunder minimum coincides with the reign of Louis XIV of France, the "Sun King."

Magnetic Solar Phenomena

1 Magnetic phenomena in the chromosphere and corona, like magnetic weather, result as constantly changing magnetic fields on the sun trap ionized gas to produce beautiful arches and powerful outbursts. Some of this solar activity can affect Earth's magnetic field and atmosphere.

This ultraviolet image of the solar surface was made by the NASA TRACE spacecraft. It shows hot gas trapped in magnetic arches extending above active regions. At visual wavelengths, you would see sunspot groups in these active regions.

Sacramento Peak Observatory

H-alpha filtergram

1a A **prominence** is composed of ionized gas trapped in a magnetic arch rising up through the photosphere and chromosphere into the lower corona. Seen during total solar eclipses at the edge of the solar disk, prominences look pink because of the three Balmer emission lines. The image above shows the arch shape suggestive of magnetic fields. Seen from above against the sun's bright surface, prominences form dark **filaments**.

Filament

H_α image

NOAA/SEL/USAF

1b Quiescent prominences may hang in the lower corona for many days, whereas eruptive prominences burst upward in hours. The eruptive prominence below is many Earth diameters long.

The gas in prominences may be 60,000 to 80,000 K, quite cold compared with the low-density gas in the corona, which may be as hot as a million Kelvin.

Trace/NASA

Far-UV image

Earth shown for size comparison

SOHO, EIT, ESA and NASA

2 Solar **flares** rise to maximum in minutes and decay in an hour. They occur in active regions where oppositely directed magnetic fields meet and cancel each other out in what astronomers call **reconnections.** Energy stored in the magnetic fields is released as short-wavelength photons and as high-energy protons and electrons. X-ray and ultraviolet photons reach Earth in 8 minutes and increase ionization in our atmosphere, which can interfere with radio communications. Particles from flares reach Earth hours or days later as gusts in the solar wind, which can distort Earth's magnetic field and disrupt navigation systems. Solar flares can also cause surges in electrical power lines and damage to Earth satellites.

This multiwavelength image shows a sunspot interacting with a neighboring magnetic field to produce a solar flare.

Hinode JAXA/NASA

2a At right, waves rush outward at 50 km/sec from the site of a solar flare 40,000 times stronger than the 1906 San Francisco earthquake. The biggest solar flares can be a billion times more powerful than a hydrogen bomb.

Helioseismology image

SOHO/MDI, ESA, and NASA

2b The solar wind, enhanced by eruptions on the sun, interacts with Earth's magnetic field and can create electrical currents up to a million megawatts. Those currents flowing down into a ring around Earth's magnetic poles excite atoms in Earth's upper atmosphere to emit photons as shown below. Seen from Earth's surface, the gas produces glowing clouds and curtains of **aurora.**

Auroras occur about 130 km above the Earth's surface.

Coronal mass ejection

Ring of aurora around the north magnetic pole

NSSDC, Holzworth and Meng

2c Magnetic reconnections can release enough energy to blow large amounts of ionized gas outward from the corona in **coronal mass ejections (CMEs).** If a CME strikes Earth, it can produce especially violent disturbances in Earth's magnetic field.

X-ray image

Coronal hole

Yohkoh/ISAS/NASA

3 Much of the solar wind comes from **coronal holes,** where the magnetic field does not loop back into the sun. These open magnetic fields allow ionized gas in the corona to flow away as the solar wind. The dark area in this X-ray image at right is a coronal hole.

In contrast, an earlier period called the Grand Maximum, lasting from about AD 1100 to about 1250, saw a warming of Earth's climate. The Vikings were able to explore and colonize Greenland, and native communities in parts of North America were forced to abandon their settlements because of long droughts. The Grand Maximum may have been caused by a small change in solar activity, but the evidence is not conclusive.

Other minima and maxima have been found in climate data taken from studies of the growth rings of trees. In good years, trees add a thicker growth ring than in poor years, so measuring tree rings can reveal the climate in the past. Evidently, solar activity can increase or decrease the solar constant very slightly and affect Earth's climate in dramatic ways. The future of our civilization on Earth may depend on our learning to understand the solar constant.

SCIENTIFIC ARGUMENT

What kind of activity would the sun have if it didn't rotate differentially?

Once again, it can help you understand a concept by constructing an argument with one factor changed. Begin by thinking about the Babcock model. If the sun didn't rotate differentially, its equator traveling faster than its higher latitudes, then the magnetic field might not get wound up, and there might not be a solar cycle. Twisted tubes of magnetic field might not form and rise through the photosphere to produce prominences and flares, although convection might tangle the magnetic field slightly and produce some activity. Is the magnetic activity that heats the chromosphere and corona driven by differential rotation or by convection? It is hard to guess; but, without differential rotation, the sun might not have a strong magnetic field and high-temperature gas above its photosphere.

This is very speculative, but speculating within a scientific argument can be revealing. For example, redo the argument above. **What do you think the sun would be like if it had no convection inside?**

What Are We? Sunlight

We live very close to a star and depend on it for survival. All of our food comes from sunlight that was captured by plants on land or by plankton in the oceans. We either eat those plants directly or eat the animals that feed on those plants. Whether you had salad, seafood, or a cheeseburger for supper last night, you dined on sunlight, thanks to photosynthesis.

Almost all of the energy that powers human civilization came from the sun through photosynthesis in ancient plants that were buried and converted to coal, oil, and natural gas. New technology is making energy from plant products like corn, soy beans, and sugar. It is all stored sunlight. Windmills generate electrical power, and the wind blows because of heat from the sun. Photocells make electricity directly from sunlight. Even our bodies have adapted to use sunlight to manufacture vitamin D.

Our planet is warmed by the sun, and without that warmth the oceans would be ice and much of the atmosphere would be a coating of frost. Books often refer to the sun as "our sun" or "our star." It is ours in the sense that we live beside it and by its light and warmth, but we can hardly say it belongs to us. It is better to say that we belong to the sun.

Study and Review

Summary

▶ The sun is very bright, and its light and infrared radiation can burn your eyes, so you must take great care in observing it. At sunset or sunrise when it is safe to look at the sun, you see the sun's photosphere, the level in the sun from which visible photons most easily escape. Dark **sunspots (p. 143)** come and go on the sun, but only rarely are they large enough to be visible to the unaided eye.

▶ The solar atmosphere consists of three layers of hot, low-density gas: the photosphere, chromosphere, and corona.

▶ The **granulation (p. 144)** of the photosphere is produced by **convection (p. 145)** currents of hot gas rising from below. Larger **supergranules (p. 145)** appear to be caused by larger convection currents deeper in the sun.

▶ The edge or **limb (p. 145)** of the solar disk is dimmer than the center. This **limb darkening (p. 145)** is evidence that the temperature in the solar atmosphere increases with depth.

▶ The chromosphere is most easily visible during total solar eclipses, when it flashes into view for a few seconds. It is a thin, hot layer of gas just above the photosphere, and its pink color is caused by the Balmer emission lines in its spectrum.

▶ **Filtergrams (p. 146)** of the chromosphere reveal **spicules (p. 146)**, flamelike structures extending upward into the lower corona.

- The corona is the sun's outermost atmospheric layer and can be imaged using a **coronagraph (p. 146)**. It is composed of a very-low-density, very hot gas extending many solar radii from the visible sun. Its high temperature—over 2,000,000 K—is believed to be maintained by the magnetic field extending up through the photosphere—the **magnetic carpet (p. 147)**—and by magnetic waves coming from below the photosphere.

- Parts of the corona give rise to the **solar wind (p. 147)**, a breeze of low-density ionized gas streaming away from the sun.

- Solar astronomers can study the motion, density, and temperature of gases inside the sun by analyzing the way the solar surface oscillates. Known as **helioseismology (p. 148)**, this field of study requires large amounts of data and extensive computer analysis.

- There are only four forces in nature: the electromagnetic force, the gravitational force, the **weak force (p. 150)**, and the **strong force (p. 150)**. In nuclear fission or nuclear fusion, the energy comes from the strong force. Physicists are working on unifying the four forces under one mathematical description.

- Nuclear reactors on Earth generate energy through **nuclear fission (p. 150)**, during which large nuclei such as uranium break into smaller fragments. The sun generates its energy through **nuclear fusion (p. 150)**, during which hydrogen nuclei fuse to produce helium nuclei.

- Hydrogen fusion in the sun proceeds in three steps known as the **proton–proton chain (p. 151)**. The first step in the chain combines two hydrogen nuclei to produce a heavy hydrogen nucleus called **deuterium (p. 151)**. The second step forms light helium, and the third step combines the light helium nuclei to form normal helium. Energy is released as **positrons (p. 151)**, **neutrinos (p. 151)**, gamma rays, and the rapid motion of particles flying away.

- Fusion can occur only at the center of the sun because charged particles repel each other, and high temperatures are needed to give particles high enough velocities to penetrate this **Coulomb barrier (p. 152)**. High densities are needed to provide large numbers of reactions.

- Neutrinos escape from the sun's core at nearly the speed of light, carrying away about 2 percent of the energy produced by fusion. Observations of fewer neutrinos than expected coming from the sun's core are now explained by the oscillation of neutrinos among three different types (flavors). The detection of solar neutrinos confirms the theory that the sun's energy comes from hydrogen fusion.

- Energy flows out of the sun's core as photons traveling through the **radiative zone (p. 152)** and closer to the surface as rising currents of hot gas and sinking currents of cooler gas in the **convective zone (p. 152)**.

- Sunspots seem dark because they are slightly cooler than the rest of the photosphere. The average sunspot is about twice the size of Earth. They appear for a month or so and then fade away, and the number of spots on the sun varies with an 11-year cycle.

- Early in a sunspot cycle, spots appear farther from the sun's equator, and later in the cycle they appear closer to the equator. This is shown in the **Maunder butterfly diagram (p. 155)**.

- Astronomers can use the **Zeeman effect (p. 155)** to measure magnetic fields on the sun. The average sunspot contains magnetic fields a few thousand times stronger than Earth's. This is part of the evidence that the sunspot cycle is produced by a solar magnetic cycle.

- The sunspot cycle does not repeat exactly each cycle, and the decades from 1645 to 1715, known as the **Maunder minimum (p. 155)**, seem to have been a time when solar activity was very low and Earth's climate was slightly colder.

- Sunspots are the visible consequences of **active regions (p. 155)** where the sun's magnetic field is strong. Arches of magnetic field can produce sunspots where the field passes through the photosphere.

- The sun's magnetic field is produced by the **dynamo effect (p. 158)** operating at the base of the convection zone.

- Alternate sunspot cycles have reversed magnetic polarity, which has been explained by the **Babcock model (p. 158)**, in which the **differential rotation (p. 158)** of the sun winds up the magnetic field. Tangles in the field arch above the surface and cause active regions visible to your eyes as sunspot pairs. When the field becomes strongly tangled, it reorders itself into a simpler but reversed field, and the cycle starts over.

- Arches of magnetic field are visible as **prominences (p. 162)** in the chromosphere and corona. Seen from above in filtergrams, prominences are visible as dark **filaments (p. 162)** silhouetted against the bright chromosphere.

- **Reconnections (p. 163)** of magnetic fields can produce powerful **flares (p. 163)**, sudden eruptions of X-ray, ultraviolet, and visible radiation plus high-energy atomic particles. Flares are important because they can have dramatic effects on Earth, such as communications blackouts.

- The solar wind originates in regions on the solar surface called **coronal holes (p. 163)**, where the sun's magnetic field leads out into space and does not loop back to the sun.

- **Coronal mass ejections, or CMEs (p. 163)**, occur when magnetic fields on the surface of the sun eject bursts of ionized gas that flow outward in the solar wind. Such bursts can produce **auroras (p. 163)** and other phenomena if they strike Earth.

- Other stars are too far away for starspots to be visible, but some stars vary in brightness in ways that show they have spots on their surfaces. Also, spectroscopic observations reveal that many other stars have spots and magnetic fields that follow long-term cycles like the sun's.

- Small changes in the **solar constant (p. 161)** over decades can affect Earth's climate and may be responsible or the Little Ice Age and other climate fluctuations in Earth's history.

Review Questions

1. Why can't you see deeper into the sun than the photosphere?
2. What evidence can you give that granulation is caused by convection?
3. How are granules and supergranules related? How do they differ?
4. How can astronomers detect structure in the chromosphere?
5. What evidence can you give that the corona has a very high temperature?
6. What heats the chromosphere and corona to a high temperature?
7. How are astronomers able to explore the layers of the sun below the photosphere?
8. Why does nuclear fusion require high temperatures?
9. Why does nuclear fusion in the sun occur only near the center?
10. How can astronomers detect neutrinos from the sun?
11. How did neutrino oscillation affect the detection of solar neutrinos by the Davis experiment?
12. What evidence can you give that sunspots are magnetic?
13. How does the Babcock model explain the sunspot cycle?
14. What does the spectrum of a prominence reveal? What does its shape reveal?
15. How can solar flares affect Earth?
16. **How Do We Know?** What does it mean when scientists say they are certain? What does scientific certainty really mean?
17. **How Do We Know?** How does consolidation extend scientific understanding?

Discussion Questions

1. What energy sources on Earth cannot be thought of as stored sunlight?
2. What would the spectrum of an auroral display look like? Why?

3. What observations would you make if you were ordered to set up a system that could warn astronauts in orbit of dangerous solar flares? Such a warning system exists.

Problems

1. The radius of the sun is 0.7 million km. What percentage of the radius is taken up by the chromosphere?

2. The smallest detail visible with ground-based solar telescopes is about 1 arc second. How large a region does this represent on the sun? (*Hint:* Use the small-angle formula, Chapter 3.)

3. What is the angular diameter of a star like the sun located 5 ly from Earth? Is the Hubble Space Telescope able to detect detail on the surface of such a star?

4. How much energy is produced when the sun converts 1 kg of mass into energy?

5. How much energy is produced when the sun converts 1 kg of hydrogen into helium? (*Hint:* How does this problem differ from Problem 4?)

6. A 1-megaton nuclear weapon produces about 4×10^{15} J of energy. How much mass must vanish when a 5-megaton weapon explodes?

7. A solar flare can release 10^{25} J. How many megatons of TNT would be equivalent?

8. The United States consumes about 2.5×10^{19} J of energy in all forms in a year. How many years could you run the United States on the energy released by the solar flare in Problem 7?

9. Use the luminosity of the sun, the total amount of energy it emits each second, to calculate how much mass it converts to energy each second.

10. If a sunspot has a temperature of 4200 K and the solar surface has a temperature of 5800 K, how many times brighter is a square meter of the surface compared to a square meter of the sunspot? (*Hint:* Use the Stefan–Boltzmann law, Chapter 7.)

11. Neglecting energy absorbed or reflected by Earth's atmosphere, the solar energy hitting 1 square meter of Earth's surface is 1370 J/s. How long does it take a baseball diamond (90 ft on a side) to receive 1 megaton of solar energy?

Learning to Look

1. Whenever there is a total solar eclipse, you can see something like the image shown at right. Explain why the shape and extent of the glowing gases is different for each eclipse.

NOAO

2. The two images at right show two solar phenomena. What are they, and how are they related? How do they differ?

NOAO

3. This image of the sun was recorded in the extreme ultraviolet by the SOHO spacecraft. Explain the features you see.

NASA/SOHO

The Family of Stars

Visual wavelength image

Guidepost

Science is based on measurement, but measurement in astronomy is very difficult. To discover the properties of stars, astronomers must use their telescopes and spectrographs in ingenious ways to learn the secrets hidden in starlight. The result is a family portrait of the stars.

Here you will find answers to five essential questions about stars:

— **How far away are the stars?**

— **How much energy do stars make?**

— **How big are stars?**

— **How much mass do stars contain?**

— **What is the typical star like?**

With this chapter, you leave our sun behind and begin your study of the billions of stars that dot the sky. In a sense, the star is the basic building block of the universe. If you hope to understand what the universe is, what our sun is, what our Earth is, and what we are, you need to understand stars.

Once you know how to find the basic properties of stars, you will be ready to trace the history of the stars from birth to death, a story that begins in the next chapter.

The center of the gas cloud around the star V838 Monocerotis is ablaze with the light of brilliant stars, but fainter stars also dot the image. The crosses on the star images are produced by light diffraction in the telescope. (NASA/Hubble Heritage Project)

Ice is the silent language of the peak;
and fire the silent language of the star.

— CONRAD AIKEN, *AND IN THE HUMAN HEART*

DOES YOUR FAMILY include some characters? The family of stars is amazingly diverse. In a photograph such as ■ Figure 9-1, stars seem to differ only slightly in color and brightness, but you are going to discover that some are huge and some are tiny, some are astonishingly hot and some are quite cool, some are ponderously massive and some are tiny little stars hardly massive enough to shine. If your family is as diverse as the family of stars, you may have some peculiar relatives.

Unfortunately, finding out what a star is like is quite difficult. When you look at a star, you look across a vast distance and see only a bright point of light. Just looking tells you almost nothing about a star's energy production, diameter, or mass. Rather than just look at stars, you have to analyze starlight with great care. Starlight is the silent language of the sky, and it speaks volumes.

9-1 Measuring the Distances to Stars

ALTHOUGH YOU WANT TO LEARN such things as the size and mass of stars, you immediately meet a detour. To find out almost anything about a star, you must know how far away it is. That quick detour will provide you with a method of measuring the distances to stars.

Distance is the most difficult measurement in astronomy, and astronomers have found a number of ways to estimate the distance to stars. Yet each of those ways depends on a direct geometrical method that is much like the method surveyors use to measure the distance across a river they cannot cross. You can begin by reviewing that method and then apply it to stars.

The Surveyor's Triangulation Method

To measure the distance across a river, a team of surveyors begins by driving two stakes into the ground a known distance apart. The distance between the stakes is the baseline of the measurement. The surveyors then choose a landmark on the opposite side of the river, a tree perhaps, thus establishing a large triangle marked by the two stakes and the tree. Using their surveying instruments, they sight the tree from the two ends of the baseline and measure the two angles on their side of the river (■ Figure 9-2).

Now that they know two angles of this large triangle and the length of the side between the angles, the surveyors can find the distance across the river by simple trigonometry. Another way to find the distance is to construct a scale drawing. For example, if the baseline is 50 m and the angles are 66° and 71°, you can draw a line 50 mm long to represent the baseline. Each millimeter on

■ **Figure 9-1**

The modern quest to understand the universe is symbolized in this photo of the Eta Carinae Nebula, roughly 7500 light-years from Earth. Only by the careful analysis of starlight have astronomers learned that the stars in the nebula are only 3 million years old and that the brightest star at lower left contains 100 times more matter than the sun. (2MASS Sky Survey and IPAC)

your drawing is worth 1 meter. Using a protractor, you can construct angles of 66° and 71° at each end of the baseline, and then, as shown in Figure 9-2, extend the two sides until they meet at *C*. Point *C* on your drawing is the location of the tree. If you measure the height of your triangle, you would find it to be 64 mm and thus conclude that the distance from the baseline to

■ **Figure 9-2**

You can find the distance *d* across a river by measuring the length of the baseline and the angles *A* and *B*, and then constructing a scale drawing of the triangle.

the tree is 64 m. Modern surveyors use calculators to do the math; but, however you solve the problem, the point is that simple triangulation can reveal the distance across a river.

The more distant an object is, the longer the baseline you need to measure its distance. You could use a baseline 50 m long to find the distance across a river; but, to measure the distance to a mountain on the horizon, you might need a baseline 1000 m long. Great distances require long baselines.

The Astronomer's Triangulation Method

To find the distance to a star, you must use a very long baseline, the diameter of Earth's orbit. If you take a photograph of a nearby star and then wait six months, Earth will have moved halfway around its orbit. You can then take another photograph of the star from the other side of Earth's orbit 2 AU (astronomical units) from the point where the first photograph was taken. Thus your baseline equals the diameter of Earth's orbit, or 2 AU, and lines to the star outline a long thin triangle (■ Figure 9-3).

You then have two photographs of the same part of the sky taken from slightly different locations in space. When you examine the photographs, you will discover that the nearby star is not in exactly the same place in the two photographs. This apparent shift in the position of the star is called *parallax*, the apparent

change in the position of an object due to a change in the location of the observer. In Chapter 4, you saw an everyday example. Your thumb, held at arm's length, appears to shift position against a distant background when you look with first one eye and then with the other (see page 56). In this case, the baseline is the distance between your eyes, and the parallax is the angle through which your thumb appears to move when you change eyes. The farther away you hold your thumb, the smaller the parallax.

Because the stars are so distant, their parallaxes are very small angles, usually expressed in arc seconds. The quantity that astronomers call **stellar parallax (p)** is half the total shift of the star, in other words, the shift as seen over a 1 AU baseline, as shown in Figure 9-3. Astronomers measure the parallax, and surveyors measure the angles at the ends of the baseline, but both measurements reveal the same thing—the shape and size of the triangle and thus the distance to the object in question.

Astronomers have defined a special unit of distance, the **parsec (pc),**[*] for use in distance calculations. A parsec is defined as the distance to an imaginary star with a parallax of 1 arc second. One parsec turns out to equal 2.06×10^5 AU, or 3.26 ly. This makes it very easy to calculate the distance to a star given the parallax. The formula is simply:

$$d = \frac{1}{p}$$

where the parallax, p, is expressed in arc seconds and the distance, d, is expressed in parsecs. For example, one of your Favorite Stars, Sirius, has a parallax of 0.379 arc seconds. That means the distance to Sirius in parsecs is 1 divided by 0.379, which equals 2.64 pc. If you want to convert to light-years, multiply 2.64 pc by 3.26 ly/pc, and you find that Sirius is 8.61 ly away.

Measuring the parallax p is very difficult because it is such a small angle. The star nearest the sun is one of your Favorite Stars, α Centauri. It has a parallax of only 0.742 arc seconds, and the more distant stars have even smaller parallaxes. To see how small these angles are, hold a piece of paper edgewise at arm's length. The thickness of the paper covers an angle of about 30 arc seconds.

The blurring caused by Earth's atmosphere smears star images and makes them about 1 arc second in diameter, and that makes it difficult to measure parallax from Earth. Even when astronomers average together many observations, they cannot measure parallax from an observatory on Earth with an uncertainty smaller than about 0.002 arc seconds. If you measure a parallax of

■ **Figure 9-3**

You can measure the parallax of a nearby star by photographing it from two points along Earth's orbit. For example, you might photograph it now and again in six months. Half of the star's total change in position from one photograph to the other is its stellar parallax, p.

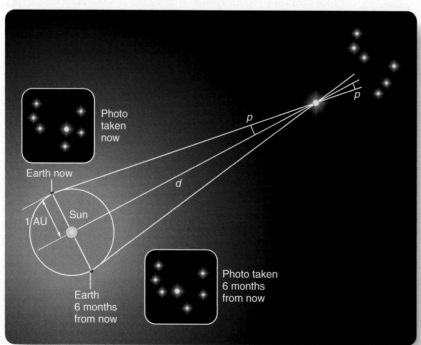

*The parsec is used throughout astronomy because it simplifies the calculation of distance. However, there are instances when the light-year is also convenient. Consequently, the chapters that follow use either parsecs or light-years as convenience and custom dictate.

0.02 arc seconds, the uncertainty is about 10 percent. Ten percent is about the largest uncertainty in a parallax measurement that astronomers can comfortably tolerate, so ground-based astronomers have not been able to measure the distance to stars farther distant than about 50 pc. Ever since the first stellar parallax was measured in 1838, ground-based astronomers have been able to measure accurate parallaxes for only about 10,000 stars.

In 1989, the European Space Agency launched the satellite Hipparcos to measure stellar parallaxes from orbit above the blurring effects of Earth's atmosphere. The satellite observed for four years, and the data were reduced by highly sophisticated software to produce two parallax catalogs in 1997. One catalog contains 120,000 stars with parallaxes 20 times more accurate than ground-based measurements. The other catalog contains over a million stars with parallaxes as accurate as ground-based parallaxes. The Hipparcos data have given astronomers new insights into the nature of stars.

The European Space Agency plans to launch the GAIA mission in a few years. It will be able to measure the parallax of a billion stars to 10 percent. NASA's planned Space Interferometry Mission will be able to measure the distances of stars out to 25,000 pc.

Proper Motion

Parallax isn't the only way to find the distances to the stars. A related technique uses the motions of the stars. All the stars in the sky, including the sun, are moving along orbits around the center of our galaxy. That motion isn't obvious over periods of years, but over the centuries it can significantly distort the shape of constellations (■ Figure 9-4). Detecting the slow drift of the stars requires high-precision measurements, but it can reveal information about the distances to the stars.

If you photograph a small area of the sky on two dates separated by 10 years or more, precise measurements would reveal that some of the stars in the photograph have moved very slightly against the background of more distant stars. This motion, expressed in units of arc seconds per year, is the **proper motion** of the stars. As examples, consider two stars from your list of Favorite Stars. Vega is a bright blue-white star in the summer sky, and it has a proper motion of 0.351 arc seconds per year. Rigel, a bright blue-white star in the winter sky, has a proper motion of only 0.002 arc seconds per year. The two stars are nearly the same brightness in the sky and nearly the same temperature, but the proper motion of Rigel is over a hundred times less than that of Vega. What does that mean?

A star might have a small proper motion if it is moving almost directly toward or away from you; then its position on the sky would change very slowly. That is unlikely, but it does happen. Another reason a star might have a small proper motion is that it could be quite far away from you. Then even if the star were moving rapidly through space, it would not have a large

The Changing Shape of the Big Dipper

100,000 years ago the Big Dipper had a different shape.

Proper motion is moving the stars of the Big Dipper across the sky.

100,000 years in the future, the Big Dipper will have a distorted shape.

■ **Figure 9-4**

Proper motion refers to the slow movement of the stars across the sky.

proper motion. That explains why Rigel, at a distance of 237 pc, has a smaller proper motion, and Vega, at a distance of only 7.76 pc, has a larger proper motion. Although Rigel is 31 times farther away than Vega, they have nearly the same brightness in the sky. Rigel must be emitting a lot more light than Vega.

Astronomers can use proper motion to look for nearby stars. If you see a star with a small (or zero) proper motion, it is probably a distant star, but a star with a large proper motion is probably quite close. You may have seen this effect if you watch birds. Distant geese move slowly across the sky, but a nearby bird flits quickly across your field of view. Proper motions can help astronomers locate nearby stars for further study.

9-2 Apparent Brightness, Intrinsic Brightness, and Luminosity

IF YOU SEE A LIGHT on a dark highway, it is hard to tell how powerful it really is. It could be the brilliant headlight on a distant truck or the dim headlight on a nearby bicycle (■ Figure 9-5).

To judge the true brightness of a light source, you need to know how far away it is. With no clues to distance, the headlight on a distant truck might look as bright as the nearby headlight on a bicycle.

Observer

How bright an object looks depends not only on how much light it emits but also on its distance.

A sixth-magnitude star just visible to your eye looks faint, but its apparent magnitude doesn't tell you how luminous it really is. Now that you know how to find the distance to stars, you can use those distances to figure out the **intrinsic brightness** of the stars. *Intrinsic* means "belonging to the thing," so the intrinsic brightness of a star refers to the total amount of light the star emits.

Brightness and Distance

When you look at a bright light, your eyes respond to the visual wavelength energy falling on your eye's retina. The apparent brightness you perceive is related to the flux of energy entering your eye. **Flux** is the energy in joules (J) per second falling on 1 square meter. Recall that a joule is about as much energy as is released when an apple falls from a table onto the floor. One joule per second is one watt, a common unit of energy consumption used, for example, to rate light bulbs.

The apparent brightness of a light source is described by the inverse square law. (You first encountered the inverse square relation in Chapter 5, where it was applied to the strength of gravity. See Figure 5-6.) If you double the distance to a light source, its brightness falls by a factor of 2^2 or 4 times. If you triple the distance, the brightness falls by a factor of 3^2, which equals 9 times. The flux of light on a surface is inversely proportional to the square of the distance from the source.

Now you can understand how the brightness of any light source depends on its distance. If you knew both the apparent magnitude of a star and its distance from Earth, you could use the inverse square law to correct for distance and learn the intrinsic brightness of the star. Astronomers do that using a special kind of magnitude scale described in the next section.

Absolute Visual Magnitude

If all stars were the same distance from Earth, you could compare one with another and decide which was emitting more light and which less. Of course, the stars are scattered at different distances, and you can't shove them around to line them up for comparison. If, however, you know the distance to a star, you can use the inverse square relation to calculate the brightness the star would have at some standard distance. Astronomers have adopted 10 pc as the standard distance and refer to the apparent visual magnitude a star would have if it were 10 pc away as its **absolute visual magnitude (M_v)**. This is an expression of the intrinsic brightness of the star.

The symbol for absolute visual magnitude is M_v. The subscript reminds you it is a visual magnitude based only on the wavelengths of light you can see. Other magnitude systems are based on other parts of the electromagnetic spectrum, such as the infrared and ultraviolet.

How does the sun stack up against other stars? Astronomers can find the sun's absolute visual magnitude because they know the distance to the sun and can measure its apparent visual magnitude. The sun is tremendously bright in the sky, but it is very close. Its absolute visual magnitude is only 4.83. If the sun were only 10 pc from Earth (not a great distance in astronomy), it would look no brighter than the faintest star in the handle of the Little Dipper.

The intrinsically brightest stars known have absolute visual magnitudes of about –8, which means that such a star 10 pc from Earth would be nearly as bright as the moon. In absolute magnitude, such stars are 13 magnitudes brighter than the sun, so they must be emitting over 100,000 times more light than the sun. Yet the intrinsically faintest stars have absolute visual magnitudes of +15 or fainter. They are ten magnitudes fainter than the sun, meaning they are emitting 10,000 times less light than the sun.

The detour to find the distance to stars had led you to absolute visual magnitude and some new insights into what stars are like.

Calculating Absolute Visual Magnitude

How exactly do astronomers find the absolute visual magnitude of a star? This question leads to one of the most important formulas in astronomy, a formula that relates a star's magnitude and its distance.

The **magnitude–distance formula** relates the apparent magnitude m_v, the absolute magnitude M_v, and the distance d in parsecs:

$$m_v - M_v = -5 + 5\log_{10}(d)$$

If you know any two of the parameters in this formula, you can easily calculate the third. If you want to find the absolute magnitude of a star, then you need to know its distance and apparent magnitude. Suppose a star has a distance of 50 pc and an apparent magnitude of 4.5. A calculator tells you that the log of 50 is 1.70, and $-5 + 5(1.70)$ equals 3.5, so you know that the star's absolute magnitude is 3.5 magnitudes brighter than its apparent magnitude. That means the absolute magnitude is 1.0 because 4.5 minus 3.5 is 1.0. (Remember that smaller numbers mean brighter magnitudes.) If this star were 10 pc away, it would look bright in the sky, a first-magnitude star.

Astronomers also use the magnitude–distance formula to calculate the distance to a star if the apparent and absolute magnitudes are known. For that purpose, it is handy to rewrite the formula in the following form:

$$d = 10^{(m_v - M_v + 5)/5}$$

If you knew that a star had an apparent magnitude of 7 and an absolute magnitude of 2, then $m_v - M_v$ is 5 magnitudes, and the distance would be 10^2 or 100 parsecs.

The magnitude difference $m_v - M_v$ is known as the **distance modulus,** a measure of how far away the star is. The larger the distance modulus, the more distant the star. You could use the magnitude–distance formula to construct a table of distance and distance modulus (■ Table 9-1).

■ **Table 9-1** | **Distance Moduli**

$m_v - M_v$	d (pc)
0	10
1	16
2	25
3	40
4	63
5	100
6	160
7	250
8	400
9	630
10	1000
.	.
.	.
.	.
15	10,000
.	.
.	.
20	100,000

The magnitude–distance formula may seem awkward at first, but a calculator makes it easy to use. The formula is important because it performs a critical function in astronomy: It allows astronomers to convert observations of distance and apparent magnitude into absolute magnitude, a measure of true brightness. Once you know the absolute magnitude, you can go one step further and figure out the total amount of energy a star is radiating into space.

Luminosity

The **luminosity (L)** of a star is the total energy the star radiates in one second. Hot stars emit a great deal of ultraviolet radiation that you can't see, and cool stars emit infrared. Because absolute visual magnitude includes only visible radiation, astronomers must add a small correction to make up for the invisible energy. Then they can calculate the luminosity of the star from its absolute magnitude.

The correction astronomers make adjusts for the radiation emitted at wavelengths humans cannot see. The absolute visual magnitudes of hot stars will underestimate their total luminosities because those stars radiate significant amounts of ultraviolet radiation. Similarly the correction for cool stars is large because they radiate significant amounts of infrared. Astronomers can correct for the missing radiation because the amount of missing energy depends only on the star's temperature. For hot and cool stars, the correction can be large, but for medium-temperature stars like the sun, the correction is small. Adding the proper correction to the absolute visual magnitude changes it into the **absolute bolometric magnitude**—the absolute magnitude the star would have if you could see all wavelengths.

To find the luminosity of a star, you compare the star with the sun. If the absolute bolometric magnitude of the star is one magnitude brighter than the sun, then it must be approximately 2.5 times more luminous. If it is five magnitudes brighter, then it must be 100 times more luminous. Astronomers would write the luminosity of the first star as 2.5 $L_\odot$ and the luminosity of the second star as 100 $L_\odot$. To find the luminosity of a star in joules per second, you can just multiply by the luminosity of the sun, 3.83×10^{26} J/s. For example, Favorite Star Aldebaran has a luminosity of about 150 $L_\odot$, which corresponds to about 6×10^{28} J/s.

Remember Favorite Stars Vega and Rigel? Earlier in this chapter you noted that they look the same in the sky, but Rigel is much further away, so it must be more luminous. Now you can calculate their luminosities and discover that Rigel is almost a thousand times more luminous than Vega.

The most luminous stars emit roughly a million times more energy than the sun, and the least luminous stars emit over a thousand times less. Although stars look similar in the sky, they can emit amazingly different amounts of energy. The most luminous emit at least a billion times more energy per second than the least luminous. Clearly, the family of stars contains some interesting characters.

SCIENTIFIC ARGUMENT

How can two stars look the same in the sky but have dramatically different luminosities?

You can answer this question by building a scientific argument that relates three factors: the appearance of a star, its true luminosity, and its distance. The farther away a star is, the fainter it looks, and that is just the inverse square law. Favorite Stars Vega and Rigel have the same apparent visual magnitude, so your eyes must be receiving the same amount of light from them. Parallax observations from the Hipparcos satellite reveal that Rigel is 31 times farther away than Vega, so Rigel is much more luminous than Vega.

Distance is often the key to understanding the brightness of stars, but temperature can also be important. Build a scientific argument to answer the following: **Why must astronomers make a correction in converting the absolute visual magnitude of very hot or very cool stars into luminosities?**

9-3 The Diameters of Stars

Now that you know the luminosities of stars, you are ready to find their diameters. You know little about stars until you know their diameters. Are they all the same size as the sun, or are some larger and some smaller?

Recall that astronomers cannot see the stars as disks through astronomical telescopes (see Chapter 6). All stars look like points of light, no matter how big the telescope. Nevertheless, there is a way to find out how big stars really are. If you know their temperatures and luminosities, you can find their diameters. This relationship will introduce you to the most important diagram in astronomy, where you will discover more of the stars' family secrets.

Luminosity, Radius, and Temperature

To use the luminosity and temperature of a star to learn its diameter, you must first understand the two factors that affect a star's luminosity, surface area and temperature. You can eat dinner by candlelight because a candle flame has a small surface area. Although the flame is very hot, it cannot radiate much heat; it has a low luminosity. However, if the candle flame were 12 ft tall, it would have a very large surface area from which to radiate, and, although it might be no hotter than a normal candle flame, its luminosity would drive you from the table (■ Figure 9-6).

In a similar way, a hot star may not be very luminous if it has a small surface area, but it could be highly luminous if it were larger and had a larger surface area from which to radiate. On the other hand, even a cool star could be luminous if it had a large surface area. Because of this dependence on both temperature and surface area, you need to separate the effects of temperature and surface area, and then you can find the diameters of stars.

Stars are spheres, and the surface area of a sphere is $4\pi R^2$. If you express radius in meters, the area is the number of square meters on the surface of the star. Each square meter radiates like a blackbody, and you will remember from Chapter 7 that the total energy given off each second from each square meter is σT^4. So the total luminosity of the star is the surface area multiplied by the energy radiated per square meter:

$$L = 4\pi R^2 \sigma T^4$$

If you divide by the same quantities for the sun, you can cancel out the constants and get a simple formula for the luminosity of a star in terms of its radius and temperature:

$$\frac{L}{L_\odot} = \left(\frac{R}{R_\odot}\right)^2 \left(\frac{T}{T_\odot}\right)^4$$

Here the symbol $\odot$ stands for the sun, and the formula says that the luminosity of a star in terms of the sun equals the radius of the star in terms of the sun squared times the temperature of the star in terms of the sun raised to the fourth power.

Suppose a star is 10 times the sun's radius but only half as hot. How luminous would it be?

$$\frac{L}{L_\odot} = \left(\frac{10}{1}\right)^2 \left(\frac{1}{2}\right)^4 = \left(\frac{100}{1}\right)\left(\frac{1}{16}\right) = 6.25$$

The star would be 6.25 times more luminous than the sun.

How can you use this formula to find the diameters of the stars? If you see a cool star that is very luminous, you know it must be very large, and if you see a hot star that is not very luminous, you know it must be very small. Suppose that a star is 40 times the luminosity of the sun and twice as hot. If you put these numbers into the formula, you get:

$$\frac{40}{1} = \left(\frac{R}{R_\odot}\right)^2 \left(\frac{2}{1}\right)^4$$

■ **Figure 9-6**

Molten lava pouring from a volcano is not as hot as a candle flame, but a lava flow has more surface area and radiates more energy than a candle flame. Approaching a lava flow without protective gear is dangerous. (Karafft/Photo Researchers, Inc.)

Solving for the radius, you get:

$$\left(\frac{R}{R_\odot}\right)^2 = \frac{40}{2^4} = \frac{40}{16} = 2.5$$

So the radius is:

$$\frac{R}{R_\odot} = \sqrt{2.5} = 1.58$$

The star is 1.58 times larger in radius than the sun.

The H–R Diagram

The **Hertzsprung–Russell (H–R) diagram,** named after its originators, Ejnar Hertzsprung and Henry Norris Russell, is a graph that separates the effects of temperature and surface area on stellar luminosities and enables astronomers to sort stars according to their diameters. Before you explore the details of the H–R diagram, try looking at a similar diagram you might use to sort automobiles.

You can plot a diagram such as ■ Figure 9-7, showing horsepower versus weight for various makes of cars. In general, the more a car weighs, the more horsepower it has. Most cars fall somewhere along the sequence of cars, running from heavy, high-powered cars at the upper left to light, low-powered models at the lower right. You might call this the main sequence of cars. But some cars have much more horsepower than normal for their weight—the sport and racing models—and lie higher in the diagram. Other cars, the economy models, have less power than normal for cars of the same weight and fall lower in the diagram. Just as this diagram sorts cars into family groups, so the H–R diagram sorts stars into groups according to size.

The H–R diagram is a graph with luminosity on the vertical axis and temperature on the horizontal axis. A star is represented by a point on the graph that marks its luminosity and its temperature. The H–R diagram in ■ Figure 9-8 also contains a scale of spectral type across the top. Because a star's spectral type is determined by its temperature, you could use either spectral type or temperature on the horizontal axis.

In an H–R diagram, the location of a point tells you a great deal about the star it represents. Points near the top of the diagram represent very luminous stars, and points near the bottom represent very-low-luminosity stars. Also, points near the right edge of the diagram represent very cool stars, and points near the left edge of the diagram represent very hot stars. Notice in the H–R diagram in Figure 9-8 how the artist has used color to represent temperature. Red stars are cool, and blue stars are hot.

Astronomers use H–R diagrams so often that they usually skip the words "the point that represents the star." Rather, they will say that a star is located in a certain place in the diagram. The location of a star in the H–R diagram has nothing to do with the

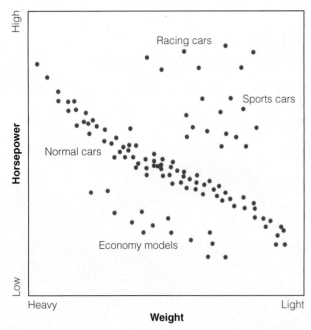

■ **Figure 9-7**

You could analyze automobiles by plotting their horsepower versus their weight and thus reveal relationships between various models. Most would lie somewhere along the main sequence of "normal" cars.

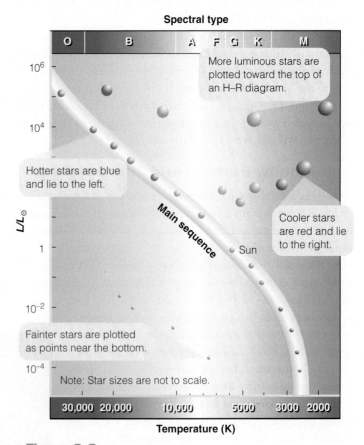

■ **Figure 9-8**

In an H–R diagram, a star is represented by a dot that shows the luminosity and temperature of the star. The background color in this diagram indicates the temperature of the stars. The sun is a yellow-white G2 star. Most stars fall along a sequence running from hot luminous stars at upper left to cool low-luminosity stars at lower right.

location of the star in space. Furthermore, a star may move in the H–R diagram as it ages and its luminosity and temperature change, but such motion in the diagram has nothing to do with the star's motion in space.

Notice that the vertical axis of the H–R diagram is an exponential scale. That's a convenient way to graph data that covers a wide range. On a graph of body weight, for example, you could plot the weight of a cat at the bottom, your own weight just above that, and above that the weight of an elephant and then a whale. You could get all of your data on one graph, but notice that an exponential scale compresses the high numbers and spreads out the low numbers. You can see that effect in the H–R diagram.

Giants, Supergiants, and Dwarfs

The **main sequence** is the region of the H–R diagram running from upper left to lower right. It includes roughly 90 percent of all normal stars. In Figure 9-8, the main sequence is represented by a curved line with dots for stars plotted along it. As you might expect, the hot main-sequence stars are more luminous than the cool main-sequence stars.

Notice in the H–R diagram that some cool stars lie above the main sequence. Although they are cool, they are luminous, and that must mean they are larger and have more surface area than main sequence stars of the same temperature. These are called **giant** stars, and they are roughly 10 to 100 times larger than the sun. There are even **supergiant** stars at the top of the H–R diagram that are over a thousand times the sun's diameter.

At the bottom of the H–R diagram lie the economy models, stars that are very low in luminosity because they are very small. At the bottom end of the main sequence, the **red dwarfs** are not only small, but they are also cool, and that gives them low luminosities. In contrast, the **white dwarfs** lie in the lower left of the H–R diagram and are lower in luminosity than you would expect, given their high temperatures. That must mean they are very small. Although some white dwarfs are among the hottest stars known, they are so small they have very little surface area from which to radiate, and that limits them to low luminosities.

The equation in the previous section can be used to draw precise lines of constant radius across the H–R diagram, and these lines slope down and to the right across the diagram because cooler stars are fainter than hotter stars of the same size. ■ Figure 9-9 plots the luminosities and temperatures of a number of well-known stars along with lines of constant radius. For example, locate the line labeled 1 $R_\odot$ (1 solar radius) and notice that it passes through the point representing the sun. Any star whose point is located along this line has a radius equal to the sun's. Next, look at the rest of the stars along the main sequence. They range from a tenth the size of the sun to about ten times as large. Even though the main sequence slopes dramatically down to the right across the diagram, most main-sequence stars are similar in size. In contrast, the white dwarfs at the lower left of the diagram are extremely small—only about the size of Earth—and the giants and supergiants at the upper right are extremely large compared to the stars of the main sequence.

Notice the great range of sizes among stars. The largest stars are 100,000 times larger than the tiny white dwarfs. If the sun were a tennis ball, the white dwarfs would be grains of sand, and the largest supergiants would be as big as football fields (■ Figure 9-10).

Now you can understand why Favorite Star Rigel is so much more luminous than Vega. They have nearly the same temperature, but Rigel is a supergiant and has a much larger surface area from which to radiate. Another of your Favorite Stars is Betelgeuse in Orion, also a supergiant. If Betelgeuse replaced the sun at the center of our solar system, it would swallow up Mercury, Venus, Earth, and Mars. The largest stars known have radii of about 7 AU; if one of them replaced the sun, it would extend nearly to the orbit of Saturn.

Interferometric Observations of Diameter

Is there any way to check the diameters predicted by the H–R diagram? One way is to use interferometers (see Chapter 6), for example the Center for High Angular Resolution Astronomy (CHARA) Array on Mount Wilson. There, six 1-meter telescopes combine their light to produce the resolving power of a virtual telescope 330 meters in diameter. Such interferometers can resolve the diameters of large, bright, nearby stars.

You can see Favorite Star Vega high in the sky on summer evenings. It is an A0 V star, and observations with the CHARA array confirm that it is about 2.5 times larger in diameter than the sun—about what you would expect from its location in the H–R diagram. The observations also reveal that it is spinning about twice a day compared to once a month for the sun and is flattened, with its poles 2300 K hotter than its equator (■ Figure 9-11).

Observations with interferometers confirm that upper-main-sequence stars are larger than the sun. Altair (A7) is about 50 percent larger than the sun, and Regulus, a B7 star bright in the sky on spring evenings, is about four times larger than the sun. Achernar, a B3 star, is still larger. All three of these stars are flattened by their rapid spin, as you can see in Figure 9-11.

Interferometric observations of giant and supergiant stars such as Betelgeuse (M2) show that they are also as large as predicted. Betelgeuse is at least 500 times the sun's diameter and can sometimes puff itself up to 800 times. In contrast, observations of red dwarfs confirm that although they are quite small, they are 15 to 20 percent bigger than expected. Evidently models of red dwarfs need further refining.

In short, interferometric observations confirm the sizes predicted by the temperatures and luminosities on the H–R

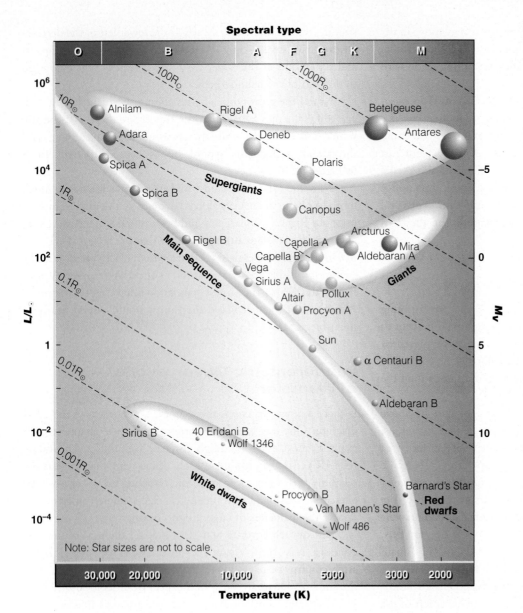

Figure 9-9

An H–R diagram showing the luminosity and temperature of many well-known stars. The dashed lines are lines of constant radius. The star sizes on this diagram are not to scale. (Individual stars that orbit each other are designated A and B, as in Spica A and Spica B.)

diagram. Stars really do range from roughly the size of Earth to over a thousand times bigger than the sun.

Luminosity Classification

A star's spectrum contains clues as to whether it is a main-sequence star, a giant, or a supergiant. The larger a star is, the less dense its atmosphere is, and that affects the widths of spectral lines.

Atoms collide often in a dense gas, their energy levels become distorted, and their spectral lines broadened. Hydrogen Balmer lines are an example. In the spectrum of a main-sequence star, the Balmer lines are broad because the star's atmosphere is dense and the hydrogen atoms collide often. In the spectrum of a giant star, the lines are narrower (■ Figure 9-12) because the giant star's atmosphere is less dense, and the hydrogen atoms collide less often. In the spectrum of a supergiant star, the Balmer lines are very narrow.

You can look at a star's spectrum and tell roughly how big it is. Size categories derived from spectra are

called **luminosity classes** because the size of the star is the dominating factor in determining luminosity. Supergiants, for example, are very luminous because they are very large. The luminosity classes are represented by the roman numerals I through V, with supergiants further subdivided into types Ia and Ib, as follows:

Luminosity Classes
Ia Bright supergiant
Ib Supergiant
II Bright giant
III Giant
IV Subgiant
V Main-sequence star

This classification scheme allows you to distinguish between the bright supergiants (Ia) such as Rigel and the regular supergiants (Ib) such as Polaris, the North Star. The star Adhara is a bright

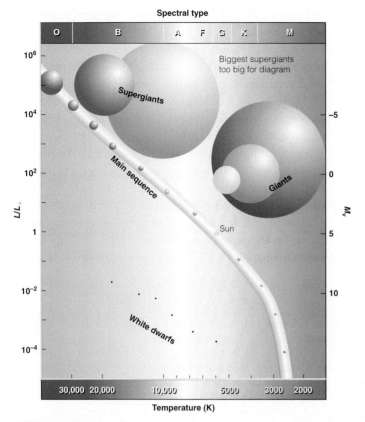

Spectral type

■ **Figure 9-10**

This H–R diagram shows the relative sizes of stars. Giant stars are 10 to 100 times larger than the sun, and white dwarfs are about the size of Earth. (The dots representing white dwarfs here are much too large.) The larger super-giants are too big for this diagram. To visualize the size of the largest stars, imagine that the sun is the size of one of your eyeballs. Then the largest supergiants would be the size of a hot air balloon.

giant (II), Aldebaran is a giant (III), and Altair is a subgiant (IV). Sirius and Vega, like the sun, are main-sequence stars (V). When you describe a star, its luminosity class appears after the spectral type, as in G2 V for the sun. White dwarfs don't enter into this classification because their spectra are peculiar. Notice that some of our Favorite Stars are unusual; next time you look at Polaris, remind yourself that it is a supergiant.

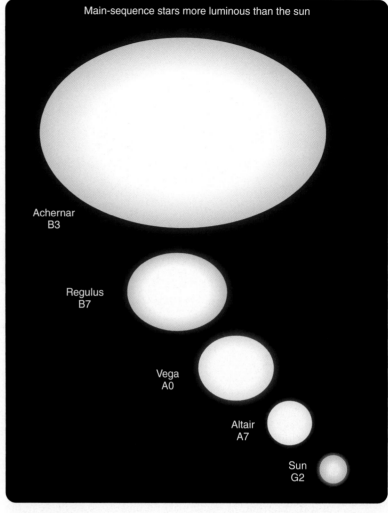

Main-sequence stars more luminous than the sun

■ **Figure 9-11**

Observations with interferometers can resolve the size and shape of some nearby stars. The stars of the upper main sequence are indeed larger than the sun, as predicted by the H–R diagram. The examples shown here are flattened by rapid rotation, but most stars rotate slower and are more nearly spherical. On the scale of this diagram, the supergiant Betelgeuse would have a diameter similar to that of a typical classroom.

The positions of the luminosity classes on the H–R diagram are shown in ■ Figure 9-13. Remember that these are rather broad clas-sifications and that the lines on the diagram are only approximate.

Luminosity effects on the widths of spectral lines

Supergiant

Giant

Main-sequence star

■ **Figure 9-12**

These schematic spectra show how the widths of spectral lines reveal a star's luminosity classifica-tion. Supergiants have very narrow spectral lines, and main-sequence stars have broad lines. In addition, certain spectral lines are more sensitive to this effect than others, so careful inspection of a star's spectrum can determine its luminosity classification.

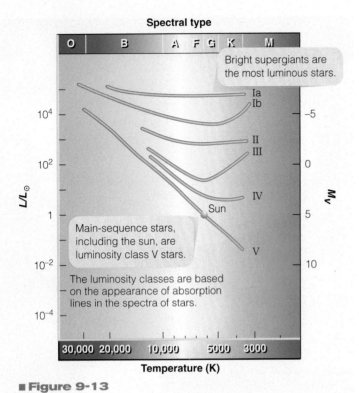

Spectral type

Bright supergiants are the most luminous stars.

Main-sequence stars, including the sun, are luminosity class V stars.

The luminosity classes are based on the appearance of absorption lines in the spectra of stars.

Temperature (K)

■ Figure 9-13

The approximate location of the luminosity classes on the H–R diagram.

A star of luminosity class III may lie slightly above or below the line labeled III. A scale of absolute magnitude has been added to the right edge of this H–R diagram for easy reference.

Luminosity classification is subtle and not too accurate, but it is important in modern astronomy. As you will see in the next section, luminosity classification provides a way to estimate the distance to stars that are too far away to have measurable parallaxes.

Spectroscopic Parallax

Astronomers can measure the stellar parallax of nearby stars, but most stars are too distant to have measurable parallaxes. These distances can be estimated from the star's spectral type, luminosity class, and apparent magnitude in a process called **spectroscopic parallax.** Spectroscopic parallax is potentially a confusing term because it does not involve an actual measurement of parallax shifts, but it is a method to tell you the distance to the star.

Spectroscopic parallax relies on the location of the star in the H–R diagram. If you record the spectrum of a star, you can determine its spectral class, and that tells you its horizontal location in the H–R diagram. You can also determine its luminosity class by looking at the widths of its spectral lines, and that tells you the star's vertical location in the diagram. Once you plot the point that represents the star in the H–R diagram, you can read off its absolute magnitude. As you learned earlier in this chapter, you

can find the distance to a star by comparing its apparent and absolute magnitudes.

For example, Favorite Star Betelgeuse is classified M2 Ib, and its apparent magnitude is about 0.4. You can plot this star in an H–R diagram such as Figure 9-13, where you would find that it should have an absolute magnitude of about –6.0 That means the distance modulus is 0.4 minus (–6.0), which is 6.4, and its distance estimated from Table 9-1 or calculated from the magnitude-distance formula is about 190 pc. Measurements made by the Hipparcos satellite are more accurate and reveal the distance to be 131 pc, with an uncertainty of 21 percent, so the result derived from spectroscopic parallax is only approximate. Obviously a direct measurement of the parallax is better, but for more distant stars spectroscopic parallax is often the only way to find their distance.

SCIENTIFIC ARGUMENT

What evidence can you give that giant stars really are bigger than the sun?

Scientific arguments are based on evidence, so you need to proceed step by step here. Stars exist that have the same spectral type as the sun but are clearly more luminous. Capella, for example, is a G star with an absolute magnitude of 0. Because it is a G star, it must have about the same temperature as the sun, but its absolute magnitude, based on its measured distance, is almost five magnitudes brighter than the sun's. A magnitude difference of five magnitudes corresponds to an intensity ratio of 100, so Capella must be about 100 times more luminous than the sun. If it has the same surface temperature as the sun but is 100 times more luminous, then it must have a surface area 100 times greater than the sun's. Because the surface area of a sphere is proportional to the square of the radius, Capella must be ten times larger in radius. That is clear observational evidence that Capella is a giant star.

In Figure 9-9, you can see that Procyon B is a white dwarf slightly warmer than the sun but about 10,000 times less luminous. Build a scientific argument based on evidence to resolve this question. **Why do astronomers conclude that white dwarfs must be small stars?**

9-4 The Masses of Stars

To UNDERSTAND STARS WELL, you must find out how much matter stars contain, that is, their masses. Do they all contain about the same mass as the sun, or are some more massive and others less? Unfortunately, it's difficult to determine the mass of a star. Looking through a telescope, you see only a point of light that reveals nothing about the mass of the star. Gravity is the key. Matter produces a gravitational field, and you can figure out how much matter a star contains if you watch another object move through the star's gravitational field. To find the masses of stars, you must study **binary stars,** pairs of stars that orbit each other.

Binary Stars in General

To measure the mass of a binary star, you need to understand orbital motion. Chapter 5 illustrated orbital motion by asking you to imagine a cannonball fired from a high mountain (see page 84). If Earth's gravity didn't act on the cannonball, it would follow a straight-line path and leave Earth forever. Because Earth's gravity pulls the cannonball away from its straight-line path, the cannonball follows a curved path around Earth—an orbit. When two stars orbit each other, their mutual gravitation pulls them away from straight-line paths and makes them both follow closed orbits around a point between the stars.

Each star in a binary system moves in its own orbit around the system's center of mass, the balance point of the system. If the stars were connected by a massless rod and placed in a uniform gravitational field such as that near Earth's surface, the system would balance at its center of mass like a playground seesaw (see page 85). If one star is more massive than its companion, then the more massive star is closer to the center of mass and travels in a smaller orbit, while the lower-mass star whips around in a larger orbit (■ Figure 9-14). The ratio of the masses of the stars M_A/M_B equals r_B/r_A, the inverse of the ratio of the radii of the orbits. If one star has an orbit twice as large as the other star's orbit, then it must be half as massive. Getting the ratio of the masses is easy, but that doesn't tell you the individual masses of the stars, which is what you really want to know. That takes further analysis.

To find the mass of a binary star system, you must know the sizes of the orbits and the orbital period—the length of time the stars take to complete one orbit. The smaller the orbits are and the shorter the orbital period is, the stronger the stars' gravity

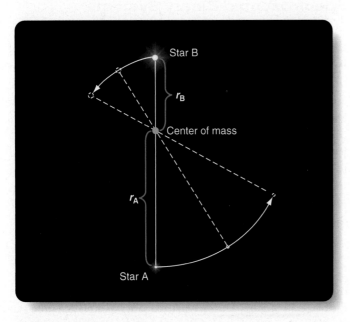

■ **Figure 9-14**

As stars in a binary star system revolve around each other, the line connecting them always passes through the center of mass, and the more massive star is always closer to the center of mass.

must be to hold each other in orbit. For example, if two stars whirl rapidly around each other in small orbits, then their gravity must be very strong to prevent their flying away from each other. Such stars would have to be very massive. From the size of the orbits and the orbital period, astronomers can figure out the masses of the stars using Newton's laws.

Calculating the Masses of Binary Stars

According to Newton's laws of motion and gravity, the total mass of two stars orbiting each other is related to the average distance a between them and their orbital period P. If the masses are M_A and M_B, then

$$M_A + M_B = \frac{a^3}{P^2}$$

In this formula, a is expressed in AU, P in years, and the mass in solar masses.

Notice that this formula is related to Kepler's third law of planetary motion (see Table 4-1). Almost all of the mass of the solar system is in the sun. For planets in our solar system, the total mass is 1 solar mass, and the formula becomes $P^2 = a^3$, which is Kepler's third law.

In a binary star system, this formula gives you a way to find the masses of the two stars. If you can find the average distance in AU between the two stars, a, and their orbital period in years, P, the sum of the masses of the two stars is just a^3/P^2.

Example 1: If you observe a binary system with a period of 32 years and an average separation of 16 AU, what is the total mass? *Solution:* The total mass equals $16^3/32^2$, which equals 4 solar masses.

Example 2: Call the two stars in the previous example A and B. Suppose star A is 12 AU away from the center of mass, and star B is 4 AU away. What are the individual masses? *Solution:* The ratio of the masses must be 12:4, which is the same as 3:1. What two numbers add up to 4 and have the ratio of 3:1? In this case, the answer is easy. Star B must be 3 solar masses, and Star A must be 1 solar mass.

Actually, figuring out the mass of a binary star system is not as easy as it might seem from this discussion. The orbits of the two stars may be elliptical; and, although the orbits lie in the same plane, that plane can be tipped at an unknown angle to your line of sight, further distorting the observed shapes of the orbits. Astronomers must find ways to correct for these distortions. In addition, astronomers analyzing binary systems must first find the distances to them so they can estimate the true size of the orbits in astronomical units. Finding the masses of binary stars requires a number of steps to get from what you can observe to what you really want to know, the masses. Constructing such sequences of steps is an important part of science (**How Do We Know? 9-1**).

Although there are many different kinds of binary stars, three types are especially useful for determining stellar masses. These are discussed separately in the next sections.

Chains of Inference

How do scientists measure something they can't detect? Sometimes scientists cannot directly observe the things they really want to study, so they must construct chains of inference that connect observable parameters to the unobservable quantities they want to know. You can't measure the mass of a star directly, so you must find a way to use what you can observe, orbital period and angular separation, to figure out step by step the parameters you need to calculate the mass.

Consider another example. Geologists can't measure the temperature and density of Earth's interior directly. There is no way to drill a hole to Earth's center and lower a thermometer or recover a sample. However, the speed of vibrations from a distant earthquake depends on the temperature and density of the rock they pass through. Geologists can't measure the speed of the vibrations deep inside Earth;

but they can measure the delays in the arrival times at different locations on the surface, and that allows them to work their way back to the speed and, finally, the temperature and density.

Chains of inference can be non-mathematical. Biologists studying the migration of whales can't follow individual whales for years at a time, but they can observe them feeding and mating in different locations; take into consideration food sources, ocean currents, and water temperatures; and construct a chain of inference that leads back to the seasonal migration pattern for the whales.

This chapter contains a number of chains of inference. Almost all sciences use chains of inference. When you can link the observable parameters step by step to the final conclusions, you gain a strong insight into the nature of science.

San Andreas fault: A chain of inference connects earthquakes to conditions inside Earth. (USGS)

Visual Binary Systems

In a **visual binary system,** the two stars are separately visible in the telescope. Only a pair of stars with large orbits can be separated visually; if the orbits are small, the telescope cannot resolve the star images, and you see only a single point of light. In a visual binary system, you can see each star moving around its orbit.

Astronomers study visual binary systems by measuring the position of the two stars directly at the telescope or in photographs. In either case, the astronomers need measurements over many years to map the orbits. The first frame of ■ Figure 9-15 shows a photograph of Favorite Star Sirius, which is a visual binary system made up of the bright star Sirius A and its white dwarf companion Sirius B. The photo was taken in 1960. Successive frames in Figure 9-15 show the motion of the two stars as observed since 1960 and the orbits the stars follow. The orbital period is 50 years, and astronomers have found accurate masses for both stars.

Visual binary systems are common; more than half of all stars are members of binary star systems, and many of those are visual binaries. Favorite Star Polaris has two stellar companions. Few visual binaries, however, can be analyzed completely. Many are so far apart that their periods are much too long for practical mapping of their orbits. Others are so close together that they are hardly visible as separate stars, and it is difficult to map the shape of their orbits. One of the stars that orbits Polaris, for instance,

orbits with a period over a thousand years, and the other is so close to Polaris that it is hardly visible even with the Hubble Space Telescope.

Spectroscopic Binary Systems

If the stars in a binary system are close together, the telescope, limited by diffraction and seeing, reveals only a single point of light. Only by looking at a spectrum, which is formed by light from both stars and contains spectral lines from both, can astronomers tell that there are two stars present and not one. Such a pair of stars is a **spectroscopic binary.**

■ Figure 9-16 shows a sequence of spectra recorded over a few days as the stars in a spectroscopic binary moved around their orbits. You can see how the spectral line in the top spectrum splits into two components that move apart, move together, merge as they cross, and then move apart again. This is the sure sign of a spectroscopic binary.

To understand the spectra in Figure 9-16, look at the diagrams in ■ Figure 9-17, which show two stars orbiting each other. In the first frame, star A is approaching while star B recedes. In the spectrum, you see a spectral line from star A Doppler shifted toward the blue end of the spectrum while the same spectral line from star B is Doppler shifted toward the red end of the spectrum. As the two stars revolve around their orbits, they alternately approach and recede, and you see small Doppler shifts moving their spectral lines apart and then back together. In a real spectroscopic binary, you

A Visual Binary Star System

The bright star Sirius A has a faint companion Sirius B (arrow), a white dwarf.

Visual

1960

Over the years astronomers can watch the two move and map their orbits.

1970

Center of mass

A line between the stars always passes through the center of mass of the system.

1980

The star closer to the center of mass is the more massive.

1990

Orbit of white dwarf

Orbit of Sirius A

The elliptical orbits are tipped at an angle to our line of sight.

■ **Figure 9-15**

The orbital motion of Sirius A and Sirius B can reveal their individual masses. (Photo: © UC Regents Lick Observatory)

Time in days

0.061
0.334
1.019
1.152
1.338
1.886
2.038
2.148
2.821
2.859
3.145
3.559
3.654
3.677

Relative intensity

654.0   655.0
Wavelength (nm)

■ **Figure 9-16**

Fourteen spectra of the star HD 80715 are shown here as graphs of intensity versus wavelength. A single spectral line (arrow in top spectrum) splits into a pair of spectral lines (arrows in third spectrum), which then merge and split apart again. These changing Doppler shifts reveal that HD 80715 is a spectroscopic binary. (Adapted from data courtesy of Samuel Barden and Harold Nations)

can't see the individual stars, but the sight of pairs of spectral lines moving back and forth across each other would alert you that you were observing a spectroscopic binary system.

At first glance, it seems that it should be easy to find the masses of the stars in a spectroscopic binary. You can find the orbital period by waiting to see how long it takes for the spectral lines to return to their starting positions. You can measure the size of the Doppler shifts to find the orbital velocities of the two stars. If you multiply velocity times orbital period, you can find the circumference of the orbit, and from that you can find the radius of the orbit. Now that you know the orbital period and the size of the orbit you should be able to calculate the mass. One important detail is missing, however. You don't know how much the orbits are inclined to your line of sight.

A Spectroscopic Binary Star System

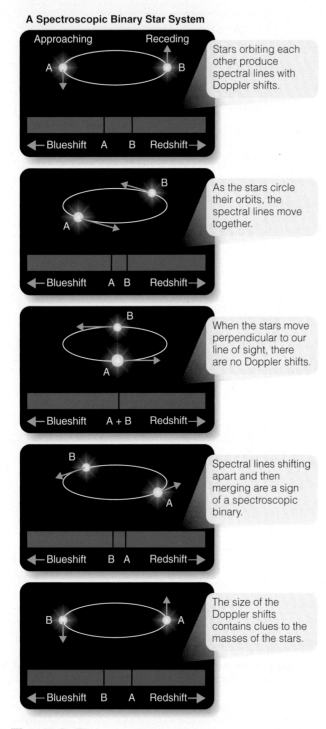

Approaching — Receding

A — B

Stars orbiting each other produce spectral lines with Doppler shifts.

←— Blueshift   A   B   Redshift —→

B

A

As the stars circle their orbits, the spectral lines move together.

←— Blueshift   A B   Redshift —→

B

A

When the stars move perpendicular to our line of sight, there are no Doppler shifts.

←— Blueshift   A + B   Redshift —→

B

A

Spectral lines shifting apart and then merging are a sign of a spectroscopic binary.

←— Blueshift   B   A   Redshift —→

B — A

The size of the Doppler shifts contains clues to the masses of the stars.

←— Blueshift   B   A   Redshift —→

■ Figure 9-17

From Earth, a spectroscopic binary looks like a single point of light, but the Doppler shifts in its spectrum reveal the orbital motion of the two stars.

Astronomers can find the inclination of a visual binary system because they can see the shape of the orbits. In a spectroscopic binary system, however, the individual stars are not visible, so the orbits can't be mapped and the inclination can't be found. Recall that the Doppler effect only reveals the radial velocity, the part of the velocity directed toward or away from the observer. Because you cannot find the inclination, you cannot correct these radial

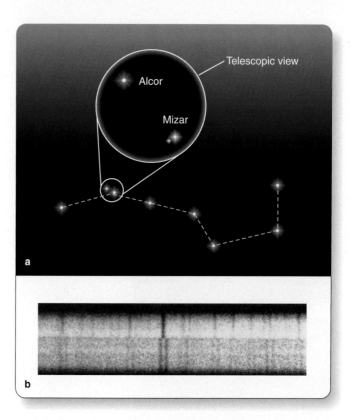

Telescopic view

Alcor

Mizar

a

b

■ Figure 9-18

(a) At the bend of the handle of the Big Dipper lie a pair of stars, Mizar and Alcor. Through a telescope you can discover that Mizar has a fainter companion and so is a member of a visual binary system. (b) Spectra of Mizar recorded at different times show that it is itself a spectroscopic binary system rather than a single star. In fact, both the faint companion to Mizar and the nearby star Alcor are also spectroscopic binary systems. (The Observatories of the Carnegie Institution of Washington)

velocities to find the true orbital velocities. Consequently, you cannot find the true masses. All you can find from a spectroscopic binary system is a lower limit to the masses.

More than half of all stars are in binary systems, and most of those are spectroscopic binary systems. Many of the familiar stars in the sky are actually pairs of stars orbiting each other (■ Figure 9-18).

You might wonder what happens when the orbits of a spectroscopic binary system lie exactly edge-on to Earth. The result is the most useful kind of binary system.

Eclipsing Binary Systems

As mentioned earlier, the orbits of the two stars in a binary system always lie in a single plane. If that plane is nearly edge-on to Earth, then the stars will appear to cross in front of each other. Imagine a model of a binary star system in which a cardboard disk represents the orbital plane and balls represent the stars, as in ■ Figure 9-19. If you see the model from the edge, then the balls that represent the stars can move in front of each other as they follow their orbits. The small star crosses in front of the large star, and then, half an orbit later, the large star crosses in front of

A small, hot star orbits a large, cool star, and you see their total light.

As the hot star crosses in front of the cool star, you see a decrease in brightness.

As the hot star uncovers the cool star, the brightness returns to normal.

When the hot star is eclipsed behind the cool star, the brightness drops.

The depth of the eclipses depends on the surface temperatures of the stars.

■ **Figure 9-19**

Imagine a model of a binary system with tennis and golf balls for stars and a disk of cardboard for the plane of the orbits. Only if you view the system edge on do you see the stars cross in front of each other.

the small star. When one star moves in front of the other, it blocks some of the light, and the star is eclipsed. Such a pair of stars is called an **eclipsing binary.**

Seen from Earth, the two stars are not visible separately. The system looks like a single point of light. But when one star moves in front of the other star, part of the light is blocked, and the total brightness of the point of light decreases. ■ Figure 9-20 shows a smaller star moving in an orbit around a larger star, first eclipsing the larger star and then being eclipsed itself as it moves behind its companion. The resulting variation in the brightness of the system is shown as a graph of brightness versus time, a **light curve.** Remember, you can't see the individual stars in an eclipsing system. Cover the stars in Figure 9-20 with your fingers and look only at the light curve. If you saw such a light curve, you would immediately recognize the point of light in the sky as an eclipsing binary.

The light curves of eclipsing binary systems contain tremendous amounts of information, but the curves can be difficult to analyze. Figure 9-20 shows an idealized system. Compare this with ■ Figure 9-21, which shows the light curve of a real system in which the stars have dark spots on their surfaces and are so close to each other that their shapes are distorted.

Once the light curve of an eclipsing binary system has been accurately observed, you can construct a chain of inference leading to the masses of the two stars. You can find the orbital period easily, and you can get spectra showing the Doppler shifts of the

■ **Figure 9-20**

From Earth, an eclipsing binary looks like a single point of light, but changes in brightness reveal that two stars are eclipsing each other. Doppler shifts in the spectrum combined with the light curve, shown here as magnitude versus time, can reveal the size and mass of the individual stars.

two stars. You can find the true orbital velocity because you don't have to untip the orbits; you know they are nearly edge-on or there would not be eclipses. Then you can find the size of the orbits and the masses of the stars.

Earlier in this chapter you used luminosity and temperature to find the radii of stars, but eclipsing binary systems provide a way

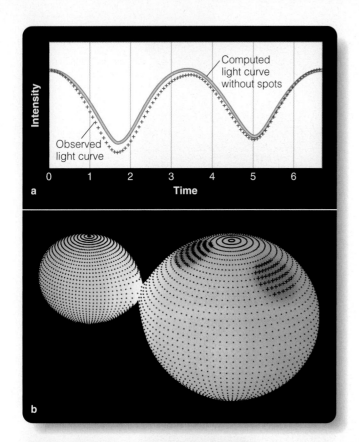

The observed light curve of the binary star VW Cephei (lower curve) shows that the two stars are so close together their gravity distorts their shapes. Slight distortions in the light curve reveal the presence of dark spots at specific places on the star's surface. The upper curve shows what the light curve would look like if there were no spots. (Graphics created with Binary Maker 2.0)

to measure the sizes of stars directly. From the light curve you can tell how long it takes for the small star to cross the large star. Multiplying this time interval by the orbital velocity of the small star gives the diameter of the larger star. You can also determine the diameter of the small star by noting how long it takes to disappear behind the edge of the large star. For example, if it takes 300 seconds for the small star to disappear while traveling 500 km/s relative to the large star, then it must be 150,000 km in diameter.

Algol (β Persei) is one of the best-known eclipsing binaries because its eclipses are visible to the naked eye. Normally, its magnitude is about 2.15, but its brightness drops to 3.4 during eclipses that occur every 68.8 hours. Although the nature of the star was not recognized until 1783, its periodic dimming was probably known to the ancients. *Algol* comes from the Arabic for "the demon," and it is associated in constellation mythology with the severed head of Medusa, the sight of whose serpentine locks turned mortals to stone (■ Figure 9-22). Indeed, in some accounts, Algol is the winking eye of the demon.

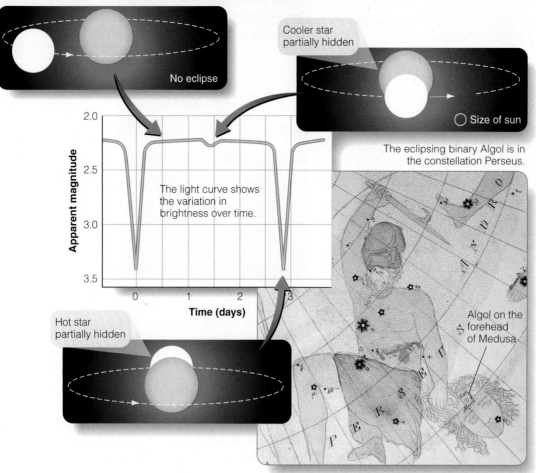

No eclipse

Cooler star partially hidden

○ Size of sun

The light curve shows the variation in brightness over time.

Hot star partially hidden

The eclipsing binary Algol is in the constellation Perseus.

Algol on the forehead of Medusa

■ Figure 9-22

The eclipsing binary Algol consists of a hot B star and a cooler G or K star. The eclipses are partial, meaning that neither star is completely hidden during eclipses. The orbit here is drawn as if the cooler star were stationary.

Basic Scientific Data

Where do large masses of scientific data come from? In a simple sense, science is the process by which scientists look at data and search for relationships, and it sometimes requires large amounts of data. For example, astronomers need to know the masses and luminosities of many stars before they can begin to understand the mass–luminosity relationship.

Compiling basic data is one of the common forms of scientific work—a necessary first step toward scientific analysis and understanding. An archeologist may spend months or even years diving to the floor of the Mediterranean Sea to study an ancient Greek shipwreck. She will carefully measure the position of every wooden timber and bronze fitting. She will photograph and recover everything from broken pottery to tools and weapons. The care with which she records data on the site pays

off when she begins her analysis. For every hour the archaeologist spends recovering an object, she may spend days or weeks in her office, a library, or a museum identifying and understanding the object. Why was there a Phoenician hammer on a Greek ship? What does that reveal about the economy of ancient Greece?

Finding, identifying, and understanding that ancient hammer contributes only a small bit of information, but the work of many scientists eventually builds a picture of how ancient Greeks saw their world. Solving a single binary star system to find the masses of the stars does not tell an astronomer a great deal about nature. Over the years, however, many astronomers have added their results to the growing data file on stellar masses. Scientific data accumulate and can be analyzed by later generations of scientists.

Collecting mineral samples can be hard work, but it is also fun. Scientists sometimes collect large amounts of data because they enjoy the process. (M. Seeds)

From the study of binary stars, astronomers have found that the masses of stars range from roughly 0.1 solar mass at the low end to over 100 solar masses at the high end. The most massive star ever found in a binary system has a mass of about 115 solar masses and orbits a companion star that is nearly as massive. A few other stars are believed to be more massive up to about 150 solar masses, but they do not lie in binary systems, so astronomers must estimate their mass.

SCIENTIFIC ARGUMENT

When you look at the light curve for an eclipsing binary system with total eclipses, how can you tell which star is hotter?
A good scientific argument is a chain of inference with no missing links. Start by assuming that the two stars in an eclipsing binary system are not the same size; then you can refer to them as the larger star and the smaller star. When the smaller star moves behind the larger star, you lose the light coming from the total area of the small star. And when the smaller star moves in front of the larger star, it blocks off light from the same amount of area on the larger star. In both cases, the same area, the same number of square meters, is hidden from your sight. That means the amount of light lost during an eclipse depends only on the temperature of the hidden surface because temperature is what determines how much a single square meter can radiate per second. When the surface of the hotter star is hidden, the brightness will fall dramatically, but when the surface of the cooler star is hidden, the brightness will not fall as much. So you can look at the light curve and point to the deeper of the two eclipses and say, "That is where the hotter star is behind the cooler star."

Now change the argument to consider the diameters of the stars. **How could you look at the light curve of an eclipsing binary with total eclipses and find the ratio of the diameters?**

9-5 A Census of the Stars

YOU HAVE LEARNED how to find the luminosities, diameters, and masses of stars, and now you can put all those data together (**How Do We Know? 9-2**) to paint a family portrait of the stars. As in any family portrait, both similarities and differences are important clues to the history of the family. As you begin trying to understand how stars are born and how they die, ask a simple question: What is the average star like? Answering that question is both challenging and illuminating.

Surveying the Stars

If you want to know what the average person thinks about a certain subject, you take a survey. If you want to know what the average star is like, you must survey the stars. Such surveys reveal important relationships among the family of stars.

Not many decades ago, surveying large numbers of stars was an exhausting task, but modern computers have changed that. Specially designed telescopes controlled by computers can make millions of observations per night, and high-speed computers can compile these data into easy-to-use databases. Those surveys produce mountains of data that astronomers can mine while searching for relationships within the family of stars.

The Family of Stars

1 What is the most common kind of star? Are some rare? Are some common? To answer those questions you must survey the stars. To do so you must know their spectral class, their luminosity class, and their distance. Your census of the family of stars produces some surprising demographic results.

1a You could survey the stars by observing every star within 62 pc of Earth. A sphere 62 pc in radius encloses a million cubic parsecs. Such a survey would tell you how many stars of each type are found within a volume of a million cubic parsecs.

62 pc

Earth

2 Your survey faces two problems.

1. The most luminous stars are so rare you find few in your survey region. There are no O stars at all within 62 pc of Earth.

2. Lower-main-sequence M stars, called red dwarfs, and white dwarfs are so faint they are hard to locate even when they are only a few parsecs from Earth. Finding every one of these stars in your survey sphere is a difficult task.

Spectral Class Color Key

- O and B
- A
- F
- G
- K
- M

The star chart in the background of these two pages shows most of the constellation Canis Major; stars are represented as dots with colors assigned according to spectral class. The brightest stars in the sky tend to be the rare, highly luminous stars, which look bright even though they are far away. Most stars are of very low luminosity, so nearby stars tend to be very faint red dwarfs.

Red dwarf
15 pc

o² Canis Majoris
B3Ia   790 pc

Red dwarf
17 pc

δ Canis Majoris
F8Ia   550 pc

σ Canis Majoris
M0Iab   370 pc

η Canis Majoris
B5Ia   980 pc

ε Canis Majoris
B2II   130 pc

Sirius A (α Canis Majoris) is the brightest star in the sky. With a spectral type of A1V, it is not a very luminous star. It looks bright because it is only 2.6 pc away.

Sirius B is a white dwarf that orbits Sirius A. Although Sirius B is not very far away, it is much too faint to see with the unaided eye.

In this histogram, bars rise from an H–R diagram to represent the frequency of stars in space.

Red dwarfs and white dwarfs are the most common kinds of stars.

2a O and B stars, super-giants, and giants are so rare their bars are not visible in this graph.

3 Luminous stars are rare but are easy to see. Most stars are very low luminosity objects. Not a single white dwarf or red dwarf is bright enough to see with the unaided eye. See H–R diagrams at right.

Brightest stars

The brightest stars in the sky tend to be highly luminous stars — upper-main-sequence stars, giants, or supergiants. They look bright because they are luminous, not because they are nearby.

Nearest stars

The nearest stars in space tend to be very faint stars — lower-main-sequence red dwarfs or white dwarfs. Nearly all of these stars are faint in the sky even though they are nearby. Only a few are visible to the unaided eye.

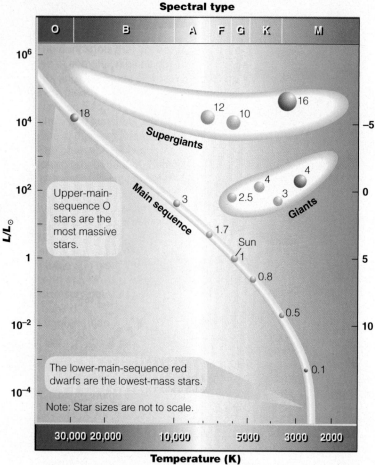

Spectral type

Upper-main-sequence O stars are the most massive stars.

The lower-main-sequence red dwarfs are the lowest-mass stars.

Note: Star sizes are not to scale.

Temperature (K)

Mass, Luminosity, and Density

If you survey enough stars and plot the data in an H–R diagram, you can see the patterns that hint at how stars are born, how they age, and how they die.

If you label an H–R diagram with the masses of the plotted stars, as in ■ Figure 9-23, you will discover that the main-sequence stars are ordered by mass. The most massive main-sequence stars are the hot stars, and as you run your eye down the main sequence, you will find successively lower-mass stars, until you reach the lowest-mass, coolest, faintest main-sequence stars.

Stars that do not lie on the main sequence are not in order according to mass. Giant stars are a jumble of different masses, and supergiants, although they tend to be more massive than giants, are in no particular order in the H–R diagram. In contrast, all white dwarfs have about the same mass, somewhere in the narrow range of from 0.5 to about 1 solar mass.

Because of the systematic ordering of mass along the main sequence, the main-sequence stars follow a **mass–luminosity relation**—the more massive a star is, the more luminous it is (■ Figure 9-24). In fact, the mass–luminosity relation can be expressed as a simple formula:

$$L = M^{3.5}$$

That is, a star's luminosity (in terms of the sun's luminosity) equals its mass (in solar masses) raised to the 3.5 power. For example, a star of 4 solar masses has a luminosity of approximately $4^{3.5}$, which equals $4 \times 4 \times 4 \times \sqrt{4}$. This equals 64×2, or 128. So a 4-solar-mass star will have a luminosity of about 128 times the luminosity of the sun. This is only an approximate equation, as shown by the red line in Figure 9-24.

Notice how large the range in luminosity is. The observed range of stellar masses extends from about 0.08 solar mass to over 100 solar masses—a factor of roughly 1000. But the range of luminosities extends from about 10^{-6} to about 10^6 solar luminosities—a factor of a trillion (10^{12}). Clearly, a small difference in mass causes a large difference in luminosity.

Although giants and supergiants do not follow the mass–luminosity relation very closely, and white dwarfs do not follow it at all, the link between mass and luminosity is critical in astronomy. In the next chapter, the mass–luminosity relation will help you understand how stars generate their energy.

What could you learn about stars from a survey of the stars near the sun? Because the sun is thought to be in a typical place in the universe, such a survey could reveal general characteristics of stars everywhere, and might reveal unexpected processes governing the formation and evolution of stars. Study **The Family of Stars** on pages 186–187 and notice three important points:

1 Taking a survey is difficult because you must be sure you get an honest sample. If you don't survey enough stars, or if you don't notice some kinds of stars, you can get biased results.

2 Most stars are faint, and luminous stars are rare. The most common kinds of stars are the lower-main-sequence red dwarfs and the white dwarfs.

3 A survey reveals that what you see in the sky is deceptive. Stars near the sun are quite faint; but luminous stars, although they are rare, are easily visible even at great distances. Many of the brighter stars in the sky are highly luminous stars that you see even though they are far away.

The night sky is a beautiful carpet of stars, but they are not all the same. Some are giants and supergiants, and some are dwarfs.

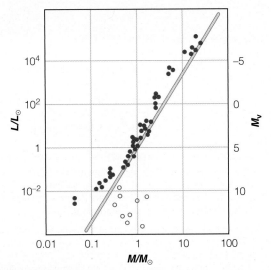

■ Figure 9-24

The mass–luminosity relation shows that the more massive a main-sequence star is, the more luminous it is. The open circles represent white dwarfs, which do not obey the relation. The red line represents the equation $L = M^{3.5}$.

The density of stars reveals another pattern in the H–R diagram. The average density of a star is its mass divided by its volume. Stars are not uniform in density but are most dense at their centers and least dense near their surface. The center of the sun, for instance, is about 100 times as dense as water; its density near the visible surface is about 3400 times less dense than Earth's atmosphere at sea level. A star's average density is intermediate between its central and surface densities. The sun's average density is approximately 1 g/cm^3—about the density of water.

Main-sequence stars have average densities similar to the sun's, but giant stars, being large, have low average densities, ranging from 0.1 to 0.01 g/cm^3. The enormous supergiants have still lower densities, ranging from 0.001 to 0.000001 g/cm^3.

These densities are thinner than the air you breathe, and if you could insulate yourself from the heat, you could fly an airplane through these stars. Only near the center would you be in any danger, for there the material is very dense—roughly three million times the density of water.

The white dwarfs have masses about equal to the sun's but are very small, only about the size of Earth. That means the matter is compressed to enormous densities. On Earth, a teaspoonful of this material would weigh about 15 tons.

Density divides stars into three groups. Most stars are main-sequence stars with densities like the sun's. Giants and supergiants are very-low-density stars, and white dwarfs are high-density stars. You will see in later chapters that these densities reflect different stages in the evolution of stars.

SCIENTIFIC ARGUMENT

What kind of stars do you see if you look at a few of the brightest stars in the sky?

This argument shows how careful you must be to interpret simple observations. When you look at the night sky, the brightest stars are mostly giants and supergiants. Most of the bright stars in Canis Major, for instance, are supergiants. Sirius, one of your Favorite Stars, is an exception. It is the brightest star in the sky, but it is just a main-sequence star that looks bright because it is very nearby, not because it is very luminous. In general, the supergiants and giants are so luminous that they stand out and look bright, even though they are not nearby. When you look at a bright star in the sky, you are probably looking at a highly luminous star—a supergiant or a giant. You can check this argument above by consulting the tables of the brightest and nearest stars in the Appendix.

Now revise your argument. **What kinds of stars do you see if you look at the stars nearest to the sun?**

What Are We? Medium

We humans are medium creatures, and we experience medium things. You can see trees and flowers and small insects, but you cannot see the beauty of the microscopic world without ingenious instruments and special methods. Similarly, you can sense the grandeur of a mountain range, but larger objects, such as stars, are too big for our medium senses. You have to use your ingenuity and imagination to experience the truth of such large objects. That is what science does for us. We live between the microscopic world and the astronomical world, and science enriches our lives by revealing the parts of the universe beyond our daily experience.

Experience is fun, but it is very limited. You may enjoy experiencing a flower by admiring its color and shape and by smelling its fragrance. But the flower is more wonderful than your experience can reveal. To truly appreciate the flower you need to understand it—how it serves its plant and how the plant came to create such a beautiful blossom.

Humans have a natural drive to understand as well as experience. You have experienced the stars in the night sky, and now you are beginning to understand them as objects ranging from hot blue O stars to cool red M dwarfs. It is natural for you to wonder why these stars are so different. As you explore that story in the following chapters, you will discover that although you have medium senses, you can understand the stars.

Summary

▶ Your goal in this chapter was to characterize the stars by finding their luminosities, diameters, and masses. Before you could begin, you needed to find their distances. Only by first knowing the distance to a star could you find its other properties.

▶ Astronomers can measure the distance to nearer stars by observing their **stellar parallaxes *(p)* (p. 169)**. The most distant stars are so far away that their parallaxes are unmeasurably small. Space telescopes above Earth's atmosphere have measured the parallaxes of a huge number of stars.

▶ Stellar distances are commonly expressed in **parsecs (p. 169)**. One parsec is 2.06×10^5 AU—the distance to an imaginary star whose parallax is 1 arc second. One parsec equals 3.26 light-years.

▶ **Proper motions (p. 170)** can give you a clue to distance because nearby stars tend to have large proper motions.

▶ The amount of light received from a star, the light **flux (p. 171)**, is related to its distance by the inverse square law. Once you know the distance to a star, you can use the **magnitude–distance formula (p. 172)** to find its **intrinsic brightness (p. 171)** expressed as its **absolute visual magnitude (M_v) (p. 171)**—the apparent magnitude the star would have if it were 10 pc away. A star's **distance modulus (p. 172)** is the difference between its apparent and absolute magnitudes.

▶ To find the energy output of a star, astronomers must correct for the light at wavelengths that are not visible to convert absolute visual magnitude into **absolute bolometric magnitude (p. 172)**, which can be converted into **luminosity (*L*) (p. 172)**, the total energy radiated by the star in one second.

▶ The **Hertzsprung–Russell (H–R) diagram (p. 174)** is a plot of luminosity versus surface temperature. It is an important graph in astronomy because it sorts the stars into categories by size.

▶ Roughly 90 percent of normal stars, including the sun, fall on the **main sequence (p. 175)**, with the more massive stars being hotter and more luminous. The **giants (p. 175)** and **supergiants (p. 175)**, however, are much larger and lie above the main sequence.

▶ **Red dwarfs (p. 175)** lie at the bottom end of the main sequence. Some of the **white dwarfs (p. 175)** are very hot stars, but they fall below the main sequence because they are so small.

▶ Observations made with interferometers confirm the sizes of stars implied by the H–R diagram and reveal that rapidly rotating stars are slightly flattened.

▶ The large sizes of the giants and supergiants mean their atmospheres have low densities and their spectra have sharper spectral lines than the spectra of main-sequence stars. In fact, it is possible to assign stars to **luminosity classes (p. 176)** by the widths of their spectral lines. Class V stars are main-sequence stars. Giant stars, class III, have sharper lines, and supergiants, class I, have extremely sharp spectral lines.

▶ Astronomers can use the locations of the luminosity classes in the H–R diagram to estimate the distances to stars in a technique called **spectroscopic parallax (p. 178)**.

▶ The only direct way to find the mass of a star is by studying **binary stars (p. 178)**. When two stars orbit a common center of mass, astronomers find their masses by observing the period and sizes of their orbits. In a **visual binary (p. 180)**, both stars are visible and the orbits can be mapped, but in a **spectroscopic binary (p. 180)** the stars are so close together they look like a single point of light, and the orbits can't be observed directly. Because the inclination of the orbit can't be found, spectroscopic binaries yield only a lower limit to the masses of the stars.

▶ In an **eclipsing binary (p. 183)**, the orbits are edge-on, and the stars cross in front of each other. The resulting brightness changes in the **light curve (p. 183)** can reveal the _____ their masses.

▶ A survey in the neighborhood of the sun shows that lower-main-sequence stars are the most common type. Giants and supergiants are rare, but white dwarfs are fairly common, although they are faint and hard to find.

▶ The **mass–luminosity relation (p. 188)** says that the more massive a star is, the more luminous it is. Main-sequence stars follow this rule closely, the most massive being the upper-main-sequence stars and the least massive the lower-main-sequence stars. Giants and supergiants do not follow the relation precisely, and white dwarfs not at all.

▶ Given the mass and diameter of a star, you can find its average density. On the main sequence, the stars are about as dense as the sun, but the giants and supergiants are very-low-density stars. Some are much thinner than air. The white dwarfs, lying below the main sequence, are tremendously dense.

Review Questions

1. Why are Earth-based parallax measurements limited to the nearest stars?

2. Why was the Hipparcos satellite able to make more accurate parallax measurements than ground-based telescopes?

3. What do the words *absolute* and *visual* mean in the definition of absolute visual magnitude?

4. What does luminosity measure that is different from what absolute visual magnitude measures?

5. Why does the luminosity of a star depend on both its radius and its temperature?

6. How can you be sure that giant stars really are larger than main-sequence stars?

7. What evidence shows that white dwarfs must be very small?

8. What observations would you make to classify a star according to its luminosity? Why does that method work?

9. Why does the orbital period of a binary star depend on its mass?

10. What observations would you make to study an eclipsing binary star?

11. Why don't astronomers know the inclination of a spectroscopic binary? How do they know the inclination of an eclipsing binary?

12. How do the masses of stars along the main sequence illustrate the mass–luminosity relation?

13. Why is it difficult to find out how common the most luminous stars are? The least luminous stars?

14. What is the most common kind of star?

15. If you look only at the brightest stars in the night sky, what kind of star are you likely to be observing? Why?

16. **How Do We Know?** What is the missing link in the chain of inference leading from observations of spectroscopic binaries to the masses of the stars?

17. **How Do We Know?** In what way is basic scientific data cumulative, and how do accumulations of such data help later scientists?

Discussion Questions

1. If someone asked you to compile a list of the nearest stars to the sun based on your own observations, how would you select your sample, what measurements would you make, and how would you analyze the measurements to detect nearby stars?

2. The sun is sometimes described as an average star. Is that true? What is the average star really like?

Problems

1. If a star has a parallax of 0.050 arc second, what is its distance in pc? In ly? In AU?

2. If a star has a parallax of 0.016 arc second and an apparent magnitude of 6, how far away is it, and what is its absolute magnitude?

3. Complete the following table:

m	M_v	d(pc)	p (arc seconds)
____	7	10	____
11	____	1000	____
____	−2	____	0.025
4	____	____	0.040

4. If a main-sequence star has a luminosity of 400 $L_\odot$, what is its spectral type? (*Hint:* See Figure 9-13.)

5. If a star has an apparent magnitude equal to its absolute magnitude, how far away is it in parsecs? In light-years?

6. If a star has an absolute bolometric magnitude that is eight magnitudes brighter than the sun, what is the star's luminosity?

7. If a star has an absolute bolometric magnitude that is one magnitude fainter than the sun, what is the star's luminosity?

8. An O8 V star has an apparent magnitude of +1. Use the method of spectroscopic parallax to estimate the distance to the star.

9. Find the luminosity of the sun, given the radius of Earth's orbit and the solar constant (Chapter 8). Make your calculation in two steps. First, use $4\pi R^2$ to calculate the surface area (in square meters) of a sphere surrounding the sun with a radius of 1 AU. Second, multiply by the solar constant to find the total solar energy passing through the sphere in 1 second. That is the luminosity of the sun. Compare your result with that in Celestial Profile 1.

10. In the following table, which star is brightest in apparent magnitude? Most luminous in absolute magnitude? Largest? Farthest away?

Star	Spectral Type	m_v
a	G2 V	5
b	B1 V	8
c	G2 Ib	10
d	M5 III	19
e	White dwarf	15

11. What is the total mass of a visual binary system if its average separation is 8 AU and its period is 20 years?

12. Measure the wavelengths of the iron lines in Figure 9-16 and plot a graph showing the radial velocities of the two stars in this system. What is the period? Assuming that the orbit is circular and edge-on, what is the total mass? What are the individual masses?

13. If the eclipsing binary in Figure 9-20 has a period of 32 days, an orbital velocity of 153 km/s, and an orbit that is nearly edge on, what is the circumference of the orbit? The radius of the orbit? The mass of the system?

14. If the orbital velocity of the eclipsing binary in Figure 9-20 is 153 km/s and the smaller star becomes completely eclipsed in 2.50 hours, what is its diameter?

15. What is the luminosity of a 4-solar-mass main-sequence star? Of a 9-solar-mass main-sequence star? Of a 7-solar-mass main-sequence star?

Learning to Look

1. Look at Figure 9-6. Why is the lava nearest the source brighter and yellower than the lava that is farther away?

2. If all of the stars in the photo here are members of the same star cluster, then they all have about the same distance. Then why are three of the brightest much redder than the rest? What kind of star are they?

NASA

10 | The Interstellar Medium

Visual wavelength image

Guidepost

You have begun your study of the sun and other stars, but now it is time to study the thin gas and dust that drifts through space between the stars. This chapter will show you how important this material is to the story of stars and will help you answer three essential questions:

- **How do astronomers study the gas and dust between the stars?**
- **What kinds of material make up the interstellar medium?**
- **How does the matter between the stars interact with the stars?**

The gas and dust between the stars is the starting point for the life story of the stars. The next four chapters will trace the birth, life, and death of stars.

Some 7500 ly from Earth and over 200 ly across, the Eta Carina Nebula is a churning cloud of gas and dust illuminated by massive newborn stars. The red-purple color is typical of excited hydrogen atoms, but helium and heavier atoms are also present. (ESO)

> *when he shall die,*
> *Take him and cut him out in little stars,*
> *And he will make the face of heaven so fine*
> *That all the world will be in love with night,*
> *And pay no worship to the garish sun.*

— WILLIAM SHAKESPEARE, *ROMEO AND JULIET*, 3.2.21

JULIET LOVED ROMEO so much she compared him to the beauty of the stars. Had she known what was between the stars, she might have compared him to that instead. True, the gas and dust between the stars is mostly invisible to human eyes, but when observed at infrared wavelengths it is strikingly beautiful, and its densest clouds are the nurseries where new stars are born. If there is beauty in vast extent and sweeping power, then the gas and dust between the stars, called the **interstellar medium** (abbreviated **ISM**), could steal worship from the garish stars.

When people use the phrase, "the vacuum of space," they reveal a **Common Misconception** that space is empty. Space is not empty; in fact, you are about to discover that the interstellar medium is both complex and, when observed at the proper wavelengths, quite beautiful (■ Figure 10-1).

10-1 | Studying the Interstellar Medium

THERE IS NOTHING SPECIAL about visible light except that you can see it. Although you begin this chapter with what you see, you will need to use all parts of the electromagnetic spectrum to understand the interstellar medium.

Nebulae

On a cold, clear winter night, Orion hangs high in the southern sky, a large constellation composed of brilliant stars. If you look carefully at Orion's sword, you will see that one of the stars is a hazy cloud (Figure 2-4). A small telescope reveals even more such clouds of gas and dust scattered around the sky. Astronomers refer to these clouds as **nebulae** (singular, nebula), from the Latin word for mist or cloud. They are visible evidence of an interstellar medium.

Read **Three Kinds of Nebulae** on pages 194–195 and notice three important points and four new terms:

1 *HII regions* are clouds of gas ionized by the ultraviolet radiation from nearby hot stars. They are often called *emission nebula* because the ionized hydrogen produces visible-wavelength photons that make the regions glow with a characteristic pink color.

2 If nearby stars are not hot enough to ionize the hydrogen in a nebula, it may still be visible to human eyes as a *reflection nebula,* produced when light is scattered by tiny dust specks mixed in with the gas.

■ **Figure 10-1**

(a) At visual wavelengths, the spaces between the stars in and around the constellation Orion seem empty. (b) An infrared image reveals the swirling clouds of the interstellar medium. (Visual: Akito Fujii; IR: NASA/IPAC courtesy Deborah Levine)

Orion Nebula

Visual   a

Far-infrared   b

Three Kinds of Nebulae

1 **Emission nebulae** are produced when a hot star excites the gas near it to produce an emission spectrum. The star must be hotter than about B1 (25,000 K). Cooler stars do not emit enough ultraviolet radiation to ionize the gas. Emission nebulae have a distinctive pink color produced by the blending of the red, blue, and violet Balmer lines. Emission nebulae are also called **HII regions**, following the custom of naming gas with a roman numeral to show its state of ionization. HI is neutral hydrogen, and HII is ionized.

In an HII region, the ionized nuclei and free electrons are mixed. When a nucleus captures an electron, the electron falls down through the atomic energy levels, emitting photons at specific wavelengths. Spectra indicate that the nebulae have compositions much like that of the sun – mostly hydrogen. Emission nebulae have densities of 100 to 1000 atoms per cubic centimeter, better than the best vacuums produced in laboratories on Earth.

Visual-wavelength image

2 A **reflection nebula** is produced when starlight scatters from a dusty nebula. Consequently, the spectrum of a reflection nebula is just the reflected absorption spectrum of starlight. Gas is surely present in a reflection nebula, but it is not excited to emit photons. See image below.

Reflection nebulae NGC 1973, 1975, and 1977 lie just north of the Orion Nebula. The pink tints are produced by ionized gases deep in the nebulae.

Visual-wavelength image

2a Reflection nebulae look blue for the same reason the sky looks blue. Short wavelengths scatter more easily than long wavelengths. See image below.

Sunlight enters Earth's atmosphere

Blue photons are scattered more easily than longer wavelengths, and blue photons enter your eyes from all directions, making the sky look blue.

2b The blue color of reflection nebulae at left shows that the dust particles must be very small in order to preferentially scatter the blue photons. Interstellar dust grains must have diameters ranging from 0.01 mm down to 100 nm or so.

2c In the star cluster called the Pleiades, the hottest stars are B6, not hot enough to ionize hydrogen in the interstellar medium. Instead, the brightest stars produce a reflection nebula as their light is scattered from interstellar dust.

Visual-wavelength image

o-Australian Observation

Reflection

Emission

Trifid Nebula

Emission

The Milky Way in Sagittarius contains two nebulae that dramatically demonstrate the difference between emission and reflection nebulae.

Visual   **Lagoon Nebula**

Daniel Good

Dark Nebula Barnard 86

Star Cluster NGC6520

Visual

Anglo-Australian Observatory/ David Malin Images

Anglo-Australian Observatory/David Malin Images

3 **Dark nebulae** are dense clouds of gas and dust that obstruct the view of more distant stars. Some are generally round, but others are twisted and distorted, as shown at the left, suggesting that even when there are no nearby stars to ionize the gas or produce a reflection nebula, there are breezes and currents pushing through the interstellar medium.

Northern Coalsack

Cygnus

Milky Way

Great Rift

Twisted by intense light from nearby stars, this dark nebula is visible because it obscures more distant stars.

Visual-wavelength image

Large dark nebulae obstruct the view of more distant stars and form holes and rifts along the Milky Way. The Great Rift extends from Cygnus to Sagittarius.

③ At visual wavelengths, *dark nebulae* are visible where dense clouds of gas and dust are silhouetted against background regions filled with stars or bright nebulae.

The different kinds of nebulae that decorate the sky are really similar objects seen in different ways much like rain clouds in Earth's atmosphere. On a sunny day, a distant cloud looks white, but overhead it blocks sunlight and looks dark. If you could see the same cloud with infrared eyes, you would see it glowing brightly with blackbody radiation. Different kinds of nebulae are regions of the interstellar medium with different relationships to starlight.

A detailed analysis of the spectra of nebulae can reveal their composition. About 70 percent of the mass in the interstellar medium is hydrogen, 28 percent is helium, and 2 percent is made up of elements heavier than helium. (Look back to Table 7-2 on page 137 and notice this is the same composition as the sun and other stars.) The density of the interstellar medium is very low, typically only 1 atom per cubic centimeter, although it can be much higher in dense clouds. Even in those clouds, the gas is 10^{15} times less dense than the air you breathe.

Almost all of this matter is a thin gas, but about 1 percent of the mass is made up of dust particles called **interstellar dust.** The dust particles are composed of carbon, silicates, iron, and even ice and organic compounds. (An organic compound is made up of molecules that have a carbon chain structure, but it does not have to originate with living things.) The particles are almost all less than 1 micron in diameter. That is only 10^{-6} meters or 1000 nm.

Certain lines in the spectra of emission nebulae are called **forbidden lines** because they are almost never seen in the spectra of excited gas on Earth. This is because transitions between certain energy levels are extremely unlikely. A normal transition might occur after 10^{-8} to 10^{-7} second, but if an electron gets caught in one of these **metastable levels,** it may be stuck for as long as an hour before it falls to a lower level and emits the proper photon. Unless a gas has an extremely low density, collisions between atoms disturb electrons caught in metastable levels long before they can make a transition downward and emit a photon. That means forbidden lines are produced only by very-low-density gas and are generally not visible in laboratories on Earth where gas densities are not low enough. The gases in Earth's upper atmosphere have low enough density to emit forbidden lines visible as aurorae (see Chapter 8).

Even in a denser than average nebula, the gas has a very low density, and an atom could go for an hour or more between collisions, giving an electron stuck in a metastable level time to decay to a lower level and emit a photon at a so-called forbidden wavelength.

Two good examples of forbidden lines are the strong green lines at 495.9 nm and 500.7 nm produced by oxygen atoms that have lost two electrons. (Following the convention for naming ions, twice-ionized oxygen is OIII. Neutral oxygen is symbolized as OI.) The oxygen ions can become excited by collision with a high-energy photon or a rapidly moving ion or electron, and the atom can emit various-wavelength photons as its electron cascades back down to lower energy levels. Some of those electrons get caught in metastable levels and eventually emit photos at forbidden wavelengths.

The forbidden lines are clear evidence that nebulae have very low densities. This is an example of how astronomers can use knowledge of atomic physics to understand astronomical objects.

Extinction and Reddening

One way to study the interstellar medium is to examine the starlight that passes through it. The interstellar medium makes distant stars appear fainter than they would if space were perfectly transparent. This phenomenon is called **interstellar extinction,** and in the neighborhood of the sun it amounts to about 1 magnitude per thousand parsecs at visual wavelengths. That is, a star 1000 pc from Earth will look about 1 magnitude fainter to human eyes than it would if space were perfectly empty. If it were 2000 pc away, it would look about 2 magnitudes dimmer, and so on. This is a dramatic effect at visual wavelengths, and it shows that the interstellar medium is not confined to a few nebulae scattered here and there. The spaces between the stars are far from empty.

The interstellar medium also affects the colors of stars. As you saw earlier, the dust particles are small, with diameters equal to or smaller than the wavelengths of light, so they scatter shorter wavelengths better than longer wavelengths. That is the reason why extinction is more severe at shorter wavelengths, and that makes stars look redder than they should be, a process called **interstellar reddening** (■ Figure 10-2). Some hot O stars, for instance, look red and not blue because of reddening.

You see reddening when you look at the setting sun. As the sun sets, sunlight must travel through a lot of air on its way to your eyes, and blue photons are more likely to be scattered. A larger proportion of red photons reach your eyes, and the setting sun looks red.

Note that interstellar reddening does not shift the wavelengths of spectral lines as does the Doppler effect. Rather, reddening changes the proportions of long- and short-wavelength photons that reach Earth, and that makes distant stars redder.

Astronomers can measure the amount of reddening by comparing two stars of the same spectral type, one of which is dimmed more than the other. If you plot the difference in brightness between the two stars against wavelength, you get a curve that shows the reddening. That is, it shows how the starlight is dimmed at different wavelengths (■ Figure 10-3). In general, the light is dimmed in proportion to the reciprocal of the wavelength, a pattern typical of scattering from small dust particles. Laboratory measurements suggest that the high extinction at about 220 nm is caused by a spectral feature of one form of carbon, evidence that some of the dust particles contain carbon.

No stars visible through center of Barnard 86, "The Black Cloud"

Stars seen through edges of nebula dimmed and reddened

Visual-wavelength image

Infrared image reveals many stars hidden behind the nebula.

Infrared image

■ Figure 10-2

Interstellar reddening makes stars seen through a cloud of gas and dust look redder than they should because shorter wavelengths are more easily scattered. If the gas and dust is especially dense, no stars are visible through the cloud at visual wavelengths except near the edges. At the longer wavelengths of the near-infrared, many stars can be detected behind the cloud. (European Southern Observatory)

In many cases, clouds of interstellar matter are so dense, they block our view at visual wavelengths, and even the less dense parts of the interstellar medium dim starlight severely. Look again at Figure 10-3 and notice how low extinction is in the infrared. The interstellar medium is highly transparent at near-infrared wavelengths (■ Figure 10-4), but at much longer infrared wavelengths, the interstellar medium glows with blackbody radiation emitted by the dust.

Interstellar Absorption Lines

As light travels through the interstellar medium, atoms can absorb specific wavelengths and form **interstellar absorption lines** in the spectra of stars. Astronomers can tell interstellar absorption lines from stellar absorption lines in a number of ways.

Some stellar spectra contain absorption lines that obviously don't belong to the stars because they represent the wrong ionization state. For example, if you looked at the spectrum of a very hot star such as an O star, you would expect to see no lines of once-ionized calcium (Ca II) because that ion cannot exist at the high temperatures found in the atmosphere of such a hot star. But many O-star spectra contain spectral lines of Ca II. These lines must have been produced not in the star's atmosphere but in the interstellar medium between the star and Earth.

The interstellar medium is highly transparent in the infrared.

A distant star is dimmed most at short wavelengths.

IR Visible UV

1000 500 300 200 125

Wavelength λ [nm]

■ Figure 10-3

Interstellar extinction, the dimming of starlight by dust between the stars, depends strongly on wavelength. Infrared radiation is only slightly affected, but ultraviolet light is strongly scattered. The strong extinction at about 220 nm is caused by a spectral feature of a form of carbon dust in the interstellar medium.

a Visible   **b** Near-infrared   **c** Mid-infrared

■ **Figure 10-4**

(a) At visual wavelengths, the Horsehead Nebula is a dark nebula extending away from a larger dark cloud. (Howard McCallon) (b) At near-infrared wavelengths, the dark nebulae are nearly transparent, and stars are visible through them. (2MASS) (c) At much longer infrared wavelengths, the clouds glow with blackbody radiation emitted by dust grains. (ISO)

The widths of the interstellar lines also give away their identities. In the atmosphere of a star, the gas is so dense that atoms collide with each other often and disturb the atomic energy levels. That blurs the spectral lines and makes them broader. Also, in a hot gas, the atoms move so rapidly that they produce small Doppler shifts, some red some blue, and that broadens the spectral lines. In contrast, interstellar gas is cold and has a very low density, so atoms collide only rarely. That means interstellar absorption lines are exceedingly sharp (■ Figure 10-5).

Interstellar lines are also found in the spectra of some spectroscopic binary stars (see Chapter 9). As the two stars orbit each other, Doppler shifts move their spectral lines apart, together, and then apart again, but the narrow interstellar lines don't move and are obviously not produced by the stars in the spectroscopic binary.

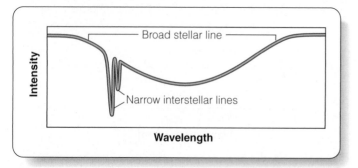

■ **Figure 10-5**

Interstellar absorption lines can be recognized because they are very narrow. Here a spectral line produced in the atmosphere of a star is so magnified that it is seen as a broad dip in the plot. In contrast, the absorption lines produced by two clouds in the interstellar medium are much narrower.

Interstellar lines are often split into two or more components. The multiple components have slightly different wavelengths and must have been produced when the light from the star passed through different clouds of gas on its way to Earth. Because individual clouds of gas have slightly different radial velocities, they produce absorption lines with slightly different Doppler-shifted wavelengths.

Interstellar Emission Lines

You expect from Kirchhoff's second law (Chapter 7) that an excited low-density gas viewed against an empty or colder background should produce an emission spectrum, and the interstellar medium does exactly that. As you also learned via Kirchoff's laws, the wavelengths of a given atom or molecule's emission lines are the same as the wavelengths of its absorption lines. Emission lines, like absorption lines, give astronomers powerful ways to study the gas and dust between the stars.

For example, cold, neutral hydrogen floating in space can emit electromagnetic radiation with a wavelength of 21 cm, which can be detected with radio telescopes. This **21-cm radiation** is an emission line.

How could cold hydrogen atoms emit radio-wavelength photons? A hydrogen atom consists of an electron and a proton, and they both spin. Because they have electric charges, that spinning generates tiny magnetic fields, and if the two particles spin in the same direction, the magnetic fields are reversed because the particles have opposite charges. If they spin opposite to each other, the magnetic fields are aligned. In cold, unexcited hydrogen there are two ways the electron can settle into the ground state—spinning one way or the other way—and that means the ground state is really two energy levels separated by a tiny amount of energy (■ Figure 10-6). If the electron is spinning one way, it can flip over and spin the other way, releasing the excess energy as a photon with a wavelength of 21 cm.

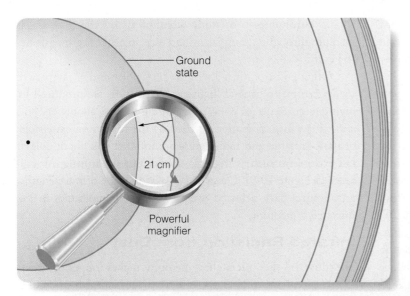

Because the proton and electron in a hydrogen atom can spin in the same or in the opposite directions, the ground state is actually two closely spaced energy levels. In this diagram, you would need a magnifying glass to distinguish the two levels. When an atom decays from the upper level to the lower level, it emits a photon with a wavelength of 21 cm.

The 21-cm radiation is a forbidden line. The transition is statistically very unlikely, and it isn't detected in laboratories on Earth because the gas is too dense and the atoms collide too often. In space, however, hydrogen atoms collide only rarely, and hydrogen atoms can go undisturbed for millions of years. That allows them to produce the 21-cm radiation, and astronomers can use that radiation to map the location of the cold, low-density gas in our galaxy (■ Figure 10-7). Also, radio waves have

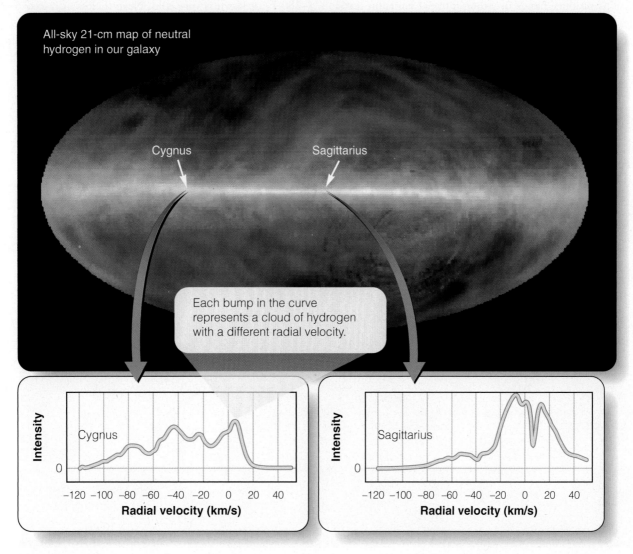

■ **Figure 10-7**

Most of the neutral hydrogen in the Milky Way Galaxy is in the plane of the disk-shaped galaxy—the bright band running from left to right. Notice how wispy and irregular the hydrogen is. (J. Dickey, UMn, F. Lockman, NRAO, SkyView) 21-cm radio observations reveal many clouds of neutral hydrogen orbiting the center of the galaxy, each with its individual Doppler shift. (Adapted from observations by Burton) such long wavelengths that they are unaffected by the tiny dust grains in the interstellar medium, allowing astronomers to observe distant clouds that would be undetectable at shorter wavelengths.

Other atoms and molecules in the interstellar medium produce emission lines in the infrared and radio parts of the spectrum. A molecule can store energy by rotating at different speeds, by vibrating as if the atoms were linked by little springs, or by twisting back and forth. When an atom makes a transition from a high-energy state to a lower energy state, it can emit the excess energy as a photon. The CO molecule is an especially powerful emitter of radio energy, as is OH. You learned in Chapter 7 that Zthe hydrogen Balmer lines lie in the visible and near-ultraviolet part of the spectrum, but other series of hydrogen lines lie in the infrared. Molecular hydrogen (H_2) and water also produce strong emission lines in the infrared. Silicate molecules contained in dust grains produce bands of strong infrared emission lines. Molecules called PAHs (polycyclic aromatic hydrocarbons) are organic molecules that float freely in space and are also found in dust grains. The strong infrared emission from PAHs allows astronomers to study conditions in the interstellar medium throughout our galaxy and even in other nearby galaxies (■ Figure 10-8).

Other emission lines lie in the ultraviolet and X-ray part of the spectrum. In general, high-energy photons are produced by high-energy events, so X-ray observations tell you about very hot, excited gas such as matter expelled by the supernova explosions of stars. Infrared and radio emission lines tell you about colder, less excited gas such as frigid gas clouds quietly drifting through space (■ Figure 10-9). Observing at a wide range of wavelengths, astronomers have detected over 150 different molecules in the interstellar medium.

Infrared Radiation from Dust

The dust in the interstellar medium makes up only about 1 percent of its total mass, and at a temperature of 100 K (–280°F) or less it is very cold. Nevertheless, it is easy to detect at infrared wavelengths.

You learned earlier that silicate molecules in dust grains produce strong spectral lines in the infrared, but the dust itself is also

■ Figure 10-8

At a distance of 23 million light-years, the galaxy M51, also known as the Whirlpool Galaxy, is similar to our Milky Way Galaxy. Infrared observations reveal it glowing from emission by complex molecules called PAHs (red). Many of these molecules are part of dust particles in the galaxy's interstellar medium. (KPNO, NASA)

Infrared

Optical

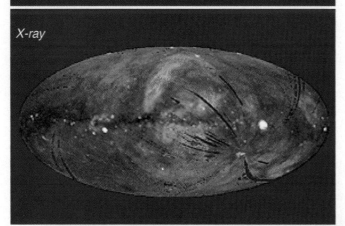

X-ray

■ **Figure 10-9**

These images of our galaxy include the entire sky spread into an oval. The infrared image shows the location of clouds of cold interstellar gas and dust made visible by blackbody radiation from dust grains. In the visual-wavelength image, dense, dusty clouds are silhouetted against distant stars. The X-ray image shows the location of very hot gas produced in most cases by the supernova explosions of dying stars. (NASA)

a powerful source of blackbody radiation. Although the dust can be very cold, 10 to 100 K, it is not at absolute zero, so it must radiate blackbody radiation, and at those temperatures, that radiation is emitted in the infrared.

You might wonder how such cold dust can be a powerful source of infrared radiation, but you must remember that the luminosity of an object depends on both its temperature and its surface area. To illustrate, imagine that you pack a solar mass of interstellar dust into a ball. It would be roughly the size of the sun. If you left that dust floating free in space, it would amount to more than a billion trillion trillion trillion (10^{45}) dust specks, each 0.001 mm in diameter or smaller. All that dust would have a surface area more than 10^{15} times larger than the sun's, and that means that even though it is very cold, the dust could radiate a huge amount of infrared radiation.

Infrared telescopes can map the interstellar medium by mapping the energy emitted by dust. Where the gas and dust are denser or where stars warm the dust, it is more luminous. ■ Figure 10-10 shows part of our Milky Way Galaxy aglow with radiation from dust at an infrared wavelength of 8 microns (8000 nm).

■ **Figure 10-10**

The Spitzer Space Telescope imaged the center of the Milky Way Galaxy at a wavelength of 8 microns (8000 nm) to reveal the distribution of the dusty interstellar medium. The brightest regions are clouds heated by young, massive stars. Individual stars can be seen as bright spots. (NASA/JPL-Caltech/S. Stolovy, Spitzer Science Center/Caltech)

Infrared image

Separating Facts from Hypotheses

When scientists disagree, what do they debate? The fundamental work of science is testing theories by comparing them with facts. The facts are evidence of how nature works, and they represent reality. Hypotheses are attempts to explain how nature works. Scientists are very careful to distinguish between the two.

Scientific facts are those observations or experimental results of which scientists are confident. Ornithologists might note that fewer mountain thrushes are returning each spring to a certain mountain valley. Counting bird populations reliably is difficult and requires special techniques, but if the scientists made the observations correctly, they can be confident of their result and treat it as a fact.

To explain the declining population of thrushes, the scientists might consider a number of hypotheses, such as global warming or chemical pollution in the food chain. The ornithologists are free to combine or adjust

their hypotheses to better explain the bird migration, but they are not free to adjust their facts. Scientific facts are the hard pebbles of reality that can't be changed.

New facts can aggravate debates that are already politically charged. The declining number of mountain thrushes, for example, could be unwelcome news because addressing the root problem might cost taxpayer dollars or hurt local business interests. Nonscientists sometimes debate an issue by trying to adjust or even deny the facts, but scientists are not free to ignore a fact because it is unpopular or inconvenient. Scientists debate an issue by arguing about which hypotheses best apply or how a hypothesis could be adjusted to fit the observed facts, but, once established, the facts themselves are not in question.

Whether scientists are measuring the density of an emission nebula or the size of a bird population, the final data become the

In science, evidence is made up of facts, which could range from precise numerical measurements to the observation of the shape of a flower. (M. Seeds)

reality against which hypotheses are tested. When Galileo said we should "read the book of nature," he meant we should consult reality as the final check on our understanding.

SCIENTIFIC ARGUMENT

What evidence can you cite that there is an interstellar medium? Everything in science is based on evidence, so your argument should discuss observations. First, there is the simple fact that certain parts of the interstellar medium are visible—the nebulae. Detailed analysis of emission and absorption lines show that all of interstellar space is filled by cold, thin gas. Extinction, reddening, and infrared observations show that some of the material is in the form of tiny dust specks.

Perhaps this is enough evidence to convince someone that the spaces between the stars are not empty, but there is more. Expand your argument. **What do infrared observations reveal about the interstellar gas?**

10-2 Components of the Interstellar Medium

YOU HAVE SEEN how astronomers can observe the interstellar medium at many different wavelengths, and those observations are the evidence against which they can test their theories (**How Do We Know? 10-1**). The observations clearly show that the interstellar medium is not uniform but is made up of different components.

Cool Clouds

The nebulae you see near hot, luminous stars are only small parts of the interstellar medium. Like the parts of a fog bank near streetlights, you see them easily because they are illuminated.

Most of the interstellar medium is invisible to human eyes and announces its presence strongly only at radio, infrared, ultraviolet, or X-ray wavelengths.

The multiple interstellar absorption lines seen in stellar spectra alerted you that some of the interstellar medium consists of clouds, and observations at infrared and radio wavelengths dramatically reveal clouds of cool gas and dust with densities of about 100 atoms per cubic centimeter. Because these clouds are not ionized, they are called **HI clouds.** They are 50 to 150 pc in diameter and have masses of a few solar masses. The gas temperature is only about 100 K. While it is easy to think of these clouds as more or less spherical blobs of gas, observations show that they are usually twisted, flattened, and tangled into chaotic shapes, as you can see in Figure 10-10—further evidence that the interstellar medium is not static and motionless.

The Intercloud Medium

The space between the cool HI clouds is filled by a hot **intercloud medium** with a temperature of a few thousand K and a density of only about 0.1 atom/cm^3. The gas is partially ionized by the ultraviolet photons in starlight; but, although it is hot, it has such a low density it does not emit noticeable visible light.

In regions where the interstellar medium is in equilibrium (in other words, where the HI clouds are not expanding or contracting), the pressure in the cool clouds and the hot intercloud medium is about the same. The pressure in a gas depends on its density and its temperature (**Focus on Fundamentals 5**). The HI clouds are cool but dense, and the gas of the intercloud

Pressure

One of the most fundamental parameters in science is **pressure,** a measure of force per unit area. If you are going to understand astronomy, you must be sure you understand pressure. Doctors measure blood pressure, and astronomers measure gas pressure, but they are really measuring the same fundamental parameter.

Pressure is expressed in the units of force per unit area. If you inflate the tires on a car, in the United States you use the unit pounds per square inch. A typical pressure might be 34 lb/in². It is important to note that this is not the total force pushing out on the inside of the tire but only the force exerted on a single square inch. When you stand, your weight exerts a force on the floor, and the pressure under your shoes is your weight divided by the surface area of your shoes' soles. A typical pressure might be only 4 lb/in². If you step on someone's toe, that is the pressure you exert. Of course, if you were wearing ice skates, your weight would be spread over a much smaller area, the area of the bottom of the blade, and

you might exert a pressure of 150 lb/in² or more. That's why skaters must be careful not to step on someone's toe. The pressure would be dangerously high.

Astronomers are most commonly interested in the behavior of matter when it is a gas, and pressure in a gas arises when atoms or molecules collide. Consider, for example, how the gas molecules colliding with the inside of a balloon exert an outward force on the rubber and keep the balloon inflated. If the gas is hot, the atoms or molecules move rapidly, and the resulting pressure is higher than for a cooler gas. If the gas is dense, there will be many gas particles colliding with the inside of the balloon, and the pressure will be higher than for a lower-density gas. In this way, pressure depends on both the temperature and the density of the gas.

Pressure and density are related, but they are not at all the same thing. Density is a measure of the amount of matter in a given volume, and pressure is a measure of the force that matter exerts on its surroundings.

Pressure pushes outward on the inside of a balloon.

A very-low-density gas and a very-high-density gas might have the same pressure if they had different temperatures.

In daily life, you think of pressure when you inflate an automobile tire, but pressure is common in nearly all of the sciences. Astronomers must consider pressure in thinking about the gas inside stars and the thin gas between the stars.

MASS | ENERGY | TEMPERATURE AND HEAT | DENSITY | **PRESSURE**

---

medium is hot but low in density. That means the two regions can have similar pressures even though their temperatures are quite different and allows the HI clouds and the intercloud medium to be stable and to coexist.

By now you are probably wondering how the intercloud medium could be ionized when it is not close to hot stars. To understand why it is ionized, imagine that you are an atom floating in the intercloud medium. Ultraviolet photons from distant stars are not common, but they do whiz past you now and then. Soon you absorb one of these photons and become ionized by losing an electron. In a denser gas, you would quickly find another electron, capture it, and become a neutral atom again, but the interstellar medium has such a low density that the gas particles are spread far apart. You must wait a very long time before an electron comes close enough for you to capture. That is why the gas of the intercloud medium is ionized; the atoms spend almost all their time waiting for an electron to wander past.

Molecular Clouds

Radio and infrared observations of the interstellar medium reveal some clouds of gas and dust with densities ranging from hundreds to a thousand particles (atoms and molecules) per cubic

centimeter. These clouds are called **molecular clouds** because they are dense enough to form molecules deep inside where the dust protects the molecules from ultraviolet photons, which would break up the fragile molecules.

Molecular clouds are very cold, only a few degrees above absolute zero, and much of the gas is in the form of molecules. Molecular hydrogen (H_2) is the main gas, but that molecule is difficult to detect, so astronomers typically study the clouds by studying radio emission from other molecules such as carbon monoxide (CO). Although CO is 10,000 times less common in the clouds than is H_2, the CO molecules are a strong source of radio emission at a wavelength of 2.6 mm in the microwave part of the radio spectrum. Over 150 other molecules including OH, N_2O (nitrous oxide, which some humans inhale), and ethyl alcohol (which some humans drink) have been detected in molecular clouds, but the overall composition of the clouds is the same as the interstellar medium in general; they are about 70 percent hydrogen, 28 percent helium, and 2 percent heavier atoms. The difference is that they are dense enough and cold enough for the atoms to link together and form molecules.

The CO molecules and the dust in the cloud tend to keep it cold. CO and dust are very good at radiating infrared radiation, and the cloud is transparent to infrared wavelengths. So the infrared photons zip out of the clouds carrying away energy, and that keeps the temperature low.

Molecular clouds contain up to a few hundred solar masses, but **giant molecular clouds** contain up to a million solar masses. They can be 100 pc (300 ly) in diameter and in their densest cores can contain 100,000 particles per cubic centimeter. The giant molecular clouds tend to form from gas that has settled toward the plane of our galaxy, and you can see a number of them as dark nebulae that obscure stars and form the Great Rift along the center of the Milky Way (p. 195). Thousands of giant molecular clouds exist in our galaxy.

Giant molecular clouds are the nests of star birth. Deep inside these great clouds, gravity can pull the matter inward and create new stars (■ Figure 10-11). That is a story you will follow in detail in the next chapter. For now, you can learn more about the interstellar medium by examining its hottest component.

Coronal Gas

The interstellar medium seems very cold, so you would hardly expect to find it emitting X-rays because such high-energy photons are commonly produced by high temperatures. Nevertheless, X-ray telescopes above Earth's atmosphere have detected X-rays from parts of the interstellar medium. This gas has been called the **coronal gas** because it has temperatures of 10^6 K or higher, similar to the sun's corona. Of course, the coronal gas in the interstellar medium is not related in any way to the actual corona of the sun.

You might expect the coronal gas to have a very high pressure because it is so hot, but actually it has a very low density. It contains only 0.003 to 0.0004 particle/cm^3. That is, you would have to search through a few hundred to a few thousand cubic centimeters of coronal gas to find a single particle—an ionized atom or an electron. Because of its very low density, the gas pressure in the coronal gas can be roughly the same as in the HI clouds, and the intercloud medium can stay in equilibrium (not expand or contract).

Coronal gas is evidently produced when a massive star dies violently in a supernova explosion. Although they are rare, such explosions blast large amounts of very hot gas outward in expanding bubbles. Gas flowing away from very hot, young stars can also produce coronal gas (■ Figure 10-12). In some cases, neighboring bubbles of coronal gas may expand into each other and merge to form larger volumes called superbubbles. Such regions are impor-

Visual + infrared image

■ **Figure 10-11**

A giant molecular cloud collapsed and began forming stars a few million years ago, including three star clusters visible in this image. Intense radiation and outflowing gas from the hottest, most luminous of these stars is eating into the dark molecular cloud and exciting some of its gases to glow. The nebula is located 210,000 ly from Earth in a nearby galaxy. (NASA, ESA, and A. Nota, STScI/ESA)

Visual + X-ray image

■ **Figure 10-12**

Intense star formation within this cloud is blowing it apart. On the right side of this image, roughly 200 hot, young, massive stars are inflating bubbles of coronal gas, shown as blue in the X-ray image. On the left side of the diagram, the expanding clouds of coronal gas come from hot stars plus a number of past supernova explosions. (X-ray: NASA/CXC/CfA/R. Tuellmann et al.; Opitcal: NASA/AURA/STScI) tant because the expanding gas may compress nearby clouds and trigger star formation. Probably about 20 percent of the space between the stars is filled with bubbles of coronal gas.

Far-ultraviolet and X-ray observations reveal that the sun is located just inside a region of coronal gas roughly 100 pc in diameter filled with hot, ionized hydrogen. This **local bubble** (or **local void**) of gas in which the sun is located was inflated when a supernova exploded near the sun within the last few million years and may be linked to other hot, transparent regions.

Observations at many wavelengths show that the interstellar medium is complex with four different components (■ Table 10-1). The exact proportions are not well known, but cool clouds probably make up very roughly 20 percent of the mass and the intercloud medium about 50 percent. The molecular clouds are dense and make up about 20 percent of the mass, and the low-density coronal gas, although it occupies a large volume, amounts to only about 10 percent of the mass in the interstellar medium. In fact the four-component picture is a simplified model of the real situation, but it is adequate to portray the general properties of the interstellar medium.

■ Table 10-1 | Four Components of the Interstellar Medium

Component	Temperature (K)	Density (atoms/cm³)	Gas State
Molecular clouds	20–50	10^3–10^5	Molecules
HI clouds	50–150	1–1000	Neutral hydrogen; other atoms ionized
Intercloud medium	10^3–10^4	0.01	Partially ionized
Coronal gas	10^5–10^6	10^{-4}–10^{-3}	Highly ionized

SCIENTIFIC ARGUMENT

If hydrogen is the most common molecule, why do astronomers depend on the CO molecule to map molecular clouds?

This scientific argument links a bit of atomic physics with the chain of inference that leads from what can be observed to what astronomers need to know. Although hydrogen is the most common atom in the universe and molecular hydrogen the most common molecule, molecules of hydrogen do not radiate easily in the radio part of the spectrum. But the much less common CO (carbon monoxide) molecule is a very efficient radiator of radio energy, so radio astronomers use it as a tracer of molecular clouds. Wherever radio telescopes reveal a great cloud of CO, you can be confident that most of the gas is molecular hydrogen.

You can also be confident that the molecular clouds contain dust, because it is the dust that protects the molecules in the cloud from the ultraviolet radiation that would otherwise break the molecules into atoms.

At the temperatures found in the interstellar medium, dust doesn't radiate very much longer-wavelength radio energy, but you can study it in the infrared. Although the dust in a molecular cloud is very cold and makes up a small percentage of the total mass, it is a very good radiator of infrared radiation. Create a new argument using the physics of infrared emission from dust to answer a different question: **How can a small mass of cold dust radiate vast amounts of infrared radiation?**

(10-3) The Gas-Star-Gas Cycle

THE INTERSTELLAR MEDIUM IS COMPLEX and, in some cases, quite beautiful, but it would be just a curiosity if it were not intimately related to stars. Stars are born from the interstellar medium, and aging stars return gas and dust back into the interstellar medium. As you learn about that cycle, you are beginning to learn about the life story of the stars that will be portrayed in the next few chapters.

Gas and Dust from Aging Stars

Astronomers have clear evidence that much of the hydrogen and helium in the interstellar medium is gas left over from the formation of our galaxy over 10 billion years ago, so that gas has never been inside stars. But some of the gas and dust that lie between the stars has been produced in stars and expelled as the stars aged.

The sun exhales gas and dust in the solar wind, but that is a gentle breeze compared to the wind blown out of aging stars. The atmospheres of those stars are so cool that some atoms can condense to form specks of dust, including carbon and silicon. The pressure of the starlight pushes those dust specks out of the star along with a powerful flow of hydrogen, helium, and other gases (■ Figure 10-13). The sun, for example, will blow away almost half of its mass in a relatively short episode before it reaches its final fate in about five billion years. Thus, part of the gas and dust in the interstellar medium has been exhaled by stars.

In later chapters, you will learn that some stars die in violent supernova explosions that blast matter outward in expanding clouds of hot gas. Much of the coronal gas in the interstellar medium is produced by supernova explosions. As those gases cool, dust condenses like soot from a candle flame, so supernovae add large amounts of dust to the interstellar medium. As you will learn in a later chapter, other types of stars end their lives less violently but also contribute substantial amounts of material to the interstellar medium.

Supernova explosions and the blasts of light and gas blowing away from the hottest stars keep the interstellar medium stirred with **shock waves,** the astronomical equivalent of sonic booms. As those shock waves sweep through the interstellar medium, they compress gas and form clouds dense enough for molecules to begin forming. Many of the molecular clouds in the galaxy have been twisted, distorted, and compressed by shock waves.

Motion of Betelgeuse with respect to the interstellar medium

Bow shock

Betelgeuse

Bow shock

Infrared image

■ **Figure 10-13**

The red giant star Betelgeuse is blowing away a powerful wind of gas and dust at 17 km/s. Where that wind collides with the interstellar medium, it forms a bow shock much like the bow wave in front of a speed boat. The bow shock is not centered on the star because it is speeding through the interstellar medium as shown by the arrow in the figure. (Ueta et al, PASJ, 2008)

A Preview of Star Formation

Molecular clouds form as the interstellar medium is compressed, and gravity and turbulence tend to concentrate these clouds to form giant molecular clouds. Such clouds are located along the spiral arms of our galaxy.

Because these clouds of gas are so cool, gravity can squeeze them to higher densities, especially if they are compressed further by a passing shock wave. The densest regions of molecular clouds can become gravitationally unstable, meaning the gravity pulling the gas together is stronger than the pressure and turbulence in the gas. As the gas falls together, the dense cores break into fragments and form clusters of stars. A single giant molecular cloud can sometimes form a number of clusters of stars.

■ **Figure 10-14**

Matter cycles from the interstellar medium to form stars and back into the interstellar medium. Slowly our galaxy is using up its star-making supplies and exhausting its reserve of the hydrogen fuel that powers newborn stars.

Aging stars exhale gas and dust into the interstellar medium.

Visual image

Gas expanding away from a supernova explosion

Stars forming from clouds of interstellar gas

The Gas-Stars-Gas Cycle

Gas and dust in the interstellar medium.

Visual image

Visual image

X-ray image

The most massive stars to form are the hottest and exhale gas most violently. Also, as you will learn in a few chapters, the most massive stars live very short lives—only a few million years—and die in violent supernova explosions blasting more gas back into the interstellar medium.

A giant molecular cloud can make lots of stars, but as supernovae begin expelling coronal gas, the molecular cloud can be ripped apart and mixed back into the general interstellar medium, and that closes the circle on the gas-stars-gas cycle (■ Figure 10-14).

As matter in our galaxy passes through this cycle, some of the mass gets incorporated into low-mass stars that live very long

times or gets trapped in remnants of stars like white dwarfs, neutron stars, and black holes that you will learn about in later chapters. Consequently, the matter in those remnants is removed from the cycle. Also, with each cycle some of the hydrogen gets fused into helium and heavier atoms like carbon, nitrogen, and oxygen. Thus, as the eons pass, our galaxy is gradually using up its star-making mass and hydrogen fuel as it forms stars. Also, with each generation of stars, the interstellar medium becomes richer in those heavier atoms, and the chemical composition of the interstellar medium slowly changes. In a later chapter, that will give you a critical clue to understanding the life story of our galaxy.

What Are We? Drifters

City dwellers see only the brightest stars scattered across the sky, but even those who live far from city lights see almost nothing between the stars. It is easy to imagine that space is empty. Only a few hazy nebulae such as that in Orion's sword hint at the hidden richness of space.

We live in a universe filled with beauty beyond our senses. Special telescopes and cameras can capture photographs of glowing gas containing brilliant stars and dark clouds of gas twisting through space. Clouds of neutral gas, cold dust, and hot bubbles of coronal gas are not visible to our eyes, but they are part of the complex beauty of the

interstellar medium. All around us, stars drift through an invisible ocean whose peaceful reaches are blasted here and there by storms of light and heat as the interstellar medium interacts with the stars.

Science enriches our lives by revealing the beauty we cannot sense directly.

Study and Review

Summary

▶ The **interstellar medium (ISM) (p. 193)**, the gas and dust between the stars, is mostly concentrated near the plane of our Milky Way Galaxy and has an average density of about one atom per cubic centimeter.

▶ A **nebula (p. 193)** is a cloud of gas in space, and an **HII region (p. 194)** (also known as an **emission nebula [p. 194]**) is produced when ultraviolet radiation from hot stars ionizes nearby gas, making it glow like a giant neon sign. The red, blue, and violet Balmer lines blend together to produce the characteristic pink-red color of ionized hydrogen.

▶ A **reflection nebula (p. 194)** is produced by gas and dust illuminated by a star that is not hot enough to ionize the gas. Rather, the dust scatters the starlight to produce a reflection of the stellar absorption spectrum. Because shorter-wavelength photons scatter more easily than longer-wavelength photons, reflection nebulae look blue. The daytime sky looks blue for the same reason.

▶ A **dark nebula (p. 195)** is a cloud of gas and dust that is noticeable because it blocks the light of distant stars. The irregular shapes

of these dark nebulae reveal the turbulence in the interstellar medium.

▶ **Interstellar dust (p. 196)** makes up roughly 1 percent of the mass of the interstellar medium. The remaining 99 percent of the mass is gas.

▶ About 70 percent of the mass of the interstellar medium is hydrogen gas, and 28 percent is helium. About 2 percent is atoms heavier than helium. This is approximately the same composition as the sun and other stars.

▶ The gas in nebulae has a low density, and the atoms collide so rarely that an electron caught in a **metastable level (p. 196)** can remain there long enough to finally fall to a lower level and emit a photon. This produces so-called **forbidden lines (p. 196)** that are not seen in laboratory spectra on Earth where the atoms in the gas collide too often.

▶ **Interstellar extinction (p. 196)**, or dimming, makes the distant stars look fainter than they should. **Interstellar reddening (p. 196)** makes distant stars appear too red because dust particles in the interstellar medium scatter blue light more easily than red light. The dependence of this extinction on wavelength shows that the scattering dust particles are very small. The dust is made of carbon, silicates, iron, ice, and other common atoms and molecules.

► The interstellar gas is cold and has a very low density, and this makes **interstellar absorption lines (p. 197)** much narrower than the spectral lines produced in stars. Such lines are usually obvious in stellar spectra because they represent ions that cannot exist in the atmospheres of the stars. Interstellar lines stand out in the spectra of spectroscopic binaries because they do not shift their wavelengths as do lines produced by the orbiting stars. Multiple interstellar lines reveal that the light has passed through more than one interstellar cloud on its way to Earth.

► The low-density gas of the interstellar medium also produces emission lines at many wavelengths. The **21-cm radiation (p. 198)** is a forbidden line produced when the electrons in hydrogen atoms change the direction of their spin and emit radio wavelength photons. This radiation allows radio astronomers to map the distribution of neutral hydrogen gas in the interstellar medium.

► Radio, infrared, and X-ray telescopes have detected emission from over 150 different molecules in the interstellar medium.

► Interstellar dust, although it is very cold, emits blackbody radiation; and, because the dust in an interstellar cloud has a huge surface area, it can emit large amounts of long-wavelength infrared radiation.

► The interstellar medium is made up of four main components. **HI clouds (p. 202)** of neutral hydrogen are cold clouds containing a few solar masses in a region 10 to 150 pc in diameter. They are separated from each other by a hotter but lower-density gas called the **intercloud medium (p. 202)**, and the two generally have similar **pressures (p. 203)** and are in equilibrium.

► Large, dense clouds of gas and dust are called **molecular clouds (p. 203)** because they are so dense molecules can form inside them. Such clouds can be mapped by the radio photons emitted by CO and OH molecules. Hydrogen molecules (H_2) do not radiate at radio wavelengths. The largest of these are called **giant molecular clouds (p. 204)** and are the sites of star formation.

► Molecules can be broken up by short-wavelength photons, but the dust in molecular clouds scatters these photons and shields the molecules in the inner part of the cloud. Because the molecules are so good at radiating energy away, they keep the clouds very cold.

► X-ray observations have detected very hot **coronal gas (p. 204)**, the fourth component of the interstellar medium. It is produced by hot gas blown away from massive stars and gas expelled from supernova explosions. Far-ultraviolet observations show that the sun is located in a **local bubble** (or **local void**) **(p. 205)** of coronal gas that was apparently produced by a supernova explosion near the sun within the last few million years.

► The interstellar medium interacts with the stars through a gas-star-gas cycle. Hot stars and supernovae expel gas and dust into the interstellar medium, and cool stars contribute more gas and dust. The gas and dust collects into giant molecular clouds where new stars form singly or in clusters. Star formation ends in a molecular cloud when hot gas from newborn massive stars and supernovae form **shock waves (p. 205)** and blow the cloud apart.

► As matter in our galaxy passes through the gas-star-gas cycle, some is trapped in low-mass stars and black holes. Also, more and more hydrogen is converted into helium and heavier elements. In this way, our galaxy is gradually using up its star-making supplies.

Review Questions

1. What evidence visible to human eyes can you cite that the spaces between the stars are not totally empty?
2. What evidence can you cite that the interstellar medium contains both gas and dust?
3. How do the spectra of HII regions differ from the spectra of reflection nebulae? Why?
4. How is the blue color of a reflection nebula related to the blue color of the daytime sky?
5. Why do distant stars look redder than their spectral types suggest?
6. Why are interstellar lines so narrow? Why do some spectral lines forbidden in spectra on Earth appear in spectra of interstellar clouds and nebulae? What does that tell you?
7. Why can the 21-cm radio emission line of neutral hydrogen be observed in the interstellar medium but not easily in the laboratory?
8. How can the HI clouds and the intercloud medium have similar pressures when their temperatures are so different?
9. Why can molecular clouds form molecules in their interiors while HI clouds cannot?
10. What produces the coronal gas?
11. How does the interstellar medium interact with stars?
12. **How Do We Know?** Why are scientists free to adjust their hypotheses but not their facts?

Discussion Questions

1. When you see distant streetlights through smog, they look dimmer and redder than they do normally. But when you see the same streetlights through fog or falling snow, they look dimmer but not redder. Use your knowledge of the interstellar medium to discuss the relative sizes of the particles in smog, fog, and snowstorms compared to the wavelength of light.
2. If you could see a few stars through a dark nebula, how would you expect their spectra and colors to differ from similar stars just in front of the dark nebula?

Problems

1. A small nebula has a diameter of 20 arc seconds and a distance of 1000 pc from Earth. What is the diameter of the nebula in parsecs? In meters? (*Hint:* Use the small-angle formula, Chapter 3.)
2. The dust in a molecular cloud has a temperature of about 50 K. At what wavelength does it emit the maximum energy? (*Hint:* Consider blackbody radiation, Chapter 7.)
3. Extinction dims starlight by about 1 magnitude per 1000 pc. What fraction of photons survives a trip of 1000 pc? (*Hint:* Consider the definition of the magnitude scale in Chapter 2.)
4. If the total extinction through a dark nebula is 10 magnitudes, what fraction of photons makes it through the cloud? (*Hint:* See Problem 3.)
5. The density of air in a child's balloon 20 cm in diameter is roughly the same as the density of air at sea level, 10^{19} particles/cm³. To how large a diameter would you have to expand the balloon to make the gas inside the same density as the interstellar medium, about 1 particle/cm³? (*Hint:* The volume of a sphere is $\frac{4}{3}\pi R^3$.)

6. If a giant molecular cloud has a diameter of 30 pc and drifts relative to neighboring clouds at 20 km/s, how long will it take to travel its own diameter?

7. An HI cloud is 4 pc in diameter and has a density of 100 hydrogen atoms/cm³. What is its total mass in kilograms? (*Hint:* The volume of a sphere is $\frac{4}{3}\pi R^3$, and the mass of a hydrogen atom is 1.67×10^{-27} kg.)

8. Find the mass in kilograms of a giant molecular cloud that is 30 pc in diameter and has a density of 300 hydrogen molecules/cm³. (*Hint:* See Problem 7.)

9. At what wavelength does the coronal gas radiate most strongly? (*Hint:* Consider blackbody radiation, Chapter 7.)

Learning to Look

NASA and the Hubble Heritage Team, STScI/AURA

1. At visual wavelengths, the bright-blue star at the center of the images in Figure 10-4 is surrounded by a blue nebula. What can you conclude about the temperature of this star?

2. The image at right shows two nebulae, one pink in the background and one black in the foreground. What kind of nebulae are these?

11 | The Formation and Structure of Stars

Infrared image

Guidepost

The last chapter introduced you to the gas and dust between the stars that are raw material for new stars. Here you will begin putting together observations and theories to learn how nature makes stars from the interstellar medium and to understand the internal structure of stars. That will answer four essential questions:

— **How do stars form?**

— **What is the evidence that theories of star formation are correct?**

— **How do stars maintain their stability?**

— **How do stars make energy?**

As you finish this chapter you will have gained a view of the exciting and energetic infancy of stars. In the next chapter, you will follow stars into their stable, slowly evolving adult life stage, called the main sequence.

This infrared image of the Great Nebula in Orion shows cool protostars (depicted as orange) deeply embedded in the gas and dust of a giant molecular cloud, as well as newborn stars that are just blowing their dust cocoons away, plus abundant raw material for new stars. (Mark McCaughrean [AI Potsdam] et al., ISAAC, VLT ANTU, ESO)

■ **Figure 11-1**

Nebula NGC 1333 is filled with newborn stars caught in the act of forming in this infrared image. (NASA/JPL-Caltech/R. A. Gutermuth, Harvard-Smithsonian CfA)

THE STARS ARE NOT ETERNAL. When you look at the sky, you see hundreds of points of light, and, amazingly enough, each one, like the sun, is a tremendous nuclear fusion reactor held together by its own gravity. The stars you see tonight are the same stars your parents, grandparents, and great-grandparents saw. Stars don't change perceptibly in a person's lifetime, even during all of human history, but they do not last forever. Stars are "born," and stars "die." This chapter begins that story.

How can you know what the life cycles and internal processes of stars are, given that you won't live long enough to see them evolve, and you can't see inside them? The answer lies in the methods of science. By constructing theories that describe how nature works and then testing those theories against evidence from observations, you can unravel some of nature's greatest secrets. In this chapter, you will see how gravity creates stars from the thin material of interstellar space. You will then learn more about how the flow of energy from the insides of stars outward toward their surfaces balances gravity and makes the stars stable, and how nuclear reactions in the cores of stars ultimately supply that energy flow. To understand this story, you will plunge from the cold gas of the interstellar medium into the hot centers of the stars themselves.

11-1 Making Stars from the Interstellar Medium

ASTRONOMERS FIND HUNDREDS of places in the sky where clouds of gas glow brightly because they are illuminated by the hottest, most massive and luminous stars, of spectral types O and B. As you will learn in detail in Chapter 12, those kinds of stars pour out such floods of energy that they can last only a few million years, so you must be seeing them pretty near where they were born. O and B stars are therefore signposts pointing to star-forming regions, which are always among the densest parts of the interstellar medium (■ Figure 11-1).

Star Birth in Giant Molecular Clouds

As you saw in the previous chapter, spectra of the interstellar medium (ISM) show that its chemical composition is basically the same as stars. By observing at far-infrared and radio wavelengths, to which interstellar dust is basically transparent, astronomers can peer inside even dense molecular clouds and find evidence that stars are forming there. In fact, the giant molecular clouds discussed in the preceding chapter are each massive enough to make thousands of new stars. But how do those large low-density clouds of cold gas and dust become comparatively small, high-density, hot stars?

Giant molecular clouds have typical diameters of 50 pc and typical masses exceeding 10^5 solar masses, vastly larger than a single star. The gas in a giant molecular cloud is about 10^{20} times less dense than a star and has temperatures of only a few degrees Kelvin. Those clouds can form into stars only if small regions of the cloud can be compressed somehow to high density and high temperature. But at least four factors resist the compression of an interstellar gas cloud, and those factors must be overcome by gravity before star formation can begin.

First, thermal energy in the gas appears as motion of the atoms and molecules. Even at the very low temperature of 10 K, the average hydrogen molecule moves at about 0.33 km/s (about 740 mph). This thermal motion would make the cloud come apart if gravity were too weak to hold it together.

Second, the interstellar medium is filled with a magnetic field. The ISM field is only about 0.0001 times as strong as Earth's magnetic field, but that is enough to act as an internal spring and prevent the gas from contracting. Neutral atoms and molecules are unaffected by a magnetic field, but ions, having an electric charge, cannot move freely through a magnetic field. Although the gas in a molecular cloud is mostly neutral, some ions are included, and that means a magnetic field can exert a force on the gas as a whole. Gravity must overcome the interstellar magnetic field to make the gas contract. Under some conditions, the ionized gas in giant molecular clouds can gradually recombine with free electrons. The resulting less-ionized gas is freer to "slip past" the magnetic field and contract. This process has been observed inside isolated molecular clouds.

Third, everything in the universe rotates. As a gas cloud begins to contract, it spins more and more rapidly as it conserves angular momentum, just as ice-skaters spin faster as they pull in their arms (see Figure 5-7). This rotation can become so rapid that it resists further contraction of the cloud.

Fourth, turbulence in the interstellar medium can prevent a cloud from contracting. In the previous chapter, you learned that nebulae are often twisted and distorted by strong currents. This turbulence can help prevent a molecular cloud from contracting.

Given these four resisting factors, it may seem surprising that any giant molecular clouds can contract at all, but radio and infrared observations show that at least some giant molecular clouds develop concentrated regions called dense cores that are roughly 0.1 pc in size and contain about 1 solar mass. A single giant molecular cloud may contain many of these dense cores, each perhaps destined to become a star.

Both theory and observation suggest that giant molecular clouds can be triggered to form stars by a passing shock wave, sometimes just called a **shock**, the astronomical equivalent of a sonic boom (■ Figure 11-2). During such a triggering event, some regions of the large cloud can be compressed to such high densities that the resisting factors can no longer oppose gravity, and star formation begins.

Shock waves that can trigger star formation are common in the interstellar medium. For example, gas flows of several sorts produce shocks when they push into colder, denser interstellar matter. Supernova explosions (Chapter 13) create powerful shock waves that rush through the interstellar medium (■ Figure 11-3a). Also, the ignition of very hot stars ionizes nearby gas and causes it to flow rapidly away (Figure 11-3b). New stars of all types seem to emit strong winds and jets while they are forming. Each of those kinds of flows can also produce shocks. A second type of star formation trigger is the collision of molecular clouds. Because the clouds are large, they are likely to run into each other occasionally, and because they contain magnetic fields they cannot easily pass through each other. A collision between such clouds can compress parts of the clouds and cause star formation. A third type of trigger is the spiral pattern of our Milky Way Galaxy (see Figure 1-11). Theory and evidence both indicate that spiral arms are shock waves that travel around the disk of the galaxy like the moving hands of a clock (Chapter 15). As a cloud passes through a spiral arm, the cloud can be compressed, and star formation may begin. Astronomers have found regions of star formation in which each of these trigger processes can be identified.

A single giant molecular cloud containing a million solar masses does not contract to form a single humongous star.

Shock Wave Triggers Star Formation

A shock wave (red) approaches an interstellar gas cloud.

The shock wave passes through and compresses the cloud.

Motions in the cloud continue after the shock wave passes.

The densest parts of the cloud become gravitationally unstable.

Contracting regions of gas give birth to stars.

■ Figure 11-2

In this summary of a computer model, an interstellar gas cloud is triggered into star formation by a passing shock wave. The events summarized here might span about 6 million years.

Evidently, collapsing clouds break into fragments, and the densest parts form a number of dense cores. Exactly why clouds divide into fragments isn't fully understood, but their rotation, magnetic fields, and turbulence apparently play important roles. Whatever the reason, when a giant cloud of interstellar matter contracts, it forms many newborn stars simultaneously.

■ **Figure 11-3**

(a) An expanding shock wave from a supernova explosion a few million years ago has compressed a nearby cloud of gas and triggered the birth of new stars. Most of the bright, young stars in this arc-shaped nebula are hidden deep in dust clouds and are not yet visible at visual wavelengths. (NASA/JPL-Caltech/V. Gorjian, NOAO) (b) Nebula N44 has given birth to a large cluster of stars. The process of star formation can spread to new regions by the effects of stars already formed. (ESO)

Heating by Contraction

You can understand how low-density clouds of interstellar gas might contract and become dense enough to make stars, but how does the cold gas become hot enough to be a star? The answer, once again, is gravity.

To see how gravity can heat the gas, shift your attention to one dense cloud core destined to become a single star. Once that small cloud of gas begins to contract, gravity draws the atoms toward the center. This means the atoms are falling, and, like all things that fall, they gain speed as they fall. In fact, astronomers refer to this early stage in the formation of a star as **free-fall collapse**. Although the atoms may have been moving slowly to start with, by the time they have fallen most of the way to the center of the cloud, they are traveling rapidly. Thermal energy is the agitation of the particles in a gas, so this increase in speed is a step toward heating the gas. However, you can't say that the gas is hot simply because all of the atoms are moving fast. The air in the cabin of a jet airplane is traveling rapidly, but it isn't hot because all of the atoms are moving in generally the same direction along with the plane. The high speed of the infalling atoms is not converted into thermal energy until their motion becomes randomized, and that happens when the atoms begin to collide with one another as they fall into the central region of the cloud. The

jumbled, random, rapid motion of the colliding atoms represents thermal energy, and so the temperature of the gas increases.

This is an important principle in astronomy. Whenever a cloud of gas contracts, the atoms move "downward" in the gravitational field, pick up speed, and collide more rapidly, and the gas grows hotter. Astronomers express this by saying that gravitational energy is converted into thermal energy. Whenever a gas cloud expands, gas atoms move "upward" against gravity and lose speed, and the gas becomes cooler. Astronomers say that in this case thermal energy is converted into gravitational energy. The principle applies not only to clouds of interstellar gas but also to contracting and expanding stars, as you will see in the following chapters.

Earlier you learned that thermal energy in random atomic motion is one of the factors that can resist gravity and keep a cloud from contracting. So, you may ask, does the contraction stop once the free-fall collapse heats the gas? The answer is no, not if there is a way for the compressed cloud to get rid of some thermal energy by radiating it away. The contracting cloud is still relatively cold; and, according to Wien's law (see Chapter 7), its material should produce very-long-wavelength radiation to which the cloud will be mostly transparent. Thus, some thermal energy generated by the collapse can escape the cloud, and contraction can continue. Astronomers know this happens because they

O B A F G K M

10^6

10^4

10^2

1

10^{-2}

10^{-4}

L/L$_\odot$

A contracting protostar grows hotter but is hidden inside its dusty cocoon and is detectable only in the infrared.

Main sequence

A newborn star becomes visible as it blows its dust cocoon away.

A protostar begins as an invisible concentration of gas deep inside a cloud.

Protostars glow in the infrared.

Infrared image

b

30,000 20,000 10,000 5000 3000 2000 1000 500 300 200 100

a

Temperature (K)

■ **Figure 11-4**

(a) This H–R diagram has been extended to very low temperatures to show schematically the contraction of a dim, cool protostar. (Illustration design by M. Seeds) (b) Protostars are normally invisible at visual wavelengths because they are cool objects and are deep inside dusty clouds of gas, but they are detectable at infrared wavelengths. (ESO)

observe far-infrared spectral emission lines, called **cooling lines**, from dense cloud cores that are evidently contracting.

Your study of gas clouds has shown how the contraction of dense cores in giant molecular clouds can begin and how this contraction heats the gas. Now you are ready to construct a detailed story of the transformation from gas cloud to star.

Protostars

To understand star formation further, you can continue to follow the contraction of a dense core as matter falls in and heats up, and the object gradually behaves more and more like a star. When the contracting core becomes hot enough, it produces short-wavelength radiation to which the core is not transparent. Then the core's thermal energy can no longer escape, and it enters a new stage of slow, rather than free-fall, contraction. Although the term is used rather loosely by astronomers, a **protostar** can be defined as a prestellar object that is compressed enough that it is opaque at all wavelengths but not so hot and compressed as to be able to generate energy by nuclear fusion, as would a main-sequence star.

Instead, a protostar shines with energy released gravitationally, from a combination of matter falling inward to the protostar plus slow contraction of the protostar itself.

Early in its life a protostar develops a higher-density region at the center and a low-density outer region, or envelope, because the material that started falling in from closer to the center races ahead of material falling from farther out. Meanwhile, material continues to flow inward from the outer parts of the cloud. In other words, the cloud contracts from the inside out, with the protostar growing deep inside a surrounding cloud of cold, dusty gas.

These enveloping clouds have been called **cocoons** because they hide the forming protostar from view. That is especially true for observations at short wavelengths. The cocoon absorbs the protostar's radiation and, growing warm, reradiates the energy as longer-wavelength infrared radiation than the radiation produced by the protostar. In other words, if you observe at short infrared wavelengths, you may be able to observe the protostar itself; at longer wavelengths, you might be able to observe its envelope. In either case, what you detect would be cooler than a star but much larger than the sun and would therefore be a very luminous infrared source, with properties placing it in the upper right part of the H–R diagram (■ Figure 11-4).

The theory of star formation takes you into an unearthly realm filled with unfamiliar processes and objects. How can anyone really know how stars are born? Although the theory of star

Theories and Proof

How do astronomers know the sun isn't made of burning coal? People say dismissively of a theory they dislike, "That's only a theory," as if a theory were just a random guess. A hypothesis is something like a guess, but of course not a random one. What scientists mean by the word *theory* is a hypothesis that has "graduated" to being confidently considered a well-tested truth. You can think of a hypothesis as equivalent to having a suspect in a criminal case and a theory as equivalent to having finished the trial and having convicted someone of the crime.

Of course, no matter how many tests and experiments you conduct, you can never prove that any scientific theory is absolutely true. It is always possible that the next observation you make will disprove the theory. And it is unfortunately sometimes true that innocent people go to jail and guilty people are free, but, occasionally, with further evidence, those legal mistakes can be fixed.

There have always been hypotheses about why the sun is hot. Some scientists once thought the sun was a ball of burning coal. Only a century ago, most astronomers accepted the hypothesis that the sun was hot because gravity was making it contract. In the late 19th century, geologists showed that Earth

was much older than the sun could be if it was powered by gravity, so the gravity hypothesis had to be wrong. It wasn't until 1920 that a new hypothesis was proposed by Sir Arthur Eddington, who suggested that the sun is powered somehow by the energy in atomic nuclei. In 1938 the German-American astrophysicist Hans Bethe showed how nuclear fusion could power the sun. He won the Nobel Prize in 1967.

The fusion hypothesis is now so completely confirmed that it is fair to call it a theory. No one will ever go to the center of the sun, so you can't *prove* the fusion theory is right. Many observations and model calculations support this theory, and in Chapter 8 you saw further evidence in the neutrinos that have been detected coming from the sun's core. Nevertheless there remains some tiny possibility that all the observations and models are misunderstood and that the theory will be overturned by some future discovery. Astronomers have tremendous confidence that the sun is powered by fusion and not gravity or coal, but a scientific theory can never be proven conclusively correct.

There is a great difference between a theory in the colloquial sense of a far-fetched guess and a scientific theory that has undergone decades of testing and confirmation with

Technically it is still a theory, but astronomers have tremendous confidence that the sun gets its power from nuclear fusion and not from burning coal. (SOHO/MDI)

observations, experiments, and models. But no theory can ever be proven absolutely true. It is up to you as a consumer of knowledge and a responsible citizen to distinguish between a flimsy guess and a well-tested theory that deserves to be treated like truth—at least pending further information.

---

formation, like all scientific theories, can never be absolutely proven, scientists have strong confidence in it because of repeated testing by observation (**How Do We Know? 11-1**). There is plenty of evidence that star formation is a continuous process; you can be sure that stars are being born right now.

11-2 The Orion Nebula: Evidence of Star Formation

IN ASTRONOMY, evidence means observations. Consequently, you can ask what observations confirm the hypotheses about star formation. Protostars are not easy to observe. Astronomers calculate that the protostar stage is only a few tenths of a percent of the lifetime of a star like the sun; and, although that is a long time in human terms, you cannot expect to catch many stars in the protostar stage. Furthermore, protostars form deep inside clouds of dusty gas that block your view at visible wavelengths, and, being cooler than full-fledged stars, they produce radiation primarily at longer wavelengths. Astronomers must therefore

depend on observations at infrared and radio wavelengths to search for protostars in their natural environment.

On a clear winter night, you can see with an unaided eye the Great Nebula of Orion as a fuzzy blob in Orion's sword. With binoculars or a small telescope, it is striking, and through a large telescope, it is breathtaking. At the center of the nebula lie four brilliant blue-white stars known as the Trapezium, the brightest in a cluster of a few hundred stars. Surrounding the stars are the glowing filaments of a nebula more than 8 pc across. Like a great thundercloud illuminated from within, the churning currents of gas and dust suggest immense power. The significance of the Orion Nebula, also known as Messier 42, lies hidden, figuratively and literally, beyond the visible nebula. This region is ripe with star formation.

Observing Star Formation

Observations provide plenty of evidence that star formation is a continuous process; you can be sure that stars are being born right now. Read **Star Formation in the Orion Nebula** on pages 216–217 and note four important points and one new term:

1 The nebula you see is only a small part of a vast, dusty molecular cloud. You see the nebula because the larger stars

Star Formation in the Orion Nebula

Side view of Orion Nebula

Hot Trapezium stars · Protostars

To Earth

Expanding ionized hydrogen

Molecular cloud

1 The visible Orion Nebula shown below is a pocket of ionized gas on the near side of a vast, dusty molecular cloud that fills much of the southern part of the constellation Orion. The molecular cloud can be mapped by radio telescopes. To scale, the cloud would be many times larger than this page. As the stars of the Trapezium were born in the cloud, their radiation has ionized the gas and pushed it away. Where the expanding nebula pushes into the larger molecular cloud, it is compressing the gas (see diagram at right) and may be triggering the formation of the protostars that can be detected at infrared wavelengths within the molecular cloud.

Hundreds of stars lie within the nebula, but only the four brightest, those in the Trapezium, are easy to see with a small telescope. A fifth star, at the narrow end of the Trapezium, may be visible on nights of good seeing.

The cluster of stars in the nebula is less than 2 million years old. This must mean the nebula is similarly young.

Trapezium

Visual-wavelength image

Credit: NASA, ESA, M. Robberto, STScI and the Hubble Space Telescope Orion Treasury Project Team

Infrared

NASA

The near-infrared image above reveals more than 50 low-mass, cool protostars.

Visual

NASA

Small dark clouds called **Bok globules**, named after astronomer Bart Bok, are found in and near star-forming regions. The one pictured above is part of nebula NGC 1999 near the Orion Nebula. Typically about 1 light-year in diameter, they contain from 10 to 1000 solar masses.

Photons with enough energy to ionize H

Energy radiated by O6 star

Energy radiated by B1 star

Energy

Wavelength (nanometers)

0   100   200   300

2 Of all the stars in the Orion Nebula, only one is hot enough to ionize the gas. Only photons with wavelengths shorter than 91.2 nm can ionize hydrogen. The second-hottest stars in the nebula are B1 stars, and they emit little of this ionizing radiation. The hottest star, however, is an O6 star 30 times the mass of the sun. At a temperature of 40,000 K, it emits plenty of photons with wavelengths short enough to ionize hydrogen. Remove that one star, and the nebula would turn off its emission.

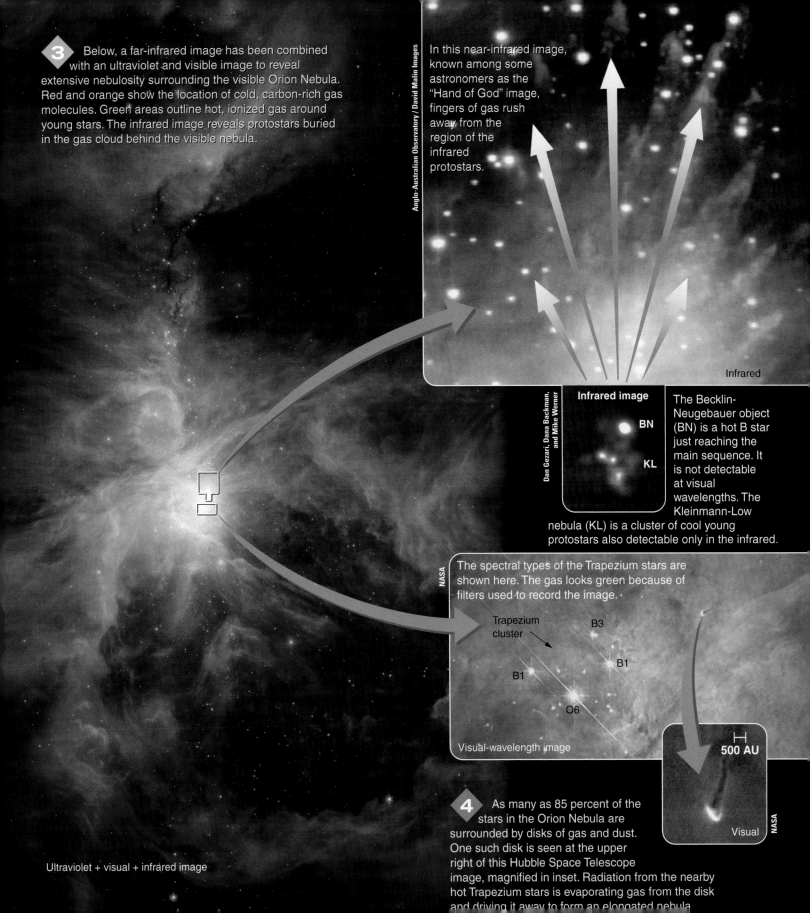

3 Below, a far-infrared image has been combined with an ultraviolet and visible image to reveal extensive nebulosity surrounding the visible Orion Nebula. Red and orange show the location of cold, carbon-rich gas molecules. Green areas outline hot, ionized gas around young stars. The infrared image reveals protostars buried in the gas cloud behind the visible nebula.

In this near-infrared image, known among some astronomers as the "Hand of God" image, fingers of gas rush away from the region of the infrared protostars.

Anglo-Australian Observatory / David Malin Images

Infrared

Dan Gezari, Dana Backman, and Mike Werner

Infrared image

BN

KL

The Becklin-Neugebauer object (BN) is a hot B star just reaching the main sequence. It is not detectable at visual wavelengths. The Kleinmann-Low nebula (KL) is a cluster of cool young protostars also detectable only in the infrared.

NASA

The spectral types of the Trapezium stars are shown here. The gas looks green because of filters used to record the image.

Trapezium cluster

B3

B1

B1

O6

Visual-wavelength image

500 AU

Visual

NASA

4 As many as 85 percent of the stars in the Orion Nebula are surrounded by disks of gas and dust. One such disk is seen at the upper right of this Hubble Space Telescope image, magnified in inset. Radiation from the nearby hot Trapezium stars is evaporating gas from the disk and driving it away to form an elongated nebula

Ultraviolet + visual + infrared image

born within it have ionized the gas and driven it outward, breaking out of the molecular cloud. Visual and infrared observations reveal small dusty clouds of gas called *Bok globules* that may be in the process of forming stars.

2 A single very hot and short-lived O star is almost entirely responsible for producing the ultraviolet photons that ionize the gas and make the nebula glow. This star is so massive that it has already become a main sequence star while its smaller siblings are still protostars.

3 Infrared observations reveal clear evidence of active star formation deeper in the molecular cloud behind the visible nebula.

4 Many of the young stars in the Orion nebula are surrounded by disks of gas and dust.

You should not be surprised to find star formation in Orion. The constellation is a brilliant pattern in the winter sky, marked by bright blue stars. Although those stars are hundreds of parsecs away, they appear bright because they are tremendously luminous. Such high-luminosity O and B stars cannot live more than a few million years. That is an astronomically short time, and they are not moving quickly, so they must have been born somewhere near where you see them now.

Are there other nebulae like the Orion Nebula? Such emission nebulae are actually quite common, and many examples shown in this chapter as well as in the previous chapter are produced by newborn stars just as is the Orion Nebula. The shape of a nebula is determined, in part, by the distribution of gas around the forming stars. The nebula around the star cluster NGC 602 is strikingly similar in shape to the Orion Nebula (■ Figure 11-5).

Contagious Star Formation

Not only can astronomers locate evidence of star formation, but they have also found evidence that star formation can stimulate more star formation. If a gas cloud produces massive stars, those massive stars ionize the gas nearby and drive it away. Where the intense radiation and hot gas pushes into surrounding gas, it can compress the gas and trigger more star formation. One sign of this process is the presence of **star-formation pillars**, columns of gas that point back toward the young massive star. Such pillars are produced by denser regions of clouds that protect the gas behind them as the blast of intense radiation and hot gas flows past (■ Figure 11-6). Another way massive stars can trigger further star formation is by exploding as a supernova. You read earlier in this chapter how such an explosion can drive a shock wave through surrounding gas and cause interstellar clouds to collapse, forming new stars (Figure 11-3a).

Like a brush fire moving through the interstellar medium, star formation can spread itself especially by creating massive stars, and astronomers have located the remains of such episodes

NGC 602

Visual wavelength image

■ **Figure 11-5**

The nebula around star cluster NGC 602 resembles the Orion Nebula. It has been inflated by radiation and winds streaming away from the cluster of hot young stars at lower right. More stars are forming where gas is compressed at upper left. (NASA/ESA, and the Hubble Heritage Team)

(■ Figure 11-7). Of course, lower-mass stars also form in the process, but they cannot trigger further star formation because they are not hot enough to ionize and drive away large amounts of gas, nor do they explode as supernovae.

The history of star formation in the constellation of Orion is written in its stars. Judging from the luminosities and estimated masses of the most prominent examples, the stars at Orion's west shoulder are less than 12 million years old, while the stars of Orion's belt are at most 8 million years old. The stars of the Trapezium at the center of the Great Nebula are no older than 2 million years. Star formation has swept across Orion from northwest to southeast, apparently beginning near Orion's west shoulder. The massive stars that formed there probably triggered the formation of the stars in Orion's belt. That star formation episode may then have caused the formation of the new stars you see today in the Great Nebula.

In the next million years, the familiar outline of the Great Nebula will change, and a new nebula may begin to form as the protostars embedded in a different part of the molecular cloud ionize the gas, drive it away, and become visible. Throughout the cloud, centers of star formation may develop and then dissipate as massive stars are born and force the gas to expand. If enough massive stars are born, they could blow the entire molecular cloud apart and bring the successive generations of star formation to a conclusion. The Great Nebula in Orion and its adjacent huge, but invisible, molecular cloud are a beautiful and dramatic example of the continuing cycles of star formation.

■ Figure 11-6

The hot, massive stars in the star cluster 30 Doradus are pouring out intense ultraviolet radiation and powerful winds of hot gas that are pushing back and compressing the surrounding nebula. Slightly denser regions in the nebula protect the gas behind them to make star-formation pillars a few light-years long that point back at the star cluster. The dense blobs are being compressed and may make more stars within the next few million years. (N. Walborn and J. Maiz- Apellániz, STScI, R. Barbá, La Plata Observatory, and NASA)

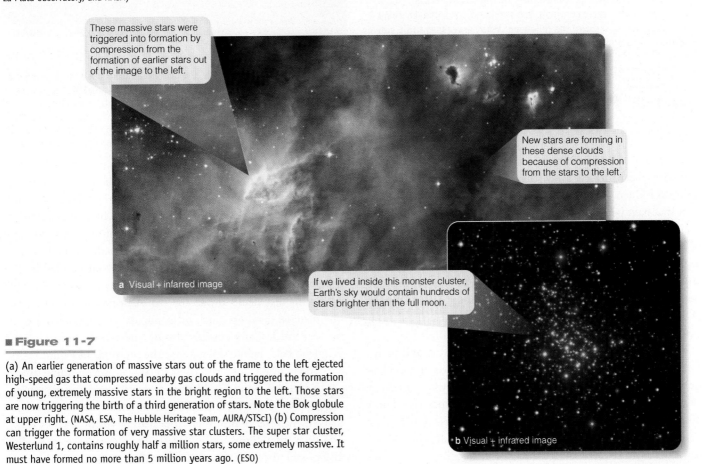

■ Figure 11-7

(a) An earlier generation of massive stars out of the frame to the left ejected high-speed gas that compressed nearby gas clouds and triggered the formation of young, extremely massive stars in the bright region to the left. Those stars are now triggering the birth of a third generation of stars. Note the Bok globule at upper right. (NASA, ESA, The Hubble Heritage Team, AURA/STScI) (b) Compression can trigger the formation of very massive star clusters. The super star cluster, Westerlund 1, contains roughly half a million stars, some extremely massive. It must have formed no more than 5 million years ago. (ESO)

11-3 Young Stellar Objects and Protostellar Disks

WHEN MOST OF THE MATERIAL in a protostar's cocoon has fallen inward or been driven away, the protostar will no longer be quite so hidden. The locations in the H–R diagram of protostars that have become detectable at visible wavelengths because their cocoons have disappeared is called the **birth line** (■ Figure 11-8). Once a star crosses the birth line and becomes visible, it continues to contract and move toward the main sequence at a pace that depends on its mass. Stars in this late stage of formation are sometimes called **Young Stellar Objects (YSOs)** or pre-main-sequence stars, to distinguish them from earlier protostellar stages.

The more massive a star, the stronger its gravity and therefore the more rapid will be its contraction. Astronomers calculate that the sun took about 30 million years from when its cloud began contracting until it became a main-sequence star, but a 30-solar-mass star would take only 30,000 years. A 0.2-solar-mass star needs as much as 1 billion years to finish forming and reach the main sequence.

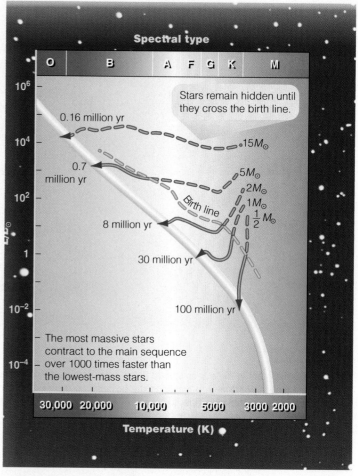

■ **Figure 11-8**

The more massive a protostar is, the faster it contracts. A 1-$M_\odot$ star requires 30 million years to reach the main sequence. (Recall that $M_\odot$ means "solar mass.") The dashed line is the birth line, where contracting protostars first become visible as they dissipate their surrounding clouds of gas and dust. Compare with Figure 11-4, which shows the evolution of a protostar of about 1 $M_\odot$ as a dashed line up to the birth line and as a solid line from the birth line to the main sequence. (Illustration design by M. Seeds)

As a contracting molecular cloud core becomes a protostar, the cloud rotates faster and faster. The rapidly spinning core of the cloud must flatten into a spinning disk like a blob of pizza dough spun into the air. Gas from the envelope that has lost its angular momentum through collisions can sink directly to the center of the cloud, where the protostar grows larger, surrounded by the disk. Other infalling material can add to the disk and then move within the disk plane toward the star. Astronomers calculate that this material gives up much of its angular momentum via collisions in the disk and possibly also by interactions with the disk's magnetic field, before sinking into the protostar (■ Figure 11-9).

Theoretically, for a protostar to have no surrounding disk at all, its original cloud would need to have zero angular momentum, which is very unlikely. Observationally, astronomers find that the majority of protostars appear to be surrounded by disks. The disks that form around protostars are called **protostellar disks**, and they are important because, as you will learn in

Formation of a Protostellar Disk

A slowly rotating cloud of gas begins to contract.

Conservation of angular momemtum spins the cloud faster and it flattens...

into a growing protostar at the center of a rotating disk of gas and dust.

■ **Figure 11-9**

The rotation of a contracting gas cloud forces it to flatten into a disk, and the protostar grows at the center. The scale of the top panel is much larger than the lower two panels.

Chapter 19, astronomers conclude that planets form within these disks. In fact, the evidence indicates that Earth formed in such a disk around the protosun 4.6 billion years ago. Because most protostars have protostellar disks, it seems likely that most stars have planetary systems.

Read **Observational Evidence of Star Formation** on pages 222–223 and notice that it makes four important points and introduces three new terms:

1 Star formation regions contain types of stars so young they must have formed recently. *T Tauri* stars, for example, are a type of star understood to still be in the slowly contracting phase.

2 Infrared observations reveal the complicated shapes of star-forming clouds that are strongly affected by radiation and winds from nearby luminous stars.

3 In the H–R diagram, newborn stars lie between the birth line and the main sequence—just where you would expect to find stars that have recently lost their dust cocoons. Young stars tend to have very active, hot coronae and chromospheres, making them prominent X-ray sources.

4 Observations provide clues about the effects of disks of gas and dust around protostars. These disks evidently cause *bipolar flows* that push into the surrounding interstellar medium and produce glowing blobs called *Herbig–Haro objects*. Images have been obtained of a few protostellar disks. Astronomers have abundant evidence that these disks are the sites of planet formation.

In some cases, these dark disks of gas and dust are clearly visible around newborn stars (■ Figure 11-10), but it isn't clear how the protostellar disk produces jets. Certainly the contracting, spinning disk contains tremendous energy, and theorists suspect that magnetic fields

Jet

Forming star hidden at center of dusty disk

Disk

■ **Figure 11-10**

In the object HH 30, a newly formed star lies at the center of a dense disk of dusty gas that is narrow near the star and thicker farther away. Although the star is hidden from you by the edge-on dusty disk, the star illuminates the inner surface of the disk. Interactions between the infalling material in the disk and the spinning star eject jets of gas along the axis of rotation. The artist's conception on the right is to help interpret what you see in the Hubble Space Telescope image on the left. (C. Burrows, STScI & ESA, WFPC 2 Investigation Definition Team, NASA)

Observations of Young Stellar Objects and Protoctellar Disks

1 The nebula around the star S Monocerotis is bright with hot stars. Such stars live short lives of only a few million years, so they must have formed recently. Such regions of young stars are common. The entire constellation of Orion is filled with young stars and clouds of gas and dust.

Nebulae containing young stars usually contain **T Tauri** stars. These stars fluctuate irregularly in brightness, and many are bright in the infrared, suggesting they are surrounded by dust clouds and in some cases by dust disks. Doppler shifts show that gas is flowing away from many T Tauri stars. The T Tauri stars appear to be newborn stars just blowing away their dust cocoons. T Tauri stars have ages ranging from 100,000 years to 100,000,000 years. Spectra of T Tauri stars show signs of an active chromosphere as we might expect from young, rapidly rotating stars with powerful dynamos and strong magnetic fields.

Visual-wavelength image

Visual

Infrared

Skyfactory.org

NASA/JPL-Caltech/W. Reach

Roughly 1000 young stars with hot chromospheres appear in this X-ray image of the Orion Nebula.

X-ray

NASA/CXC/SAO

3 The star cluster NGC 2264, imbedded in the nebula on this page, is only a few million years old. Lower-mass stars have not yet reached the main sequence, and the cluster contains many T Tauri stars (open circles), which are found above and to the right of the main sequence, near the birth line. The faintest stars in the cluster were too faint to be observed in this study.

2 The Elephant Trunk (above) is a dark nebula compressed and twisted by radiation and winds from a luminous star beyond the left edge of this image. Infrared observations reveal that it contains six protostars (pink objects, lower edge) not detected at visual wavelengths.

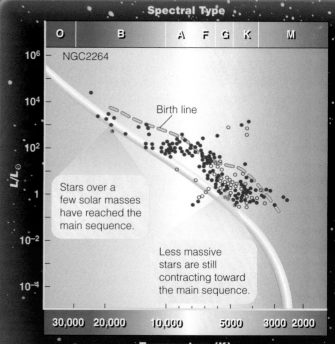

Spectral Type

O   B   A F G K   M

10^6 NGC2264

10^4

Birth line

10^2

Stars over a few solar masses have reached the main sequence.

1

$L/L_\odot$

10^{-2}

Less massive stars are still contracting toward the main sequence.

10^{-4}

30,000   20,000   10,000   5000   3000 2000

Temperature (K)

HH34S

Visual

NASA

Visual

Gas jet

Young star

HH34N

4 At the center of this image, a newborn star is emitting powerful jets to left and right. Where the jets strike the interstellar medium, they produce **Herbig–Haro objects**. The inset shows how irregular the jet is. Such jets can be over a light-year long and contain gas traveling at 100 km/s or more.

Herbig–Haro object

Jet

4a Herbig–Haro objects, named after the two astronomers who first described them, are small nebulae that fluctuate in brightness. They appear to be produced by flickering jets from newborn stars exciting the interstellar medium.

Dusty disk

NASA

Jet

Herbig–Haro object

4b Matter flowing into a protostar swirls through a thick disk and, by a process believed to involve magnetic fields, ejects high-energy jets in opposite directions. Observation of these **bipolar flows** is evidence that protostars are surrounded by disks because only disks could focus the flows into jets.

4c Radiation and winds from massive stars have shaped this nebula, Messier 16, and a recent supernova has heated some of the dust (red). Shock waves from the explosion will destroy the Eagle Nebula star-formation pillars (inset) within about 1000 years. Erosion of part of the Eagle Nebula has exposed small fingers and globules of denser gas. About 15 percent of those have formed protostars.

Visual

Visual

Visual

NASA

250 AU

NASA

Infrared image

4d Protostellar disks observed in the Orion Nebula. Radiation and winds from hot stars nearby are evaporating and distorting the disks. The disk pictured above is seen silhouetted against the nebula, with light from the protostar embedded in the disk's center apparent at its upper edge. Although bigger than the present size of our solar system, such disks are understood to be sites of planet formation.

become twisted tightly around the disk. Exactly how those fields eject hot gas away from the stars is not completely understood, but the presence of a confining disk is thought to explain why material flows out in two streams along the axis of rotation. The detection of these jets was one of the first pieces of evidence that substantial disks often surround protostars.

Some evidence of stellar youth is not obvious. An **association** is a widely distributed star cluster that is not held together by its own gravity—its stars wander away as the association ages. It is not clear why some gas clouds give birth to compact star clusters held together by their own gravity and others give birth to larger associations not bound together. You can conclude, however, that associations must consist of young stars because the stars wander apart astronomically quickly. The constellation Orion, a known region of star formation, is filled with T Tauri stars in a **T association**. T Tauri stars are relatively low-mass pre-main-sequence objects ranging from roughly 0.5 to 2 solar masses. **OB associations**, fairly obviously, are extended groups of more massive O and B stars. Associations of stars that are journeying away from each other as we watch are clear evidence of recent star formation.

When a protostar becomes hot enough, it can drive away the gas and dust of the protostellar disk as well as any remaining traces of its cocoon. Just as the sun exhales a solar wind, stars produce a **stellar wind**, which can be quite vigorous for hot, young stars. Also, when photons encounter gas atoms or dust specks in space, the photons can exert **radiation pressure**. Stellar winds and radiation pressure combine to blow disks and remnant cocoons apart. As you learned in the previous section, the most luminous stars are even capable of eroding the cocoon and disk material of their neighbors (Figure 11-6). You can recognize that process in the overall shape of the Eagle Nebula (page 223) as well as in the smaller pillars within that nebula.

SCIENTIFIC ARGUMENT

What evidence can you cite that stars in so-called star-forming regions are actually young?
This is a very good example of building a scientific argument because you must cite different forms of evidence to confirm a hypothesis. First, you should note that some extremely luminous stars can't live very long, so when you see such stars, such as the hot blue stars in Orion, you know they must have formed in the last few million years. Many regions of gas and dust contain bright, hot stars that are caught in the act of blowing their nebulae apart; those stars must also have formed recently, or the nebulae would be gone already.

You have other evidence when you look at T Tauri stars. They: (1) are usually associated with interstellar gas and dust concentrations, (2) have H–R diagram locations just above the main sequence where you expect stars to be that are still contracting, and (3) often have protostellar disks that are easily destroyed and cannot last long.

There seems to be no doubt that star formation is an ongoing process, and you can revise your argument to discuss how it happens. **What evidence can you cite that protostars are often surrounded by disks of gas and dust?**

11-4) Stellar Structure

How would you go about making a star? It's simple, really. All you need is something, maybe a light-year-sized broom, to gather together a star's mass of interstellar medium, and gravity will do the rest. The object that forms in that way is also simple.

What Keeps a Star Stable?

If there is a single idea in stellar astronomy that can be called crucial, it is the concept of balance. In this section you will discover that stars are held together by their own gravity balanced by the support of their internal heat and pressure. This story will lead your imagination into a region where you yourself can never go—the heart of a star.

Consider the structure of a star, using the basic concept of balance. What is meant here by structure is the variation in temperature, density, pressure, composition, and so on, between the surface of the star and its center. You can think more easily about stellar structure if you imagine that the star is divided into many concentric shells like those in an onion (■ Figure 11-11). You can

■ **Figure 11-11**

To discuss the structure of a star, it is helpful to divide its interior into concentric shells, much like the layers in an onion. This model is, of course, only an aid to your imagination. Stars are not really divided into separable layers.

then focus on the temperature, pressure, and density in each shell. These helpful shells exist only in the imagination; stars do not actually have such separable layers.

The weight of each layer of a star must be supported by the layer below. (The words *down* or *below* are conventionally used to refer to regions closer to the center of a star.) Picture a pyramid of people in a circus stunt—the people in the top row do not have to hold up anybody else; the people in the next row down are holding up the people in the top row, and so on. In a star that is stable, the deeper layers must support the weight of all of the layers above. The inside of a star is made up of gas, so the weight pressing down on a layer must be balanced by gas pressure in that layer. If the pressure is too low, the weight from above will compress and push down the layer; and if the pressure is too high, the layer will expand and lift the layers above.

This balance between weight and pressure is called **hydrostatic equilibrium**. *Hydro* (from the Greek word for water) tells you the material is a fluid, which by definition includes the gases of a star, and *static* tells you the fluid is stable, neither expanding nor contracting. ■ Figure 11-12 shows this hydrostatic balance in the imaginary layers of a star. The weight pressing down on each layer is shown by lighter red arrows, which grow larger with increasing depth to represent the weight growing larger. The pressure in each layer is shown by darker red arrows. The important point here is that you can be absolutely sure, from this simple argument, that the pressure inside a star must grow larger with increasing depth to support the weight and keep the star stable, even if you can't directly examine the inside of a star.

The pressure in a gas depends on the temperature and density of the gas. Near the surface there is not much weight pressing down, so the pressure does not need to be high for stability. Deeper in the star, the pressure must be higher, which means that the temperature and density of the gas must also be higher. In other words, the principle of hydrostatic equilibrium tells you that stars must have high temperature, pressure, and density inside to support their own weight and be stable. Although the law of hydrostatic equilibrium can tell you some things about the inner structure of stars, you also need to know how energy flows within the star to completely understand its structure.

Energy Transport

The surface of a star radiates light and heat into space and would quickly cool if that energy were not replaced. Because the inside of the star is hotter than the surface, energy must flow outward to the surface, where it radiates away. This flow of energy through each shell determines its temperature, which, as you saw earlier, determines how much weight that shell can balance. The movement of energy from the inside to the surface of a star thus plays a crucial role in determining the star's structure.

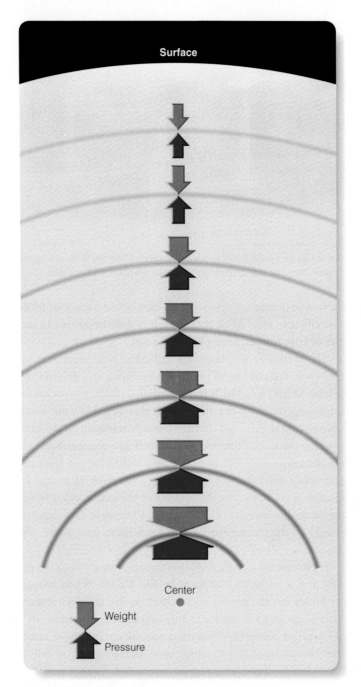

■ Figure 11-12

The law of hydrostatic equilibrium says the pressure in each layer must balance the weight on that layer. Consequently, as the weight increases from the surface of a star to its center, the pressure must also increase.

The law of **energy transport** says that energy must flow from hot regions to cooler regions either by conduction, convection, or radiation. Conduction is the most familiar form of heat flow. If you hold the bowl of a spoon in a candle flame, the handle of the spoon grows warmer as heat, in the form of motion among the atoms of the spoon, is conducted from atom to atom up the handle (■ Figure 11-13). But conduction is not a significant cause of

■ **Figure 11-13**

The three modes by which energy may be transported from the flame of a candle, as shown here, are the three modes of energy transport within a star.

heat flow in normal stars because radiation or convection are much more efficient, even in their centers; it is only important in rare types of stars with extremely high densities.

The transport of energy by radiation is another familiar experience. Put your hand near a candle flame, and you can feel the heat. What you actually feel are infrared photons—packets of energy—radiated by the flame and absorbed by your hand. Radiation is the principal means of energy transport in the interiors of most stars. Photons are absorbed and reemitted in random directions over and over as energy works its way from the hot interior toward the cooler surface. The flow of energy by radiation is controlled by the **opacity** of the gas, in other words its resistance to movement of radiation. Opacity in turn depends strongly on the temperature: A hot gas is more transparent, less opaque, than a cool gas.

If the opacity is high, radiation cannot flow through the gas easily, and it backs up like water behind a dam. When enough heat builds up, the gas begins to churn as hot gas rises upward and cool gas sinks downward. This heat-driven circulation of a fluid is called convection, the third way energy can move inside a star. You are familiar with convection: The rising wisp of smoke above a candle flame is carried by convection. Energy is carried upward in these convection currents as rising hot gas (red in the right-hand diagram within Figure 11-13) and as sinking cool gas (blue in the right-hand diagram within Figure 11-13). Convection is important not only because it carries energy but also because it mixes the gas.

11-5 The Source of Stellar Energy

IN THE PREVIOUS SECTION YOU LEARNED that the sun and other stars are stable because their centers have very high temperature and, therefore, pressure. Stars are born when gravity pulls

interstellar matter together. When the density and temperature at the centers of the new stars become high enough, nuclear fusion begins making energy. This supplies the energy that keeps the core hot enough, with high enough pressure, so that the star remains stable. In this section, you will learn the details of how that happens.

A Review of the Proton–Proton Chain

In Chapter 8 you visited the center of the sun and discovered that it creates energy through hydrogen fusion in a series of nuclear reactions called the proton–proton chain (see Figure 8-9). That reaction begins with the fusion of two protons, which are hydrogen nuclei. Protons have positive charges and repel each other electrically. As you learned earlier, electrical force is also called the Coulomb force, so the resistance of protons to being combined is called the Coulomb barrier. High-speed collisions are required to penetrate the Coulomb barrier, and high speed for atoms and subatomic particles means high temperature. Consequently, the proton–proton chain cannot effectively occur if the gas temperature is lower than about 4 million Kelvin.

You also discovered that the gas must be dense if the proton–proton chain is to produce significant energy. The fusion of two protons is unlikely, even if they collide, so a huge number of collisions are necessary to produce a few fusion reactions. Furthermore, a single cycle through the proton–proton chain produces only a tiny amount of energy, so a vast number of fusion reactions are needed to supply enough energy to support a star. The higher the gas density for a given temperature, the larger will be the number of fusion reactions.

Those are the reasons why the proton–proton chain produces energy only near the sun's center, where the temperature and density are high. In fact, only about the innermost 30 percent of the sun's radius is hot enough to support fusion. The rest of the sun, farther from the center, isn't hot and dense enough.

You might expect other stars to fuse hydrogen the same way the sun does, and you would be right for most stars. Some stars, however, can fuse hydrogen using a different recipe, and that makes a big difference to their structure and lifetimes.

The CNO Cycle

Main-sequence stars more massive than 1.1 solar masses are hot enough to fuse hydrogen into helium using the **CNO cycle**, a hydrogen fusion process that uses carbon, nitrogen, and oxygen as stepping-stones.

Look carefully at ■ Figure 11-14 and notice the steps in the CNO cycle. The cycle begins with a carbon-12 nucleus absorbing a proton and becoming nitrogen-13, which decays to become carbon-13. The carbon-13 nucleus absorbs a second proton and becomes nitrogen-14, which absorbs a third proton and becomes oxygen-15. The oxygen-15 decays to become nitrogen-15, which absorbs a fourth proton, ejects a helium

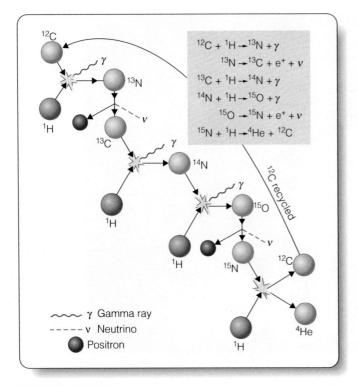

$$
\begin{aligned}
^{12}C + {}^{1}H &\rightarrow {}^{13}N + \gamma \\
^{13}N &\rightarrow {}^{13}C + e^{+} + \nu \\
^{13}C + {}^{1}H &\rightarrow {}^{14}N + \gamma \\
^{14}N + {}^{1}H &\rightarrow {}^{15}O + \gamma \\
^{15}O &\rightarrow {}^{15}N + e^{+} + \nu \\
^{15}N + {}^{1}H &\rightarrow {}^{4}He + {}^{12}C
\end{aligned}
$$

$\sim\sim\sim$ γ Gamma ray

$-----$ ν Neutrino

● Positron

■ **Figure 11-14**

The CNO cycle uses ^{12}C as a catalyst to combine four hydrogen nuclei (^{1}H) to make one helium nucleus (^{4}He) plus energy. The carbon nucleus reappears at the end of the process, ready to start the cycle over.

nucleus, and becomes carbon-12. Notice that carbon-12 begins the cycle and ends the cycle, so the carbon-12 nucleus can be recycled over and over. Notice also that, along the way, four protons combine to make a helium nucleus. This CNO cycle has the same outcome as the proton–proton chain, but it is different in an important way.

The CNO cycle begins with a carbon nucleus combining with a proton, a hydrogen nucleus. Because a carbon nucleus has a positive charge six times higher than a proton, the Coulomb barrier is higher for this reaction than for the proton–proton chain. Temperatures higher than 16 million Kelvin are required so that significant numbers of protons are able to penetrate the Coulomb barrier of a carbon nucleus. In comparison, the proton–proton chain can make energy at temperatures as low as 4 million K. The CNO cycle therefore needs much hotter gas to operate than does the proton–proton chain. The temperature at the very center of the sun is estimated to be 15 million K, which is why the sun makes nearly all of its energy from the proton–proton chain and only a little from the CNO cycle.

The CNO cycle and the proton–proton chain both fuse hydrogen to make helium. The temperature sensitivity of the CNO cycle means that O and B stars, with the highest temperature cores, create nearly all of their energy via the CNO cycle. As you have learned, O and B stars have very high luminosities and short lifetimes, making them prominent advertisements of star-forming regions.

Inside Stars

One important point for you to consider is that it is not correct to say "the sun's core is hot because nuclear reactions occur there." That statement reverses cause and effect. Rather, it is correct to say the sun and other stars have nuclear reactions in their cores because the temperature is hot enough there. You observe the sun to be stable; therefore, it must have a certain temperature, pressure, and density in its core. It would have about that same temperature in its core even if somehow you could magically turn off the nuclear reactions. But then, without a source of energy to replace the luminosity pouring out into space, the sun would gradually lose its internal energy and start slowly contracting again, as was true during its protostellar phase before the nuclear reactions started.

In Chapter 9, you discovered that the stars on the main sequence are ordered according to mass. Combining this with what you know about hydrogen fusion reveals that there are two kinds of main-sequence stars: (1) massive stars, on the upper main sequence, fuse hydrogen into helium via the CNO cycle, in which carbon, nitrogen, and oxygen nuclei act as catalysts but are not consumed; (2) low-mass stars, on the lower main sequence, including the sun, fuse hydrogen into helium via the proton–proton chain.

Viewed from the outside, those two types of stars differ only in size, temperature, and luminosity, but inside they are quite different. The upper-main-sequence stars are more massive and thus must have higher central temperatures to be able to stand against their own gravity. Those high central temperatures allow the star to fuse hydrogen on the CNO cycle, and that affects the internal structure of the star.

You have learned that the CNO cycle is extremely temperature sensitive. To illustrate, if the central temperature of the sun rose by 10 percent, energy production by the proton–proton chain would rise by about 46 percent, but energy production by the CNO cycle would shoot up 350 percent. This means that the more massive stars generate almost all of their energy in a tiny region at their very centers where the temperature is highest. A 10-solar-mass star, for instance, generates 50 percent of its energy in its central 2 percent of mass.

This concentration of energy production at the very center of the star causes a "traffic jam" as the energy tries to flow away from the center. Transport of energy by radiation can't drain away the energy fast enough, and the central core of the star churns in convection as hot gas rises upward and cooler gas sinks downward. Farther from the center, the traffic jam is less severe, and the energy can flow outward as radiation. This

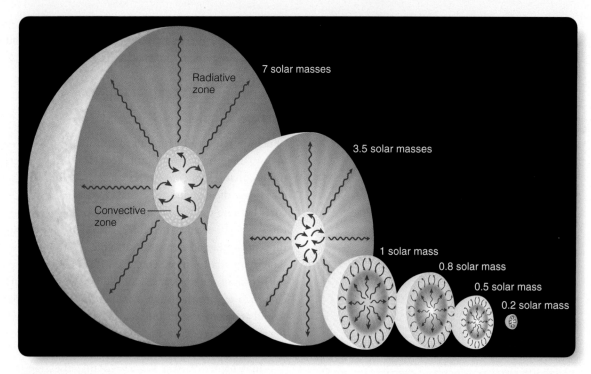

■ **Figure 11-15**

Inside stars. The more massive stars have small convective cores and radiative envelopes. Lower-mass stars, including the sun, have radiative cores and convective envelopes. The lowest-mass stars are convective throughout. The "cores" of the stars where nuclear fusion occurs (not shown) are smaller portions of the interiors. (Illustration design by M. Seeds)

means that massive stars have convective cores at their centers and radiative envelopes extending from their cores to their surfaces (■ Figure 11-15).

Main-sequence stars with less than about 1.1 solar masses cannot get hot enough to fuse much hydrogen on the CNO cycle. They generate nearly all of their energy by the proton–proton chain, which is not as sensitive to temperature, and thus the energy generation occurs in a larger region in the star's core. The sun, for example, generates 50 percent of its energy in a region that contains 11 percent of its mass. Because the energy generation is not concentrated at the very center of the star, no traffic jam develops, and the energy flows outward as radiation. Only near the surface, where the gas is cooler and therefore more opaque, does convection stir the gas. Consequently, the less massive stars on the main sequence, including the sun, have radiative cores and convective envelopes, the opposite of higher-mass stars.

The lowest-mass stars have a slightly different kind of structure. For stars less than about 0.4 solar mass, the gas is relatively cool compared to the inside of more massive stars, and the radiation cannot flow outward easily. As a result, the entire bulk of these low-mass stars is stirred by convection.

The stars in the evening sky look much the same, but you have discovered that they are a diverse group, both outside and inside. Different kinds of stars make their energy in different ways and have different internal structures. Those structures are determined by the principle of balance. But, can a star "lose" its balance? How do stars maintain their stability?

11-6 The Pressure– Temperature Thermostat

NEWBORN STARS CONTRACT and heat up until nuclear fusion begins. The energy flowing outward from the core heats the layers of gas, raises the pressure, and stops the contraction. This leads to an interesting question: How does the star manage to make just enough energy to stop contracting but not to start expanding? The key is the relationship between pressure and temperature that acts like a thermostat to keep the star burning steadily.

Consider what would happen if the reactions begin to produce too much energy. Normally, the nuclear reactions generate just enough energy to balance the inward pull of gravity. If the star makes slightly too much energy, the extra energy flowing out of the star would force its layers to expand slightly, lowering the central temperature and density and slowing the nuclear reactions until the star regained stability. Thus, a star has a built-in regulator that keeps its nuclear reactions from occurring too rapidly.

The same thermostat keeps the reactions from dying down. Suppose the nuclear reactions begin making too little energy. Then the star would contract slightly, increasing the central temperature and density, which would in turn increase the nuclear energy generation until the star regained stability.

The stability of a star depends on this relation between pressure and temperature. If an increase or decrease in temperature produces a corresponding change in pressure, the thermostat functions correctly, and the star is stable. You will discover in the next chapter how the thermostat accounts for the relationship between mass and luminosity of main-sequence stars. In Chapter 13, you will see what happens to a star when the thermostat breaks down completely and the nuclear fires rage unregulated.

SCIENTIFIC ARGUMENT

What would happen if the sun stopped generating energy?
Sometimes one of the best ways to test your understanding is to build an argument based on an altered situation. Stars are supported by the outward flow of energy generated by nuclear fusion in their interiors. That energy keeps each layer of the star just hot enough for the gas pressure to support the weight of the layers above. Each layer in the star must be in hydrostatic equilibrium; that is, the inward weight must be balanced by outward pressure. If the sun stopped making energy in its interior, nothing would happen at first, but over many thousands of years the loss of energy from its surface would reduce the sun's ability to withstand its own gravity, and it would begin to contract. You wouldn't notice much for 100,000 years or so, but eventually the sun would lose its battle with gravity.

Stars are elegant in their simplicity—nothing more than a cloud of gas held together by gravity and warmed from the inside by nuclear fusion. Now build a different argument. **How does the star manage to make exactly the right amount of energy to support its weight?**

What Are We?   Myth-Makers and Explainers

On cold winter nights when the sky is clear and the stars are bright, Jack Frost paints icy lacework across your windowpane. That's a fairy tale, of course, but it is a graceful evocation of the origin of frost. We humans are explainers, and one way to explain the world around us is to create myths.

An ancient Aztec myth tells the story of the origin of the moon and stars. The stars, known as the Four Hundred Southerners, and the moon, the goddess Coyolxauhqui, plotted to murder their unborn brother, the great war god Huitzilopochtli. Hearing their plotting, he leaped from the womb fully armed, hacked Coyolxauhqui into pieces, and chased the stars away. You can see the Four Hundred Southerners scattered across the sky, and each month you can see the moon chopped into pieces as it passes through its phases.

Stories like these explain the origins of things and can make our universe seem more understandable. Science is a natural extension of our need to explain the world. The stories have become sophisticated scientific theories and are tested over and over against reality, but we humans build those theories for the same reason people used to tell myths.

Study and Review

Summary

- Stars are born from the gas and dust of the interstellar medium.

- The existence of massive, hot stars, such as the prominent stars of Orion, that cannot live very long is strong evidence that stars have formed recently.

- The gravity of giant molecular clouds makes them contract, but that is resisted by thermal energy in the gas and by magnetic fields, rotation, and turbulence. In at least some cases, clouds are compressed by passing shock waves, also known as **shocks (p. 212),** and star formation is triggered. The birth of massive stars can produce shock waves that trigger further star formation.

- The cold gas of interstellar space heats up as it contracts because the atoms fall inward in **free-fall collapse (p. 213)** and pick up speed. In other words, the gas is converting gravitational energy into thermal energy. The thermal energy of the contracting cloud can leak out, allowing the rapid collapse to continue, as long as the material remains transparent to spectral **cooling lines (p. 214).**

- Collapsing clouds dense enough to be opaque slow their contraction and become **protostars (p. 214).** Protostars form deep inside dusty **cocoons (p. 214)** and are not directly visible at visual wavelengths until the cocoons dissipate.

- The visible Orion Nebula is only a small part of a much larger dusty molecular cloud. Ionization by ultraviolet photons from the hottest star is lighting up the nebula and making it glow brightly.

- Only one star in the Orion Nebula is hot enough to emit the ultraviolet photons that ionize the gas and make the nebula glow.

- Infrared observations reveal clear evidence of active star formation deeper in the molecular cloud just to the northwest of the Trapezium.

- Many stars visible in the Orion Nebula are surrounded by disks of gas and dust. Such disks do not last long and are clear evidence that the stars are very young.

- **Bok globules (p. 216)** are small dark nebulae, some of which may be contracting to form stars. **Star-formation pillars (p. 218)** are formed when hot gas rushes away from newborn stars and encounters denser blobs of gas and dust.

- Protostars become visible as they cross the **birth line (p. 220)** in the H–R diagram. **T Tauri (p. 222)** stars have just emerged from their cocoons and are located between the birth line and the main sequence in the H–R diagram. Stars that are nearing the main sequence stage are generally termed **Young Stellar Objects (YSOs) (p. 220).**

- Many, perhaps most, protostars form surrounded by dusty **protostellar disks (p. 220),** and jets of gas can be emitted as **bipolar flows (p. 223)** along the axis of the spinning disk. Where the jets push into the surrounding gas, they can form nebulae called **Herbig–Haro objects (p. 223).**

- **Associations,** including **T associations** and **OB associations (p. 224),** are groups of stars born together but not bound by their mutual gravity. The presence of these associations in an area is evidence of recent star formation.

- Protostars and YSOs produce **stellar winds (p. 224)** and **radiation pressure (p. 224)** that can blow their remaining disk and cocoon material away and affect neighboring protostars.

- The law of **hydrostatic equilibrium (p. 225)** says that the weight pressing down on a layer of gas in a star must be balanced by the pressure in the gas. That shows that the inner layers of stars must be hotter because they must support more weight.

- The law of **energy transport (p. 225)** states that energy must flow from the hot stellar core to the cooler surface by conduction, radiation, or convection. The **opacity (p. 226)** of a gas is its resistance to the flow of radiation. In regions where the opacity of the gas does not permit radiation to carry away enough energy, the gas can churn in convection. One reason convection is important in stellar evolution is that it can mix material between inner and outer parts of stars. Conduction is less efficient than radiation or convection except in a few rare types of stars with very high densities.

- Many stars make their energy the same way the sun does using the proton–proton chain, which only operates at temperatures above 4 million degrees K needed to overcome the Coulomb barrier of electrical repulsion between positively charged atomic nuclei. The **CNO cycle (p. 226)** is more efficient, but it requires a higher temperature than the proton–proton chain because of the larger repulsion by carbon, etc. nuclei. Both processes combine four hydrogen nuclei to make one helium nucleus plus energy.

- The CNO cycle is highly temperature sensitive, so stars more massive than 1.1 solar masses, being hotter inside, make energy via the CNO cycle. Less massive stars, including the sun, make energy via the proton–proton chain.

- The temperature sensitivity of the CNO cycle causes energy production in upper-main-sequence stars to occur in a very small region near the center, and the cores of the stars are convective zones. These stars are radiative in their outer layers.

- The proton–proton chain is not very sensitive to temperature, so the energy generation of lower-main-sequence stars, including the sun, is more widely spread through the star's core, and the deep interior is radiative. The outer layers of these stars are convective.

- The lowest-mass stars are so cool that their gases are relatively opaque and they are convective throughout.

Review Questions

1. What factors resist the contraction of a cloud of interstellar matter?

2. Explain the different ways a giant molecular cloud can be triggered to contract.

3. What evidence is there that: (a) star formation has occurred recently? (b) protostars really exist? (c) the Orion region is actively forming stars?

4. How does a contracting protostar convert gravitational energy into thermal energy?

5. How does the geometry of bipolar flows and Herbig–Haro objects support the hypothesis that protostars are surrounded by rotating disks?

6. Describe the principle of hydrostatic equilibrium as it relates to the internal structure of a star.

7. How does energy get from the core of a star, where it is generated, to the surface, where it is radiated into space?

8. How does the CNO cycle differ from the proton–proton chain? How is it similar?

9. How does the extreme temperature sensitivity of the CNO cycle affect the structure of stars?

10. How does the pressure–temperature thermostat control the nuclear reactions inside stars?

11. **How Do We Know?** How would you respond to someone's comment about star formation, "That's only a theory"?

12. **How Do We Know?** Why can't scientists prove a scientific theory is totally correct?

Discussion Questions

1. Ancient astronomers, philosophers, and poets assumed that the stars were eternal and unchanging. Is there any observation they could have made or any line of reasoning that could have led them to conclude that stars don't live forever?

2. How does hydrostatic equilibrium relate to hot-air ballooning?

Problems

1. The expanding bubble of hot gas inflated by the cluster of new stars in its center, shown in Figure 11-3b, has a diameter of about 100 ly. If the bubble is 170,000 ly from Earth, what is the observed diameter of the bubble in arc seconds? (*Hint:* Use the small-angle formula, Chapter 3.)

2. If a giant molecular cloud is 50 pc in diameter and a shock wave can sweep through it in 2 million years, how fast is the shock wave going in kilometers per second?

3. If a giant molecular cloud has a mass of 10^{35} kg and it converts 1 percent of its mass into stars during a single encounter with a shock wave, how many stars can it make? Assume the stars each contain 1 solar mass.

4. If a protostellar disk is 200 AU in radius and the disk plus the forming star together contain 2 solar masses, what is the orbital speed at the outer edge of the disk in kilometers per second? (*Hint:* See Chapter 5.)

5. If a contracting protostar is five times the radius of the sun and has a temperature of only 2000 K, how luminous will it be? (*Hint:* See Chapter 9.)

6. The gas in a bipolar flow can travel as fast as 100 km/s. If the length of the jet is 1 ly, how long does it take for a blob of gas to travel from the protostar to the end of the jet?

7. If a T Tauri star is the same temperature as the sun but is ten times more luminous, what is its radius? (*Hint:* See Chapter 9.)

8. Circle all of the ^{1}H and ^{4}He nuclei in Figure 11-14 and explain how the CNO cycle can be summarized by 4 ^{1}H $\Rightarrow$ ^{4}He + energy.

9. How much energy is produced when the CNO cycle converts 1 kg of mass into energy? Is your answer different if the mass is fused by the proton–proton chain?

10. If the Orion Nebula is 8 pc in diameter and has a density of about 600 hydrogen atoms/cm^3, what is its total mass? (*Hint:* The volume of a sphere is $\frac{4}{3}\pi R^3$.)

11. The hottest star in the Orion Nebula has a surface temperature of 40,000 K. At what wavelength does it radiate the most energy? (*Hint:* See Chapter 7.)

Learning to Look

1. In Figure 11-7, a dark globule of dusty gas is located at top right. What do you think that globule would look like if you could see it from the other side?

2. Compare the nebula in Figure 11-3b with the image of the Orion Nebula on page 216. How are these two nebulae related?

3. Locate the star-formation pillars in Figure 11-6. What are they pointing at?

4. The star at right appears to be ejecting a jet of gas. What is happening to this star?

STScI and NASA

12 | Stellar Evolution

Visual wavelength image

Massive red supergiant star V838 Monocerotis is evolving rapidly. In early 2002, it flared up, and the expanding light is illuminating gas that was probably ejected in an earlier outburst. Spikes are produced by diffraction in the telescope. (NASA and The Hubble Heritage Team, AURA/STScI)

Guidepost

Stars form from the interstellar medium and reach stability by fusing hydrogen in their cores. This chapter is about the long stable middle age of stars on the main sequence, and their old age as they swell to become giant stars. Here you will answer four essential questions:

— **Why is there a main sequence of stellar luminosities and surface temperatures?**

— **Why is there a simple relationship between the masses and luminosities of main-sequence stars?**

— **How does a star change as it exhausts its hydrogen?**

— **What evidence do astronomers have that stars really do evolve?**

This chapter is about how stars live. The next two chapters are about how stars die and the strange objects they leave behind.

We should be unwise to trust scientific inference very far when it becomes divorced from opportunity for observational test.

— SIR ARTHUR EDDINGTON, *THE INTERNAL CONSTITUTION OF THE STARS*

EVERY STAR HAD A BEGINNING, and every star will someday have an ending, but in between the stars produce the light and energy that make our universe beautiful. The stars above you seem eternal, but their existence depends on the fusion of nuclear fuels in their cores; and, even as you look at them, they are using up their fuels and drawing closer to their ends.

In this chapter, you will see the full interplay of theory and evidence used to describe how stars change as they consume their nuclear fuels. As the quotation that opens this chapter warns, theory alone is never enough. At each step, astronomers must compare their theories with the evidence.

12-1) Main-Sequence Stars

THE INSIDES OF STARS are forever beyond direct observation, so astronomers must use theories to describe how stars work. Nevertheless, astronomers test those theories at every opportunity against reality by making observations of real stars. That has produced one of the greatest triumphs of modern astronomy—the recognition that stars are not eternal and that mere humans can understand them.

Stellar Models

Astronomers can build mathematical models that describe the insides of stars, and the key to those models is balance. Every star is balanced between two forces, gravity that tries to make it contract and internal pressure that tries to make it expand. As you learned in Chapter 11, a star's internal layers are balanced in hydrostatic equilibrium. By defining the layers mathematically, astronomers can discuss the conditions at different levels inside the star—what they call the "structure" of the star (■ Figure 12-1).

The internal structure of a star can be described by four simple laws of physics, two of which you have already met in Chapter 11. In addition to the law of hydrostatic equilibrium, the law of energy transport describes how energy flows from hot to cool regions by radiation, convection, or conduction.

To these two laws you can add two basic laws of nature. The **conservation of mass law** says that the total mass of the star must equal the sum of the masses in its shells with the added requirement that the mass be smoothly distributed through the star. No gaps are allowed. The **conservation of energy law** says that the amount of energy flowing out the top of a shell in the

Surface of star

■ **Figure 12-1**

Structure in a star refers to the temperature, density, pressure, and so on, in each layer. Because each layer, like an acrobat in a circus stunt, must support the weight of everything above, astronomers can compute the conditions in each layer from the surface down to the center. Compare with Figure 11-12.

star must be equal to the amount of energy coming in at the bottom of the shell plus whatever energy is generated within the shell. This means that the energy leaving the surface of the star, its luminosity, must equal the sum of the energy generated in all of the shells inside the star. This is like saying that the total number of new cars driving out of a factory must equal the sum of cars manufactured on each assembly line. No car can vanish into nothing or appear from nothing. Energy in a star may not vanish without a trace or appear out of nowhere.

The four laws of stellar structure, described in general terms in ■ Table 12-1, can be written as mathematical equations. By solving those equations numerically using computer programs, astronomers can build a mathematical model of the inside of a star.

If you wanted to build a model of a star, you would have to divide the star into at least 100 concentric shells and then write down the four equations of stellar structure for each shell. You would then have 400 equations that would have a total of 400 unknowns, namely, the temperature, density, mass, and energy flow in each shell. Solving 400 equations simultaneously is not easy, and the first such solutions, calculated by hand before the

1. Hydrostatic equilibrium	The weight on each layer is balanced by the pressure in that layer.
2. Energy transport	Energy moves from hot to cool by radiation, convection, or conduction.
3. Conservation of mass	Total mass equals the sum of the shell masses. No gaps are allowed.
4. Conservation of energy	Total luminosity equals the sum of the energies generated in each shell.

Notice that stellar models are quantitative; that is, properties are assigned specific numerical values. Earlier in this book, you used models that were qualitative—the Babcock model of the sun's magnetic cycle, for instance. Both kinds of models are useful, but a quantitative model can reveal deeper insights into how nature works because it incorporates the precision of mathematics (**How Do We Know? 12-1**).

Stellar models let astronomers understand the inside of a star, and they can also look into a star's past and future. In fact, astronomers can use models like a time machine to follow the evolution of a star over billions of years. To look into a star's future, astronomers can use a stellar model to determine how fast the star uses its fuel in each of its shells. As the fuel is consumed, the chemical composition of the gas changes, the opacity changes, and the amount of energy generated declines. By calculating the rates of these changes, astronomers can predict what the star will be like a few million years in the future. They can then repeat the process over and over and, step by step, follow the evolution of the star as it ages.

Although this sounds simple, it is actually a highly challenging problem involving nuclear and atomic physics, thermodynamics, and sophisticated computational methods. Only since the 1950s have computers made the rapid calculation of stellar models possible, and many of the advances in astronomy since then have been heavily influenced by the use of such models to study the structure and evolution of stars. The summary of star formation in the previous chapter is based on thousands of stellar

invention of electronic computers, took months of work. Now a properly programmed computer can solve the equations for a simple model in a few seconds and print a table of numbers that represent the conditions in each shell of the star. Such a table is a **stellar model.**

The table shown in ■ Figure 12-2 shows a model of the sun containing only 10 layers, but it is based on a model with many more layers. The bottom line in the table, for radius equal to 0.00, represents the center of the sun, and the top line, for radius equal to 1.00, represents the surface. The other lines in the table show the temperature and density in each shell, the mass inside each shell, and the fraction of the sun's luminosity that is flowing outward through the shell. You can use such a model to understand many things about the sun. For example, the model shows that all of the sun's energy is generated near the center. No energy is generated in the outer layers.

$R/R_\odot$	T (10^6 K)	Density (g/cm^3)	$M/M_\odot$	$L/L_\odot$
1.00	0.006	0.00	1.00	1.00
0.90	0.60	0.009	0.999	1.00
0.80	1.2	0.035	0.996	1.00
0.70	2.3	0.12	0.990	1.00
0.60	3.1	0.40	0.97	1.00
0.50	4.9	1.3	0.92	1.00
0.40	5.1	4.1	0.82	1.00
0.30	6.9	13.	0.63	0.99
0.20	9.3	36.	0.34	0.91
0.10	13.1	89.	0.073	0.40
0.00	15.7	150.	0.000	0.00

$$\frac{dM}{dr} = 4\pi r^2 \rho$$

$$\frac{dL}{dr} = 4\pi r^2 \rho \varepsilon$$

$$\frac{dP}{dr} = -\frac{GM}{r^2}\rho$$

$$\frac{dT}{dr} = \frac{-3}{16\pi ac}\frac{\bar{\kappa}\rho}{T^3}\frac{L}{r^2}$$

■ **Figure 12-2**

A stellar model is a table of numbers that represent conditions inside a star. Such tables can be computed using the four laws of stellar structure, shown here in mathematical form. The table in this figure describes the sun. (Illustration design by Mike Seeds.)

Mathematical Models

How can scientists study aspects of nature that cannot be observed directly? One of the most powerful methods in science is the mathematical model, a group of equations carefully designed to mimic the behavior of objects and processes that scientists want to study. Astronomers build mathematical models of stars to study the structure hidden deep inside them. Models can speed up the slow evolution of stars and slow down the rapid processes that generate energy. Stellar models are based on only four equations, but other models are much more complicated and may require many more equations.

For example, scientists and engineers designing a new airplane don't just cross their fingers, build it, and ask a test pilot to try it out. Long before any metal parts are made, mathematical models are created to test whether the wing design will generate enough lift, whether the fuselage can support the strain, and whether the rudder and ailerons can safely control the plane during takeoff, flight, and landing. Those mathematical models are put through all kinds of tests: Can a pilot fly with one engine shut down? Can the pilot recover from sudden turbulence? Can the pilot land in a crosswind? By the time the test pilot rolls the plane down the runway for the first time, the mathematical models have flown many thousands of miles.

Scientific models are only as good as the assumptions that go into them and must be compared with the real world at every opportunity. If you are an engineer designing a new airplane, you can test your mathematical models by making measurements in a wind tunnel. Models of stars are much harder to test against reality, but they do predict some observable things. Stellar models predict the existence of a main sequence, the mass–luminosity relation, the observed numbers of giant and supergiant stars, and the shapes of H–R diagrams.

Before any new airplane flies, engineers build mathematical models to test its stability. (The Boeing Company)

Without mathematical models, astronomers would know little about the lives of the stars, and designing new airplanes would be a very dangerous business.

models. You will continue to rely on theoretical models as you study main-sequence stars in the next section and the deaths of stars in the next chapter.

Why Is There a Main Sequence?

Astronomers have confidence in their stellar models because the physics that goes into the models is well understood. Another reason for confidence is that the models are constantly checked against reality by comparing them with observations of real stars. With that confidence, astronomers can use the models to understand stars better. For example, the models explain why there is a main sequence.

Models of stars show that there is a main sequence because the centers of contracting protostars eventually grow hot enough to begin nuclear fusion. Deuterium, the heavy isotope of hydrogen, is the first nuclear fuel to fuse, but it is rare and produces little energy; stellar models show that it has no real effect on a contracting star. Hydrogen fusion is the big powerhouse; when it begins, it produces enough energy to stop the star's contraction. Stars reach equilibrium somewhere along the main sequence. Hot stars are more luminous, and cool stars are less luminous, as you would expect. There is, however, a question about the main sequence that you can now resolve by thinking about stellar models. Why does the luminosity of a star depend on its mass?

In Chapter 9, you used pairs of stars orbiting each other in binary systems to find the masses of stars and discovered that the masses of main-sequence stars are ordered along the main sequence. In other words, the least massive stars are at the bottom of the

H–R diagram, and the most massive stars are at the top. Further, you discovered a direct relationship between the mass of a star and its luminosity—the mass–luminosity relation. This is one of the most fundamental observations in astronomy, and stellar models can tell you why there must be a mass–luminosity relation.

The keys to understanding the mass–luminosity relation are the law of hydrostatic equilibrium, which says that pressure must balance weight, and the pressure–temperature thermostat, which regulates energy production. You have seen that a star's internal pressure stays high because the generation of thermonuclear energy keeps its interior hot. Because more massive stars have more weight pressing down on the inner layers, their interiors must have high pressures and thus must be hotter. For example, the temperature at the center of a 15-solar-mass star is about 34,000,000 K, more than twice the central temperature of the sun.

Because massive stars have hotter cores, their pressure–temperature thermostats are set higher. The nuclear fuel at the center of a 15-solar-mass star fuses over 3000 times more rapidly than the fuel at the center of the sun. The rapid reactions produce more energy, which flows outward toward the cooler surface, heating each level in the star and enabling it to support the weight pressing inward. When all that energy reaches the surface, it radiates into space and makes the star highly luminous. There is a mass–luminosity relation because each star must support its weight by generating nuclear energy, and more massive stars have more weight to support.

The main sequence is elegant in its simplicity, but it has more secrets to reveal. To understand the main-sequence stars even better, you should next look at its upper and lower ends.

The Upper End of the Main Sequence

Models of stellar structure give astronomers a way to think about the extreme ends of the main sequence, the most massive and least massive stars. The former are rare, but the latter are common. Nevertheless, both are very difficult to study.

Taken together, theory and observation predict that there is an upper limit to the mass of stars. First, astronomers don't find stars more massive than about 100 solar masses. Observations show that, as gas clouds contract, they can fragment to form two or more stars. The more mass a gas cloud contains, the more likely it is to fragment, so there aren't many extremely massive stars because most large gas clouds break into smaller fragments and form multiple-star systems.

Even if a very massive star does begin to form, stellar models reveal that the most massive stars (roughly 50 to 150 solar masses) are unstable. To support the tremendous weight in such stars, the internal gas must be very hot, and that means it must emit floods of radiation that flow outward through the star. The resulting radiation pressure blows gas away from the star's surface in powerful stellar winds. This mass loss from very massive stars could reduce a 60-solar-mass star to less than 30 solar masses in only a million years.

This process sets an upper limit on the masses of stars, but it is difficult to test the theory because it is hard to find truly massive stars. Most of the O and B stars in the sky have masses of 10 to 25 solar masses. The survey of stars at the end of Chapter 9 revealed that the stars at the upper end of the main sequence are very rare, so astronomers must search to great distances to find just a few. Nevertheless, a few stars are known that are thought to be very massive, and their spectra contain blueshifted emission lines. Kirchhoff's laws tell you that emission lines come from excited low-density gas, and the blueshift must be caused by a Doppler shift produced because the gas is coming toward Earth. These stars are losing mass.

■ Figure 12-3 shows a famous star, Eta Carinae. Observations suggest it is actually a binary containing two massive stars of 60 and 70 solar masses. The stars may have formed with about 100 solar masses each, but they are losing mass rapidly. An eruption in 1841 made Eta Carinae the second brightest star in the sky and ejected the two expanding lobes of dusty gas you can see in the picture. Although the star has faded, it is still very active, and more recent eruptions have ejected jets and an equatorial disk of gas and dust. Massive stars like Eta Carinae are clearly unstable.

The Lower End of the Main Sequence

The lower end of the main sequence is also difficult to study, not because the stars are rare but because they are dim. If a red dwarf from the lower end of the main sequence replaced the sun, it would shine only a few times brighter than the full moon. Such stars are very common, but they are difficult to find even when they are only a few light-years away.

a Visual-wavelength image   **b** Visual-wavelength image

■ **Figure 12-3**

(a) This star-formation nebula in the constellation Carina contains the massive star Eta Carinae. (NOAO/AURA/NSF) (b) Eta Carinae is actually two stars in a binary system, and they are so massive they are rapidly losing mass and inflating two lobes with a disk of ejected material between like a plate pressed between two basketballs. Each lobe is about half a light-year in diameter. Gas outside the lobes is high speed gas expelled in the outburst of 1841. (J. Hester/ Arizona State Univ. NASA)

Stellar models predict that there are star-like objects even fainter than red dwarfs. Objects less massive than 0.08 solar mass cannot get hot enough in their cores to ignite hydrogen fusion. These **brown dwarfs** slowly contract, convert their gravitational energy into thermal energy, and radiate it away. A low-mass red dwarf containing 0.08 solar mass and fusing hydrogen has a surface temperature of about 2500 K, but brown dwarfs should have even lower temperatures, giving them a dull muddy-red color—thus the term "brown dwarf." Brown dwarfs were difficult to find because they are so faint, but large surveys and infrared studies have turned up lots of them. Some are located in binary systems with normal stars (■ Figure 12-4), but large numbers are free-floating objects without stellar companions.

Brown dwarfs are clearly different from normal stars. Some brown dwarfs have methane bands in their spectra, and that means they must be quite cool. Methane molecules would be broken up at the temperatures of true stars. Color variations suggest that some brown dwarfs may be cool enough to have changing weather patterns.

The discovery of brown dwarfs has created a controversy. Are they failed stars, or are they planets? To discuss this, astronomers use a unit of mass related to Jupiter, the giant planet in our solar system. Jupiter is 1000 times less massive than the sun, and astronomers refer to the mass of brown dwarfs in Jupiter masses. A contracting mass containing more than 80 Jupiter masses can get hot enough to fuse hydrogen and become a red dwarf star. Consequently, a brown dwarf must be less than about 80 Jupiter masses. Because they can't get hot enough to fuse hydrogen, brown dwarfs can't be true stars. But astronomers tend to think of a planet as a non-luminous body that orbits a star, so can a brown dwarf floating free in space be called a planet?

Brown dwarfs more massive than 13 Jupiter masses go through a phase during their formation when they can fuse deuterium, a heavy isotope of hydrogen, so some astronomers draw the line between brown dwarfs and planets at 13 Jupiter masses. By this definition, a brown dwarf would be an object with more than 13 and fewer than 80 Jupiter masses. However, deuterium fusion does not last very long, does not generate much energy, and does not stop the brown dwarf from cooling. Not everyone agrees that this is a good dividing line.

Another approach to the question of distinguishing brown dwarfs from planets is to consider how these objects form. A star forms from the contraction of a gas cloud, but astronomers know that planets form from the accumulation of solid bits of matter in disk-shaped nebulae around stars (a subject discussed in Chapter 19). In that case, free-floating brown dwarfs can't be planets. A problem with this definition is that it is difficult or impossible to tell how a mature low-mass object in a binary system originally formed, so if you use this definition, you won't necessarily know whether a given object should be called a brown dwarf or a planet.

The controversy over brown dwarfs is really an argument over the meaning of the words *star* and *planet* and doesn't really change astronomers' understanding. Brown dwarfs are the lowest mass objects at the bottom of the main sequence, and because they cannot sustain nuclear fusion, they must radiate away their thermal energy and slowly cool over billions of years.

■ **Figure 12-4**

Only 12.7 ly from the sun, a brown dwarf orbits a small star. Photographic effects give the brown dwarf a blue cast in the image, but if you could visit it, you would see an object slightly larger than the planet Jupiter glowing muddy red with a temperature just over 1000 K. Observations of brown dwarfs suggest that some have shifting weather patterns, as shown in the artist's impression. (ESO)

Star

Brown dwarf

Infrared

Images blurred by seeing. The true diameter of the star in this photo is less than 0.1 mm. The brown dwarf is smaller.

Artist's impression

Brown dwarf

The Life of a Main-Sequence Star

A normal main-sequence star supports its weight by fusing hydrogen into helium, but its supply of hydrogen is limited. As it consumes hydrogen, the chemical composition in its core changes, and the star evolves. Mathematical models of stars allow astronomers to follow that evolution.

Hydrogen fusion combines four nuclei into one. Consequently, as a main-sequence star consumes its hydrogen, the total number of nuclei in its interior decreases. Each newly made helium nucleus exerts the same pressure as one hydrogen nucleus; because the gas has fewer nuclei, its total pressure is less. This unbalances the gravity–pressure stability, and gravity squeezes the core of the star more tightly. As the core contracts, its temperature and density increase, and the nuclear reactions burn faster, releasing more energy and making the star more luminous. This additional energy flowing outward through the envelope forces the outer layers to expand and cool, making the star slightly larger, brighter, and cooler.

As a result of these gradual changes in main-sequence stars, the main sequence is not actually a sharp line across the H–R diagram but rather a band (■ Figure 12-5). When a star begins its stable life fusing hydrogen, it settles on the lower edge of this band, called the **zero-age main sequence (ZAMS).** As it combines hydrogen nuclei to make helium nuclei, the point that represents the star's luminosity and surface temperature moves upward and to the right, eventually reaching the upper edge of the main sequence just as the star exhausts nearly all of the hydrogen in its center. Astronomers find that main-sequence stars are plotted throughout this band depending on the stage of their main-sequence lives.

These gradual changes in the sun will spell trouble for Earth. When the sun began its main-sequence life about 5 billion years ago, it had only about 70 percent of its present luminosity. By the time the sun leaves the main sequence in another 5 billion years, it will have twice its present luminosity. By that time, the average temperature on Earth will have climbed by at least 55°C (about 100°F). As this happens over the next few billion years, the polar caps will melt, the oceans will evaporate, and much of the atmosphere will vanish into space. (This is not related to the current global warming, which affects Earth's climate much more quickly and is not caused by the sun.) Clearly, the future of Earth as the home of life is limited by the evolution of the sun.

Once a star leaves the main sequence, it evolves rapidly and soon dies. The average star spends about 90 percent of its life fusing hydrogen on the main sequence. This explains why about 90 percent of all normal stars are main-sequence stars. You are most likely to see a star during its long, stable visit to the main sequence.

How long a star spends on the main sequence depends on its mass (■ Table 12-2). Massive stars have lots of fuel, but they use it rapidly and live short lives. Low-mass stars conserve their fuel and shine for billions of years. For example, a 25-solar-mass star will exhaust its hydrogen and die in only about 7 million years, whereas the sun can fuse hydrogen for about 10 billion years. This means, for one thing, that astronomers think that life is unlikely to develop on planets orbiting massive stars. These stars do not live long enough for life to get started and evolve into complex creatures. You will learn about this problem in detail in Chapter 26.

Red dwarfs have low masses and use their fuel so slowly they should survive for hundreds of billion years. Because the universe seems to be only about 14 billion years old, red dwarfs must still

Spectral type

The Aging of Main-Sequence Stars

10 million years

Stars exhaust the last of the hydrogen in their cores as they leave the main sequence.

$15M_\odot$

640 million years

$3M_\odot$

10 billion years

Present sun

Initial sun

Newly formed stars begin life at the lower edge of the main sequence.

ZAMS

Temperature (K)

■ **Figure 12-5**

Contracting protostars reach stability at the lower edge of the main sequence, the zero-age main sequence (ZAMS). As a star converts hydrogen in its core into helium, its position in the H–R diagram moves slowly across the main sequence, becoming slightly more luminous and slightly cooler. Once a star consumes all of the hydrogen in its core, it can no longer remain a stable main-sequence star. More massive stars age rapidly, but less-massive stars use up the hydrogen in their cores more slowly and live longer main-sequence lives.

Table 12-2 | Main-Sequence Stars

Spectral Type	Mass (sun = 1)	Luminosity (sun = 1)	Approximate Years on Main Sequence
O5	40	405,000	1×10^6
B0	15	13,000	11×10^6
A0	3.5	80	440×10^6
F0	1.7	6.4	3×10^9
G0	1.1	1.4	8×10^9
K0	0.8	0.46	17×10^9
M0	0.5	0.08	56×10^9

be in their infancy. None of them have exhausted their hydrogen fuel yet.

Vast numbers of faint, low-mass stars fill the sky. Look at page 187 and recall how much more common the lower-main-sequence stars are than the massive O and B stars. Main-sequence K and M stars are so faint they are difficult to locate, but they are very common. Nature makes more low-mass stars than massive stars, but that is not sufficient to explain the excess. An additional factor is the stellar lifetimes. Because low-mass stars not only form more often but also live long lives, there are many more of them in the sky than massive stars. The O and B stars are luminous and easy to locate; but, because of their fleeting lives, there are never more than a few on the main sequence at any one time.

The Life Expectancies of Stars

You have compared stellar lifetimes in a qualitative way; but, to really understand how stars evolve, you must be able to calculate how long they can survive. In fact, you can calculate the approximate life expectancy of a star from its mass.

Because main-sequence stars consume their fuel at an approximately constant rate, you can estimate the amount of time a star spends on the main sequence—its life expectancy, T—by dividing the amount of fuel by the rate of fuel consumption. You have made calculations like this before. If you drive a truck that carries 20 gallons of fuel and uses 2 gallons of fuel per hour, you know the truck can run for 10 hours.

The amount of fuel a star has is proportional to its mass, and the rate at which it burns its fuel is proportional to its luminosity; that means you could make a first estimate of the star's life expectancy by dividing mass by luminosity. Astronomers observe that 2-solar-mass main-sequence stars are about 11 times more luminous than the sun. Stars with 2 solar masses have 2 times as much fuel as the sun, but consume that fuel 11 times as quickly as the sun does, so they should live only

about 2/11, or 18 percent, as long as the sun. Notice that stars larger than the sun have shorter lifetimes because their fuel consumption rates are so much faster. You can make the calculation even easier if you remember from Chapter 9 that the mass–luminosity relation says that the luminosity of a main-sequence star is approximately proportional to $M^{3.5}$. The life expectancy then is:

$$T = \frac{M}{L} = \frac{M}{M^{3.5}} \text{ or } T = \frac{1}{M^{2.5}}$$

This means that you can estimate the life expectancy of a star by dividing 1 by the star's mass raised to the 2.5 power. If you express the mass in solar masses, the life expectancy will be in solar lifetimes.

For example, how long can a 4-solar-mass star live, relative to the sun?

$$T = \frac{1}{4^{2.5}} = \frac{1}{(4 \cdot 4 \cdot \sqrt{4})} = \frac{1}{32} \text{ solar lifetimes}$$

Detailed studies of models of the sun show that the sun, presently 5 billion years old, can last another 5 billion years. So, a solar lifetime is approximately 10 billion years, and a 4-solar-mass star will last about (10 billion)/32, or about 310 million, years.

This estimation of stellar life expectancies is very approximate. For example, the model ignores mass loss, which may affect the life expectancies especially of both very luminous and very faint stars. Nevertheless, it serves to illustrate an important point. Stars that are only slightly more massive than the sun have dramatically shorter lifetimes on the main sequence.

SCIENTIFIC ARGUMENT

Why is there a main sequence?
Some scientific arguments test a theory by comparing it to observations. You can begin with the simple fact that the weight of a star's material must be balanced by pressure, the principle of hydrostatic equilibrium. A contracting protostar is not quite in equilibrium, and gravity squeezes it tighter and tighter. As it contracts, its interior heats up; and, when it gets hot enough to fuse hydrogen into helium, the pressure–temperature thermostat takes over and regulates energy production so that the star makes just enough energy to support its own weight. That means that massive stars, having more weight to support, must have higher internal pressures and therefore must make more energy. Energy must flow from hot to cool, so that energy flows from the hot core of the star out to the cooler surface and is radiated into space. Massive stars, having more weight to support, must have their pressure temperature thermostats set higher, and that makes them more luminous. They reach stability with luminosities and surface temperatures that place them along the upper main sequence on the H–R diagram. Less massive stars support less weight and reach stability along the lower main sequence. There is a main sequence because stars in this stable life stage fuse hydrogen to support their own weight.

Now revise your argument. **Why do massive stars have such short life expectancies?**

12-2 Post-Main-Sequence Evolution

IN EARLIER CHAPTERS, you probably had questions about giant stars: Why are giant stars so large? Why do they have such low densities? And, why are they so uncommon? Now you are ready to answer those questions by learning about the evolution of stars after they leave the main sequence.

Expansion into a Giant

To understand how stars evolve, you must remember that they are not well mixed; that is, their interiors are not stirred. The centers of lower-mass stars like the sun are radiative, meaning the energy moves as radiation and not as circulating currents of heated gas. The gas does not move deep inside such stars, and that means they are not mixed at all. More massive stars have convective cores that mix the central regions (Figure 11-15), but these regions are not very large, and so, for the most part, these stars, too, are not mixed. (The lowest-mass stars are an exception that you will examine in the next chapter.)

In this respect, a star is like a campfire that is not stirred; the ashes accumulate at the center, and the fuel in the outer parts never gets used. Nuclear fusion consumes hydrogen nuclei and produces helium nuclei, the "ashes" that accumulate at the star's center. Because nothing mixes the interior of the star, the helium nuclei remain where they are in the center, and the hydrogen in the star's outer parts is not mixed down to the center where it could be fused.

The helium ashes that accumulate in the star's core cannot fuse into heavier elements because the temperature is too low. As a result, the core eventually becomes an inert ball of helium. As this happens, the energy production in the core falls, and the weight of the outer layers forces the core to contract.

Although the contracting helium core cannot generate nuclear energy, it does grow hotter because it converts gravitational energy into thermal energy (see Chapter 11). The rising temperature heats the unprocessed hydrogen just outside the core, hydrogen that was never before hot enough to fuse. When the surrounding hydrogen becomes hot enough, it ignites in a thin, spherical shell. Like a grass fire moving outward from an exhausted campfire, the hydrogen-fusing shell slowly burns outward, leaving helium ash behind and increasing the mass of the helium core.

During this stage in its evolution, the star overproduces energy; that is, it produces more energy than it needs to balance its own gravity. The contracting helium core converts gravitational energy into thermal energy. Some of this energy heats the helium core, and some of that heat leaks outward through the star. At the same time, the hydrogen-fusion shell also produces energy as the contracting core brings fresh hydrogen closer to the center of the star and heats it to high temperature. The result is a flood of energy flowing outward, forcing the outer layers of the star to puff up and expand the star into a giant (■ Figure 12-6).

The expansion of the envelope dramatically changes the star's location in the H–R diagram. As the outer layers of gas expand, energy is absorbed in lifting and expanding the gas. The loss of that energy lowers the temperature of the gas. Consequently, the point that represents the star in the H–R diagram moves quickly to the right (in less than a million years for a star of 5 solar masses but in about 150 million years for a 1 solar mass star) (■ Figure 12-7). As the radius of a giant star continues to increase, the enlarging surface area makes the star more luminous, moving its point also upward in the H–R diagram. One of your Favorite Stars, Aldebaran, the glowing red eye of Taurus the bull, is a red giant, with a diameter 25 times that of the sun but with only half its surface temperature.

A medium-mass star like the sun evolves to become a giant, but more massive stars evolve across the upper H–R diagram and become supergiants, stars even larger than giants. Consider two more Favorite Stars. Betelgeuse (α Orionis) is a very cool, red supergiant over 800 times the diameter of the sun. Rigel (β Orionis) is a supergiant 50 times larger than the sun. It may seem odd to say that Rigel, a blue star, has expanded and cooled. At a temperature of 12,000 K, Rigel is hot and looks quite blue to your eyes. But when it was on the main sequence, Rigel had a much hotter surface. Even so, it would not have

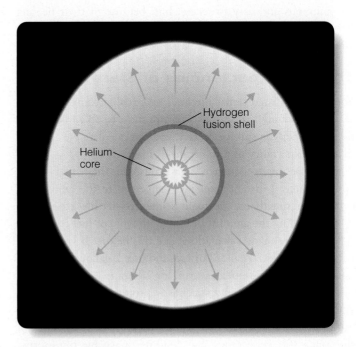

■ Figure 12-6

When a star runs out of hydrogen at its center, it ignites a hydrogen-fusion shell. The helium core contracts and heats while the envelope expands and cools. (For a scale drawing, see Figure 12-9.)

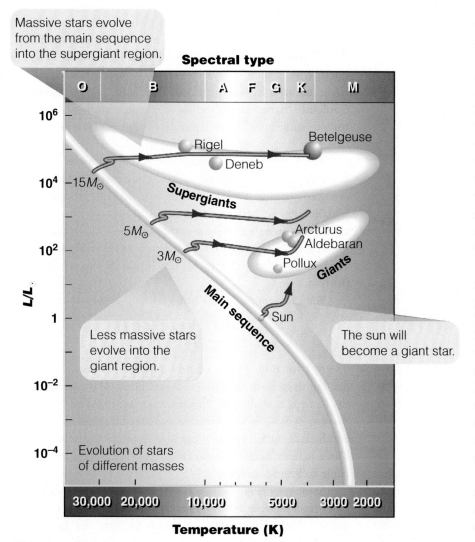

Spectral type

O   B   A F G K   M

10⁶

Rigel

Betelgeuse

Deneb

10⁴ −15M☉

Supergiants

5M☉

Arcturus
Aldebaran

10²

3M☉

Pollux **Giants**

$L/L_⊙$

1

Main sequence

Sun

Less massive stars evolve into the giant region.

The sun will become a giant star.

10⁻²

10⁻⁴ Evolution of stars of different masses

30,000 20,000   10,000   5000   3000 2000

Temperature (K)

■ **Figure 12-7**

The evolution of a massive star moves the point that represents it in the H–R diagram to the right of the main sequence into the region of the supergiants such as Rigel and Betelgeuse. The evolution of a medium-mass star moves its point in the H–R diagram into the region of the giants such as those shown here.

looked much bluer because you cannot see the ultraviolet radiation that the hottest stars emit. Any star as hot or hotter than Rigel will look blue to your eyes, as shown in Figure 7-6. So, even though Rigel is blue, it is indeed a star that has expanded and cooled.

Now you can understand a few things you noticed in earlier chapters. Giants and supergiants are large because they have expanded, and they have very low densities for the same reason. Also, the giant and supergiant region of the H–R diagram contains a jumble of different mass stars because all main-sequence stars funnel through this part of the diagram as they die. (See Figure 9-23.)

Degenerate Matter

Although the hydrogen-fusion shell can force the envelope of the star to expand, it cannot stop the contraction of the helium core. Because the core is not hot enough to fuse helium, gravity squeezes it tighter, and it becomes very small. If you were to represent the helium core of a giant star with a baseball, the outer envelope of the star would be about the size of a baseball stadium. Yet the core would contain about 12 percent of the star's mass. When gas is compressed to such extreme densities, it begins to behave in surprising ways that can affect the evolution of a star.

Normally, the pressure in a gas depends on its temperature. The hotter a gas is, the faster its particles move, and the more pressure it exerts. The gas inside a star is ionized, so there are two kinds of particles, atomic nuclei and free electrons. Under normal conditions the gas in a star follows the same pressure–temperature laws as other gases, but if the gas is compressed to very high densities, as in the core of a giant star, two laws of quantum mechanics come into play, and the difference between electrons and nuclei becomes important.

First, quantum mechanics says that the moving electrons confined in the star's core can have only certain amounts of energy, just as the electron in an atom can occupy only certain energy levels (see Chapter 7). You can think of these permitted energies as the rungs of a ladder. An electron can occupy any rung but not the spaces between.

The second quantum mechanical law (called the Pauli exclusion principle) says that two identical electrons cannot occupy the same energy level. Because electrons spin in one direction or the other, two electrons can occupy a single energy level if they spin in opposite directions. That level is then completely filled, and a third electron cannot enter because, whichever way it spins, it will be identical to one or the other of the two electrons already in the level.

A low-density gas has few electrons per cubic centimeter, so there are plenty of energy levels available (■ Figure 12-8). If a gas becomes very dense, however, nearly all of the lower energy levels are occupied. In such a gas, a moving electron cannot slow down; slowing down would decrease its energy, and there are no open energy levels for it to drop down to. It can speed up only if it can absorb enough energy to leap to the top of the energy ladder, where there are empty energy levels.

When a gas is so dense that its electrons are not free to change their energy, astronomers call it **degenerate matter.**

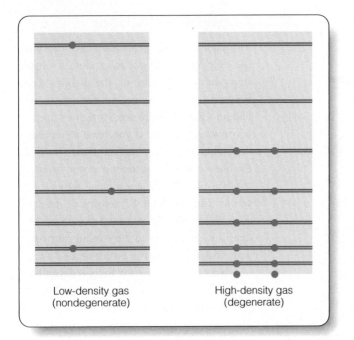

■ **Figure 12-8**

Electron energy levels are arranged like rungs on a ladder. In a low-density gas, many levels are open, but in a degenerate gas, all lower-energy levels are filled.

Although it is a gas, it has two peculiar properties that can affect the star. First, the degenerate gas resists compression. To compress the gas, you must push against the moving electrons, and changing their motion means changing their energy. That requires tremendous effort because you must boost them to the top of the energy ladder. That is why degenerate matter, though still a gas, is harder to compress than the toughest hardened steel.

Second, the pressure of degenerate gas does not depend on temperature. To see why, note that the pressure depends on the speed of the electrons, which cannot be changed without tremendous effort. The temperature, however, depends on the motion of all the particles in the gas, both electrons and nuclei. If you add heat to the gas, most of that energy goes to speed up the motions of the nuclei, which move slowly and don't contribute much to the pressure. Only a few electrons can absorb enough energy to reach the empty energy levels at the top of the energy ladder. That means that changing the temperature of the gas has almost no effect on the pressure.

These two properties of degenerate matter become important when stars end their main-sequence lives. Eventually, many stars collapse into white dwarfs, and you will discover that these tiny stars are made of degenerate matter. But, long before that, the cores of some giant stars become so dense that they are degenerate, a situation that can produce a cosmic bomb.

Helium Fusion

Hydrogen fusion leaves behind helium ash, which cannot fuse at the relatively low temperatures of hydrogen fusion. Helium nuclei (two protons plus two neutrons) have a positive charge twice that of a hydrogen nucleus (a proton), which means the Coulomb barrier is higher. At the temperature of hydrogen fusion, helium nuclei move too slowly and collide too gently to fuse.

As the star becomes a giant star, fusing hydrogen in a shell, its inner core of helium ash contracts and grows hotter. It may even become degenerate. Finally, as the temperature approaches 100,000,000 K, helium nuclei begin to fuse together to make carbon. Because three helium nuclei are needed to make a carbon nucleus, and because a helium nucleus is called an alpha particle, astronomers often refer to helium fusion as the **triple alpha process**.

You can summarize the helium-fusing process in two steps:

$$^4\text{He} + {}^4\text{He} \rightarrow {}^8\text{Be} + \gamma$$
$$^8\text{Be} + {}^4\text{He} \rightarrow {}^{12}\text{C} + \gamma$$

The first reaction actually absorbs a little bit of energy from the gas, but the second reaction produces almost 80 times more than the first reaction absorbs. This process is complicated by the fact that beryllium-8 is very unstable and may break apart, back into two helium nuclei, before it can absorb another helium nucleus. Three helium nuclei can also form carbon directly, but such a triple collision is unlikely.

Some stars begin helium fusion gradually, but stars in a certain mass range begin helium fusion with an explosion called the **helium flash**. This explosion occurs because the gas in the helium core becomes degenerate with a density that can reach 1,000,000 g/cm³. On Earth, a teaspoon of this material would weigh as much as a large truck. Because pressure no longer depends on temperature in a degenerate gas, the pressure–temperature thermostat that controls the nuclear fusion reactions no longer works.

When the helium ignites, it generates energy, which raises the temperature. But because the pressure–temperature thermostat is not working in the degenerate gas, the core does not respond to the higher temperature by expanding. Rather, the higher temperature forces the reactions to go faster, which makes more energy, which raises the temperature, which makes the reactions go faster, and so on. The ignition of helium fusion in a degenerate gas results in a runaway explosion so violent that for a few minutes the helium core generates 10^{14} times more energy per second than the sun. That's about 100 times the energy generated by all the stars in the Milky Way Galaxy.

Although the helium flash is sudden and powerful, it does not destroy the star. In fact, if you were observing a giant star as it experienced a helium flash, you would probably see no outward evidence of an eruption. The helium core is quite small

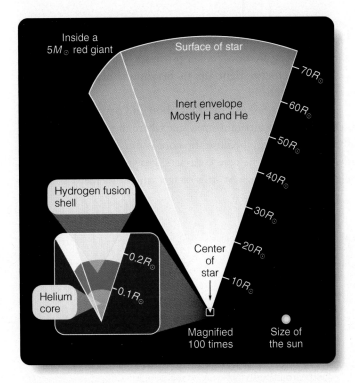

■ **Figure 12-9**

When a star runs out of hydrogen at its center, the core of helium contracts to a small size, becomes very hot, and begins nuclear fusion in a shell (blue). The outer layers of the star expand and cool. The red giant star shown here has an average density much lower than the air at Earth's surface. Here $M_\odot$ stands for the mass of the sun, and $R_\odot$ stands for the radius of the sun. (Illustration design by Mike Seeds)

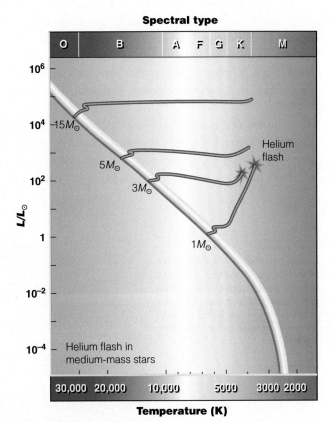

■ **Figure 12-10**

Stars like the sun suffer a helium flash, but more massive stars begin helium fusion without a helium flash. Stars less than 0.4 times the mass of the sun cannot get hot enough to ignite helium. The zero-age main sequence is shown here in red at the lower edge of the main sequence.

(■ Figure 12-9), and all of the energy of the explosion is absorbed by the distended envelope. Also, the helium flash is a very short-lived event. In a matter of minutes, the core of the star becomes so hot it is no longer degenerate, the pressure–temperature thermostat brings the helium fusion under control, and the star proceeds to fuse helium steadily in its core. You will learn about this post-helium-flash evolution later.

Astronomers calculating models of stellar evolution find that the sun and other medium-mass main-sequence stars will eventually undergo a helium flash, but not all stars do. Stars less massive than about 0.4 solar mass never get hot enough to ignite helium, and stars more massive than about 3 solar masses ignite helium before their cores become degenerate (■ Figure 12-10). In such stars, pressure always depends on temperature, so the pressure–temperature thermostat keeps the helium fusion under control.

If the helium flash occurs only in some stars and is a very short-lived event that is hardly visible from outside the star, why is it important? The answer is that it limits the reliability of the mathematical models astronomers use to study stellar evolution. Massive stars are not very common, and low-mass stars evolve so slowly that it is hard to find evidence of low-mass stellar evolution. For those reasons, studies of stellar evolution largely depend

on medium-mass stars, which do experience the helium flash. But the helium flash occurs so rapidly and so violently that computer programs cannot follow the changes in a star's internal structure in detail. To follow the evolution of medium-mass stars like the sun past the helium flash, astronomers must make assumptions about the way the helium flash affects stars' internal structures.

There is another reason why you should think about the helium flash. By seeing what happens when the pressure–temperature thermostat is turned off, you can appreciate its importance in maintaining the stability of stars. In the next chapter you will meet stars that explode violently because nuclear fusion becomes unregulated.

Post-helium-flash evolution is generally understood, and you can trace the stages in the following discussion in ■ Figure 12-11. After the gas ceases to be degenerate, helium fusion proceeds under the control of the pressure–temperature thermostat. Throughout these events, the hydrogen fusion shell continues to produce energy, but the new helium fusion energy produced in the core makes the core expand. That expansion absorbs energy previously used to support the outer layers of the star. As a result, the outer layers contract, and the surface of the star grows slightly hotter. In the H–R diagram, the point that represents the star initially moves down toward lower luminosity and then to the left toward higher temperature. Later, as the star stabilizes fusing helium in its core, its luminosity recovers, but its surface grows hotter.

Helium fusion produces carbon, and some of the carbon nuclei absorb helium nuclei to form oxygen. A few of the oxygen nuclei absorb helium nuclei to form neon and then magnesium. Some of these reactions release neutrons, which, having no charge, are more easily absorbed by nuclei to gradually build even heavier nuclei. These reactions are not important as energy producers. They are slow-cooker processes that form small traces of heavier elements right up to beryllium, nearly four times heavier than iron.

The nuclear "ashes," mostly carbon and oxygen, accumulate at the center of a medium-mass star where they cannot fuse rapidly to make energy because the core is not hot enough. As the ashes accumulate, the core contracts, grows hotter, and ignites a helium fusion shell. At this stage, the star has two shells

■ **Figure 12-11**

When a main-sequence star exhausts the hydrogen in its core, it evolves rapidly to the right in the H–R diagram as it expands to become a cool giant. It then follows a looping path (enlarged) as it fuses helium in its core and then fuses helium in a shell. Compare with Figure 12-7.

producing energy. A hydrogen fusion shell continues to move outward, leaving behind helium ash; a helium fusion shell moves outward into the helium, leaving behind carbon–oxygen ash. As the star's carbon–oxygen core contracts, its outer layers expand, and its point in the H–R diagram moves back toward the right, completing a loop, as you can see in Figure 12-11.

Fusing Elements Heavier Than Helium

Understanding the evolution of stars after helium exhaustion requires great sophistication in computer models. As usual, what happens depends on the mass of the star. The inert core of carbon–oxygen ash contracts and becomes hotter, but only in stars more massive than about 4 solar masses can the core reach temperatures as high as 600,000,000 K, hot enough to fuse carbon. Subsequently, these stars can fuse neon, oxygen, silicon, and other heavy elements.

Carbon fusion in a star begins a complex network of reactions illustrated in ■ Figure 12-12, where each circle represents a possible nucleus and each arrow represents a different nuclear reaction. Nuclei can react by capturing a proton, capturing a neutron, capturing a helium nucleus, or by combining directly with other nuclei. Unstable nuclei can decay by ejecting an electron, ejecting a positron, ejecting a helium nucleus, or splitting into fragments.

As you can tell from all the arrows in Figure 12-12, the fusion of elements heavier than helium is not simple. Astronomers who model the structure and evolution of massive stars must use sophisticated nuclear physics to compute the amount of energy produced and to follow the changes in chemical composition that occur as the stars fuse carbon and heavier elements. Stars in this stage of their evolution develop complex internal structure as they fuse one heavy element after another in concentric shells. Like great spherical cakes with many layers, the stars can fuse a number of different elements simultaneously in different shells.

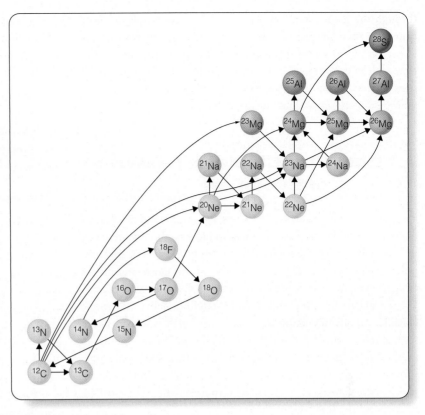

■ **Figure 12-12**

Carbon fusion involves many possible reactions that build numerous heavy nuclei.

Eventually, all stars face collapse. Less massive stars cannot get hot enough to ignite the heavier nuclei. The more massive stars that can ignite heavy nuclei consume their fuels at a tremendous rate, so they run through their available fuel quickly (■ Table 12-3). No matter what the star's mass, it will eventually run out of usable fuels, and gravity will win the struggle with pressure. You will explore the ultimate deaths of stars in the next chapter.

The time a star spends as a giant or supergiant is small compared with its life on the main sequence. The sun, for example, will spend about 10 billion years as a main-sequence star but only about a billion years as a giant. The more massive stars pass

■ **Table 12-3 | Nuclear Reactions in Massive Stars**

Nuclear Fuel	Nuclear Products	Minimum Ignition Temperature	Main-Sequence Mass Needed to Ignite Fusion	Duration of Fusion in a 25-$M_\odot$ Star
H	He	4×10^6K	$0.1\ M_\odot$	7×10^6 yr
He	C, O	120×10^6K	$0.4\ M_\odot$	0.5×10^6 yr
C	Ne, Na, Mg, O	0.6×10^9K	$4\ M_\odot$	600 yr
Ne	O, Mg	1.2×10^9K	~$8\ M_\odot$	1 yr
O	Si, S, P	1.5×10^9K	~$8\ M_\odot$	~0.5 yr
Si	Ni to Fe	2.7×10^9K	~$8\ M_\odot$	~1 day

through the giant stage even more rapidly. Because of the short time stars spend as giants, you will see relatively few giants. This illustrates an important principle in astronomy: The shorter the time a given evolutionary stage takes, the less likely you are to see stars in that particular stage. That explains why you see a great many main-sequence stars but few giants (see page 187).

12-3 Star Clusters: Evidence of Evolution

THE THEORY OF STELLAR EVOLUTION is so complex and involves so many assumptions that astronomers would have little confidence in it were it not for the evidence provided by clusters of stars. By observing and comparing the properties of star clusters of different ages, you can see clear evidence of the evolution of stars.

To grasp the difficulty of understanding stellar evolution, consider an analogy. Suppose a visitor to Earth who had never seen a tree wandered through a forest for an hour looking at mature trees, fallen seeds, young saplings, rotting logs, and rising sprouts. Could such an observer understand the life cycle of trees? Astronomers face the same problem when they try to understand the life story of the stars.

Humans do not live long enough to see stars evolve. You see only a momentary glimpse of the universe as it appears during your lifetime, a snapshot in which all the stages in the life cycle of the stars are represented. Unscrambling these stages and putting them in order is a difficult task. Only by looking at selected groups of stars—star clusters—can you see the pattern.

Observing Star Clusters

Plotting each star in a star cluster on an H–R diagram freezes a moment in the cluster's history and makes the evolution of the stars visible. The stars in a cluster all formed at about the same time from the same cloud of gas, so they are all about the same age and have the same chemical composition. The differences you see among stars in a cluster must arise from differences in mass, and that is what makes stellar evolution visible. Study **Star Cluster H–R Diagrams** on pages 248–249 and notice three important points and four new terms:

1 There are two kinds of star clusters, *open clusters* and *globular clusters*. They look different, but their stars evolve in similar ways. You will learn more about these clusters in a later chapter.

2 You can estimate the age of a star cluster by observing the *turnoff point* in the distribution of the points that represent its stars in the H–R diagram.

3 Finally, notice that the shape of a star cluster's H–R diagram is governed by the evolutionary path the stars take. The H–R diagrams of older clusters are especially clear in outlining how stars evolve away from the main sequence to the giant region, then move left along the *horizontal branch* before evolving back into the giant region. By comparing clusters of different ages, you can visualize how stars evolve almost as if you were watching a film of a star cluster evolving over billions of years.

Were it not for star clusters, astronomers would have little confidence in the theories of stellar evolution. Star clusters make that evolution visible and assure astronomers that they really do understand how stars are born, live, and die.

The Evolution of Star Clusters

What you know about star formation and stellar evolution can help you understand star clusters and how they evolve.

A star cluster is formed when a cloud of gas contracts, fragments, and forms a group of stars. As you recall from Chapter 11, some groups of stars, called associations, are so widely scattered that the group is not held together by its own gravity. The stars in an association wander away from each other rather quickly. Some groups of stars are more compact; even after the stars become luminous and the gas and dust are blown away, gravity holds the group together as a star cluster.

Open clusters are not as old or as crowded as the globular clusters, and that helps explain their appearance. Close encounters between stars are rare in an open cluster where the stars are farther apart, and such clusters have an irregular appearance. The globular clusters appear to be nearly perfect globes because the stars are much closer together and encounters between stars are more common. The globular clusters have had time to evenly distribute the energy of motion among all of the stars so they have settled into a more uniform, spherical shape.

As a star cluster ages, some stars traveling a bit faster than others can escape. Globular clusters are compact and massive and have survived for 11 billion years or more. A star cluster with only a few widely distributed stars may evaporate completely as its stars escape one by one. Our sun may have formed in a star cluster 5 billion years ago, but there is no way to trace it back to its family home even if that star cluster still exists.

SCIENTIFIC ARGUMENT

Why is it only lower-mass stars that outline the horizontal branch?

This argument depends on timing. If a star cluster is young, it may contain a few massive stars, but because massive stars are so rare and evolve so rapidly you are unlikely to see more than a few of these stars evolving through the giant or supergiant regions of the H–R diagram. Lower-mass stars are very common and evolve slowly, so, in an older star cluster, you can see lots of stars in various stages of the post-main-sequence evolution. That outlines the horizontal branch.

Now construct a different argument. **What evidence can you cite that giant stars are main-sequence stars that have expanded to large diameters?**

12-4 Variable Stars: Evidence of Evolution

IT IS A **Common Misconception** that the stars are constant and unchanging. Stellar models show that stars slowly evolve as they consume their fuels, and the evidence from star clusters confirms these slow changes in structure. But is this enough evidence to be certain? One of the most important principles of science is that theories must be checked against all known evidence. Some stars that vary in brightness provide evidence of stellar evolution and illustrate once more the importance of energy flowing outward through the layers of the stars.

A **variable star** is any star that changes its brightness in a periodic way. Some variable stars are eclipsing binaries (see Chapter 9), but many others are single stars that grow brighter and fainter because of internal processes. These stars are often called **intrinsic variables** to distinguish them from eclipsing binaries. Of these intrinsic variables, two related kinds are centrally important to modern astronomy, even though the first star of that class was discovered centuries ago.

Cepheid and RR Lyrae Variable Stars

In 1784, the deaf and mute English astronomer John Goodricke, then 19 years old, discovered that the star δ Cephei is variable, changing its brightness by almost a magnitude over a period of 5.37 days (■ Figure 12-13a). Goodricke died at the age of 21, but his discovery ensures his place in the history of astronomy. Since 1784, hundreds of stars like δ Cephei have been found, and they are now known as **Cepheid variable stars**.

Cepheid variables are supergiant or bright giant stars of spectral type F or G. The fastest complete a cycle—bright to faint to bright again—in about two days, whereas the slowest take as long as 60 days. A plot of a variable's magnitude versus time, known as a light curve, shows a typical rapid rise to maximum brightness and a slower decline (Figure 12-13b). Some Cepheids change their brightness by only 0.01 magnitude (about 1 percent), while others change by more than a magnitude. One of your Favorite Stars, Polaris, the North Star, is a Cepheid with a period of 3.9696 days and a very small amplitude. A related type of star, the **RR Lyrae variable stars**, are giant stars that are fainter than the Cepheids and pulsate with periods of less than a day.

Studies of Cepheids and RR Lyrae stars reveal two related facts of great importance. First, there is a **period–luminosity relation** that connects the period of pulsation of a Cepheid to its luminosity. The longer-period Cepheids are about 40,000 times more luminous than the sun, while the shortest-period Cepheids are only a few hundred times more luminous than the sun. Second, there are two types of Cepheids. Type I Cepheids,

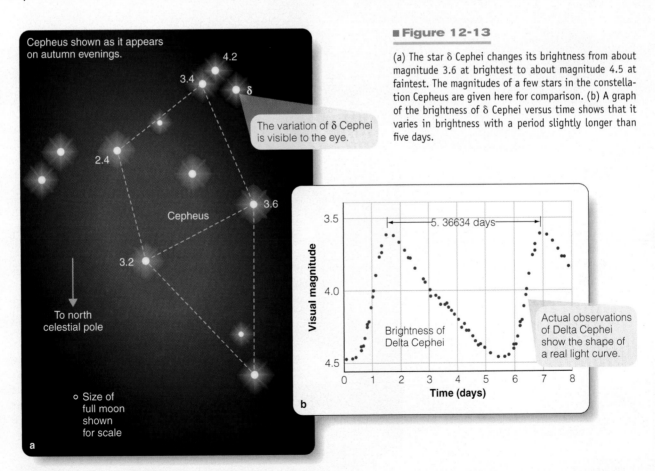

■ Figure 12-13

(a) The star δ Cephei changes its brightness from about magnitude 3.6 at brightest to about magnitude 4.5 at faintest. The magnitudes of a few stars in the constellation Cepheus are given here for comparison. (b) A graph of the brightness of δ Cephei versus time shows that it varies in brightness with a period slightly longer than five days.

Cepheus shown as it appears on autumn evenings.

The variation of δ Cephei is visible to the eye.

Cepheus

To north celestial pole

○ Size of full moon shown for scale

a

Brightness of Delta Cephei

Actual observations of Delta Cephei show the shape of a real light curve.

5. 36634 days

Visual magnitude

Time (days)

b

Star Cluster H-R Diagrams

1 An **open cluster** is a collection of 10 to 1000 stars in a region about 25 pc in diameter. Some open clusters are quite small and some are large, but they all have an open, transparent appearance because the stars are not crowded together.

In a star cluster each star follows its orbit around the center of mass of the cluster.

AURA/NOAO/NSF

Visual-wavelength image

**Open Cluster
The Jewel Box**

1a A **globular cluster** can contain 10^5 to 10^6 stars in a region only 10 to 30 pc in diameter. The term "globular cluster" comes from the word "globe," although globular cluster is pronounced like "glob of butter." These clusters are nearly spherical, and the stars are much closer together than the stars in an open cluster.

**Globular Cluster
47 Tucanae**

Anglo-Australian Observatory / David Malin Images

Visual-wavelength image

Astronomers can construct an H–R diagram for a star cluster by plotting a point to represent the luminosity and temperature of each star.

Spectral type

The Hyades Star Cluster

The most massive stars have died

Only a few stars are in the giant stage.

Main sequence

Giants

The lower-mass stars are still on the main sequence.

The faintest stars were not observed in the study.

Temperature (K)

2 The H–R diagram of a star cluster can make the evolution of stars visible. The key is to remember that all of the stars in the star cluster have the same age but differ in mass. The H–R diagram of a star cluster provides a snapshot of the evolutionary state of the stars at the time you happen to be alive. The diagram here shows the 650-million-year-old star cluster called the Hyades. The upper main sequence is missing because the more massive stars have died, and our snapshot catches a few medium-mass stars leaving the main sequence to become giants.

As a star cluster ages, its main sequence grows shorter like a candle burning down. You can judge the age of a star cluster by looking at the **turnoff point**, the point on the main sequence where stars evolve to the right to become giants. Stars at the turnoff point have lived out their lives and are about to die. Consequently, the life expectancy of the stars at the turnoff point equals the age of the cluster.

From theoretical models of stars, you could construct a film to show how the H–R diagram of a star cluster changes as it ages. You can then compare (left) with observation (right) to understand how stars evolve. Note that the time step for each frame in this film increases by a factor of 10.

Highest-mass stars evolving. Low-mass stars still contracting.

10^6 y

10^7 y

Upper main sequence stars have died.

10^8 y

10^9 y

Only the lower-mass stars remain on the main sequence.

10^{10} y

NGC2264
Age 10^6 yr

$L/L_\odot$

10^6
10^4
10^2
1
10^{-2}
10^{-4}

Faintest stars not observed.

Pleiades
Age 10^8 yr

$L/L_\odot$

10^6
10^4
10^2
1
10^{-2}
10^{-4}

Turnoff point

Faintest stars not observed.

M67
Age 4×10^9 yr

$L/L_\odot$

10^6
10^4
10^2
1
10^{-2}
10^{-4}

Turnoff point

Faintest stars not observed.

30,000   10,000   5000 3000
Temperature (K)

NGC 2264 is a very young cluster still embedded in the nebula from which it formed. Its lower-mass stars are still contracting, and it is rich in T Tauri stars.

Visual

The nebula around the Pleiades is produced by gas and dust through which the cluster is passing. Its original nebula dissipated long ago.

Visual

M67 is an old open cluster. In photographs, such clusters have a uniform appearance because they lack hot, bright stars. Compare with the Jewel Box on the opposite page.

Visual

...ar cluster H–R diagrams resemble the last frame in ..., which tells you that globular clusters are very old.

Theory

Evolution of a globular cluster star

Main sequence

Helium shell fusion

Helium core fusion

Globular cluster main sequence

30,000 20,000   10,000   5000   3000 2000
Temperature (K)

Observation

Globular cluster M3

Horizontal Branch

Giant stars

Main-sequence stars

Faintest stars not observed

30,000 20,000   10,000   5000   3000 2000
Temperature (K)

3a The H–R diagrams of globular clusters have very faint turnoff points showing that they are very old clusters. The best analysis suggests these clusters are about 11 billion years old.

The **horizontal branch** stars are giants fusing helium in their cores and then in shells. The shape of the horizontal branch outlines the evolution of these stars.

The main-sequence stars in globular clusters are fainter and bluer than the zero-age main sequence. Spectra reveal that globular cluster stars are poor in elements heavier than helium, and that means their gases are less opaque. That means energy can flow outward more easily, which makes the stars slightly smaller and hotter. Again the shape of star cluster H–R diagrams illustrates principles of stellar evolution.

including δ Cephei itself, have chemical compositions like that of the sun, but type II Cepheids and the RR Lyrae stars are poor in elements heavier than helium. These facts are clues that will help you understand variable stars as evidence of stellar evolution.

Pulsating Stars

Why would a star pulsate? Why should there be a period–luminosity relation? Why are there two types of Cepheids? The answers to these questions will reveal some of the deepest secrets of the stars. To find the answers, you should start with the H–R diagram.

Remember that after a star leaves the main sequence, it fuses hydrogen in a shell, and the point that represents it in the H–R diagram moves to the right as the star becomes a cool giant. When it ignites helium in its core, the star contracts and grows hotter, and the point in the diagram moves to the left. Soon, however, the helium core is exhausted; helium fusion continues only in a shell, forcing the star to expand again; and the point in the H–R diagram moves back to the right, completing a loop. Because giant stars evolve through these stages, their sizes and temperatures change in complicated ways. Certain combinations of size and temperature make a star unstable, causing it to pulsate as an intrinsic variable star. In the H–R diagram, the region where size and temperature lead to pulsation is called the **instability strip**, as shown in the H–R diagram in ■ Figure 12-14.

What makes variable stars pulsate? Start with a stable star. You could make a stable star pulsate temporarily if you squeezed it and then released it. The star would rebound outward, and it might oscillate in and out for a few cycles, but the oscillation would eventually run down because of friction. The energy of the moving gas would be converted to heat and radiated away, and the star would return to stability with each layer of gas in hydrostatic equilibrium. To make a star pulsate continuously, some process must drive the oscillation, just as a spring in a windup clock is needed to keep it ticking.

Studies using stellar models show that variable stars in the instability strip pulsate like beating hearts because of an energy-absorbing layer in their outer envelopes. This layer is the region where helium is partially ionized. Above this layer, the temperature is too low to ionize helium, and below the layer it is hot enough to ionize all of the helium. Like a spring, the helium ionization zone can absorb energy when it is compressed and release it when the zone expands, and that is enough to keep the star pulsating.

You can follow this pulsation in your imagination. As the outer layers of a pulsating star expand, the ionization zone expands, and the ionized helium becomes less ionized and releases stored energy, which gives the expanding gas a little boost and the expansion goes a little faster. The surface of the star overshoots its equilibrium position—it expands too far—and eventually falls back. As the surface layers contract, the ionization zone is compressed and becomes more ionized, which absorbs energy. Robbed of some of their energy, the layers of the star can't support the weight, and they compress a little faster. This allows the contraction to go even faster, and the in-falling layers overshoot the equilibrium point until the pressure inside the star slows them to a stop and makes them expand again.

Cepheids change their radius by 5 to 10 percent as they pulsate, and this motion can be detected by observing Doppler shifts in their spectra. When the stars expand, the surface layers approach, and astronomers see a blueshift. When they contract, the surface layers recede, and astronomers see a redshift. Although a 10 percent change in radius seems like a large change, it affects only the outer layers of the star. The center of the star is much too dense to be affected.

Only stars in the instability strip have their helium ionization zone at the right depth to act as a spring and drive the pulsation. In cool stars, the zone is too deep and cannot overcome the weight of the layers above it. That is, the spring is overloaded and can't expand. In hot stars, the helium ionization zone lies near the surface, and there is little weight above it to compress it. That is, the spring never gets squeezed. The stars in the instability strip have the right combination of temperature and radius for the helium ionization zone to fall exactly where it is most effective, and that is why those stars pulsate.

Now you can also understand why there is a period–luminosity relation. The more massive stars are larger and more luminous. When they cross the instability strip, they cross higher in the H–R diagram. But the larger a star is, the more slowly it pulsates—just as when large bells vibrate. They go "bong" whereas little bells go "ding." Pulsation period depends on size, which depends on mass, and mass also determines luminosity. So the most luminous Cepheids at the top of the instability strip are also the largest and pulsate most slowly. Less luminous Cepheids are smaller and pulsate faster. If you plot the average brightnesses of the variable stars against their periods of pulsation, you can clearly see the relationship between luminosity and period. Look at the right half of Figure 12-14 to see this relationship.

You know enough about stars to understand why there are two types of Cepheid variable stars. Type I Cepheids have chemical abundances roughly like those of the sun, but type II Cepheids are poor in elements heavier than helium. That means the gases in type II Cepheids are not as opaque as the gases in type I Cepheids. The all-important energy flowing outward can escape more easily in type II Cepheids, and they reach a slightly different equilibrium. For stars of the same period of pulsation, type II Cepheids are less luminous, as you can see from the graph in Figure 12-14.

In the H–R diagram, the RR Lyrae stars lie at the lower end of the instability strip. They are a bit smaller and hotter than Cepheids, but they pulsate for the same reason.

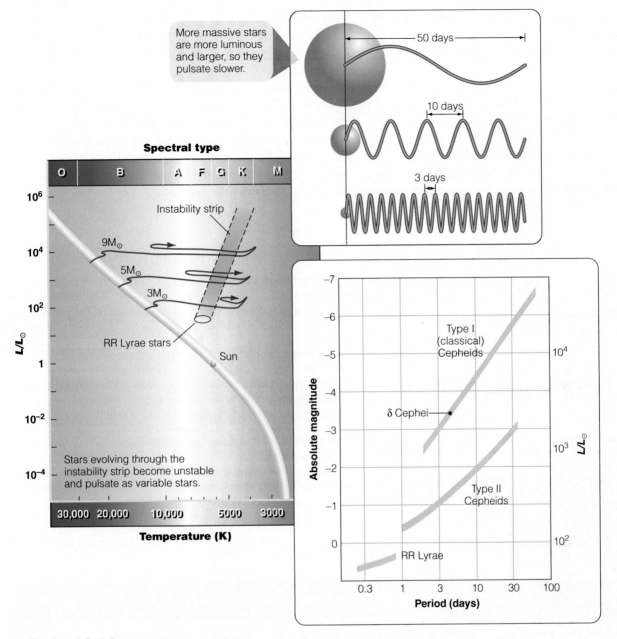

Spectral type

More massive stars are more luminous and larger, so they pulsate slower.

50 days

10 days

3 days

Instability strip

9M☉

5M☉

3M☉

RR Lyrae stars

Sun

Stars evolving through the instability strip become unstable and pulsate as variable stars.

Type I (classical) Cepheids

δ Cephei

Type II Cepheids

RR Lyrae

■ Figure 12-14

More massive stars are larger and more luminous and pulsate with longer periods than less massive stars. Consequently there is a period–luminosity relation: Type I and type II Cepheids have slightly different chemical compositions. The RR Lyrae stars have lower luminosities and shorter periods.

Period Changes in Variable Stars

Some Cepheids have been observed to change their periods of pulsation, and those changes are evidence that stars really do evolve.

The evolution of a star may carry it through the instability strip a number of times, and each time it can become a variable star. If you could watch a star as it entered the instability strip, you could see it begin to pulsate. Similarly, if you could watch a star leave the instability strip, you would see it stop pulsating.

Such an observation would be dramatic evidence that the stars are evolving. But, stars evolve so slowly that these events are rare.

One famous Cepheid, RU Camelopardalis, was observed to stop pulsating temporarily. Its pulsations died away in 1966, and many astronomers assumed that it had stopped pulsating because it was leaving the instability strip, but its pulsations resumed in 1967, so that star's exact situation is not well understood. Remember your Favorite Star, Polaris? It may be going through a similar change now, although it does not lie near the edge of the instability strip in the H–R diagram. There may be other factors affecting the evolution of Polaris that astronomers have not discovered yet.

Clearer evidence of stellar evolution can be found in the slowly changing periods of Cepheid variables. Even a tiny change in period can become easily observable because it accumulates, just as a clock that gains a second each day becomes obviously fast over a time as long as a year. Some Cepheids have periods that are growing shorter, and others have periods that are growing longer. These changes occur because the stars are evolving and changing their average radii; contraction shortens the period, and

expansion lengthens the period. The star X Cygni, for example, has a period that is gradually growing longer (■ Figure 12-15). These changes in the periods of pulsating stars provide definite evidence that the stars are evolving.

Some other kinds of variable stars lie outside the instability strip because their pulsation is driven by different mechanisms. It is sufficient here to discuss the Cepheids. They are common, they illustrate important ideas about stellar structure, and their changing periods make stellar evolution clearly evident. Also, you will use Cepheids in later chapters to study the distances to galaxies and the fate of the universe.

■ **Figure 12-15**

Like a clock running just a bit slow, the Cepheid variable star X Cygni has been reaching maximum brightness later and later for most of this century. This is shown by the upward curve in this graph of its observed minus predicted times of maximum brightness. As it evolves to the right across the instability strip, it is slowly expanding, and its period is growing longer by 1.46 seconds per year.

SCIENTIFIC ARGUMENT

What evidence can you cite to show that stars really are evolving?

Some processes occur so slowly that they cannot be observed over a human lifetime, so scientists must infer the process from observations. Stellar evolution occurs over billions of years, but because astronomers can plot H–R diagrams of star clusters having different ages, they can see how stellar evolution affects the stars. The H–R diagrams can be assembled into a sequence that makes stellar evolution obvious. Variable stars provide further evidence because tiny changes in radius produce correspondingly tiny changes in period of pulsation. Because those changes accumulate and make the stars run "fast" or "slow," astronomers can detect the effect of stellar evolution.

Now build a scientific argument that is based on theory. **How do stellar models allow astronomers to understand why Cepheid and RR Lyrae stars pulsate?**

What Are We?   Snapshooters

A human lifetime is less than a century, and that is a mere flicker of a moment in the history of the universe. What we see in the sky during our lives is just a snapshot that freezes the action. The stars form gradually and evolve over billions of years. We humans see none of that action. Our snapshot shows us the many stages of star birth and evolution, but we see

almost none of the changes through which stars pass.

Look again at Section 1-2, "When Is Now?" The entire 10,000-year history of human civilization is only a tiny fraction of the history of the universe. In that time, a few of the most massive stars may have evolved slightly, but the vast majority of stars have not changed since

humans on Earth began building the first cities.

Only by the application of human ingenuity have astronomers figured out how stars work, how they are born, how they evolve, and, as you will see in the next chapter, how they die. Our human life spans are only snapshots, but they reveal that we are part of a complex and evolving universe.

Study and Review

Summary

▶ Astronomers compute **stellar models (p. 234)** of the interiors of stars based on four simple laws of stellar structure. Two of the laws are the **conservation of mass law (p. 233)** and the **conservation of energy law (p. 233).** The third, the law of hydrostatic equilibrium, says that the star must balance the weight of its layers by its internal pressure. The fourth law says that energy can flow outward only by conduction, convection, or radiation.

▶ Mathematical stellar models show how rapidly a star uses its fuel in each layer, and that allows astronomers to step forward in time and follow the evolution of the star as it ages.

▶ There is a main sequence of stellar luminosities and temperatures because stars support their weight by hydrogen fusion. As energy flows outward, it heats the gas of the star, and pressure in the gas balances the inward pull of gravity.

▶ The mass–luminosity relation for main-sequence stars is explained by the requirement that a star support the weight of its layers by its internal pressure. The more massive a star is, the more weight it must support, and the higher its internal pressure must be. To keep its pressure high, it must be hot and generate large amounts of energy. Thus, the mass of a star determines its luminosity.

▶ Extremely massive stars are quite rare. Contracting gas clouds tend to fragment and produce pairs, groups, or clusters of stars and not extremely massive stars. Also, massive stars tend to blow matter away in strong stellar winds, and that rapidly reduces their mass.

▶ Stars less massive than 0.08 solar mass can't get hot enough to fuse hydrogen. Objects less massive than this become **brown dwarfs (p. 237)** and slowly cool as they radiate away their thermal energy. Many brown dwarfs have been observed.

▶ The **zero-age main sequence (ZAMS) (p. 238)** is the line in the H–R diagram where contracting stars begin fusing hydrogen and reach stability. As a star ages, it moves slightly upward and to the right, making the main sequence a band rather than a narrow line.

▶ The life expectancy of a main-sequence star depends on its mass. The more massive stars have more fuel but use their fuels rapidly and remain on the main sequence only a few million years. The sun, a medium-mass star, will last a total of about 10 billion years, and the least massive stars can survive for many hundreds of billion years.

▶ When a main-sequence star exhausts its hydrogen, its core contracts, and it begins to fuse hydrogen in a shell around its core. The outer parts of the star—its envelope—swell, and the star becomes a giant. Because of this expansion, the surface of the star cools, and it moves toward the right in the H–R diagram. The most massive stars move across the top of the diagram as supergiants.

▶ Because the core of a giant star contracts and the envelope expands, the average density of the star is very low, but the core, where the nuclear fusion occurs, is small and very dense.

▶ When the core of the star becomes hot enough, helium fusion, known as the **triple alpha process (p. 242),** begins first in the core and then in a shell. This causes the star to describe a loop in the giant region of the H–R diagram.

▶ If the matter in the core becomes **degenerate (p. 241)** before helium ignites, the pressure of the gas does not depend on its temperature, and when helium ignites, the core explodes in the **helium flash (p. 242).** Although the helium flash is violent, the star absorbs the extra energy and quickly brings the helium-fusing reactions under control.

▶ Helium fusion produces carbon and oxygen. Other nuclear reactions, which are not important sources of energy, slowly cook the matter during helium fusion and produce small amounts of heavy elements.

▶ If a star is massive enough, it can ignite carbon and other fuels after helium fusion. Each fuel fuses more rapidly, producing heavier and heavier elements.

▶ Because all the stars in a cluster have about the same chemical composition and age, you can see the effects of stellar evolution in the H–R diagram of a cluster. Massive stars evolve faster than low-mass stars, so in a given cluster the most massive stars leave the main sequence first.

▶ There are two types of star clusters. **Open clusters (p. 248)** contain 10 to 1000 stars and have an open, transparent appearance. **Globular clusters (p. 248)** contain 10^5 to 10^6 stars densely packed into a spherical shape. The open clusters tend to be young to middle aged, but globular clusters tend to be as old as 11 billion years. Also, globular clusters tend to be poor in elements heavier than helium.

▶ You can judge the age of a cluster by looking at the **turnoff point (p. 248),** the location on the main sequence where the stars turn off to the right and become giants. The life expectancy of a star at the turnoff point equals the age of the cluster.

▶ H–R diagrams of old star clusters such as globular clusters show how giant stars ignite helium fusion in their cores and evolve to the left in the diagram along the **horizontal branch (p. 249).**

▶ **Variable stars (p. 247)** are those that change in brightness. **Intrinsic variable stars (p. 247)** change in brightness because of internal processes and not because they are member of eclipsing binaries.

▶ The **Cepheid** and **RR Lyrae variable stars (p. 247)** are intrinsic variables with properties that lie in an **instability strip (p. 250)** in the H–R diagram; they contain a layer in their envelopes that stores and releases energy as they expand and contract. Stars outside the instability strip do not pulsate because the layer is too deep or too shallow to make the stars unstable.

▶ The Cepheids obey a **period–luminosity relation (p. 247)** because more massive stars, which are more luminous, are larger and pulsate more slowly.

▶ Some Cepheids have periods that are slowly changing, showing that the evolution of the star is gradually changing the star's average radius and thus its period of pulsation. Thus, some intrinsic variable stars show direct evidence of stellar evolution.

Review Questions

1. Why is there a main sequence?
2. Why is there a lower end to the main sequence? Why is there an upper end?
3. What is a brown dwarf?
4. Why is there a mass–luminosity relation?
5. Why does a star's life expectancy depend on mass?
6. Why do expanding stars become cooler and more luminous?
7. What causes the helium flash? Why does it make it difficult for astronomers to understand the later stages of stellar evolution?
8. How do some stars avoid the helium flash?
9. Why are giant stars so low in density?
10. Why are lower-mass stars unable to ignite more massive nuclear fuels such as carbon?

11. How can you estimate the age of a star cluster?

12. How do star clusters confirm that stars evolve?

13. How do some variable stars show that stars are evolving?

14. **How Do We Know?** How can mathematical models allow scientists to study processes that are hidden from human eyes or happen too fast or too slowly for humans to experience?

Discussion Questions

1. How do you know that the helium flash occurs if it cannot be observed? Can you accept an event as real if you can never observe it?

2. Can you think of ways that chemical differences could arise in stars in a single star cluster? Consider the mechanism that triggered their formation.

Problems

1. In the model shown in Figure 12-2, how much of the sun's mass is hotter than 13,000,000 K?

2. What is the life expectancy of a 16-solar-mass star? Of a 50-solar-mass star?

3. How massive could a star be and still survive for 5 billion years?

4. If the sun expanded to a radius 100 times its present radius, what would its density be? (*Hint:* The volume of a sphere is $\frac{4}{3}\pi R^3$.)

5. If a giant star 100 times the diameter of the sun were 1 pc from Earth, what would its angular diameter be? (*Hint:* Use the small-angle formula, in Chapter 3.)

6. What fraction of the volume of a 5-solar-mass giant star is occupied by its helium core? (*Hints:* See Figure 12-9. The volume of a sphere is $\frac{4}{3}\pi R^3$.)

7. If the stars at the turnoff point in a star cluster have masses of about 4 solar masses, how old is the cluster?

8. If an open cluster contains 500 stars and is 25 pc in diameter, what is the average distance between the stars? (*Hints:* On average, what share of the volume of the cluster surrounds each star? The volume of a sphere is $\frac{4}{3}\pi R^3$.)

9. Repeat Problem 8 for a typical globular cluster containing a million stars in a sphere 25 pc in diameter.

10. If a Cepheid variable star has a period of pulsation of 2 days and its period increases by 1 second, how late will it be in reaching maximum light after 1 year? After 10 years? (*Hint:* How many cycles will it complete in a year?)

Learning to Look

1. In the photograph of the Pleiades on page 249 there are no bright red stars. Use the H–R diagram to explain why the brightest stars are blue. Have there ever been bright red stars in this cluster?

2. Look at the photograph of the star cluster M67 on page 249. Why are there no bright blue stars in this cluster?

3. The star cluster in the photo at the right contains many hot, blue, luminous stars. Sketch its H–R diagram and discuss its probable age.

NASA/Walborn, Maiz-Apellaniz, and Barba

13 | The Deaths of Stars

Visual-wavelength image

Guidepost

Perhaps you were surprised in earlier chapters to learn that stars are born and grow old. Modern astronomers can tell the story of the stars right to the end. Here you will learn how stars die, and as you follow the story you will see how astronomers have tested their theories against evidence to answer four essential questions:

— **How will the sun die?**

— **Why are there so many white dwarf stellar remnants?**

— **What happens if an evolving star is in a binary system?**

— **How do massive stars die?**

Astronomy is exciting because it is about us. As you think about the deaths of stars, you are also thinking about the safety of Earth as a home for life and about the ultimate fate of our sun, our Earth, and the atoms of which you are made.

This nebula cataloged as NGC 2438 was produced by an aging sun-like star that swelled to become a giant and then ejected its outer layers into space. Here red emission is produced by nitrogen atoms, green by hydrogen, and blue by oxygen. (NASA, ESA, Hubble Heritage team, and K. Noll, STScI)

Natural laws have no pity.

— ROBERT HEINLEIN, *THE NOTEBOOKS OF LAZARUS LONG*

GRAVITY IS PATIENT. In the previous chapter you saw how stars resist their own gravity by generating energy through nuclear fusion. The energy keeps their interiors hot, and the resulting high pressure balances gravity and prevents the stars from collapsing. However, stars have only so much fuel, and it eventually runs out. When the stars exhaust their fuel, gravity wins, and the stars die (■ Figure 13-1).

The mass of a star is critical in determining its fate. Lower-mass stars like the sun die relatively gentle deaths, but massive stars explode violently. In addition, stars that orbit close to another star can have their evolution modified in peculiar ways. To follow the evolution of stars to their graves, you can sort the stars into two categories: lower-main-sequence stars, including the sun, and upper-main-sequence stars.

13-1 Lower-Main-Sequence Stars

THE STARS OF THE LOWER MAIN SEQUENCE have relatively low masses, and they face similar fates as they exhaust their nuclear fuels.

NGC 2440

Visual-wavelength image

As you learned in the previous chapter, when a star exhausts one nuclear fuel, its interior contracts and grows hotter until the next nuclear fuel ignites. The interior of a star heats up as contraction converts gravitational energy into thermal energy. That presents a problem for lower-main-sequence stars. Low-mass stars don't have a lot of gravitational energy, so they can't get very hot, and that limits the fuels they can ignite. The lowest-mass stars, for example, cannot get hot enough to ignite helium fusion.

As you will learn in the next sections, structural differences divide the lower-main-sequence stars into two subgroups—very-low-mass stars and medium-mass stars such as the sun. The critical difference between the two groups is the extent of interior convection (see Figure 11-15). If the star is convective throughout its interiror, so that the hydrogen fuel is constantly mixed, the resulting evolution of the star is strongly affected.

Red Dwarfs

Stars less massive than about 0.4 solar mass—the red dwarfs—can survive a long time. They have very small masses, and consequently they have very little weight to support. Their pressure–temperature thermostats are set low, and they consume their hydrogen fuel very slowly. If you calculate the life expectancy of one of these stars (see Chapter 12), you will discover a red dwarf can be expected to live more than ten times longer than the sun. Furthermore, they are totally convective, and that mixes the interiors of those stars like pots of soup that are constantly stirred. Hydrogen is consumed and helium accumulates uniformly throughout these lowest-mass stars, and that has two important consequences for them.

First, because red dwarf stars are completely mixed and can fuse all their hydrogen, their lives are extra prolonged. Models of a 0.1-solar-mass red dwarf predict it would take 2 billion years to contract to the main sequence and 6 trillion years (6000 billion years) to use up its hydrogen fuel.

The second consequence is that red dwarfs use up their hydrogen uniformly throughout their

■ **Figure 13-1**

Astronomers find evidence of dying stars all around the sky. This small nebula formed within the last few thousand years when an aging giant star expelled its outer layers. The remains of the star collapsed to form a hot white dwarf at the center of the nebula. The sun may suffer this fate in about 5 billion years. (NASA, ESA, and K. Noll, STScI) interiors. That means they never develop a hydrogen fusion shell, and they never become giant stars. They slowly convert their hydrogen into helium, a fuel they are not massive enough to ignite, and will finally die slow, unremarkable deaths by contracting to form white dwarfs.

You will learn in a later chapter about evidence that the universe is only about 14 billion years old, so no red dwarf should have exhausted its fuel yet. Every red dwarf that has ever been born is still a main sequence star, still fusing hydrogen into helium, still shining. Then why are there so many white dwarfs? There must be another way to make white dwarfs.

Sun-like Stars

Stars like the sun with masses between roughly 0.4 and 4 solar masses* fuse hydrogen, and later, helium, but they cannot get hot enough to ignite carbon, the next fuel in the sequence (see Table 12-3). When they reach that impasse, they can no longer maintain their stability, and for a second time their interiors contract while their envelopes expand, turning them into red giants again. The carbon–oxygen core is a dead end for these stars.

As the helium fusion shell burns outward, it leaves its ashes behind, and that increases the mass of the carbon-oxygen core. Because the core can't get hot enough to fuse carbon, it cannot resist the weight pressing down on it, so it contracts. The energy released by the contracting core, plus the energy generated in the helium- and hydrogen-fusion shells, flows outward and makes the envelope of the star expand and cool further.

This forces the star to become a very large giant the second time around. Its radius may become as large as the radius of Earth's orbit, and its surface can become as cool as 2000 K. Such a star can lose large amounts of mass from its surface.

Mass Loss from Sun-like Stars

It's not hard to find evidence that stars like the sun lose mass. Observations show that the sun itself is losing mass through the solar wind, a gentle breeze of gas that blows outward from the solar corona and carries mass into space. The sun loses only about 0.001 solar mass per billion years. Even over the entire lifetime of the sun, the solar wind would not significantly reduce the sun's mass.

The spectra of stars contain clear evidence of mass loss. Ultraviolet and X-ray spectra of many stars reveal strong emission lines, and you can use Kirchhoff's laws to conclude that the star's outer layers must be highly ionized. That means the stars must have hot chromospheres and coronas like the sun's and must have stellar winds blowing outward. You can find further evidence in the spectra of some giant stars, which contain

---

*This mass limit is uncertain, as are many of the masses stated here. The evolution of stars is highly complex, and such parameters are not precisely known.

blueshifted absorption lines. The blueshifts are Doppler shifts produced as the gas flowing out of the star moves toward Earth.

Giant stars lose mass much more rapidly than the sun. Because the spectra of some of these stars do not show the characteristic X-ray emission, you must assume that they do not have hot coronas; but other processes could drive mass loss. Giant stars are so large that gravity is weak at their surfaces, and convection in the cool gas can drive shock waves outward that propel mass loss. In addition, some giants are so cool that specks of carbon dust condense in their atmospheres, just as soot can condense in a fireplace. The pressure of the star's radiation can push this dust and any atoms that collide with the dust completely out of the star.

Another process that can cause mass loss in giant stars is periodic eruptions in the helium fusion shell. The triple-alpha process that fuses helium into carbon is extremely sensitive to temperature, and that can make the helium-fusion shell so unstable that it experiences eruptions called **thermal pulses**. Every few hundred thousand years, the shell can erupt and suddenly produce energy equivalent to a million times the luminosity of the sun. Almost all of that energy goes into lifting the outer layers of the star and driving gas away from the surface.

Rapid mass loss can affect stars dramatically. Observations show that some giant stars are losing mass so rapidly that they can shed an entire solar mass in only 100,000 years, a short time in the evolution of a star. That means that a star that began its existence on the main sequence with a mass of 8 solar masses might reduce its mass to only 3 solar masses in half a million years once it becomes a giant.

Stellar mass loss confuses the story of stellar evolution. Astronomers would like to be able to say that stars more massive than a certain limit will evolve one way, and stars less massive will evolve another way. But giant stars may lose enough mass to alter their own evolution. As a result, you need to consider both the initial mass a star has on the main sequence and the mass it retains after later stages of mass loss. Because astronomers don't know exactly how effective mass loss is, it is difficult to be exact about the mass limits in any discussion of stellar evolution.

Planetary Nebulae

When a medium-mass star like the sun becomes a distended giant, its atmosphere cools. As it cools, it becomes more opaque, and light has to push against it to escape. At the same time, the fusion He shell becomes so narrow it is unstable and begins to flare, which also pushes the atmosphere outward. Because of this outward pressure, an aging giant can expel its outer atmosphere in repeated surges to form one of the most beautiful objects in astronomy, a **planetary nebula**, so called because through a small telescope some of them look like the greenish-blue disk of a planet like Uranus or Neptune. In fact, a planetary nebula has nothing to do with a planet. It is composed of ionized gases expelled by a dying star.

Read **The Formation of Planetary Nebulae** on pages 260–261 and notice four things:

1 You can understand what planetary nebulae are like by using simple observational principles such as Kirchhoff's laws and the Doppler effect.

2 Notice the model that astronomers have developed to explain planetary nebulae. The real nebulae are more complex than the simple model of a slow wind and a fast wind, but that model provides a way to organize the observed phenomena.

3 Oppositely directed jets (much like bipolar flows from protostars) produce many of the asymmetries seen in planetary nebulae.

4 The star itself must contract into a white dwarf.

Most astronomy books say that the sun will form a planetary nebula, but that is questionable. To ionize the gas and light up a planetary nebula, a star must become a white dwarf with a temperature of at least 25,000 K. Mathematical models show that a collapsing star of less than 0.55 solar mass can take as long as a million years to heat up enough to ionize its nebulae, and by that time, the expelled gases are long gone. Models of the sun are not precise enough to indicate how much mass will be left once it ejects its outer layers. If it is left with too little mass, it may heat too slowly to make a planetary nebula. Also, some research suggests that to eject a planetary nebula, a star needs a close binary companion to speed up its spin. The sun, of course, has no close binary companion. This is an area of active research, and there are no firm conclusions.

Medium-mass stars die by ejecting gas into space and contracting into white dwarfs. You have found evidence regarding the deaths of some medium-mass stars in observations of planetary nebulae. Now you can turn your attention to the evidence revealed by the white dwarf remnants themselves.

White Dwarfs

White dwarfs are among the most common stars. The census of stars in Chapter 9 revealed that white dwarfs and red dwarfs, although very faint, are common (page 187). Now you can recognize white dwarfs as the remains of medium-mass stars that fused hydrogen and then helium, failed to ignite carbon, drove away their outer layers, and finally collapsed to form white dwarfs. The billions of white dwarfs in our galaxy are the remains of medium-mass stars like the sun.

The first white dwarf discovered was the faint companion to one of your Favorite Stars, Sirius. In that visual binary system, the bright star is Sirius A. The white dwarf, Sirius B, is 10,000 times fainter than Sirius A. The orbital motions of the stars (shown in Figure 9-15) reveal that the white dwarf's mass is 0.98 solar mass, and its blue-white color tells you that its surface is hot, about 25,000 K. Although it is very hot, it has a very low luminosity, so it must have a small surface area—in fact, it is roughly the size of Earth. Dividing its mass by its volume reveals that it is very dense—over 2×10^6 g/cm^3. On Earth, a teaspoonful of Sirius B material would weigh more than 11 tons (■ Figure 13-2). Basic observations and simple physics lead to the conclusion that white dwarfs are astonishingly dense.

A normal star is supported by energy flowing outward from its core, but a white dwarf cannot generate energy by nuclear fusion. It has exhausted its hydrogen and helium fuels and converted them into carbon and oxygen. When a star collapses into a white dwarf, it converts gravitational energy into thermal energy. Its interior becomes very hot, but it cannot get hot enough to fuse its carbon-oxygen interior. Instead the star contracts until it becomes degenerate. Although a tremendous amount of energy flows out of its hot interior, it is not the energy flow that supports the star. As you learned in the previous chapter, a white dwarf is supported against its own gravity by the inability of its degenerate electrons to pack into a smaller volume. In this case, the properties of white dwarfs, objects as big as Earth, are determined by the properties of subatomic particles. Astronomers often find that the causes of natural phenomena lead step by step into the subatomic world (**How Do We Know? 13-1**).

■ **Figure 13-2**

The degenerate matter from inside a white dwarf is so dense that a lump the size of a beach ball would, transported to Earth, weigh as much as an ocean liner.

Toward Ultimate Causes

How do scientist's search for natural causes lead into the world of subatomic particles? Scientists search for causes. They are not satisfied to know that a certain kind of star dies by exploding. They want to know why it explodes. They want to find the causes for the natural events they see, and that search for ultimate causes often leads into the atomic world.

For example, why do icebergs float? When water freezes, it becomes less dense than liquid water, so it floats. That answers the question, but you can search for a deeper cause.

Why does ice float? Why is it less dense than water? Water molecules are made up of two hydrogen atoms bonded to an oxygen atom, and the oxygen is so good at attracting electrons, the hydrogen atoms are left needing a bit more negative charge, and they are attracted to atoms in nearby molecules.

That means the hydrogen atoms in water are constantly trying to stick to other molecules. When water is warm, the thermal motion prevents these hydrogen bonds from forming; but when water freezes, the hydrogen atoms link the water molecules together. Because of the angles at which the bonds form, the molecules leave open spaces between molecules, and that makes ice less dense than water.

But scientists can continue their search for causes. Why do electrons have negative charge? What is charge? Nuclear particle physicists are trying to understand those properties of matter. Sometimes the properties of very large things such as supernovae are determined by the properties of the tiniest particles. Science is exciting because the simple observation that ice floats in your lemonade can lead you toward ultimate causes and some of the deepest questions about how nature works.

Ice has a low density and floats because of the way electrons (blue) link to oxygen (red) when water freezes.

The interior of a white dwarf is mostly carbon and oxygen nuclei floating among a whirling storm of degenerate electrons. It is these degenerate electrons that exert the pressure needed to support the star's weight, but most of the star's mass is represented by the carbon and oxygen ions. Theory predicts that, as the star cools, these ions lock together to form a crystal lattice, so there may be some truth in the image of aging white dwarfs as great crystals of carbon and oxygen. Near the surface, where the pressure is lower, a layer of ionized gases makes up a hot atmosphere.

The tremendous surface gravity of a white dwarf—100,000 times that of Earth—affects its atmosphere in strange ways. The heavier atoms in the atmosphere tend to sink, leaving the lightest gases at the surface. Astronomers see some white dwarfs with atmospheres of almost pure hydrogen, whereas others have atmospheres of nearly pure helium (gas that was never close enough to the core to be fused into carbon). Still others, for reasons not well understood, have atmospheres that contain traces of heavier atoms. In addition, the powerful surface gravity pulls the white dwarf's atmosphere down into a very shallow layer. If Earth's atmosphere were equally shallow, people on the top floors of skyscrapers would have to wear oxygen masks.

Clearly, a white dwarf is not a true star. It generates no nuclear energy, is almost totally degenerate, and, except for a thin layer at its surface, contains no gas. Instead of calling a white dwarf a star, you can call it a **compact object**. In the next chapter, you will meet two other types of compact objects that are remnants of burned-out stars—neutron stars and black holes.

A white dwarf's future is bleak. Degenerate matter is a very good thermal conductor, so heat flows to the surface and escapes into space, and the white dwarf gets fainter and cooler, so the point representing its luminosity and temperature moves downward and to the right in the H–R diagram. As it radiates energy into space, its temperature gradually falls, but it cannot shrink any smaller because its degenerate electrons cannot get closer together. Because the white dwarf contains a tremendous amount of heat, it needs billions of years to radiate that heat through its small surface area. Eventually, such objects may become cold and dark, so-called **black dwarfs**. Our galaxy is not old enough to contain black dwarfs. The coolest white dwarfs in our galaxy are just a bit cooler than the sun.

One more important and interesting fact about white dwarfs is predicted by mathematical models. The equations predict that if you added mass to a white dwarf, its radius would *shrink*, because added mass would increase its gravity and squeeze it tighter. If you added enough to raise its total mass to about 1.4 solar masses, its radius would shrink to zero

The Formation of Planetary Nebulae

1 Simple observations tell astronomers what planetary nebulae are like. Their angular size and their distances indicate that their radii range from 0.2 to 3 ly. The presence of emission lines in their spectra assures us that they are excited, low-density gas. Doppler shifts show they are expanding at 10 to 20 km/s. If you divide radius by velocity, you find that planetary nebulae are no more than about 10,000 years old. Older nebulae evidently become mixed into the interstellar medium.

Astronomers find about 3000 planetary nebulae in the sky. Because planetary nebulae are short-lived formations, you can conclude that they must be a common part of stellar evolution. Medium-mass stars up to a mass of about 8 solar masses are destined to die by forming planetary nebulae.

The Helix Nebula is 2.5 ly in diameter, and the radial texture shows how light and winds from the central star are pushing outward.

NASA/JPL-Caltech/ESA   Visual + Infrared

2 The process that produces planetary nebulae involves two stellar winds. First, as an aging giant, the star gradually blows away its outer layers in a slow breeze of low-excitation gas that is not easily visible. Once the hot interior of the star is exposed, it ejects a high-speed wind that overtakes and compresses the gas of the slow wind like a snowplow, while ultraviolet radiation from the hot remains of the central star excites the gases to glow like a giant neon sign.

2a The Cat's Eye, below, lies at the center of an extended nebula that must have been exhaled from the star long before the fast wind began forming the visible planetary nebula. See other images of the nebula on opposite page.

Slow stellar wind from a red giant

Fast wind from exposed interior

The gases of the slow wind

You see a planetary nebula

Visual

The Cat's Eye Nebula

Roman Corradi/Nordic Optical Telescope

3 Images from the Hubble Space Telescope reveal that asymmetry is the rule in planetary nebulae rather than the exception. A number of causes have been suggested. A disk of gas around a star's equator might form during the slow-wind stage and then deflect the fast wind into oppositely directed flows. Another star or planets orbiting the dying star, rapid rotation, or magnetic fields might cause these peculiar shapes. The Hour Glass Nebula seems to have formed when a fast wind overtook an equatorial disk (white in the image). The nebula Menzel 3, as do many planetary nebulae, shows evidence of multiple ejections.

Some shapes suggest bubbles being inflated in the interstellar medium. The Cat's Eye is shown at left, below, and on the facing page.

Visual

The Cat's Eye Nebula

Visual + X-ray

The Cat's Eye Nebula

The purple glow in the image above is a region of X-ray bright gas with a temperature measured in millions of degrees. It is apparently driving the expansion of the nebula.

Visual

Menzel 3

Visual

The Hour Glass Nebula

NASA

Some planetary nebulae, such as M2-9, are highly elongated, and it has been suggested that the Ring Nebula, at left, is a tubular shape that happens to be pointed roughly at Earth.

NASA

M2-9

Visual

M57 The Ring Nebula

Visual

Infrared

Jet

Disk

Jet

NASA

The Egg Nebula

At visual wavelengths, the Egg Nebula is highly elongated, as shown below. The infrared image at left reveals an irregular, thick disk from which jets of gas and dust emerge. Such beams may create many of the asymmetries in planetary nebulae.

4 Once an aging giant star blows its surface into space to form a planetary nebula, the remaining hot interior collapses into a small, intensely hot object containing a carbon and oxygen interior surrounded by hydrogen and helium fusion shells and a thin atmosphere of hydrogen. The fusion gradually dies out, and the core of the star evolves to the left of the conventional H–R diagram to become the intensely hot nucleus of a planetary nebulae. Mathematical models show that these nuclei cool slowly to become white dwarfs.

10^6 Nuclei of planetary nebulae.

10^4

10^2

Supergiants

Main sequence

$L/L_\odot$

1

Giants

10^{-2}

Mathematical model of an 0.8-solar-mass stellar remnant contracting to become a white dwarf.

White dwarfs

10^{-4}

100,000 50,000 30,000   10,000   5000

Temperature (K)

JPL/NASA

The Egg Nebula

Visual

(■ Figure 13-3). This is called the **Chandrasekhar limit** after Subrahmanyan Chandrasekhar, the astronomer who discovered it. It seems to imply that a star more massive than 1.4 solar masses cannot become a white dwarf unless it sheds mass in some way.

As you saw earlier in this chapter, aging giant stars do lose mass (■ Figure 13-4). This suggests that stars more massive than the Chandrasekhar limit can eventually die as white dwarfs if they reduce their mass. Theoretical models show that an 8-solar-mass star should be able to reduce its mass to 1.4 solar masses before it collapses. Consequently, a wide range of medium-mass stars eventually die as white dwarfs. No wonder white dwarfs are so common.

SCIENTIFIC ARGUMENT

What evidence can you cite to show that large numbers of stars die by producing planetary nebula?

You can begin your argument by noting that planetary nebulae are only a light-year or so in radius and that Doppler shifts show that they are expanding at 10 to 20 km/s. Dividing the radius by the velocity tells you that a typical planetary nebula is only about 10,000 years old. That means that the nebulae don't last very long. Nevertheless, astronomers find almost 3000 of them visible in the sky. To be so common but so short lived, planetary nebulae must be produced in large numbers as medium-mass stars blow their outer layers into space.

Now review more evidence. **Use Favorite Star Sirius to explain how you know that white dwarfs are very dense.**

13-2 The Evolution of Binary Stars

SO FAR YOU HAVE BEEN THINKING about the deaths of stars as if they were all single objects that never interact. But more than half of all stars are members of binary star systems. Most such binaries are far apart, so one of the stars can swell into a giant and eventually collapse without affecting the companion star. In some binary systems, however, the two stars orbit close together. When the more massive star begins to expand, it interacts with

■ Figure 13-3

The more massive a white dwarf, the smaller its radius. Stars more massive than the Chandrasekhar limit of 1.4 solar masses at the ends of their lives cannot become white dwarfs.

■ Figure 13-4

Stars can lose mass if they are very hot, very large, or both. The massive red supergiant VY Canis Majoris is ejecting gas in loops, arcs, and knots as it ages. A young massive star such as WR124 constantly loses mass into space. Warmed dust in these gas clouds can make them glow in the infrared. (VY Canis Majoris: NASA, ESA, R. Humphreys; WR124: NASA)

Light from the eruption of a supergiant star illuminates gas and dust ejected previously.

V838 Mon

Visual

WR 124

Massive star WR124 is ejecting mass in a violent stellar wind.

Visual

its companion star in complicated ways. These interacting binary stars are fascinating objects, and they are important because they help explain observed phenomena such as nova explosions. In the next chapter, you will see how they can also help astronomers search for black holes.

Mass Transfer

Binary stars can sometimes interact by transferring mass from one star to the other. The gravitational fields of the two stars, combined with the rotation of the binary system, define a dumbbell-shaped volume around the pair of stars called the **Roche lobes**. The gravity of each star controls the motion of matter inside its Roche lobe. The surface of this volume is called the **Roche surface**. The size of the Roche lobes depends on the mass of the stars and on the distance between the stars. If the stars are far apart, the lobes are very large, and the stars easily hang on to their own material. If the stars are close together, however, the lobes are small and can interfere with the evolution of the stars. Matter inside each star's Roche lobe is gravitationally bound to the star, but matter that crosses the Roche surface and leaves a star's Roche lobe can fall into the other star or leave the binary system completely.

The **Lagrangian points** are places in the orbital plane of a binary star system where a bit of matter can reach stability. For astronomers, the most important of these points is the **inner Lagrangian point**, where the two Roche lobes meet (■ Figure 13-5). If matter can leave a star and reach the inner Lagrange point, it can flow onto the other star. Thus, the inner Lagrangian point is the connection through which the stars can transfer matter.

In general, there are only two ways matter can escape from a star and reach the inner Lagrangian point. First, if a star has a strong stellar wind, some of the gas blowing away from it can pass through the inner Lagrangian point and be captured by the other star. Second, if an evolving star expands so far that it fills its Roche lobe, which can occur if the stars are close together and the lobes are small, then matter can overflow through the inner Lagrangian point onto the other star. Mass transfer driven by a stellar wind tends to be slow, but mass can be transferred rapidly from an expanding star.

Evolution with Mass Transfer

Mass transfer between binary stars can affect the evolution of both stars in surprising ways. In fact, it provides the explanation of a problem that puzzled astronomers for many years.

In some binary systems, the less massive star has become a giant, while the more massive star is still on the main sequence. That seems backward. If more massive stars evolve faster than lower-mass stars, how could the low-mass star leave the main sequence first? This is called the Algol paradox, after the binary system Algol (also known as Beta Persei) (see Figure 9-22).

Mass transfer explains how this could happen. Imagine a close binary system that contains a 5-solar-mass star and a 1-solar-mass companion (■ Figure 13-6). The two stars formed at the same time, so the more massive star must evolve faster and leave the main sequence first. When it expands into a giant, it fills its Roche surface and transfers matter to the low-mass companion. The massive star shrinks into a lower-mass star, and the companion gains mass to become a more massive main-sequence star. If you observed such a system after the mass transfer ended, you would see a binary system like Algol, which contains a 5-solar-mass main-sequence star and a 1-solar-mass giant.

Another exotic result of the evolution of close binary systems is the possible merging of the stars. Astronomers see many binaries in which both stars have expanded to fill their Roche surfaces and now spill mass out into space. If the stars are close enough together and expand rapidly enough, theorists believe, the two stars could merge into a single, rapidly rotating giant star. Most giants rotate slowly because they conserved angular momentum and slowed their rotation as they expanded. Examples of rapidly rotating giant stars are known, however, and they are thought to be the result of merged binary stars. Inside the distended envelope of such a star, the cores of the two stars may even continue to orbit each other until friction slows them down and they sink to the center.

Mass transfer can lead to dramatic violence. The first four frames of Figure 13-6 show how mass transfer could have produced a system like Algol. The last frame shows an additional stage in which the giant star has expelled its outer layers and

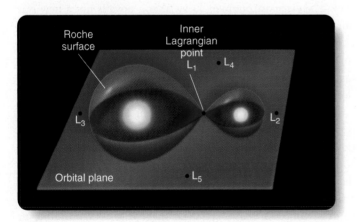

■ Figure 13-5

A pair of binary stars control the region of space located inside the Roche surface. The Lagrangian points are locations of stability, with the inner Lagrangian point making a connection through which the two stars can transfer matter.

The Evolution of a Binary System

Star B is more massive than Star A.

Star B becomes a giant and loses mass to Star A.

Star B loses mass, and Star A gains mass.

Star A is a massive main-sequence star with a lower-mass giant companion—an Algol system.

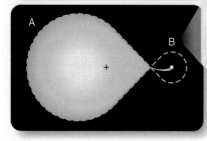

Star A has now become a giant and loses mass back to the white dwarf that remains of Star B.

■ **Figure 13-6**

A pair of stars orbiting close to each other can exchange mass and modify their evolution.

collapsed to form a white dwarf. The more massive companion has expanded and now transfers matter back onto the white dwarf. Such systems can become the site of tremendous explosions. To see how this can happen, you need to consider in detail how mass falls into a star.

Accretion Disks

Matter flowing from one star to another cannot fall directly into the star. Rather, because of conservation of angular momentum, it must flow into a whirling disk around the star.

As you learned in Chapter 5, angular momentum refers to the tendency of a rotating object to continue rotating. All rotating objects possess some angular momentum; and, in the absence of external forces, an object maintains (conserves) its total angular momentum. For a common example, consider a bathtub full of water. Gentle currents in the water give it some angular momentum, but you can't see its slow circulation until you pull the stopper. Then, as the water rushes toward the drain, conservation of angular momentum forces it to form a whirlpool.

In a binary star system, mass transferred through the inner Lagrangian point toward one of the stars must conserve its angular momentum. If the star is small enough, as in the case of a white dwarf, the mass will form a rapidly rotating whirlpool around the star called an **accretion disk** (■ Figure 13-7).

Two important things happen in an accretion disk. First, the gas in the disk grows very hot due to friction and tidal forces. The disk also acts as a brake, shifting angular momentum outward in the disk and allowing the innermost matter to fall into the white dwarf. The interior parts of an accretion disk around a white dwarf are violent places. The temperature of the gas can exceed a million Kelvin, causing the gas to emit X-rays, and the matter falling inward can produce a violent explosion when enough accumulates on the white dwarf.

Nova Explosions

Astronomers occasionally see a **nova**, what seems to be a new star that appears in the sky, grows brighter, then fades away after a few weeks (■ Figure 13-8). In fact, *nova* is the Latin word for "new." Modern astronomers know that a nova is not a new star but an old star flaring up. After a nova fades, astronomers can photograph the spectrum of the remaining faint point of light. Invariably, they find a short-period spectroscopic binary containing a normal star and a white dwarf. A nova is evidently an explosion involving a white dwarf.

Observational evidence can tell you how nova explosions occur. As the explosion begins, spectra show blueshifted absorption lines, which tells you the gas is dense and coming toward you at a few thousand kilometers per second. After a few days, the spectral lines change to emission lines, telling you the gas has thinned enough to become transparent. The blueshifts remain, so you can conclude that a spherical shell of gas is continuing to expand into space.

Nova explosions occur in binary systems when mass transfers from a normal star through the inner Lagrangian point into an accretion disk around a white dwarf. As the matter loses its angular momentum in the accretion disk, it spirals inward and eventually settles onto the surface of the white dwarf. Because the

■ **Figure 13-7**

Matter from an evolving red giant falls into a white dwarf and forms a whirling accretion disk. Friction and tidal forces can make the disk very hot. Such systems can lead to nova explosions on the surface of the white dwarf as shown in this artist's impression. (David A. Hardy, www.astroart.org, and PPARC)

temperature so high that the CNO cycle begins. With no pressure–temperature thermostat to control the fusion, the temperature shoots to 100 million degrees in seconds. The temperature quickly rises high enough to force the gas to expand, and it is no longer degenerate. But it is too late for the pressure-temperature thermostat to cause the non-degenerate gas to become stable. By the time the gas begins to expand, enough energy has been released to blow the surface layers of the white dwarf into space as a violently expanding shell of hot gas, visible from Earth as a nova.

The explosion of its surface hardly disturbs the white dwarf or its companion star. Mass transfer quickly resumes, and a new layer of fuel begins to accumulate. How fast the fuel builds up depends on the rate of mass transfer. Accordingly, you can expect novae (the plural of nova) to repeat each time an explosive layer accumulates. Many novae probably take thousands of years to build an explosive layer, but some take only a few years (■ Figure 13-9).

matter came from the surface of a normal star, it is rich in unused nuclear fuel, mostly hydrogen. As it accumulates on the surface of the white dwarf, it forms a layer of unprocessed fuel.

As the layer of fuel grows deeper, it becomes hotter and denser. Compressed by the white dwarf's gravity, the gas becomes degenerate, much like the core of a sun-like star approaching the helium flash. In such a gas, the pressure–temperature thermostat does not work, so the layer of unfused hydrogen is a thermonuclear bomb waiting to explode. By the time the white dwarf has accumulated about 100 Earth masses of hydrogen, the temperature at the base of the hydrogen layer reaches millions of degrees, and the density is 10,000 times the density of water. Suddenly, the nuclear reactions of the proton–proton chain begin to fuse the hydrogen, and the energy released drives the

The End of Earth

Astronomy is about us. Although this chapter has discussed the deaths of stars, it has also been discussing the future of our planet. The sun is a medium-mass star and will eventually die by becoming a giant, possibly producing a planetary nebula, and collapsing into a white dwarf. That will spell the end of Earth.

Evolutionary models of the sun suggest that it may survive for an additional 6 billion years or so, but it is already growing more luminous as it fuses hydrogen into helium. In about 5 billion years, it will exhaust hydrogen in its core, begin burning hydrogen in a shell, and swell into a red giant star about 30 times its present radius. Later, helium fusion will ignite in the core and the sun will contract somewhat, becoming a horizontal branch star. Then, when the helium fuel is exhausted in its core and helium fusion begins in a shell, the sun will have another episode as a red giant. That second red giant version of the sun will be about as large as the orbit of Earth, so that will mark the end of our world. Before that, the sun's increasing luminosity will certainly evaporate Earth's oceans, drive away the atmosphere, and even vaporize much of Earth's crust. Astronomers are still uncertain about some of the details, but computer models that include

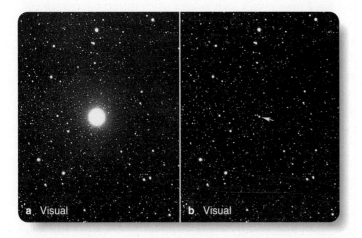

■ **Figure 13-8**

Nova Cygni 1975, near its maximum apparent brightness of about second magnitude, and later when it had declined to about eleventh magnitude. (Photo© UC Regents)

■ **Figure 13-9**

Nova T Pyxidis erupts about every two decades, expelling shells of gas into space. The shells of gas are visible from ground-based telescopes, but the Hubble Space Telescope reveals much more detail. The shell consists of knots of excited gas that presumably form when a new shell collides with a previous shell. (M. Shara and R. Williams, STScI; R. Gilmozzi, ESO; and NASA)

tidal effects predict that the expanding sun eventually will engulf and destroy Mercury, Venus, and Earth. While it is a giant star, the sun will have a strong wind and lose a substantial fraction of its mass into space. The atoms that were once in Earth will be part of the expanding nebula around the sun. Your atoms will be part of that nebula. If the white dwarf remnant sun becomes hot enough, it will ionize the expelled gas and light it (and you) up as a planetary nebula.

There is no danger that the sun will explode as a nova; it has no binary companion. And, as you will see in the next section, the sun is not massive enough to die the violent death of the massive stars.

The most important lesson of astronomy is that we are part of the universe and not just observers. The atoms we are made of are destined to return to the interstellar medium in just a few billion years. That's a long time, and it is possible that the human race will migrate to other planetary systems before then. That might save the human race, but much of our planet will return to being stardust.

SCIENTIFIC ARGUMENT

How does spectroscopic evidence tell you what a nova explosion is like?

For this argument you need to use your knowledge of basic spectroscopy. As soon as a nova is seen, astronomers rush to telescopes to record spectra, and they see blueshifted absorption lines. The blueshifts are Doppler shifts showing that the near side of the object is coming toward Earth. The absorption lines must be formed by fairly dense gas seen through thinner gas, much like the atmosphere of a star, so the surface of the star must be expanding rapidly outward. Later the spectrum becomes an emission spectrum, and Kirchhoff's laws tell you that the gas must have thinned and become transparent. The continued blueshift shows that the expansion is continuing.

Now review the post-explosion evidence. **How do observations of novae long after they have faded provide evidence that white dwarfs are involved?**

13-3 The Deaths of Massive Stars

YOU HAVE SEEN that low- and medium-mass stars die relatively quietly as they exhaust their hydrogen and helium and then eject their surface layers, in some cases forming planetary nebulae. In contrast, massive stars live spectacular lives and then destroy themselves in violent explosions.

Nuclear Fusion in Massive Stars

Stars on the upper main sequence have too much mass to die as white dwarfs, but their evolution begins much like that of their lower-mass cousins. They consume the hydrogen in their cores and ignite hydrogen fusion shells; as a result, they expand into giants or, for the most massive stars, supergiants. Next, their cores contract and fuse helium—first in the core and then in a shell, producing a carbon–oxygen core.

A massive star can lose significant mass as it ages; but, if it still has a mass over 4 solar masses when its carbon–oxygen core contracts, it can ignite carbon fusion at a temperature of about 1 billion Kelvin. Carbon fusion produces more oxygen and neon. As soon as the carbon is exhausted in the core, the core contracts, and carbon ignites in a shell. This pattern of core ignition and shell ignition continues with fuel after fuel, and the star develops the layered structure as shown in ■ Figure 13-10, with a hydrogen fusion shell above a helium fusion shell above a carbon fusion shell above … After carbon fuses, oxygen, neon, and magnesium fuse to make silicon and sulfur, and then the silicon fuses to make iron.

The fusion of successive nuclear fuels goes faster and faster as the massive star evolves. Recall that massive stars must consume their fuels rapidly to support their great weight, but other factors also cause the heavier fuels like carbon, oxygen, and silicon to fuse at increasing speeds. For one thing, the amount of energy released per fusion reaction decreases as the mass of the fusing atom increases. To support its weight, a star must fuse

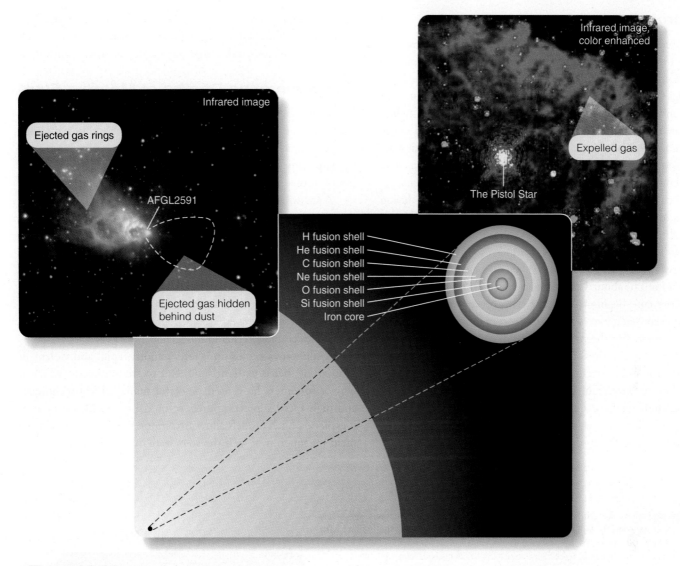

■ Figure 13-10

Massive stars live fast and die young. The two shown here are among the most massive stars known, containing 100 solar masses or more. They are rapidly ejecting gas into space. (See also Figure 12-3.) The centers of these massive stars develop Earth-size cores (magnified 100,000 times in this figure) composed of concentric layers of gases undergoing nuclear fusion. The iron core at the center leads eventually to a star-destroying explosion. (AFGL 2591: Gemini Observatory/NSF/C. Aspin; The Pistol Star: NASA)

oxygen much faster than it fused hydrogen. Also, there are fewer nuclei in the core of the star by the time heavy nuclei begin to fuse. Four hydrogens make a helium nucleus, and three heliums make a carbon, so there are 12 times fewer nuclei of carbon available for fusion than there were hydrogen. This means the fusion of heavy elements goes very quickly in massive stars (■ Table 13-1). Model calculations indicate that hydrogen core fusion can last 7 million years in a 25-solar-mass star, but that same star will fuse the oxygen in its core in six months and its silicon in a day.

■ Table 13-1 | Heavy-Element Fusion in a 25-$M_\odot$ Star

Fuel	Time	Percentage of Lifetime
H	7,000,000 years	93.3
He	500,000 years	6.7
C	600 years	0.008
O	0.5 years	0.000007
Si	1 day	0.00000004

The Iron Core

Heavy-element fusion ends with iron because nuclear reactions that use iron as a fuel cannot produce energy. Nuclear reactions can produce energy if they proceed from less tightly bound nuclei to more tightly bound nuclei. As shown in Figure 8-8, both nuclear fission and nuclear fusion produce nuclei that are more tightly bound than the starting fuel. Look again at Figure 8-8 and notice that iron is the most tightly bound nucleus of all. No nuclear reaction, fission or fusion, that starts with iron can produce a more tightly bound nucleus, and that means that iron is a dead end.

When a massive star develops an iron core, nuclear fusion cannot produce energy, and the core contracts and grows hotter. The shells around the core burn outward, fusing lighter elements into heavier elements and leaving behind more iron, which further increases the mass of the core. When the mass of the iron core exceeds a limit of about 1.3 to 2 solar masses, it must collapse.

As the core begins to collapse, two processes can make it contract even faster. Heavy nuclei in the core capture high-energy electrons, removing thermal energy from the gas. This robs the gas of some of the pressure it needs to support the crushing weight of the outer layers. Also, temperatures are so high that many photons have gamma-ray wavelengths and are capable of breaking more massive nuclei into less massive nuclei. In the process, the gamma rays are absorbed, which robs the gas of energy and allows the core to collapse even faster.

Although a massive star may live for millions of years, its iron core—about 500 km in diameter—collapses in only a few thousandths of a second, triggering a star-destroying explosion.

The Supernova Deaths of Massive Stars

In the 1930s, astronomers realized that some of the novae that had been seen in the sky were much more luminous and longer lasting than the others, and they dubbed such an object a **supernova** (plural, **supernovae**). Modern astronomers understand that a supernova is caused by the violent, explosive death of a massive star.

A few novae appear in the sky each year, but supernovae are so rare that only one or two supernovae are observed each century in our galaxy. Astronomers know that supernovae occur because they occasionally are seen to flare in other galaxies, and because telescopes reveal the shattered remains of these titanic explosions (■ Figure 13-11). Modern theory predicts that the collapse of the core in a massive star can eject the outer layers of the star to produce one of the most common kinds of supernova explosions. You will learn about another kind of supernova explosion later in this section.

A supernova explosion is rare, remote, rapid, and violent. It is an event that is extremely difficult to study directly, which is why astronomers have used powerful mathematical techniques and high-speed supercomputers to model the inside of a star as it explodes. Such models allow astronomers, in a sense, to experiment on supernovae as if the stars were in a laboratory.

■ **Figure 13-11**

Supernova explosions are rare in any one galaxy, but each year astronomers see a few erupt in other galaxies. In our own galaxy, astronomers find expanding shells filled with hot, low-density gas produced by past supernova explosions. (Pinwheel: NOAO/AURA/NSF/ G. Jacoby, B. Bohannan & M. Hanna; Tycho's Supernova: NASA/CXC/Rutgers/J. Warren & J. Hughes et al.; N63A: NASA/CXC/Rutgers/J. Warren et al., STScI/U.Ill/Y. Chu; ATCA/U.Ill/J. Dickel et al.)

Supervona in the Pinwheel Galaxy

Visual

G292.0+1.8

Age 1600 years

X-ray image

N63A

Age 2000 to 5000 yr

X-ray blue
Optical green
Radio red

Gas as hot as 10 million K fills the expanding shells.

Those models reveal that the key to a supernova explosion is the collapse of the iron core. This collapse allows the rest of the star's interior to fall inward, creating a tremendous "traffic jam" as all the nuclei fall toward the center. It is as if all the residents of Indiana suddenly tried to drive their cars as fast as possible into the center of Indianapolis. There would be a tremendous traffic jam downtown, and as more cars rushed in, the traffic jam would spread outward into the suburbs. Similarly, as the inner core of the star falls inward, a shock wave (a traffic jam) develops and begins to move outward. Such a shock wave was first thought to be the cause of the supernova explosion. Computer models revealed, however, that the shock wave spreading outward through the collapsing star stalls within a few hundredths of a second. Matter falling inward smothers the shock wave and pushes it back into the star. Those computer models wouldn't successfully explode.

Then why does the star explode? Theory predicts that 99 percent of the energy released as the core collapses appears in the form of the subatomic particles known as neutrinos (see Chapter 8). In the sun, neutrinos zip outward unimpeded by the gas of the solar layers, but in a collapsing star the gas is billions of times denser than the gas in the sun, nearly as dense as an atomic nucleus. That gas is nearly opaque to neutrinos, and they are partially absorbed by the gas. Not only does the tremendous burst of neutrinos remove energy from the core and allow it to collapse even faster, but when the neutrinos are absorbed outside the core they heat those layers. For some years, astronomers thought that these neutrinos could spread energy across the shock wave and, within a quarter of second or so, reaccelerate the stalled shock wave. The computer models, however, still refused to explode.

The final ingredient that the models needed was turbulent convection. When the collapse begins, the very center of the star forms a highly dense core, the beginnings of a neutron star, and the in-falling material bounces off that core. As the temperature shoots up, the bouncing material produces highly turbulent convection currents that give the stalled shock wave an outward boost (■ Figure 13-12). Within a second or so, the shock wave begins to push outward again, and after just a few hours it bursts out through the surface, blasting the star apart in a supernova explosion.

Of course, supernova explosions occur in silence. Science fiction movies and television have led to the **Common Misconception** that explosions in space are accompanied by deeply satisfying sonic booms. But space is nearly a vacuum, so there can be no sound. Some of the most violent events in the universe make no noise at all.

The supernova visible from Earth is the brightening of the star as its outer layers are blasted outward. As the months pass, the cloud of gas expands, thins, and begins to fade. The way it fades can tell astronomers about the death throes of the star. Essentially all of the iron in the core of the star is destroyed when the core collapses, but the violence in the outer layers during the explosion can produce densities and temperatures high enough to trigger nuclear fusion reactions that produce as much as half a solar mass

The Exploding Core of a Supernova

The core of a massive supergiant has begun to collapse at the lower left corner of this model.

Matter continues to fall inward (blue and green) as the core expands outward (yellow) creating a shock wave.

To show the entire star at this scale, this page would have to be 30 kilometers in diameter.

Only 0.4 s after beginning, violent convection in the expanding core (red) pushes outward.

The shock wave will blow the star apart as a neutron star forms at the extreme lower left corner.

■ **Figure 13-12**

As the iron core of a massive star begins to collapse, intensely hot gas triggers violent convection. Even as the outer parts of the core continue to fall inward, the turbulence blasts outward and reaches the surface of the star within hours, creating a supernova eruption. This diagram is based on mathematical models and shows only the exploding core of the star. (Courtesy Adam Burrows, John Hayes and Bruce Fryxell) of radioactive nickel-56. The nickel gradually decays to form radioactive cobalt, which decays to form normal iron. The rate at which the supernova fades matches the rate at which these radioactive elements decay. Thus the destruction of iron in the core of the star is matched by the production of iron through nuclear fusion and eventual radioactive decay in the expanding outer layers.

The presence of nuclear fusion in the outer layers of supernovae testifies to the violence of the explosion. A typical supernova is equivalent to the explosion of 10^{28} megatons of TNT—about 5 million solar masses of high explosive.

Supernovae may seem powerful and remote, but you have a personal connection with the deaths of stars. All of the atoms in your body heavier than helium but lighter than iron were cooked up in red giant stars. Some were made in medium-mass stars and expelled in planetary nebula. Even more were made inside massive stars and blasted into space in supernova explosions. Short-lived nuclear fusion reactions taking place during supernova explosions created iron and rare elements heavier than iron such as the iodine in your thyroid gland, and platinum, gold, and silver. You are made of atoms that were created by the stars, and your jewelry comes from star explosions.

Collapsing massive stars can trigger one kind of cosmic violence, but astronomers have observed more than one kind of supernova.

Types of Supernovae

Supernovae are rare, and only a few have been seen in our galaxy, but astronomers have been able to observe supernovae occurring in other galaxies (■ Figure 13-13). From data accumulated over

The Whirlpool Galaxy

Supernova 2005cs was seen exploding in a nearby galaxy in July 2005.

Ultraviolet + near infrared

The star that exploded is visible in a photo of the galaxy made months earlier.

Visual

The star that became the supernova was a 10-solar-mass red supergiant.

Near-infrared

■ **Figure 13-13**

Robotic telescopes search every night for supernovae flaring in other galaxies. When one is seen, astronomers can obtain spectra and record the supernova's rise in brightness and its decline to study the physics of exploding stars. If a supernova is seen in a nearby galaxy, it is sometimes possible to identify the star in earlier photos. (NASA, ESA. W. Li and S. Filippenko, Berkeley, S. Beckwith, STScI, and The Hubble Heritage Team, STScI/AURA) decades, astronomers have noticed that there are two main types. **Type I supernovae** have spectra that contain no hydrogen lines. They reach a maximum brightness about 4 billion times more luminous than the sun and then decline rapidly at first and then more slowly. **Type II supernovae** have spectra containing hydrogen lines. They reach a maximum brightness up to about 0.6 billion times more luminous than the sun (less than type I supernovae), decline to a temporary standstill, and then fade rapidly. The light curves in ■ Figure 13-14 summarize the behavior of the two types of supernovae.

The evidence is clear that type II supernovae occur when a massive star develops an iron core and collapses. Such supernovae occur in or near regions of active star formation. These are the regions where you would expect to find massive stars. Also, the spectra of type II supernovae contain hydrogen lines, as you would expect from the explosion of a massive star that contains large amounts of hydrogen in its outer layers.

Type I supernovae show no hydrogen in their spectra, which means they can't be caused by the deaths of typical massive stars. In fact, there are two kinds of type I supernovae, and they have dramatically different causes. Both involve binary stars.

A **type Ia supernova** occurs when a white dwarf gaining mass in a binary star system exceeds the Chandrasekhar limit and collapses. The collapse of a white dwarf is different from the collapse of a massive star because the white dwarf contains usable nuclear fuel—mainly carbon. As the collapse begins, the temperature shoots up, but the gas cannot halt the collapse because it is degenerate, and the pressure–temperature thermostat is turned off in the core. Even as carbon fusion begins, the increased temperature cannot increase the pressure and make the gas expand and slow the reactions. The lack of a thermostat

■ **Figure 13-14**

Type I supernovae decline rapidly at first and then more slowly, but type II supernovae pause for about 100 days before beginning a steep decline. Supernova 1987A was odd in that it did not rise directly to maximum brightness. These light curves have been adjusted to the same maximum brightness. Generally, type II supernovae are about two magnitudes fainter than type I.

makes the collapsing white dwarf into a bomb. The carbon–oxygen core fuses suddenly in violent nuclear reactions called **carbon deflagration** and produces a wide range of heavier nuclei. The word *deflagration* means to be totally destroyed by fire, in this case by nuclear fusion. In a flicker of a stellar lifetime, the white dwarf is consumed, with the resulting heavy nuclei and outer layers blasted away in a violent explosion that at its brightest is three to six times more luminous than a type II supernova. The white dwarf is destroyed with nothing left behind but an expanding cloud of hot gas. Of course, you would see no hydrogen lines in the spectrum of a type Ia supernova because white dwarfs contain at most only a little hydrogen in their outer layers.

You might wonder why a white dwarf gaining mass doesn't erupt in a nova explosion and blast the mass away. Mathematical models show that the nova eruption does not necessarily blow away all of the mass the white dwarf has gained. So it is possible for a white dwarf to gain mass, erupt a number of times as a nova, and eventually become so massive it collapses in a type Ia supernova explosion.

The less common **type Ib supernovae** are thought to occur when a massive star in a binary system loses its hydrogen-rich outer layers to its companion star. The remains of the massive star continue to evolve, develop an iron core, and collapse, producing a supernova explosion that lacks hydrogen lines in the spectrum. Some astronomers have referred to these as "peeled" supernovae, meaning that the massive star has had its hydrogen-rich outer layers peeled away by its binary companion.

To summarize, a type II supernova is caused by the collapse of a massive star. A type Ia is caused by the collapse of a white dwarf. A type Ib is caused by the collapse of a massive star that has lost its outer envelope of hydrogen. The distinction is evident even in the location of these supernovae. Type II and type Ib supernovae are caused by the collapse of massive stars, which don't live very long. Those types of supernovae are seen near regions of active star formation. In contrast, type Ia supernovae are caused by the collapse of white dwarfs, and it takes a long time for the evolution of stars to produce white dwarfs. That's why type Ia supernovae are seen in regions where star formation took place long ago.

There may be other types of supernovae caused by other processes that can make a massive star explode. For example, SN 2005gl has been identified with a very luminous, hot supergiant, and astronomers did not expect such a star to explode (■ Figure 13-15). That supernova remains a puzzle. Supernovae are so rare, Earth's astronomers may not have seen every type that can occur.

Much of what you have learned so far about supernovae has been based on theory, so it is time to compare theory with observations of real supernova explosions. These frequent reality checks are a distinguishing characteristic of science.

Visual-wavelength images

■ **Figure 13-15**

(a) SN 2005gl was seen erupting in the galaxy NGC 266, 215 million light-years from Earth. (b) In a 1997 image, the star is visible as a highly luminous blue supergiant, a class of star not expected to explode as a supernova. (c) In a 2007 image recorded after the explosion had faded away, the star is gone. (a. Puckett Observatory; b. and c. NASA, ESA, A. Gal-Yam, Weizmann Inst. of Science, Israel)

Observations of Supernovae

In AD 1054, Chinese astronomers saw a "guest star" appear in the constellation now known as Taurus, the bull. The star quickly became so bright it was visible in the daytime. After a month's time, it slowly faded, taking almost two years to vanish from sight. When modern astronomers turned their telescopes to the location of the guest star, they found a cloud of gas about 1.4 pc in radius, expanding at 1400 km/s. Projecting the expansion back in time, they concluded that it must have begun about nine centuries ago, just when the Taurus guest star made its visit. From this and other evidence, astronomers conclude that the nebula, now called the Crab Nebula because of its shape (■ Figure 13-16), marks the site of the 1054 supernova.

The glowing filaments of the Crab Nebula appear to be excited gas flung outward by the explosion, but the hazy glow in the inner nebula is something else. Radio observations show that the gas in the nebula is emitting **synchrotron radiation**—electromagnetic energy radiated by high-speed electrons spiraling through a magnetic field. Electrons moving at different velocities radiate at different wavelengths, so synchrotron radiation is spread over a wide range of wavelengths. The foggy glow in the Crab Nebula is synchrotron radiation at the relatively short wavelengths of visible light, which means the electrons must be traveling at tremendous speeds. In the nine centuries since the Crab supernova explosion, the electrons should have radiated their energy away and slowed down. Evidently they

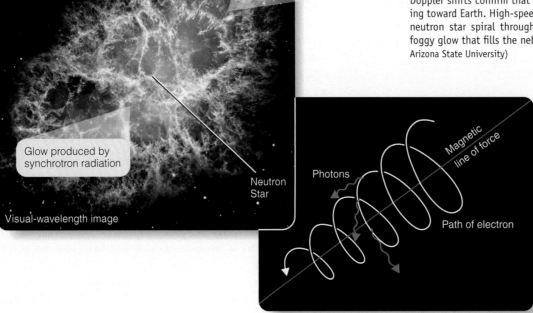

The Crab Nebula

Filaments of gas rush away from the site of the supernova of AD 1054.

Glow produced by synchrotron radiation

Neutron Star

Visual-wavelength image

Magnetic line of force

Photons

Path of electron

■ **Figure 13-16**

The Crab Nebula is located in the constellation Taurus the Bull, just where Chinese astronomers saw a brilliant "guest star" in AD 1054. Over tens of years, astronomers can measure the motions of the filaments as they expand away from the center. Doppler shifts confirm that the near side of the nebula is moving toward Earth. High-speed electrons produced by the central neutron star spiral through magnetic fields and produce the foggy glow that fills the nebula. (NASA, ESA, J. Hester and A. Loll, Arizona State University) have not, so there must be an energy source in the Crab Nebula that is producing very-high-speed electrons. You will use this clue in the next chapter and discover a neutron star at the center of the Crab Nebula.

In contrast, Kepler's supernova of 1604 left nothing behind but a cloud of gas and dust. Astronomers analyzing the chemical content of the cloud conclude the explosion was a type Ia supernova, so it would not have formed a neutron star or black hole. In fact, a team of astronomers has found the companion star that spilled mass onto the white dwarf. When the white dwarf exploded, the companion star was suddenly freed and its orbital velocity carried it away into space. It is seen today rushing away from the site of the explosion.

A supernova fades to obscurity in a year or two, but it produces an expanding shell of gas, originally expelled at 10,000 to 20,000 km/s, called a **supernova remnant**. As the supernova remnant cools, some of the gas condenses to form dust, and that makes supernovae one of the biggest sources of the dust in the interstellar medium. As you learned earlier, there are several processes that cause a supernova remnant to remain visible long after the explosion itself is over. Another such process is collision of the expanding shell of gas and dust with the surrounding interstellar medium that can sweep up even more gas and excite it to produce a glowing nebula.

Supernova remnants look quite delicate and do not survive very long—a few tens of thousands of years—before they gradually mix with the interstellar medium and vanish. The Crab Nebula is a young remnant, only about 950 years old, and it isn't very large, only a few parsecs in diameter. Older remnants can be larger. Some supernova remnants are detectable only at radio and X-ray wavelengths. They have become too tenuous to emit much visible light, but the collision of the expanding hot gas with the interstellar medium can generate radio and X-ray radiation and allows astronomers to create images of them at these non-visible wavelengths. In general, supernova remnants are low-density shells of gas expanding into the interstellar medium (■ Figure 13-17). You saw in Chapter 11 that the compression of the interstellar medium by expanding supernova remnants can trigger star formation.

The supernova remnant Cassiopia A (Cas A) is only about 300 years old, although there is no record of a supernova being seen at that location. The Chandra X-ray Observatory has recorded a series of X-ray images beginning in 2001 (Figure 13-17), and they allow astronomers to see the gas cloud expanding. Detailed studies reveal jets rich in silicon and iron. Infrared images made by the Spitzer Space Telescope combined with ground-based observations have allowed astronomers to create a three-dimensional model of the remnant. These studies show that the outer layers of the star were ejected in a spherical shell, but parts of the stars' interior were ejected in a flattened disk. Theoretical models have not yet explained that geometry.

The Crab Nebula is important because it is a young supernova remnant linked to a supernova explosion that was actually seen to occur. Supernovae are rare, and only a few have been visible to the naked eye during all of recorded history. Arab astronomers recorded one in 1006, and the Chinese saw the Crab supernova in 1054. The guest stars of 185, 386, 393, and 1181 may also have been supernovae. European astronomers observed two—one in 1572 (Tycho's supernova) and one in 1604 (Kepler's supernova). Most supernovae are discovered in distant galaxies, but those are faint and difficult to study.

The Supernova of 1987

For the 383 years following Kepler's supernova in 1604, no naked-eye supernova was seen. Then, in late February 1987, the news raced around the world: Astronomers in Chile had discovered a naked-eye supernova in the Large Magellanic Cloud, a small galaxy very near our Milky Way Galaxy (■ Figure 13-18). Because the supernova was only 20 degrees from the south celestial pole, it could be studied only from southern latitudes. It was named SN 1987A to denote the first supernova discovered in 1987.

The hydrogen-rich spectrum suggested that the supernova was a type II, caused by the collapse of the core of a massive star. As the months passed, however, the light curve proved to be odd in that it paused for a few weeks before rising to its final maximum (see Figure 13-14). From photographs of the area made some years before, astronomers were able to determine that the star that exploded, cataloged as Sanduleak −69°202, was not the expected red supergiant but rather a hot, blue supergiant of about 20 solar masses and 50 solar radii, not extreme for a supergiant. Theorists now believe that the star was chemically poor in elements heavier than helium and had consequently contracted and heated up after a phase as a cool, red supergiant, during which it had lost mass into space. The brightening of the supernova may have gone through a pause because much of the energy of the explosion went into blowing apart the smaller, denser-than-usual star and making it expand.

The brightening of the expanding gases after the first few weeks seems to have been caused by the decay of radioactive nickel into cobalt, which emitted gamma rays that heated the expanding shell of gas and made it brighter. About 0.07 solar mass of nickel was produced, about 20,000 times the mass of Earth.

The cobalt atoms are also unstable, but they decay more slowly, so it was not until some time later, after much of the nickel had decayed, that the decay of cobalt into iron began providing energy to keep the expanding gas hot and luminous. Although these processes had been predicted, they were clearly observed in SN 1987A. Gamma rays from the decay of cobalt to iron were detected above Earth's atmosphere, and cobalt and iron are clearly visible in the infrared spectra of the supernova.

■ Figure 13-17

A supernova remnant is an expanding bubble of hot gas created by a supernova explosion. As the remnant expands and pushes into neighboring gas, it can emit radiation at many wavelengths. (Cygnus Loop: Mikael Svalgaard; SN1006: NASA/CXC/J. Hughes et al.; Cas A: NASA/CXC/GSFC/ U. Hwang et al.)

As the expanding gases dimmed, photographs revealed bright rings of gas (look again at Figure 13-18). Comparison with mathematical models shows that the rings were produced by two stellar winds. When the star was a red supergiant, it expelled a slow stellar wind. Later, when it became a blue supergiant, it expelled a fast stellar wind. The interaction of these two winds, shaped by a magnetic field and illuminated by the supernova explosion, produces the rings. Compare this with the rings seen in some of the planetary nebulae shown on page 261.

Two independent observations confirm that SN 1987A probably gave birth to a neutron star. As you learned earlier, theory predicts that as a massive star's core collapses into a neutron star it should liberate a tremendous blast of neutrinos that leave the star hours before the shock wave from the interior blows the star apart. Two independent neutrino detectors, one in Ohio and one in Japan, recorded a burst of neutrinos passing through Earth at 2:35:41 AM EST on February 23, 1987, a few hours before the supernova was seen. The data show that the neutrinos rushed toward Earth from the direction of the supernovae. The detectors caught only 19 neutrinos during a 12-second interval, but recall that neutrinos hardly ever react with normal matter. Even though only 19 were detected, the full flood of neutrinos must have been immense. Within a few seconds of that moment, roughly 20 trillion neutrinos passed

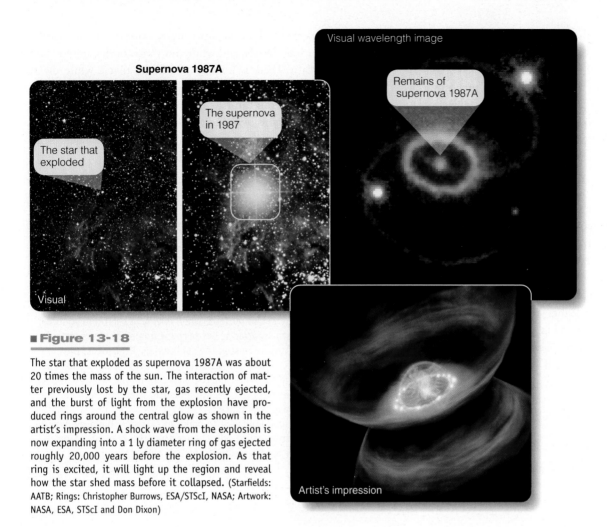

Supernova 1987A

The star that exploded

The supernova in 1987

Visual

Visual wavelength image

Remains of supernova 1987A

Artist's impression

■ **Figure 13-18**

The star that exploded as supernova 1987A was about 20 times the mass of the sun. The interaction of matter previously lost by the star, gas recently ejected, and the burst of light from the explosion have produced rings around the central glow as shown in the artist's impression. A shock wave from the explosion is now expanding into a 1 ly diameter ring of gas ejected roughly 20,000 years before the explosion. As that ring is excited, it will light up the region and reveal how the star shed mass before it collapsed. (Starfields: AATB; Rings: Christopher Burrows, ESA/STScI, NASA; Artwork: NASA, ESA, STScI and Don Dixon)

harmlessly through each human body on Earth. The detection of the neutrino blast confirms that the collapsing core gave birth to a neutron star.

Over time the expanding gas shell of the supernova will continue to thin and cool, and eventually astronomers on Earth will be able to peer inside and see what is left of Sanduleak −69°202. Will they see the expected neutron star, or will theories need further revision? For the first time in almost 400 years, astronomers can observe a bright supernova to test their theories.

Local Supernovae and Life on Earth

Although supernovae are rare events, they are very powerful and could affect life on planets orbiting nearby stars. In fact, supernovae explosions long ago may have affected Earth's climate and the evolution of life.

If a supernova were to occur within a few light years of Earth, the human race would have to abandon the surface and live below ground for at least a few decades. The burst of gamma rays and high-energy particles from the supernova explosion could kill many life forms and cause serious genetic damage in others. The only way to avoid this radiation would be to move the population into tunnels below Earth's surface. Of course, if a supernova did occur, there would not be time to dig enough tunnels.

Even if you could survive in tunnels long enough for the radioactivity on Earth's surface to subside, you might not like Earth when you emerged. Genetic mutation induced by radioactivity might alter plant and animal life so seriously that the human population could not be supported. After all, humans depend almost totally on grass for food. The basic human foods—milk, butter, eggs, wheat, tomatoes, lettuce, and meat (Big Macs, in other words)—are grass and similar vegetation processed into different forms. Seafood is merely processed ocean plankton and plant life, which might also be altered or damaged by a local supernova explosion.

Even if a supernova were 25 to 100 ly away, it could seriously damage Earth's ozone layer and alter the climate dramatically. Local supernovae have been suggested as a possible cause of occasional climate changes and extinctions in Earth's past. It is almost certain that, as the sun moves through space, supernovae explode near enough to affect Earth every few hundred million years. A close call could trigger an extinction.

Is there any evidence that supernovae really affect Earth? In 1979, scientists studying Antarctic ice cores containing very old ice noticed that ice from the years 1181, 1320, 1572, and 1604 contains high abundances of nitrates. Bright supernovae were seen in the years 1181, 1572, and 1604. Ultraviolet radiation from those supernovae might have altered Earth's upper atmosphere and produced acid rain that was recorded in the ice as nitrates. But what of the ice from 1320? In 1999, X-ray astronomers noticed a supernova remnant in the southern sky. When they calculated its age, they found the supernova should have occurred about 1320. It isn't clear why there is no historical record of this supernova or why the nitrates appear in Antarctic ice cores but not in Greenland ice cores. In any case, this evidence may be a warning that even distant supernova explosions can affect Earth in subtle ways.

A study of cores from the seafloor has revealed a deposit of the isotope iron-60 in a layer that was laid down at the time of the Pliocene-Pleistocene extinction about 2 million years ago. Iron-60 is produced in supernova explosions and has a half-life of only 1.5 million years. To reach Earth before it decayed, this iron must have been produced in a supernova explosion no more than 100 ly away. Some scientists wonder if the Pliocene-Pleistocene extinction was caused by a nearby supernova explosion.

Earth seems to be fairly safe at the moment. No star within 500 ly is known to be a massive giant capable of exploding as a type II supernova. Type Ia supernovae, however, are caused by collapsing white dwarfs, and white dwarfs are both common and hard to locate. There is no way to be sure that a white dwarf teetering on the edge of the Chandrasekhar limit does not lurk near us in space. You can take comfort, however, in the rarity of supernova explosions, which seem to occur within our view only a few times per millenium. Earth faces greater dangers from human ignorance than from exploding stars.

SCIENTIFIC ARGUMENT

Why does a type II supernova explode?

For this argument you need to review theory rather than evidence. A type II supernova occurs when a massive star reaches the end of its usable fuel and develops an iron core. The iron is the final ash produced by nuclear fusion, and it cannot fuse because iron is the most tightly bound nucleus. When energy generation begins to decrease, the star contracts, but because iron can't ignite there is no new energy source to stop the contraction. In seconds, the core of the star falls inward, and a shock wave moves outward. Aided by a flood of neutrinos and sudden convective turbulence, the shock wave blasts the star apart; seen from Earth, it brightens as its surface gases expand into space.

Now revise your argument to consider evidence. **What evidence can you cite to support the theory that the core of a type II supernova can form a neutron star?**

What Are We?   Stardust

You are made of atoms that were cooked up inside stars. Gravity draws matter together to make stars, and although nuclear fusion delays gravity's final victory, stars must eventually die. That process of star life and star death manufactures atoms heavier than helium and spreads them back into the interstellar medium, where they can become part of the gas clouds that form new stars. All of the atoms in your body except for the hydrogen were made inside stars.

Some of your atoms, such as the carbon, were cooked up in the cores of medium-mass stars like the sun and were puffed out into space when those stars died and produced planetary nebulae. Some of your atoms, such as the calcium in your bones, were made inside massive stars and were blown out into space during a type II supernova explosion. Many of the iron atoms in your blood were made by the sudden fusing of carbon when white dwarfs collapsed in type Ia supernova explosions. In fact, a few of your heavier atoms, such as iodine in your thyroid gland, selenium in your nerve cells, and gold in your class ring, were produced in the raging violence of supernova explosions.

You are made of atoms scattered into space long ago by the violent deaths of stars. What are we? We are stardust.

Summary

▶ Red dwarfs less massive than about 0.4 solar mass are completely mixed internally by convection. They cannot ignite a hydrogen fusion shell, so they cannot become giant stars. Because they have little weight to support and can fuse nearly all of their hydrogen fuel, they will remain on the main sequence for many times the present age of the universe and then contract to become white dwarfs. The universe is not old enough for any white dwarfs to have formed in this way.

▶ Medium-mass stars between about 0.4 and 4 solar masses, including the sun, become cool giants and fuse helium but cannot fuse carbon. While they are giants, they lose mass into space, a process that is helped by **thermal pulses (p. 257)** in their helium fusion shells. Finally such stars collapse to become white dwarfs.

▶ If the collapsed star becomes hot enough, it can ionize the gas it has ejected first as a slow wind and later as a fast wind to produce a **planetary nebula (p. 257)**.

▶ White dwarfs are the remains of sun-like stars that have collapsed until their gas becomes degenerate. Because white dwarfs are small, dense, and generate no fusion energy, they are sometimes called **compact objects (p. 259)**, along with neutron stars and black holes. Because white dwarfs have no nuclear fuels they will slowly cool off and eventually become **black dwarfs (p. 259)**. The universe is not old enough yet for any black dwarfs to have formed.

▶ A white dwarf cannot support its own weight by its degenerate pressure if its mass is greater than the **Chandrasekhar limit (p. 262)** of 1.4 solar masses. Medium-mass stars up to about 8 solar masses can lose enough mass during their lives to shrink under the Chandrasekhar limit and die as white dwarfs. This explains the large number of white dwarfs found in space.

▶ Two stars orbiting each other control two regions of space called **Roche lobes (p. 263)**. The surface of these lobes is called the **Roche surface (p. 263)**. The **Lagrangian points (p. 263)** mark places of stability in the system, and mass can flow from one star to the other through the **inner Lagrangian point (p. 263)**.

▶ Close binary stars evolve in complex ways because they can transfer mass from one star to the other. This explains why some binary systems contain a main-sequence star more massive than its giant companion—the Algol paradox.

▶ Mass is transferred from an evolving star through an **accretion disk (p. 264)** around the receiving star. Accretion disks can become hot enough to emit light and even X-rays.

▶ Mass transferred onto the surface of a white dwarf can build up a layer of fuel that fuses suddenly in a **nova (p. 264)** explosion. A white dwarf can erupt repeatedly so long as mass transfer continues to form new layers of fuel.

▶ Stars more massive than about 8 solar masses cannot lose mass fast enough to reduce their mass low enough to die by ejecting a planetary nebula and collapsing into a white dwarf. Such massive stars must die more violent deaths.

▶ The end of Earth will come in about 5 billion years when the sun expands, goes through two red giant phases, and engulfs Earth. Most of the atoms now on Earth's surface will be blown outward to rejoin the interstellar medium. If the sun collapses quickly enough into a hot white dwarf, the gas it has expelled will be excited to glow as a planetary nebula.

▶ The massive stars on the upper main sequence fuse nuclear fuels up to iron but cannot generate further nuclear energy because iron is the most tightly bound of all atomic nuclei. When a massive star forms an iron core, the core collapses and triggers a **supernova (p. 268)** explosion known as a **type II supernova (p. 271)**.

▶ A **type I supernova (p. 271)** has no hydrogen lines in its spectra. A **type Ia supernova (p. 271)** can occur when mass transferred onto a white dwarf pushes it over the Chandrasekhar limit and the white dwarf collapses suddenly, fusing all of its carbon at once in a burst of **carbon deflagration (p. 271)**. Type Ia supernovae have no hydrogen lines because white dwarfs contain very little hydrogen.

▶ A **type Ib supernova (p. 271)** occurs when a massive star in a binary system loses its outer layers of hydrogen due to mass transfer. Later its iron core can collapse, and it can explode as a type Ib supernova, which lacks hydrogen lines.

▶ Many atoms heavier than iron are produced inside supergiant stars and then blown into space by supernova explosions. Many other heavy atoms are produced by fusion reactions that take place during supernova explosions.

▶ **Supernova remnants (p. 273)** are the expanding shells of gas ejected by supernova explosions. They are filled with hot gas. The Crab Nebula is a supernova remnant formed by the supernova of AD 1054.

▶ The hazy glow in the Crab Nebula is produced by **synchrotron radiation (p. 272)** and is evidence that some energy source remains in the nebula. Observations have found a neutron star there.

▶ The supernova of 1987 is believed to have been produced by a peculiar type II supernova explosion. Neutrinos from the explosion were detected on Earth and are evidence that the star's iron core collapsed, presumably forming a neutron star, although it has not yet been detected.

▶ Supernova explosions near Earth could alter the ozone layer, change Earth's climate, and produce some of the extinctions that are seen in the fossil record.

Review Questions

1. Why can't the lowest-mass stars become giants?
2. Presumably, all the white dwarfs in our galaxy were produced by sun-like stars of medium mass. Why couldn't any of these white dwarfs have been produced by the deaths of the lowest-mass stars?
3. What evidence can you cite that stars can lose mass?
4. What kind of spectrum does the gas in a planetary nebula produce? Where does it get the energy to radiate?
5. The coolest stars at the center of planetary nebulae are about 25,000 K. Why don't astronomers see planetary nebulae containing cooler central stars? (*Hint:* What kind of photons excite the gas in a planetary nebula?)
6. As white dwarfs cool, they move toward the lower right in the H–R diagram (Figure 9-9 and page 261), maintaining constant radius. Why don't they contract as they cool?
7. All white dwarfs are about the same mass. Why?
8. Why have no white dwarfs cooled to form black dwarfs in our galaxy?
9. What happens to a star in a close binary system when it becomes a giant?
10. Why do novae repeat while supernovae do not?
11. Why can't stars generate energy from iron fusion?
12. How could you use spectra to tell the difference between a type I supernova and a type II supernova? Why does this difference arise?
13. What processes produce type I and type II supernovae?
14. Why do supernova remnants emit X rays?
15. **How Do We Know?** How could you trace the ultimate causes of supernova explosions back to the behavior of subatomic particles?

Discussion Questions

1. How certain can you be that the sun will never explode as a supernova? What does it mean when a scientist uses the word *certainty*?

2. If humans could live for millions of years, they might notice stars that had exploded repeatedly as novas finally being destroyed in supernova explosions. What could account for this?

Problems

1. Use the formula in Chapter 12 to compute the life expectancy of a 0.4-solar-mass star. Why might this be an underestimate if the star is fully mixed?

2. The Ring Nebula in Lyra is a planetary nebula with an angular diameter of 76 arc seconds and a distance of 5000 ly. What is its linear diameter? (*Hint:* Use the small-angle formula, Chapter 3.)

3. If the Ring Nebula is about a light-year in diameter and expanding at a velocity of 15 km/s, typical of planetary nebulae, how old is it? (*Hint:* 1 ly = 9.46×10^{12} km, and 1 year = 3.16×10^7 s.)

4. Suppose that a planetary nebula is 1.0 pc in diameter and the Doppler shifts in its spectrum show that it is expanding at 30 km/s. How old is it? (*Hint:* See Problem 3.)

5. A planetary nebula photographed 20 years ago and then photographed again today has increased its radius by 0.6 arc seconds. If Doppler shifts in its spectrum show that it is expanding at a velocity of 20 km/s, how far away is it? (*Hints:* First figure out how many parsecs it has increased in radius in 20 years. Then use the small-angle formula, Chapter 3.)

6. The Crab Nebula is now 1.35 pc in radius and is expanding at 1400 km/s. About when did the supernova occur?

7. The Cygnus Loop is now 2.6° in diameter and lies about 500 pc distant. If it is 10,000 years old, what was its average velocity of expansion? (*Hint:* Find its radius in parsecs first, using the small-angle formula, Chapter 3.)

8. The supernova remnant Cassiopeia A (Cas A) is expanding in radius at a rate of about 0.5 arc seconds per year. Doppler shifts show that the velocity of expansion is about 5700 km/s. How far away is the nebula?

9. Cassiopeia A has a radius of about 2.5 arc minutes. If it is expanding at 0.5 arc seconds per year, when did the supernova explosion occur? (Note that there is no record of a supernova being seen at that time.)

Learning to Look

1. What processes caused a medium-mass star to produce the nebula shown here? The nebula is now about 0.1 ly in diameter and still expanding. What will happen to it?

2. The image here combines X-ray (blue), visible (green), and radio (red) images. Observations show the sphere is expanding at a high speed and is filled with very hot gas. What kind of object produced this nebula? Roughly how old do you think it must be?

14 | Neutron Stars and Black Holes

Artist impression

Guidepost

In the last two chapters you have traced the story of stars from birth to death. By now you are asking a simple question, "What's left?" The answer depends on the mass of the star. You already know that stars like the sun produce white dwarf corpses, but more massive stars leave behind the strangest beasts in the cosmic zoo.

Now you are ready to meet neutron stars and black holes, and your exploration will answer four essential questions:

How does theory predict the existence of neutron stars?

How do astronomers know neutron stars really exist?

How does theory predict the existence of black holes?

How can astronomers be sure that black holes really exist?

This chapter will show you more striking examples of how astronomers combine observations and theory to understand nature.

This chapter ends the story of individual stars, but it does not end the story of stars. In the next chapter, you will begin exploring the giant communities in which stars live— the galaxies.

A neutron star containing roughly the mass of the sun and only about 10 km in radius draws matter inward through a whirling disk of gas hot enough to emit X-rays. (NASA/Dana Berry)

*Almost anything is easier
to get into than out of.*

— AGNES ALLEN

GRAVITY ALWAYS WINS. No matter how long a star struggles to withstand its own gravity, it must eventually exhaust its fuels and die by collapsing. Those stars that do not destroy themselves in the process become one of three types of compact objects—white dwarfs, neutron stars, or black holes. Almost all of the energy available has been squeezed out of compact objects, and you find them in their final, high-density states.

You studied white dwarfs in the previous chapter. Here you will study the most extreme of the compact objects, and you need to compare evidence and theory with great care. Theory predicts the existence of these objects; but, by their nature, they are difficult to detect. To confirm the theories, astronomers have searched for real objects that can be identified as having the properties predicted by theory. That is, they have searched out real neutron stars and real black holes. No hero ever set off on a more difficult quest.

14-1 Neutron Stars

A **NEUTRON STAR** CONTAINING A LITTLE OVER 1 SOLAR MASS compressed to a radius of about 10 km can be left behind by a type II supernova. For comparison, a white dwarf has about the same mass but is about the size of Earth. A neutron star's density is so high that physicists calculate that the matter is stable only as a fluid of neutrons. Theory predicts that such an object would spin a number of times a second, be nearly as hot at its surface as the inside of the sun, and have a magnetic field a trillion times stronger than Earth's. Two questions should occur to you immediately. First, how could any theory predict such a wondrously unbelievable object? And second, do neutron stars really exist?

Theoretical Prediction of Neutron Stars

The neutron was discovered in the laboratory in February 1932. Only two years later, in January 1934, Caltech astronomers Walter Baade and Fritz Zwicky published a seminal paper. They showed that some novae in historical records were much more luminous than most and suggested that these were caused by the explosive collapse of a massive star in an explosion they named a supernova. The core of the star, they proposed, would form a small and tremendously dense sphere of neutrons, and Zwicky coined the term *neutron star.*

Over the following years, scientists applied the principles of quantum mechanics to see if such an object was indeed possible. Neutrons spin in much the way that electrons do, which means that neutrons must obey the Pauli exclusion principle. In other words, if neutrons are packed together tightly enough, they can

become degenerate just as electrons do. White dwarfs are supported by degenerate electrons, and quantum mechanics predicts that an even denser mass of neutrons could support itself by the pressure of degenerate neutrons.

How does the core of a collapsing star become a mass of neutrons? Nuclear physics provides an explanation. As the supernova begins, the core collapses inward. If the collapsing core is more massive than the Chandrasekhar limit of 1.4 solar masses, then it cannot reach stability as a white dwarf because the weight is too great to be supported by degenerate electrons. The collapse of the core continues, and the atomic nuclei are broken apart by gamma rays. Almost instantly, the increasing density forces the freed protons to combine with electrons and become neutrons by this reaction:

$$e + p \rightarrow n + \nu$$

A side result is the production of a neutrino. Remember from the previous chapter that the burst of neutrinos (ν) during a supernova explosion helps blast the envelope of the star away, and the core is left behind as a neutron star.

Which stars produce neutron stars as remnants? As you saw in the previous chapter, a star of 8 solar masses or less can lose enough mass to die by forming a planetary nebula and then leaving behind a white dwarf. More massive stars also lose mass rapidly, but model calculations indicate they cannot shed mass fast enough to reduce their mass below the Chandrasekhar limit, so it seems likely that they must die in supernova explosions. Theoretical calculations suggest that stars that begin life on the main sequence with roughly 8 to 20 solar masses will leave behind neutron stars. Stars even more massive than that are thought to form black holes.

How massive can a neutron star be? That is a critical question and a difficult one to answer because scientists don't know the strength of pure neutron material. They can't make such matter in the laboratory, so its properties must be predicted theoretically. The most widely accepted calculations suggest that a neutron star cannot be more massive than about 3 solar masses. If a neutron star were more massive than that, the degenerate neutrons would not be able to support the weight, and the object would collapse (presumably into a black hole). Two of the most massive neutron stars observed have masses of 1.94 and 2.74 solar masses, which confirms the theory.

How big are neutron stars? Mathematical models predict that a neutron star should be only 10 or so kilometers in radius (■ Figure 14-1), which, combined with a typical mass, means it must have a density of almost 10^{15} g/cm^3. On Earth, a sugar-cube-sized lump of this material would weigh 100 million tons. This is roughly the density of an atomic nucleus, so you can think of a neutron star as matter with absolutely all of the empty space squeezed out of it.

Simple physics, the same physics you have used in previous chapters to understand normal stars, predicts that neutron stars

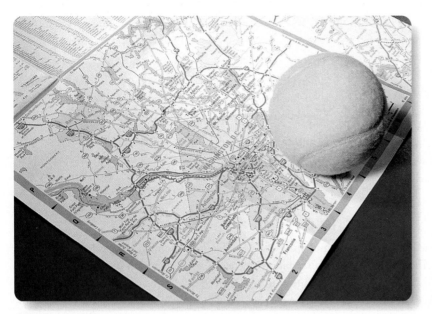

■ Figure 14-1

A tennis ball and a road map illustrate the relative size of a neutron star. Such an object, containing slightly more than the mass of the sun, would fit with room to spare inside the beltway around Washington, D.C. (Photo by M. Seeds)

When the star collapses, the magnetic field is squeezed into a smaller volume, which can make the field as much as a billion times stronger. Because some stars start with magnetic fields over 1000 times stronger than the sun's, a neutron star could have a magnetic field as much as a trillion times stronger than the sun's. For comparison, that is about 10 million times stronger than any magnetic field ever produced in the laboratory.

Theory predicts the properties of neutron stars, but it also predicts that they should be difficult to observe. Neutron stars are very hot, so from your understanding of blackbody radiation you can predict they will radiate most of their energy in the gamma-ray and X-ray part of the spectrum, radiation that could not be observed in the 1940s and 1950s because astronomers could not put their telescopes above Earth's atmosphere. Also, the small surface areas of neutron stars mean that they will be faint objects. Consequently, astronomers of the mid-20th century were not surprised that none of the newly predicted neutron stars had been found. Neutron stars were, at that point, entirely theoretical objects.

should be hot, spin rapidly, and have strong magnetic fields. You have seen that contraction heats the gas in a star. As gas particles fall inward, they pick up speed; and, when they collide, their high speeds become thermal energy. The sudden collapse of the core of a massive star to a radius of 10 km should heat it to a trillion degrees. Astronomers calculate that neutron stars should initially cool rapidly from that astonishingly high temperature because neutrinos can escape from their entire volume and carry energy away. After a few years neutron stars will cool down to a mere million degrees or so, and neutrinos won't be produced in bulk. From that point on, neutron stars should cool slowly because the heat can escape only from the surface, and neutron stars are so small they have little surface from which to radiate.

The principle of conservation of angular momentum predicts that neutron stars should spin rapidly. All stars rotate because they form from swirling clouds of interstellar matter. As a star collapses, it must rotate faster because it conserves angular momentum. Recall the example of an ice skater spinning slowly with her arms extended and then speeding up as she pulls her arms closer to her body (see Figure 5-7). In the same way, a collapsing star must spin faster as it pulls its matter closer to its axis of rotation. If the sun collapsed to a radius of 10 km, its period of rotation would increase from once every 25 days to over 20 times a second. You might expect the collapsed core of a massive star to rotate in the range of 10 to 100 times a second.

It isn't hard to understand why a neutron star should have a powerful magnetic field. The gas of a star is ionized, and that means the magnetic field cannot move easily through the gas.

The Discovery of Pulsars

In November 1967, Jocelyn Bell, a graduate student at Cambridge University in England, found a peculiar pattern in the data from a radio telescope. Unlike other radio signals from celestial bodies, this was a series of regular pulses (■ Figure 14-2). At first she and the leader of the project, Anthony Hewish, thought the signal was interference from Earthly sources, but they found it day after day in the same place in the sky. Clearly, it was celestial in origin.

Another possibility, that it came from a distant civilization, led them to consider naming it LGM, for Little Green Men. But within a few weeks, the team found three more objects in other parts of the sky pulsing with different periods. The objects were clearly natural, and the team dropped the name LGM in favor of

■ Figure 14-2

The 1967 detection of regularly spaced pulses in the output of a radio telescope led to the discovery of pulsars. This record of the radio signal from the first pulsar, CP 1919, contains regularly spaced pulses (marked by ticks). The period is 1.33730119 seconds.

pulsar—a contraction of *pulsing star.* The pulsing radio source Bell had observed with her radio telescope was the first known pulsar.

As more pulsars were found, astronomers argued over their nature. The periods ranged from 0.033 to 3.75 seconds and each one was nearly as exact as an atomic clock. However, months of observation showed that many of the periods were slowly growing longer by a few billionths of a second per day. Whatever produced the regular pulses had to be highly precise, nearly as exact as an atomic clock, but also gradually slowing down.

It was easy to eliminate possibilities. Pulsars could not be ordinary stars. A normal star, even a small white dwarf, is much too big to pulse that fast. Nor could a star with a hot spot on its surface spin fast enough to produce the pulses. Even a small white dwarf would fly apart if it spun 30 times a second.

The pulses themselves gave the astronomers a clue. The pulses lasted only about 0.001 second, placing an upper limit on the size of the object producing the pulse. If a white dwarf blinked on and then off in that interval, you would not see a 0.001-second pulse. That's because the point on the white dwarf closest to Earth would be about 6000 km closer to you, and light from that spot would arrive 0.022 second before the light from the bulk of the white dwarf. So its short blink would be smeared out into a longer pulse. This is an important principle in astronomy—an object cannot change its brightness appreciably in an interval shorter than the time light takes to cross its diameter. If pulses from pulsars are no longer than 0.001 second, then the objects cannot be larger than 300 km (190 miles) in diameter, and could be much smaller.

Only a neutron star is small enough to be a pulsar. In fact, a neutron star is so small that it couldn't pulsate slowly enough, but it can spin as fast as 1000 times a second without flying apart. The missing link between pulsars and neutron stars was found in 1968, when astronomers discovered a pulsar at the heart of the Crab Nebula (Figure 13-16). The Crab Nebula is a supernova remnant, and theory predicts that some supernovae leave behind neutron stars. The short pulses and the discovery of the pulsar in the Crab Nebula were strong evidence that pulsars are neutron stars.

A Model Pulsar

As you have noticed before, scientists often work by building a model of a natural phenomenon—not a physical model made of plastic and glue, but an intellectual conception of how nature works in a specific instance. The scientists' model may be limited and incomplete, but it helps them organize their understudying.

The modern model of a pulsar has been called the **lighthouse model** and is shown in **The Lighthouse Model of a Pulsar** on pages 284–285. Notice three important points:

 A pulsar does not pulse but rather emits beams of radiation that sweep around the sky as the neutron star rotates. If the beams do not sweep over Earth, the pulses will not be detectable by Earth's radio telescopes.

 The mechanism that produces the beams involves extremely high energies and is not fully understood.

Modern space telescopes observing from above Earth's atmosphere can image details around young neutron stars and even locate isolated neutron stars whose beams of electromagnetic radiation do not sweep over Earth.

Neutron stars are not simple objects, and modern astronomers need to use both general relativity and quantum mechanics to try to understand them. Nevertheless, astronomers know enough to tell the life story of pulsars.

The Evolution of Pulsars

When a pulsar first forms, it is spinning fast, perhaps a hundred times a second. The energy it radiates into space comes from its energy of rotation, so as it blasts beams of radiation outward, its rotation slows. The average pulsar is apparently only a few million years old, and the oldest are about 10 million years old. Presumably, older neutron stars rotate too slowly to generate detectable radio beams.

You can expect that a young neutron star should emit powerful beams of radiation. The Crab Nebula is an example. Only about 950 years old, the Crab pulsar is so powerful it emits photons all across the electromagnetic spectrum, at radio, infrared, visible, X-ray, and gamma-ray wavelengths (■ Figure 14-3). Careful measurements of its brightness with high-speed instruments show that it blinks twice for every rotation. When one beam sweeps almost directly over Earth, astronomers detect a strong pulse. Half a rotation later, the edge of the other beam brushes over Earth, and astronomers detect a weaker pulse.

Only the most energetic pulsars produce short-wavelength photons and thus pulse at visible wavelengths. The Crab Nebula pulsar is young and powerful, and it produces visible pulses. So does another young pulsar called the Vela pulsar (located in the Southern Hemisphere constellation Vela). Compared with most pulsars, the Vela pulsar is fast, pulsing about 11 times a second and, like the Crab Nebula pulsar, is located inside a supernova remnant. Its age is estimated at a relatively young 20,000 to 30,000 years.

The Fermi Gamma-Ray Space Telescope has detected a new kind of pulsar that pulses in pure gamma rays. It is not clear how these pulses are produced, but because gamma rays are extremely short-wavelength, high-energy photons, the process must involve very high energies. At least one of those gamma-ray pulsars is located inside a supernova remnant that is only about 10,000 years old.

The electromagnetic energy in the beams is only a small part of the energy emitted by a pulsar. Roughly 99.9 percent of the energy flowing away from a pulsar is carried as a **pulsar wind** of high-speed atomic particles. This can produce small, high-energy nebulae near a young pulsar (■ Figure 14-4).

High-speed images of the Crab Nebula pulsar show it pulsing at visual wavelengths and at X-ray wavelengths. (© AURA, Inc., NOAO, KPNO) The period of pulsation is 33 milliseconds, and each cycle includes two pulses as its two beams of unequal intensity sweep over Earth. (Courtesy F. R. Harnden Jr., from *The Astrophysical Journal,* published by the University of Chicago Press; © 1984 The American Astronomical Society)

Variation in light intensity

Main pulse

Secondary pulse

Pulsar blinks twice each cycle.

Time (milliseconds)

Variation in X-ray intensity

Pulsar blinking at X-ray wavelengths.

Time (milliseconds)

Ring and jets produced by pulsar wind

3000-year-old supernova remnant G54.1+0.3

Pulsar

X-ray image

X-ray image

Pulsar PSR0540–69 located in a 1000-year-old supernova remnant

X-ray image

Pulsar wind nebula

Pulsar

Supernova remnant G11.2–0.3 formed by supernova of AD 386

Motion of pulsar through space

Vela pulsar

Rings and jets produced by pulsar wind

X-ray image

The Vela supernova remnant is 15 times larger than this image.

■ Figure 14-4

The effects of pulsar winds can be seen at X-ray wavelengths. The high-energy gas of the winds is sometimes detectable, as is the interaction of the winds with surrounding gas. Not all pulsars have detectable winds. (NASA/CXC/SAO/U. Mass; F. Lu/McGill; V. Kaspi)

The Lighthouse Model of a Pulsar

1 Astronomers think of pulsars not as pulsing objects but rather as objects emitting beams. As they spin, the beams sweep around the sky; when a beam sweeps over Earth, observers detect a pulse of radiation. Understanding the details of this lighthouse model is a challenge, but the implications are clear. Although a neutron star is only a few kilometers in radius, it can produce powerful beams. Also, observers tend to notice only those pulsars whose beams happen to sweep over Earth.

In this artist's conception, gas trapped in the neutron star's magnetic field is excited to emit light and outline the otherwise invisible magnetic field.

Beams of electromagnetic radiation would probably be invisible unless they excited local gas to glow.

What color should an artist use to paint a neutron star? With a temperature of a million degrees, the surface emits most of its electromagnetic radiation at X-ray wavelengths. Nevertheless, it would probably look blue-white to your eyes.

2 How a neutron star can emit beams is one of the challenging problems of modern astronomy, but astronomers have a general idea. A neutron star contains a powerful magnetic field and spins very rapidly. The spinning magnetic field generates a tremendously powerful electric field, and the field causes the production of electron–positron pairs. As these charged particles are accelerated through the magnetic field, they emit photons in the direction of their motion, which produce powerful beams of electromagnetic radiation emerging from the magnetic poles.

As in the case of Earth, the magnetic axis of a neutron star could be inclined to its rotational axis.

The rotation of the neutron star will sweep its beams around like beams from a lighthouse.

While a beam points roughly toward Earth, observers detect a pulse.

While neither beam is pointed toward Earth, observers detect no energy.

Beams may not be as exactly symmetric as in this model.

pulsars show that they are surrounded by disks of excited matter and emit powerful jets of excited gas. The disks and jets are shaped by electromagnetic fields, and the jets may curve if they encounter magnetic fields.

3C58

Neutron star

X-ray image

The pulsar 3C58 above was produced by the supernova seen in AD 1181. It pulses 15 times per second and is ejecting jets in both directions.

The pulsar B1509-58 at right is only 1700 years old, young for a pulsar. It is ejecting a thin jet almost 20 ly long. The nebulosity at the top of the image is part of the enclosing supernova remnant excited by energy from the pulsar.

Crab Nebula Pulsar

Neutron star

X-ray image

NASA/CXC/SAO/P. Slane et al.

The Crab Nebula Pulsar above was produced by the supernova of AD 1054. It pulses 30 times a second, and X-ray images can detect rapid flickering changes in the disk.

B1509-58

Neutron star

X-ray image

X-ray image of Puppis supernova remnant

Neutron star

Hubble Space Telescope visual-wavelength image

Neutron star

3a If a pulsar's beams do not sweep over Earth, observers detect no pulses, and the neutron star is difficult to find. A few such objects are known, however. The Puppis A supernova remnant is about 4000 years old and contains a point source of X-rays believed to be a neutron star. The isolated neutron star in the right-hand image has a temperature of 700,000 K.

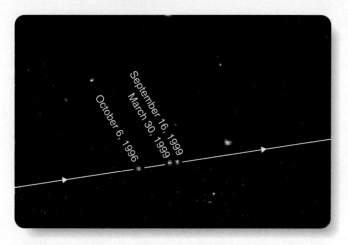

September 16, 1999
March 30, 1999
October 6, 1996

■ **Figure 14-5**

Many neutron stars have high velocities through space. Here the neutron star known as RXJ 185635-3754 was photographed on three different dates as it rushed past background stars. (V. Kaspi/NASA)

You might expect to find all pulsars inside supernova remnants, but the statistics must be examined with care. Many supernova remnants probably do contain pulsars, but their beams never sweep over Earth. Also, some pulsars move through space at high velocity (■ Figure 14-5), quickly leaving their supernova remnants behind. Evidently supernova explosions can occur asymmetrically, perhaps because of the violent turbulence in the exploding core, and that can kick a neutron star away with a high velocity through space. Some supernovae probably occur in binary systems and fling the two stars apart at high velocity. In any case, pulsars are known to have such high velocities that many probably escape the disk of our galaxy. Finally, you must remember that a pulsar can remain detectable for 10 million years or so, but a supernova remnant cannot survive more than about 50,000 years before it is mixed into the interstellar medium. For all these reasons, you should not be surprised that most pulsars are not in supernova remnants and that most supernova remnants do not contain pulsars.

Astronomers conclude that the 1987 explosion of Supernova 1987A formed a neutron star. As you read in the previous chapter, a burst of neutrinos was detected passing through Earth; theory predicts that the collapse of a massive star's core into a neutron star produces such a burst of neutrinos, so the detection of the neutrinos is evidence that the supernova produced a neutron star. At first the neutron star will be hidden at the center of the expanding shells of gas ejected into space; but, as the gas expands and thins, astronomers expect someday to be able to detect the neutron star. Even if its beams don't sweep over Earth, astronomers should eventually be able to detect its X-ray and gamma-ray emission. Although no neutron star has yet been detected, astronomers continue to watch the site, hoping to see a newborn pulsar.

One reason pulsars are so fascinating is the extreme conditions found in spinning neutron stars. To see natural processes of even greater violence, you have only to look at pulsars in binary systems.

Binary Pulsars

Nearly 2000 pulsars are now known, and some are located in binary systems. These pulsars are of special interest because astronomers can learn more about the neutron star by studying the orbital motions of the binary. Also, in some cases, mass can flow from the companion star onto the neutron star, and that produces high-energy violence.

The first binary pulsar was discovered in 1974 when astronomers Joseph Taylor and Russell Hulse noticed that the pulse period of the pulsar PSR 1913+16 was changing. The period first grew longer and then grew shorter in a cycle that took 7.75 hours. Thinking of the Doppler shifts seen in spectroscopic binaries, the radio astronomers realized that the pulsar had to be in a binary system with an orbital period of 7.75 hours. When the orbital motion of the pulsar carries it away from Earth, astronomers see the pulse period lengthen slightly—a redshift. Then, when the pulsar rounds its orbit and approaches Earth, they see the pulse period shorten slightly—a blueshift. From these changing Doppler shifts, Taylor and Hulse calculated the radial velocity of the pulsar around its orbit just as if it were a spectroscopic binary star. The resulting graph of radial velocity versus time was then analyzed to find the shape of the pulsar's orbit (■ Figure 14-6). The analysis of PSR 1913+16 showed that the binary system consists of two neutron stars, one of which is "silent," separated by a distance roughly equal to the radius of our sun.

Yet another surprise was hidden in the motion of PSR 1913+16. In 1916, Einstein's general theory of relativity described gravity as a curvature of space-time. Einstein realized that any rapid change in a gravitational field should spread outward at the speed of light as **gravitational radiation**. Gravity waves have not been detected yet, but Taylor and Hulse were able to show that the orbital period of the binary pulsar is slowly growing shorter because the stars are radiating orbital energy away as gravitational radiation and gradually spiraling toward each other. (Normal binary stars are too far apart and orbit too slowly to emit significant gravitational radiation.) Taylor and Hulse won the Nobel Prize in 1993 for their work with binary pulsars.

Dozens of pulsars have been found orbiting stars of various kinds; by analyzing the Doppler shifts in their pulse periods, astronomers can estimate the masses of the neutron stars. Typical masses are about 1.4 solar masses, in good agreement with models of neutron stars.

In 2004, radio astronomers announced the discovery of a double pulsar: two pulsars that orbit each other in only 2.4 hours. The spinning beams from both pulsars sweep over Earth (■ Figure 14-7). One spins 44 times a second, and the other spins

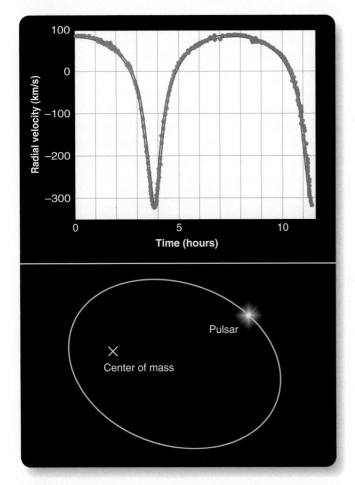

■ **Figure 14-6**

The radial velocity of pulsar PSR 1913+16 can be found from the Doppler shifts in its pulsation. Analysis of the radial velocity curve allows astronomers to determine the pulsar's orbit. Here the center of mass does not appear to be at a focus of the elliptical orbit because the orbit is inclined to the line of sight from Earth. (Adapted from data by Joseph Taylor and Russell Hulse)

■ **Figure 14-7**

Artist's impression of the double pulsar. One star must have exploded to form a pulsar, and later the other star did the same. Gravitational radiation causes the neutron stars to spiral toward each other, and they will merge in 85 million years, presumably then triggering a violent explosion. (John Rowe Animations)

once every 2.8 seconds. This system is a pulsar jackpot because the orbits are nearly edge-on to Earth and the powerful magnetic fields and the gas trapped in the fields eclipse each other, giving astronomers the chance to study their size and structure. Furthermore, the theory of general relativity predicts that these pulsars are emitting gravitational radiation and that their separation is decreasing by 7 mm per year. The two neutron stars will merge in 85 million years, presumably to trigger a violent explosion. In the meantime, the steady decrease in orbital period can be measured, giving astronomers a further test of general relativity and gravitational radiation.

In addition to producing gravitational radiation, a neutron star's intense gravitational field means that binary pulsars can be sites of tremendous violence if matter is transferred from a star to a neutron star. The gravitational field is so strong that an astronaut stepping onto the surface of a neutron star would be instantly smushed into a layer of matter only 1 atom thick.

Matter falling into this gravitational field releases titanic amounts of energy. If you dropped a single marshmallow onto the surface of a neutron star from a distance of 1 AU, it would hit with an impact equivalent to a 3-megaton nuclear warhead. In general, a particle falling from a large distance to the surface of a neutron star will release energy equivalent to $0.2\ mc^2$, where m is the particle's mass at rest and c is the speed of light. Even a small amount of matter flowing from a companion star to a neutron star can generate high temperatures and release X-rays and gamma rays.

Hercules X-1 is an example of such an active system; it contains a 2-solar-mass star and a neutron star that orbit each other with a period of 1.7 days (■ Figure 14-8). Matter flowing from the normal star into an accretion disk around the neutron star reaches temperatures of millions of degrees and emits a powerful X-ray glow. Interactions of the gas with the neutron star's magnetic field produce beams of X-rays that sweep around with the rotating neutron star (Figure 14-8b). Earth receives a pulse of X-rays every time a beam points this way. The X-rays shut off completely every 1.7 days when the neutron star is eclipsed behind the normal star. Hercules X-1 is a complex system with many different high-energy processes going on simultaneously, but this quick sketch serves to illustrate how complex and powerful such binary systems are during mass transfer.

The X-ray source 4U 1820-30 illustrates another way neutron stars can interact with normal stars. In this system, a neutron star and a white dwarf orbit their center of mass with a

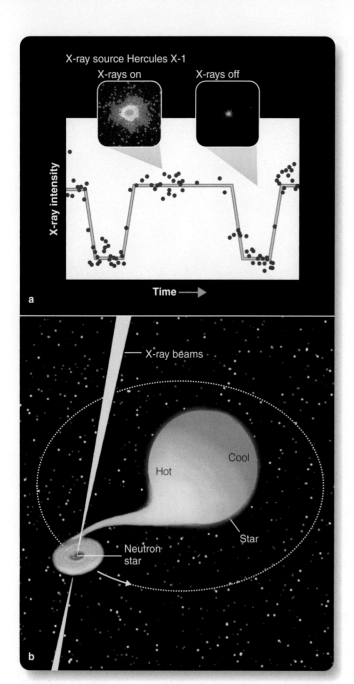

■ Figure 14-8

Sometimes the X-ray pulses from Hercules X-1 are on, and sometimes they are off. A graph of X-ray intensity versus time looks like the light curve of an eclipsing binary. (Insets: J. Trümper, Max-Planck Institute) (b) In Hercules X-1, matter flows from a star into an accretion disk around a neutron star producing X-rays, which heat the near side of the star to 20,000 K compared with only 7000 K on the far side. X-rays turn off when the neutron star is eclipsed behind the star.

period of only 11 minutes (■ Figure 14-9a and b). The separation between the two objects is only about one-third the distance between Earth and the moon. To explain how such a very close pairing could originate, theorists suggest that a neutron star collided with a giant star and went into an orbit inside the star. (Recall the low density of the outer envelope of giant stars.) The

neutron star would gradually eat away the giant star's envelope from the inside, and the star would collapse into a white dwarf. Matter still flows from the white dwarf into an accretion disk and then down to the surface of the neutron star (Figure 14-9c), where it accumulates in a degenerate layer until it ignites helium fusion to produce a burst of X-rays. Objects called **X-ray bursters** are thought to be such binary systems involving mass transferred to a neutron star, and the bursts repeat each time a large enough layer of degenerate fuel accumulates. Notice the similarity between this mechanism and that responsible for novae (see Chapter 13).

The Fastest Pulsars

Your knowledge of pulsars suggests that newborn pulsars should blink rapidly, and old pulsars should blink slowly. In fact, the handful that blink the fastest may be quite old. One of the fastest known pulsars is cataloged as Terzan 5ad in the constellation Sagittarius. It pulses 716 times a second and is slowing down only slightly. The energy stored in the rotation of a neutron star at this rate is equal to the total energy of a supernova explosion, so it seemed difficult at first to explain this pulsar. It now appears that Terzan 5ad is an old neutron star that has gained mass and rotational energy from a companion in a binary system. Like water hitting a mill wheel, the matter falling on the neutron star has spun it up to 716 rotations per second. With its weak magnetic field, it slows down very gradually and will continue to spin rapidly for a very long time.

A number of other very fast pulsars have been found. They are generally known as **millisecond pulsars** because their pulse periods and therefore their periods of rotation are almost as short as a millisecond (0.001 s). This rapid rotation produces some fascinating physics. If a neutron star 10 km in radius spins 716 times a second, as does Terzan 5ad, then its equator must be traveling about 45,000 km/s. That is fast enough to flatten the neutron star into an ellipsoidal shape and is nearly fast enough to break it up. The fastest known pulsar, XTEJ1739-285, spins 1122 times a second. It appears to have been spun up by matter flowing from its companion star and is very near the breakup speed for an object composed of pure neutrons.

The hypothesis that the millisecond pulsars are spun up by mass transfer from a companion star is quite reasonable, but astronomers demand evidence, and evidence has been found. For example, the pulsar PSR J 1740-5340 has a period of 42 milliseconds and is orbiting a bloated red star from which it is gaining mass. This appears to be a pulsar caught in the act of being spun up to high speed. For another example, consider the X-ray source XTEJ1751-305, a pulsar with a period of only 2.3 milliseconds. X-ray observations show that it is gaining mass from a companion star. The orbital period is only 42 minutes, and the mass of the companion star is only 0.014 solar mass. The evidence suggests this neutron star has devoured all but the last morsel of its binary partner.

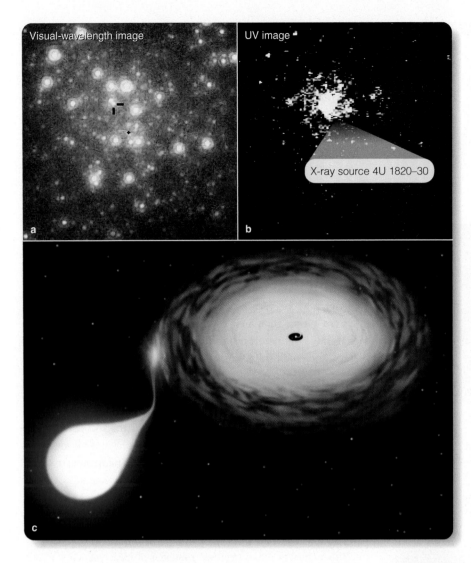

Visual-wavelength image

UV image

a

b

X-ray source 4U 1820–30

c

■ Figure 14-9

(a) At visible wavelengths, the center of star cluster NGC 6624 is crowded with stars. (b) In the ultraviolet, one object stands out, an X-ray source consisting of a neutron star orbiting a white dwarf. (c) An artist's conception shows matter flowing from the white dwarf into an accretion disk around the neutron star. (a and b, Ivan King and NASA/ESA)

"Show me," say scientists; and, in the case of neutron stars, the evidence seems so strong that astronomers have great confidence that such objects really do exist. Other theories that describe their formation, their evolution, and how they emit beams of radiation are less certain, but continuing observations at many wavelengths are expanding astronomers' understanding of these last embers of massive stars. In fact, precise observations have turned up some objects no one expected.

Pulsar Planets

Because a pulsar's period is so precise, astronomers can detect tiny variations by comparing their observations with atomic clocks. When astronomers checked pulsar PSR B1257+12, they found variations in the period of pulsation much like those caused by the orbital motion of a binary pulsar (■ Figure 14-11a). However, in the case of PSR B1257+12, the

Although some millisecond pulsars have binary companions, some are solitary neutron stars. A pulsar known as the Black Widow may reveal how a fast pulsar can lack a companion. The Black Widow has a period of 1.6 milliseconds, meaning it is spinning 622 times per second, and it orbits with a low-mass companion. Presumably the neutron star was spun up by mass flowing from the companion, but spectra show that the blast of radiation and high-energy particles from the neutron star is now boiling away the surface of the companion. The Black Widow has eaten its fill and is now evaporating the remains of its companion. It will soon be a solitary millisecond pulsar (■ Figure 14-10).

■ Figure 14-10

The Black Widow pulsar and its companion star are moving rapidly through space, creating a shock wave like the bow wave of a speedboat. The shock wave confines high-energy particles shed by the pulsar into an elongated cocoon (red). (X-ray: NASA/CXC/ASTRON/B. Stappers et al.; Optical: AAO/J. Bland-Hawthorn & H. Jones)

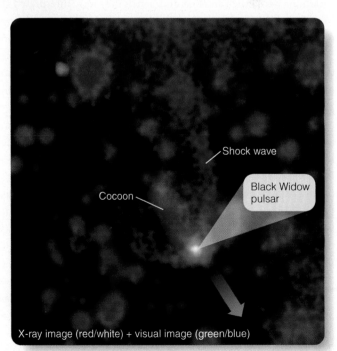

Shock wave

Cocoon

Black Widow pulsar

X-ray image (red/white) + visual image (green/blue)

■ Figure 14-11

(a) The dots in this graph are observations showing that the period of pulsar PSR1257+12 varies from its average value by a fraction of a billionth of a second. The blue line shows the variation that would be produced by planets orbiting the pulsar. (b) As the planets orbit the pulsar, they cause it to wobble by less than 800 km, a distance that is invisibly small in this diagram. (Adapted from data by Alexander Wolszczan)

variations were much smaller; and, when they were interpreted as Doppler shifts, it became evident that the pulsar was being orbited by at least two objects with planet-like masses of 4.1 and 3.8 Earth masses. The gravitational tugs of these planets make the pulsar wobble about the center of mass of the system by no more than 800 km, producing the observed tiny changes in period (Figure 14-11b).

Astronomers greeted this discovery with both enthusiasm and skepticism. As usual, they looked for ways to test the hypothesis. Simple gravitational theory predicts that planets in the same system should interact and slightly modify each other's orbits. When the data were analyzed, that interaction was found, further confirming the existence of the planets. In fact, later data revealed the presence of a third planet with only 1/40 the mass of Earth, about twice the mass of Earth's moon. This illustrates the astonishing precision of studies based on pulsar timing.

Astronomers wonder how a neutron star can have planets. The three planets that orbit PSR B1257+12 are closer to the pulsar than Venus is to the sun. Any planets that orbited a star that closely would have been absorbed or vaporized when the star

expanded to become a supergiant. Furthermore, the supernova explosion would have suddenly reduced the mass of the star and allowed any orbiting planets to escape from their orbits. So how can planets exist there? One suggestion is that these planets are the remains of a stellar companion that was devoured by the neutron star. In fact, PSR B1257+12 spins very fast (161 pulses per second), suggesting that it was spun up in a binary system. However, the Spitzer Space Telescope observing in the infrared has detected a ring of gas and dust around a different rapidly spinning neutron star. If supernova explosions can leave such rings of material behind, then planets could form from the accumulation of matter in the rings.

PSR B1257+12 is not unique. Another planet has been found orbiting a neutron star that is part of a binary system with a white dwarf. Because this system is located in a very old star cluster and contains a white dwarf, astronomers suspect that the planet may be very old, dating back to the formation of that system rather than being debris from the supernova explosion that made the neutron star. Planets probably orbit other neutron stars, and small shifts in the timing of the pulses may eventually reveal their presence.

You can imagine what these worlds might be like. Formed from the remains of elderly stars, they might have chemical compositions richer in heavy elements than Earth. You can imagine visiting these worlds, landing on their surfaces, and hiking across their valleys and mountains. Above you, the neutron star would glitter in the sky, a tiny point of light.

SCIENTIFIC ARGUMENT

Why are neutron stars easier to detect at X-ray wavelengths?
This argument draws together a number of ideas you know from previous chapters. First, recall that a neutron star is very hot because of the heat released when it contracts to a radius of 10 km. It could easily have a surface temperature of 1,000,000 K, and Wien's law (see Chapter 7) tells you that such an object will radiate most intensely at a very short wavelength—X-rays. Normal stars are much cooler and emit only weak X-rays unless they have hot accretion disks. At visual wavelengths, stars are bright, and neutron stars are faint, but at X-ray wavelengths, the neutron stars stand out from the crowd.

Now build a new argument as if you were seeking funds for a research project. **What observations would you make to determine whether a newly discovered pulsar was young or old, single or a member of a binary system, alone or accompanied by planets?**

14-2 Black Holes

YOU HAVE NOW STUDIED white dwarfs and neutron stars, two of the three end states of dying stars. Now it's time to think about the third end state—black holes.

Although the physics of black holes is difficult to discuss without using sophisticated mathematics, simple logic is sufficient to predict that they should exist. The problem is to confirm that they are real. What objects observed in the heavens could be real black holes? More difficult than the search for neutron stars, the quest for black holes has nevertheless met with success.

You can begin by considering a simple question. How fast must an object travel to escape from the surface of a celestial body?

Escape Velocity

Suppose you threw a baseball straight up. How fast must you throw it if it is not to come down? Of course, gravity will always pull back on the ball, slowing it, but if the ball is traveling fast enough to start with, it will never come to a stop and fall back. Such a ball will escape from Earth.

In Chapter 5 you learned that the escape velocity is the initial velocity an object needs to escape from a celestial body (■ Figure 14-12). Whether you are discussing a baseball leaving Earth or a particle escaping a collapsing star, escape velocity depends on two things, the mass of the celestial body and the distance from the center of mass to the escaping object. If the celestial body has a large mass, its gravity is strong, and you need a high velocity to escape; but, if you begin your journey farther from the center of mass, the velocity needed is less. For example, to escape from Earth, a spaceship would have to leave Earth's surface at 11 km/s (25,000 mph), but if you could launch spaceships from the top of a tower 1000 miles high, the escape velocity would be only 10 km/s (22,000 mph).

If you could make an object massive enough or small enough, its escape velocity could be greater than the speed of light. Relativity says that nothing can travel faster than the speed of light, so even photons, which have no mass, would be unable to escape. Such a small, massive object could never be seen because light could not leave it.

Long before Einstein and relativity, the Reverend John Mitchell, a British gentleman astronomer, realized the peculiar consequences of Newton's laws of gravity and motion. In 1783, he pointed out that an object 500 times the radius of the sun but of the same density would have an escape velocity greater than the speed of light. Then, "all light emitted from such a body would be made to return towards it." Mitchell didn't know it, but he was talking about a black hole.

Schwarzschild Black Holes

If the core of a star contains more than 3 solar masses when it collapses, no force can stop it. It cannot stop collapsing when it reaches the density of a white dwarf because degenerate electrons cannot support that weight, and it cannot stop when it reaches the density of a neutron star because not even degenerate neutrons can support that weight. No force remains to stop the object from collapsing to zero radius.

■ **Figure 14-12**

Escape velocity, the velocity needed to escape from a celestial body, depends on mass. The escape velocity at the surface of a very small body would be so low you could jump into space. Earth's escape velocity is much larger, about 11 km/s (25,000 mph).

As an object collapses, its density and the strength of its surface gravity increase. If an object collapses to zero radius, its density and gravity become infinite. Mathematicians call such a point a **singularity**, but in physical terms it is difficult to imagine an object of zero radius. Some theorists believe that a singularity is impossible and that the laws of quantum physics must somehow halt the collapse at some subatomic radius roughly 10^{20} times smaller than a proton. Astronomically, it seems to make little difference.

If the contracting core of a star becomes small enough, the escape velocity in the region of space around it is so large that no light can escape. This means you can receive no information about the object or about the region of space near it. Because it emits no light, such a region is called a **black hole**. If the core of an exploding star collapsed into a black hole, the expanding outer layers of the star could produce a supernova remnant, but the core would vanish without a trace.

To understand black holes, you should consider relativity. In 1916, Albert Einstein published a mathematical theory of space and time that became known as the general theory of relativity. Einstein treated space and time as a single entity called space-time. His equations showed that gravity could be described as a curvature of space-time, and almost immediately the astronomer Karl Schwarzschild found a way to solve Einstein's equations to describe the gravitational field around a single, non-rotating, electrically neutral lump of matter. That solution contained the first general relativistic description of a black hole, and non-rotating, electrically neutral black holes are now known as Schwarzschild black holes. In recent decades, theorists such as Roy Kerr and Stephen Hawking have found ways to apply the sophisticated mathematical equations of the general theory of relativity and quantum mechanics to describe charged, rotating black holes. For this discussion, the differences are minor, and you may proceed as if all black holes were Schwarzschild black holes.

Schwarzschild's solution shows that if matter is packed into a small enough volume, then space-time curves back on itself. Objects can follow paths that lead into the black hole, but no path leads out, so nothing can escape. Because not even light can escape, the inside of the black hole is totally beyond the view of an outside observer. The **event horizon** is the boundary between the isolated volume of space-time and the rest of the universe, and the radius of the event horizon is called the **Schwarzschild radius**, R_S. A collapsing stellar core must shrink inside its Schwarzschild radius to become a black hole (■ Figure 14-13).

Although Schwarzschild's work was highly mathematical, his conclusion is quite simple. The Schwarzschild radius (in meters) depends only on the mass of the object (in kilograms):

$$R_S = \frac{2GM}{c^2}$$

In this simple formula, G is the gravitational constant, M is the mass, and c is the speed of light. A bit of arithmetic shows that a 1-solar-mass black hole has a Schwarzschild radius of 3 km, a 10-solar-mass black hole has a Schwarzschild radius of 30 km, and so on (■ Table 14-1). Even a very massive black hole would not have a very large event horizon.

Every object has a Schwarzschild radius determined by its mass, but not every object is a black hole. For example, Earth has a Schwarzschild radius of about 1 cm, meaning that it could become a black hole if you squeezed it inside that radius. Fortunately, Earth will not collapse spontaneously to become a black hole because the strength of the rock and metal in its interior is sufficient to support its weight. Only exhausted stellar cores more massive than about 3 solar masses can form black holes under the sole influence of their own gravity.

It is a **Common Misconception** to think of black holes as giant vacuum cleaners that will eventually suck in everything in the universe. A black hole is just a gravitational field, and at a reasonably large distance its gravity is no greater than that of a normal object of similar mass. If the sun were replaced by a 1-solar-mass black hole, the orbits of the planets would not change at all. ■ Figure 14-14 illustrates this by representing gravitational fields as curvature of the fabric of space-time. Normal, uncurved space-time is represented by a flat plane, and the presence of a mass such as a star curves the plane to produce a depression. The extreme curvature around a black hole produces a deep funnel-shaped surface in this graphic representation. You can see from the graphs that the gravity of a black hole becomes extreme only when you approach close to it.

Now you can check off another **Common Misconception** that may strike you as silly. Because of special effects in movies and TV, some people think black holes should actually look like funnels. Of course, the graphs of the strength of gravity around black holes look like funnels, but black holes themselves are not shaped like funnels. If you could approach a black hole,

■ **Figure 14-13**

A black hole forms when an object collapses to a small size (perhaps to a singularity) and the escape velocity becomes so great light cannot escape. The boundary of the black hole is called the event horizon because any event that occurs inside is invisible to outside observers. The radius of the black hole R_S is the Schwarzschild radius.

■ **Table 14-1** I **The Schwarzschild Radius**

	Mass ($M_\odot$)	Radius
Star	10	30 km
Star	3	9 km
Star	2	6 km
Sun	1	3 km
Earth	0.000003	0.9 cm

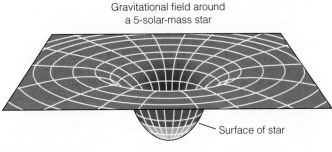

Gravitational field around
a 5-solar-mass star

— Surface of star

Gravitational field around
a 5-solar-mass black hole

To the event horizon →

■ Figure 14-14

If you fell into the gravitational field of a star, you would hit the star's surface before you fell very far. Because a black hole is so small, you could fall much deeper into its gravitational field and eventually cross the event horizon. At a distance, the two gravitational fields are the same.

you might be able to see hot gas swirling inward, but you wouldn't be able to see the black hole itself.

Leaping into a Black Hole

Before you can search for real black holes, you must understand what theory predicts about a black hole. To explore that idea, you can imagine leaping, feet first, into a Schwarzschild black hole.

If you were to leap into a black hole of a few solar masses from a distance of 1 AU, the gravitational pull would not be very large, and you would fall slowly at first. Of course, the longer you fell and the closer you came to the center, the faster you would travel. Your wristwatch would tell you that you fell for about two months by the time you reached the event horizon.

Your friends who stayed behind would see something different. They would see you falling more and more slowly as you came closer to the event horizon because, as explained by general relativity, time slows down in curved space-time. This is known as **time dilation**. In fact, your friends would never actually see you cross the event horizon. To them you would fall more and more slowly until you seemed hardly to move. Generations later, your descendants could focus their telescopes on you and see you still inching closer to the event horizon. You, however, would have sensed no slowdown and would conclude that you had reached the event horizon after about two months.

Another relativistic effect would make it difficult to see you with normal telescopes. As light travels out of a gravitational field, it loses energy, and its wavelength grows longer. This is known as the **gravitational redshift**. Although you would notice no effect as you fell toward the black hole, your friends would need to observe at longer and longer wavelengths to detect you.

While these relativistic effects seem merely peculiar, other effects would be quite unpleasant. If you were falling feet first, you would feel your feet, which would be closer to the black hole, being pulled in more strongly than your head. This is a tidal force, and at first it would be minor. But as you got closer to the black hole, the tidal force would become very large. Another

tidal force would compress you as both your left and your right side fell toward the center of the black hole. For any black hole with a mass like that of a star, the tidal forces would crush you sideways and stretch you lengthwise long before you reached the event horizon (■ Figure 14-15). The friction from such severe distortions of your body would heat you to millions of degrees, and you would emit X-rays and gamma rays. (Needless to say, this would render you inoperative as a thoughtful observer.)

Some years ago a popular book suggested that you could travel through the universe by jumping into a black hole in one place and popping out of another somewhere far across space. That might make for good science fiction, but tidal forces would make it an unpopular form of transportation even if it worked. You would certainly lose your luggage.

Your imaginary leap into a black hole is not frivolous. You now know how to find a black hole: Look for a strong source of X-rays. It may be a black hole into which matter is falling.

The Search for Black Holes

Do black holes really exist? The first X-ray telescopes reached orbit in the 1970s, and that allowed astronomers to begin searching for evidence of black holes. They tried to find one or more objects that were obviously black holes. That very difficult search is a good illustration of how the unwritten rules of science help scientists understand nature (**How Do We Know? 14-1**).

A black hole alone is totally invisible because nothing can escape from its event horizon, but if matter flows into a black hole, it will whirl through an accretion disk and become hot enough to emit X-rays before it reaches the event horizon. An isolated black hole in space will not have much matter flowing into it, but a black hole in a binary system might receive a steady flow of matter transferred from the companion star. This suggests you can search for black holes by looking closely at X-ray binaries.

Some X-ray binaries such as Hercules X-1 contain a neutron star, and they will emit X-rays much as would a binary containing a black hole. You can tell the difference in two ways. If the

■ Figure 14-15

Leaping feet first into a black hole. A person of normal proportions (left) would be distorted by tidal forces (right) long before reaching the event horizon around a typical black hole of stellar mass. Tidal forces would stretch the body lengthwise while compressing it laterally. Friction from this distortion would heat the body to high temperatures.

The first X-ray binary suspected of harboring a black hole was Cygnus X-1, the first X-ray object discovered in the constellation Cygnus. It contains a supergiant B0 star and a compact object orbiting each other with a period of 5.6 days. Astronomers suspected that the X-rays were emitted by matter from the star flowing into the compact object. The object is invisible, but Doppler shifts in the spectrum reveal the motion of the B0 star around the center of mass of the binary. From the geometry of the orbit, astronomers were able to calculate that the mass of the compact object had to be greater than 3.8 solar masses, well above the maximum for a neutron star.

To confirm that black holes existed, astronomers needed a conclusive example, an object that couldn't be anything else. Cygnus X-1 didn't quite pass that test when it was first discovered. Perhaps the B0 star was not a normal star and its portion of the system mass was incorrectly estimated, or perhaps the system contained a third star. Either possibility would distort the analysis. At the time, astronomers could not conclusively show that Cygnus X-1 contained a black hole.

It took years of work to understand Cygnus X-1. Further observations and analysis show that the star has a mass of about 25 solar masses, and the compact object is about 10 times the mass of the sun. Astronomers conclude that matter flows from the B0 star as a strong stellar wind, and much of that matter gets caught in a hot accretion disk about five times larger in diameter than the orbit of Earth's moon. The inner few hundred kilometers of the disk has a temperature of about 2 million Kelvin—hot enough to radiate X-rays (■ Figure 14-16). The evidence is now strong that Cyg X-1 contains a black hole.

As X-ray telescopes have found many more X-ray-emitting objects, the list of black hole candidates has grown to dozens. A few of these objects are shown in ■ Table 14-2. Each candidate is a compact object surrounded by a hot accretion disk in a close X-ray binary system. Some of the binary systems are easier to

compact object emits pulses, you know it is a neutron star because the neutron star has a solid surface relative to which hot spots and beams are anchored and spin into and out of Earth's view. With no solid surface, a black hole would not be able to emit an extended series of regular pulses. Another clue depends on the mass of the object. If the mass of the compact object is greater than about 3 solar masses, it cannot be a neutron star; it must be a black hole.

■ Figure 14-16

The X-ray source Cygnus X-1 consists of a supergiant B0 star and a compact object orbiting each other. Gas from the B0 star's stellar wind flows into the hot accretion disk around the compact object, and the X-rays astronomers detect come from the disk. (Don Dixon/cosmographica.com)

Checks on Fraud in Science

How do you know scientists aren't just making stuff up? The unwritten rules of science make fraud difficult, and the way scientists publish their research makes it almost impossible. Scientists depend on each other to be honest, but they also double-check everything.

For example, all across North America, black-capped chickadees sing the same quick song. Some people say it sounds like *Chick-a-dee-dee-dee,* but others say it sounds like *Hey-sweetie-sweetie-sweetie.* You could invent tables of data and publish a paper reporting that you had recorded chickadees around Ash Lake in northern Minnesota that sing a backward song: *Sweetie-sweetie-sweetie-hey.* Experts of brain development and animal learning would be amazed, and your research might secure you praise from your colleagues, a job offer at a prestigious university, or a generous grant—but only if you could get away with it.

The first step in your scheme would be to publish your results in a scientific journal. Because the journal's reputation rests on the accuracy of the papers it publishes, the editor sends all submitted papers to one or more experts for peer review. Those world experts on chickadees would almost certainly notice things wrong with your made-up data tables. On their recommendation, the editor would probably refuse to publish your paper.

Even if your faked data fooled the peer reviewers, you would probably be found out once the paper was published. Experts on bird song would read your paper and flock to Ash Lake to study the bird songs themselves. By the next spring, you would be found out—and the journal would be forced to publish an embarrassing retraction of your article.

One of the rules of science is that good results must be repeatable. Scientists routinely repeat the work of others, not only to check the results but as a way to start a new research topic. When someone calls a news conference and announces a new discovery, other scientists begin asking, "How does this fit with other observations? Has this been checked? Has this been peer reviewed?" Until a result has been published in a peer-reviewed journal, scientists treat it with extra care. Fraud isn't unheard of in science. But because of peer review and the requirement of repeatability in science, bad research, whether the result of carelessness or fraud, is usually exposed quickly.

Chickadees always sing the same song. Hey-Sweety-Sweety-Sweety. (Steve and Dave Maslowski/Photo Researchers, Inc.)

■ **Table 14-2 | Nine Black Hole Candidates**

Object	Location	Companion Star	Orbital Period	Mass of Compact Object
Cygnus X-1	Cygnus	B0 supergiant	5.6 days	10 $M_\odot$
LMC X-3	Dorado	B3 main-sequence	1.7 days	~10 $M_\odot$
A0620-00	Monocerotis	K main-sequence	7.75 hours	10 ± 5 $M_\odot$
V404 Cygni	Cygnus	K main-sequence	6.47 days	12 ± 2 $M_\odot$
GRO J1655-40	Scorpius	F–G main-sequence	2.61 days	6.9 ± 1 $M_\odot$
QZ Vul	Vulpecula	K main-sequence	8 hours	10 ± 4 $M_\odot$
4U 1543-47	Lupus	A main-sequence	1.123 days	2.7−7.5 $M_\odot$
V4641 Sgr	Sagittarius	B supergiant	2.81678 days	8.7−11.7 $M_\odot$
XTEJ1118+480	Ursa Major	K main-sequence	0.170113 days	>6 $M_\odot$

analyze than others, but, in the end, it has become clear that at least some of these compact objects are clearly too massive to be neutron stars and must be black holes. The evidence is now overwhelming: Black holes really do exist.

Another way to confirm that black holes are real is to search for evidence of their distinguishing characteristic—event horizons—and that search too has been successful. In one study, astronomers selected 12 X-ray binary systems, six of which seemed to contain neutron stars and six of which were thought to contain black holes. Using X-ray telescopes, the astronomers monitored the systems, watching for telltale flares of energy as blobs of matter fell into the accretion disks and spiraled inward. In the six systems thought to contain neutron stars, the astronomers could detect final bursts of energy when the blobs of matter finally impacted the surfaces of the

Black Hole X-Ray Nova

Matter spiraling into a neutron star hits the surface with a detectable burst of energy.

Neutron Star X-Ray Nova

Matter spiraling into a black hole vanishes with no detectable burst of energy.

■ Figure 14-17

Gas spiraling into an accretion disk grows hot; and, as it nears the central object, a strong gravitational redshift makes it appear redder and dimmer. Systems containing a neutron star emit bursts of energy when the gas hits the surface of the neutron star, but such bursts are not seen for systems containing black holes. In those systems, the matter vanishes as it approaches the event horizon. This is direct observational evidence of an event horizon around black holes. (NASA/CXC/SAO)

neutron stars. In the six systems suspected of containing black holes, however, the blobs of matter spiraled inward through the accretion disks and vanished without final bursts of energy. Evidently, those blobs of matter had vanished as they approached the event horizons (■ Figure 14-17). This is dramatic evidence that event horizons are real.

The evidence shows that black holes really do exist. The problem now is to understand how these objects interact with the matter flowing into them through accretion disks to produce high-energy jets and outbursts.

SCIENTIFIC ARGUMENT

If relativistic effects slow time and prevent you from seeing matter cross the event horizon, how can infalling matter disappear without a trace?
This argument brings together observations and theory. Astronomers observed flares when matter hit the surfaces of neutron stars, but observed no flares when matter fell into a black hole. Although time slows near the event horizon, remember the gravitational redshift. Hot matter flowing into a black hole can emit X-rays, but as the matter nears the event horizon, the gravitational redshift lengthens the wavelengths dramatically. The matter vanishes, not because you see it cross the event horizon but because its photons are shifted to undetectably long wavelengths.

Now build a new argument to review a basic principle. **Why does matter become hot as it falls into a black hole?**

14-3 Compact Objects with Disks and Jets

MATTER FLOWING INTO A NEUTRON STAR or a black hole forms an accretion disk, and that can produce some surprising phenomena. Astronomers are just beginning to understand these peculiar effects.

Jets of Energy from Compact Objects

Observations show that some compact objects are emitting jets of gas and radiation in opposite directions. These jets are similar to the bipolar outflows ejected by protostars but much more powerful. You have seen in the X-ray images on page 285 that some young pulsars, including the Crab Nebula pulsar, are ejecting jets of highly excited gas. The Vela pulsar does the same (Figure 14-4). Systems containing black holes can also eject jets. The black hole candidate GRO J1655-40 has been observed at radio wavelengths sporadically ejecting oppositely directed jets at 92 percent the speed of light.

One of the most powerful examples of this process is an X-ray binary called SS 433. Its optical spectrum shows sets of spectral lines that are Doppler shifted by about one-fourth the speed of light, with one set shifted to the red and one set shifted to the blue. Furthermore, the two sets of lines shift back and forth across each other with a period of 164 days. At the time of its discovery, news media reported, with a smirk, that astronomers had discovered an object that was both approaching and receding at a fantastic speed, but astronomers recognized the Doppler shifts as evidence of oppositely directed jets.

Apparently, SS 433 is a binary system in which a compact object (probably a black hole) pulls matter from its companion star and forms an extremely hot accretion disk. Jets of high-temperature gas blast away from the disk in beams aimed in opposite directions. As the disk precesses, it sweeps these beams around the sky once every 164 days, and telescopes on Earth detect light from gas carried outward in both beams. One beam produces a redshift, and the other produces a blueshift.

It's not clear how an accretion disk can produce jets. Accretion disks around neutron stars and black holes are very small, spin fast, and grow very hot. Somehow the hot gas in the disk can emit powerful beams of gas and radiation along the disk's axis of rotation (■ Figure 14-18). The exact process isn't well understood, but it seems to involve magnetic fields that get caught in the accretion disk and are twisted into tightly wound tubes that squirt gas and radiation out of the disk and confine it in narrow beams. You can recognize the geometry of SS 433 in Figure 14-18.

Such pairs of jets are a prototype that illustrates how the gravitational field around a compact object can produce powerful beams of radiation and matter. You will meet this phenomenon again in a later chapter when you study peculiar galaxies.

■ Figure 14-18

In this artist's impression, matter from a normal star flows into an accretion disk around a compact object. Processes in the spinning disk eject gas and radiation in jets perpendicular to the disk. (© 2005, Fahad Sulehria, www.novacelestia.com)

Gamma-Ray Bursts

The Cold War plays a minor part in the story of neutron stars and black holes. In 1963, a nuclear test ban treaty was signed, and by 1968, the United States was able to put a series of satellites in orbit to watch for nuclear tests that were violations of the treaty. A nuclear detonation emits gamma rays, so the satellites were designed to watch for bursts of gamma rays coming from Earth. The experts were startled when the satellites detected about one gamma-ray burst a day coming from space. When those data were finally declassified in 1973, astronomers realized that the bursts might be coming from neutron stars and black holes. These bursts are now known as **gamma-ray bursts** (abbreviated **GRBs**).

The Compton Gamma Ray Observatory reached orbit in 1991 and immediately began detecting gamma-ray bursts at the rate of a few a day. Its observations showed that the intensity of the gamma rays rises to a maximum in seconds and then fades away quickly; a burst is usually over in a few seconds to a minute. Data from the Compton Observatory also showed that the gamma-ray bursts were coming from all over the sky and not from any particular region. This helped astronomers eliminate some hypotheses.

For example, there was a hypothesis that the gamma-ray bursts were being produced by relatively common events involving the stars in our galaxy, but the results from the Compton Observatory eliminated that possibility. If the gamma-ray bursts were produced among stars in our galaxy, you would expect to see them most often along the Milky Way where there are lots of stars. That the bursts occurred all over the sky meant that they were being produced by rare events in distant galaxies.

Gamma-ray bursts are hard to study because they occur without warning and fade so quickly; but, starting in 1997, new satellites in orbit were able to detect gamma-ray bursts. Such studies showed that there are two kinds of gamma-ray bursts. Short bursts last less than 2 seconds, but longer bursts can go on for many seconds. Specialized satellites can detect bursts, quickly determine their location in the sky, and immediately alert astronomers on the ground. When telescopes on Earth swiveled to image the locations of the bursts, they detected fading glows that resembled supernovae (■ Figure 14-19), suggesting that long gamma-ray bursts are produced by a certain kind of supernova explosion.

Theory proposes that a star more massive than some upper limit of about 20 solar masses can exhaust its nuclear fuel and collapse directly into a black hole. Models show that the collapsing star would conserve angular momentum and spin very rapidly, slowing the collapse of the equatorial parts of the star. The poles of the star would fall in quickly, and that would focus beams of intense radiation and ejected gas that would blast out along the axis of rotation. Such an eruption has been called a **hypernova** (■ Figure 14-20). If one of those beams were pointed at Earth, it could produce a powerful gamma-ray burst. Evidently the long gamma-ray bursts are produced by hypernovae.

Short gamma-ray bursts don't seem to be associated with hypernovae. Some repeat, and these repeating bursts seem to be produced by neutron stars with magnetic fields 100 times stronger than that in a normal neutron star. Dubbed **magnetars**, these objects can produce bursts of gamma rays when shifts in the

Visual-wavelength image

Visual-wavelength image

Host galaxy

Visual-wavelength image

■ Figure 14-19

Alerted by gamma-ray detectors on satellites, observers used one of the VLT 8.2-meter telescopes on a mountaintop in Chile to image the location of a gamma-ray burst only hours after the burst. The image at top left shows the fading glow of the eruption. The image at top right, recorded 13 years before, reveals no trace of an object at the location of the gamma-ray burst. The Hubble Space Telescope image at bottom was recorded a year later and reveals a very faint galaxy at the location of the gamma-ray burst. (ESO and NASA)

A Hypernova Explosion

The collapsing core of a massive star drives its energy along the axis of rotation because . . .

the rotation of the star slows the collapse of the equatorial regions.

Within seconds, the remaining parts of the star fall in.

Beams of gas and radiation strike surrounding gas and generate beams of gamma rays.

The gamma-ray burst fades in seconds, and a hot accretion disk is left around the black hole.

■ Figure 14-20

The collapse of the cores of extremely massive stars can produce hypernova explosions, which are thought to be the source of gamma-ray bursts longer than 2 seconds. (NASA/Skyworks Digital)

magnetic field break the crust of the neutron stars—causing "starquakes"—and release large amounts of energy (■ Figure 14-21). One of those objects produced a burst of gamma rays that reached Earth in 1998 and was strong enough to temporarily ionize Earth's upper atmosphere, disrupting radio communication worldwide.

Eruptions on the surfaces of magnetars may be common. Changes in the Cassiopeia A supernova remnant (Figure 13-17) appear to have been caused by an eruption on the central neutron star that occurred about 1953. The Fermi Gamma-Ray

Space Telescope in orbit has detected a neutron star producing rapid-fire eruptions as often as 100 times in 20 minutes. Such eruptions also are thought to be somehow related to starquakes in the crusts of magnetars.

Not all short gamma-ray bursts are produced by magnetars. Some bursts have occurred in parts of distant galaxies where you

■ Figure 14-21

Some neutron stars appear to have magnetic fields up to 1000 times stronger than those in a normal neutron star. These magnetars can produce bursts of gamma rays when shifts in the magnetic field rupture the rigid crust of the neutron star. (NASA/CXC/M. Weiss)

would not expect to find the young, massive stars that produce magnetars or hypernovae, and the afterglows don't resemble fading supernovae. These bursts may be produced by the merger of two neutron stars that orbited around each other, radiated orbital energy as gravitational radiation, and spiraled into each other. Such a merger would produce a violent explosion as the two neutron stars merged to form a black hole.

Other short gamma-ray bursts are probably produced by the merger of a neutron star and a black hole. As these objects spiral into each other, the neutron star is ripped apart and swallowed by the black hole. That could produce a gamma-ray burst, but the burst and its fading afterglow should be different from that produced by the merger of two neutron stars. Astronomers are

now working to distinguish between these two kinds of short gamma-ray bursts.

In 2008 the Swift orbiting telescope detected an intense gamma-ray burst that originated in a galaxy 7.5 billion light years from Earth. The burst was so powerful that for about one minute, its visual-wavelength component was bright enough to see with the unaided eye. If you had been looking directly at it, you would have seen it appear as a star slightly brighter than those in the Little Dipper. Another powerful gamma-ray burst detected by Swift in 2008 originated in a galaxy 12.2 billion light-years away. In spite of the distance, it was one of the brightest gamma-ray bursts ever detected. Astronomers suspect that these bursts were produced by hypernova collapses of massive stars in which one of the jets was aimed directly at Earth.

Could a gamma-ray burst occur near Earth? The nearest known binary pulsar is only about 2000 ly from Earth. If a gamma-ray burst occurred at that distance, the gamma rays would shower Earth with radiation equivalent to a 10,000-megaton nuclear blast, equivalent to a full-scale nuclear war between superpowers. (The largest single bombs ever made were a few tens of megatons.) The gamma rays could create enough nitric oxide in the atmosphere to produce intense acid rain and also would destroy the ozone layer, exposing life on Earth to deadly levels of solar ultraviolet radiation. Gamma-ray bursts can occur relatively near the Earth as often as every few hundred million years and could be one of the causes of the mass extinctions that show up in the fossil record.

Does it surprise you that such astonishing events as merging neutron stars and hypernovae produce something so common that gamma-ray telescopes observe one or more every day? Remember that these events are so powerful they can be detected over very great distances. There may be 30,000 neutron star binaries in each galaxy, and there are billions of galaxies within range of gamma-ray telescopes. Earthlings are treated to the entire observable universe's display of these cosmic catastrophes.

What Are We? Abnormal

Look around. What do you see? A table, a chair, a tree? It's all normal stuff. The world we live in is familiar and comfortable, but astronomy reveals that "normal" isn't normal at all. The universe is, for the most part, utterly unlike anything you have ever experienced.

Throughout the universe, gravity makes clouds of gas form stars, and in turn the stars generate energy through nuclear fusion in their cores, which delays gravity's final

victory. But gravity always wins. You have learned that stars of different masses die in different ways, but you have also discovered that they always reach one of three end states: white dwarfs, neutron stars, or black holes. However strange these compact objects are, they are common. They are normal.

The physics of compact objects is extreme and violent. You are not accustomed to objects as hot as the surface of a

neutron star, and you have never experienced the environment near a black hole, where gravity is so strong it would pull you to pieces.

The universe is filled with things that are so violent and so peculiar they are almost unimaginable, but they are so common they deserve the label "normal." Next time you are out for a walk, look around and notice how beautiful Earth is and recall how unusual it is compared to the rest of the universe.

Summary

▶ When a supernova explodes, the core collapses to very small size. Theory predicts that the collapsing core cannot support itself as a white dwarf if its mass is greater than 1.4 solar masses, the Chandrasekhar limit. If its mass lies between 1.4 solar masses and about 3 solar masses, it can halt its contraction and form a **neutron star (p. 280)**.

▶ A neutron star is supported by the pressure of the degenerate neutrons. Theory predicts that a neutron star should be about 10 km in radius, spin very fast because it conserves angular momentum as it contracts, and have a powerful magnetic field.

▶ **Pulsars (p. 282)**, rapidly pulsing radio sources, were discovered in 1967. The **lighthouse model (p. 282)** explains pulsars as spinning neutron stars that emit beams of radiation from their magnetic poles. As they spin, they sweep the beams around the sky like lighthouses; if the beams sweep over Earth, astronomers detect pulses. The short pulses and the discovery of a pulsar in the supernova remnant called the Crab Nebula were key evidence that pulsars are neutron stars.

▶ A spinning neutron star slows as it radiates its energy into space. Most of the energy emitted by a pulsar is carried away as a **pulsar wind (p. 282)**.

▶ Theory predicts that a neutron star cannot have a mass greater than about 3 solar masses. Dozens of pulsars have been found in binary systems, and those objects allow astronomers to estimate the masses of the neutron stars. Such masses are consistent with the predicted masses of neutron stars.

▶ Observations of the first binary containing two neutron stars revealed that the system is losing orbital energy by emitting **gravitational radiation (p. 286)**.

▶ In some binary systems, mass flows into a hot accretion disk around the neutron star and causes the emission of X-rays. **X-ray bursters (p. 288)** are systems in which matter accumulates on the surface of the neutron star and explodes.

▶ The fastest pulsars, the **millisecond pulsars (p. 288)**, appear to be old pulsars that have been spun up to high speed by mass flowing from binary companions.

▶ Planets have been found orbiting at least one neutron star. They may be the remains of a companion star that was mostly devoured by the neutron star, or they may have formed from a ring of gas and dust left orbiting the neutron star after the supernova explosion.

▶ If the collapsing core of a supernova has a mass greater than 3 solar masses, then it must contract to a very small size—perhaps to a **singularity (p. 291)**, an object of zero radius. Near such an object, gravity is so strong that not even light can escape, and the region is called a **black hole (p. 291)**.

▶ The outer boundary of a black hole is the **event horizon (p. 292)**; no event inside is detectable. The radius of the event horizon is the **Schwarzschild radius, R_S (p. 292)**, amounting to only a few kilometers for a black hole of stellar mass.

▶ If you were to leap into a black hole, your friends who stayed behind would see two relativistic effects. They would see your clock slow relative to their own clock because of **time dilation (p. 293)**. Also, they would see your light redshifted to longer wavelengths because of the **gravitational redshift (p. 293)**.

▶ You would not notice these effects, but you would feel powerful tidal forces that would deform and heat your mass until you grew hot enough to emit X-rays. Any X-rays you emitted before reaching the event horizon could escape.

▶ To search for black holes, astronomers must look for binary star systems in which mass flows into a compact object and emits X-rays. If the mass of the compact object is greater than about 3 solar masses, then the object is presumably a black hole. A number of such objects have been located.

▶ Clues that an X-ray source is caused by accretion into a black hole rather than onto a neutron star are lack of sustained regular pulsations and lack of flares when blobs of material in the accretion disk arrive at the central compact object.

▶ Black holes and neutron stars at the center of accretion disks can eject powerful jets of gas and radiation. Such jets have been detected.

▶ **Gamma-ray bursts (p. 297)** appear to be related to violent events involving neutron stars or black holes. Bursts longer than 2 seconds appear to arise during **hypernovae (p. 297)**, the collapse of massive stars to form black holes.

▶ Some short gamma-ray bursts are produced by shifts in the powerful magnetic fields in a type of pulsar called **magnetars (p. 297)**, whereas other bursts probably represent the merger of binary compact objects such as neutron-star pairs or neutron-star/black-hole pairs.

Review Questions

1. How are neutron stars and white dwarfs similar? How do they differ?
2. Why is there an upper limit to the mass of neutron stars?
3. Why do you expect neutron stars to spin rapidly?
4. If neutron stars are hot, why aren't they very luminous?
5. Why do you expect neutron stars to have a powerful magnetic field?
6. Why did astronomers conclude that pulsars actually could not be pulsating stars?
7. What does the short length of pulsar pulses tell you?
8. How does the lighthouse model explain pulsars?
9. What evidence can you cite that pulsars are neutron stars?
10. Why would astronomers naturally assume that the first discovered millisecond pulsar was relatively young?
11. How can a neutron star in a binary system generate X-rays?
12. If the sun has a Schwarzschild radius, why isn't it a black hole?
13. How can a black hole emit X-rays?
14. What evidence can you cite that black holes really exist?
15. How can mass transfer into a compact object produce jets of high-speed gas? X-ray bursts? Gamma-ray bursts?
16. Discuss the possible causes of gamma-ray bursts.
17. **How Do We Know?** How does peer review make fraud rare in science?

Discussion Questions

1. In your opinion, has the link between pulsars and neutron stars been sufficiently tested to be called a theory, or should it be called a hypothesis? What about the existence of black holes?
2. Why wouldn't an accretion disk orbiting a giant star get as hot as an accretion disk orbiting a compact object?

Problems

1. If a neutron star has a radius of 10 km and rotates 716 times a second, what is the speed of the surface at the neutron star's equator in terms of the speed of light?

2. Suppose that a neutron star has a radius of 10 km and a temperature of 1,000,000 K. How luminous is it? (*Hint:* See Chapter 9.)

3. A neutron star and a white dwarf have been found orbiting each other with a period of 11 minutes. If their masses are typical, what is their average separation? Compare the separation with the radius of the sun, 7×10^5 km. (*Hint:* See Chapter 9.)

4. If the accretion disk around a neutron star has a radius of 2×10^5 km, what is the orbital velocity of a particle at its outer edge? (*Hint:* Use circular velocity, Chapter 5.)

5. What is the escape velocity from the surface of a typical neutron star? How does that compare with the speed of light? (*Hint:* See Chapter 5.)

6. If Earth's moon were replaced by a typical neutron star, what would the angular diameter of the neutron star be as seen from Earth? (*Hint:* Use the small-angle formula, Chapter 3.)

7. If the inner accretion disk around a black hole has a temperature of 1,000,000 K, at what wavelength will it radiate the most energy? What part of the spectrum is this in? (*Hint:* Use Wien's law, Chapter 7.)

8. What is the orbital period of a bit of matter in an accretion disk 2×10^5 km from a 10-solar-mass black hole? (*Hint:* Use circular velocity, Chapter 5.)

9. If an X-ray binary consists of a 20-solar-mass star and a neutron star orbiting each other every 13.1 days, what is their average separation? (*Hint:* See Chapter 9.)

Learning to Look

1. The X-ray image at the right shows the supernova remnant G11.2–0.3 and its central pulsar in X-rays. The blue nebula near the pulsar is caused by the pulsar wind. How old do you think this system is? Discuss the appearance of this system a million years from now.

NASA/McGill, V. Kaspi et al.

2. What is happening in the artist's impression at the right? How would you distinguish between a neutron star and a black hole in such a system?

CXC/M. Weiss

15 | The Milky Way Galaxy

Guidepost

You have traced the life stories of stars from their birth in clouds of gas and dust to their deaths as white dwarfs, neutron stars, or black holes. Now you are ready to step back and view stars in vast communities called galaxies. This chapter focuses on our home galaxy, the Milky Way, and addresses four essential questions:

— **How do you know that you live in a galaxy?**

— **How do you know that our Milky Way is a spiral galaxy, and what are the spiral arms?**

— **What lies at the center of the Milky Way Galaxy?**

— **How did the Milky Way Galaxy form and evolve?**

Discovering the Milky Way Galaxy by answering these questions will be one more step toward understanding the universe as a whole. In the chapters that follow, you will leave your home galaxy and voyage out among the billions of other galaxies that fill the depths of the universe.

The stars of our home galaxy, the Milky Way, rise behind a telescope dome and the highly polished surface of a submillimeter telescope at the La Silla European Southern Observatory in Chile. (ESO and Nico Housen)

The Stars Are Yours.

—JAMES PICKERING

THE STARS ARE YOURS is the title of a popular astronomy book written by James Pickering in 1948. The point of the title is that the stars belong to everyone equally, and you can enjoy the stars as if you owned them.

Next time you admire the night sky, recall that every star you see is part of the star system in which you live. You will learn in this chapter how evidence reveals that you are inside a great wheel of stars, a galaxy. The Milky Way Galaxy is over 80,000 ly in diameter and contains more than 100 billion stars. It is your galaxy because you live in it, but you are also a product of it, because the stars in the Milky Way Galaxy made many of the atoms in your body. You begin this chapter by pondering the notion that the stars belong to you, but when you reach the end of the chapter, you may realize that you also belong to the stars.

15-1 The Discovery of the Galaxy

IT SEEMS ODD to say that astronomers discovered something that is all around us, but it isn't obvious that we live in a galaxy. You might ask, "How do we know what our galaxy is like? Nobody has ever seen it from the outside." Because all scientific knowledge is based on evidence, you need to know a few facts about our galaxy to get started. The more interesting question is, how did astronomers come to know those facts? That story makes up one of the great adventures in astronomy.

The Great Star System

Since ancient times, humanity has been aware of a hazy band of light around the sky (■ Figure 15-1). The ancient Greeks named that band *galaxies kuklos,* the "milky circle." The Romans changed the name to *via lactia,* meaning "milky road" or "milky way." It was not until Galileo used his telescope in 1610 that anyone realized the Milky Way is made of a huge number of stars.

Almost every celestial object you can see with your unaided eyes is part of the Milky Way Galaxy. The only exception viewable from Earth's northern hemisphere is the Andromeda Galaxy (also known as Messier 31, abbreviated M31), which is barely visible as a faint patch of light in the constellation Andromeda.* As you will learn later in this chapter, our galaxy, if seen from a distance, would look similar to the Andromeda Galaxy (Figure 15-1b).

Galileo's telescope revealed that the glowing Milky Way is made up of stars, and later astronomers realized that the sun must

---

*Consult the star charts at the end of this book to locate the Milky Way and the Andromeda Galaxy, labeled M31 on the chart.

be located in a great wheel-shaped cloud of stars, which they called the star system. That star system appears, from our location inside it, as the band of the Milky Way you see encircling the sky. In 1750, Thomas Wright (1711–1786), drawing on the technology of the time, referred to the wheel-shaped star system as the grindstone universe, by analogy with the thick disks of stone used in mills. Wright used the term *universe* because, so far as was known at the time, the Milky Way star system was the entire universe.

The English astronomer Sir William Herschel (1738–1822) and his sister Caroline Herschel (1750–1848) set out to map the three-dimensional distribution of stars in the Milky Way. They assumed that they could see to the outer boundaries of the Milky Way in all directions. They hypothesized that by counting the number of stars that were visible in different directions they could find the relative distances to the edges of the star distribution. If they saw many stars in one direction, they reasoned that the edge of the Milky Way in that direction is far away. If their telescope revealed fewer stars in another direction, they concluded that edge must be closer. Calling their method "star gauging," they counted stars in 683 directions in the sky and outlined a model of the star system. Their data indicated that the stars were arranged in a disk shape with the sun near the center, apparently confirming the "grindstone model" (■ Figure 15-2). In some directions the Herschels saw very few stars, and these "holes in the sky" produced great irregularities along the edge of their diagram, as shown in Figure 15-2.

The model proposed by the Herschels was widely accepted and studied by other astronomers. The Herschels were not able to measure the size of the star system, but later astronomers attempted to do so by various means. Those efforts culminated with the early-20th-century work of Jacobus Kapteyn (1851–1922), who made a comprehensive analysis of the magnitudes, numbers, and motions of Milky Way stars. Kapteyn concluded that the star system's disk is about 10 kiloparsecs in diameter and 2 kiloparsecs thick. A **kiloparsec (kpc)** is 1000 pc.

The Herschels assumed that they could see to the edge of the star system, but that was not correct. They were actually seeing only as far into the Milky Way as the interstellar dust permitted. At the time the Herschels did their work, astronomers did not understand that the interstellar medium blocks the passage of light (see Chapter 10). Because the Herschels counted roughly similar numbers of stars in most directions around the Milky Way, they incorrectly concluded that the sun is near the center of the star system. Furthermore, modern astronomers know that the "holes in the sky" observed by the Herschels are not empty but are actually especially dense interstellar clouds completely blocking the view of stars beyond them.

Imagine an analogous situation, with you standing in a crowd of people within a very dense fog. You might get the mistaken impression that the crowd extends only as far away as you can see in the fog. Your view reaches roughly the same distance in all directions, so you would think you were near the center of

(a) Nearby stars look bright, and people around the world group them into different constellations. Nevertheless, the vast majority of the stars in our galaxy merge into a faintly luminous path that circles the sky, the Milky Way. This artwork shows the location of a portion of the Milky Way near a few bright winter constellations. (See Figure 15-3 and the star charts at the end of this book to locate other sections of the Milky Way in your sky.) (b) This photograph of the Andromeda Galaxy, a spiral galaxy about 2.5 million ly from Earth, shows approximately what our galaxy would look like if you could view it from the same distance. (AURA/NOAO/NSF)

Gemini

Taurus

Orion

Canis Major

a

b   Visual-wavelength image

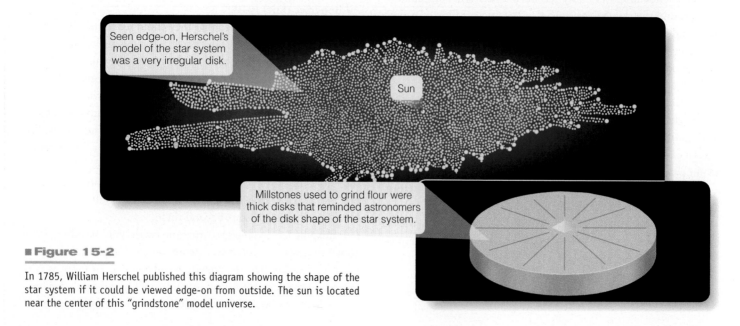

Seen edge-on, Herschel's model of the star system was a very irregular disk.

Sun

Millstones used to grind flour were thick disks that reminded astronomers of the disk shape of the star system.

■ Figure 15-2

In 1785, William Herschel published this diagram showing the shape of the star system if it could be viewed edge-on from outside. The sun is located near the center of this "grindstone" model universe.

the crowd. The real size of the crowd, and the location of its true center, would be unknown to you. Modern astronomers know that the Milky Way Galaxy is much larger than Kapteyn estimated, and that the sun is not at its center. How the human race realized the truth about our location in the universe is an adventure that begins with a woman studying stars that pulsate and leads to a man studying distant star clusters.

Variable Stars and the Size of the Milky Way

Until early in the 20th century no one knew that humanity lives inside a galaxy. That began to change around 1920 when an astronomer named Harlow Shapley (1885–1972) discovered how big our star system really is. Besides being one of the turning points of modern astronomy, Shapley's study illustrates one of the most common techniques in astronomy. If you want to understand how astronomers know things about the universe, then Shapley's story is worth tracing in detail.

You learned in Chapter 12 that star clusters come in two quite different types, open clusters and globular clusters (see page 246). Shapley began his research on the star system by noticing that, although open star clusters are scattered all along the Milky Way, more than half of all globular clusters lie in or near the constellation Sagittarius. The globular clusters seem to be distributed in a great cloud with a center located in the direction of Sagittarius (■ Figure 15-3). Shapley assumed that the orbital motion of these clusters is controlled by the gravitation of the entire star system, and, for that reason, he concluded that the center of the star system could not be near the sun but must lie somewhere toward Sagittarius.

To find the distance to the center of the star system and thus the size of the star system as a whole, Shapley needed to find the distance to the star clusters, but that was difficult to do. The clusters are much too far away to have measurable parallaxes. They do, however, contain variable stars (see Chapter 12), and those were the beacons Shapley needed to find the distances to the clusters.

■ **Figure 15-3**

Nearly half of cataloged globular clusters (red dots) are located in or near Sagittarius and Scorpius. A few of the brighter globular clusters, labeled with their catalog designations, are visible in binoculars or small telescopes. Constellations are shown as they appear above the southern horizon on a summer night as seen from latitude 40° N, typical for most of the United States. (M52: NOAO/AURA/NSF; M19: Doug Williams, N. A. Sharp/NOAO/AURA/NSF)

Open cluster M52 in Cassiopeia

Open clusters lie along the Milky Way all around the sky.

Visual-wavelength image

Globular cluster M19

Globular clusters are scattered over the entire sky but are strongly concentrated toward Sagittarius.

Visual-wavelength image

Calibration

How do you take the temperature of a vat of molten steel? Astronomers often say that Shapley "calibrated" the Cepheids for the determination of distance, meaning that he did all the detailed background work to determine the luminosities of Cepheids. After that, he and other astronomers could use his calibrated period–luminosity diagram to find the distance to other Cepheids without repeating the detailed calibration.

Calibration is actually very common in science because it saves a lot of time and effort. For example, engineers in steel mills must monitor the temperature of molten steel, but they can't dip in a thermometer. Instead, they can use handheld devices that measure the color of molten steel. You recall from Chapter 7 that the color of blackbody radiation is determined by its temperature. Molten steel emits visible and infrared radiation that is nearly perfect blackbody radiation, so the manufacturer can calibrate the engineer's devices to convert the measured color to a temperature displayed on digital readouts. The engineers don't have to repeat the calibration every time; they just point their instrument at the molten steel and read off the temperature. Astronomers have made the same kind of color–temperature calibration for stars.

As you read about any science, notice how calibrations are used to simplify common measurements. But notice, too, how important it is to get the calibration right. An error in calibration can throw off every measurement made with that calibration.

An infrared video camera calibrated to measure temperature allows bakers to monitor the operation of their ovens. (Courtesy of FLIR Systems, Inc.)

Shapley knew about the work of Henrietta Leavitt (1868–1921), who in 1912 had shown that a Cepheid variable star's period of pulsation is related to its brightness. Leavitt worked on stars whose distances were unknown, so she was unable to find their absolute magnitudes (meaning their luminosities), but astronomers realized that the Cepheids could be a powerful tool in astronomy if their true luminosities could be discovered.

Cepheids are giant and supergiant stars and so are relatively rare. None lies close enough to Earth to have a measurable parallax, but their proper motions—slow movements across the sky—can be measured. The more distant a star is, the smaller its proper motion tends to be, so proper motions contain clues to distance. Ejnar Hertzsprung (co-inventor of the H–R diagram) made an early attempt to determine the absolute magnitudes of the Cepheids, but Shapley went further. He found 11 Cepheids with measured proper motions and used a statistical process to find their average distance and thus their average absolute magnitude. Then, he could erase Leavitt's *apparent* magnitudes from the vertical axis of the period–luminosity diagram (see Figure 12-14) and write in *absolute* magnitudes, representing true luminosities. All of the stars in the diagram were thus **calibrated** as standard light sources that astronomers could use to find distances. Calibrations like this one are important tools in science (**How Do We Know? 15-1**).

Finding distances using Cepheid variable stars is so important in astronomy that you should pause to examine the process. Suppose you studied an open star cluster and discovered that it contained a type I Cepheid variable star with a period of 10 days and an average apparent magnitude of 10.5. How far away is the cluster? Using the period–luminosity diagram (see Figure 12-14), you will find that the absolute magnitude of the star must be about −3. Then the distance modulus (see Chapter 9) is:

$$m_V - M_V = 10.5 - (-3) = 13.5$$

You can then solve the magnitude–distance formula to find the distance:

$$d = 10^{(m - M_V + 5)/5}$$

If you substitute the given apparent magnitude and absolute magnitude in the formula, you can determine that the distance is equal to $10^{3.7}$ pc, which equals about 5000 pc. This is one of the most common calculations in astronomy.

Once Shapley had calibrated the period–luminosity relation, he could use it to find the distance to any cluster in which he could identify those types of variable stars. By taking a series of photographic plates over a number of nights, Shapley was able to pick out the variable stars in a cluster, measure their average apparent magnitude, and find their periods of pulsation. Because the periods were very short, he knew the variable stars he saw in the clusters were the lowest-luminosity variable stars (now called RR Lyrae variables). Knowing that, he could read their absolute magnitude off the period–luminosity diagram. With the apparent magnitude and the absolute magnitude, he could calculate the distance to the star cluster.

This worked well for the nearer globular clusters, but variable stars in more distant clusters were too faint for him to detect. Shapley estimated the distances to these more distant clusters by calibrating the diameters of the clusters. For the

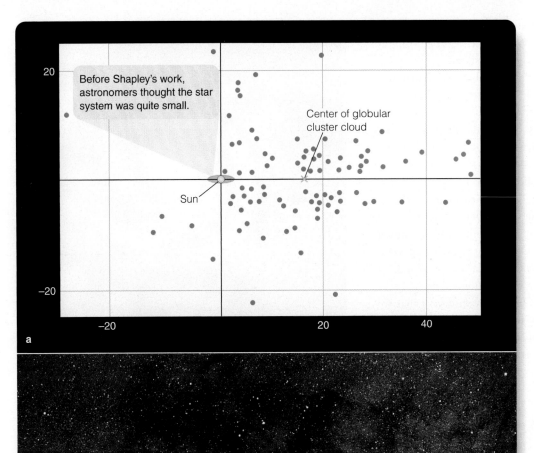

■ **Figure 15-4**

(a) Shapley's study of globular clusters showed that they were not centered on the sun, at the origin of this graph, but rather formed a great cloud centered far away in the direction of Sagittarius. Distances on this graph are given in thousands of parsecs, corresponding to Shapley's original calibration that produced values more than 2 times larger than the modern calibration. (b) Looking toward Sagittarius at visual wavelengths, you see nothing to suggest that this is the center of the galaxy. Interstellar dust and gas block your view. Only the distribution of globular clusters told Shapely the sun lay far from the center of the star system. (Daniel Good)

clusters whose distance he knew, he could use their angular diameters and the small-angle formula (see Chapter 3) to calculate linear diameters in parsecs. He found that the nearby clusters are about 25 pc in diameter, which he assumed is the average diameter of all globular clusters. He then used the angular diameters of the more distant clusters to find their distances. This is another illustration of calibration in astronomy.

Shapley later wrote that it was late at night when he finally plotted the directions and distances to the globular clusters on graph paper and found that, just as he had supposed, they formed a great swarm whose center lay many thousands of light-years in the direction of Sagittarius, confirming his suspicion that the center of the star system was not near the sun but was far away in Sagittarius (■ Figure 15-4). He found the only other person in the building, a cleaning lady, and the two stood looking at his graph as he explained that they were the only two people on Earth who understood that humanity lives, not near the center of a small star system, but in the suburbs of a vast wheel of stars.

How did Shapley avoid the problem of obscuration by interstellar dust that limited earlier work by Kapteyn, the Herschels, and other astronomers? Shapley was able to see the globular clusters at great distances because they lie outside the plane of the galaxy (Figure 15-4) and are not dimmed much by the interstellar medium.

After Shapley's work, astronomers more strongly suspected that some of the faint patches of light visible through telescopes were other star systems. Within a few years they found evidence that the faint patches of light were indeed other galaxies much like our own Milky Way Galaxy. Today the largest telescopes can detect an estimated 100 billion galaxies similar to our own. Our home galaxy is special only in that it is our home.

Shapley's study of star clusters led to the discovery that we live in a galaxy and that the universe is filled with similar galaxies. Like Copernicus, Shapley moved us from the center to the outskirts. A careful analysis of the structure of the galaxy will tell you the details about our real location.

15-2) Structure of the Galaxy

ASTRONOMERS COMMONLY GIVE the diameter of our galaxy as approximately 25 kpc, or 80,000 ly, and place the sun about two-thirds of the way from the center to the edge (■ Figure 15-5). Note that this is only the diameter of the easily detected part of our galaxy. Later in this chapter you will learn that the entire galaxy, some parts of which are not easy to observe, is much larger than 25 kpc in diameter.

The disk of the galaxy is often referred to as the **disk component**. It contains most of the galaxy's stars and nearly all of its gas and dust. Because the disk is home to the giant molecular clouds within which stars form (see Chapter 11), nearly all star formation in our galaxy takes place in the disk. Most of the stars in the disk are middle- to lower-main-sequence stars like the sun, a few are red giants and white dwarfs, and fewer still are brilliant blue O and B stars. Although those hot, massive stars are rare, they are so luminous that they provide much of the light from the disk.

Although astronomers can survey the locations and distances of the stars, they cannot cite a single number for the thickness of the disk because it lacks sharp boundaries. Also, the thickness of the disk depends on the kind of object studied. Stars like the sun, with ages of a few billion years, lie within about 500 pc above and below the central plane. In comparison, the youngest stars, including the O and B stars and the gas and dust from which these young stars form, are confined to a thin disk extending only about 50 pc above and below the plane (■ Figure 15-6). In proportion to its diameter

■ Figure 15-5

An artist's conception of our Milky Way Galaxy, seen face-on and edge-on. Note the position of the sun and the distribution of globular clusters in the halo. Hot blue stars light up the spiral arms. Only the inner halo is shown here. At this scale, the entire halo would be larger than a dinner plate. (©2003, 2004 Three Rivers Foundation)

of about 25 kpc, the disk of the galaxy is thinner than a thin pizza crust.

The disk of the galaxy contains both stellar associations and open star clusters. Associations are groups of 10 to a few hundred stars so widely scattered in space that their mutual gravity cannot hold them permanently together. From the turnoff points in their H–R diagrams (see Chapter 12), you can tell that they are very young groups of stars. The stars move together through space (■ Figure 15-7) because they formed from a single interstellar cloud and haven't had time to wander apart yet since they formed.

The second kind of cluster in the disk is the open cluster (see Figure 15-3), a group of 100 to a few thousand stars in a region about 25 pc in diameter. Because they have more stars in less space than associations, open clusters are more firmly

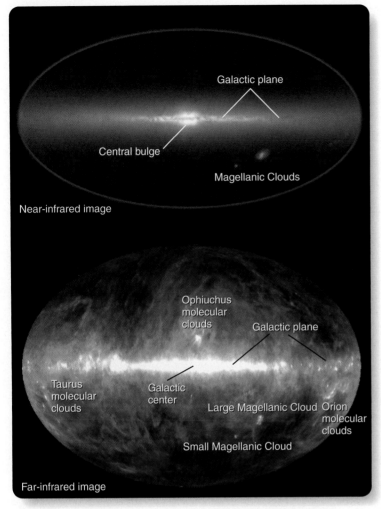

In these infrared images, the entire sky has been projected onto ovals with the center of the galaxy at the center. The central plane of the Milky Way extends from left to right. At near-infrared wavelengths, the central bulge is prominent, and dust clouds block your view. At longer wavelengths, the dust emits blackbody radiation and glows brightly. (Near-IR: 2MASS; Far-IR: DIRBE image courtesy Henry Freudenreich)

bound by gravity. Although they lose stars occasionally, they can survive for a long time, and the turnoff points in their H–R diagrams give ages from a few million to a few billion years.

If you look "up" or "down," out of the galaxy's disk, you are looking away from the dust and gas, so you can see into the galaxy's **halo**, a spherical cloud of stars and star clusters that contains almost no gas and dust. Because the halo contains no dense gas clouds, it cannot make new stars. Halo stars are old, cool, lower-main-sequence stars; red giants; and white dwarfs. It is difficult to judge the extent of the halo, but it could have as much as 10 times the diameter of the visible disk.

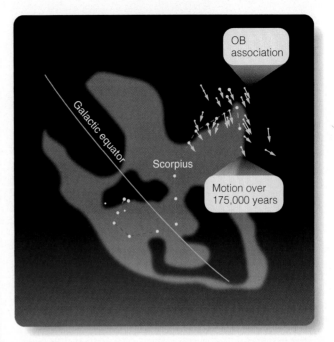

Figure 15-7

Many of the stars in the constellation Scorpius are members of an OB association that evidently formed recently from a single cloud of gas. As the stars orbit the center of our galaxy, they are moving together southwest along the Milky Way.

Around the center of our galaxy lies the **central bulge**, a flattened cloud of billions of stars about 6 kpc in diameter (see Figure 15-5). Like the halo, it contains little gas and dust. Astronomers often refer to the halo and the central bulge together as the **spherical component** of the galaxy. The central bulge is the most crowded part of the spherical component. Visible above and below the plane of the galaxy and through gaps in the obscuring dust, the central bulge contains mostly stars that are old and cool like the stars in the halo.

The halo includes roughly 200 globular clusters, each of which contains 50,000 to a million stars in a sphere a few tens of parsecs in diameter (refer again to Figure 15-3). Because they contain so many stars in such a small region, the clusters hold together very well gravitationally and have survived for billions of years. From the turnoff points in their H–R diagrams, you can tell their average age is about 11 billion years.

Orbital motions are quite different in the two components of the galaxy. Disk stars follow nearly circular orbits that lie in the plane of the galaxy (■ Figure 15-8a). Halo stars and globular clusters, however, follow highly elongated orbits tipped steeply to the plane of the disk (Figure 15-8b). Although the diagram shows these orbits as elliptical, the gravitational influence of the thick bulge forces them into curves that haven't had time to wander apart yet. The dramatic difference between the motions of halo stars and disk stars will be important evidence when you consider the formation of the galaxy later in this chapter.

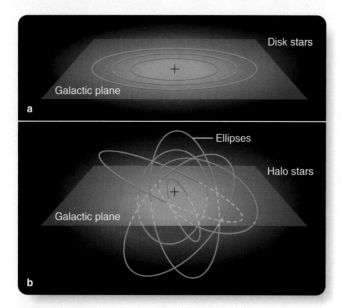

■ Figure 15-8

(a) Stars in the galactic disk have nearly circular orbits that lie in the plane of the galaxy. (b) Stars in the halo have randomly oriented, highly eccentric, elongated orbits.

From the shape and size of our galaxy, astronomers conclude that we live in a spiral galaxy (■ Figure 15-9). The most impressive features of these disk galaxies are the spiral arms—long spiral patterns of bright stars, HII regions, star clusters, and clouds of gas and dust. The sun is located near the inside edge of one of these spiral arms. You will see later in this chapter how astronomers can observe the spiral arms in our own galaxy.

This analysis of the components of our galaxy may leave you wondering about one critical question: How much matter does our galaxy contain? To answer that question, you can measure our galaxy's rotation.

The Mass of the Galaxy

To find the mass of an object, astronomers must observe the motion of another object orbiting it, just as in a binary star system. Humans don't live long enough to see stars move significantly along their orbits around the galaxy, but astronomers can observe the radial velocities, proper motions, and distances of stars and then calculate the sizes and periods of their orbits. The results can reveal the mass of the galaxy.

Stars in the disk of the galaxy follow nearly circular orbits that lie in the plane of the disk (look again at Figure 15-8a). By observing the radial velocities of stars and other objects in various directions, astronomers conclude that the sun orbits the center of our galaxy at about 220 km/s, moving in the direction of Cygnus. The evidence suggests the sun's orbit is nearly circular, so given the distance to the center of our galaxy, 8.0 kpc, you can find the circumference of the sun's orbit by multiplying by 2π. If you divide the circumference of its orbit by its orbital velocity, you will discover that the sun has an orbital period of about 220 million years.

■ Figure 15-9

Our galaxy resembles the spiral galaxies visible through large telescopes. (a) Seen edge-on, spiral galaxies have central bulges and dust-filled disks. (Todd Boroson/NOAO/AURA/NSF) (b) Seen face-on, the spiral arms are dramatically outlined by hot O and B stars, emission nebulae, and dust. (ESO)

When you studied binary stars in Chapter 9, you saw that the total mass (in solar masses) of a binary star system equals the cube of the separation of the stars a (in AU) divided by the square of the period P (in years):

$$M = \frac{a^3}{P^2}$$

You can use the same equation here to find the mass of the galaxy. The radius of the sun's orbit around the galaxy is about 8000 pc, and each parsec contains 2.06×10^5 AU. Multiplying, you find that the radius of the sun's orbit is 1.65×10^9 AU. The orbital period is 220 million years, so the mass is:

$$M = \frac{(1.65 \times 10^9)^3}{(220 \times 10^6)^2} = 0.93 \times 10^{11} \, M_\odot$$

This is only a rough estimate because it does not include any mass lying outside the orbit of the sun. Allowing for that overlooked mass yields a lower limit to the total mass for our galaxy of at least 4×10^{11} (four hundred billion) solar masses.

The rotation of our galaxy is actually the orbital motion of each of its stars around the center of mass. Stars at different distances from the center revolve around the center of the galaxy with different periods, so stars starting near each other will draw apart as time passes (■ Figure 15-10), a situation called differential rotation. (Recall that differential rotation was first defined regarding the sun in Chapter 8.)

To fully describe the rotation of our galaxy, astronomers graph orbital velocity versus radius to produce a **rotation curve** (■ Figure 15-11). If all of the mass of the galaxy were concentrated near its center, you would expect to see orbital velocities decrease as you move away from the center. That is what you see in our solar system, where nearly all of the mass is concentrated in the sun. For that reason this is called **Keplerian motion**, referring to Kepler's laws. In contrast, the best observations of the rotation curve of the Milky Way show that orbital velocities in the outer disk are constant or even increasing with distance from the center of the galaxy. Those high orbital velocities indicate that the larger orbits enclose more mass and imply that our galaxy has much more mass than is contained within the radius of the sun's orbit.

■ Figure 15-10

The differential rotation of the galaxy means that stars at different distances from the center have different orbital periods. In this example, the star just inside the sun's orbit has a shorter period and pulls ahead of the sun, while the star outside falls behind.

Both observational evidence and mathematical models show that the extra mass lies in an extended halo sometimes called a **galactic corona** that may extend up to 10 times farther than the edge of the visible disk and could contain more than a trillion (10^{12}) solar masses. Most of that mass is invisible, neither emitting nor absorbing light, so astronomers refer to it as **dark matter**. Some of the mass in the galactic corona is made up of low-luminosity stars and white dwarfs, but much of the mass must be some other form of matter. You will learn more about the problem of dark matter in the following two chapters. The nature of dark matter is one of the fundamental unknowns in modern astronomy.

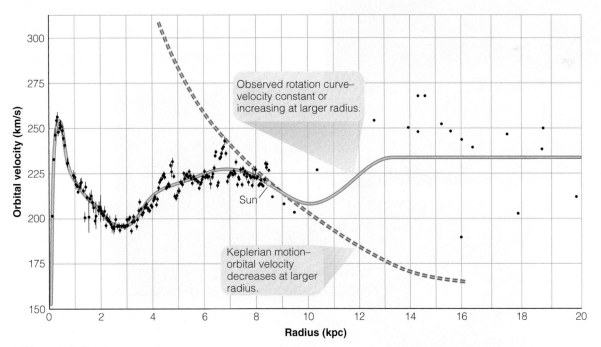

■ Figure 15-11

The rotation curve of our galaxy is plotted here as orbital velocity versus radius. Data points show measurements made by radio telescopes. Observations outside the orbit of the sun are much more uncertain, and the data points scatter widely. Orbital velocities do not decline outside the orbit of the sun, as you would expect if most of the mass of the galaxy were concentrated toward the center (Keplerian motion). Rather, the curve is approximately flat at great distances, suggesting that the galaxy contains significant mass outside the orbit of the sun. (Adapted from a diagram by Françoise Combes)

15-3) Spiral Arms and Star Formation

THE MOST STRIKING FEATURE of galaxies like the Milky Way is their patterns of spiral arms that wind outward through the disk. These arms contain swarms of hot, blue stars; clouds of dust and gas; and young star clusters. The young objects suggest that the spiral arms involve star formation, but, as you try to understand the spiral arms, you need to consider two problems. First, how can anyone be sure our galaxy has spiral arms if interstellar dust obstructs our view? Second, why doesn't the differential rotation of the galaxy destroy the arms? The solution to both problems involves star formation.

Tracing the Spiral Arms

As you have already learned, O and B stars are often found in associations and are very luminous. Thus, they are easy to detect across great distances. Unfortunately, at those great distances their parallax is too small to measure, so their distances must be found by other means, usually by spectroscopic parallax (see Chapter 9). Astronomers find that OB associations are not located randomly but lie along segments of three spiral arms near the sun (■ Figure 15-12). Those arms have been named for the

■ **Figure 15-12**

(a) Nearby young O and B stars in our galaxy fall along bands that appear to be segments of spiral arms. (b) Many of the galaxies in the sky are disk shaped like our galaxy, and most of those galaxies have spiral arms. (c) Images of other galaxies show that spiral arms are marked especially by hot luminous stars and emission nebulae that must be very young. This should make you suspect that spiral arms are related to star formation. (Images: NASA, Hubble Heritage Team)

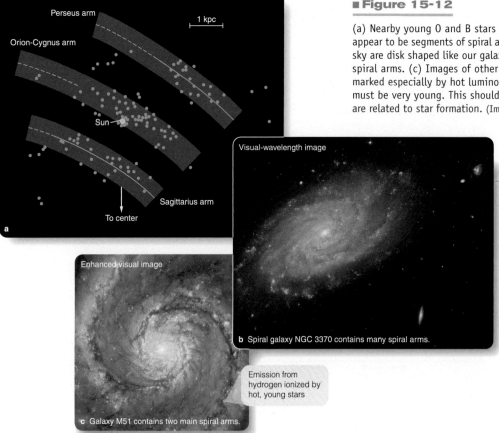

Perseus arm

Orion-Cygnus arm

1 kpc

Sun

Sagittarius arm

To center

a

Visual-wavelength image

b Spiral galaxy NGC 3370 contains many spiral arms.

Enhanced visual image

Emission from hydrogen ionized by hot, young stars

c Galaxy M51 contains two main spiral arms.

prominent constellations through which they pass. Astronomers can use infrared and radio telescopes to penetrate the interstellar dust and gas, locate more distant OB associations, and trace the spiral arms even farther.

Objects used to map spiral arms are called **spiral tracers**. Aside from OB associations, spiral tracers include young open star clusters, clouds of hydrogen ionized by hot stars (emission nebulae), and certain higher-mass variable stars. Notice that all spiral tracers are young objects, formed recently, astronomically speaking. O stars, for example, live for only a few million years. If their orbital velocity is about 200 km/s, they cannot move more than about 500 pc in their lifetimes. This is less than the width of a spiral arm. Because they don't live long enough to move away from the spiral arms, they must have formed there.

Studies of other galaxies show that their spiral arms are also marked by hot blue stars and other spiral tracers, as in our galaxy (Figure 15-12c). The youth of spiral tracers is an important clue about spiral arms. Obviously spiral arms are associated with star formation. Before you can follow this clue, you need to extend your map of spiral arms to show the entire galaxy.

Radio Maps of Spiral Arms

The dust that blocks the view at visual wavelengths is transparent to radio waves because radio wavelengths are much larger than the diameter of the dust particles. If you point a radio telescope at a section of the Milky Way, you will receive signals from gas clouds along your line of sight in spiral arms at various distances across the galaxy. Signals from different clouds can be separated by measuring the Doppler shifts of the spectral lines.

Radio astronomers use the strong spectral line emission from carbon monoxide (CO) to map the location of giant molecular clouds in the plane of the galaxy. Recall from Chapter 11 that those clouds are sites of active star formation. Maps constructed from such observations reveal that the giant molecular clouds are located along the spiral arms (■ Figure 15-13).

Observing at a wavelength of 21 cm allows detection of atomic hydrogen (see Figures 10-6 and 10-7), warmer than the material in molecular clouds (■ Figure 15-14). Just as for the molecular clouds, analysis of the radial velocity data requires that astronomers start with estimates of the orbital velocities at different distances from the center of the galaxy. Because those velocities are not precisely known and because turbulent motions in the gas distort the radial velocities, the atomic hydrogen map doesn't trace a perfect spiral pattern. In the direction toward the center of the galaxy there is an additional problem. There, the orbital motions of gas clouds are perpendicular to the line of

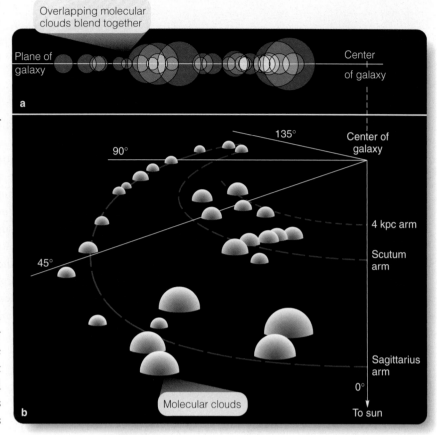

■ **Figure 15-13**

(a) At the wavelength emitted by the CO molecule, astronomers find many molecular clouds along the Milky Way, but the clouds overlap in a confusing jumble. By using a model of the rotation of the galaxy and the radial velocities of the clouds, radio astronomers can estimate the distances to each cloud and use them to map spiral arms. (b) This map represents the view from a point 2 kpc directly above the sun. The molecular clouds, shown here as hemispheres extending above the plane of our galaxy, are located along spiral arms. Angle labels indicate galactic longitudes. (Adapted from a diagram by T. M. Dame, B. G. Elmegreen, R. S. Cohen, and P. Thaddeus)

sight, and all of the radial velocities are zero. That is why the map in Figure 15-14 is empty in the wedge-shaped region directly toward the center.

Radio maps combined with studies at infrared and visible wavelengths can be used to paint a picture of our galaxy viewed from the inside. Clearly we live in a spiral galaxy, but the spiral pattern appears to be slightly irregular, with many branches and gaps. The stars you see in Orion, for example, appear to be in a detached segment of a spiral arm, referred to as a "spur."

In addition to helping map the arrangement of spiral arms, infrared observations indicate that the central bulge of our galaxy is not a sphere but rather an elongated bar pointing partially away from Earth. The spiral arms may stem from a ring that encloses this bar. In the next chapter, you will see that such

This 21-cm radio map of our galaxy confirms that concentrations of neutral hydrogen gas lie approximately in a spiral, but the pattern is complex and suggests branches and spurs. (Adapted from a radio map by Gart Westerhout)

structures are common in other galaxies. By combining observations of our own galaxy with studies of other galaxies, astronomers can construct a best guess at what the Milky Way Galaxy might look like viewed from outside (■ Figure 15-15).

One important fact revealed by the radio maps is that spiral arms are regions of higher gas density. Spiral tracers tell you that the arms contain young objects, so you suspect they must also have active star formation. Radio maps confirm your suspicion by telling you that the material needed to make stars is abundant and concentrated in spiral arms.

■ **Figure 15-15**

(a) This model of our galaxy is based on far-infrared observations of dust and includes four spiral arms with no branches springing from a ring around a central bar. (Courtesy Henry Freudenreich) (b) This artist's impression of a two-armed model is based on observations with the Spitzer infrared space telescope. Notice the larger central bar. (NASA/JPL-Caltech/R. Hurt, SSC)

The Spiral Density Wave Theory

Just what are spiral arms? You can be sure they are not physically connected structures like bands of magnetic field that hold the gas in place. If they were, the differential rotation of the galaxy would destroy them within just a few hundred million years, winding them up and tearing them apart like paper streamers caught on the wheel of a speeding car. Yet spiral arms are common in galaxies (■ Figure 15-16), so they must last for billions of years.

Astronomers conclude that spiral arms are dynamically stable—they retain the same appearance even though the gas, dust, and stars in them are constantly changing. To see how this works, think of the traffic jam behind a slow-moving truck. Seen from an airplane, the traffic jam would be stable, moving slowly down the highway. But you could watch an individual car approach from behind, slow down, wait its turn, finally reach the front of the jam, pass the truck, and resume speed. The individual cars in the jam are constantly changing, but the traffic jam itself is a dynamically stable shape, moving at its own speed along the highway.

In the **density wave theory**, the galaxy's spiral arms are dynamically stable regions of compression that move slowly around the galaxy, just as the truck moves slowly down the highway. Gas clouds moving at orbital velocity around the galaxy overtake the slow-moving arms from behind and slam into the gas already in the arms. The sudden compression of the gas can trigger the collapse of the gas clouds and the formation of new stars (see Chapter 11). Newly formed stars and the remaining gas eventually move on through the arm and emerge from the front of the slow-moving arm to resume their travels around the galaxy (■ Figure 15-17).

The Spiral Density Wave

Orbiting gas clouds overtake the spiral arm from behind.

The compression of a gas cloud triggers star formation.

Massive stars are highly luminous and light up the spiral arm.

The most massive stars die quickly.

Low-mass stars live long lives but are not highly luminous.

Visual-wavelength image

■ Figure 15-16

Typical of spiral galaxies, M83 has a two-armed spiral pattern with prominent dust lanes and bright O and B stars along the arms. This galaxy's spiral also contains branches and spurs. (European Southern Observatory)

■ Figure 15-17

According to the spiral density wave theory, star formation occurs as gas clouds pass through spiral arms.

Science depends on evidence, so you should ask what evidence astronomers have that spiral arms are caused by spiral density waves. Spiral tracers are the key. Stars of all masses are forming in spiral arms, but the O and B stars live such short lifetimes that they die before they can move out of the spiral arm. These massive, high-luminosity stars, along with gas and dust, confirm that spiral arms are sites of star formation. Lower-mass stars, such as the sun, can't be used as spiral tracers. They also form in spiral arms, but, because they live so long, they leave the arms in which they were born and circle the galaxy many times. The sun probably formed as part of an association in a star-forming region within a spiral arm almost 5 billion years ago, escaped from that association, and has circled the galaxy about 20 times, passing through spiral arms many times. Therefore, plotting the locations of sunlike stars does not reveal the spiral pattern because such stars live too long.

Giant molecular clouds and thick dust in the arms (■ Figure 15-18) are evidence that material is compressed in the arms and fostering active star formation. These clouds can convert up to 30 percent of their mass into stars. The Orion complex and the Ophiuchus dark cloud are examples of regions filled with infrared protostars (see Chapter 11). Such a cloud can form stars for 10 to 100 million years before it is disrupted by radiation pressure and winds from the most massive new stars. At their normal speeds, clouds need about that long to pass through a spiral arm.

The evidence seems to fit the spiral density wave theory well, but the theory has two problems. First, how does the complicated spiral disturbance begin, and how is it sustained? Computer models indicate that spiral density waves should slowly die out in about a billion years, so something must regenerate the spiral wave. Other models show that the disk of the galaxy is naturally unstable to (affected by) certain types of disturbances, just as a guitar string is unstable to certain vibrations. Any sudden jostling—the rumble of a passing truck, for example—can set the string vibrating at its natural frequencies. Similarly, minor fluctuations in the galaxy's disk, such as supernova explosions, might be able to regenerate the spiral waves.

Another possibility is that large gravitational perturbations can generate a spiral density wave. As you learned earlier, observations show that the center of our galaxy is not a sphere but a bar. The rotation of that bar could continuously disturb the disk of the galaxy and stimulate the formation of a spiral density wave. A close encounter with a passing galaxy could also stimulate a spiral pattern.

The second problem for the density wave theory involves the spurs and branches observed in the arms of our own and other galaxies. Computer models of density waves produce regular, simple two-armed spiral patterns. Some galaxies, called **grand-design** galaxies, do indeed have symmetric two-armed patterns, but others do not (■ Figure 15-19). Some galaxies have a great many short spiral segments, giving them a fluffy appearance, but no overall grand design. These galaxies have been termed **flocculent**, meaning "woolly." Our galaxy seems to be intermediate between the extremes of flocculent versus grand-design. How can astronomers explain these variations in the spiral pattern? Perhaps the answer lies in a process that sustains star formation once it begins.

■ **Figure 15-18**

Besides bright stars, spiral arms also contain clouds of gas and dust. In the Andromeda Galaxy, dust clouds glow brightly in the infrared and outline the spiral arms. (NASA/JPL-Caltech/K. Gordon and NOAO/AURA/NSF)

Self-Sustaining Star Formation

Star formation is a critical process in the creation of spiral arms. It not only makes spiral arms visible but may also shape the spiral pattern itself.

Star formation can control the shape of spiral patterns if the birth of stars in a cloud of gas is able to renew itself by triggering the formation of more new stars. Consider a newly formed star cluster with a single massive star. There are several ways in which this massive star can compress the surrounding gas to trigger more star formation: by sending out strong winds and bipolar jets as it forms, by the pressure of its intense radiation (■ Figure 15-20), or by the explosive expansion caused by its eventual death as a supernova. Examples of such **self-sustaining star formation** have been found. The Orion complex, consisting of the Great

M100

a

NGC 300

b

Visual-wavelength images

■ **Figure 15-19**

(a) Some galaxies are dominated by two spiral arms; but, even in these galaxies, minor spurs and branches are common. Spiral density waves can generate the two-armed, grand-design pattern, but self-sustained star formation may be responsible for the irregularities. (b) Many spiral galaxies do not appear to have two dominant spiral arms. Spurs and branches suggest that star formation is proceeding rapidly in such galaxies. (Anglo-Australian Telescope Board)

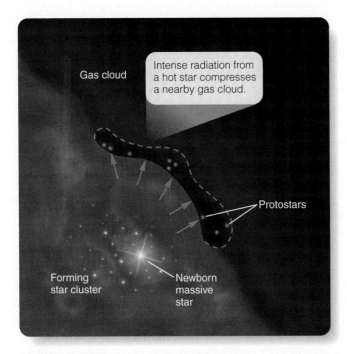

Gas cloud

Intense radiation from a hot star compresses a nearby gas cloud.

Protostars

Forming star cluster

Newborn massive star

■ **Figure 15-20**

Most stars in a star cluster are too small and too cool to affect nearby gas clouds; but, once a massive star forms, it becomes so hot and so luminous its radiation can push gas away and compress a nearby gas cloud. In the densest regions of the compressed cloud, new stars can begin forming.

Nebula in Orion and the star formation buried deep in the dark interstellar clouds behind the nebula, is such a region (see Chapter 11).

Self-sustaining star formation can produce growing clumps of new stars, and the differential rotation of the galaxy can drag the inner edge ahead and let the outer edge lag behind to produce a cloud of star formation shaped like a segment of a spiral arm: a spur (■ Figure 15-21). Mathematical models of galaxies filled with such segments of spiral arms do have a spiral appearance but without the strong two-armed pattern of the grand-design spirals. Astronomers suspect that a spiral density wave can generate beautiful two-armed spiral patterns, but the self-sustaining star formation process produces the branches and spurs so prominent in flocculent galaxies.

The discussion of star formation in spiral arms illustrates the understanding of nature in terms of processes. The spiral density wave creates graceful arms, but it is the star formation in the arms that makes them stand out so prominently. Self-sustaining star formation can act in some galaxies to modify the spiral arms and produce branches and spurs. In some galaxies, it can make

Self-Sustaining Star Formation

Differential rotation drags the inner edge of a gas cloud ahead of its outer edge.

Center of galaxy

A cloud can become elongated by continuing differential rotation.

Star formation in a gas cloud can produce massive stars whose high luminosity . . .

and supernova explosions can compress surrounding gas and trigger more star formation.

If star formation continues long enough, a cloud can be elongated into a spiral segment.

■ Figure 15-21

Self-sustaining star formation may be able to produce long clouds of young stars that look like segments of spiral arms.

the spiral pattern flocculent. By searching out and understanding the details of such natural processes, astronomers can begin to understand the overall structure and evolution of the universe we live in.

15-4 The Nucleus

THE MOST MYSTERIOUS REGION of our galaxy is its very center, the nucleus. At visual wavelengths, this region is totally hidden by dust that dims the light it emits by 30 magnitudes. If a trillion (10^{12}) photons of light left the center of the galaxy on a journey to Earth, only one of those photons would make it through the dust. Consequently, visual-wavelength images reveal nothing about the nucleus. Observations at infrared and radio wavelengths can see through the interstellar material, and those images show a region of tremendously crowded stars orbiting in the nucleus at high velocity. To understand what is happening in the innermost regions of our galaxy, you need to carefully compare observations and hypotheses.

Observations of the Galactic Nucleus

If you look up at the Milky Way on a dark night, you might notice a slight thickening in the direction of the constellation Sagittarius, but nothing specifically identifies this as the direction of the heart of the galaxy. Even Shapley's study of globular clusters identified the location only approximately. The first complete infrared map of the central bulge made by Eric Becklin in 1968 showed the location of intense radiation where the stars are most crowded together, the gravitational core of the galaxy. High-resolution radio maps of that stellar center revealed a complex collection of radio sources, with one, **Sagittarius A*** (abbreviated Sgr A* and usually pronounced "sadge A-star"), lying at the exact location of the galactic nucleus.

Observations show that Sgr A* is less than 1 AU in diameter but is a strong source of radio energy as well as X-ray emission (short-wavelength X-rays can also penetrate interstellar dust and gas). The tremendous amount of infrared radiation coming from the central area appears to be produced by crowded stars and by dust warmed by those stars. But what could be as small as Sgr A* and produce so much radio and X-ray energy?

Read **Sagittarius A*** on pages 320–321 and notice three important points:

1 Observations at radio and infrared wavelengths reveal complex structures near Sgr A* caused by magnetic fields and by rapid star formation. Supernova remnants show that massive stars have formed there recently and exploded at the ends of their lives.

2 The center is crowded. Tremendous numbers of stars heat the dust, which emits strong infrared radiation.

3 Finally, there is evidence that Sgr A* is a supermassive black hole into which gas is flowing.

A supermassive black hole is an exciting idea, but scientists must always be aware of the difference between adequacy and necessity. A supermassive black hole is adequate to explain the observations, but is it necessary? Could there be other explanations? For example, some astronomers have suggested that gas flowing inward could trigger tremendous bursts of star formation. Such hypotheses have been considered and tested against the evidence, but none appears to be adequate to explain all the observations. So far, the only hypothesis that seems adequate is that our galaxy's nucleus is home to a supermassive black hole.

Meanwhile, observations are allowing astronomers to refine their models. For instance, Sgr A* is not as bright in X-rays as it should be if it has a hot accretion disk with matter constantly flowing into the black hole. Observations of X-ray and infrared flares lasting only a few hours suggest that mountain-size blobs of matter may occasionally fall into the black hole and be ripped apart and heated by tides. But the black hole seems to be mostly dormant, lacking a fully developed hot accretion disk because little matter is flowing into it at the present time.

Such a supermasssive black hole could not be the remains of a single dead star. It contains too much mass. It probably formed when the galaxy first formed over 13 billion years ago. In later chapters you will see that such supermassive black holes are found at the centers of many galaxies.

SCIENTIFIC ARGUMENT

Why do astronomers think the center of our galaxy contains a large mass?
Because scientific arguments usually hinge on evidence, they often involve discussions of measurement—one of the keys to science. The best way to measure the mass of an astronomical object is to watch something orbit around it. Then, you can use Kepler's third law to find the mass inside the orbit. Because of gas and dust, astronomers can't see to the center of our galaxy at visual

wavelengths, but infrared observations can detect individual stars orbiting Sgr A*. The star S0-2 has been particularly well observed, but a number of stars can be followed as they orbit the center. The sizes and periods of these orbits, interpreted using Kepler's laws, reveal that Sgr A* contains roughly 4 million solar masses.

Now build a new argument to analyze a different observation. **The strong infrared radiation at wavelengths longer than 4 microns (4000 nm) implies vast numbers of stars crowded into the center. Why?**

15-5) Origin and History of the Galaxy

JUST AS DINOSAURS LEFT BEHIND fossilized footprints, our galaxy has left behind clues about its youth. The stars of the spherical component are old and must have formed long ago when the galaxy was very young.

Stellar Populations

In the 1940s, astronomers realized that there are two families of stars in the galaxy. They form and evolve in similar ways, but they differ in the abundances of atoms that are heavier than helium—atoms that astronomers call **metals.** (Note that this is not the way the word *metal* is defined by non-astronomers.) **Population I stars** are metal-rich, containing 2 to 3 percent metals, whereas **Population II stars** are metal-poor, containing only about 0.1 percent metals or less. The difference may seem small, but it is dramatically evident in spectra (■ Figure 15-22).

Population I stars belong to the disk component of the galaxy and are sometimes called disk population stars. They have nearly circular orbits in the plane of the galaxy and are relatively young stars that formed within the last few billion years. The sun is a Population I star, as are the type I Cepheid variables discussed in this chapter and in Chapter 12.

Population II stars belong to the spherical component of the galaxy and are sometimes called the halo population stars. These stars have randomly tipped orbits ranging from circular to highly elliptical. They are old stars that formed when the galaxy was young. The metal-poor globular clusters are part of the halo population, as are the RR Lyrae and type II Cepheids.

Since the discovery of stellar populations, astronomers have realized that there is a gradation between populations. Extreme Population I stars are found only in the spiral arms. Slightly less metal-rich Population I stars, called intermediate Population I stars, are located throughout the disk. The sun is an intermediate Population I star. Stars that are even less metal rich, such as stars in the central bulge, belong to the intermediate Population II. The most metal-poor stars are those in the halo, including those in globular clusters. Those are referred to as extreme Population II stars.

1   There is so much interstellar dust in the plane of the Milky Way that you cannot observe the nucleus of our galaxy at visual wavelengths. The image below is a radio image of the innermost 300 pc. Many of the feature are supernova remnants (labeled SNR), and a few are star formation clouds. Peculiar features such as threads, the Arc, and the Snake may be gas trapped in magnetic fields. At the center of the image lies Sagittarius A, the location of the nucleus of our galaxy.

Arc

Radio image

The radio map above shows Sgr A and the Arc filaments, 50 parsecs long. The image was made with the VLA radio telescope. The contents of the white box are shown on the opposite page.

Sgr D HII

Sgr D SNR

SNR 0.9 + 0.1

Sgr B2

Sgr B1

Apparent angular size of the moon for comparison

Arc

New SNR 0.3 + 0.0

Threads

The Cane

Background galaxy

Threads

Sgr A

2   Infrared photons with wavelengths longer than 4 microns (4000 nm) are emitted almost entirely by warm interstellar dust. The radiation at those wavelengths coming from Sagittarius is intense, indicating that this region contains lots of dust, and is crowded with stars that warm the dust.

Radio image

Sgr C

The Pelican

Coherent structure?

Snake

Sgr E

SNR 359.1 − 00.5

Infrared image

2MASS

1a This high-resolution radio image of Sgr A (within the white box in the small-scale map on the opposite page) reveals a spiral swirl of gas around an intense radio source known as Sgr A*, about 3 pc across, this spiral lies in a low-density cavity inside a larger disk of neutral gas. The arms of the spiral are thought to be streams of matter flowing into Sgr A* from the inner edge of the larger disk (drawing at right).

Sgr A*

Radio image

N. Killeen and Kwok-Yung Lo

Evidence of a Black Hole in the Nucleus of Our Galaxy

3 Since the middle 1990s, astronomers have been able to use large infrared telescopes and active optics to follow the motions of stars orbiting around Sgr A*. A few of those orbits are shown here. The size and period of the orbit allows astronomers to calculate the mass of Sgr A* using Kepler's third law. The orbital period of the star SO-2, for example, is 15.2 years, and the semimajor axis of its orbit is 950 AU. The combined motions of the observed stars suggest that Sgr A* has a mass of 4 million solar masses.

The Chandra X-ray Observatory has imaged Sgr A* and detected over 2000 other X-ray sources in the area.

NASA/CXC/MIT/F.K. Baganoff et al.

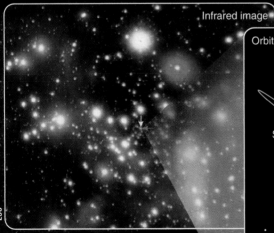

Infrared image

ESO

At its closest, SO-2 comes within 17 light-hours of Sgr A*. Alternative theories that Sgr A* is a cluster of stars, of neutron stars, or of stellar black holes are eliminated. Only a single black hole could contain so much mass in so small a region.

Orbits of stars near Sgr A*

SO-16
SO-2
SO-1
Sgr A*
SO-19
SO-1
SO-20

1 light-day

For comparison, the diameter of the planetary region of our solar system, defined by Neptune's orbit, is half a light-day.

3a A black hole with a mass of 4 million solar masses would have an event horizon with a size on the scale of this diagram smaller than the period at the end of this sentence. A slow dribble of only 0.0002 solar mass of gas per year flowing into the black hole could produce the observed energy. A sudden increase, such as when a star falls in, could produce a violent eruption.

The evidence of a massive black hole at the center of our galaxy seems conclusive. It is much too massive to be the remains of a dead star, however, and astronomers conclude that it probably formed as the galaxy first took shape.

a

Many metal lines

H$_\gamma$ H$_\beta$ H$_\alpha$

Pop I

Pop II

Few metal lines

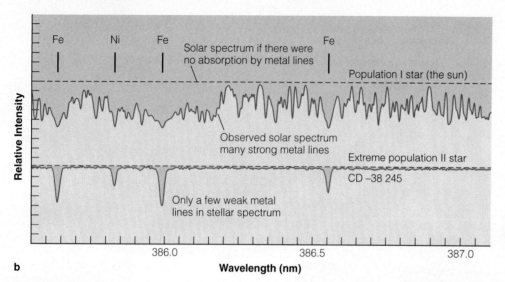

b

Fe   Ni   Fe   Fe

Solar spectrum if there were no absorption by metal lines

Population I star (the sun)

Observed solar spectrum many strong metal lines

Extreme population II star

CD –38 245

Only a few weak metal lines in stellar spectrum

Relative Intensity

386.0   386.5   387.0

Wavelength (nm)

■ **Figure 15-22**

(a) The difference between spectra of Population I stars and Population II stars is dramatic. Examine the upper spectrum here and notice the hundreds of faint spectral lines. The lower spectrum has fewer and weaker lines. (AURA/NOAO/NSF) (b) A graph of such spectra reveals overlapping absorption lines of metals completely blanketing the Population I spectrum. The lower spectrum is that of an extremely metal-poor star with only a few weak metal lines of iron (Fe) and nickel (Ni). This Population II star contains about 10,000 times less metal than the sun. (Adapted from an ESO illustration)

The two populations of stars in our galaxy are clearly different. They have different chemical compositions, are located in different parts of the galaxy, follow different shaped orbits, and have different ages (■ Table 15-1). These differences are clues to the origin of the galaxy, but to follow those clues you need to consider the origin of the elements.

The Element-Building Process

You can use what you have learned about stellar structure and stellar evolution (Chapters 11 to 13) to understand the origin of the metals. Remember that in astronomy jargon, the term *metals*

refers to all of the chemical elements heavier than helium. When the universe began, it contained only hydrogen and helium atoms. (You will learn about the evidence that supports this statement in Chapter 18.) All of the other chemical elements have been produced by **nucleosynthesis**, the process that fuses hydrogen and helium to make the heavier elements. Telling the story of a process from beginning to end is an important part of science (**How Do We Know? 15-2**).

When our galaxy formed sometime after the beginning of the universe, the gas contained about 90 percent hydrogen atoms, 10 percent helium atoms, and almost no heavier atoms.

■ **Table 15-1 | Stellar Populations**

	Population I		Population II	
	Extreme	**Intermediate**	**Intermediate**	**Extreme**
Location	Spiral arms	Disk	Central bulge	Halo
Metals (%)	3	1.6	0.8	Less than 0.8
Shape of orbit	Circular	Slightly elliptical	Moderately elliptical	Highly elliptical
Average age (yr)	100 million and younger	0.2–10 billion	2–10 billion	10–13 billion

Nature as Processes

How is getting a cold like stars building the chemical elements? Science, at first glance, seems to be nothing but facts; but, in many cases, you can organize the facts into the story of a process. For example, astronomers try to assemble the sequence of events that led to the formation of the chemical elements. If you understand that process, you have command over a lot of important facts in astronomy.

A process is a sequence of events that leads to some result or condition, and much of science is focused on understanding how these natural processes work. Biologists, for example, try to understand how a virus reproduces. They must figure out how the virus tricks the immune system to leave it alone, penetrates the wall of a healthy cell, injects viral DNA, commandeers the cell's resources to make new viruses, and finally destroys the cell

to release the new virus copies. A biologist may spend her life studying a specific step, but the ultimate goal of science is to tell the entire story of the process.

As you study any science, be alert for processes as organizing themes. When you see a process in science, ask yourself a few basic questions. What conditions prevailed at the beginning of the process? What sequence of steps occurred? Can some steps occur simultaneously, or must one step occur before another can occur? What is the final state that this process produces?

Recognizing a process and learning to tell its story will help you remember a lot of details, but that is not the real value of a scientific process. Identifying a process and learning to tell its story helps you understand how nature works and explains why the universe is the way it is.

A virus is a collection of molecules that cannot reproduce until it penetrates into a living cell.
(Russell Knightly Media, rkm.com.au)

Therefore, the first stars to form had to be metal poor. Succeeding generations of stars manufactured heavier atoms, and the metal abundance of the galaxy gradually increased.

As you learned in Chapters 12 and 13, medium-mass stars like the sun cannot ignite carbon fusion; but, during helium shell fusion, the heat and density can trigger low-level nuclear reactions that cook the gas to produce small amounts of elements heavier than helium. When the aging star pushes away its surface layers to produce a planetary nebula, some of those elements are spread back into the interstellar medium.

The most massive stars fuse elements up to iron and simultaneously cook the gas in their cores to produce small amounts of many different atoms, including sulfur and calcium. When those stars die in supernova explosions, traces of those elements are spread back into the interstellar medium. Furthermore, the supernova explosion itself can fuse nuclei into atoms much heavier than iron. These rare atoms, such as gold, platinum, and uranium, also get spread back into space where they may become part of newly forming stars and planets.

Metals are actually quite rare in the universe. Traditionally, astronomers graph the abundance of the elements using an exponential scale, but if you replot the data using a linear scale, you can see how rare these atoms are (■ Figure 15-23).

When you observe Population II stars, such as those in the halo, you are looking at the survivors of the early generations of

stars in our galaxy. The first stars formed from gas that was metal poor, and the survivors of these early generations are low-mass, long-lived stars. Their spectra, which indicate the composition of their atmospheres and not their cores, still show the composition of the metal-poor gas from which they formed. Population I stars such as the sun formed more recently, after the interstellar medium had been enriched in metals, and their spectra show stronger metal lines. Stars forming now show even stronger metal lines.

Galactic Fountains

Supernova remnants are rich in metals and eventually mix back into the interstellar medium. In fact, supernovae continuously stir and enrich the interstellar medium. But a larger-scale process may be even more efficient at spreading newly created metals throughout the disk of the galaxy where they can be incorporated into the newly forming stars.

In Chapter 10, you saw how neighboring supernova remnants can merge to form a superbubble of hot gas (Figure 10-9b). A supernova remnant may be only a few tens of parsecs in diameter, but a superbubble can be more than ten times bigger. The denser gas of the galactic disk tends to confine an expanding superbubble, but the disk is only a few hundred parsecs thick. If a superbubble breaks out of the denser gas of the galactic disk, it can spew hot gas high above the plane of the galaxy in a **galactic**

a

b

fountain (■ Figure 15-24). As this gas cools and falls back into the disk, it can spread metals through the galaxy.

Galactic fountains are difficult to observe directly, but isolated clouds of gas have been found high in the halo, and cool clouds have been found falling toward the disk. Some of these may be material from outside the galaxy that is falling inward for the first time, but the lower-velocity clouds only a few thousand parsecs above the disk may be cooling gas that was spewed out of the disk by fountains. It seems likely that this process contributes to spreading metals through the disk. Either way, it is evident that supernovae create metals and mix them back into the interstellar medium where they can be incorporated into newly forming stars.

Because the recycling of stellar nucleosynthesis products means that the metal abundance of newborn stars increases as the galaxy ages, astronomers can use metal abundance as an index to the ages of the components of our galaxy. The halo is old, and the disk is younger.

The Age of the Milky Way

Because astronomers know how to find the age of star clusters, they can estimate the age of our galaxy. The process sounds straightforward, but uncertainties make the easy answer hard to interpret.

The oldest open clusters are 9 to 10 billion years old. These ages come from the turnoff points in their H–R diagrams (see Chapter 12), but finding the age of an old cluster is difficult because old clusters change so slowly. Also, the exact location of the turnoff point depends on chemical composition, which differs slightly among clusters. Finally, open clusters are not strongly bound by their gravity, so older open clusters may have dissipated as their stars wandered away. It is reasonable to suppose that the galactic disk is somewhat older than the oldest remaining open clusters, which suggests that the disk is at least 10 billion years old.

Globular clusters have faint turnoff points in their H–R diagrams and are clearly old, but finding these ages is difficult. Again, slight differences in chemical composition make noticeable differences when calculating the stellar models from which ages are determined. Also, to find the age of a cluster, astronomers must know its distance. Precise parallaxes from the Hipparcos satellite have allowed astronomers to more accurately calibrate the Cepheid and RR Lyrae variable stars, and careful studies with the newest large telescopes have refined the chemical compositions and better defined the H–R diagrams of globular clusters. The best analysis of all of the data suggests that the average globular clusters are about 11 billion years old, although some globular clusters are younger than that, and some are older. Studies of the oldest globular clusters suggest that the halo of our galaxy is at least 13 billion years old.

Observations of stellar populations and clusters show that the disk is younger than the halo. You can combine these ages with the process of nucleosynthesis to tell the story of our galaxy.

Formation of the Galaxy

The lack of metals in the spherical component of the galaxy tells you it is very old, a fossil left behind by the galaxy when it was young and drastically different from its present disk shape. The study of element building and stellar populations leads to the fundamental question, "How did our galaxy form?"

In the 1950s, astronomers began to develop a hypothesis sometimes called the **monolithic collapse hypothesis** to explain the formation of our galaxy. Recent observations, however, are forcing a major revision of that hypothesis.

The monolithic collapse hypothesis says that the galaxy formed from a single large cloud of turbulent gas over 13 billion years ago. That cloud contracted to form our galaxy. As gravity pulled the gas inward, the cloud began to fragment into smaller clouds; and, because the gas was turbulent, the smaller clouds had random velocities. That caused the stars and star clusters that formed from these fragments to have orbits with a wide range of shapes; a few were circular, most were elliptical, and some were extremely elliptical. The orbits were also inclined at different angles, resulting in a spherical cloud of stars—the spherical component of the galaxy. Of course, these first stars were metal poor because no stars had existed earlier to enrich the gas with metals.

The second stage in this hypothesis accounts for the formation of the disk component. As the gas clouds in the originally spherical cloud collided, turbulent motions in the gas canceled out, as do eddies in recently stirred coffee, and the cloud was left with a uniform rotation. A rotating, low-density cloud of gas cannot remain spherical. A star is spherical because its high internal pressure balances its gravity; but, in a low-density cloud, the internal pressure is much too low to support the weight. Like a blob of pizza dough spun in the air, the cloud must flatten into a disk (■ Figure 15-25), eventually producing the galaxy's disk.

This contraction from a sphere into a disk must have taken billions of years, and while that happened the metal abundance gradually increased as generations of stars were born from the gradually flattening gas cloud. The stars and globular clusters of the halo were left behind by the cloud as it flattened, and subsequent generations of stars formed in flatter distributions. The gas distribution in the galaxy now is so flat that the youngest stars are confined to a disk only about 100 parsecs thick. These stars are metal rich and have nearly circular orbits.

The monolithic collapse hypothesis accounts for many of the Milky Way's properties. Advances in technology, however, have improved astronomical observation, and, beginning in the 1980s, contradictions between theory and observation arose. For example, not all globular clusters have the same age, but, surprisingly, some of the youngest clusters seem to be in the outer halo. In contrast, the monolithic collapse hypothesis says that the halo formed first and predicts that the clusters within it should either have a uniform age or the most distant ones should be slightly older. Another problem is that the oldest stars are observed to be metal poor but not completely metal free. There must have been at least a few massive stars to create these metals during a generation before the formation of the oldest stars now seen in the halo.

Can the original hypothesis be modified to explain these observations? Astronomers suspect that the galaxy began as a

Origin of the Halo and Disk

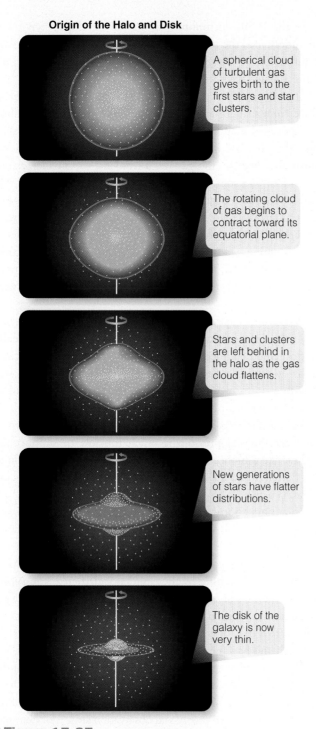

A spherical cloud of turbulent gas gives birth to the first stars and star clusters.

The rotating cloud of gas begins to contract toward its equatorial plane.

Stars and clusters are left behind in the halo as the gas cloud flattens.

New generations of stars have flatter distributions.

The disk of the galaxy is now very thin.

■ **Figure 15-25**

The "monolithic collapse" model for the origin of our galaxy begins with a spherical gas cloud that flattens into a disk.

large gas cloud containing almost no metals. Models of metal-free stars show that they are very massive, so that first generation of stars evolved rapidly and exploded as supernovae, which enriched the gas cloud with traces of metals. None of those massive first-generation stars survive, but the metals they created are detectable in the oldest Population II stars.

■ **Figure 15-26**

The Large and Small Magellanic clouds, shown here rising above the Walter Baade Telescope's dome at the Magellan Observatory in Chile, are small galaxies that orbit close to the Milky Way Galaxy. A long trail of stars and gas stretching halfway around the sky reveals that they are being ripped apart, and the Milky Way Galaxy is absorbing their stars, gas, and dust. (Kris Koenig/Coast Learning Systems)

It seems likely that the central bulge and halo formed from such a gas cloud or from the accumulation of a number of gas clouds. A thick but low-density disk of stars may have formed at this early stage. This would explain the age of the central bulge and the metals in both the oldest stars in the halo and those scattered above and below the disk. The thin part of the disk could have formed later as more gas fell into the galaxy and settled into the gas clouds of the disk where the stars are forming today.

Perhaps entire galaxies were captured by the growing Milky Way Galaxy. Astronomers have found streams and rings of scattered stars surrounding our galaxy and suspect they were produced when smaller galaxies were captured, pulled apart, and absorbed by our home galaxy (■ Figure 15-26). You will see dramatic evidence in the next chapter that such galaxy mergers do occur.

If the young Milky Way Galaxy absorbed a few small but partially evolved galaxies, then some of the globular clusters astronomers see in the halo may be hitchhikers. This would explain the range of globular cluster ages. In fact, some astronomers hypothesize that our galaxy formed through a rapid merger of a number of smaller pregalaxy clouds of gas and stars with later additions of infalling gas and other small galaxies.

The problem of the formation of our galaxy is frustrating because the hypotheses are incomplete. Almost everyone prefers certainty to confusion, but astronomers are still gathering observations and testing hypotheses. The older monolithic collapse hypothesis has proven inadequate to explain all of the observations, and astronomers are attempting to refine the observations and devise new theories. The metal abundances and ages of the stars in our galaxy seem to be important clues, but metal abundance and age do not tell the whole story. Astronomer Bernard Pagel was thinking of this when he said, "Cats and dogs may have the same age and metallicity, but they are still cats and dogs."

SCIENTIFIC ARGUMENT

Why do metal-poor stars have the most eccentric orbits?

A good argument makes connections between ideas, and sometimes those connections are not obvious. Certainly, the metal abundance of a star cannot affect its orbit, so an analysis must not confuse cause and effect with the relationship between these two factors. Both chemical composition and orbital shape depend on a third factor—age. The oldest stars are metal poor because they formed before there had been many supernova explosions to create and scatter metals into the interstellar medium. Those stars formed long ago when the galaxy was young and motions were not organized into a disk, so the stars tended to take up randomly shaped orbits, many of which are quite elongated and eccentric. Consequently, today, the most metal-poor stars tend to follow the most eccentric orbits.

Nevertheless, even the oldest stars known in our galaxy contain some metals. They are metal poor, not metal free. Adjust your argument. **Where did these metal-poor stars get their metals?**

What Are We? Children of the Milky Way

Hang on tight. The sun, with Earth in its clutch, is ripping along at about 220 km/s (that's 490,000 mph) as it orbits the center of the Milky Way Galaxy. We live on a wildly moving ball of rock in a large galaxy that humanity calls home, but the Milky Way is more than just our home. Perhaps "parent galaxy" would be a better name.

Except for hydrogen atoms, which have survived unchanged since the universe began, you and Earth are made of metals—atoms heavier than helium. There is no helium in your body, but there is plenty of carbon, nitrogen, and oxygen. There is calcium in your bones and iron in your blood. All of those atoms and more were cooked up inside stars or in their supernova deaths.

Stars are born in the galaxy's disk when clouds of gas orbiting the center of the galaxy collide with the gas in spiral arms and are compressed. That process has given birth to generations of stars, and each generation has produced elements heavier than helium and spread them back into the interstellar medium. The abundance of metals has grown slowly in the galaxy. About 4.6 billion years ago a cloud of gas enriched in those heavy atoms slammed into a spiral arm and produced the sun, Earth, and you. You have been cooked up by the Milky Way--your parent galaxy.

Summary

▶ The hazy band of the Milky Way is our wheel-shaped galaxy seen from within, but its size and shape are not obvious. William and Caroline Herschel counted stars at many locations over the sky to show that our star system seemed to be shaped like a grindstone with the sun near the center.

▶ Later astronomers studied the distributions of stars, but because gas and dust in space blocked their view of distant stars, they concluded the star system was only about 10 **kiloparsecs (p. 303)** in diameter with the sun at the center.

▶ In the early 20th century, Harlow Shapley **calibrated (p. 306)** Cepheid variable stars to find the distance to globular clusters, demonstrating that our galaxy is much larger than what we can see and that the sun is not at the center.

▶ Modern observations suggest that our galaxy contains a **disk component (p. 308)** about 80,000 ly in diameter and that the sun is two-thirds of the way from the center to the visible edge. The **central bulge (p. 309)** around the center and an extensive **halo (p. 309)** containing old stars and little gas and dust make up the **spherical component (p. 309)**.

▶ The mass of the galaxy can be found from its **rotation curve (p. 311)**. Kepler's third law reveals that the galaxy contains at least 100 billion solar masses. If stars orbited in **Keplerian motion (p. 311)**, more distant stars would orbit more slowly. They do not, and that shows that the halo must contain much more mass than is visible. Because the mass in this **galactic corona (p. 311)** is not emitting detectable electromagnetic radiation, astronomers call it **dark matter (p. 311)**.

▶ You can trace the spiral arms through the sun's neighborhood by using **spiral tracers (p. 313)** such as OB associations; but, to extend the map over the entire galaxy, astronomers must use radio telescopes to see through the gas and dust.

▶ The most massive stars live such short lives they don't have time to move from their place of birth. Because they are found scattered along the spiral arms, astronomers conclude that the spiral arms are sites of star formation.

▶ The spiral **density wave theory (p. 315)** suggests that the spiral arms are regions of compression that move around the disk. When an orbiting gas cloud overtakes the compression wave, the gas cloud is compressed and forms stars. A density wave produces a two-armed **grand-design (p. 316)** spiral galaxy.

▶ Another process, **self-sustaining star formation (p. 316)**, may act to modify the arms with branches and spurs as the birth of massive stars triggers the formation of more stars by compressing neighboring gas clouds. This may account for the wooly appearance of **flocculent (p. 316)** galaxies.

▶ The nucleus of the galaxy is invisible at visual wavelengths, but radio, infrared, and X-ray radiation can penetrate the gas and dust. These wavelengths reveal crowded central stars and warmed dust.

▶ The very center of the Milky Way Galaxy is marked by a radio source, **Sagittarius A* (p. 318)**. The core must be less than an astronomical unit in diameter, but the motions of stars around the center show that it must contain roughly 4 million solar masses. A supermassive black hole is the only object that could contain so much mass in such a small space.

▶ The oldest star clusters reveal that the disk of our galaxy is younger than the halo, and the oldest globular clusters appear to be about 13 billion years old. So our galaxy must have formed about 13 billion years ago.

▶ Stellar populations are an important clue to the formation of our galaxy. The first stars to form, termed **Population II stars (p. 319)**, were poor in elements heavier than helium—elements that astronomers call **metals (p. 319)**. As generations of stars manufactured metals in a process called **nucleosynthesis (p. 322)** and spread them back into the interstellar medium, the metal abundance of more recent generations increased. **Population I stars (p. 319)**, including the sun, are richer in metals.

▶ **Galactic fountains (p. 323–324)** produced by expanding supernova remnants may help spread metals throughout the disk.

▶ Because the halo is made up of Population II stars and the disk is made up of Population I stars, astronomers conclude that the halo formed first and the disk later.

▶ The **monolithic collapse hypothesis (p. 325)**, that the galaxy formed from a single, roughly spherical cloud of gas and gradually flatted into a disk, does not match all of the current evidence and has been amended to include mergers with other galaxies and infalling gas contributing to the disk.

Review Questions

1. Why is it difficult to specify the dimensions of the disk and halo?
2. Why didn't astronomers before Shapley realize how large the galaxy is?
3. What evidence can you cite that our galaxy has a massive corona?
4. Explain why some star clusters lose stars more slowly than others.
5. Contrast the motion of the disk stars and that of the halo stars. Why do their orbits differ?
6. Why are metals less abundant in older stars than in younger stars?
7. Why do metal-poor stars have a wider range of orbital shapes than metal-rich stars like the sun?
8. What evidence contradicts the monolithic collapse hypothesis for the origin of our galaxy?
9. Why are all spiral tracers young?
10. Why couldn't spiral arms be physically connected structures? What would happen to them?
11. What kind of galaxy would the spiral density wave produce if it acted alone?
12. Why does self-sustaining star formation produce clouds of stars that look like segments of spiral arms?
13. Describe the kinds of observations you would make to study the galactic nucleus.
14. Why must astronomers use infrared telescopes to observe the motions of stars around Sgr A*?
15. What evidence can you cite that the nucleus of the galaxy contains a supermassive energy source that is very small in size?
16. **How Do We Know?** Calibration simplifies complex measurements, but how does that make the work of later astronomers dependent on the expertise of the astronomer who did the calibration?
17. **How Do We Know?** The story of a process makes the facts easier to remember, but that is not the true goal of the scientist. What is the real value of understanding a scientific process?

Discussion Questions

1. How would this chapter be different if interstellar dust did not scatter light?
2. Why doesn't the Milky Way circle the sky along the celestial equator or the ecliptic?

Problems

1. Make a scale sketch of our galaxy in cross section. Include the disk, sun, nucleus, halo, and some globular clusters. Try to draw the globular clusters to scale.

2. Because of dust, astronomers can see only about 5 kpc into the disk of the galaxy at visual wavelengths. What percentage of the galactic disk does that include? (*Hint:* Consider the area of the entire disk versus the area visible from Earth.)

3. The fastest passenger aircraft, the Concorde, could fly 0.59 km/s (1320 mph). How long would it take to reach the sun? The galactic center? (*Hint:* 1 pc = 3.1×10^{13} km.)

4. If a typical halo star has an orbital velocity of 250 km/s, how long does it take to pass through the disk of the galaxy? Assume that the disk is 1000 pc thick.

5. If the RR Lyrae stars in a globular cluster have apparent magnitudes of 14, how far away is the cluster? (*Hints:* Use the magnitude–distance formula, and see Figure 12-14.)

6. If interstellar dust makes an RR Lyrae variable star look 1 magnitude fainter than it should, by how much will you overestimate its distance? (*Hint:* Use the magnitude–distance formula or Table 9-1.)

7. If a globular cluster is 10 arc minutes in diameter and 8.0 kpc away, what is its diameter? (*Hint:* Use the small-angle formula, Chapter 3.)

8. If you assume that a globular cluster 4.0 arc minutes in diameter is actually 25 pc in diameter, how far away is it? (*Hint:* Use the small-angle formula, Chapter 3.)

9. If the sun is 4.6 billion years old, how many times has it orbited the galaxy?

10. If the true distance to the center of the galaxy is 7 (instead of 8) kpc and the orbital velocity of the sun is 220 km/s, what is the minimum mass of the galaxy? (*Hint:* Use Kepler's third law.)

11. What temperature would interstellar dust have to have to radiate most strongly at 100 μm? (*Hint:* 1 μm = 1000 nm. Use Wien's law, Chapter 7.)

12. Infrared radiation from the center of our galaxy with a wavelength of about 2 μm (2×10^{-6} m) comes mainly from cool stars. Use this wavelength as λ_{max} and find the temperature of the stars.

13. If an object at the center of our galaxy has a linear diameter of 10 AU, what will its angular diameter be as seen from Earth? (*Hint:* Use the small-angle formula, Chapter 3.)

Learning to Look

1. Why does the galaxy shown at the right have so much dust in its disk? How big do you suppose the halo of this galaxy really is?

NASA/Hubble Heritage Team/STScI/AURA

2. Why are the spiral arms in the galaxy at the right blue? What color would the halo be if it were bright enough to see in this photo?

NASA/Hubble Heritage Team and A. Riess, STScI

16 | Galaxies

Visual wavelength image

Guidepost

Our Milky Way Galaxy is only one of the many billions of galaxies visible in the sky. This chapter will expand your horizon to discuss the different kinds of galaxies and their complex histories. Here you can expect answers to five essential questions:

— **What do galaxies look like?**

— **How do astronomers measure the distances to galaxies?**

— **How do galaxies differ in size, luminosity, and mass?**

— **Do other galaxies contain supermassive black holes and dark matter, as does our galaxy?**

— **Why are there different kinds of galaxies?**

As you begin studying galaxies, you will discover they are classified into different types, and that will lead you to insights into how galaxies form and evolve. In the next chapter, you will discover that some galaxies are violently active, and that will give you more clues to the evolution of galaxies.

Even if your spaceship could travel at the speed of light, it would take you 29 million years to reach the Sombrero Galaxy, also known as M104, one of the closest galaxies to our Milky Way Galaxy. (NASA/ESA/Hubble Heritage Team/STScI/AURA)

A hypothesis or theory is clear, decisive, and positive, but it is believed by no one but the man who created it. Experimental findings, on the other hand, are messy, inexact things which are believed by everyone except the man who did that work.

— HARLOW SHAPLEY, *THROUGH RUGGED WAYS TO THE STARS*

SCIENCE FICTION HEROES FLIT EFFORTLESSLY between the stars, but almost none travels between the galaxies. As you leave your home galaxy, the Milky Way, behind, you will voyage out into the depths of the universe, out among the galaxies, into space so deep it is unexplored even in fiction.

Before you can begin to understand the life stories of the galaxies, you need to gather some basic data. How many kinds of galaxies are there? How big are they? How massive are they? You can characterize the family of galaxies just as you characterized the family of stars in Chapter 9.

16-1 The Family of Galaxies

LESS THAN A CENTURY AGO, astronomers did not know for certain that there are such things as galaxies. Nineteenth-century telescopes revealed faint nebulae scattered among the stars, and some were spiral shaped. Astronomers argued about the nature of these faint nebulae, but it was not understood until the 1920s that some were other galaxies much like our own; and it was not until recent decades that astronomical telescopes could fully reveal their tremendous beauty and intricacy (■ Figure 16-1).

■ **Figure 16-1**

A century ago, photos of galaxies looked like clouds of haze. Modern images of these relatively nearby spiral galaxies reveal dramatically beautiful objects filled with newborn stars and clouds of gas and dust. (NGC 4414, ESO 510-G13, NGC 3341a and 3341b: Hubble Heritage Team, AURA/STScI/NASA; M83: ESO)

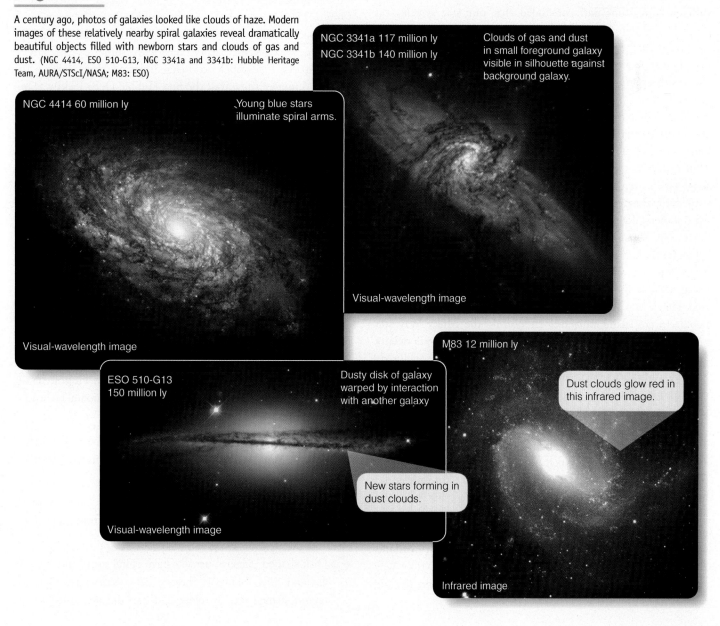

NGC 4414 60 million ly — Young blue stars illuminate spiral arms.
Visual-wavelength image

NGC 3341a 117 million ly
NGC 3341b 140 million ly — Clouds of gas and dust in small foreground galaxy visible in silhouette against background galaxy.
Visual-wavelength image

ESO 510-G13 150 million ly — Dusty disk of galaxy warped by interaction with another galaxy
New stars forming in dust clouds.
Visual-wavelength image

M83 12 million ly — Dust clouds glow red in this infrared image.
Infrared image

The Discovery of Galaxies

Galaxies are faint objects, so they were not noticed until telescopes had grown large enough to gather significant amounts of light. In 1845, William Parsons, third Earl of Rosse in Ireland, built a telescope 72 in. in diameter. It was, for some years, the largest telescope in the world. Parsons lived before the invention of astronomical photography, so he had to view the faint nebulae directly at the eyepiece and sketch their shapes. He noticed that some have a spiral shape, and they became known as **spiral nebulae**. Parsons immediately concluded that the spiral nebulae were great spiral clouds of stars. The German philosopher Immanuel Kant in 1755 had proposed that the universe was filled with great wheels of stars that he called **island universes**. Parsons adopted that term for the spiral nebulae.

Not everyone agreed that the spiral nebulae were clouds of stars lying outside our own star system. An alternative point of view was that our Milky Way star system was alone in an otherwise empty universe. Sir William Herschel had counted stars in different directions and concluded that our star system was shaped approximately like a grindstone (see Figure 15-2). Beyond the edge of this grindstone star system, space was supposed to be a limitless void. The spiral nebulae, in this view, were nothing more than whirls of gas and faint stars within our star system.

The debate over the spiral nebulae could not be resolved in the 19th century because the telescopes were not large enough and photographic plates, when they became available in the late 1800s, were not sensitive enough. The spiral nebulae remained foggy swirls even in the best photographs, and astronomers continued to disagree over their true nature. In April 1920, two astronomers debated the issue at the National Academy of Science in Washington, D.C. Harlow Shapley of Mount Wilson Observatory had recently shown that the Milky Way was a much larger star system than had been thought. He argued that the spiral nebulae were just objects within the Milky Way star system. Heber D. Curtis of Lick Observatory argued that the spiral nebulae were island universes far outside the Milky Way star system. Historians of science mark this **Shapley–Curtis debate** as a turning point in modern astronomy, but it was inconclusive. Shapley and Curtis cited the right evidence but drew incorrect conclusions. The disagreement was finally resolved, as is often the case in astronomy, by evidence from a bigger telescope.

On December 30, 1924, Mount Wilson astronomer Edwin Hubble (for whom the Hubble Space Telescope is named) announced that he had taken photographic plates of a few bright galaxies using the new 100-in. telescope. Not only could he detect individual stars in the spiral nebulae, but he could identify some of the stars as Cepheid variables with apparent magnitudes of about 18. For the brightest Cepheids, which are supergiants, to appear that faint, they had to be very distant. This meant that spiral nebulae must be outside the Milky Way star system. They are galaxies, separate from ours, and rivaling ours in size.

How Many Galaxies Are There?

Like leaves on the forest floor, galaxies carpet the sky. Pick any direction in the sky away from the dust and gas of the Milky Way, and you are looking deep into space. Photons that have traveled for billions of years enter your eye, but they are too few to register on your retina. Only the largest telescopes can gather enough light to detect distant galaxies.

When astronomers chose a relatively empty spot on the sky near the Big Dipper and used the Hubble Space Telescope to record an extremely long exposure of 10 days' duration, they found thousands of galaxies crowded into the image. That image, now known as a Hubble Deep Field, contains a few relatively nearby galaxies along with many others that are as much as 10 billion light-years away (■ Figure 16-2).

Since the first Hubble Deep Field was recorded, other deep fields have been imaged in other parts of the sky and at other wavelengths. The GOODS program (Great Observatories Origins Deep Survey) has used the Hubble Space Telescope with other space telescopes such as the Spitzer Space Telescope and the Chandra X-ray Observatory and with some of the largest ground-based telescopes to image selected deep fields. The GOODS images show that the first Hubble Deep Field was not unusual; the entire sky appears to be just as thickly covered with galaxies.

The GOODS study of distant galaxies is especially amazing when you think that, less than a century ago, humanity did not know that we live in a galaxy or that the universe contained other galaxies. Today telescopes are capable of detecting a few hundred billion galaxies, and new, larger telescopes will reveal even more. The discovery of galaxies was one of the turning points in the history of astronomy.

The Shapes of Galaxies

Look at the galaxies in the Hubble Deep Field (Figure 16-2), and you will see galaxies of different shapes. Some are spiral, some are elliptical, and some are irregular. Astronomers classify galaxies according to their shapes in photographs made at visual wavelengths using a system developed by Edwin Hubble in the 1920s. Such systems of classification are a fundamental technique in science (**How Do We Know? 16-1**).

Read **Galaxy Classification** on pages 334–335 and notice three important points and four new terms that describe the main types of galaxies:

1 Many galaxies have no disk, no spiral arms, and almost no gas and dust. These *elliptical galaxies* range from huge giants to small dwarfs.

2 Disk-shaped galaxies usually have spiral arms and contain gas and dust. Many of these *spiral galaxies* have a central region shaped like an elongated bar and are called *barred*

Foreground star in our galaxy

Visual-wavelength image

■ Figure 16-2

An apparently empty spot on the sky only 1/30 the diameter of the full moon contains over 1500 galaxies in this extremely long time exposure known as the Northern Hubble Deep Field. Only four stars are visible in this image; they are sharp points of light with diffraction spikes produced by the telescope optics. Presumably the entire sky is similarly filled with galaxies. (R. Williams and the Hubble Deep Field Team, STScI, NASA)

spiral galaxies. (As you learned in Chapter 15, the Milky Way Galaxy is a barred spiral.) A few disk galaxies contain little gas and dust.

③ Finally, notice the *irregular galaxies,* which are generally shapeless and tend to be rich in gas and dust.

The amount of gas and dust in a galaxy strongly influences its appearance. Galaxies rich in gas and dust usually have active star formation and emission nebulae and contain hot, bright stars. That gives these galaxies a blue tint. Galaxies that are poor in gas and dust contain few or none of these highly luminous blue stars and no emission nebulae and consequently look redder and have a much more uniform appearance.

Spiral galaxies are clearly disk shaped, but the true, three-dimensional shape of elliptical galaxies isn't obvious from images. Some are spherical, but the more elongated elliptical galaxies could be shaped like flattened spheres (hamburger bun shaped) or like elongated spheres (American football shaped). Some may even have three different diameters; they are longer than they are thick and thicker than they are wide, like a flattened loaf of bread. Statistical studies suggest that all of these shapes are represented among elliptical galaxies.

Edwin Hubble devised the classification system for galaxies by looking at visual-wavelength images, but infrared images reveal the location of the vast majority of stars—stars that are not as luminous as the hot stars that produce most of the light. These studies suggest that the structures of many galaxies are dominated by the gravitational fields of large masses of low-luminosity cool stars. For example, some spiral galaxies that appear at visible wavelengths to lack bars actually have massive bars that are evident in infrared images. As you think about galaxies, you should remember that their classification is based on where the light comes from and not necessarily where most of the mass is located.

1 **Elliptical galaxies** are round or elliptical, contain no visible gas and dust, and have few or no bright stars. They are classified with a numerical index ranging from 1 to 7; E0s are round, and E7s are highly elliptical. The index is calculated from the largest and smallest diameter of the galaxy used in the following formula and rounded to the nearest integer.

$$\frac{10(a - b)}{a}$$

Outline of an E6 galaxy

AURA/NOAO/NSF

Visual-wavelength image

The Leo 1 dwarf elliptical galaxy is not many times bigger than a globular cluster.

Anglo-Australian Telescope Board

Visual

M87 is a giant elliptical galaxy classified E1. It is several times larger in diameter than our own galaxy and is surrounded by a swarm of over 500 globular clusters.

2 **Spiral galaxies** contain a disk and spiral arms. Their halo stars are not visible, but presumably all spiral galaxies have halos. Spirals contain gas and dust and hot, bright O and B stars, as shown at right and below. The presence of short-lived O and B stars alerts us that star formation is occurring in these galaxies. Sa galaxies have larger nuclei, less gas and dust, and fewer hot, bright stars. Sc galaxies have small nuclei, lots of gas and dust, and many hot, bright stars. Sb galaxies are intermediate.

Anglo-Australian Telescope Board

Sa

Visual   NGC 3623

BAR

Sb

NGC 3627   Visual

Sc

2a Roughly 2/3 of all spiral galaxies are **barred spiral galaxies** classified SBa, SBb, and SBc. They have an elongated nucleus with spiral arms springing from the ends of the bar, as shown at left. Our own galaxy is a barred spiral.

NGC 1365   Visual

NGC 2997   Visual

2b Some disk galaxies are rich in dust, which is concentrated along their spiral arms. NGC 4013, shown below, is a galaxy much like ours, but seen edge-on, its dust is dramatically apparent.

NASA/ESA/Hubble Heritage T

Dust visible in spiral arm crossing in front of more distant galaxy.

NASA/ESA/Hubble Heritage Team/STScI/AURA

Visual

Visual

NGC 2207 and IC 216

Dust in spiral galaxies is most common in the spiral arms. Here the spiral arms of one galaxy are silhouetted in front of a more distant galaxy.

G. J. Jacoby, M. J. Pierce/AURA/NOAO, NSF

The galaxy IC 4182 is a dwarf irregular galaxy only about 4 million parsecs from our galaxy.

2c Galaxies with an obvious disk and nuclear bulge but no visible gas and dust and few or no hot bright stars are classified as S0 (pronounced "Ess Zero"). Compare this galaxy with the edge-on spiral above.

Visual

Visual

3 Irregular galaxies (classified Irr) are a chaotic mix of gas, dust, and stars with no obvious nuclear bulge or spiral arms. The Large and Small Magellanic Clouds are visible to the unaided eye as hazy patches in the southern hemisphere sky. Telescopic images show that they are irregular galaxies that are interacting gravitationally with our own much larger galaxy. Star formation is dramatic in the Magellanic Clouds. The bright pink regions are emission nebulae excited by newborn O and B stars. The brightest nebula in the Large Magellanic Cloud is called the Tarantula Nebula.

Tarantula Nebula

Small Magellanic Cloud

Large Magellanic Cloud

Visual

Visual

AURA/NOAO/NSF

Classification in Science

What does a flamingo have in common with a *T. rex*? Classification is one of the most basic and most powerful of scientific tools. Establishing a system of classification is often the first step in studying a new aspect of nature, and it can produce unexpected insights.

Charles Darwin sailed around the world from 1831 to 1836 with a scientific expedition aboard the ship HMS *Beagle*. Everywhere he went, he studied the living things he saw and tried to classify them. For example, he classified different types of finches he saw on the Galapagos Islands based on the shapes of their beaks. He found that those that fed on seeds with hard shells had thick, powerful beaks, whereas those that picked insects out of deep crevices had long, thin beaks. His classifications of these and other animals led him to think about how natural selection shapes creatures to survive in their environment, which led him to understand how living things evolve.

Years after Darwin's work, paleontologists classified dinosaurs into two orders, lizard-hipped and bird-hipped dinosaurs. This classification, based on the shapes of dinosaur hip joints, helped the scientists understand patterns of evolution of dinosaurs. It also led to the conclusion that modern birds, including the finches that Darwin saw on the Galapagos, evolved from dinosaurs.

Astronomers use classifications of galaxies, stars, moons, and many other objects to help them see patterns, trace evolutions, and generally make sense of the astronomical world. Whenever you encounter a scientific discussion, look for the classifications on which it is based. Classifications are the orderly framework on which much of science is built.

The careful classification of living things has revealed that the birds, including this flamingo, are descended from dinosaurs. (M. Seeds)

It is surprisingly difficult to figure out what proportions of galaxies are elliptical, spiral, or irregular. In catalogs of galaxies, about 70 percent are spiral, but that is because spiral galaxies are luminous and easy to notice because they contain hot, bright stars and clouds of ionized gas. Most ellipticals are fainter and harder to notice. Small galaxies such as dwarf ellipticals and dwarf irregulars are actually very common, but they are hard to detect. From careful statistical studies, astronomers estimate that ellipticals are actually more common than spirals and that irregulars make up only about 25 percent of all galaxies.

Why are there different kinds of galaxies? That is a key question you will explore in the rest of this chapter.

SCIENTIFIC ARGUMENT

What color are galaxies?
Scientific arguments must be based on evidence, and evidence means observations. But you need to be careful and analyze even the simplest observations with care. Different kinds of galaxies have different colors, depending mostly on how much gas and dust they contain. If a galaxy contains large amounts of gas and dust, it probably contains lots of young stars, and a few of those young stars will be massive, hot, luminous O and B stars. They will produce most of the light and give the galaxy a distinct blue tint. In contrast, a galaxy that contains little gas and dust will contain few young stars. It will lack O and B stars, and instead the most luminous stars in such a galaxy will be red giants and supergiants. They will give the galaxy a red tint. Because the light from a galaxy is a blend of the light from billions of stars, the colors are only tints. Nevertheless, the most luminous stars in a galaxy determine the overall color. From this you can conclude that elliptical galaxies tend to be red, and the disks of spiral galaxies tend to be blue.

Now create your own scientific argument and analyze a different kind of observation. **Why are most cataloged galaxies spiral in spite of the fact that the most common kind of galaxy is elliptical?**

16-2 Measuring the Properties of Galaxies

LOOKING BEYOND THE EDGE of our Milky Way Galaxy, astronomers find billions of galaxies filling space as far as anyone can see. What are the properties of these star systems? What are the diameters, luminosities, and masses of galaxies? Just as in your study of stellar characteristics (see Chapter 9), the first step in your study of galaxies is to find out how far away they are. Once you know a galaxy's distance, its size and luminosity are relatively easy to find. Later in this section, you will see that, just as for stars, finding the masses of galaxies is more difficult.

Distance

The distances to galaxies are so large that it is not convenient to measure them in light-years, parsecs, or even kiloparsecs. Instead, astronomers use the unit **megaparsec (Mpc)**, or 1 million pc. One Mpc equals 3.26 million ly, or approximately 3×10^{19} km (2×10^{19} miles).

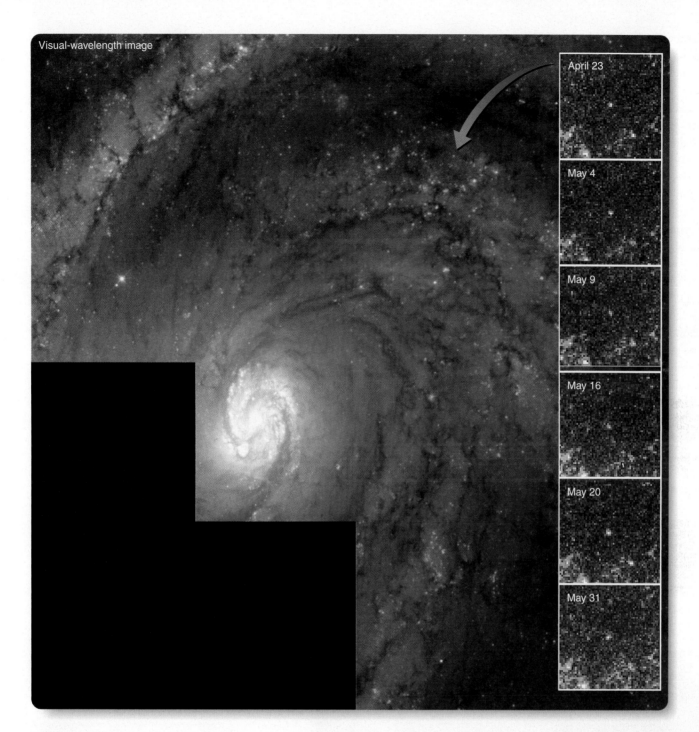

Visual-wavelength image

April 23

May 4

May 9

May 16

May 20

May 31

■ Figure 16-3

The vast majority of spiral galaxies are too distant for Earth-based telescopes to detect Cepheid variable stars. The Hubble Space Telescope, however, can locate Cepheids in some of these galaxies, as it has in the bright spiral galaxy M100. From a series of images taken on different dates, astronomers can locate Cepheids (inset), determine the period of pulsation, and measure the average apparent brightness. They can then deduce the distance to the galaxy—16 Mpc (52 million ly) for M100. (J. Trauger, JPL; Wendy Freedman, Observatories of the Carnegie Institution of Washington; and NASA)

To find the distance to a galaxy, astronomers must search among its stars, nebulae, and star clusters for familiar objects whose luminosity or diameter they know. Such objects are called **distance indicators** because they can be used to find the distance to a galaxy. Most distance indicators are objects whose brightness is known, and astronomers often refer to them as **standard candles**. If you can find a standard candle in a galaxy, you can judge its distance.

Cepheid variable stars are reliable distance indicators because their period is related to their luminosity. The period–luminosity relation has been calibrated (see Figure 12-14 as well as "How Do We Know? 15-1"), so you can use the period of the star's variation to find its absolute magnitude. Then, by comparing its absolute and apparent magnitudes, you can find its distance. ■ Figure 16-3 shows a galaxy in which the Hubble Space Telescope detected Cepheids.

Even with the Hubble Space Telescope, Cepheids are not visible in galaxies much beyond 30 Mpc (100 million ly), so astronomers must search for less common but brighter distance indicators and calibrate them using nearby galaxies that contain both indicators. For example, by studying nearby galaxies with distances known from Cepheids, astronomers have found that the brightest globular clusters have absolute magnitudes of about −10. If you found globular clusters in a more distant galaxy, you could assume that the brightest of the globular clusters have absolute magnitudes of −10 and use that information to calculate the distance.

Astronomers can use globular clusters in a different way. Studies of nearby globular clusters with known distance show that they are about 25 pc in diameter. If astronomers can detect globular clusters in a distant galaxy, they can assume the clusters are about 25 pc in diameter, measure their angular diameter, and calculate the distance to the galaxy from the small-angle formula. This shows that a distance indicator can be an object of known absolute magnitude or known diameter.

Astronomers can calibrate type Ia supernovae, those produced by the collapse of a white dwarf, because the white dwarf always collapses at the same mass limit, so the explosions reach approximately the same maximum luminosity. When type Ia supernovae occur in galaxies with distances that are known from Cepheid variables and other distance indicators, astronomers can find the absolute magnitude of the supernovae at peak brightness. An example is shown in ■ Figure 16-4. When astronomers see a type Ia supernova in a more distant galaxy, they observe the apparent magnitude of the supernova at maximum and compare that with the known absolute magnitude these supernovae reach at maximum to find the distance to the galaxy. As you will see in Chapter 18, this is a critical calibration in modern measurements of the size and age of the universe.

Cepheids and globular clusters are invisible in the most distant galaxies, and supernovae are rare. Consequently, to measure the greatest distances, astronomers have calibrated the total luminosity of the galaxies themselves. For example, studies of nearby galaxies show that a normal large spiral galaxy like the Milky Way has a luminosity of about 16 billion times that of the sun. If you see a spiral galaxy far away, you can measure its apparent magnitude and estimate its distance. Of course, it is important to recognize the different types of galaxies, and that is difficult to do at great distances, as you can see by looking at the fainter galaxies in Figure 16-2. Averaging the distances to the brightest spiral galaxies in a cluster can reduce the uncertainty in this method.

Notice how astronomers use calibration to build a **distance scale** reaching from the nearest galaxies to the most distant visible galaxies. Often astronomers refer to this as the "distance pyramid" or the "distance ladder" because each step depends on the steps below it. The most dependable step is the Cepheid variable stars, but notice that Cepheid distance indicators depend on astronomers' understanding of the luminosities of the stars in the H–R diagram, and that rests on a lower step in the ladder—measurements of the parallax of stars. Stellar parallaxes in turn depend on measuring the size of Earth's orbit around the sun, which finally rests on the bottom step, measuring the size of Earth itself. The distance ladder ultimately connects the size of Earth to the most distant galaxies in the universe.

The most distant visible galaxies are over 3000 Mpc (10 billion ly) away, and at such distances you see an effect akin to time travel. When you look at a galaxy that is millions of light-years away, you do not see it as it is now but as it was millions of years ago when its light began the journey toward Earth. When you look at a distant galaxy, you look back into the past by an amount called the **look-back time,** a time in years equal to the distance in light years the light from the galaxy traveled to reach Earth.

You may have experienced something like a look-back time if you have ever made a long-distance phone call carried by satellite or watched a TV newscaster interview someone via satellite.

■ Figure 16-4

While dinosaurs roamed Earth, a white dwarf in the galaxy NGC 1309 collapsed and exploded as a type Ia supernova, and the light from that explosion reached Earth in 2002. Astronomers found Cepheid variable stars in the galaxy, so they can determine that it is 100 million light-years away, and that allowed them to find the absolute magnitude of the supernova at its brightest. By combining observations of many supernovae, astronomers were able to calibrate type Ia supernovae as distance indicators. (Lick: W. Li and A. V. Filippenko, Berkeley; HST: NASA, ESA, The Hubble Heritage Team, STScI/AURA and A. Riess, STScI)

A half-second delay occurs as a radio signal carries a question 23,000 miles out to a satellite then back to Earth, then carries the answer out to the satellite and again back to Earth. That half-second look-back delay can make people hesitate on long-distance phone calls and produces a seemingly awkward delay in TV interviews.

The look-back time to nearby objects is usually not significant. For example, the look-back time across a football field is a tiny fraction of a second. The look-back time to the moon is 1.3 seconds, to the sun only 8 minutes, and to the nearest star a bit over 4 years. The Andromeda Galaxy has a look-back time of over 2 million years, but that is a mere eyeblink in the lifetime of a galaxy. If you look at more distant galaxies, the look-back time becomes an appreciable part of the age of the universe. You will learn about evidence in Chapter 18 that the universe began almost 14 billion years ago. When you look at the most distant visible galaxies, you are looking back over 10 billion years to a time when the universe was significantly different. The look-back time becomes an important factor as you begin to think about the origin and evolution of galaxies.

The Hubble Law

Although astronomers must work carefully to measure the distance to a galaxy, they often estimate such distances using a simple relationship that was first noticed at about the same time astronomers were beginning to understand the nature of galaxies.

In 1913, Vesto Slipher at Lowell Observatory reported on the spectra of some of the faint, nebulous objects in the sky. Their spectra seemed to be composed of a mixture of stellar spectra: Some had Doppler shifts that suggested rotation; most had redshifts as if they were receding; and the faintest had the largest redshifts. Within two decades, astronomers concluded that the faint objects are galaxies similar to our own Milky Way and that the galaxies are indeed receding from us in a general expansion.

In the 1920s, astronomers Edwin Hubble and Milton Humason were able to measure the distances to a number of galaxies using Cepheid variable stars. In 1929, they published a graph that plotted the apparent velocity of recession versus distance for their galaxies. The points in the graph fell along a straight line (■ Figure 16-5). The straight-line relation from Hubble's diagram can be written as the simple equation

$$V = Hd$$

That is, the apparent velocity of recession V equals the distance d in millions of parsecs times the constant H. This relation between redshift and distance is known as the **Hubble law**, and the constant H is known as the **Hubble constant**. Modern measurements of distance show that H equals about 70 km/s/Mpc.*

---

*H has the units of a velocity divided by a distance. These are usually written as km/s/Mpc, meaning km per second per Mpc.

■ **Figure 16-5**

Edwin Hubble's first diagram of the apparent velocities of recession and distances of galaxies did not probe very deeply into space, and the vertical axis was later recalibrated. These data did show, however, that the galaxies are receding from one another.

The Hubble law has important implications. It is commonly interpreted to show that the universe is expanding. In Chapter 18, you will study this expansion, but here you can use the Hubble law first as a practical way to estimate the distance to a galaxy.

Simply stated, a galaxy's distance equals its apparent velocity of recession divided by H. For example, if a galaxy has an apparent radial velocity of 700 km/s, and H is 70 km/s/Mpc, then the distance to the galaxy is 700 divided by 70, or about 10 Mpc. This makes it relatively easy to estimate the distances to galaxies because a large telescope can photograph the spectrum of a galaxy and determine its apparent velocity of recession even when it is too distant to have visible distance indicators.

Diameter and Luminosity

Once you find the distance to a galaxy from distance indicators or the Hubble law, you can calculate its diameter and its luminosity. With a good telescope and the right equipment, you could easily photograph a galaxy and measure its angular diameter in arc seconds. If you knew the distance, you could use the small-angle formula (see Chapter 3) to find its linear diameter. If you also measured the apparent magnitude of a galaxy, you could use the magnitude-distance formula to find its absolute magnitude and from that its luminosity (see Chapter 9).

The results of such observations show that galaxies differ dramatically in size and luminosity. Irregular galaxies tend to be small, 1 to 25 percent the size of our galaxy, and of low luminosity. Although they are common, they are easy to overlook. Our Milky Way Galaxy is large and luminous compared with most spiral galaxies, though astronomers know of a few spiral galaxies that are even larger and more luminous. The largest is nearly four times bigger in diameter and about 10 times more luminous. Elliptical galaxies cover a wide range of diameters and luminosities. The largest, called giant ellipticals, are five times the size of

Visual-wavelength image

■ **Figure 16-6**

The small galaxy cluster known as Hickson Compact Group 87 appears to contain three spiral galaxies and one elliptical. It is not known whether the small spiral galaxy is in the distant background or is part of the group, but it could be a group member. Note the contrast between the sizes of the galaxies. (Hubble Heritage Team, STScI/AURA/NASA)

our Milky Way, but many elliptical galaxies are very small dwarf ellipticals only 1 percent the diameter of our galaxy.

To put galaxies in perspective, you can use an analogy. If our galaxy were an 18-wheeler, the smallest dwarf galaxies would be the size of pocket-size toy cars, and the largest giant ellipticals would be the size of jumbo jets. Even among spiral galaxies that appeared similar in shape, the sizes could range from that of a go-cart to that of a large bus (■ Figure 16-6).

Clearly, the diameter and luminosity of a galaxy do not determine its type. Some small galaxies are irregular, and some are elliptical. Some large galaxies are spiral, and some are elliptical. Later in this chapter you can build a hypothesis for the origin and evolution of galaxies, but first, you need to add a third basic parameter—mass.

Mass

Although the mass of a galaxy is difficult to determine, it is an important quantity. It tells you how much matter the galaxy contains, which in turn provides clues to the galaxy's origin and evolution. In this section, you will examine two fundamental ways to find the masses of galaxies.

One way to find the mass of a galaxy is to watch it rotate. All you need to know is the radius of the galaxy (in AU) and the orbital period (in years) of the stars orbiting at the galaxy's outer edge. Then you can use Newton's version of Kepler's third law to find the mass, just as you found the mass of binary stars in Chapter 9.

Of course, you don't live long enough to see a galaxy rotate, so you must find the stars' orbital periods using a chain of inference. You could find the orbital velocity of the stars from the Doppler effect. If you focus the image of the galaxy on the slit of a spectrograph, you see a bright spectrum formed by the bright nucleus of the galaxy, in addition to fainter emission lines produced by ionized gas in the disk of the galaxy. Because the galaxy rotates, one side moves away from Earth and one side moves toward Earth, so the emission lines would be redshifted on one side of the galaxy and blueshifted on the other side. You could measure those changes in wavelength, use the Doppler formula to find the velocities, and plot a diagram showing the velocity of rotation at different distances from the center of the galaxy—a diagram called a **rotation curve**. The artwork in ■ Figure 16-7a shows the process of creating a rotation curve, and Figure 16-7b shows a real galaxy, its spectrum, and its rotation curve.

Of course, once you know the orbital velocity and the radius of a star's orbit around a galaxy, you can calculate its orbital period. You followed this procedure in the previous chapter to estimate the mass of the Milky Way Galaxy. The circumference of the orbit (2π times the radius) divided by the orbital velocity equals the orbital period. So knowing the velocity and size of an orbit tells you the orbital period, and from that you can find the mass. That is why the rotation curve of a galaxy is so important; it contains all the information you need to find the mass of the galaxy, and the method is known as the **rotation curve method**. It is the most accurate way to find the mass, but it works only for the nearer galaxies, whose rotation curves can be observed. More distant galaxies appear so small astronomers cannot measure the radial velocity at different points across the galaxy.

You should note one warning about masses found from rotation curves. Recent studies of our own galaxy and others show that the outer parts of the rotation curve do not decline to lower velocities as you would expect if most of the mass lies in the inner part of the galaxy. As in the case of the rotation curve of the Milky Way Galaxy (see Figure 15-11), this indicates that the galaxies contain large amounts of mass outside this radius, perhaps in extended galactic coronae. Because the rotation curve method can be applied only to nearby galaxies and because it cannot determine the masses of galactic coronas, astronomers have looked at another way to find the masses of galaxies.

The **cluster method** of finding the masses of galaxies depends on the motions of galaxies within a cluster. If you measured the radial velocities of many individual galaxies in a cluster, you would find that some velocities are larger than others. You could ask how massive a cluster of that size must be to hold itself together, given the range of velocities in the cluster. That is the same as asking how massive the cluster must be to have an escape velocity larger than the velocity of the fastest galaxy. Solving this problem would tell you the mass of the entire cluster. Dividing the total mass of the cluster by the number of galaxies in the cluster yields the average mass of the galaxies. This method

Figure 16-7

(a) In the upper panel's artwork representation, an astronomer has placed the image of the galaxy over a narrow slit so that light from the galaxy can enter the spectograph and produce a spectrum. A very short segment of the spectrum shows an emission line redshifted on the receding side of the rotating galaxy and blueshifted on the approaching side. Converting those Doppler shifts into velocities, the astronomer can plot the galaxy's rotation curve (right). (b) Real data are shown in the lower panel. Galaxy NGC 2998 is shown over the spectrograph slit, and the segment of the spectrum includes three emission lines. (Courtesy Vera Rubin)

contains the built-in assumption that the cluster is not flying apart. If it is, your result is too large. Because it seems likely that most clusters are held together by their own gravity, the method is probably valid.

A related way of measuring a galaxy's mass is called the **velocity dispersion method**. It is really a version of the cluster method. Instead of observing the motions of galaxies in a cluster, you could observe the motions of matter within a galaxy. In the spectra of some galaxies, broad spectral lines indicate that stars and gas are moving at high velocities. If you assume the galaxy is bound by its own gravity, you can ask how massive it must be to

hold this moving matter within the galaxy. This method, like the one before, assumes that the system is not coming apart.

Measuring the masses of galaxies reveals two things. First, the range of masses is wide—from 1 million times smaller than the Milky Way Galaxy to 50 times larger (■ Table 16-1). And second, galaxies contain dark matter spread through extended galactic coronae, just as does our Milky Way Galaxy.

One last region remains to be explored. What lies in the centers of galaxies? Our Milky Way Galaxy contains a 4 million-solar-mass black hole at its center. Do all galaxies contain similar objects?

■ Table 16-1 | The Properties of Galaxies*

	Elliptical	Spiral	Irregular
Mass	0.0001–50	0.005–2	0.0005–0.15
Diameter	0.01–5	0.2–1.5	0.05–0.25
Luminosity	0.00005–5	0.005–10	0.00005–0.1

*In units of the mass, diameter, and luminosity of the Milky Way Galaxy

Supermassive Black Holes in Galaxies

Rotation curves show the motions of the outer parts of a galaxy, but it is also possible to detect the Doppler shifts of stars orbiting very close to the centers. Although these motions are not usually shown on rotation curves, they reveal something astonishing.

Measurements show that the stars near the centers of most galaxies are orbiting very rapidly. To hold stars in such small, short-period orbits, the centers of galaxies must contain millions or even billions of solar masses in a very small region. The evidence shows that the nuclei of many galaxies contain supermassive black holes. The Milky Way contains a supermassive black hole at its center (see Chapter 15), and evidently that is typical of galaxies.

Such a supermassive black hole cannot be the remains of a dead star. That would amount to only a few solar masses. Rather, a supermassive black hole either formed as the galaxy formed or accumulated mass over billions of years as matter sank into the center of the galaxy. Measurements show that the mass of a supermassive black hole is related to the mass of the central bulge. A galaxy with a large central bulge has a supermassive black hole whose mass is greater than the black hole in a galaxy with a small central bulge. Rare galaxies lacking central bulges usually also lack supermassive black holes (■ Figure 16-8). This suggests that the supermassive black holes formed long ago as the galaxies formed. Of course, matter has continued to drain into the black holes, but they do not appear to have grown dramatically since they formed.

A billion-solar-mass black hole sounds like a lot of mass, but note that it is roughly 1 percent of the mass of a galaxy. The 4-million-solar-mass black hole at the center of the Milky Way Galaxy contains only one-thousandth of 1 percent of the mass of our galaxy. In the next chapter you will discover that these supermassive black holes can produce titanic eruptions, but they still represent only a small fraction of the mass of a galaxy.

Dark Matter in Galaxies

Given the size and luminosity of a galaxy, astronomers can make a rough guess as to the amount of matter it should contain. They know how much light stars produce, and they know about how much matter there is between the stars, so it is quite possible to estimate very roughly the mass of a galaxy from its luminosity. But when astronomers compare their estimates with measured masses of galaxies, they find that the measured masses are 10 times larger than the masses that can be seen. This must mean that nearly all galaxies contain dark matter. Theorists conclude that dark matter must be made up of some as yet undiscovered subatomic particles that do not interact with normal matter, with each other, or with light. Dark matter is detectable only through its gravitational field.

X-ray observations reveal more evidence of dark matter. X-ray images of galaxy clusters show that many of them are filled with very hot, low-density gas. The amount of gas present is much too small to account for the dark matter. Rather, the gas is

Visual-wavelength image

■ Figure 16-8

The galaxy M33 is near our Milky Way Galaxy, and it can be studied in detail. The velocities at the center of the galaxy are low, showing that it does not contain a supermassive black hole at its center. It also lacks a central bulge, and that confirms the observation that, with few exceptions, the mass of a supermassive black hole is related to the size of a galaxy's central bulge. (Bill Schoening/AURA/NOAO/NSF)

Gas in the Coma Cluster has a temperature over 100 million K.

b   X-ray image

a   Visual-wavelength image

■ **Figure 16-9**

(a) The Coma cluster of galaxies contains at least 1000 galaxies and is especially rich in E and S0 galaxies. Two giant galaxies lie near its center. Only the central area of the cluster is shown in this image. If the cluster were visible in the sky, it would span eight times the diameter of the full moon. (Gregory Bothun, University of Oregon) (b) In false colors, this X-ray image of the Coma cluster shows it filled and surrounded by hot gas. Note that the two brightest galaxies are visible in the X-ray image. (NASA/CXC/SAO/A. Vikhlinin et al.)

important because it is very hot and its rapidly moving atoms have not leaked away. Evidently the gas is held in the cluster by a strong gravitational field. To have a high enough escape velocity to hold the hot gas, the cluster must contain much more matter than what astronomers can observe directly. The detectable galaxies in the Coma cluster, for instance, amount to only a small fraction of the total mass of the cluster (■ Figure 16-9).

Dark matter is a significant issue. Observations of galaxies and clusters of galaxies show that approximately 90 percent of the matter in the universe is dark matter. The universe you see—the kind of matter that you and the stars are made of—has been compared to the foam on an invisible ocean.

Gravitational Lensing and Dark Matter

When you solve a math problem and get an answer that doesn't seem right, you check your work for a mistake. Astronomers using Newton's laws (for example, calculations of orbital velocity and escape velocity) to measure the mass of galaxies find evidence of large amounts of dark matter, so they look for ways to check their work. Fortunately, there is another way to detect dark matter that does not depend on Newton's laws. Astronomers can follow a light beam.

Albert Einstein described gravity as a curvature of space-time (see Chapter 5). The presence of mass actually distorts space-time, and that is what you feel as gravity. He predicted that a light beam traveling through a gravitational field would be deflected by the curvature of space-time much as a golf ball is deflected as it rolls over a curved putting green. That effect has been observed and is a strong confirmation that Einstein's theories are correct.

Gravitational lensing occurs when light from a distant object passes a nearby massive object and is deflected by the gravitational field. The gravitational field of the nearby object is actually a region of curved space-time that acts as a lens to deflect the passing light. Astronomers can use gravitational lensing to detect dark matter when light from very distant galaxies passes through a cluster of galaxies on its way to Earth and is deflected by the strong curvature. The distortion can produce multiple images of the distant galaxies and distort them into arcs. The amount of the distortion depends on the mass of the cluster of galaxies (■ Figure 16-10a). Observations of gravitational lensing made with very large telescopes reveal that clusters of galaxies contain far more matter than what can be seen. That is, they contain large amounts of dark matter. This confirmation of the existence of dark matter is independent of Newton's laws and gives astronomers great confidence that dark matter is real.

Dark matter is difficult to detect, and it is even harder to explain. The halos of galaxies contain faint objects such as white dwarfs, red dwarfs, and brown dwarfs, but not nearly enough to be the dark matter. It can't be black holes and neutron stars, because astronomers don't find the X-rays those objects would emit. Remember, there must be roughly 10 times more dark matter than visible matter, and such a huge number of black holes and neutron stars would produce X-rays that should be easy to detect.

Dark matter is so peculiar a few scientists have speculated that it isn't real, and that some quirk of gravity makes it seem that there is dark matter in the universe. Observations contradict this idea. Visual observations have identified two clusters of galaxies that passed through each other about 100 million years ago. X-ray observations show that the hot gas in the clusters collided and was swept out of the clusters by the collision, but gravitational lensing measurements show that the clusters still contain dark matter. As predicted by theory, the dark matter did not collide as the gas did and is still in the clusters. You can see the gas as the pink areas in Figure 16-10b and the locations of the dark matter as the purple areas. This shows that dark matter really exists and is not a quirk of gravitational theory.

Dark matter remains one of the fundamental unresolved problems of modern astronomy. You will learn more about this problem in Chapter 18 when you try to understand how dark matter affects the nature of the universe, its past, and its future.

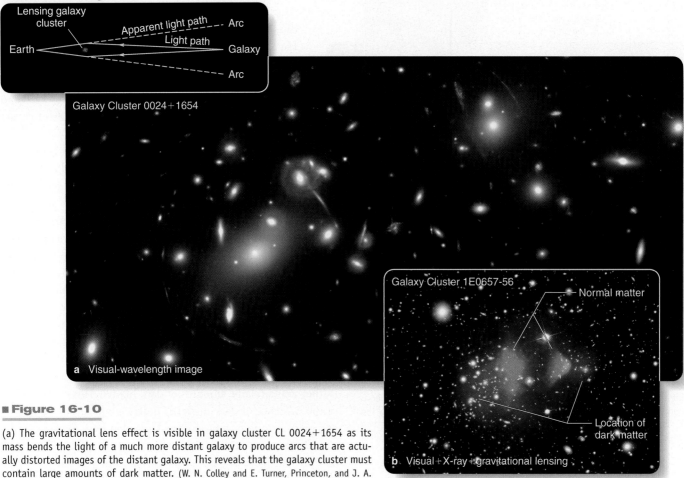

Gravitational lensing

Lensing galaxy
cluster

Apparent light path --- Arc

Light path

Earth

Galaxy

Arc

Galaxy Cluster 0024+1654

a   Visual-wavelength image

Galaxy Cluster 1E0657-56

Normal matter

Location of
dark matter

b   Visual+X-ray+gravitational lensing

■ **Figure 16-10**

(a) The gravitational lens effect is visible in galaxy cluster CL 0024+1654 as its mass bends the light of a much more distant galaxy to produce arcs that are actually distorted images of the distant galaxy. This reveals that the galaxy cluster must contain large amounts of dark matter. (W. N. Colley and E. Turner, Princeton, and J. A. Tyson, Bell Labs, and NASA) (b) When two galaxy clusters passed through each other, normal matter (pink) collided and was swept out of the clusters, but the dark matter (purple), detected by gravitational lensing, was not affected. (NASA/CXC/CfA/STScI/ Magellan/ESO WFI)

SCIENTIFIC ARGUMENT

Why do you have to know the distance to a galaxy to find its mass?
A good scientific argument proceeds step by step in a chain of inference with no gaps. This is a good example. To find the mass of a galaxy, you need to know the size of the orbits and the orbital periods of stars at the galaxy's outer edge and then use Kepler's third law to find the mass inside the orbits. Measuring the orbital velocity of the stars as the galaxy rotates is easy if you can obtain a rotation curve from a spectrum. But you must also know the radii of the stars' orbits in meters or astronomical units. That is where the distance comes in. Once you know the distance to the galaxy, you can use the small-angle formula to convert the radius in arc seconds into a radius in parsecs, in AU, or in meters. If your measurement of the distance to the galaxy isn't accurate, you will get inaccurate radii for the orbits and will compute an inaccurate mass for the galaxy.

Many different measurements in astronomy depend on the calibration of the distance scale. Build a step-by-step argument to analyze the following problem. **What would happen to your measurements of the diameters and luminosities of the galaxies if astronomers discovered that the Cepheid variable stars were slightly more luminous than had been thought?**

16-3) The Evolution of Galaxies

Your goal in this chapter is to build a theory to explain the evolution of galaxies. In Chapter 15 you considered the origin of our own Milky Way Galaxy; presumably, other galaxies formed similarly. But why did some galaxies become spiral, some elliptical, and some irregular? An important clue to that mystery lies in the clustering of galaxies.

Clusters of Galaxies

Single, isolated galaxies are rare. Instead, most galaxies occur in clusters containing a few to a few thousand galaxies in volumes 1 to 10 Mpc across (■ Figure 16-11). Our Milky Way Galaxy is a member of a small cluster, and surveys have cataloged thousands of other clusters.

For purposes of this study, you can sort clusters of galaxies into rich clusters and poor clusters. **Rich clusters** contain a thousand or more galaxies, mostly ellipticals, scattered through a

■ **Figure 16-11**

The Hercules galaxy cluster is named after the constellation in which it is found. It is a small cluster containing roughly a hundred galaxies, both elliptical and spiral. It lies over 500 million light-years from our galaxy. (NOAO/AURA/NSF)

Visual-wavelength image

NORTH

volume roughly 3 Mpc (10^7 ly) in diameter. Such a cluster is nearly always condensed; that is, the galaxies are more crowded near the cluster center. At their centers, such clusters often contain one or more giant elliptical galaxies.

The Virgo cluster is an example of a rich cluster. It contains over 2500 galaxies and is about 18 Mpc (59 million ly) from our galaxy. The Virgo cluster, like most rich clusters, is centrally condensed and contains the giant elliptical galaxy M87 at its center (page 334).

X-ray observations have found that many of these rich clusters are filled with a hot gas—an intracluster medium. Some of this gas has presumably been driven out of galaxies by supernovae explosions, but much of it appears to be left over from the formation of galaxies.

Poor clusters contain fewer than a thousand (and often only a few) galaxies spread through a region that can be as large as a rich cluster. That means the galaxies are more widely separated.

Our Milky Way Galaxy is a member of a poor cluster known by the unimaginative name of the Local Group (■ Figure 16-12a). The total number of galaxies in the Local Group is uncertain, but it probably contains about 40 galaxies scattered irregularly through a volume roughly 1 Mpc in diameter. Of the brighter galaxies, 15 are elliptical, 4 are spiral, and 13 are irregular.

The total number of galaxies in the Local Group is uncertain because some galaxies lie in the plane of the Milky Way Galaxy and are difficult to detect. For example, a small galaxy known as the Sagittarius Dwarf has been found on the far side of our own galaxy, where it is almost totally hidden behind the star clouds of Sagittarius (Figure 16-12b). Even closer to the Milky Way Galaxy is the Canis Major Dwarf Galaxy (Figure 16-12c). This galaxy was found by mapping the distribution of red supergiants detected by the 2MASS infrared survey. There are certainly other small galaxies in our Local Group that have not been detected yet.

Poor galaxy clusters tend not to be centrally condensed; rather, they tend to have subclusters with smaller galaxies crowded around larger galaxies. The Local Group illustrates this subclustering. The two largest galaxies, the Milky Way Galaxy and the Andromeda Galaxy, are the centers of two subclusters. The Milky Way Galaxy is accompanied by the Magellanic Clouds and at least seven other dwarf galaxies. The Andromeda Galaxy is attended by more dwarf elliptical galaxies and a small spiral, M33 (look again at Figure 16-8). The Andromeda Galaxy and our Milky Way Galaxy, with their retinues of smaller galaxies, are known to be moving toward each other and will almost certainly collide within a few billion years.

From all of this, you can draw an important conclusion: Galaxies do not live in isolation. They are usually found in clusters, often interact with nearby companions, and may even collide with each other. That leads to a critical clue hidden in the clusters of galaxies—the relative abundance of the different types of galaxies.

■ Figure 16-12

(a) The Local Group. Our galaxy is located at the center of this diagram. The vertical lines giving distances from the plane of the Milky Way are solid above the plane and dashed below. (b) The Sagittarius Dwarf Galaxy (Sgr Dwarf) lies on the other side of our galaxy. If you could see it in the sky, its minor axis would be 17 times wider than the full moon. (c) The Canis Major Dwarf Galaxy, shown in this simulation, is even closer to the Milky Way Galaxy. It is the remains of a small galaxy that is being pulled apart by our galaxy and is hidden behind the stars of the constellation Canis Major. (Nicolas Martin and Rodrigo Ibata, Strasbourg Observatory)

In general, rich clusters tend to contain 80 to 90 percent E and S0 galaxies and a few spirals. In other words, galaxies that are crowded together tend to be E or S0 rather than spirals. Poor clusters contain a larger percentage of spirals. Among the rare isolated galaxies that are not in clusters, 80 to 90 percent are spirals. Somehow the environment around a galaxy helps determine its type.

Astronomers suspect that collisions between galaxies are an important process. In a rich cluster, the galaxies are much closer together, and they must collide with each other more often than galaxies in a poor cluster. Could such collisions explain the excess of elliptical galaxies in the rich clusters? Astronomers have discovered that galaxy smashups are both important and entertaining.

Colliding Galaxies

Galaxies should collide fairly often. The average separation between galaxies is only about 20 times their diameter. Like two blindfolded elephants blundering about under a circus tent, galaxies should bump into each other once in a while. Stars, on the other hand, almost never collide. In the region of the galaxy near the sun, the average separation between stars is about 10^7 times their diameters. Consequently, a collision between two stars inside a galaxy is about as likely as collision between two gnats flitting about in a football stadium.

Read **Interacting Galaxies** on pages 348–349 and notice four important points and three new terms:

1 Interacting galaxies can distort each other with tides producing *tidal tails* and shells of stars. They may even trigger the formation of spiral arms. In fact, large galaxies can even absorb smaller galaxies, a process called *galactic cannibalism*.

2 Interactions between galaxies can trigger rapid star formation.

3 Evidence left inside galaxies in the form of motions and multiple nuclei reveals that they have suffered past interactions and mergers.

4 Finally, the beautiful *ring galaxies* are understood to be bull's-eyes left behind by high-speed collisions.

Evidence of galaxy mergers is all around you. Our Milky Way Galaxy is a cannibal galaxy snacking on the nearby Magellanic Clouds. Furthermore, our galaxy's tides are pulling the Sagittarius Dwarf Galaxy apart, and the Canis Major Dwarf Galaxy has been almost completely digested as tides have pulled stars away to form great streamers wrapped around the Milky Way Galaxy (■ Figure 16-13). Our galaxy has almost certainly dined on other small galaxies.

Infrared observations of the nearby Andromeda Galaxy show that it contains two dusty rings, a small inner ring and a larger outer ring. These appear to have been produced when the dwarf elliptical galaxy M32 plunged through the galaxy nearly perpendicular to the disk. You can see the rings in Figure 16-13b, and you can locate M32 below and to the left of the nucleus of the Andromeda Galaxy in Figure 15-1

You have seen the evidence that collisions and mergers between galaxies are common and can produce dramatic changes in the structure of the galaxies; now you are ready to evaluate a hypothesis that may explain how galaxies form and evolve.

The Origin and Evolution of Galaxies

The test of any scientific understanding is whether you can put all the evidence and theory together to tell the history of the objects studied. Can you describe the origin and evolution of the galaxies? Just a few decades ago, it would have been impossible, but the evidence from space telescopes and new-generation telescopes on Earth, combined with advances in computer modeling and theory, allows astronomers to outline the story of the galaxies.

Before you begin, you should eliminate a few older ideas immediately. It is so easy to imagine that galaxies normally evolve from one type to another that you could call that a **Common Misconception**. But an elliptical galaxy cannot become a spiral galaxy or an irregular galaxy because ellipticals contain almost no gas and dust from which to make new stars. That means elliptical galaxies can't be young galaxies. But you can also argue that spiral and irregular galaxies cannot evolve into elliptical galaxies because spiral and irregular galaxies contain old stars as well as young stars. The old stars tell you that spiral and irregular galaxies can't be young. The galaxy classes tell you something important, but a single galaxy does not change from one class to another any more than a cat can change into a dog.

Stream of stars ripped from galaxy

Location of sun

Canis Major Galaxy

a   Artist's impression

Small ring

Large ring

b   Infrared

■**Figure 16-13**

Interactions with small galaxies: (a) As shown in this mathematical model, the Canis Major Dwarf Galaxy has orbited around the Milky Way Galaxy a number of times, and tides have ripped stars and gas away to form streamers. (Nicolas Martin and Rodrigo Ibata, Strasbourg Observatory) (b) A small inner ring and a large outer ring in the Andromeda Galaxy are evidence that a dwarf galaxy passed through perpendicular to the disk of the larger galaxy about 200 million years ago. (NASA/JPL D. Block)

Interacting Galaxies

1 When two galaxies collide, they can pass through each other without stars colliding because the stars are so far apart relative to their sizes. Gas clouds and magnetic fields do collide, but the biggest effects may be tidal. Even when two galaxies just pass near each other, tides can cause dramatic effects, such as long streamers called **tidal tails.** In some cases, two galaxies can merge and form a single galaxy.

Tidal Distortion

Small galaxy passing near a massive galaxy.

Gravity of a second galaxy represented as a single massive object

1a When a galaxy swings past a massive object such as another galaxy, tides are severe. Stars near the massive object try to move in smaller, faster orbits while stars farther from the massive object follow larger, slower orbits. Such tides can distort a galaxy or even rip it apart.

Galaxy interactions can stimulate the formation of spiral arms

In this computer model, two uniform disk galaxies pass near each other.

The small galaxy passes behind the larger galaxy so they do not actually collide.

Tidal forces deform the galaxies and trigger the formation of spiral arms.

The upper arm of the large galaxy passes in front of the small galaxy.

A photo of the well-known Whirlpool Galaxy resembles the computer model.

Visual

Allen Beechel

Visual false-color image

The Mice are a pair of galaxies whipping around each other and being distorted.

Computer model of the Mice

Allen Beechel

1b The merger of galaxies is called **galactic cannibalism.** Models show that merging galaxies spiral around their common center of mass while tides rip stars away and form shells.

Computer model

François Schweizer and Alar Toomre

Shells of stars

Such shells have been found around elliptical galaxies such as NGC 5128. It is peculiar in many ways and even has a belt of dusty gas. The shells revealed in this enhanced image are evidence that the giant galaxy has cannibalized at least one smaller galaxy. The giant galaxy itself may be the result of the merger of two large galaxies.

NOAO

Visual enhanced image

NOAO

2 The collision of two galaxies can trigger firestorms of star formation as gas clouds are compressed. Galaxies NGC 4038 and 4039 have been known for years as the Antennae because the long tails visible in Earth-based photos resemble the antennae of an insect. Hubble Space Telescope images reveal that the two galaxies are blazing with star formation. Roughly a thousand massive star clusters have been born.

Spectra show that the Antennae galaxies are 10 to 20 times richer in elements such as magnesium and silicon than the Milky Way. Such metals are produced by massive stars and spread by supernova explosions.

The Antennae

Brad Whitmore, STScI/NASA

Ground-based visual image

Hubble Space Telescope visual image

3 Evidence of past galaxy mergers shows up in the motions inside some galaxies. NGC 7251 is a highly distorted galaxy with tidal tails in this ground-based image.

Visual

This Hubble Space Telescope image of the core of the galaxy reveals a small spiral spinning backward in the heart of the larger galaxy.

This rotation suggests that NGC 7251 is the remains of two oppositely rotating galaxies that merged about a billion years ago.

An X-ray image of the Antennae shows clouds of very hot gas heated by supernovae exploding 30 times more often than in our own galaxy.

X-ray image

NASA/CXC/SAO/
G. Fabbiano et al.

3a Radio evidence of past mergers: Doppler shifts reveal the rotation of the spiral galaxy M64. The upper part of the galaxy has a redshift and is moving away from Earth, and the bottom part of the galaxy has a blueshift and is approaching. A radio map of the core of the galaxy reveals that it is rotating backward. This suggests a merger long ago between two galaxies that rotate in opposite directions.

Rotation of galaxy M64

Redshift

Blueshift

Robin Braun NRAO/AUI/NSF

4 The Cartwheel galaxy below was once a normal galaxy but is now a **ring galaxy.** One of its smaller companions has plunged through at high speed almost perpendicular at the Cartwheel's disk. That has triggered a wave of star formation, and the more massive stars have exploded leaving behind black holes and neutron stars. Some of those are in X-ray binaries, and that makes the outer ring bright in X-rays.

Purple = X-ray
Blue = UV
Green = Visible
Red = Infrared

Evidence of galactic cannibalism: Giant elliptical galaxies in rich clusters sometimes have multiple nuclei, thought to be the densest parts of smaller galaxies that have been absorbed and only partly digested.

Multiple nuclei

Visual false-color image

Composite: NASA/JPL/
Caltech/P. Appleton et al.
X-ray: NASA/CXC/A. Wolter
& G. Trinchieri

Another old idea held that a galaxy that formed from a rapidly rotating cloud of gas would have lots of angular momentum and would contract slowly to form a disk-shaped spiral galaxy. A cloud of gas that rotated less rapidly would contract faster, form stars quickly, use up all of its gas and dust, and become an elliptical galaxy. This reflects the original hypothesis that galaxies formed from the top down—from a single large cloud of gas. That idea is mentioned in the previous chapter as the "monolithic collapse hypothesis." Modern evidence clearly shows that galaxies form partly from the bottom up—from the gradual accumulation of smaller clouds of gas and stars and, in some cases, entire galaxies. Collisions and mergers dominate the history of the galaxies.

Ellipticals appear expecially to be the product of galaxy collisions and mergers. They are devoid of gas and dust because it was used up in the rapid star formation triggered by the interaction. In fact, astronomers see many **starburst galaxies** that are very luminous in the infrared because a recent collision has triggered a burst of star formation that is heating the dust (■ Figure 16-14), which reradiates the energy in the infrared. Some of these galaxies are a hundred times more luminous than our Milky Way Galaxy but so deeply shrouded in dust that they are very dim at visible wavelengths. Such **ultraluminous infrared galaxies (ULIRGs)** show evidence of tidal tails and are probably the result of the merger of three or more galaxies that

triggered firestorms of star formation and generated tremendous clouds of dust. The Antennae Galaxies (page 349) contain over 15 billion solar masses of hydrogen gas and will become a starburst galaxy as the ongoing merger continues to trigger rapid star formation. As these galaxies use up the last of their gas and dust making stars, they will probably become normal elliptical galaxies or merge to form a single elliptical.

Another process can help clear the gas and dust out of elliptical galaxies. Supernovae in a starburst galaxy can blow away the remaining gas and dust, and a burst of rapid star formation produces lots of supernova explosions.

In this way, a few collisions and mergers could leave a galaxy with no gas and dust from which to make new stars and could scramble the orbits of the remaining stars to produce an elliptical shape. Astronomers now suspect that most elliptical galaxies are formed by the merger of at least two or three galaxies of comparable size.

In contrast, spirals have never suffered major collisions. Their thin disks are delicate and would be destroyed by the tidal

■ Figure 16-14

Rapid star formation: (a) NGC 1569 is a starburst galaxy filled with clouds of young stars and supernovae. At least some starbursts are triggered by interactions between galaxies. (ESA/NASA/P. Anders) (b) The dwarf irregular galaxy NGC 1705 began a burst of star formation about 25 million years ago. (NASA/ESA/Hubble Heritage Team/AURA/STScI) (c) The inner parts of M64, known as the "Black Eye Galaxy," are filled with dust produced by rapid star formation. Radio observations (page 349) show that the inner part of the galaxy rotates backward compared to the outer part of the galaxy, a product of a merger. Where the counterrotating parts of the galaxy collide, star formation is stimulated. (NASA/ESA/Hubble Heritage Team/STScI/AURA)

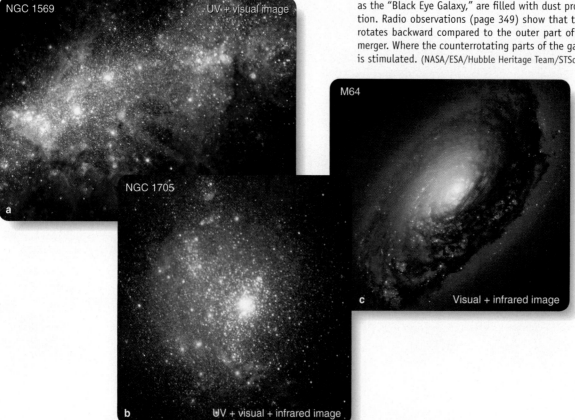

NGC 1569 — UV + visual image

NGC 1705

M64 — Visual + infrared image

b — UV + visual + infrared image

forces generated during a collision with a massive galaxy. Also, they retain plenty of gas and dust and continue making stars, so they have never experienced a major starburst triggered by a merger.

Of course, spiral galaxies can safely cannibalize smaller galaxies with no ill effects. The small galaxies do not generate strong tides to distort a full-sized galaxy. You have seen plenty of evidence of cannibalism in our own galaxy, and some astronomers suspect that much of the halo consists of the remains of cannibalized galaxies. Evidently our Milky Way Galaxy has not collided with a galaxy of size comparable to itself, so far. Such a collision would trigger rapid star formation, use up gas and dust, scramble the orbits of stars, and destroy the thin disk. However, other evidence indicates that our galaxy will merge with the approaching Andromeda Galaxy, and the final result probably will be a large elliptical galaxy.

Just as people do, spiral galaxies may need some interaction to fully develop. Only one in 10,000 galaxies is isolated from its neighbors; and, although most of these are disk galaxies, many are flocculent without a strong two-armed spiral pattern. Some isolated galaxies are rich in gas and dust but have little star formation. All of this suggests, as was discussed in the previous chapter, that continuous gentle gravitational interactions with neighboring galaxies is necessary to stimulate spiral structure and star formation.

Earlier, the Virgo cluster was cited as a rich cluster, so you may find it surprising to learn that it contains lots of spiral galaxies. Rich clusters are supposed to contain few spirals. Astronomers hypothesize that the cluster is so massive that the galaxies orbit the center of mass of the cluster at such high speeds that they rush past each other too quickly to interact strongly. The galaxies are whittled down a bit, but many are still disk galaxies with spiral patterns.

Barred spiral galaxies may also be the products of tidal interactions. Mathematical models show that bars are not stable and eventually dissipate. Tidal interactions with other galaxies may regenerate the bars. Well over half of all spiral galaxies have bars, suggesting that these tidal interactions are common.

Other processes can alter galaxies. The S0 galaxies retain a disk shape but lack gas and dust. Although they could have lost gas and dust during starburst episodes, they may also have lost it as they orbited through the gas in their respective clusters. A galaxy moving rapidly through the thin gas filling a cluster would encounter a tremendous wind that could blow the galaxy's gas and dust away. In this way, a disk-shaped spiral galaxy could be reduced to an S0 galaxy. For example, X-ray observations show that the Coma cluster contains thin, hot gas between the galaxies (Figure 16-9), and astronomers have located, in a similar cluster, a galaxy in the act of plunging through such gas and being stripped of its gas and dust (■ Figure 16-15).

Small galaxies may be produced in a number of ways. The dwarf ellipticals are too small to be produced by mergers, but

Visible (white)
X-ray (purple)
Radio (red)

■ **Figure 16-15**

The distorted galaxy C153 is orbiting through the thin gas in its home cluster of galaxies at 2000 km/s (4.5 million mph). At that speed, it feels a tremendous wind stripping gas out of the galaxy in a trail 200,000 ly long. Such galaxies could quickly lose almost all of their gas and dust. (NASA, W. Keel, F. Owen, M. Ledlow, and D. Wang)

they could be fragments of galaxies ripped free during interactions. Another possibility is that the dwarf ellipticals are small galaxies that have plunged through the gas in a cluster of galaxies and lost their gas and dust. In contrast, the irregular galaxies may be small fragments splashed from larger galaxies during collisions but retaining enough gas and dust to continue forming stars.

Other factors must influence the evolution of galaxies. The hot gas in galaxy clusters warns that galaxies rarely form in isolation. Cooler gas clouds may fall into galaxies and add material for star formation. These processes are just beginning to be understood.

A good theory helps you understand how nature works, and astronomers are beginning to understand the exciting and complex story of the galaxies. Nevertheless, it is already clear that galaxy evolution bears some resemblance to a pie-throwing contest.

The Farthest Galaxies

Observations made with the largest and most sophisticated telescopes are taking astronomers back to the age of galaxy formation. At great distances the look-back time is so great that the universe can be seen as it was soon after the galaxies began to form. There were more spirals then and fewer ellipticals. On the whole, galaxies long ago were more compact and more irregular than they are now. The observations also show that galaxies were closer together long ago; about a third of all distant galaxies are in close pairs, but only 7 percent of nearby galaxies are in pairs. The observational evidence clearly supports the hypothesis that galaxies have evolved by merger.

At great distances, astronomers see tremendous numbers of small, blue, irregularly shaped galaxies that have been called blue dwarfs. The blue color indicates that they are rapidly forming stars, but the role of these blue dwarfs in the formation of galaxies is not clear. Blue dwarf galaxies are not found at small look-back times, so they no longer exist in the present universe. They may be clouds of gas and stars that were absorbed long ago in the formation of larger galaxies, or they may have used up their gas and dust and faded into obscurity.

At the limits of the largest telescopes, astronomers see faint red galaxies (■ Figure 16-16). They look red from Earth because of their great redshifts. The floods of ultraviolet light emitted by these star-forming galaxies have been shifted into the far-red part of the spectrum. Their look-back times are so great that they appear as they were when the universe was only a billion years old. These galaxies seem to be among the first to begin shining after the beginning of the universe, a story told in Chapter 18.

SCIENTIFIC ARGUMENT

How did elliptical galaxies get that way?

Telling the story of a natural object is a goal that lies at the heart of science, and many scientific arguments tell such tales. A growing body of evidence suggests that elliptical galaxies have been subject to collisions in their past and that spiral galaxies have not. During collisions, a galaxy can be driven to use up its gas and dust in a burst of star formation, and the resulting supernova explosions can help drive gas and dust out of the galaxy. This explains why elliptical galaxies now contain little star-making material. The beautiful disk typical of spiral galaxies is very orderly, with all the stars following similar orbits. When galaxies collide, the stellar orbits get scrambled, and an orderly disk galaxy could be converted into a chaotic swarm of stars typical of elliptical galaxies. It seems likely that elliptical galaxies have had more complex histories than spiral galaxies have had.

When scientists create a scientific argument to tell the story of a natural object, they use evidence to make the story as true as it can be. Expand your argument. **What evidence can you cite to support the story in the preceding paragraph?**

Visual-wavelength image

■ Figure 16-16

Arrows point to three very distant red galaxies. The look-back time to these galaxies is so large that they appear as they were when the universe was only a billion years old. Such highly redshifted galaxies are believed to be among the first to form stars and begin shining after the beginning of the universe about 14 billion years ago. (NASA, H.-J. Yan, R. Windhorst and S. Cohen, Arizona State University)

What Are We? Small and Proud

Do you feel insignificant yet? You are riding a small planet orbiting a humdrum star that is just one of at least 100 billion stars in the Milky Way Galaxy, and you have just learned that there are at least a 100 billion galaxies visible with existing telescopes. When you look at galaxies you are looking across voids deeper than human imagination. You can express such distances with numbers and say a certain galaxy is 5 billion light-years from Earth, but the distance is truly beyond human comprehension. Furthermore, looking at distant galaxies also leads you back in time. You see distant galaxies as they were billions years ago. The realm of the galaxies is deep space and deep time.

Some people say astronomy makes them feel humble; but, before you agree, consider that you can feel small without feeling humble. Size is not necessarily the same thing as significance. We humans live out our little lives on our little planet, but our tiny brains are able to figure out some of the most profound mysteries of the universe. We are exploring deep space and deep time and coming to understand what galaxies are and how they evolve. Most of all, we humans are beginning to understand what we are. That's something to be proud of.

Summary

▶ Through 19th-century telescopes, galaxies looked like hazy **spiral nebulae (p. 332)**. Some astronomers said they were other star systems sometimes called **island universes (p. 332)**, but others said they were clouds of gas inside the Milky Way system. The controversy culminated in the **Shapley-Curtis debate (p. 332)** in 1920.

▶ A few years later, with the construction of larger telescopes, astronomers could identify stars, including Cepheid variable stars, in the spiral nebulae. That showed that the spiral nebulae were galaxies.

▶ Astronomers divide galaxies into three classes—**elliptical (p. 334)**, **spiral (p. 334)**, and **irregular (p. 335)**—with subclasses specifying the galaxy's shape.

▶ Elliptical galaxies contain little gas and dust and cannot make new stars. Consequently, they lack hot, blue stars and have a reddish tint.

▶ Spiral galaxies contain more gas and dust in their disks and support active star formation, especially along the spiral arms. Some of the newborn stars are massive, hot, and blue, and that gives the spiral arms a blue tint. About two-thirds of spirals, including our Milky Way Galaxy, are **barred spiral galaxies (p. 334)**.

▶ The halo and central bulge of a spiral galaxy usually lack gas and dust and contain little star formation. The halos and central bulges have a reddish tint because they lack hot, blue stars.

▶ Irregular galaxies have no obvious shape but contain gas and dust and support star formation.

▶ Galaxies are so distant astronomers measure their distances in **megaparsecs (Mpc) (p. 336)**—millions of parsecs.

▶ Astronomers find the distance to galaxies using **distance indicators (p.337)**, sometimes called **standard candles (p. 337)**, objects of known luminosity. The most accurate distance indicators are the Cepheid variable stars. Globular clusters and type Ia supernovae explosions have also been calibrated as distance indicators.

▶ By calibrating additional distance indicators, astronomers have built a **distance scale (p. 338)**.

▶ When astronomers look at a distant galaxy, they see it as it was when it emitted the light now reaching Earth. The **look-back time (p. 338)** to distant galaxies can be a significant fraction of the age of the universe.

▶ According to the **Hubble law (p. 339)**, the apparent velocity of recession of a galaxy equals its distance times the **Hubble constant (p. 339)**. Astronomers can estimate the distance to a galaxy by observing its redshift, calculating its apparent velocity of recession, and then dividing by the Hubble constant.

▶ Once the distance to a galaxy is known, its diameter can be found from the small-angle formula and its luminosity from the magnitude-distance relation.

▶ Astronomers measure the masses of galaxies in two basic ways. The **rotation curve (p. 340)** of a galaxy shows the orbital motion of its stars, and astronomers can use the **rotation curve method (p. 340)** to find the galaxy's mass.

▶ The **cluster method (p. 340)** uses the velocities of the galaxies in a cluster to find the total mass of the cluster. The **velocity dispersion method (p. 341)** uses the velocities of the stars in a galaxy to find the total mass of the galaxy.

▶ Galaxies come in a wide range of sizes and masses. Some dwarf ellipticals and dwarf irregular galaxies are only a few percent of the size and luminosity of our galaxy, but some giant elliptical galaxies are five times larger than the Milky Way Galaxy.

▶ Stars near the centers of galaxies are following small orbits at high velocities, which suggests the presence of supermassive black holes in the centers of most galaxies.

▶ The mass of a galaxy's supermassive black hole is proportional to the mass of its central bulge. This shows that the supermassive black holes must have formed when the galaxy formed.

▶ Observations of individual galaxies show that galaxies contain 10 to 100 times more dark matter than visible matter.

▶ The hot gas held inside some clusters of galaxies and the **gravitational lensing (p. 343)** caused by the mass of galaxy clusters reveal that the clusters must be much more massive than can be accounted for by the visible matter—further evidence of dark matter.

▶ **Rich clusters (p. 344)** of galaxies contain thousands of galaxies with fewer spirals and more ellipticals. **Poor clusters (p. 345)** of galaxies contain few galaxies with a larger proportion of spirals. This is evidence that galaxies evolve by collisions and mergers.

▶ When galaxies collide, tides twist and distort their shapes and can produce **tidal tails (p. 348)**.

▶ Large galaxies can absorb smaller galaxies in what is called **galactic cannibalism (p. 348)**. There is clear evidence that our own Milky Way Galaxy is devouring some of the small galaxies that orbit nearby and that our galaxy has consumed other small galaxies in the past.

▶ Shells of stars, counterrotating parts of galaxies, streams of stars in the halos of galaxies, and multiple nuclei are evidence that galaxies can merge.

▶ **Ring galaxies (p. 349)** are produced by high-speed collisions in which a small galaxy plunges through a larger galaxy perpendicular to its disk.

▶ The compression of gas clouds can trigger rapid star formation, producing **starburst galaxies (p. 350)**. The rapid star formation can produce lots of dust, which is warmed by the stars to emit infrared radiation, making the galaxy an **ultraluminous infrared galaxy (ULIRG) (p. 350)**.

▶ The merger of two larger galaxies can scramble star orbits and drive bursts of star formation to use up gas and dust. Most large ellipticals have evidently been produced by past mergers.

▶ Spiral galaxies have thin, delicate disks and appear not to have suffered mergers with large galaxies.

▶ A galaxy moving through the gas in a cluster of galaxies can be stripped of its own gas and dust and may become an S0 galaxy.

▶ Rare isolated galaxies tend to be spirals and lack a bar or a strong two-armed spiral pattern, which suggests that gentle interactions with neighbors are needed to stimulate the formation of bars and spiral arms.

▶ At great distance and great look-back times, the largest telescopes reveal that galaxies were smaller, more irregular, and closer together. There were more spirals and fewer ellipticals long ago.

▶ At the largest distances, astronomers find small irregular clouds of stars that may be the original objects that fell together to begin forming galaxies when the universe was very young.

Review Questions

1. If a civilization lived on a planet in an E0 galaxy, do you think they would have a "Milky Way" band of starlight in their sky? Why or why not?

2. Why can't the evolution of galaxies go from elliptical to spiral? From spiral to elliptical?

3. If all elliptical galaxies had three different diameters, you would never see an elliptical galaxy with a circular outline on a photograph. True or false? Explain your answer. (*Hint:* Can a football ever cast a circular shadow?)

4. What is the difference between an Sa and an Sb galaxy? Between an S0 and an Sa galaxy? Between an Sb and an SBb galaxy? Between an E7 and an E0 galaxy?

5. Why wouldn't white dwarfs make good distance indicators?

6. Why isn't the look-back time important among nearby galaxies?

7. Explain how the rotation curve method of finding a galaxy's mass is similar to the method used to find the masses of binary stars.

8. Explain how the Hubble law allows you to estimate the distances to galaxies.

9. How can collisions affect the shape of galaxies?

10. What evidence can you cite that galactic cannibalism really happens?

11. Describe the future evolution of a galaxy that astronomers now see as a starburst galaxy. What will happen to its interstellar medium?

12. Why does the gas held in a cluster of galaxies help determine the nature of the galaxies in a cluster?

13. **How Do We Know?** Classification helped Darwin understand how creatures evolve. How has classification helped you understand how galaxies evolve?

Discussion Questions

1. From what you know about star formation and the evolution of galaxies, do you think irregular galaxies should be bright or faint in the infrared? Why or why not? What about starburst galaxies? What about elliptical galaxies?

2. Imagine that you could observe a few gas clouds at such a high look-back time that they are just beginning to form one of the first galaxies. Further, suppose you discovered that the gas was metal rich. Would that support or contradict your understanding of galaxy formation?

Problems

1. If a galaxy contains a type I (classical) Cepheid with a period of 30 days and an apparent magnitude of 20, what is the distance to the galaxy? (*Hints:* See Figure 12-4 and the definition of distance modulus in Chapter 9.)

2. If you find a galaxy that contains globular clusters that are 2 arc seconds in diameter, how far away is the galaxy? (*Hints:* Assume that a globular cluster is 25 pc in diameter and use the small-angle formula in Chapter 3.)

3. If a galaxy contains a supernova that at its brightest has an apparent magnitude of 17, how far away is the galaxy? (*Hint:* Assume that the absolute magnitude of the supernova is −19 and see the definition of distance modulus in Chapter 9.)

4. If you find a galaxy that is the same size and mass as our Milky Way Galaxy, what orbital velocity would a small satellite galaxy have if it orbited 50 kpc from the center of the larger galaxy? (*Hint:* See Chapter 15.)

5. Find the orbital period of the satellite galaxy described in Problem 4.

6. If a galaxy has an apparent radial velocity of 2000 km/s and the Hubble constant is 70 km/s/Mpc, how far away is the galaxy? (*Hint:* Use the Hubble law.)

7. If you find a galaxy that is 20 arc minutes in diameter and you measure its distance to be 1 Mpc, what is its diameter?

8. Suppose you found a galaxy in which the outer stars have orbital velocities of 150 km/s. If the radius of the galaxy is 4 kpc, what is the orbital period of the outer stars? (*Hints:* 1 pc = 3.08×10^{13} km, and 1 yr = 3.16×10^{7} seconds.)

9. A galaxy has been found that is 5 kpc in radius and whose outer stars orbit the center with a period of 200 million years. What is the mass of the galaxy? On what assumptions does this result depend?

10. Among the globular clusters orbiting a distant galaxy, the fastest is traveling 420 km/s and is located 11 kpc from the center of the galaxy. Assuming the globular cluster is just barely gravitationally bound to the galaxy, what is the mass of the galaxy? (*Hint:* The galaxy had a slightly faster globular cluster, but it escaped some time ago. What is the escape velocity?)

Learning to Look

1. Study Figure 16-2. Which galaxies do you suppose are the nearest ones, and which are farthest away? How is your estimate based on your own calibration of galaxy size and luminosity?

2. Hubble's first determination of the Hubble constant was too high because the calibration of Cepheid variable stars he used was not very good. Use his original diagram shown in Figure 16-5 to estimate his first determination of the Hubble constant.

3. This image of M33 has emission by ionized hydrogen enhanced as bright pink. Discuss the location of these clouds of gas and explain how that provides important evidence toward understanding spiral arms.

P. Massey, Lowell Obs.; N. King, STScI; S. Holmes, College of Charleston; G. Jacoby, WIYN/AURA/NSF

4. In the image at right you see two interacting galaxies; one is nearly face-on and the other is nearly edge-on. Discuss the shapes of these galaxies and describe what is happening.

WIYN/NOAO/AURA/NSF

17 | Active Galaxies and Supermassive Black Holes

Visual (white) + radio (orange)

Size of Milky Way Galaxy

Guidepost

In the last few chapters, you have explored our own and other galaxies, and now you are ready to stretch your scientific imagination and study some of the most powerful objects in nature. Supermassive black holes at the centers of galaxies are common but extreme. To study them, you will be combining many of the ideas you have discovered so far to answer four essential questions:

— **What makes some galaxy cores active?**

— **How do supermassive black holes erupt?**

— **How did supermassive black holes form and evolve?**

— **How do supermassive black holes affect the evolution of their host galaxies and galaxy clusters?**

The formation and evolution of supermassive black holes leads your astronomical curiosity outward into space and backward in time to the era of galaxy formation. In the next chapter, you will take the next step and try to understand the birth and evolution of the entire universe.

Like cosmic fireworks, the galaxy NGC 1316 (Fornax A) has erupted to expel two lobes visible at radio wavelengths. The size of the Milky Way Galaxy is shown for comparison. (Image courtesy of Barbara Harris)

Somewhere something incredible is waiting to be known.

— CARL SAGAN

Supermassive black holes containing millions or even billions of solar masses lurk at the centers of many galaxies. Such monsters can release tremendous energy and cause eruptions that dwarf the largest supernovae. Yet most supermassive black holes in galaxy centers are not erupting. Why? The study of supermassive black holes will introduce you to some of the most extreme conditions in the universe.

17-1 Active Galactic Nuclei

With the construction of the first large radio telescopes in the 1950s, astronomers discovered that some galaxies, dubbed **radio galaxies,** were bright at radio wavelengths. Later, when telescopes went into orbit, these galaxies were found to be emitting energy at other wavelengths as well, and they became known as **active galaxies.** Modern observations show that the energy comes from the nuclei of the galaxies, which are now known as **active galactic nuclei (AGN).** Only a few percent of galaxies are active, so your first step is to meet these peculiar galaxies.

Seyfert Galaxies

In 1943, Mount Wilson astronomer Carl Seyfert published a study of spiral galaxies. Observing at visual wavelengths, Seyfert found that some spiral galaxies have small, highly luminous nuclei with peculiar spectra (■ Figure 17-1). These galaxies are now known as **Seyfert galaxies.**

The spectrum of a galaxy is the blended spectra of billions of stars, and consequently weak spectral lines get washed out. Galaxy spectra contain only a few of the strongest absorption lines found in stellar spectra. But spectra of Seyfert galaxy nuclei contain broad emission lines. Emission lines are produced by a hot, low-density gas, so the gas in the nuclei of Seyfert galaxies must be highly excited. The width of the spectral lines suggests large Doppler shifts produced by high velocities in the nuclei; gas approaching Earth produces blueshifted spectral lines, and gas going away produces redshifted lines. The combined light of gas approaching and receding, therefore, contains broad spectral lines showing that the velocities at the center of Seyfert galaxies are roughly 10,000 km/s, about 30 times greater than velocities at the center of normal galaxies. Something violent is happening in the cores of Seyfert galaxies.

About 2 percent of spiral galaxies appear to be Seyfert galaxies, and they are classified into two categories. Type 1 Seyfert galaxies are very luminous at X-ray and ultraviolet wavelengths and have the typical broad emission lines with sharp, narrow cores. Rapidly moving gas produces the broad part of the lines, but some lower-velocity gas must also be present to produce the

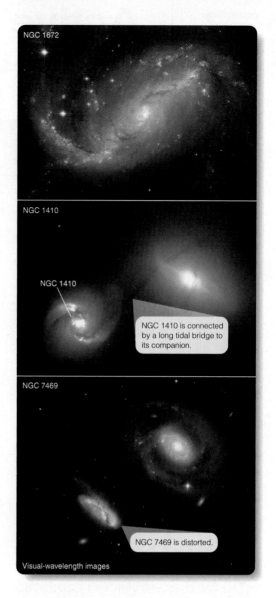

NGC 1672

NGC 1410

NGC 1410

NGC 1410 is connected by a long tidal bridge to its companion.

NGC 7469

NGC 7469 is distorted.

Visual-wavelength images

■ **Figure 17-1**

Seyfert galaxies are spirals with small, highly luminous nuclei. Some are interacting with nearby companions and appear distorted with tidal tails and bridges. (All images: NASA, ESA, Hubble Heritage Team, STScI/AURA-ESA/Hubble Collaboration; NGC 1410: Wm. Keel, Univ. of Alabama; NGC 7469: A. Evans, Univ. of Virginia, NRAO/Stony Brook)

narrow cores. Type 2 Seyfert galaxies have much weaker X-ray emission and have emission lines that are narrower than those of type 1 Seyfert galaxies but still broader than spectral lines produced by a normal galaxy.

The brilliant nuclei of Seyfert galaxies fluctuate rapidly, especially at X-ray wavelengths. A Seyfert nucleus can change its X-ray brightness by a significant amount in only minutes. As you learned when you studied neutron stars, an object cannot change its brightness in a time shorter than the time it takes light to cross its diameter. If the Seyfert nucleus can change in a few minutes, then it cannot be more than a few light-minutes in diameter—about the size of Earth's orbit. In spite of their small size, the cores of

Statistical Evidence

How can statistics be useful if they can't be specific? Some scientific evidence is statistical. Observations suggest, for example, that Seyfert galaxies are more likely to be interacting with a nearby companion than a normal galaxy is. This is statistical evidence, so you can't be certain that any specific Seyfert galaxy will have a companion. How can scientists use statistical evidence to learn about nature when statistics contain built-in uncertainty?

Meteorologists use statistics to determine how frequently storms of a certain size are likely to occur. Small storms happen every year, but medium-sized storms may happen on average only every ten years. Hundred-year storms are much more powerful but occur much less frequently—on average only once in a hundred years.

Those meteorological statistics can help you make informed decisions—as long as you understand the powers and limitations of

statistics. Would you buy a house protected from a river by a levee that was not designed to withstand a hundred-year storm? In any one year, the chance of your house being destroyed would be only 1 in 100. You know the storm will hit eventually, but you don't know when. If you buy the house, a storm might destroy the levee the next year, but you might own the house for your whole life and never see a hundred-year storm. The statistics can't tell you anything about a specific year.

Before you buy that house, there is an important question you should ask the meteorologists. "How much data do you have on storms?" If they have only ten years of data, then they don't really know much about hundred-year storms. If they have three centuries of data, then their statistical data are significant.

Sometimes people dismiss important warnings by saying, "Oh, that's only statistics." Scientists can use statistical

Statistics can tell you that a bad storm will eventually hit, but it can't tell you when. (Marko Georgiev/Getty Images)

evidence if it passes two tests. It cannot be used to draw conclusions about specific cases, and it must be based on large enough data samples so the statistics are significant. With these restrictions, statistical evidence can be a powerful scientific tool.

Seyfert galaxies produce tremendous amounts of energy. The brightest emit a hundred times more energy than the entire Milky Way Galaxy.

Lots of energy is produced in a very small volume with extremely high temperatures and velocities. What does that remind you of? Astronomers conclude that the centers of these galaxies contain supermassive black holes orbited by hot accretion disks through which matter is flowing into the black hole.

In the previous chapter, you saw evidence that most galaxies contain supermassive black holes at their centers. But most

galaxies are not erupting. The shapes of Seyfert galaxies provide an important clue. About 25 percent of Seyfert galaxies have peculiar shapes suggesting that they have had tidal interactions with other galaxies (■ Figure 17-2). There is also statistical evidence (**How Do We Know? 17-1**) that Seyfert galaxies are more common in interacting pairs of galaxies than in isolated galaxies. These clues hint that Seyfert galaxies may have been triggered into activity by collisions or interactions with companions. You will find more such evidence as you study other kinds of active galaxies.

NGC 7674

Tidal tail

Tidal tail

Seyfert galaxy NGC 7674 is distorted with faint tidal tails.

a   Visual-wavelength image   b   False-color visual-wavelength image

■ **Figure 17-2**

(a) The Seyfert galaxy NGC 7674 is part of a small, compact group of galaxies and is interacting with its smaller companion. Tidal tails are visible extending to the left and to the upper right. (b) The tidal tails are more easily visible in this enhanced image. (a: NASA, ESA, Hubble Heritage Team, STScI/AURA-ESA/Hubble Collaboration and A. Evans, Univ. of Virginia, NRAO/Stony Brook; b: John W. Mackenty, Institute for Astronomy, University of Hawaii)

Double-Lobed Radio Sources

Beginning in the 1950s, radio astronomers found that some sources of radio energy in the sky consisted of pairs of radio-bright regions. When optical telescopes studied the locations of these radio sources, they revealed galaxies located between the two regions emitting radio energy, and the galaxies were dubbed **double-lobed radio galaxies.** Unlike Seyfert galaxies, which emit intense radiation from their cores, these radio galaxies are producing energy from two external radio lobes.

Study **Cosmic Jets and Radio Lobes** on pages 360–361 and notice four important points and two new terms:

1 The shapes of radio lobes suggest that they are inflated by jets of excited gas emerging from the nucleus of the central galaxy. This has been called the *double-exhaust model.* The presence of *hot spots* and synchrotron radiation shows that the jets are very powerful.

2 Active galaxies that have jets and radio lobes are often deformed or interacting with other galaxies.

3 The complex shapes of some jets and radio lobes can be explained by the motions of the active galactic nuclei. A good example of this is 3C 31 (the 31st source in the *Third Cambridge Catalog of Radio Sources*) with its twisting radio lobes.

4 These jets are consistent with matter falling into a central supermassive black hole. You have seen similar jets produced by accretion disks around protostars, neutron stars, and stellar mass black holes; although the details are not entirely understood, the same process seems to be producing all of these jets.

The evidence shows that the cores of many galaxies are occupied by supermassive black holes with matter flowing inward. As the matter falls toward the center, it releases tremendous gravitational energy and becomes intensely hot. The hot accretion disks can emit X-rays and eject jets in opposite directions.

In fact, the violence of these active galaxies is so great it can influence entire clusters of galaxies. The Perseus galaxy cluster contains thousands of galaxies and is one of the largest objects in the universe. One of its galaxies, NGC 1275, is one of the largest galaxies known. It is pumping out jets of high-energy particles, heating the gas in the galaxy cluster, and inflating low-density bubbles that distort the huge gas cloud (■ Figure 17-3). The hot gas observed in galaxy clusters is heated to multimillion-degree temperatures as galaxy after galaxy goes through eruptive stages that can last for hundreds of millions of years. NGC 1275 is erupting now, and it is so powerful and has heated the surrounding gas so hot that it may temporarily interrupt supply of gas to its central supermassive black hole, eventually choking off the eruption and curtailing further growth of the black hole. Astronomers speculate that there may be a

■ Figure 17-3

Active galaxy NGC 1275, also known as radio source Perseus A, lies in the Perseus galaxy cluster and is spewing out jets and streamers of high-energy particles that are inflating low-density cavities in the hot gas. Galaxy clusters commonly contain such hot gas, and active galaxies may be the main source of energy that heats the gas. The entire galaxy cluster is roughly 50 times larger in diameter than this image. (NASA/CXC/IoA/A. Fabian et al.)

maximum size for supermassive black holes set by this cycle of self-limiting activity.

Quasars

Through the 1950s, radio astronomers became familiar with celestial radio sources that were either huge clouds of gas or distant radio galaxies, so they were surprised in the early 1960s when some radio sources turned out to look like stars in visual-wavelength photographs (■ Figure 17-4). First called quasi-stellar objects, they were soon referred to as **quasars.** Many more quasars have been found over the years, and most are radio silent. The radio astronomers stumbled over those emitting radio energy because they were easy to notice. From their discovery, quasars have been a puzzle to astronomers.

The spectra of quasars were strange in that they contained a few unidentified emission lines superimposed on a continuous spectrum. In 1963, Maarten Schmidt at Hale Observatories tried redshifting the hydrogen Balmer lines to see if they could be made to agree with the lines in the spectrum of the quasar known as 3C 273. At a redshift of 15.8 percent, three lines clicked into place (■ Figure 17-5). Other quasar spectra quickly yielded to this approach, revealing even larger redshifts.

■ Figure 17-4

Quasars have starlike images clearly different from the images of even very distant galaxies. Although quasars look like stars, their spectra are unlike the spectra of stars or galaxies. The spikes on these images were produced by diffraction in the telescope. (C. Steidel, Caltech, NASA)

Numerically the redshift z is the change in wavelength $\Delta\lambda$ divided by the unshifted wavelength λ_0:

$$\text{redshift} = \frac{\Delta\lambda}{\lambda_0}$$

According to the Hubble law, these large redshifts imply very large distances. The first quasars studied were the brighter ones, but surveys have found many more. For example, the Sloan Digital Sky Survey discovered 90,000. Most of these quasars have very high redshifts and lie very far from Earth.

Many quasar redshifts are greater than 1.0, and that may strike you as impossible. The Doppler formula implies that such objects must have velocities greater than the speed of light. But the redshifts of the galaxies and quasars are not produced by the Doppler effect. As you will discover in the next chapter, the redshifts are produced by the expansion of the universe, and astronomers must use the equations of general relativity to interpret them. Redshifts greater than 1.0 are not a problem and merely indicate great distance.

Although the quasars are far away, they are not very faint. A typical galaxy at such a distance would be faint and extremely difficult to detect, but quasars show up on photographs as noticeable points of light. If you put the apparent brightnesses and huge distances of quasars into the magnitude–distance relation, you will discover that quasars are ultraluminous, having 10 to 1000 times the luminosity of a large galaxy.

Soon after quasars were discovered, astronomers detected fluctuations in brightness over times as short as a few hours. Those rapid fluctuations show that quasars are small objects, not more than a few light-hours in diameter—smaller than our solar system.

By the late 1960s, astronomers trying to understand quasars faced a problem: How could quasars be ultraluminous but also very small? What could make 10 to 1000 times more energy than a galaxy in a region as small as our solar system? Since that time, new, large telescopes in space and on Earth's surface have revealed

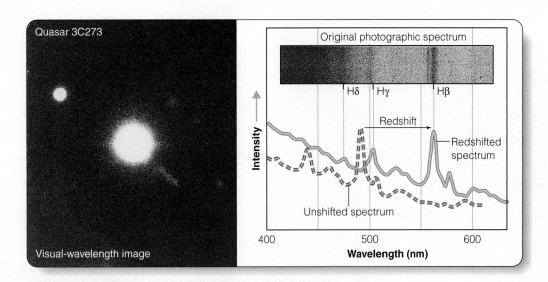

■ Figure 17-5

This image of 3C 273 shows the bright quasar at the center surrounded by faint fuzz. Note the jet protruding to lower right. The original photographic plate holding a spectrum of 3C 273 contains three hydrogen Balmer lines, H_δ, H_γ, and H_β. The spectrum is redshifted by 15.8 percent. The dashed line shows the unshifted position of the spectrum. (Image and photographic spectrum courtesy of Maarten Schmidt)

Cosmic Jets and Radio Lobes

1 Many radio sources consist of two bright lobes — double-lobed radio sources — with a galaxy, often a peculiar or distorted galaxy, located between them. Evidence suggests these active galaxies are emitting jets of high-speed gas that inflate the lobes as cavities in the intergalactic medium. This has been called the **double-exhaust model.** Where the jets impact the far side of the cavities, they create **hot spots.**

Size of Milky Way Galaxy

Hot spot

Radio image

Hot spots lie on the leading edge of a lobe where the jet pushes into the surrounding gas.

NRAO

Jet

Jet

Hot spot

1a Cygnus A, the brightest radio source in Cygnus, is a pair of lobes with jets leading from the nucleus of a highly disturbed galaxy. In this false-color image, the areas of strongest radio signals are shown in red and the weakest in blue. Because the radio energy detected is synchrotron radiation, astronomers conclude that the jets and lobes contain very-high-speed electrons, usually called relativistic electrons, spiraling through magnetic fields about 1000 times weaker than Earth's field. The total energy in a radio lobe is about 10^{53} J — what you would get if you turned the mass of a million suns directly into energy.

Visible galaxy

Used with permission, Fosbury R. A. E., Vernet, J., Villar-Martin, M., Cohen, M. H., Ogle, P. M., Tran, H. D. & Hook, R. N. 1998, Optical continuum structure of Cygnus A. "KNAW colloquium on: The most distant radio galaxies," Amsterdam, 15–17 October 1997, Roettgering, H., Best, P., and Lehnert M. eds (Reidel).

2 The radio galaxy NGC 5128 lies between two radio lobes, and, like many active galaxies, is strangely distorted. The dust ring rotates about an axis perpendicular to the ring, but the spherical cloud of stars rotates about an axis that lies in the plane of the ring. NGC 5128 appears to be two galaxies, a giant elliptical and a spiral, passing through each other. This has triggered multiple eruptions. An earlier eruption has produced a large outer pair of lobes, and a more recent eruption has produced an inner pair.

NASA/CXC/NRAO/VLA

Infrared

Nucleus

Radio = Red
X-ray = Blue

The combined radio and X-ray image at the left shows a high-energy jet at the very center of the galaxy pointing to the upper left into the northern radio lobe.

If the outer radio lobes of Centaurus A were visible to your eyes, they would look 10 times larger than the full moon.

Radio (green)

X-ray (blue)

Visual + radio + X-ray

Radio galaxy 3C31 NGC 383

NRAO/AUI/NSF

Visual (blue) + Radio (red)

from NGC 1265 are being left behind as the galaxy moves rapidly through the gas of the intergalactic medium. Twists in the tails are presumably caused by motions of the active nucleus.

Direction of motion

Radio image

NRAO/AUI/NSF and C. O'Dea & F. Owen

3a Radio galaxy 3C31 is one of a chain of galaxies. It has ejected jets from its core that twist, presumably because the active nucleus is orbiting another object such as the nucleus of a recently absorbed galaxy.

3b The radio source 3C75 is produced by two galaxies experiencing a close encounter. As the active nuclei whip around each other, their jets twist and turn. The size of the visible galaxies would be about the size of cherries at the scale of this image.

Nucleus

Nucleus

Radio image

NRAO/AUI/NSF and F.N. Owen, C.P. O'Dea, M. Inoue, & J. Eilek

4 High-energy jets appear to be caused by matter flowing into a supermassive black hole in the core of an active galaxy. Conservation of angular momentum forces the matter to form a whirling accretion disk around the black hole. How that produces a jet is not entirely understood, but it appears to involve magnetic fields that are drawn into the accretion disk and tightly wrapped to eject high-temperature gas. The twisted magnetic field confines the jets in a narrow beam and causes synchrotron radiation.

4a Jets from active galaxies may have velocities from thousands of kilometers per second up to a large fraction of the speed of light. Compare this with the jets in bipolar flows, where the velocities are only a few hundred kilometers per second. Active-galaxy jets can be millions of light-years long. Bipolar-flow jets are typically a few light-years long. The energy is different, but the geometry is the same.

Black hole

Magnetic field lines

Accretion disk

4b Excited matter traveling at very high speeds tends to emit photons in the direction of travel. Consequently, a jet pointed roughly toward Earth will look brighter than a jet pointed more or less away. This may explain why some radio galaxies have one jet brighter than the other, as in Cygnus A shown at the top of the opposite page. It may also explain why some radio galaxies appear to have only one jet. The other jet may point generally away from Earth and be too faint to detect, as in the case of NGC 5128, also shown on the opposite page.

Adapted from a diagram by Ann Field, NASA, STScI

that quasars are often surrounded by hazy features whose spectra resemble those of normal galaxies. Evidently, quasars are located in galaxies. In addition, radio telescopes have revealed that some quasars are ejecting jets and inflating radio lobes. The evidence is now overwhelming that quasars are the active cores of very distant galaxies. In other words, quasars are the most extreme kind of active galactic nuclei.

17-2 Supermassive Black Holes

IN THE PREVIOUS TWO CHAPTERS, you learned that many galaxies contain supermassive black holes at their centers. Why do such objects produce eruptions, and how did they form?

Disks and Jets

Matter flowing inward toward a black hole spins very fast and becomes very hot. It spins because it must conserve angular momentum as it sinks inward where it forms a flattened disk around the central black hole. Supermassive black holes have stronger gravity than stellar-mass black holes and produce faster spins for the in-falling matter and higher temperatures. Even a supermassive black hole is surprisingly small. A 10-million-solar-mass black hole would be only one-fifth the diameter of Earth's orbit, so the matter can get close to the black hole and orbit very fast. The in-falling matter heats up because it picks up speed; and, as it collides with other matter, those high velocities become thermal energy. That is, matter falling inward converts gravitational energy into thermal energy and becomes hot.

Theoretical calculations predict that the high temperature "puffs up" the inner part of the disk and makes it thick. Closer to the black hole, an orbiting particle is unstable and must spiral into the black hole, so the black hole is hidden deep inside an empty central well. Farther out, the disk is thinner and cooler, but the outermost part of the disk, according to calculations, is a fat, cool torus (doughnut shape) of dusty gas.

Astronomers can't see black holes, but in some active galaxies, the Hubble Space Telescope can detect the outer parts of the central disks (■ Figure 17-6). Spectra reveal the speed of rotation, and Kepler's third law yields the mass of the central object. Some supermassive black holes have masses of a few million solar masses, like the one in the center of our Milky Way Galaxy, but the most massive contain billions of solar masses.

The inner part of the accretion disk around a supermassive black hole can reach temperatures of millions of degrees and emit X-rays. In fact, cosmic ray detectors on Earth have observed ultra-high-energy particles that come from places in the sky occupied by active galactic nuclei. These powerful supermassive black holes and their hot accretion disks may be filling the universe with high-speed particles packing the wallop of major league fastballs.

No one knows exactly how the supermassive black hole and its disk produce jets of gas and radiation, but magnetic fields are a factor. Because the disk is at least partially ionized, magnetic fields are trapped in the gas of the disk, drawn inward, and wound up. Theorists suggest that this creates powerful magnetic tubes extending along the axis of rotation, channeling hot gas

NGC, 4261

Visual (white) radio (orange)

Visual-wavelength image

800 ly

Perpendicular to the axis of the jets leading into radio lobes, this disk encloses 1.2 billion solar masses.

■ **Figure 17-6**

The elliptical galaxy NGC 4261 is ejecting jets and inflating radio lobes. High-resolution images show that the core contains a small, bright nucleus orbited by a spinning disk. The orbital velocity and size of the disk confirm that the central object is a supermassive black hole. (L. Ferrarese, Johns Hopkins University, and NASA) outward in opposite directions. The jets seem to originate very close to the supermassive black hole and are then focused and confined by the enclosing magnetic tubes.

The mechanism that produces jets is understood in only a general way, but astronomers are now trying to work out the details. How can supermassive black holes explain all of the different kinds of active galaxies that are observed?

The Search for a Unified Model

When a field of research is young, scientists find many seemingly different phenomena, such as Seyfert galaxies, double-lobed radio galaxies, quasars, cosmic jets, and so on. As the research matures, scientists begin seeing similarities and eventually are able to unify the different phenomena as different aspects of a single process. This organization of evidence and theory into logical arguments that explain how nature works is the real goal of science. Astronomers studying active galaxies have developed a **unified model** of active galaxy cores that is well supported by evidence. A monster black hole is the centerpiece.

According to the unified model, what you see when you view the core of an active galaxy depends on how the black hole's accretion disk is tipped with respect to your line of sight. You should note that the accretion disk may be tipped at a steep angle to the plane of its galaxy, so just because you see a galaxy face-on doesn't mean you are looking at the accretion disk face-on.

If you view the accretion disk edge-on, you cannot see the central area at all because the thick dusty torus blocks your view. Instead, you see gas lying above and below the central disk, gas that is excited by intense radiation coming from the black hole down in the central well. Because this gas is farther from the center, it is cooler, orbits more slowly, and has smaller Doppler shifts and thus narrower spectral lines (■ Figure 17-7). This might account for the type 2 Seyfert galaxies.

■ **Figure 17-7**

The features visible in the spectrum of an AGN depend on the angle at which it is viewed. The unified model, shown in cross section, suggests that matter flowing inward passes first through a large, opaque torus; then into a thinner, hotter disk; and finally into a small, hot cavity around the black hole. Telescopes viewing such a disk edge-on would see only narrow spectral lines from cooler gas, but a telescope looking into the central cavity would see broad spectral lines formed by the hot gas. This diagram is not to scale. The central cavity may be only 0.01 pc in radius, while the outer torus may be 1000 pc in radius. (Artist's impression: NASA)

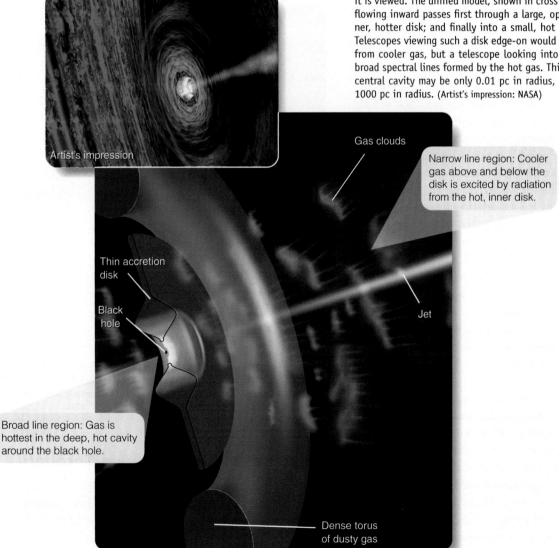

Artist's impression

Gas clouds

Narrow line region: Cooler gas above and below the disk is excited by radiation from the hot, inner disk.

Thin accretion disk

Black hole

Jet

Broad line region: Gas is hottest in the deep, hot cavity around the black hole.

Dense torus of dusty gas

If the accretion disk is tipped slightly, you may be able to see some of the intensely hot gas in the central cavity. This region emits broad spectral lines because the hot gas is orbiting at high velocities and the high Doppler shifts smear out the lines. Type 1 Seyfert galaxies may be explained by this phenomenon.

What happens if you look directly into the central cavity? According to the unified model, you would be looking directly into the high-energy jet—down the dragon's throat. A few such objects have been found; they have a featureless spectrum and fluctuate in brightness in only hours.

The unified model is far from complete. The actual structure of accretion disks is poorly understood, as is the process by which the disks produce jets. The unified model does not explain all of the differences among active galaxies and quasars. Rather, it is a model that provides some clues to what is happening in active galactic nuclei.

Triggering Eruptions

Most galaxies contain supermassive black holes at their centers, but only a few percent of galaxies have active galactic nuclei. That must mean that most of the supermassive black holes are dormant. They are sleeping.

What could trigger a supermassive black hole to erupt? The answer is something that you studied back in Chapter 5—tides. In the previous chapter you saw how tides twist interacting galaxies and rip matter away into tidal tails, but mathematical models show that those same interactions can also throw matter inward. A sudden flood of matter flowing into the accretion disk around a supermassive black hole would trigger it into eruption. This explains why active galaxies are often distorted; they have been twisted by tidal forces as they interacted or merged with another galaxy. Some active galaxies have nearby companions, and you can suspect that the companions are guilty of tidally distorting the other galaxy and triggering an eruption by tossing material into its central supermassive black hole.

Tidal forces between galaxies span distances of 100,000 ly or more, but the same bit of physics becomes important when matter comes very close to a supermassive black hole. ■ Figure 17-8 shows how a passing star would be ripped apart by tidal forces and at least partially consumed by a black hole. Inflowing gas, dust, and an occasional star would be an energy feast for a supermassive black hole.

Observations support the idea that galaxy interactions trigger active galactic nuclei. You have seen that many active galaxies are distorted. Images of some quasars reveal that they are embedded in galaxies that are distorted and lie near other distorted galaxies (■ Figure 17-9). Furthermore, in a survey of active galactic nuclei, over a third were found to originate in double objects. That is, the active nucleus is orbiting an object of similar mass. Evidently, these objects are the result of galaxy mergers in which the two original galaxies' supermassive black holes have sunk to the center of the new combined galaxy and are spiraling toward each other.

Star Falling into a Black Hole

A star, perhaps disturbed by an encounter with another star, drifts toward a supermassive black hole.

As the near side of the star tries to orbit faster than the far side, the star is torn apart by tidal forces.

Most of the mass of the star is flung away from the black hole…

but roughly 1 percent falls into the black hole as an accretion disk forms.

■ **Figure 17-8**

Orbiting X-ray telescopes observing active galaxies sometimes detect X-ray flares equaling the energy of a supernova explosion. Such flares are evidently caused when a star wanders too close to the supermassive black hole at the center of the galaxy and tidal forces rip the star apart. (ESA)

Supermassive Black Holes Through Time

When you look at a photo of galaxies with large redshifts, the look-back time is large, and you see the universe as it was long ago. The light journeying from such a great distance carries information about how the galaxies formed and developed.

■ Figure 17-9

The bright object at the center of each of these images is a quasar. Fainter objects around and near the quasars are galaxies distorted by collisions and tidal interactions. (J. Bahcall, Institute for Advanced Study, Mike Disney, University of Wales, NASA)

Astronomers have been able to measure the masses of a few dozen supermassive black holes by observing the speed of matter whirling around them. Interestingly, those masses are correlated with the masses of the host galaxies' central bulges. In each case, the mass of the black hole is about 0.5 percent the mass of the surrounding central bulge. But, for disk galaxies, there is no relationship between the masses of the black holes and the masses of the disks. This bit of statistics provides an intriguing insight into how galaxies formed soon after the universe began. Somehow, the formation process for supermassive black holes in the centers of galaxies was connected with the formation of their central bulges, but not their disks.

In the next chapter, you will see evidence that the universe began 13.7 billion years ago and that it has been expanding ever since. Within a few hundred million years, the first clouds of gas began forming stars and falling together to form the great star clouds that became the nuclear bulges of galaxies. The supermassive black holes formed at the same time. In fact, some evidence suggests that the black holes formed first and pulled matter inward to form central bulges. Matter flooding into these black holes would have triggered powerful outbursts, which because of the large look-back times could be visible from Earth today. The

formation of a central bulge was evidently a violent process. Astronomers hypothesize that the increasing power of outbursts from the growing central black hole in a forming galaxy would have been able to push away infalling gas and limit the material available to form the stars of the central bulge.

In a spiral galaxy such as the Milky Way, the disk with its spiral arms and bright stars seems a dominant part of the galaxy. But recall from Chapter 15 that the disk formed late as matter gradually settled into the galaxy. By that stage, the central bulge and black hole had already formed, and the gradual development of the outer disk didn't trigger a violent eruption. "Disk formation is wimpy," said one astronomer.

Some of the most distant quasars could have been caused by the formation of supermassive black holes, but these extremely distant objects are difficult to image with existing telescopes. Most of the quasars and other active galaxies that astronomers see with today's telescopes have been triggered into eruption by the interaction and collision of galaxies, a process that throws matter into the central black holes. When the universe was young and had not expanded very much, galaxies were closer together and collided more often. Also, as small galaxies fell inward and formed halos around larger galaxies (see Chapter 16), more matter would have been fed inward to the supermassive black holes and triggered more eruptions.

Astronomers have interpreted these observations to imply that in the first half of the history of the universe, each galaxy merged with other galaxies as often as three times every billion years. Most mergers were with smaller galaxies, but a few would have been with larger galaxies and triggered eruptions visible from Earth today as quasars.

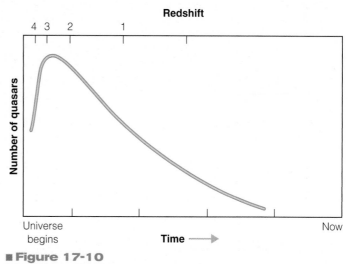

■ Figure 17-10

At large look-back times, you see the universe as it was long ago. Between redshifts of about 2 and 3, you look back to a time when galaxies were closer together and were actively forming, merging, and interacting. That produced quasars. More recently, quasars have become less common.

Quasars are most common with redshifts over 2 and less common with redshifts above 3 (■ Figure 17-10). The largest quasar redshifts are over 6, but such high-redshift quasars are quite rare. Evidently astronomers see few quasars at high red-shifts because they are looking back to an age when the universe was so young it had not yet formed many galaxies. At redshifts between about 2 and 3, galaxies were actively growing, colliding, and merging, and quasars were about 1000 times more common than they are now. Nevertheless, even during the age of quasars, quasar eruptions must have been unusual. At any one time, only a small fraction of galaxies had quasars erupting in their cores. As smaller galaxies were gobbled up and expansion of the universe (Chapter 18) carried the galaxies away from each other, galaxy formation became less active, interactions between galaxies became rare, and quasars became even less common.

"Then where are all the dead quasars?" an astronomer asked recently. "There is no way to get rid of supermassive black holes, so all of the galaxies that had short-lived quasars must still have those supermassive black holes." Where are all those dead quasars today? You know where to look—the cores of galaxies.

Many galaxies, perhaps the majority of large galaxies, contain supermassive black holes at their centers, but the black holes have consumed most of the nearby gas, dust, and stars and are now dormant. Our own Milky Way Galaxy could have had a quasar at its core long ago, but now its central supermassive black hole is on a strict diet. A slow trickle of matter flowing into the black hole could explain the mild activity seen there. Occasional interactions between galaxies can throw matter inward and nudge the dragon, awaking a sleeping supermassive black hole into eruption as a Seyfert galaxy or a double-lobed radio galaxy.

The active galaxies are not a rare kind of galaxy. They are normal galaxies passing through a stage that many galaxies experience: They are not really peculiar. They are an important part of the story of the formation and evolution of galaxies.

SCIENTIFIC ARGUMENT

What do the distorted shapes of active galaxies tell you?
Seyfert galaxies and the galaxies located between double radio lobes are often distorted and have tidal tails. Also, the galaxies that are faintly visible around quasars are also typically twisted out of shape. These distortions must be caused by tidal interactions with nearby galaxies or by mergers, and such tides can throw matter inward toward the supermassive black hole at the center of a galaxy and trigger an eruption.

Now build a new scientific argument. **Why were quasars rare when the universe was young, and why are they rare today?**

What Are We? Changed

Next time you are in a shopping mall, glance at the people around you. How many of them, do you suppose, know that galaxies can erupt or that there was an age of quasars? The vast majority of people have no idea how their lives fit into the story of the universe. Most people don't know what they are. They eat pizza and watch TV without understanding that they are part of a universe in which galaxy collisions trigger supermassive black holes to erupt in titanic explosions.

Astronomy is changing you. As you learn more about stars and galaxies and quasars, you are learning more about yourself and your connection with nature. "Perspective" can mean a view of things in their true relationships. As you study astronomy, you are gaining perspective. Our galaxy, our sun, our planet, and the local shopping mall take on new meaning when you think astronomically.

Summary

- First called **radio galaxies (p. 356)**, **active galaxies (p. 356)** are now known to emit energy at many wavelengths. Because the energy comes from their cores, they are known also as **active galactic nuclei (AGN) (p. 356)**.

- **Seyfert galaxies (p. 356)** are spiral galaxies with small, highly luminous cores and spectra that show the nuclei contain highly excited gas.

- **Double-lobed radio galaxies (p. 358)** emit radio energy from areas on either side of the galaxies. As described by the **double-exhaust model (p. 360)**, these lobes are inflated by jets ejected from the nuclei of the galaxies. Where the jets have an impact on surrounding gas, they form **hot spots (p. 360)**.

- Jets from active galaxies are at least in part responsible for heating the gas trapped in clusters of galaxies.

- The **quasars (p. 358)** have a starlike appearance but very large redshifts that imply they are very distant. To be visible at such distances, quasars must be ultraluminous. Yet rapid fluctuations in brightness show that quasars must be small, with diameters of only a few light hours, comparable in size to our solar system.

- The best images show that quasars are embedded in galaxies that are often distorted or have close companions. From this, astronomers conclude that quasars are the highly luminous cores of very distant active galaxies.

- Matter flowing into a supermassive black hole must conserve angular momentum and form an accretion disk. Observations indicate that these accretion disks are thick and dusty at great distances from the central black hole but thin and hot closer in. The closest part of the disk is puffed up, and the black hole is hidden deep in a cavity at the center. A few such disks have been imaged in the cores of active galaxies, and measurement of their rotation velocities permit determination of the masses of the black holes.

- The spinning accretion disk pulls in and winds up the magnetic field, and by a process not yet fully understood, this magnetic field ejects and focuses two jets of radiation and high-speed gas in opposite directions along the axis of rotation.

- Supermassive black holes erupt only when large amounts of matter flow inward, so most galaxies have dormant cores with little mass falling inward. During galaxy interactions and collisions, tides can throw matter into the galaxy centers and trigger eruptions. This explains why active galaxies are often distorted or have nearby companions.

- Because quasars lie at great distances, astronomers see them as they were long ago—over 10 billion years ago—when the universe was young and just forming galaxies.

- According to the **unified model (p. 363)**, what you see depends on the tilt of the accretion disk. If you see into the narrow cavity at the center, you see broad spectral lines produced by hot, high velocity gas. If you see the disk edge-on, you cannot see into the cavity and can detect only narrow spectral lines. If the jet from the black hole points directly at you, you see a featureless spectrum.

- Because the mass of a supermassive black hole is related to the mass of the galaxy's central bulge around it, astronomers conclude that the black holes formed soon after the beginning of the universe when the first gas clouds fell together to form the central bulges.

- Mergers with smaller galaxies are thought to have built the halos of galaxies and may have triggered eruptions of the cores. However, the formation of the large disks that lie outside the central bulges occurred as gas settled into the galaxies. That process was not violent and didn't trigger eruptions.

- Some of the most distant quasars may be erupting because of the formation of supermassive black holes, but most activity is triggered by interactions and collisions with other galaxies. Collisions were more common in the past before the universe had expanded very far and separated galaxies.

- The age of quasars, at redshifts from about 2 to 3, was a time when galaxies were actively growing and merging.

- The supermassive black holes that once produced quasar eruptions are now mostly dormant because very little mass is flowing into them. A galaxy can be triggered to become an active galaxy if new mass falls into the black hole.

Review Questions

1. What is the difference between the terms *radio galaxy* and *active galaxy*?
2. What statistical evidence suggests that Seyfert galaxies have suffered recent interactions with other galaxies?
3. What evidence shows that the energy source in a double-lobed radio galaxy lies at the center of the galaxy?
4. How does the peculiar rotation of NGC 5128 help explain the origin of this active galaxy?
5. What evidence shows that quasars are ultraluminous but must be small?
6. What evidence is there that quasars occur in distant galaxies?
7. How does the unified model explain the two kinds of Seyfert galaxies?
8. Why are there few quasars at low redshifts and at high redshifts but many at redshifts between about 2 and 3?
9. Why did galaxies collide more often in the distant past than they do now?
10. **How Do We Know?** How would you respond to someone who said, "Oh, that's only statistics"?

Discussion Questions

1. Why do quasars, active galaxies, SS 433, and protostars have similar geometry?
2. Astronomers normally refer to the unified *model* of AGN and not to the unified *hypothesis* or unified *theory*. In your opinion, which of the words seems best?
3. Do you think that our galaxy has ever been an active galaxy? Could it have hosted a quasar when it was young?

Problems

1. The total energy stored in a radio lobe is about 10^{53} J. How many solar masses would have to be converted to energy to produce this energy? (*Hints:* Use $E = mc^2$. One solar mass equals 2×10^{30} kg.)
2. If the jet in NGC 5128 is traveling at 5000 km/s and is 40 kpc long, how long will it take for gas to travel from the core of the galaxy to the end of the jet? (*Hint:* 1 pc equals $3 = 10^{13}$ km.)
3. Cygnus A is roughly 225 Mpc away, and its jet is about 50 arc seconds long. What is the length of the jet in parsecs? (*Hint:* Use the small-angle formula, Chapter 3.)
4. Use the small-angle formula to find the linear diameter of a radio source with an angular diameter of 0.0015 arc second and a distance of 3.25 Mpc.

5. If the active core of a galaxy contains a black hole of 10^6 solar masses, what will the orbital period be for matter orbiting the black hole at a distance of 0.33 AU? (*Hint:* See circular velocity in Chapter 5.)

6. If a quasar is 1000 times more luminous than an entire galaxy, what is the absolute magnitude of such a quasar? (*Hint:* The absolute magnitude of a bright galaxy is about −21.)

7. If the quasar in Problem 6 were located at the center of our galaxy, what would its apparent magnitude be? (*Hints:* Use the magnitude-distance formula and ignore dimming by dust clouds.)

8. Re-calculate Problem 7 assuming 30 magnitudes of extinction at visual wavelengths between Earth and the center of the Milky Way Galaxy.

9. If the Hubble constant is 70 km/s/Mpc and a quasar has an apparent velocity of recession of 45,000 km/s, how far away is it?

10. The hydrogen Balmer line H_β has a wavelength of 486.1 nm. It is shifted to 563.9 nm in the spectrum of 3C 273. What is the redshift of this quasar? (*Hint:* What is $\Delta\lambda$?)

Learning to Look

1. The image at right combines visual (blue) with radio (red) to show the galaxy radio astronomers call Fornax A. Explain the features of this image. Is it significant that the object is a distorted elliptical galaxy in a cluster?

NRAO/AUI

2. Explain the features of this radio image of the galaxy IC 708.

NRAO/AUI

3. A radio image of quasar 3C 334 is shown at the right. There are two jets, so why do you see only one? What does it mean that this looks so much like a radio image of a double-lobed radio galaxy?

NRAO/AUI

18 | Modern Cosmology

Guidepost

Since Chapter 1, you have been on an outward journey through the universe. Now you have reached the limit of your travels in space and time and can study the universe as a whole. The ideas in this chapter are among the biggest and most difficult in all of science. Can you imagine a limitless universe, or the first instant of time?

As you explore cosmology, you will find answers to three essential questions:

— **Does the universe have an edge and a center?**

— **How do you know that the universe began with a big bang?**

— **How has the universe evolved, and what will be its fate?**

Once you have finished this chapter, you will have a modern insight into the nature of the universe, as well as where you are and what you are. After that, with an understanding of the big picture, it will be time to focus back on how your local neighborhood, the solar system, fits in—the subject of the rest of this book.

All of the energy and matter in the universe, including the matter in your body, began in the big bang. In this computer model of the evolution of the universe soon after the big bang, matter is being drawn together to form great clouds of galaxies. (MPA and Jörg Colberg)

The Universe, as has been observed before, is an unsettlingly big place, a fact which for the sake of a quiet life most people tend to ignore.

— DOUGLAS ADAMS *THE RESTAURANT AT THE END OF THE UNIVERSE*

LOOK AT YOUR THUMB. The matter in your body was present in the fiery beginning of the universe. **Cosmology,** the study of the universe as a whole, can tell you where your matter came from, and it can tell you where your matter is going.

Cosmology is a mind-bendingly weird subject, and you can enjoy it for its strange ideas. It is fun to think about space stretching like a rubber sheet, invisible energy pushing the universe to expand faster and faster, and the origin of vast walls of galaxy clusters. Notice that this is better than speculation—it is all supported by evidence. Cosmology, however strange it may seem, is a serious and logical attempt to understand the structure and evolution of the entire universe.

This chapter will help you climb the cosmology pyramid (■ Figure 18-1) one step at a time. You already have some ideas about what the universe is like. Start with those ideas, test them against observations, and compare them with scientific theories. Step by step, you can build a modern understanding of cosmology. Each step in the pyramid is small, but it leads to some astonishing insights into how the universe works and how you came to be a part of it.

18-1 Introduction to the Universe

MANY PEOPLE HAVE AN IMPRESSION of the universe as a vase sphere of space filled with stars and galaxies (■ Figure 18-2). As you begin exploring the real universe, you need to become aware of your assumptions so they do not mislead you. The first step is to deal with an assumption so obvious that most people don't think about it, for the sake of a quiet life.

The Edge–Center Problem

In your daily life you are accustomed to boundaries. Rooms have walls, athletic fields have boundary lines, countries have borders, oceans have shores. It is natural to think of the universe also as having an edge, but that idea can't be right.

If the universe had an edge, imagine going to that edge. What would you find there: A wall of some type? A great empty space? Nothing? Even a child can ask: If there is an edge to the universe, what's beyond it? A true edge would have to be more than just an end of the distribution of matter. It would have to be an end of space itself. But, then, what would happen if you tried to reach past, or move past, that edge?

An edge to the universe violates common sense, and modern observations (which you will study later in this chapter) indicate that the universe could be infinite and would therefore have no

■ Figure 18-2

The entire sky is filled with galaxies. Some lie in clusters of thousands, and others are isolated in nearly empty voids between the clusters. In this image of a typical spot on the sky, the brightest objects are nearby stars; their "spikes" are caused by diffraction in the telescope. All other objects are galaxies ranging from the relatively close face-on spiral at upper right to the most distant galaxies visible only in the infrared, shown as red in this composite image. (R. Williams, STScI HDF-South Team, NASA)

■ Figure 18-1

Climbing the cosmology pyramid step by step isn't very difficult, and it leads to some fascinating ideas about the origin and evolution of the universe.

edge. Perhaps even more important, if the universe has no edge, then it cannot have a center. You find the centers of things—pizzas, football fields, oceans, galaxies—by referring to their edges. If the universe has no edge, then it cannot have a center.

It is a **Common Misconception** to imagine that the universe has a center, but, as you just realized, that is impossible. As you study cosmology, you should take care to avoid thinking that there is a center of the universe.

The Idea of a Beginning

Of course you have noticed that the night sky is dark. That is an important observation because, you may be surprised to learn, seemingly reasonable assumptions about the universe can lead to the conclusion that the night sky actually should glow blindingly bright. This conflict between observation and theory is called **Olbers's paradox** after Heinrich Olbers, a physician and astronomer who publicized the problem in 1826. (*Problem* or *question* might be more accurate words than *paradox*.) Olbers was not the first person to pose this question; the problem of the dark night sky was first discussed by Thomas Digges in 1576 and was further analyzed by astronomers such as Johannes Kepler in 1610 and Edmund Halley in 1721. Olbers gets the credit through an accident of scholarship on the part of modern scientists who were not aware of the earlier discussions.

The point made by Olbers seems simple. Suppose you assume, as did most scientists in Olbers's time, that the universe is infinite in size, infinite in age, **static** (a fancy word for unchanging overall), and filled with stars. If you look in any direction, your line of sight must eventually run into the surface of a star. (The clumping of stars into galaxies and galaxies into clusters can be shown mathematically to make no difference.) Look at ■ Figure 18-3, which uses the analogy of lines of sight in a forest. (The use of analogies in science is discussed in **How Do We Know? 18-1**.) When you are deep in a forest, every line of sight ends at a tree trunk, and you cannot see out of the forest.

By analogy to the view from inside a forest, every line of sight from Earth into space should eventually end at the surface of a star. Of course, the more distant stars would be fainter than nearby stars because of the inverse square law. However, the farther you look into space, the larger the volume you are viewing and the more stars are included; the two effects cancel out. The result would be that the entire sky should be as bright as the surface of an average star—like suns crowded "shoulder to shoulder," covering the sky from horizon to horizon. It should not get dark at night.

Astronomers and physicists who study cosmology, called **cosmologists,** now believe they understand why the sky is dark. Olbers's paradox makes an incorrect prediction because it is based on incorrect assumptions. The universe may be infinite in size, but it is neither infinitely old nor static. The essence of modern cosmologists' answer to Olbers's question was suggested first by Edgar Allan Poe in 1848. Poe proposed that the night sky is

■ Figure 18-3

(a) Every direction you look in a forest eventually reaches a tree trunk, and you cannot see out of the forest. (Photo courtesy Janet Seeds) (b) If the universe is infinite and filled with stars, then any line from Earth should eventually reach the surface of a star. This assumption leads to a prediction that the night sky should glow as brightly as the surface of the average star, a puzzle commonly referred to as Olbers's paradox.

Reasoning by Analogy

How do scientists use analogies? "The economy is overheating, and it may seize up," an economist might say. Economists like to talk in analogies because economics is often abstract, and one of the best ways to think about abstract problems is to find a more approachable analogy. Rather than discussing details of the national economy, you might be able to make conclusions about how the economy works by thinking about how a gasoline engine works.

Much of astronomy is abstract, and cosmology is the most abstract subject in astronomy. Furthermore, cosmology is highly mathematical, and unless you are prepared to learn some difficult mathematics, you instead have to use analogies, such as lines of sight in a forest.

Reasoning by analogy is a powerful technique. An analogy can reveal unexpected insights and lead you to further discoveries.

Carrying an analogy too far, however, can be misleading. You might compare the human brain to a computer, and that would help you understand how data flow in and are processed and how new data flow out, but the analogy is flawed. For example, although data in computers are stored in specific locations, memories are stored in the brain in a distributed form. No single brain cell holds a specific memory. So, if you carry the analogy too far, it can mislead you. Whenever you reason using analogies, you should be alert for their limitations.

As you study any science, be alert for analogies. They are tremendously helpful, but you have to be careful not to carry them too far.

The analogy between a human brain and a computer is of only limited use. (Blend Images/SuperStock)

dark because the universe is not infinitely old but came into existence at some finite time in the past. The more distant stars are so far away that light from them has not yet reached Earth. That is, if you look far enough away, the look-back time approaches the age of the universe, and you see to a time before the first stars began to shine. The night sky is dark because the universe had a beginning. You can now answer Olbers's question, and understand why the night sky is dark, by revising your original assumptions about the universe.

The answer to Olbers's question is a powerful idea because it clearly illustrates the difference between the universe and the **observable universe.** The universe is everything that exists, and it could be infinite. The observable universe, in contrast, is the part (maybe a very small part) that you can see from Earth using the most powerful telescopes. You will learn later in this chapter about evidence that the universe is around 14 billion years old. That means you can't observe objects farther away than a look-back time of around 14 billion years. Do not confuse the observable universe, which is huge but finite, with the universe as a whole, which might be infinite.

There is a **Common Misconception** that the universe is unchanging overall and not evolving. In the next section you will discover that the universe is actually changing. Observations reveal an **expanding universe.**

Cosmic Expansion

In 1929, Edwin Hubble published his discovery that the sizes of galaxy redshifts are proportional to galaxy distances. Nearby galaxies have small redshifts, and more distant galaxies have large redshifts. You learned this as the Hubble law in Chapter 16, when you used it to estimate the distances to galaxies. Those galaxy redshifts imply that galaxies are receding from each other and that the universe is expanding.

■ Figure 18-4 shows spectra of galaxies in galaxy clusters at various distances. The Virgo cluster is relatively nearby, and its redshift is small. The Hydra cluster is very distant, and its redshift is so large that the two dark spectral lines formed by ionized calcium are shifted from near-ultraviolet wavelengths well into the visible part of the spectrum.

The expansion of the universe does not imply that Earth has a special location. To see why, look at ■ Figure 18-5, which shows an analogy to baking raisin bread. As the dough rises, it pushes the raisins away from each other at speeds that are proportional to distance. Two raisins that were originally close to each other are pushed apart slowly, but two raisins that were far apart, having more dough between them, are pushed apart faster. If bacterial astronomers lived on a raisin in the raisin bread, they could observe the redshifts of the other raisins and derive a bacterial

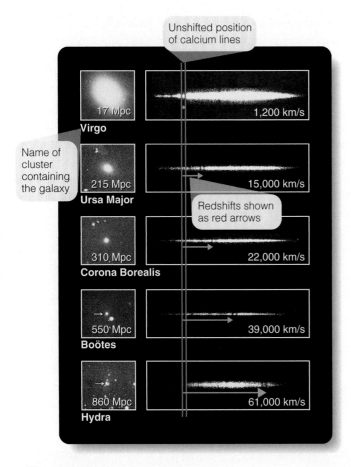

Unshifted position of calcium lines

Name of cluster containing the galaxy

17 Mpc
Virgo
1,200 km/s

215 Mpc
Ursa Major
15,000 km/s

Redshifts shown as red arrows

310 Mpc
Corona Borealis
22,000 km/s

550 Mpc
Boötes
39,000 km/s

860 Mpc
Hydra
61,000 km/s

■ **Figure 18-4**

These galaxy spectra extend from the near-ultraviolet at left to the blue part of the visible spectrum at right. The two dark absorption lines of once-ionized calcium are prominent in the near-ultraviolet. The redshifts in galaxy spectra are expressed here as apparent velocities of recession. Note that the apparent velocity of recession is proportional to distance, which is known as the Hubble law. (Caltech)

Hubble law. They would conclude that their universe was expanding uniformly. It does not matter which raisin the bacterial astronomers lived on, they would get the same Hubble law—no raisin has a special viewpoint. Similarly, astronomers in any galaxy will see the same law of expansion—no galaxy has a special viewpoint.

When you look at Figure 18-5, you see the edge of the loaf of raisin bread, and you can identify a center to the loaf. The raisin bread analogy to the universe stops working when you consider the crust—the edge--of the bread. Remember that the universe cannot have an edge or a center, so there is no center to the expansion. The raisin bread analogy is useful but also imperfect.

18-2 The Big Bang Theory

NOW YOU ARE READY to take a historic step up the cosmology pyramid. The expansion of the universe led cosmologists to conclude that the universe must have begun with an event of cosmic intensity.

Necessity of the Big Bang

Imagine that you have a video of the expanding universe and run it backward. You would see the galaxies getting closer to each other. There is no center to the expansion of the universe, so you would not see galaxies approaching a single spot. Rather, you would see the spaces between galaxies shrinking and the distances between all galaxies decreasing. Eventually, as your video ran back toward the beginning, galaxies would begin to merge. If you ran the video far enough back, you would see the matter and energy of the universe compressed into a high-density, high-temperature state. The expanding universe must have begun from this moment of extreme conditions that cosmologists call the **big bang.**

How long ago did the universe begin? You can estimate the age of the universe with a simple calculation. If you need to drive to a city 100 miles away, and you can travel 50 miles per hour, you divide distance by rate of travel and learn the travel time—in this example, 2 hours. In an analogous fashion, to find the age of the universe, you can divide the distance between two galaxies by the speed with which they are moving away from each other and find out how much time they have taken to reach their present separation.

The Hubble constant, H, has units km/s per Mpc, which is a velocity divided by a distance. This makes your task simple. If

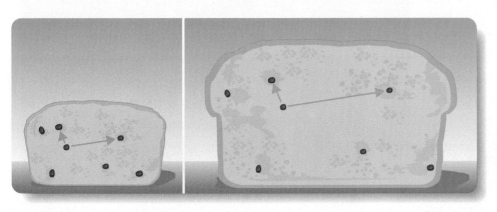

■ **Figure 18-5**

An illustration of the raisin bread analogy for the expansion of the universe. As the dough rises, raisins are pushed apart with velocities proportional to distance. A colony of bacteria living on any raisin will find that the redshifts of the other raisins are proportional to their distances.

you calculate $1/H$, you have a distance divided by velocity, in other words, a time. To finish the division and get an age, you need to convert megaparsecs into kilometers, and then the distances will cancel out and leave you with an age in seconds. To convert seconds to years, you divide by the number of seconds in a year. If you make these simple changes in units, the age of the universe in years is approximately 10^{12} divided by H in its normal astronomical units, km/s/Mpc:

$$\tau_H = \frac{10^{12}}{H}$$

This estimate of the age of the universe is known as the **Hubble time.** For example, if H is 70 km/s/Mpc, that leads to an estimated age for the universe of $\frac{10^{12}}{70}$, or 14 billion, years. The time you calculate by this procedure is the same no matter which two galaxies you pick. You will fine-tune your estimate later in this chapter, but for the moment you can conclude that basic observations of the universe, especially the recession of the galaxies, require that the expansion of the universe began about 14 billion years ago.

The phrase *big bang* was invented by early critics of that theory, and the label gives a misimpression. Do not think of an edge or a center when you think of the big bang. It is a very **Common Misconception** that the big bang was an explosion and that the galaxies are flying away from the location of that explosion. Instead, try to imagine the entire universe. At the time of the big bang, all of the matter that now composes galaxies, stars, people, and atoms was much closer together. But, like the universe now, the early universe also had no center and no edge. The big bang filled the entire universe, happening everywhere at the same moment as the matter of the universe began to draw apart. A more accurate term than *big bang* might be *big stretch*.

Although your imagination tries to visualize the big bang as a localized event, you should keep firmly in mind the correct picture that the big bang did not occur at a single place but filled the entire volume of the universe. The matter of which you are made was part of that big bang, so you are inside the remains of that event, and the universe continues to expand around you. You cannot point to any particular place and say, "The big bang occurred over there." This is a brain-straining (stretching?) idea, but you will find

more information to help you understand it better later in this chapter when you study the nature of space and time.

Your instinct also is to think of the big bang as an event that happened long ago and can no longer be observed, like the Gettysburg Address. Amazingly, the effect of look-back time makes it possible to observe the big bang now, directly. The look-back time to nearby galaxies is "only" a few million years; the look-back time to more distant galaxies is a large fraction of the age of the universe (■ Figure 18-6).

Suppose you look between the distant galaxies, seeing even farther away and farther back in time. You should be able to detect the hot gas that filled the universe long ago, right after the big bang, before the first stars and galaxies formed. The big bang occurred everywhere, and, in whatever direction you look, at great distance you can see back to the age when the universe was filled with hot gas (■ Figure 18-7).

The radiation that comes from such a great distance has a large redshift. The most distant visible objects are faint galaxies and quasars, with redshifts around 10. In contrast, the radiation from the hot gas right after the big bang has a redshift of about 1100. That means the light emitted as visible and near-infrared light by the hot gas in the early universe arrives at Earth as far-infrared, microwave, and radio waves. You can't see it with your

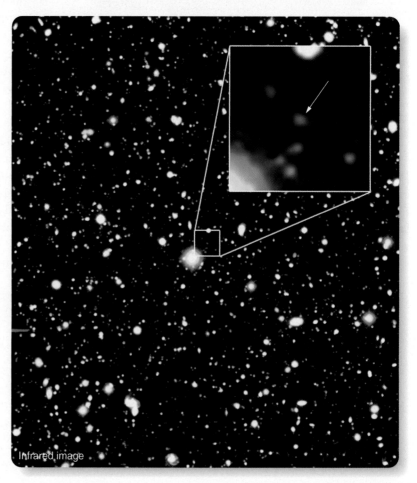

Infrared image

■ **Figure 18-6**

This faint galaxy is one of the most distant ever found. It has a redshift of 6.964 implying that it is 12.88 billion light-years from Earth. It appears as it was only 850 million years after the big bang when the light began its journey toward Earth. (Subaru: Masanori Iye et al.)

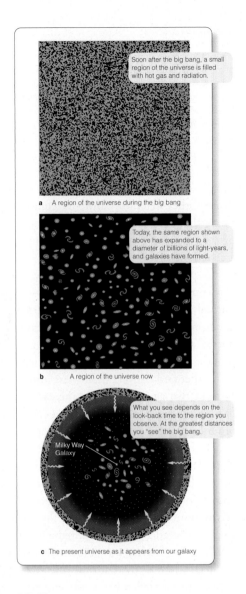

a A region of the universe during the big bang

Soon after the big bang, a small region of the universe is filled with hot gas and radiation.

b A region of the universe now

Today, the same region shown above has expanded to a diameter of billions of light-years, and galaxies have formed.

What you see depends on the look-back time to the region you observe. At the greatest distances you "see" the big bang.

Milky Way Galaxy

c The present universe as it appears from our galaxy

■ **Figure 18-7**

This diagram shows schematically the expansion of a small part of the universe. Although the universe is now filled with galaxies, the look-back time distorts what you see. Nearby you see galaxies, but at greater distances, the look-back time reveals the universe at earlier stages, before galaxies formed. At very great distances, the big bang is detectable as infrared, microwave, and radio energy arriving from the hot gas that filled the universe soon after the big bang.

eyes, but it can be detected with infrared and radio telescopes. Unlike the Gettysburg Address, the big bang can still be observed by the radiation it emitted. That amazing discovery is the subject of the next section.

The Cosmic Background Radiation

The story of the discovery of radiation from the time of the big bang begins in the mid-1960s when two Bell Laboratories physicists, Arno Penzias and Robert Wilson, were measuring the brightness of the sky at radio wavelengths (■ Figure 18-8). Their measurements showed a strange extra signal in the system, which they first attributed to the infrared glow from pigeon droppings inside the antenna. Perhaps they would have enjoyed scraping out the antenna more if they had known they would win the 1978 Nobel Prize in physics for the discovery they were about to make.

When the antenna was cleaned, they again measured the radio brightness of the sky and found the low-level noise was still there. The pigeons were innocent, but what was causing the extra signal?

The explanation for the noise goes back decades earlier. In 1939, astronomers noticed that spectra of some molecules in the interstellar medium showed they were bathed in radiation from a source with a temperature of 2 to 3 K. In 1948, physicist George Gamow predicted that the gases in the universe right after the big bang would have been hot and should have emitted strong blackbody radiation (see Chapter 7). A year later, physicists Ralph Alpher and Robert Herman pointed out that the large redshift of the big bang material relative to Earth would lengthen the wavelengths of that radiation into the microwave part of the spectrum, with a blackbody temperature they estimated as 5 K. In the mid-1960s Robert Dicke at Princeton concluded the radiation should be just strong enough to detect with newly developed techniques. Dicke and his team began building a receiver. When Penzias and Wilson heard of Dicke's work, they recognized the mysterious extra signal they had detected as radiation from the big bang, the **cosmic microwave background** radiation.

The detection of the background radiation was tremendously exciting, but cosmologists wanted confirmation. Theory predicted that the radiation should have a spectrum like blackbody radiation coming from a very cool source, but the critical observations could not be made from the ground because Earth's atmosphere is opaque at the predicted blackbody peak wavelength. It was not until 1990 that satellite measurements confirmed the background radiation has exactly a blackbody spectral distribution, with an apparent temperature of $2.725 +/- 0.002$ K —close to the original prediction.

It may seem strange that the gas of the big bang seems to have a temperature of just 2.7 degrees above absolute zero, but recall the tremendous redshift. Observers on Earth receive radiation that has a redshift of about 1100—that is, the wavelengths of the photons are about 1100 times longer than when they were emitted. The gas clouds that originally emitted the photons had a temperature of about 3000 K, and they emitted blackbody radiation with a λ_{max} of about 1000 nm (Wien's law, Chapter 7). Although that wavelength is in the near-infrared, the gas would also have emitted enough visible light to be seen glowing orangered if there had been a human eye present at the time. The redshift has made the wavelengths of the background radiation about 1100 times longer on arrival at Earth than when they were

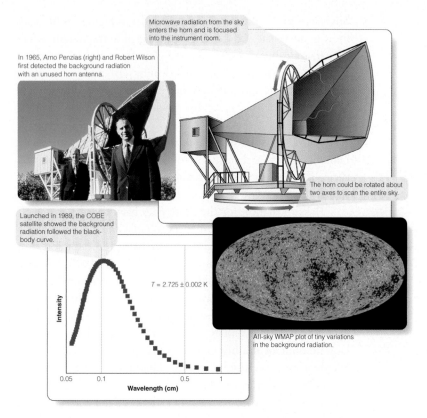

In 1965, Arno Penzias (right) and Robert Wilson first detected the background radiation with an unused horn antenna.

Microwave radiation from the sky enters the horn and is focused into the instrument room.

The horn could be rotated about two axes to scan the entire sky.

Launched in 1989, the COBE satellite showed the background radiation followed the black-body curve.

$T = 2.725 \pm 0.002$ K

Intensity

0.05   0.1   0.5   1
Wavelength (cm)

All-sky WMAP plot of tiny variations in the background radiation.

When the cosmic microwave background radiation was first detected in 1965, technology did not allow measurements at many wavelengths. Not until infrared detectors could be put in space was it conclusively shown that the background radiation has a blackbody spectrum, as predicted by theory. (Photo, AT&T Archives; WMAP plot, NASA)

density, they refer to Einstein's equation $E = mc^2$. Using that equation, you can express a given amount of radiation energy per volume as if it were matter of a certain density.)

If photons have enough energy, two photons can convert into a pair of particles—a particle of normal matter and a particle of **antimatter.** When an antimatter particle meets its matching particle of normal matter—when an antiproton meets a normal proton, for example—the two particles annihilate each other and convert their mass into energy in the form of two gamma rays. In the early universe, the photons were gamma rays and had enough energy to produce proton–antiproton pairs or neutron–anti-neutron pairs. When these particles collided with their antiparticles, they converted their mass back into photons. Thus, the early universe was filled with a dynamic soup of energy flickering from photons into particles and back again.

While all this went on, the expansion of the universe caused the temperature of the radiation to drop, reducing the energy of the photons. When the universe was 0.0001 second old, its temperature had fallen to 10^{12} K. By that time, the average energy of the radiation photons had fallen below the energy equivalent to the mass of a proton or a neutron, so the gamma rays could no longer produce such heavy particles. Those particles that did exist combined with their antiparticles and quickly converted their mass into energy.

It would seem that all of the protons and neutrons should have been annihilated with their antiparticles; but, for reasons that are poorly understood, a small excess of normal particles existed. For every billion protons annihilated by antiprotons, one survived with no antiparticle to destroy it. Consequently, you live in a world of normal matter, and antimatter is very rare.

Although the gamma ray photons did not have enough energy when the universe was older than about 0.0001 second to produce any more protons and neutrons, they could still produce electrons and positrons (antielectrons; see Chapter 8), which are about 1800 times less massive than protons and neutrons. That process continued until the universe was about 1 minute old, at which time the expansion had cooled to the point at which there were no remaining photons with enough energy to create

emitted, so λ_{max} is now about 1 million nm, or 1 mm. That is why the hot gas of the big bang seems to be about 2.7 K, 1100 times cooler than it actually was.

The first few steps up the cosmology pyramid have not been very difficult. Simple observations of the darkness of the night sky and the redshifts of the galaxies tell you that the universe must have had a beginning, and you have seen that the cosmic microwave background radiation is clear evidence of the big bang, that the early universe was hot and dense. Theorists can combine these observations with modern physics to add some details to the story of how the big bang occurred.

Photon and Particle Soup

Cosmologists cannot begin their history of the big bang at time zero, because no one understands the physics of matter and energy under such extreme conditions, but they can come surprisingly close. If you could visit the universe when it was only 10 millionths of a second old, you would find it filled with high-energy photons having a temperature well over 1 trillion (10^{12}) K and a density of 5×10^{18} kg/m³, greater than the density of an atomic nucleus. (When cosmologists say the photons have a given temperature, they mean the photons have the same spectrum as blackbody radiation emitted by an object of that temperature.) Consequently, the photons in the early universe were gamma rays, with very short wavelength and therefore very high energy. (When cosmologists say that the radiation had a certain electron–positron pairs. Again, most of the electrons and positrons combined to form photons, and only one in a billion electrons survived. Cosmologists can calculate, based on the known properties of subatomic particles and the characteristics of the universe as a whole, that the protons, neutrons, and electrons of which our universe is now made were produced during the first minute of its history.

A Few Minutes of Nucleosynthesis

The universal soup of hot gas and radiation continued to cool. Photons with high enough energy can break up an atomic nucleus, so the formation of stable nuclei could not occur until the universe had cooled enough. By the time the universe was about 2 minutes old, protons and neutrons could link to form deuterium, the nucleus of a heavy hydrogen atom, without being immediately broken apart. By the end of the third minute, further reactions began converting deuterium into helium.

Almost no atoms heavier than helium could be built in the big bang, because there are no stable nuclei with atomic weights of 5 or 8 (in units of the hydrogen atom). Nuclei of atomic weights 5 and 8 are radioactive and decay almost instantly back into smaller particles. Cosmic element building during the big bang had to proceed step by step, like someone hopping up a flight of stairs (■ Figure 18-9). The lack of stable nuclei at atomic

■ **Figure 18-9**

Cosmic element building. During the first few minutes of the big bang, temperatures and densities were high, and nuclear reactions built heavier elements. Because there are no stable nuclei with atomic weights of 5 or 8, the process built very few atoms heavier than helium.

weights of 5 and 8 meant there were missing steps in the stairway, and the step-by-step reactions had great difficulty jumping over these gaps during the few minutes of the big bang. As a result, cosmologists can calculate that only a tiny amount of lithium (atomic weight 7) would have been produced during the big bang, and no heavier elements.

By the time it was 3 minutes old, the universe had become so cool that almost all nuclear reactions had stopped. By the time it was 30 minutes old, the nuclear reactions had ended completely, and about 75 percent of the mass of the universe was in the form of protons—hydrogen nuclei. The rest was almost entirely helium nuclei. That composition, set during the first minutes of the universe, is the composition observed now for the oldest stars. Formation of elements with atomic weights greater than lithium had to wait for relatively slow-cooking nucleosynthesis processes in stars (see Chapters 12 and 13), beginning many millions of years after the big bang.

Radiation and Matter, Recombination and Reionization

After the era of nucleosynthesis, as the young universe continued to expand and cool, it went through a further sequence of four important changes. Originally, the universe was so hot that the gas was totally ionized, and the electrons were not attached to nuclei. The free electrons interacted with photons so easily that a photon could not travel very far before it encountered an electron and was deflected. The photons interacted continuously with the matter, and the radiation and matter cooled together at a rate set by the expansion rate of the universe. In those circumstances, the universe was dominated by its radiation.

The first change occurred when the universe reached an age calculated by cosmologists of about 50,000 years. Then, the density of energy in the form of photons became less than the density of the gas. Before that time, ordinary matter could not clump together because the intense sea of photons smoothed the gas out. As you will learn in the next section, dark matter, which does not interact with photons, was able to start clumping much earlier. After the 50,000-year mark, when the density of the universe's radiation permanently became less than that of its ordinary (baryonic) matter, ordinary matter could begin to draw together under the influence of the gravitational attraction of dark matter to form the clouds that eventually became galaxies.

The expansion of the universe spread the particles of the still-ionized gas farther and farther apart. When the universe reached an age of about 400,000 years, the second important change began. By then, the free electrons were spread so far apart that the photons could travel for thousands of parsecs before being deflected by an electron. In other words, the universe started to become transparent. At approximately the same time, the third important change happened. As the falling temperature of the universe reached 3000 K, protons were able to capture and hold free electrons to form neutral hydrogen, a process called **recombination.** (This term is a little misleading, because the particles had never been together stably before; *combination* would be more accurate.) As the free electrons were gobbled up, the gas became essentially completely transparent, and the photons could travel through the gas without being deflected (■ Figure 18-10).

After recombination, although the gas continued to cool, the photons no longer interacted with the gas, and consequently the photons retained the blackbody temperature that the gas had at recombination. Those photons, which started their journey with a blackbody temperature of 3000 K, are observed now as the cosmic microwave background radiation. Remember that the large redshift—the expansion of the universe—has stretched the wavelengths of the background radiation so that it appears now to have a temperature of about 2.7 K.

After recombination, the gas that originated in the big bang was neutral, warm, and transparent. As the universe continued to expand and cool, the glow from the warm gas faded into infrared wavelengths. The universe entered what cosmologists call the **dark age,** a period lasting about 400 million years until the formation of the first stars. During that interval the universe expanded in darkness.

The fourth remarkable change happened as the first stars began to form, ending the dark age. The gas from which the first stars formed contained almost no metals and was therefore highly transparent. Mathematical models show that stars formed from this metal-poor gas would have been very massive, very luminous, and very short lived. That first violent burst of massive star formation produced enough ultraviolet light to begin ionizing the gas, and astronomers now, looking back to the most distant visible quasars and galaxies, can see traces of that **reionization** era in the universe (■ Figure 18-11). Reionization not only marked the end of the dark age, it was the beginning of the age of stars and galaxies in which you live now.

Look carefully at ■ Figure 18-12; it summarizes the story of the big bang, from the sorting out of stable particles in the earliest moments, through formation of helium in the first 3 minutes, up to the eras of energy–matter equality, recombination, and finally reionization of the gas. It may seem amazing that mere humans limited to Earth can draw such a diagram, but remember that it is based on evidence and on the best understanding of how matter and energy interact (**How Do We Know? 18-2**).

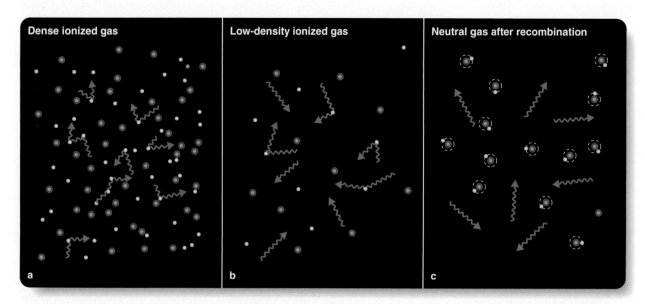

Dense ionized gas   **Low-density ionized gas**   **Neutral gas after recombination**

a   b   c

■**Figure 18-10**

Photons scatter from electrons (blue) easily but hardly at all from the much more massive protons (red). (a) When the universe was very dense and ionized, photons could not travel very far before they scattered off an electron. This made the gas opaque. (b) As the universe expanded, the electrons were spread farther apart, and the photons could travel farther; this made the gas more transparent. (c) After recombination, most electrons were locked to protons to form neutral atoms, and the gas became highly transparent.

■ **Figure 18-11**

In this artist's conception of reionization, the first stars produce floods of ultraviolet photons that ionize the gas in expanding bubbles. Such a storm of star formation ended the dark age, during which the universe expanded in darkness. Spectra of the most distant quasars reveal that those first galaxies were surrounded by neutral gas that had not yet been fully ionized. Thus the look-back time allows modern astronomers to observe the age of reionization. (K. Lanzetta, SUNY, A. Schaller for STScI, and NASA)

■ **Figure 18-12**

During the first few minutes of the big bang, some hydrogen was fused to produce helium, but the universe quickly became too cool for such fusion reactions to continue. The rate of cooling increased as matter began to dominate over radiation. Recombination freed the radiation from the influence of the gas, and reionization was caused by the birth of the first stars. Note how the exponential scale in time stretches early history and compresses recent history.

SCIENTIFIC ARGUMENT

How do you know there was a big bang?

A good scientific argument combines evidence and theory to describe how nature works, and this question calls for a detailed argument. The cosmic microwave background radiation consists of photons emitted by warm gas after the big bang, so when astronomers detect those photons, they are in a sense "seeing" the big bang. Of course, all scientific evidence must be interpreted, so you need to understand how the big bang could produce radiation all around the sky before you can accept the background radiation as evidence. First, you must remember that the big bang event filled the entire universe with hot, dense gas. The big bang didn't happen in a single place; it happened everywhere. At recombination, the expansion of the universe reached the stage where the matter became transparent, and the radiation that had previously been trapped, bouncing between matter particles, was freed to travel through space. Now, that radiation from the age of recombination arrives from all over the sky. It is all around you because you are part of the big bang event, and as you look out into space to great distance, you look back in time and see the hot gas in any direction you look. You can't see the radiation as visible light because the large redshift has lengthened the wavelengths by a factor of 1100 or so, but you can detect the radiation as photons with infrared, microwave, and radio wavelengths.

With this interpretation, the cosmic microwave background radiation is powerful evidence that there was a big bang. That tells you how the universe began, but your argument includes an important point. **Why do you think the universe cannot have a center or an edge?**

Science: A System of Knowledge

What is the difference between believing in the big bang and understanding it? If you ask a scientist, "Do you believe in the big bang?" she or he may hesitate before responding. The question implies something incorrect about the way science works.

Science is a system of knowledge and process but does not operate as a system of belief. Science is an attempt to understand logically how nature works and is based on observations and experiments used to test and confirm hypotheses and theories. A scientist does not really believe in even a well-confirmed theory in the way people normally use the word *believe*. Rather, the scientist understands the theory and recognizes how different pieces of evidence support or contradict the theory.

There are other ways to know things, and there are many systems of belief. Religions, for example, are systems of belief that are not entirely based on observation. In some cases, a political system is also a system of belief; many people believe that democracy is the best form of government and do not ask for, or expect, evidence supporting that belief. A system of belief can be powerful and lead to deep insights, but it is different from science.

Scientists try to be careful with words, so thoughtful scientists would not say they *believe* in the big bang. They would say that the evidence is overwhelming that the big bang really did occur and that they are compelled, by a logical analysis of both the observations and the theory, to conclude that the theory is very likely correct. In this way scientists try to be objective and reason without distortion by personal feelings and prejudices.

A scientist once referred to "the terrible rule of evidence." Sometimes the evidence forces a scientist to a conclusion she or he does not like, but science is not a system of

Scientific knowledge is based objectively on evidence such as that gathered by spacecraft. (NASA/WMAP Science Team)

belief, so the personal preferences of each scientist must take second place to the rule of evidence.

Do you believe in the big bang? Or, instead, do you have confidence that the theory is right because of your analysis of the evidence? There is a big difference.

18-3 Space and Time, Matter and Energy

How CAN THE BIG BANG have happened everywhere? To solve the puzzle, you need to put seemingly reasonable expectations aside and look carefully at how space and time behave on cosmic scales.

Looking at the Universe

The universe looks about the same in whichever direction you observe; in cosmologist language the universe is described as being **isotropic.** Of course, if you look toward a galaxy cluster you see more galaxies than in other directions, but that is only a local variation. On the average, you see similar numbers of galaxies in every direction. Furthermore, the background radiation is almost perfectly uniform across the sky. The universe is observed to be very isotropic.

The universe also seems about the same everywhere; in cosmologist language the universe is described as being **homogeneous.** (Note that this is a different property than the universe being isotropic.) Of course, there are local variations; some regions contain more galaxies and some less. Also, because the universe evolves, at large look-back times you see galaxies at an earlier developmental stage. But, if you account for those well-understood variations, then the universe seems to be, on average, the same everywhere.

The universe is observed to be isotropic and homogeneous. Those two properties don't have to go together; for an intellectual exercise, you can try to imagine arrangements that are isotropic but not homogeneous, or homogeneous but not isotropic. The fact that the universe is both isotropic and homogeneous leads to the **cosmological principle,** which says that any observer in any galaxy sees the same general properties for the universe. As you just learned, this overall principle intentionally overlooks minor local and evolutionary variations. The cosmological principle implies there are no special places in the universe. What you see from the Milky Way Galaxy is typical of what all intelligent creatures see from their respective home galaxies. Furthermore, the cosmological principle states, in a new form, the idea that the universe can have no center or edge. A center or an edge would be a special place, and the cosmological principle says there are no special places.

The Cosmic Redshift

Einstein's theory of general relativity, published in 1916, describes space and time together as the fabric of the universe, called space-time. That idea will give you a new insight into the meaning of the phrase *expanding universe.*

General relativity describes space-time as if it is made of stretching rubber, and that explains one of the most important observations in cosmology—the redshifts. It is a **Common Misconception** that cosmological redshifts are Doppler shifts of galaxies flying away through space. Instead, except for relatively small, local motions within clusters of galaxies, galaxies are at rest. They are being *separated* from each other as space-time expands. Also, as space-time expands, it stretches any photon traveling through space so that its wavelength increases. Photons from distant galaxies spend more time traveling through space and are stretched more, in other words have larger redshifts, than photons from nearby galaxies. That is why redshift depends on distance (■ Figure 18-13).

What are the cosmological redshifts?

A distant galaxy emits a short-wavelength photon toward our galaxy.

Grid shows expansion of space-time.

The expansion of space-time stretches the photon to longer wavelength as it travels.

The farther the photon has to travel, the more it is stretched.

When the photon arrives at our galaxy, you see it with a longer wavelength—a redshift that is proportional to distance.

■ **Figure 18-13**

Like a rubber sheet, space-time stretches, moving the galaxies away from each other and increasing the wavelength of photons as they travel through space-time.

Astronomers often express redshifts as if they were actual radial velocities, but the redshifts of the galaxies are not Doppler shifts. That is why this book is careful to refer to a galaxy's *apparent* velocity of recession. Some textbooks convert cosmological redshifts to velocities using Einstein's relativistic Doppler formula, but that formula applies to motion through space and not to the behavior of space-time itself, so that formula should not be used in a cosmological context. The Hubble law still applies: Redshifts can be used to find the distance to galaxies because redshifts show how much the universe has expanded, and thus how much time has elapsed, since the photons started on their journey.

Model Universes

Almost immediately after Einstein published his general relativity theory, other theorists were able to solve the sophisticated mathematics and compute simplified descriptions of the behavior of space-time and matter. The resulting model universes dominated cosmology throughout the 20th century.

The equations allowed three possibilities. Space-time might be curved in either of two different ways, or it might have no curvature at all. Most people find these curved models difficult to imagine, and modern observations have shown that the simplest model, without curvature, is almost certainly correct, so you don't have to wrap your brain around the curved models. You might, however, like to know a few of their most important properties.

Some models described space-time as being curved back on itself to form a **closed universe.** You would not notice this curvature in daily life; it would only be evident in measurements involving very distant objects. Throughout the 20th century, observations could not eliminate closed models, so they were considered a real possibility. Closed universe models have finite volumes, but, because space-time is curved back on itself, a closed universe nevertheless would have no edge and no center. Such closed models predicted that the expansion of the universe would eventually become a contraction that would bring all of the matter and energy back to the high-density big bang state, which was sometimes called the "big crunch."

Other models described an uncurved, **flat universe.** That is the kind of space-time you would expect from your daily life, with the same rules of geometry that you learned in high school, even for cosmological distances. Flat models are infinite, have no edge or center, and expand forever.

A third kind of model described an **open universe.** Such models contain curved space-time but are not curved back on themselves. Like the flat models, open models are infinite, have no center or edge, and expand forever.

Cosmologists of the 20th century struggled to find reasons or observations that would allow them to choose among these three kinds of models. The main clue was density. According to general relativity, the overall curvature of space-time is

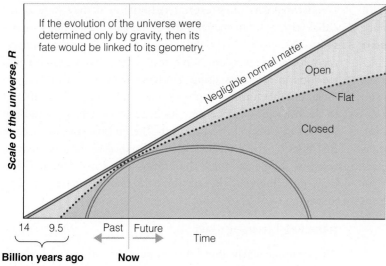

If the evolution of the universe were determined only by gravity, then its fate would be linked to its geometry.

Scale of the universe, R

Negligible normal matter

Open

Flat

Closed

14   9.5   Past | Future

Billion years ago   Now   Time

■ Figure 18-14

Illustrations of some simple universe models that depend only on the effect of gravity, without including dark energy. Open universe models expand without end, and the corresponding curves fall in the region shaded orange. Closed models expand and then contract again (red curve, one example). A flat universe (dotted line) marks the boundary between open and closed universe models. The relationship between estimated age and actual age of the universe depends on the curvature of space-time in universe models without dark energy. The age of the universe for each model is shown on the graph as the horizontal distance from "Now" back to the time when the universe scale factor R equaled 0.

determined by the average density of matter plus energy in the universe. Cosmologists could calculate that space-time is flat if the average density of the universe equals a **critical density** of 9×10^{-27} kg/m³. If the average density of the universe is more than the critical density, the universe must be closed; and if it is less, the universe must be open. Attempts to measure the actual value of the universe's density, however, were difficult and inconclusive.

These three kinds of universe models are illustrated in ■ Figure 18-14, which compares the expansions versus time of the different models. The parameter R on the vertical axis is a measure of the extent to which the universe has expanded. You can think of R, in a simplified way, as the average distance between galaxies. In the figure you can see that closed universes expand and then contract while both flat and open universes expand forever.

Notice that you can't find the actual age of the universe unless you know whether it is open, closed, or flat. The Hubble time is the age the universe would have if it were totally open, which would mean it contained almost no matter. If, instead, the universe is dense enough to have flat geometry, then its age would be $\frac{2}{3}$ of the Hubble time. If H is about 70 km/sec/Mpc, as astronomers have measured, and the universe is flat, then it

should be only 9.5 billion years old. Astronomers know of globular star clusters that are significantly older than that, so this was known as the age problem: How can the universe be younger than some of the objects in it?

Modern observations show that the universe is flat, and later in this chapter you will see how the evidence eliminated curved models and solved the age problem. For now, however, you can think about a different puzzle. If the universe is flat, then its average density must exactly equal the critical density. Yet when cosmologists added up the matter that could be detected, they found only a few percent of the critical density. They wondered if the dark matter made up the rest.

Dark Matter in Cosmology

There is more to the universe than meets the eye. In Chapters 15 and 16, you discovered that the Milky Way Galaxy and other galaxies have much stronger gravitational fields than would be predicted based on the amount of stars visible. Their gravitational fields are much stronger than expected even when you add in the gravity of the gas and dust that would be contained in the galaxies. Galaxies must contain dark matter.

This is not a small issue. Look at ■ Figure 18-15. Gravitational lensing is dramatic evidence of dark matter. The galaxy cluster in the figure contains so much dark matter that it warps space-time and focuses the images of more distant galaxies into short arcs of light. The universe contains much more dark matter than normal matter. Looking at the universe of visible matter in galaxies is like looking at a tree and seeing only the leaves.

The available evidence shows that dark matter is not the same as the normal matter you are made of. To follow that argument, you need to estimate the density of normal matter, and you can start with what is known about conditions right after the big bang.

As you have learned, during the first few minutes of the big bang, nuclear reactions converted some protons into helium and a very small amount into other elements. How much of elements heavier than helium could be produced was controlled by the density of normal matter during the big bang. For example, if the density of matter had been high so that there were lots of normal particles such as protons and neutrons flying around, they would have collided with the deuterium nuclei and converted most of them into helium. On the other hand, if the density of normal particles had been relatively low, more deuterium would have survived intact without being converted to helium.

Figure 18-9 shows that there is a gap between helium and lithium; there is no stable nucleus with atomic mass 5, so regular nuclear reactions during the first few minutes of the big bang had difficulty converting helium into lithium. If, however, the density of protons and neutrons was high enough, a few nuclear reactions could have leaped the gap and produced a small amount of the isotope lithium-7.

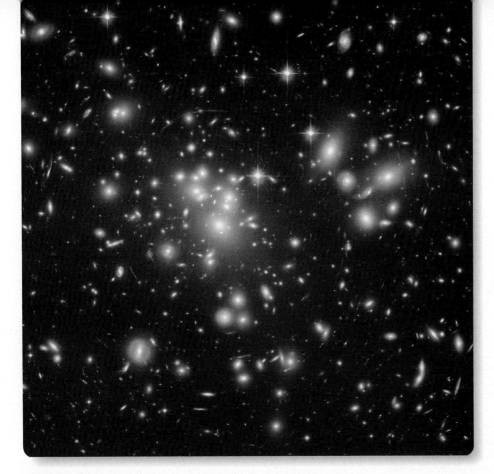

■ Figure 18-15

Gravitational lensing shows that galaxy clusters contain much more mass than what is visible. The yellowish galaxies in this image are members of a relatively nearby cluster of galaxies. Most of the objects in this image are blue or red images of very distant galaxies focused by the gravitational field of the cluster. Some of these imaged galaxies may be over 13 billion light-years away. That they can be seen at all is evidence that the foreground galaxy cluster contains large amounts of dark matter. (NASA, Benites, Broadhurst, Ford, Clampin, Hartig, Illingworth, ACS Science Team and ESA)

Both deuterium and lithium are destroyed in stars, so astronomers have attempted the difficult task of studying clouds of gas at large look-back times that had not yet been altered by nuclear reactions in stars. As shown in ■ Figure 18-16, the amount of deuterium observed now in the universe sets a lower limit on the density of the universe relative to the critical density, and the observed abundance of lithium-7 sets an upper limit. The surprising conclusion from these observations and calculations is that normal matter from which you, Earth, and the stars are made cannot make up more than 5 percent of the critical density. Yet observations of gravitational effects show that galaxies and galaxy clusters contain much larger amounts of matter than that, which can't be normal matter but instead must be dark matter.

The protons and neutrons that make up normal matter belong to a family of subatomic particles called *baryons,* so

cosmologists believe that most of the dark matter cannot be baryons. Only a few percent of the mass in the universe can be ordinary baryonic matter; the dark matter must be **nonbaryonic** matter.

Some theorists thought that neutrinos, particles that are predicted to be very abundant in the universe yet are not baryons, might have enough mass to make up the dark matter, but modern measurements show that neutrinos are not massive enough. Some particle physics theories predict the existence of a new type of particle that are labeled **WIMPs** (weakly interacting massive particles), but they have not been detected with certainty in the laboratory. The true nature of dark matter remains one of the major mysteries of astronomy.

Theoretical models of galaxy formation in the early universe provide more hints about the nature of dark matter. If dark matter is composed of particles that were moving at, or near, the speed of light when matter and energy had equal density, that is referred to as **hot dark matter.** Such fast-moving particles do not clump together easily and could not have stimulated the formation of objects as small as galaxies and clusters of galaxies. Instead, the most successful models of galaxy formation require that the dark matter is actually made up of **cold dark matter,** meaning the particles move slowly and can clump into relatively small structures.

Nonbaryonic dark matter does not interact significantly with normal matter or with photons, which is why you can't see it. This also means that dark matter was not affected by the intense radiation that dominated the universe when it was very young. So long as radiation dominated the universe, it prevented clouds of normal matter from contracting to begin forming galaxies. But the dark matter was immune to the radiation, and the dark matter could contract to form clumps while the universe was very young. In other words, dark matter could have given galaxy formation a head start soon after the big bang. Models with cold, nonbaryonic dark matter are most successful at predicting the formation of galaxies and clusters of galaxies with the right size and at the right time in the history of the universe to match the observations.

Although the evidence is very strong that plenty of dark matter exists, it is still not abundant enough to make the universe flat. Dark matter constitutes less than 30 percent of the critical density. As you will see later in this chapter, there is more to the universe than meets the eye, more even than dark matter.

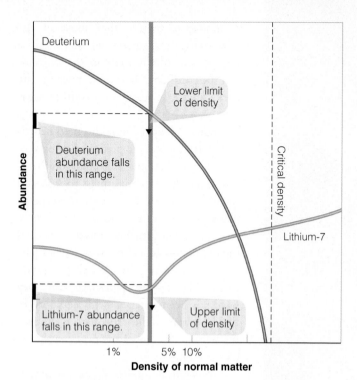

Figure 18-16

This diagram compares observation with theory. Theory predicts how much deuterium (blue curve) and lithium-7 (red curve) you would observe for different densities of normal matter. The observed density of deuterium falls in a narrow range shown at upper left and sets a lower limit on the possible density of normal matter. The observed density of lithium-7, shown at lower left, sets an upper limit. This means the true density of normal matter must fall in a narrow range represented by the green column. Certainly, the density of normal matter is much less than the critical density.

SCIENTIFIC ARGUMENT

Why do cosmologists think that dark matter can't be baryonic?
Good scientific arguments always fall back on evidence. In this case the evidence is very compelling. Small amounts of isotopes like deuterium and lithium-7 were produced by nuclear reactions in the first minutes of the big bang, and the resulting abundance of those elements depends strongly on how many protons and neutrons were available at that time. Because those particles belong to the family of particles called baryons, physicists refer to normal matter as baryonic. Measurement of the abundances of deuterium and lithium-7 show that the universe cannot contain more baryons than about 5 percent of the critical density. Yet, observations of galaxies and galaxy clusters show that dark matter must make up almost 30 percent of the critical density. Consequently, cosmologists conclude that the dark matter must be made up of nonbaryonic particles.

Finding the dark matter is important because the density of matter in the universe determines the curvature of space-time. Now build a new argument. **How does the modern understanding of space-time explain cosmic redshifts?**

18-4) 21st-Century Cosmology

IF YOU ARE A LITTLE DIZZY from the weirdness of expanding space-time and dark matter, make sure you are sitting down before you read further. As the 21st century began, astronomers made a discovery that startled all cosmologists: The expansion of the universe is actually accelerating. You'll have to go back a couple of decades to understand how that amazing new discovery nevertheless fits well with some of the things you have learned already in this chapter.

Inflation

By 1980, accumulating evidence had made the big bang theory widely accepted by cosmologists, but it faced two problems that led to the development of a new theory—a revised big bang with an important addition.

One of the problems is called the **flatness problem.** The properties of the universe appear to be close to the dividing line between being open or closed; that is, the geometry of the universe seems nearly flat, and therefore its density is close to the critical density. Given the vast range of possibilities, from zero to infinity, it seems peculiar that the density of the universe is close to the critical value. If dark matter is as common as the measurements indicate, the universe's density must be within a factor of three of the critical density.

Even a small departure from critical density when the universe was young would be magnified by subsequent expansion. To be so near critical density now, the density of the universe during its first moments must have been within 1 part in 10^{49} of the critical density. So the flatness problem can be stated as: Why is the universe so close to perfectly flat?

The second problem with the original big bang theory is called the **horizon problem.** This is related to the observed isotropy of the cosmic microwave background radiation. When astronomers make a correction for the motion of Earth, they see the same intensity and temperature of background radiation in all directions to a precision of better than 1 part in 1000. Yet when you observe background radiation coming from two points in the sky separated by an angle larger than about 1 degree, you are looking at two bits of matter that seemingly should never have been connected from the time of the big bang up to the time when the radiation was emitted. In other words, when recombination occurred and the gas of the big bang became transparent to the background radiation, the universe was not old enough for any form of energy to have traveled from one of those two regions to the other. Thus, according to the standard big bang theory, the two spots you observe had not had enough time, since the start of the big bang, to exchange energy and equalize their temperatures. (The term *horizon* is used in this context because the two spots are said to lie beyond their respective light-travel horizons.) Then, how did every part of the entire big bang universe get to be so nearly the same temperature at the time of recombination?

The key to these two problems and to others involving subatomic physics may lie with the hypothesis called the **inflationary universe.** That hypothesis predicts there was a sudden enormous expansion called *inflation* when the universe was very young, even more extreme than that predicted by the original big bang theory.

To understand the inflationary universe, you need to recall that physicists know of only four forces—gravity, the electromagnetic force, the strong force, and the weak force (see Chapter 8). You are familiar with gravity; you fought it to get out of bed this morning. The electromagnetic force is responsible for making magnets stick to refrigerator doors and cat hair stick to sweaters charged with static electricity, as well as holding electrons in orbit around atomic nuclei and being intimately connected with processes that make light and radiation. The strong force holds atomic nuclei together, and the weak force is involved in certain kinds of radioactive decay.

For many years, theorists have tried to unify these forces; that is, they have tried to describe all four forces as aspects of a single mathematical law. A century ago, James Clerk Maxwell showed that the electric force and the magnetic force were really the same effect, and physicists now count them as a single electromagnetic force. Similarly, in the 1960s, theorists succeeded in unifying the electromagnetic force and the weak force in what is now called the electroweak force. Those two forces operate effectively as a single unified force, but only in very high-energy processes. At lower energies the electromagnetic force and the weak force behave differently. Now, theorists have proposed ways of unifying the electroweak force with the strong force at even higher energies. These new theories are called **grand unified theories, or GUTs.**

According to the inflationary universe hypothesis, the universe expanded and cooled until about 10^{-36} seconds after the big bang, when it became cool enough that the electroweak force and the strong force began to disconnect from each other; that is, they began to behave in different ways (■ Figure 18-17). Cosmologists calculate that this change would have released tremendous energy, which then suddenly inflated the universe by a size factor of 10^{50} or larger. At the start of inflation, the part of the universe that is now observable from Earth is estimated to have been 35 orders of magnitude smaller than a proton, but it suddenly inflated to roughly a meter across and then continued its slower expansion to its present extent.

Early rapid inflation of the universe can solve both the flatness problem and the horizon problem. The sudden inflation of the universe would have forced whatever curvature it had before that moment toward a value of zero, just as inflating a balloon makes regions on its surface flatter. Consequently, you now live

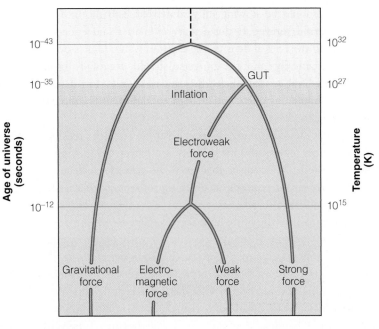

■ **Figure 18-17**

When the universe was very young and hot (top), the four forces of nature were indistinguishable in behavior. As the universe began to expand and cool, the forces "separated," meaning that they began to have different characteristics, which released a huge amount of energy and triggered a sudden rapid inflation in the size of the universe.

in a universe that is almost perfectly flat because of that long-ago moment of inflation. In addition, because what is now the entire observable part of the universe was only about 10^{-59} light seconds across when the universe was about 10^{-36} seconds old, it would have had enough time to equalize its temperature before inflation occurred. As a result, you now live in a universe in which the background radiation has the same temperature in all directions.

The inflationary theory predicts that the universe is almost perfectly flat, which means that the actual density equals the critical density. A theory can never be used as evidence, of course, but the beauty and simplicity of the inflationary theory has given many cosmologists confidence that the universe must be flat. Observations, however, seem to say that the universe does not contain enough matter (ordinary baryonic matter plus nonbaryonic dark matter) to be flat. Can there be more to the universe than baryonic matter and dark matter? What could be weirder and more obscure than dark matter? Read on.

The Acceleration of the Universe

Both common sense and the theory of general relativity suggest that as the galaxies recede from each other, the expansion should be slowed by gravity trying to pull the galaxies toward each other. How much the expansion is slowed should depend on the amount of matter in the universe. If the density of matter and energy in the universe is less than the critical density, the expansion should be slowing only somewhat, and the universe should expand forever. If the density of matter and energy is greater than the critical density, the expansion should be slowing down dramatically, and the universe should eventually begin contracting. Notice that this is the same as saying a low-density universe should be open and a high-enough-density universe should be closed.

For decades, astronomers struggled to measure the redshifts and distances to very distant galaxies and detect the slowing of the expansion. Detecting a change in the rate of expansion is difficult because it requires accurate measurements of the distances to very remote galaxies.

The launch of the Hubble Space Telescope in 1990 made it possible to measure distances to galaxies with unprecedented accuracy, and two competing research teams began using the same technique of calibrating type Ia supernovae as distance indicators. As you learned in Chapter 13, a type Ia supernova occurs when a white dwarf gains matter from a companion star, exceeds the Chandrasekhar limit, and collapses in a supernova explosion. Because all such white dwarfs should collapse at the same mass threshold, they should all produce explosions of the same size and luminosity, which makes them good distance indicators.

The two teams calibrated type Ia supernovae by locating such supernovae occurring in nearby galaxies, with distances known from Cepheid variables and other reliable distance indicators. Once the peak luminosity of type Ia supernovae had been determined, they could be used to find the distances of much more distant galaxies.

Both teams announced their results in 1998. They agree that the expansion of the universe is not slowing down. Contrary to expectations, it is speeding up! That is, the expansion of the universe is accelerating (■ Figure 18-18).

The announcement that the expansion of the universe is accelerating was totally unexpected, and astronomers immediately began testing it. This result depends critically on the calibration of type Ia supernovae as distance indicators, and some astronomers suggested that the calibration might be wrong (look back to Figure 12-14 and "How Do We Know? 15-1"). Problems with the calibration have been ruled out subsequently by supernovae observed at even greater distances. The universe really does seem to be expanding faster and faster, rather than slowing down.

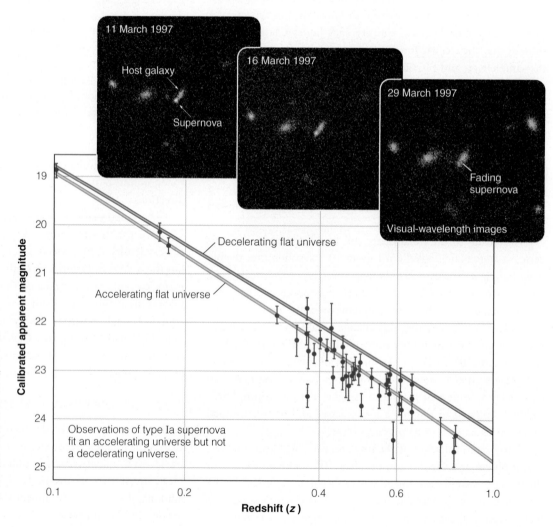

■ Figure 18-18

From the way supernovae fade over time, astronomers can identify those that are type Ia. Once calibrated, the peak brightness of each of those supernovae could be compared with their respective redshifts, revealing that distant type Ia supernovae were about 25 percent fainter than expected. That must mean they are farther away than expected, given their redshifts. This is strong evidence that the expansion of the universe is accelerating. (ESO)

Dark Energy and Acceleration

If the expansion of the universe is accelerating, then there must be a force of repulsion in the universe that counteracts gravity, and cosmologists are struggling to understand what it could be. One possibility leads back to 1916.

When Albert Einstein published his theory of general relativity in 1916, he recognized that his equations describing space-time implied that the galaxies could not float unmoving in space because their gravity would pull them toward each other. The only solutions seemed to be either a universe that was contracting under the influence of gravity or a universe in which the galaxies were rushing away from each other so rapidly that gravity could not pull them together. In 1916, cosmologists did not yet know that the universe was expanding, so Einstein made what he later thought was a mistake.

To balance the attractive force of gravity, Einstein added a constant to his equations called the **cosmological constant,** represented by an uppercase lambda (Λ). That constant represents a force of repulsion that balances the gravitational attraction between galaxies so the universe would not contract or expand. Thirteen years later, in 1929, Edwin Hubble announced his observations indicating that the universe is expanding, and Einstein said introducing the cosmological constant was his biggest blunder. Modern cosmologists think he may have been right after all.

One explanation for the acceleration of the universe is that there is, after all, a cosmological constant, representing a type of antigravity force that is part of the fabric of space-time and causes a continuing acceleration in the expansion of the universe. Because the cosmological constant by definition remains constant with time, the universe would have experienced this acceleration throughout its history.

Another solution is to suppose that totally empty space, the vacuum, contains energy that drives the acceleration. This is an interesting possibility because theoretical physicists have long discussed the idea of a vacuum energy for reasons based on the behavior of subatomic particles. Cosmologists label a universal vacuum energy as **quintessence.** Unlike the cosmological constant, the effect of quintessence would not necessarily remain constant over time.

Whatever the correct explanation might be, whether a cosmological constant antigravity force, or a universal vacuum energy, or something else, the observed acceleration of the universe's expansion is evidence that a type of unknown energy is spread throughout space. Cosmologists refer to it as **dark energy,** an energy that drives the acceleration of the universe but does not contribute to the formation of starlight or the cosmic microwave background radiation.

You will recall that acceleration and dark energy were first discovered when astronomers found that supernovae a few billion light-years away were slightly fainter than expected based on their redshifts. The acceleration of the expansion has made those supernovae a bit farther away than originally estimated from their redshifts, and so they look fainter. Since that discovery, astronomers have continued to find even more distant type Ia supernovae, some as distant as 12 billion light-years. The more distant of those supernovae are not too faint; they are too bright! That reveals even more about dark energy ($\blacksquare$ Figure 18-19).

Unlike the medium-distant supernovae, the very distant supernovae are a bit too bright because they are not as far away as expected, and that confirms a theoretical prediction based on dark energy. When the universe was young, galaxies were closer together so their gravitational pull on each other was stronger than the effect of dark energy and slowed the expansion. That makes the very distant supernovae a bit too bright. As space-time expanded, it moved the galaxies farther apart, their gravitational pull on each other became weaker than dark energy, and acceleration began. That makes the medium-distant supernovae a bit too faint. In other words, the observations show that sometime about 6 billion years ago (when the universe was 55 percent of its present age), the universe shifted gears from deceleration to acceleration. The calibration of type Ia supernovae allows astronomers to observe this change from deceleration to acceleration.

Furthermore, dark energy can help you understand the curvature of the universe. The theory of inflation makes the specific prediction that the universe is flat. Recent observations you will learn about in the rest of this chapter confirm that prediction. Dark energy seems to explain how the universe can have enough matter plus energy to be flat. As you have already learned, $E = mc^2$ means that energy and matter are equivalent. Thus, the dark energy is equivalent to an amount of mass spread through space. Baryonic matter plus dark matter makes up about one-third of the critical density, and dark energy appears to make up the remaining two-

$\blacksquare$ **Figure 18-19**

Follow-up observations of extremely distant galaxies located in the GOODs deep fields have detected type Ia supernovae. The upper images here show the supernovae, and the lower images show the galaxies before the supernovae erupted. These supernovae confirm the original discovery that the expansion of the universe is accelerating and are distant enough to eliminate concerns that the calibration of type Ia supernovae was wrong. (NASA, ESA, and Adam Riess, STScI)

Visual + infrared images

thirds. That is, when you include dark energy, the total density of the universe equals the critical density, which makes the universe flat.

Step by step, you have been climbing the cosmological pyramid. Each step has been small and logical, but look where it has led you. You now know some of nature's deepest secrets, but you can imagine there are yet more steps above yet to be found, and more secrets to explore.

The Age and Fate of the Universe

Acceleration helps with another problem. The Hubble constant equals 70 km/s/Mpc, and earlier in this chapter you calculated the Hubble time, an estimate of the age of the universe, and found it was about 14 billion years. Further, you calculated a more precise estimate of the universe's age on the assumption that its geometry is flat, which gives an age of two-thirds of the Hubble time, or $\frac{2}{3}$ times 14 billion years, which equals about 9 billion years. That was a puzzle because the globular star clusters are older than that. Now you are really ready to solve the age problem and then consider the fate of the universe.

If the expansion of the universe has been accelerating, then it must have been expanding slower in the past, and the galaxies would have taken longer to arrive at the average separations you can observe now. That means the universe can be flat but nevertheless older than two-thirds of the Hubble time. The latest estimates suggest that acceleration makes the age of a flat universe almost 14 billion years, coincidentally about the same as the simple Hubble time estimate. That age is clearly older than the oldest known star clusters, which solves the age problem.

For many years, cosmologists have enjoyed saying, "Geometry is destiny." Thinking of open, closed, and flat universe models, they concluded that the density of a model universe determines its geometry, and its geometry determines its fate. By this they meant that if the universe is open it must therefore expand forever, whereas if it is closed, it must eventually begin contracting. But that is true only if the behavior of the universe as a whole is ruled completely by gravity. If dark energy causes an acceleration that can dominate gravity, then geometry is NOT destiny, and, depending on the precise properties of dark energy, even a closed universe might expand forever.

The ultimate fate of the universe depends on the nature of dark energy. If dark energy is described by the cosmological constant, then the force driving acceleration does not change with time, and our flat universe will expand forever with the galaxies getting farther and farther apart and using up their gas and dust making stars, and stars dying, until each galaxy is isolated, burnt out, dark, and alone. If, however, dark energy is described by quintessence, then the force may be increasing with time, and the universe might accelerate faster and faster as space pulls the galaxies away from each other, eventually pulling the galaxies apart, then pulling the stars apart, and finally tearing individual atoms apart. This possibility has been called the **big rip.**

Probably there will be no big rip; critically important observations made by the Chandra X-ray Observatory have been used to measure the amount of hot gas and dark matter in almost 30 galaxy clusters. Because the distance of each cluster is one of the variables in the calculations, the X-ray astronomers could compare the amount of hot gas and dark matter and solve for distance. The farthest of the clusters is 8 billion light-years away. These observations are important for two reasons. First, the redshifts and distance of these galaxies independently confirm the conclusion from the supernova observations that the expansion of the universe first decelerated but changed to accelerating about 6 billion years ago. Second, the Chandra results almost completely rule out quintessence. If dark energy is described by the cosmological constant and not by quintessence, then there will be no big rip (■ Figure 18-20).

■ **Figure 18-20**

X-ray observations of hot gas in galaxy clusters confirm that in its early history the universe was decelerating because gravity was stronger than the dark energy. As expansion weakened the influence of gravity, dark energy began to cause acceleration. The evidence is not conclusive, but it most directly supports the cosmological constant form of dark energy and weighs against quintessence, which means the universe may not undergo a "big rip." This diagram is only schematic, and the two curves are drawn separated for clarity; at the present time, the two curves have not diverged from each other. (NASA/CXC/IoA/S. Allen et al.)

The distribution of brighter galaxies in the sky reveals the great Virgo cluster (center), containing over 1000 galaxies only about 17 Mpc away. Other clusters fill the sky, such as the more distant Coma cluster just above the Virgo cluster in this diagram. The Virgo cluster is linked with others to form the Local Supercluster.

The Origin of Large-Scale Structure

On the largest scales, the universe is isotropic. That is, it looks the same in all directions. But, on smaller scales, there are irregularities. The sky is filled with galaxies and clusters of galaxies that seem to be related to their neighbors in even larger aggregations that astronomers call **large-scale structure.** Studies of large-scale structure lead to insights about how the universe has evolved.

When you look at galaxies in the sky you see them in clusters ranging from a few galaxies to thousands, and those clusters appear to be grouped into **superclusters** (■ Figure 18-21). The Local Supercluster, in which you live, is a roughly disk-shaped swarm of galaxy clusters 50 to 75 Mpc in diameter. By measuring the redshifts and positions of hundreds of thousands of galaxies in great slices across the sky, astronomers have been able to create maps revealing that superclusters are not scattered at random. They are distributed in long, narrow **filaments** and thin walls that outline great **voids** nearly empty of galaxies (■ Figure 18-22).

This large-scale structure is a problem because the cosmic microwave background radiation is very uniform, and that means the gas of the big bang must have been extremely uniform at the time of recombination. Yet the look-back time to the

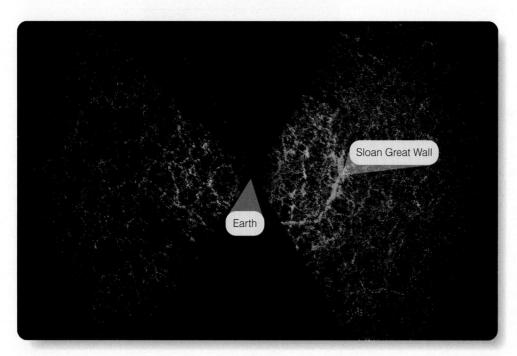

Nearly 70,000 galaxies are plotted in this double slice of the universe extending outward in the plane of Earth's equator. The nearest galaxies are shown in red and the more distant in green and blue. The galaxies form filaments and walls enclosing nearly empty voids. The Sloan Great Wall is almost 1.4 billion light-years long and is the largest known structure in the universe. The most distant galaxies in this diagram are roughly 3 billion light-years from Earth. (Sloan Digital Sky Survey)

farthest galaxies and quasars is about 93 percent of the way back to the big bang. How did the uniform gas at the time of recombination become lumpy and coagulate so quickly to form galaxies? How did it make clusters of galaxies and the supermassive black holes we observe as quasars (see Chapter 17) so early in the history of the universe?

Baryonic matter is so rare in the universe that cosmologists can calculate that it did not have enough gravity to pull itself together quickly after the big bang. As you learned earlier, cosmologists have evidence that dark matter is nonbaryonic and therefore immune to the intense radiation that prevented normal matter from contracting. Dark matter, in contrast, was able to collapse into clouds and then attract normal matter to begin the formation of galaxies, clusters, and superclusters. Mathematical models have been made to describe this process, and cold dark matter does seem capable of jump-starting the formation of structure of the right sizes and in the right amount of time (■ Figure 18-23).

But what started the clumping of the dark matter? Theorists say that space is filled with tiny, random quantum mechanical fluctuations smaller than the smallest atomic particles. At the moment of inflation, those tiny fluctuations would have been stretched to very large but very subtle variations in gravitational fields that could have stimulated the formation of galaxy superclusters, filaments, and walls. The structure you see in Figure 18-22 may be the present-day ghostly traces of microscopic random fluctuations in the infant universe.

The Two-Degree-Field Redshift Survey mapped the position and redshift of 250,000 galaxies and 30,000 quasars. As expected, the galaxies are spread in filaments and walls, and a statistical analysis of the distribution matches the prediction of inflation and shows that the universe expansion is accelerating. This is an important result because it is yet another confirmation of acceleration that is independent of the brightness of type Ia supernovae or X-ray–emitting gas in galaxy clusters. When a hypothesis is confirmed by observations of many different types, scientists have much more confidence that it is a true description of nature.

Curvature of the Universe

Astronomers continue to search for more ways to confirm that the universe is flat and that its expansion is accelerating. One way to measure the curvature of space-time is to measure the size of things at great look-back times; for example, observing irregularities in the background radiation. That type of measurement is yielding impressive results.

The background radiation is nearly isotropic—it looks almost exactly the same in all directions after effects of Earth's motion and emission by material in the foreground are taken into account. After those corrections are made to a map of the background radiation and the average intensity is subtracted from each spot on the sky, minor irregularities are evident. That is, some spots on the sky look a tiny bit hotter and brighter, or cooler and fainter, than

Growth of Structure in the Universe

Soon after the big bang, radiation and hot gas are almost uniformly spread through the universe.

Cold dark matter, immune to the influence of light, can contract to form clouds…

which pull in normal gas to form superclusters of galaxies. Gravity continues to pull clusters together.

Statistical tests show the distribution in this model universe resembles the observed distribution of galaxies.

■ Figure 18-23

This computer model traces the formation of structure in the universe from soon after the big bang to the present. (Adapted from a model by Kauffmann, Colberg, Diaferio, & White: Max-Planck Institut für Astronomie)

the average (■ Figure 18-24; also look back at Figure 18-8). Those irregularities contain lots of information.

The inflation-modified big bang theory of the universe makes specific predictions about the angular sizes of the variations you should find in the background radiation. Observations made by the COBE satellite in 1992 detected the variations with the largest diameter, but detecting smaller variations is critical for testing the theory. Six teams of astronomers have built specialized telescopes to make these observations. Some have flown under balloons high in the atmosphere, and others have observed from the ice of Antarctica. Extensive observations of the background

■ **Figure 18-24**

Data from the WMAP spacecraft were used to make this far-infrared map of the entire sky. The infrared glow from dust in our solar system and in the Milky Way Galaxy has been removed to reveal slight irregularities in the temperature of the cosmic microwave background radiation. Red and yellow spots are slightly warmer than the green and blue spots. (NASA/WMAP Science Team)

radiation have been made by the Wilkinson Microwave Anisotropy Probe (WMAP). In 2009 the Planck space telescope was launched to do an even more thorough job.

It is a **Common Misconception** that explosions in space produce sound. Science-fiction movies imply that sound can travel through a vacuum and that exploding space ships make big *kabooms.* That's not true now, of course, but the early universe was dense enough that sound could travel through the gas, and the big bang did make a noise. A theorist described it as "a descending scream, building to a deep rasping roar, and ending in a deafening hiss." The pitch of the sound was about 50 octaves too low for you to hear, but those powerful sound waves did have an effect on the universe. They determined the size of the irregularities now detectable in the cosmic microwave background radiation.

Theory predicts that most of the irregularities in the hot gas of the big bang should be about one degree in diameter if the universe is flat. If the universe were open, the most common irregularities would be smaller. Careful measurements of the size of the irregularities in the cosmic background radiation show that the observations fit the theory very well for a flat universe, as you can see in ■ Figure 18-25. Not only is the theory of inflation confirmed, an exciting result itself, but these data show that the universe is flat, meaning space-time has no overall curvature, which indirectly confirms the existence of dark energy and the acceleration of the universe.

Cosmologists can analyze those microwave background irregularities using sophisticated mathematics to find out how frequently spots of different angular sizes occur. The calculations confirm that spots about 1 degree in diameter are the most common, but spots of other sizes occur as well, and it is possible to plot a graph such as ■ Figure 18-26 to show how frequently different sizes of irregularities occur.

The data points from the WMAP observations follow a wiggling line in Figure 18-26, and the size and positions of those wiggles tell cosmologists a great deal about the universe. The details of the curve show that the universe is flat, accelerating, and will expand forever. The age of the universe derived from the data is 13.7 billion years. Furthermore, the smaller peaks in the curve reveal that the universe contains 4.6 percent baryonic (normal) matter, 23.3 percent nonbaryonic dark matter, and 72.1 percent dark energy. The Hubble constant is confirmed to be 71 km/s/Mpc. The inflationary theory is confirmed, and the data give more support to the cosmological constant version of dark energy, although quintessence is not quite ruled out. Hot dark matter is ruled out. The dark matter needs to be cold dark matter to clump together rapidly enough after the big bang to make the galaxy clusters and superclusters we observe. In fact, a model based on these data predicts that the first stars began to produce light when the universe was only about 400 million years old.

Simulated data
Closed model universe
Larger spots

Simulated data
Flat model universe
Spots about 1 degree in diameter

Simulated data
Open model universe
Smaller spots

Observational data

■ **Figure 18-25**

You can see the difference yourself. Compare the observations of the irregularities in the background radiation in the far right panel with the three simulations starting from the left. The observed size of the irregularities fits best with cosmological models having flat geometry. Detailed mathematical analysis confirms your visual impression: The universe is flat. (Courtesy of the BOOMERANG Collaboration)

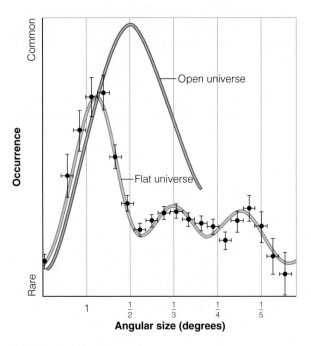

■ **Figure 18-26**

This graph shows how commonly irregularities of different sizes occur in the cosmic microwave background radiation. Irregularities of about 1 degree in diameter are most common. Models of the universe that are open or closed are ruled out. The data fit a flat model of the universe very well. Crosses on data points show the uncertainty in the measurements.

Please reread the preceding paragraph. Especially to people who have been working in the field for years, that collection of firm facts is mind-blastingly amazing. WMAP and other studies of the cosmic microwave background radiation and the distribution of galaxies have revolutionized cosmology. At last, astronomers have accurate observations against which to test theories. The values of the basic cosmic parameters are known to a precision of 1 percent or better.

On reviewing these results, one cosmologist announced that "Cosmology is solved!" but that might be premature. Cosmologists don't understand dark matter or the dark energy that drives the acceleration, so in a sense, over 95 percent of the universe is not understood. Hearing this, another cosmologist suggested a better phrase was "Cosmology in crisis!" Certainly there are further mysteries to be explored, but cosmologists are growing more confident that they can describe the origin and evolution of the universe.

SCIENTIFIC ARGUMENT

How does inflation theory solve the flatness problem?

This question requires a carefully constructed argument. The flatness problem can be stated as a question: Why is the universe so flat? After all, the density of matter in the universe could be anything from zero to infinite, but the observed sizes of variations in the cosmic background radiation show that the universe is flat, and therefore the average density of the universe is very close to the critical density (Figures 18-25 and 18-26). Furthermore, the density must have been astonishingly close to the critical density when the universe was very young, or it would not be as close as it is now. The inflationary theory solves this problem by proposing that the universe had a moment of rapid inflation when it was a tiny fraction of a second old. That inflation drove the universe toward flatness just as blowing up a balloon makes a spot on the balloon flatter and flatter.

Understanding theory in cosmology is critically important, but science depends on evidence. Now build another argument based on evidence. **What evidence can you cite that the expansion of the universe is accelerating?**

As you climbed the cosmology pyramid, you negotiated many steps. Most were easy, and all were logical. They have carried you up to some sweeping views, and you have traced the origin of the universe, the formation of the chemical elements, the birth of galaxies, and the births and deaths of stars. You now have a perspective that few humans share.

We are by-products of two cosmic processes, gravitational contraction and nuclear fusion. Gravity created instabilities in the hot matter of the big bang and triggered the formation of clusters of galaxies. Further contraction of that material formed individual galaxies and then stars within the galaxies. As stars began to shine through the universe, nuclear fusion in their cores began to cook hydrogen and helium into the heavier atoms from which humans are made.

As you review the history and structure of the universe, it is wise to recognize the mysteries that remain; but note that they are mysteries that may be solved rather than mysteries that are unknowable. Only a century ago, humanity didn't know there were other galaxies, or that the universe was expanding, or that stars generate energy by nuclear fusion. Human curiosity has solved many of the mysteries of cosmology and will solve more during your lifetime.

Study and Review

Summary

▶ **Cosmology (p. 370)** is the study of the structure and history of the universe as a whole. Astronomers and physicists who do research in cosmology are called **cosmologists (p. 371).**

▶ Cosmologists conclude that it is impossible for the universe to have an edge because an edge would introduce logical inconsistencies. In other words, an edge to the universe does not make sense.

▶ If the universe has no edge, then it cannot have a center.

▶ The darkness of the night sky leads to the conclusion that the universe is not infinitely old. If the universe were infinite in extent, infinite in age, and **static (p. 371)**, then every spot on the sky would glow as brightly as the surface of a star. This problem, commonly labeled **Olbers's paradox (p. 371)**, implies that the universe had a beginning and is evolving.

▶ The **observable universe (p. 372)**, the part you can see from Earth with a large telescope, is limited in size. It may be only a tiny portion of the entire universe, which could be infinite.

▶ Edwin Hubble's 1929 discovery that the redshift of a galaxy is proportional to its distance, now known as the Hubble law, shows that the galaxies appear to be moving away from each other. That phenomenon is called the **expanding universe (p. 372).**

▶ Tracing the expansion of the universe backward in time brings you to imagine an initial high-density, high-temperature state commonly called the **big bang (p. 373).**

▶ A rough estimate of the age of the universe based on the presently observed expansion rate is called the **Hubble time (p. 374).**

▶ Although the expanding universe began from the big bang, it has no center. The galaxies do not move away from a single point. Cosmologists understand that galaxies remain approximately in their respective positions and are carried away from each other as the space between them expands.

▶ The **cosmic microwave background (p. 375)** radiation is blackbody radiation with a temperature of about 2.73 K, spread nearly uniformly over the entire sky. This radiation is the light from the big bang, freed from the gas at the time of **recombination (p. 378)** and now red-shifted by a factor of 1100.

▶ The background radiation is clear evidence that the universe began with a big bang.

▶ During the earliest moments of the universe, matter and **antimatter (p. 376)** particles continually flashed in and out of existence. A slight excess of ordinary matter remained after most of the matter and anti-matter particles annihilated each other.

▶ During the first few minutes of the big bang, nuclear fusion converted some of the hydrogen into helium but was unable to make many other heavy atoms because no stable nuclei exist with weights of 5 or 8. Now, hydrogen and helium are common in the universe, but heavier atoms are rare.

▶ After recombination, for a period of hundreds of millions of years called the **dark age (p. 378)**, the universe expanded in darkness until the first stars came into existence. Astronomers have observed signs of **reionization (p. 378)** of the universe caused by that first generation of stars.

▶ The chemical composition of the oldest stars is about 75 percent hydrogen and 25 percent helium, which is what models of the big bang nuclear processes would predict. This is further evidence supporting the big bang theory.

▶ The universe is **isotropic (p. 380)** and **homogeneous (p. 380).** In other words, in its major features, the universe respectively looks the same in all directions from Earth and appears to have the same properties in all locations.

▶ Isotropy and homogeneity lead to the **cosmological principle (p. 380)**, the idea that there are no special places in the universe. Except for minor local differences, every place is the same, and the view from every place is the same.

- Einstein's theory of general relativity explains that cosmic redshifts are caused by wavelengths of photons stretching as they travel through expanding space-time.

- **Closed universe (p. 381)** models are finite in size, but their space-time is curved back on itself so they have no edge or center.

- **Flat universe (p. 381)** models have uncurved space-time and are infinite. Modern observations show that the universe is probably flat.

- **Open universe (p. 381)** models have curved space-time, but it is not curved back on itself. Such universes are infinite. Open model universes contain less than the **critical density (p. 382)** and closed model universes more. If the universe is flat, then its density must equal the critical density.

- The amounts of deuterium and lithium-7 in the universe shows that normal baryonic matter can make up only about 5 percent of the critical density. Dark matter must be **nonbaryonic (p. 383)** and makes up less than 30 percent of the critical density.

- One suggestion for what dark matter might be is a hypothetical type of subatomic particle labeled **WIMPs (p. 383).** The observed ranges of sizes and masses for galaxy clusters disagrees with models that assume rapidly moving **hot dark matter (p. 383)** particles that would not clump together easily and, instead, agrees with models that assume slowly moving, readily-clumping **cold dark matter (p. 383).**

- The **inflationary universe (p. 385),** a modification to the big bang theory, proposes that the universe briefly expanded dramatically, just a tiny fraction of a second after the big bang.

- The energy to drive inflation would have been released when the four forces of nature changed their respective properties to become different as the universe cooled in its earliest moments. This "separation" of forces is predicted by **grand unified theories (GUTs) (p. 385)** that explain the forces of nature as being aspects of a single force and that are unified only in particle interactions with very high energies.

- Inflation explains the **flatness problem (p. 384)** because the large expansion forced the universe to become flat, just as a spot on an inflating balloon becomes flatter as the balloon inflates.

- Inflation explains the **horizon problem (p. 384)** because what is now the observable part of the universe was so small before inflation that energy could move and equalize the temperature everywhere in that volume.

- Observations of type Ia supernovae reveal the surprising fact that the expansion of the universe is speeding up. Cosmologists propose that this acceleration is caused by energy present in empty space labeled **"dark energy" (p. 387).**

- The nature of dark energy is unknown. It may be described by Einstein's **cosmological constant (Λ) (p. 387)**, or its strength may change with time, which cosmologists label **"quintessence" (p. 387)**. Some models of quintessence predict an ever-accelerating expansion leading to a **"big rip" (p. 388)** that eventually would tear all the objects, even the atoms, of the universe apart.

- Corrected for acceleration, the observed value of the Hubble constant implies that the universe is 13.7 billion years old.

- The sudden inflation of the universe is hypothesized to have magnified tiny quantum mechanical fluctuations in the density of matter and energy. These very wide but very weak differences in density caused dark matter, followed by baryonic matter, to draw together and produce the present-day **large-scale structure (p. 389)** consisting of galaxy **superclusters (p. 389)** arranged in great walls and **filaments (p. 389)** outlining enormous **voids (p. 389).**

- Statistical observations of the large-scale structure of the universe and the size of irregularities in the cosmic microwave background confirm that it is flat and contains 4.6 percent baryonic matter, 23.3 percent dark matter, and 73.1 percent dark energy.

- The mass equivalent of dark energy added to dark matter and baryonic matter makes the observed density of the universe equal to the critical density, thereby confirming the prediction made by inflation theory that the universe is flat.

Review Questions

1. How does the darkness of the night sky tell you something important about the universe?

2. How can Earth be located at the center of the observable universe if you accept the cosmological principle?

3. Why can't an open universe have a center? How can a closed universe not have a center?

4. What evidence shows that the universe is expanding? What evidence shows that it began with a big bang?

5. Why couldn't atomic nuclei exist when the age of the universe was less than 2 minutes?

6. Why are measurements of the present density of the universe important?

7. How does the inflationary universe theory resolve the flatness problem? How does it resolve the horizon problem?

8. If the Hubble constant were really 100 instead of 70 km/s/Mpc, much of what astronomers understand about the evolution of stars and star clusters would have to be wrong. Explain why. (*Hint:* What would the age of the universe be?)

9. What is the evidence that the universe was very uniform during its first 400,000 years?

10. What is the difference between hot dark matter and cold dark matter? What difference does that make to cosmology?

11. What evidence can you cite that the expansion of the universe is accelerating?

12. What evidence can you cite that the universe is flat?

13. **How Do We Know?** Reasoning by analogy often helps make complicated systems or abstract ideas easier to understand. Why do you have to be careful when using analogies?

14. **How Do We Know?** The word *believe* has a meaning in normal conversation that does not really apply to scientific work. Why might cosmologists hesitate to use the word "believe" when they talk about the big bang?

Discussion Questions

1. Do you think Copernicus would have accepted the cosmological principle? Why or why not?

2. If you reject any model of the universe that has an edge in space because you can't comprehend such a thing, shouldn't you also reject any model of the universe that has a beginning? Isn't a beginning like an "edge" in time, or is there a difference?

Problems

1. Use the data in Figure 18-4 to plot a velocity–distance diagram, calculate the Hubble constant *H,* and estimate the Hubble time.

2. If a galaxy is 9.0 Mpc away from Earth and recedes at 510 km/s, what is *H?* What is the Hubble time? How old would the universe be, assuming space-time is flat and there has been no acceleration of the universe's expansion? How would acceleration change your answer?

3. What was the wavelength of maximum intensity for radiation from the gas of the big bang at the time of recombination? By what factor

is that different from the wavelength of maximum intensity of the cosmic microwave background radiation observed now?

4. Pretend that galaxies are spaced evenly, 2 Mpc apart, and the average mass of a galaxy is 10^{11} solar masses. What is the average density of matter in the universe? (*Hints:* The volume of a sphere is $\frac{4}{3}\pi r^3$, and the mass of the sun is 2×10^{30} kg.)

5. Figure 18-14 is based on an assumed Hubble constant of 70 km/s/Mpc. How would you change the diagram to fit a Hubble constant of 50 km/s/Mpc?

6. Hubble's first estimate of the Hubble constant was 530 km/s/Mpc. His distances were too small by a factor of about 7 because of a calibration error. If he had not had that calibration problem, what value for H would he have obtained?

7. What was the maximum age of the universe predicted by Hubble's first estimate of the Hubble constant (in Problem 6)?

Learning to Look

1. Explain why some of the galaxies in this photo have elongated, slightly curved images. What do such observations tell you about the universe?

NASA/ACS Science Team/ESA

2. The image at the right shows irregularities in the background radiation. Why isn't the background radiation perfectly uniform? What does the size of these irregularities tell you?

Courtesy of BOOMERANG Collaboration

19 | The Origin of the Solar System

Guidepost

You have studied the appearance, origin, structure, and evolution of stars, galaxies, and the universe itself. So far, though, your studies have left out one important type of object—planets. Now it is time to correct that omission. In this chapter, once you learn the evidence for how the solar system formed, you can understand how the processes you have been studying produced Earth, your home planet.

As you explore our solar system in space and time, you will find answers to four essential questions:

What is the theory for the origin of the solar system?

What are the observed properties of the solar system that the theory of its origin can explain?

How do planets form?

What do astronomers know about other planetary systems?

In the next three chapters, you will explore in more detail each of the planets, plus asteroids, comets, and meteoroids. By studying the origin of the solar system before studying the individual objects in it, you give yourself a better framework for understanding these fascinating worlds.

The human race lives on a planet in a planetary system that appears to have formed in a nebula around the protostar that became the sun. This artist's impression shows such a nebular disk around a forming star. (NASA/JPL-Caltech)

What place is this?

Where are we now?

— CARL SANDBURG, "GRASS"

MICROSCOPIC CREATURES LIVE in the roots of your eyelashes. Don't worry. Everyone has them, and they are harmless.* They hatch, fight for survival, mate, lay eggs, and die in the tiny spaces around the roots of your eyelashes without doing any harm. Some live in renowned places—the eyelashes of a glamorous movie star, for example—but the tiny beasts are not self-aware; they never stop to say, "Where are we?"

You can study the solar system for many reasons. You can study Earth and its sibling planets because, as you are about to discover, there are almost certainly more planets in the universe than stars. Above all, you can study the solar system because it is your home in the universe. Because humans are an intelligent species, we have the ability and the responsibility to wonder where we are and what we are. Our kind has inhabited this solar system for several million years, but only within the last few hundred years have we begun to understand what the solar system is.

19-1 The Great Chain of Origins

YOU ARE LINKED through a great chain of origins that leads backward through time to the instant when the universe began, 13.7 billion years ago. The gradual discovery of the links in that chain is one of the most exciting adventures of the human intellect. In earlier chapters, you studied some of that story: the origin of the universe in the big bang, the formation of galaxies, the origin of stars, and the growth of the chemical elements. Now you will explore further to consider the origin of planets.

The History of the Atoms in Your Body

The universe began in the big bang (see Chapter 18). By the time the universe was a few minutes old, the protons, neutrons, and electrons in your body had come into existence. You are made of very old matter.

Although those particles formed quickly, they were not linked together to form many of the atoms that are common today. Most of the matter in the early universe was hydrogen, and about 25 percent was helium. Although your body does not contain helium, it does contain many of those ancient hydrogen

atoms unchanged since the universe began. Evidence indicates that almost no atoms heavier than helium were made in the big bang.

Within a few hundred million years after the big bang, matter began to collect to form galaxies containing billions of stars. You have learned that nuclear reactions inside stars are where low-mass atoms such as hydrogen are combined to make heavier atoms (see Chapters 12 and 13). Generation after generation of stars cooked the original particles, fusing them into atoms such as carbon, nitrogen, and oxygen that are common in your body. Even the calcium atoms in your bones were assembled inside stars.

Massive stars produce iron in their cores, but much of that iron is destroyed when the core collapses and the star explodes as a supernova. Most of the iron on Earth and in your body was produced instead by carbon fusion in type Ia supernova explosions and by the decay of radioactive atoms in the expanding matter ejected by type II supernovae. Atoms heavier than iron such as gold, silver, and iodine are created by rapid nuclear reactions that can occur only during supernova explosions. Iodine is critical to the function of your thyroid gland, and you probably have gold and silver jewelry or dental fillings. Realize that these types of atoms, which are part of your life on Earth, were made during the violent deaths of massive stars long ago.

Our galaxy contains at least 100 billion stars, of which the sun is one. Astronomers have a variety of evidence that the sun formed from a cloud of gas and dust almost 5 billion years ago, and the atoms in your body were part of that cloud. How the sun took shape, how the cloud gave birth to the planets, how the atoms in your body found their way onto Earth and into you, make up the story of this chapter. As you explore the origin of the solar system, keep in mind the great chain of origins that created the atoms. As the geologist Preston Cloud remarked, "Stars have died that we might live."

Early Hypotheses for the Origin of Earth and the Solar System

The earliest descriptions of Earth's origin are myths and folktales that go back beyond the beginning of recorded history. In the time of Galileo, the telescope gave philosophers observational evidence on which to base rational explanations for natural phenomena. While people like Copernicus, Kepler, and Galileo tried to find logical explanations for the motions of Earth and the other planets, other philosophers began thinking about the origin of Earth and its sibling planets.

The first physical theory for the solar system's origin was proposed by the French philosopher and mathematician René Descartes (1596–1650). Because he lived and wrote before the time of Newton, Descartes did not recognize that gravitation is the dominant force in the universe. Rather, he believed that force was communicated by contact between bodies and that the entire

---

Demodex folliculorum has been found in 97 percent of individuals and is a characteristic of healthy skin.

universe was filled with vortices of whirling invisible particles. In 1644, he proposed that the sun and planets formed when a large vortex contracted and condensed. His hypothesis explained the general properties of the solar system known at the time.

A century later, in 1745, the French naturalist Georges-Louis de Buffon (1707–1788) proposed an alternative hypothesis that the planets were formed when a passing comet collided with or passed close to the sun and pulled matter out of the sun. He did not know that the solid parts of comets are small, insubstantial bodies, but later astronomers modified his hypothesis to propose that a star, rather than a comet, interacted with the sun. According to the modified hypothesis, matter ripped from the sun and the other star condensed to form the planets, which were driven into orbit around the sun by the motion of the two stars' collision. (■ Figure 19-1a). This **passing star hypothesis** was popular off and on for two centuries, but it contains serious flaws. First, stars are very small compared to the distances between them, so they collide very infrequently. Only a tiny fraction of stars in our galaxy have ever suffered a collision or close

encounter with another star. More important, the gas pulled from the sun and the star would be much too hot to condense to make planets, and it would have dispersed instead. Furthermore, even if planets did form, they would not go into stable orbits around the sun.

The hypotheses of Descartes and Buffon fall into two broad categories. Descartes proposed an **evolutionary hypothesis** involving common, gradual processes to produce the sun and planets. If it were correct, stars with planets would be very common. Buffon's idea, on the other hand, is a **catastrophic hypothesis.** It involves unlikely, sudden events to produce the solar system, and thus implies that planetary systems are very rare. While your imagination may enjoy picturing the spectacle of colliding stars, modern scientists have observed that nature usually changes gradually in small steps rather than in sudden, dramatic events. The modern theory for the origin of the planets, based on abundant evidence, is evolutionary rather than catastrophic (**How Do We Know? 19-1**).

The modern theory of the origin of the solar system had its true beginning with Pierre-Simon de Laplace (1749–1827), a brilliant French astronomer and mathematician. In 1796, he combined Descartes's vortex idea with Newton's laws of gravity and motion to produce a model of a rotating cloud of matter that contracted under its own gravitation and flattened into a disk—the **nebular hypothesis.** As the disk grew smaller, it had to conserve angular momentum and spin faster and faster. Laplace reasoned that, when it was spinning as fast as it could, the disk would shed its outer edge to leave behind a ring of matter. Then the disk could contract further, speed up again, and leave another ring. In this way, he imagined, the contracting disk would leave behind a series of rings, each of

■**Figure 19-1**

(a) The passing star hypothesis proposed that the sun was hit by, or had a very close encounter with, another star. Matter torn from the sun and the other star formed planets orbiting the sun and, perhaps, the other star. This is an example of a catastrophic hypothesis. (b) Originally proposed in the 18th century by Laplace, the nebular hypothesis proposed that a contracting disk of matter around the sun conserved angular momentum, spun faster, and shed rings of matter that then formed planets. This is an example of an evolutionary hypothesis.

which could become a planet circling the newborn sun at the center of the disk (Figure 19-1b).

According to the nebular hypothesis, the sun should be spinning very rapidly, or, to put it another way, the sun should have most of the angular momentum of the solar system. (Recall from Chapter 5 that angular momentum is the tendency of a rotating object to continue rotating.) As astronomers studied the planets and the sun, however, they found that the sun rotates relatively slowly and that the planets moving in their orbits actually have most of the angular momentum in the solar system. In fact, the rotation of the sun contains only about 0.3 percent of the angular momentum of the solar system. Because the nebular hypothesis could not explain this **angular momentum problem,** it was never fully successful, and astronomers instead considered various versions of the passing star hypothesis for over a century. Today astronomers have a consistent theory for the origin of our solar system that is a modified version of the nebular hypothesis.

The Solar Nebula Theory

By 1940, astronomers were beginning to understand how stars form and how they generate their energy, and it became clear that the origin of the solar system was linked to that story.

The modern explanation of the origin of the planets is the **solar nebula theory,** which proposes that the planets, including Earth, formed in a rotating disk of gas and dust that surrounded the sun as it formed (■ Figure 19-2). Laplace's nebular hypothesis included a disk, but his process depended on rings of matter left behind as the disk contracted. Also, it was not based on a clear understanding of how gas and dust behave in such a disk. In the solar nebula theory, the planets grew within the disk by carefully described physical processes. This evolutionary hypothesis is so comprehensive and explains so many of the observations, both of our solar system and of other systems, that it can be considered to have "graduated" from being just a hypothesis to being properly called a theory. Astronomers are continuing to refine the details of that theory.

You have seen clear evidence that disks of gas and dust are common around young stars. Bipolar flows from protostars (see Chapter 11) were some of the first clues to the existence of such disks, but modern techniques can image the disks directly (■ Figure 19-3). The evidence is strong that our own planetary system formed in such a disk-shaped cloud around the sun. When the sun became luminous enough, the remaining gas and dust were blown away into space, leaving the planets orbiting the sun.

According to the solar nebula theory, our Earth and the other planets of the solar system formed billions of years ago as the sun condensed from a cloud of gas and dust. If planet formation is a natural part of star formation, most stars should have planets.

The Solar Nebula Theory

A rotating cloud of gas contracts and flattens...

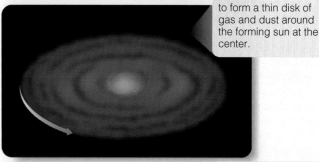

to form a thin disk of gas and dust around the forming sun at the center.

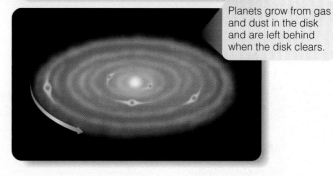

Planets grow from gas and dust in the disk and are left behind when the disk clears.

■ **Figure 19-2**

The solar nebula theory implies that the planets formed along with the sun. The scale of the top panel is much larger than the lower two panels.

SCIENTIFIC ARGUMENT

Why does the solar nebula theory imply planets are common?
Often, the implications of a theory are more important in building a scientific argument than the theory itself. The solar nebula theory is an evolutionary theory; and, if it is correct, the planets of our solar system formed from the disk of gas and dust that surrounded the sun as it condensed from the interstellar medium. That suggests it is a common process. Most stars form with disks of gas and dust around them, and planets should form in such disks. Planets should therefore be very common in the universe.

Now build a new scientific argument. **Why would a catastrophic hypothesis for the formation of the solar system suggest that planets are not common?**

Two Kinds of Theories: Catastrophic and Evolutionary

How big a role have sudden, catastrophic events played in the history of the solar system? Many theories in science can be classified as either evolutionary, in that they involve gradual processes, or catastrophic, in that they depend on sudden, unlikely events. Scientists have generally preferred evolutionary theories. Nevertheless, catastrophic events do occur.

Some people prefer catastrophic theories, perhaps because they like to see spectacular violence from a safe distance, which may explain the success of movies that include lots of car crashes and explosions. Also, catastrophic theories resonate with scriptural accounts of cataclysmic events and special acts of creation. Thus, many people have an interest in catastrophic theories.

Most scientific theories are evolutionary. Such theories do not depend on unlikely events or special acts. For example, geologists study theories of mountain building that are evolutionary and describe mountains being pushed up slowly as millions of years pass. The evidence of erosion and the folded rock layers show that the process is gradual. Because most such natural processes are evolutionary, scientists sometimes find it difficult to accept any theory that depends on catastrophic events.

You will see in this and later chapters that catastrophes do occur. For example, the planets are bombarded by debris from space, and some of those impacts are very large. As you study astronomy or any other natural science, notice that most theories are evolutionary but that you need to allow for the possibility of unpredictable catastrophic events.

Mountains evolve to great heights by rising slowly, not catastrophically. (Janet Seeds)

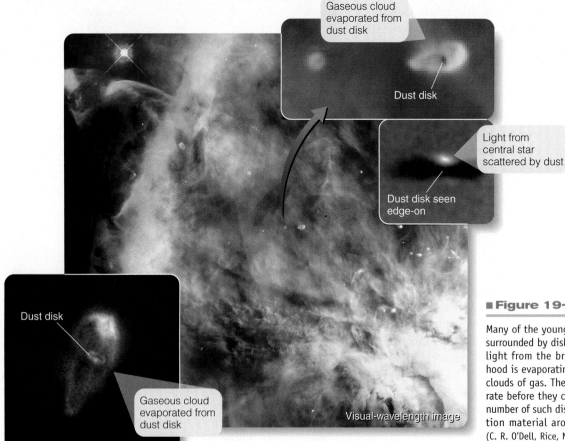

Gaseous cloud evaporated from dust disk

Dust disk

Light from central star scattered by dust

Dust disk seen edge-on

Dust disk

Gaseous cloud evaporated from dust disk

Visual-wavelength image

■ Figure 19-3

Many of the young stars in the Orion Nebula are surrounded by disks of gas and dust, but intense light from the brightest star in the neighborhood is evaporating the disks to form expanding clouds of gas. These particular disks may evaporate before they can form planets, but the large number of such disks shows that planet construction material around young stars is common. (C. R. O'Dell, Rice, NASA; Dark Disk: M. McCaughrean, Max-Planck Inst. für Astronomie, C. R. O'Dell, NASA; Lower left inset: J. Bally, H. Throop, C. R. O'Dell, NASA)

19-2 A Survey of the Solar System

To test their hypotheses about how the solar system was born, astronomers searched the present solar system for evidence of its past. In this section, you will survey the solar system and compile a list of its most significant characteristics that are potential clues to how it formed.

You can begin with the most general view of the solar system. It is, in fact, almost entirely empty space (look back to Figure 1-7). Imagine reducing the scale of the solar system until Earth is the size of a grain of table salt, about 0.3 mm (0.01 in.) in diameter. The moon is a speck of pepper about 1 cm (0.4 in.) away, and the sun is the size of a small plum located 4 m (13 ft) from Earth. Jupiter is an apple seed 20 m (66 ft) from the sun. Neptune, at the edge of the planetary zone, is a large grain of sand over 120 m (400 ft) from the central plum. Although your model solar system would be larger than a football field, you would need a powerful microscope to detect the asteroids orbiting between Mars and Jupiter. The planets are tiny specks of matter scattered around the sun—the last remains of the solar nebula.

Revolution and Rotation

The planets revolve* around the sun in orbits that lie close to a common plane. The orbit of Mercury, the closest planet to the sun, is tipped 7.0° to Earth's orbit The rest of the planets' orbital planes are inclined by no more than 3.4°. As you can see, the solar system is basically flat and disk shaped.

The rotation of the sun and planets on their axes also seems related to the rotation of the disk. The sun rotates with its equator inclined only 7.2° to Earth's orbit, and most of the other planets' equators are tipped less than 30°. The rotations of Venus and Uranus are peculiar, however. Venus rotates backward compared with the other planets, whereas Uranus rotates on its side with its equator almost perpendicular to its orbit. You will explore these planets in detail in Chapters 21 and 23, but later in this chapter you will be able to understand how they might have acquired their peculiar rotations.

There is a preferred direction of motion in the solar system—counterclockwise as seen from the north, like the curl of the fingers of your right hand if you point your thumb toward your eyes. All the planets revolve counterclockwise around the sun; and with the exception of Venus and Uranus they rotate counterclockwise on their axes. Furthermore, nearly all of the moons in the solar system, including Earth's moon, orbit around their respective planets counterclockwise. With only a few exceptions,

---

*Recall from Chapter 2 that the words *revolve* and *rotate* refer to different types of motion. A planet revolves around the sun but rotates on its axis. Cowboys in the Old West didn't carry revolvers. They actually carried rotators. And you don't rotate your tires every 6 months, you actually revolve them.

most of which are understood, revolution and rotation in the solar system follow a single theme. Apparently, these motions today are related to the original rotation of a disk of solar system construction material.

Two Kinds of Planets

Perhaps the most striking clue to the origin of the solar system comes from the obvious division of the planets into two groups, the small Earth-like worlds and the giant Jupiter-like worlds. The difference is so dramatic that you are led to say, "Aha, this must mean something!" Study **Terrestrial and Jovian Planets** on pages 402–403, notice three important points, and learn two new terms:

1 The two kinds of planets are distinguished by their location. The four inner *Terrestrial planets* are quite different from the four outer *Jovian planets*.

2 Craters are common. Almost every solid surface in the solar system is covered with craters.

3 The two groups of planets are also distinguished by properties such as presence or absence of rings and numbers of moons. A theory of the origin of the planets needs to explain these properties.

The division of the planets into two groups is a clue to how our solar system formed. The present properties of individual planets, however, don't tell everything you need to know about their origins. The planets have all evolved since they formed. For further clues about the origin of the planets, you can look at smaller objects that have remained largely unchanged since soon after the birth of the solar system.

Space Debris

The sun and planets are not the only products of the solar nebula. The solar system is littered with three kinds of space debris: asteroids, comets, and meteoroids. Although these objects represent a tiny fraction of the mass of the system, they are a rich source of information about the origin of the planets.

The **asteroids,** sometimes called minor planets, are small rocky worlds, most of which orbit the sun in a belt between the orbits of Mars and Jupiter. More than 100,000 asteroids have orbits that are charted, of which about 2000 follow paths that bring them into the inner solar system where they can potentially collide with a planet. Earth has been struck many times in its history. It is a **Common Misconception** that the asteroids are the remains of a planet that broke apart. In fact, planets are held together very tightly by their gravity and do not "break apart." Astronomers recognize the asteroids as debris left over from the failure of a planet to form at a distance of about 3 AU from the sun.

About 200 asteroids are more than 100 km (60 mi) in diameter, and tens of thousands are estimated to be more than 10 km

Terrestrial and Jovian Planets

1 The distinction between the Terrestrial planets and the Jovian planets is dramatic. The inner four planets, Mercury, Venus, Earth, and Mars, are **Terrestrial planets,** meaning they are small, dense, rocky worlds with little or no atmosphere. The outer four planets, Jupiter, Saturn, Uranus, and Neptune, are **Jovian planets,** meaning they are large, low-density worlds with thick atmospheres and liquid or ice interiors.

Planetary orbits to scale. The Terrestrial planets lie quite close to the sun, whereas the Jovian planets are spread far from the sun.

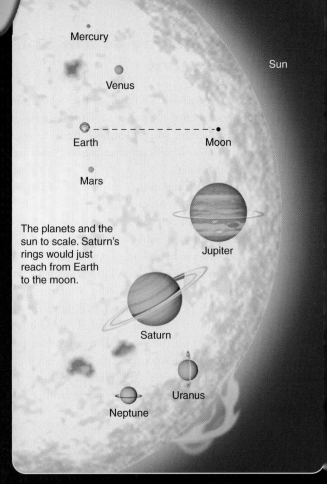

The planets and the sun to scale. Saturn's rings would just reach from Earth to the moon.

1a Of the Terrestrial planets, Earth is most massive, but the Jovian planets are much more massive. Jupiter is over 300 Earth masses, and Saturn is nearly 100 Earth masses. Uranus and Neptune are 15 and 17 Earth masses.

Mercury is only 40 percent larger than Earth's moon, and its weak gravity cannot retain a permanent atmosphere. Like the moon, it is covered with craters from meteorite impacts.

2 Craters are common on all of the surfaces in the solar system that are strong enough to retain them. Earth has about 150 impact craters, but many more have been erased by erosion. Besides the planets, the asteroids and nearly all of the moons in the solar system are scarred by craters. Ranging from microscopic to hundreds of kilometers in diameter, these craters have been produced over the ages by meteorite impacts. When astronomers see a rocky or icy surface that contains few craters, they know that the surface is young.

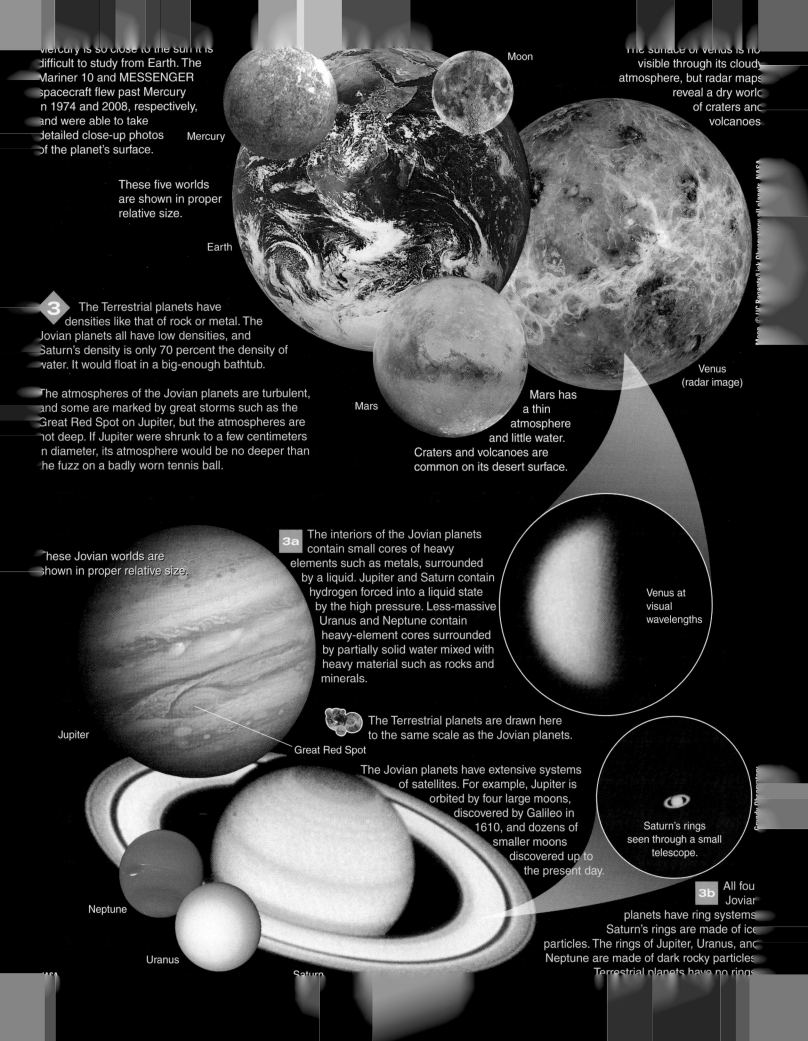

Mercury is so close to the sun it is difficult to study from Earth. The Mariner 10 and MESSENGER spacecraft flew past Mercury in 1974 and 2008, respectively, and were able to take detailed close-up photos of the planet's surface.

Mercury

These five worlds are shown in proper relative size.

Earth

Moon

The surface of Venus is not visible through its cloudy atmosphere, but radar maps reveal a dry world of craters and volcanoes.

3 The Terrestrial planets have densities like that of rock or metal. The Jovian planets all have low densities, and Saturn's density is only 70 percent the density of water. It would float in a big-enough bathtub.

The atmospheres of the Jovian planets are turbulent, and some are marked by great storms such as the Great Red Spot on Jupiter, but the atmospheres are not deep. If Jupiter were shrunk to a few centimeters in diameter, its atmosphere would be no deeper than the fuzz on a badly worn tennis ball.

Mars

Venus
(radar image)

Mars has a thin atmosphere and little water. Craters and volcanoes are common on its desert surface.

These Jovian worlds are shown in proper relative size.

3a The interiors of the Jovian planets contain small cores of heavy elements such as metals, surrounded by a liquid. Jupiter and Saturn contain hydrogen forced into a liquid state by the high pressure. Less-massive Uranus and Neptune contain heavy-element cores surrounded by partially solid water mixed with heavy material such as rocks and minerals.

Venus at visual wavelengths

Jupiter

Great Red Spot

The Terrestrial planets are drawn here to the same scale as the Jovian planets.

The Jovian planets have extensive systems of satellites. For example, Jupiter is orbited by four large moons, discovered by Galileo in 1610, and dozens of smaller moons discovered up to the present day.

Saturn's rings seen through a small telescope.

Neptune

Uranus

Saturn

3b All four Jovian planets have ring systems. Saturn's rings are made of ice particles. The rings of Jupiter, Uranus, and Neptune are made of dark rocky particles. Terrestrial planets have no rings.

(6 mi) in diameter. There are probably a million or more that are larger than 1 km (0.6 mi) and billions that are smaller. Because the largest are only a few hundred kilometers in size, Earth-based telescopes can detect no details on their surfaces, and even the Hubble Space Telescope can image only the largest features.

Spectroscopic observations indicate that asteroid surfaces are a variety of rocky and metallic materials. Photographs returned by robotic spacecraft show that asteroids are generally irregular in shape and covered with craters (■ Figure 19-4). These observations will be discussed in detail in Chapter 25, but in this quick survey of the solar system you have enough information to conclude that the solar nebula included elements that compose rock and metals and that collisions have played an important role in the solar system's history.

Since 1992, astronomers have discovered more than a thousand small, dark, icy bodies orbiting in the outer fringes of the solar system beyond Neptune. This collection of objects is called the **Kuiper belt** after astronomer Gerard Kuiper (KYE-per), who predicted their existence in the 1950s. There are probably 100 million bodies larger than 1 km in the Kuiper belt, many more than in the asteroid belt, and a successful theory should also explain how they came to be where they are. You will find out more about the origin of the Kuiper belt in Chapter 24.

In contrast to the rocky asteroids and dark Kuiper belt objects, the brightest **comets** can be seen with the naked eye and are impressively beautiful objects (■ Figure 19-5). Most comets are faint, however, and are difficult to locate even at their brightest. A comet may take months to sweep through the inner solar system, during which time it appears as a glowing ball with an extended tail of gas and dust.

The nuclei of comets are ice-rich bodies, a few kilometers or tens of kilometers in diameter (similar in size to asteroids), that are sometimes described as "dirty snowballs" or "icy mudballs," left over from the origin of the planets. From this you can conclude that at least some parts of the solar nebula had abundant icy material. You will see more evidence about the composition and history of comets in Chapter 25.

A comet nucleus remains frozen and inactive while it is far from the sun. As the nucleus moves along its elliptical orbit into the inner solar system, the sun's heat begins to vaporize the ices, releasing gas and dust. The pressure of sunlight and the solar wind push the gas and dust away, forming a long tail. The motion of the nucleus along its orbit, the effects of sunlight, and the outward flow of the solar wind can create comet tails that are long and straight or gently curved, but in any case the tail of a comet always points approximately away from the sun (Figure 19-5b), no matter what direction the comet itself is moving. The beautiful tail of a comet can be longer than an AU, but, again, note that it is produced by a relatively tiny nucleus only a few kilometers in diameter.

Unlike the stately comets, **meteors** flash across the sky in momentary streaks of light (■ Figure 19-6). They are commonly called "shooting stars." Of course, they are not stars but small bits of rock and metal colliding with Earth's atmosphere and bursting into incandescent vapor because of friction with the air about 80 km (50 mi) above the ground. This vapor condenses to form dust that settles slowly to Earth, adding about 40,000 tons per year to the planet's mass.

Visual-wavelength images

a

b

■ **Figure 19-4**

(a) Over a period of three weeks, the NEAR spacecraft approached the asteroid Eros and recorded a series of images arranged here in an entertaining pattern showing the irregular shape and 5-hour rotation period of the asteroid. Eros is 34 km (21 mi) long. (b) This close-up of the surface of Eros shows an area about 11 km (7 mi) from top to bottom. (Johns Hopkins University, Applied Physics Laboratory, NASA)

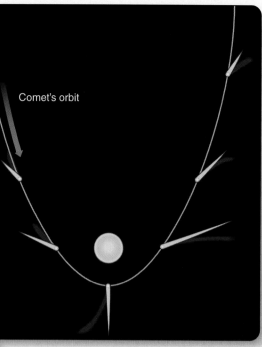

Comet's orbit

■ **Figure 19-5**

Comets orbit the sun in long, elliptical orbits and become visible when the sun's heat vaporizes its ices and pushes the gas and dust into a tail pointing away from the sun. (a) A comet may remain visible in the evening or morning sky for weeks as it moves through the inner solar system. Although comets are moving rapidly along their orbits, they are so distant that, on any particular evening, a comet seems to hang motionless in the sky. Comet Hyakutake is shown here near Polaris in 1996. (Mike Terenzoni) (b) A comet in a long, elliptical orbit becomes visible when the sun's heat vaporizes its ices and pushes the gas and dust away in a tail. (Celestron International)

Technically, the word *meteor* refers to the streak of light in the sky. In space, before its fiery plunge, the object is called a **meteoroid,** and any part of it that survives its fiery passage to Earth's surface is called a **meteorite.** Most meteoroids are specks of dust, grains of sand, or tiny pebbles. Almost all the meteors you see in the sky are produced by meteoroids that weigh less than 1 gram. Only rarely is a meteoroid massive and strong enough to survive its plunge and reach Earth's surface.

Thousands of meteorites have been found, and you will learn more about their various types in Chapter 25. Meteorites are mentioned here for one specific clue they can give you concerning the solar nebula: Meteorites can reveal the age of the solar system.

The Age of the Solar System

According to the solar nebula theory, the planets should be about the same age as the sun. The most accurate way to find the age of a rocky body is to bring a sample into the laboratory and analyze the radioactive elements it contains.

When a rock solidifies, it incorporates known percentages of the chemical elements. A few of these elements have forms, called isotopes (see Chapter 7), that are radioactive, meaning they gradually decay into other isotopes. For example, potassium-40, called a parent isotope, decays into calcium-40 and argon-40, called daughter isotopes. The **half-life** of a radioactive substance is the time it takes for half of the parent isotope atoms to decay into daughter isotope atoms. The abundance of a radioactive substance gradually decreases as it decays, and the abundances of the daughter substances gradually increase (■ Figure 19-7). The half-life of potassium-40 is 1.3 billion years. If you also have information about the abundances of the elements in the original rock, you can measure the present abundances and find the age of the rock. For example, if you study a rock and find that only 50 percent of the potassium-40 remains and the rest has become a mixture of daughter isotopes, you could conclude that one half-life must have passed and that the rock is 1.3 billion years old.

Potassium isn't the only radioactive element used in radioactive dating. Uranium-238 decays with a half-life of 4.5 billion

Visual-wavelength image

■ Figure 19-6

A meteor is a sudden streak of glowing gases produced by a bit of material falling into Earth's atmosphere. Friction with the air vaporizes the material about 80 km (50 mi) above Earth's surface. (Daniel Good)

years to form lead-206 and other isotopes. Rubidium-87 decays into strontium-87 with a half-life of 47 billion years. Any of these substances can be used as a radioactive clock to find the age of mineral samples.

Of course, to find a radioactive age, you need to get a sample into the laboratory, and the only celestial bodies of which scientists have samples are Earth, the moon, Mars, and meteorites. The oldest Earth rocks so far discovered and dated are tiny zircon crystals from Australia that are 4.4 billion years old. That does not mean that Earth formed 4.4 billion years ago. As you will see in the next chapter, the surface of Earth is active, and the crust is continually destroyed and reformed with material welling up from beneath the crust. Those types of processes tend to dilute the daughter atoms and spread them away from the parent atoms, effectively causing the radioactive clocks to reset to zero. The radioactive age of a rock is actually the length of time since the material in that rock was last melted. Consequently, the dates of these oldest rocks tells you only a lower limit to the age of Earth, in other words, that Earth is *at least* 4.4 billion years old.

One of the most exciting goals of the Apollo lunar landings was to bring lunar rocks back to Earth's laboratories where their ages could be measured. Because the moon's

A mineral sample containing radioactive atoms ∴, which decay into daughter atoms ∵

Percentage of radioactive and daughter atoms in the mineral

100

50

100

Percentage remaining

1/2 remain

1/4 remain

1/8 remain

Percentage of radioactive atoms remaining

50

0

0   1   2   3   4   5   6

Age in half-lives

■ Figure 19-7

(a) The radioactive atoms (red) in a mineral sample decay into daughter atoms (blue). Half the radioactive atoms are left after one half-life, a fourth after two half-lives, an eighth after three half-lives, and so on. (b) Radioactive dating shows that this fragment of the Allende meteorite is 4.56 billion years old. It contains a few even older interstellar grains, which formed long before our solar system. (R. Kempton, New England Meteoritical Services)

surface is not geologically active like Earth's surface, some moon rocks might have survived unaltered since early in the history of the solar system. In fact, the oldest moon rocks are 4.5 billion years old. That means the moon must be *at least* 4.5 billion years old.

Although no one has yet been to Mars, over a dozen meteorites found on Earth have been identified by their chemical composition as having come from Mars. Most of these have ages of only a billion years or so, but one has an age of approximately 4.5 billion years. Mars must be at least that old.

The most important source for determining the age of the solar system is meteorites. Radioactive dating of meteorites yields a range of ages, but there is a fairly precise upper limit—many meteorite samples have ages of 4.56 billion years old, and none are older. That figure is widely accepted as the age of the solar system and is often rounded to 4.6 billion years. The true ages of Earth, the moon, and Mars are also assumed to be 4.6 billion years, although no rocks from those bodies have yet been found that have remained unaltered for that entire stretch of time.

One last celestial body deserves mention: the sun. Astronomers estimate the age of the sun to be about 5 billion years, but that is not a radioactive date because we have no samples of radioactive material from the sun. Instead, an independent estimate for the age of the sun can be made using helio-seismological observations and mathematical models of the sun's interior (see Chapters 8 and 12). This yields a value of about 5 billion years, plus or minus 1.5 billion years, a number that is in agreement with the age of the solar system derived from the age of meteorites.

Apparently, all the bodies of the solar system formed at about the same time, some 4.6 billion years ago. You can add this as the final item to your list of characteristic properties of the solar system (■ Table 19-1).

■ **Table 19-1** | **Characteristic Properties of the Solar System**

1. Disk shape of the solar system
   Orbits in nearly the same plane
   Common direction of rotation and revolution
2. Two planetary types
   Terrestrial—inner planets; high density
   Jovian—outer planets; low density
3. Planetary rings and large satellite systems
   Yes for Jovian Planets (Jupiter, Saturn, Uranus, and Neptune)
   No for Terrestrial Planets (Mercury, Venus, Earth, and Mars)
4. Space debris—asteroids, comets, and meteoroids
   Composition, Orbits
      Asteroids in inner solar system, composition like
         Terrestrial planets
      Comets in outer solar system, composition like
         Jovian planets
5. Common age of about 4.6 billion years measured or inferred for Earth, the moon, Mars, meteorites, and the sun

---

SCIENTIFIC ARGUMENT

In what ways does the solar system resemble a disk?
Notice that this argument is really a summary of pieces of evidence. First, the general shape of the solar system is that of a disk. The orbit of Mercury is inclined 7° to the plane of Earth's orbit, and the rest of the planets are in orbits inclined less than that. In other words, the planets are confined to a thin disk with the sun at its center.

Second, the motions of the sun and planets also follow this disk theme. The sun and most of the planets rotate in the same direction, counterclockwise as seen from the north, with their equators near the plane of the solar system. Also, all of the planets revolve around the sun in that same direction. The objects in our solar system mostly move in the same direction, which further reflects a disk theme.

One of the basic characteristics of our solar system is its disk shape, but another dramatic characteristic is the division of the planets into two groups. Build an argument to detail that evidence. **What are the distinguishing differences between the Terrestrial and Jovian planets?**

19-3) The Story of Planet Building

THE CHALLENGE FOR modern planetary scientists is to compare the characteristics of the solar system with predictions of the solar nebula theory, so they can work out details of how the planets formed.

The Chemical Composition of the Solar Nebula

Everything astronomers know about the solar system and star formation suggests that the solar nebula was a fragment of an interstellar gas cloud. Such a cloud would have been mostly hydrogen with some helium and small amounts of the heavier elements.

That is precisely what you see in the composition of the sun (look back at Table 7-2). Analysis of the solar spectrum shows that the sun is mostly hydrogen, with a quarter of its mass being helium and only about 2 percent being heavier elements. Of course, nuclear reactions have fused some hydrogen into helium, but this happens in the sun's core and has not affected the composition of its surface and atmosphere, which are the parts you can observe directly. That means the composition revealed in the sun's spectrum is essentially the composition of the gases from which the sun formed.

This must have been the composition of the solar nebula, and you can also see that composition reflected in the chemical compositions of the planets. The inner planets are composed of rock and metal, and the outer planets are rich in low-density gases such as hydrogen and helium. The chemical composition of Jupiter resembles the composition of the sun. Furthermore, if you allowed low-density gases to escape from a blob of stuff with the same overall composition as the sun or Jupiter, the relative proportions of the remaining heavier elements would resemble Earth's chemical composition.

The Condensation of Solids

An important clue to understanding the process that converted the nebular gas into solid matter is the variation in density among solar system objects. You have already noted that the four inner planets are small and have high density, resembling Earth, whereas the outermost planets are large and have low density, resembling Jupiter.

Even among the four Terrestrial planets, you will find a pattern of slight differences in density. Merely listing the observed densities of the Terrestrial planets does not reveal the pattern clearly because Earth and Venus, being more massive, have stronger gravity and have squeezed their interiors to higher densities. The **uncompressed densities**—the densities the planets would have if their gravity did not compress them, or to put it another way, the average densities of their original construction materials—can be calculated using the actual densities and masses of each planet (■ Table 19-2). In general, the closer a planet is to the sun, the higher its uncompressed density.

This density variation originated when the solar system first formed solid grains. The kind of matter that could condense in a particular region depended on the temperature of the gas there. In the inner regions, the temperature was evidently 1500 K or so. The only materials that can form grains at that temperature are compounds with high melting points, such as metal oxides and pure metals, which are very dense. Farther out in the nebula it was cooler, and silicates (rocky material) could also condense, in addition to metal. These are less dense than metal oxides and metals. Mercury, Venus, Earth, and Mars are evidently composed of a mixture of metals, metal oxides, and silicates, with proportionately more metals close to the sun and more silicates farther from the sun.

■ Table 19-3 | The Condensation Sequence

Temperature (K)	Condensate	Planet (Estimated Temperature of Formation; K)
1500	Metal oxides	Mercury (1400)
1300	Metallic iron and nickel	
1200	Silicates	
1000	Feldspars	Venus (900)
680	Troilite (FeS)	Earth (600)
		Mars (450)
175	H$_2$O ice	Jovian (175)
150	Ammonia–water ice	
120	Methane–water ice	
65	Argon–neon ice	Pluto (65)

Even farther from the sun there was a boundary called the **ice line** beyond which water vapor could freeze to form ice particles. Yet a little farther from the sun, compounds such as methane and ammonia could condense to form other types of ice. Water vapor, methane, and ammonia were abundant in the solar nebula, so beyond the ice line the nebula would have been filled with a blizzard of ice particles, mixed with small amounts of silicate and metal particles that could also condense there. Those ices are low-density materials. The compositions of Jupiter and the other outer planets are a mix of ices plus relatively small amounts of silicates and metal.

The sequence in which the different materials condense from the gas as you move away from the sun toward lower temperature is called the **condensation sequence** (■ Table 19-3). It suggests that the planets, forming at different distances from the sun, should have accumulated from different kinds of materials in a predictable way.

People who have read a little bit about the origin of the solar system may hold the **Common Misconception** that the matter in the solar nebula was sorted by density, with the heavy rock and metal sinking toward the sun and the low-density gases being blown outward. That is not the case. The chemical composition of the solar nebula was originally roughly the same throughout the disk. The important factor was temperature: The inner nebula was hot, and only metals and rock could condense there, whereas the cold outer nebula could form lots of ices along with metals and rock. The ice line seems to have been between Mars and Jupiter, and it separates the region for formation of the high-density Terrestrial planets from that of the low-density Jovian planets.

The Formation of Planetesimals

In the development of a planet, three processes operate to collect solid bits of matter—rock, metal, ice—into larger bodies called

■ Table 19-2 | Observed and Uncompressed Densities

Planet	Observed Density (g/cm³)	Uncompressed Density (g/cm³)
Mercury	5.44	5.30
Venus	5.24	3.96
Earth	5.50	4.07
Mars	3.94	3.73

planetesimals, which eventually build the planets. The study of planet building is the study of these processes: condensation, accretion, and gravitational collapse, each of which will be described in detail in this section.

According to the solar nebula theory, planetary development in the solar nebula began with the growth of dust grains. These specks of matter, whatever their composition, grew from microscopic size first by condensation, then by accretion.

A particle grows by **condensation** when it adds matter one atom or molecule at a time from a surrounding gas. Snowflakes, for example, grow by condensation in Earth's atmosphere. In the solar nebula, dust grains were continuously bombarded by atoms of gas, and some of those stuck to the grains. A microscopic grain capturing a layer of gas molecules on its surface increases its mass by a much larger fraction than a gigantic boulder capturing a single layer of molecules. That is why condensation can increase the mass of a small grain rapidly, but, as the grain grows larger, condensation becomes less effective.

The second process is **accretion,** the sticking together of solid particles. You may have seen accretion in action if you have walked through a snowstorm with big, fluffy flakes. If you caught one of those "flakes" on your glove and looked closely, you saw that it was actually made up of many tiny, individual flakes that had collided as they fell and accreted to form larger particles. In the solar nebula, the dust grains were, on average, no more than a few centimeters apart, so they collided frequently and could accrete into larger particles.

When the particles grew to sizes larger than a centimeter, they would have been subject to new processes that tended to concentrate them. One important effect was that the growing solid objects would have collected into the plane of the solar nebula. Small dust grains could not fall into the plane because the turbulent motions of the gas kept them stirred up, but larger objects had more mass, and gas motions could not have prevented them from settling into the plane of the spinning nebula. Astronomers calculate this would have concentrated the larger solid particles into a relatively thin layer about 0.01 AU thick that would have made further growth more rapid. There is no clear distinction between a very large grain and a very small planetesimal, but you might consider an object to be a planetesimal when its diameter approaches a kilometer (0.6 mi) or so (■ Figure 19-8).

This concentration of large particles and planetesimals into the plane of the nebula is analogous to the flattening of a forming galaxy, and a process also found in galaxies may have become important once the plane of planetesimals formed. Computer models show that the rotating disk of particles should have been gravitationally unstable and would have been disturbed by spiral density waves resembling the much larger ones found in spiral galaxies. Those waves could have further concentrated the planetesimals and helped them coalesce into objects up to 100 km (60 mi) in diameter.

Visual-wavelength image

■ **Figure 19-8**

What did the planetesimals look like? You can get a clue from this photo of the 5-km-wide nucleus of Comet Wild 2 (pronounced *Vildt-two*). Whether rocky or icy, the planetesimals must have been small, irregular bodies, scarred by craters from collisions with other planetesimals. (NASA)

Through these processes, the theory proposes, the nebula became filled with trillions of solid particles ranging in size from pebbles to tiny planets. As the largest began to exceed 100 km in diameter, a third process began to affect them, and a new stage in planet building began, the formation of protoplanets.

The Growth of Protoplanets

The coalescing of planetesimals eventually formed **protoplanets,** the name for massive objects destined to become planets. As these larger bodies grew, a new process helped them grow faster and altered their physical structure.

If planetesimals had collided at orbital velocities, it is unlikely that they would have stuck together. A typical orbital velocity in the solar system is about 10 km/s (22,000 mph). Head-on collisions at this velocity would vaporize the material. However, the planetesimals were all moving in the same direction in the nebular plane and didn't collide head on. Instead, they merely "rubbed shoulders," so to speak, at low relative velocities. Such gentle collisions would have been more likely to combine planetesimals than to shatter them.

Some adhesive effects probably helped. Sticky coatings and electrostatic charges on the surfaces of the smaller planetesimals probably aided formation of larger bodies. Collisions would have fragmented some of the surface rock; but, if the planetesimals were large enough, their gravity could have held on to some fragments to form a layer of soil composed of crushed rock. Such a relatively soft soil layer on the surfaces of larger planetesimals may have been effective in trapping smaller bodies.

The largest planetesimals would grow the fastest because they had the strongest gravitational field. Their stronger gravity could attract additional material, and they could also hold on to a cushioning layer to trap fragments. Astronomers calculate that the largest planetesimals would have grown quickly to protoplanetary dimensions, sweeping up more and more material.

Protoplanets had to begin growing by accumulating solid material because they did not have enough gravity to capture and hold large amounts of gas. In the warm solar nebula, the atoms and molecules of gas were traveling at velocities much larger than the escape velocities of modest-sized protoplanets. Therefore, in their early development, the protoplanets could grow only by attracting solid bits of rock, metal, and ice. Once a protoplanet approached a size of 15 Earth masses or so, however, it could begin to grow by **gravitational collapse,** the rapid accumulation of large amounts of in-falling gas from the nebula.

The theory of protoplanet growth into planets supposes that all the planetesimals had about the same chemical composition. The planetesimals accumulated to form a planet-sized ball of material with homogeneous composition throughout. Once the planet formed, heat would begin to accumulate in its interior from the decay of short-lived radioactive elements.

The violent impacts of in-falling particles would also have released energy called **heat of formation.** These two heating sources would eventually have melted the planet and allowed it to differentiate. **Differentiation** is the separation of material according to density. Once a planet melted, the heavy metals such as iron and nickel, plus elements chemically attracted to them, would settle to the core, while the lighter silicates and related materials floated to the surface to form a low-density crust. The scenario of planetesimals combining into planets that subsequently differentiated is shown in ■ Figure 19-9.

The process of differentiation depends partly on the presence of short-lived radioactive elements whose rapid decay would have released enough heat to melt the interior of planets. Astronomers know such radioactive elements were present because very old rock from meteorites contains daughter isotopes such as magnesium-26. That isotope is produced by the decay of aluminum-26 with a half-life of only 0.74 million years. The aluminum-26 and similar short-lived radioactive isotopes are gone now, but they must have been produced in a supernova explosion that occurred shortly before the formation of the solar nebula. In fact, some astronomers suspect that supernova explosions could have triggered the formation of the sun and other stars by compressing interstellar clouds (see Figure 11-2 and 11-3). Thus, our solar system may exist because of a supernova explosion that occurred about 4.6 billion years ago.

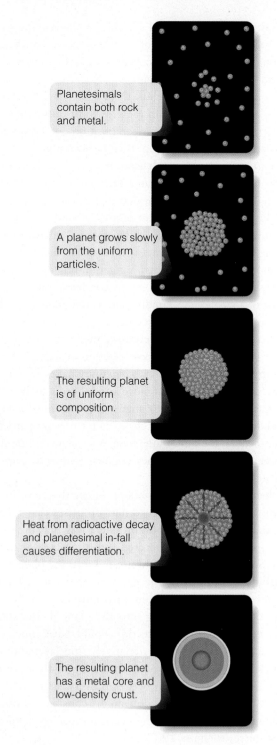

■ Figure 19-9

This simple model of planet building assumes planets formed from accretion and collision of planetesimals that were of uniform composition, containing both metals and rocky material, and that the planets later differentiated, meaning they melted and separated into layers by density and composition.

If planets formed by accretion of planetesimals and were later melted by radioactive decay and heat of formation, then Earth's early atmosphere may have consisted of a combination of gases delivered by planetesimal impacts and released from the planet's interior during differentiation. The creation of a planetary atmosphere from a planet's interior is called **outgassing.** Given the location of Earth in the solar nebula, gases released from its interior during differentiation would not have included as much water as Earth now has. So, some astronomers think that Earth's water and even some of its present atmosphere and biosphere accumulated late in the formation of the planet as Earth swept up volatile-rich planetesimals. These icy planetesimals would have formed in the cool outer parts of the solar nebula and could have been scattered toward the Terrestrial planets by encounters with the Jovian planets, creating a comet bombardment.

According to the solar nebula theory, the Jovian planets could begin growing by the same processes that built the Terrestrial planets. However, in the inner solar nebula, only metals and silicates could form solids, so the Terrestrial planets grew slowly. In contrast, the outer solar nebula contained not just solid bits of metals and silicates but also plentiful ices. Astronomers calculate that the Jovian planets would have grown faster than the Terrestrial planets and quickly become massive enough to begin even faster growth by gravitational collapse, drawing in large amounts of gas from the solar nebula. The Terrestrial planet zone did not include ice particles, so those planets developed relatively slowly and never became massive enough to grow further by gravitational collapse.

The Jovian planets must have reached their present size in no more than about 10 million years, before the sun become hot and luminous enough to blow away the remaining gas in the solar nebula, removing the raw material for further Jovian growth. As you will learn in the next section, disturbances from outside the forming solar system may have reduced the time available for Jovian planet formation even more severely. The Terrestrial planets, in comparison, grew from solids and not from the gas, so they could have continued to grow by accretion from solid debris left behind after the gas was removed. Mathematical models indicate that the Terrestrial planets were at least half

finished within 10 million years but could have continued to grow for another 20 million years or so.

The solar nebula theory has been very successful in explaining the formation of the solar system. But there are some problems, and the Jovian planets are the troublemakers.

The Jovian Problem

New information about the star formation process makes it hard to explain the formation of the Jovian parents, and this has caused astronomers to expand and revise the theory of planet formation (■ Figure 19-10).

The new information is that gas and dust disks around newborn stars don't last long. Earlier you saw images of dusty gas disks around the young stars in the Orion star-forming region (Figure 19-2 and Chapter 11). Those disks are being evaporated by intense ultraviolet radiation from hot O and B stars forming nearby. Astronomers have calculated that nearly all stars form in clusters containing O and B stars, so this evaporation may happen to most disks. Even if a disk did not evaporate quickly, the gravitational influence of the crowded stars in a cluster could strip away the outer parts of the disk. Those are troublesome observations because they seem to indicate that disks can't last longer than about 7 million years at most, and many evaporate within the astronomically very short span of 100,000 years or so. That's not long enough to grow a Jovian planet by the combination of condensation, accretion, and gravitational collapse proposed in the standard solar nebular theory.

Yet, Jovian planets are common. In the final section of this chapter, you will see evidence that astronomers have found planets orbiting other stars, and almost all of those planets have the mass of Jovian planets. There may also be many Terrestrial planets orbiting those stars that are too small for astronomers to detect at present, but the important point is that there are lots of Jovian planets around.

■ Figure 19-10

The Jovian worlds pose a problem for modern astronomers. Planet-forming nebulae are blown away in only a few million years by nearby luminous stars, so Jovian planets must form more quickly than initial calculations predicted. Newer research suggests that accretion followed by gravitational collapse can build Jovian planets in about a million years. Under certain conditions, direct gravitational collapse may form some large planets in just thousands of years.

Mathematical models of the solar nebula have been computed using specially built computers running programs that take weeks to finish a calculation. The results show that the rotating gas and dust of the solar nebula could have become unstable and formed Jovian planets by skipping straight to the step of gravitational collapse. That is, massive planets may have been able to form by **direct collapse** of gas without first forming a dense core by condensation and accretion of solid material. Jupiters and Saturns can form in these direct collapse models in only a few hundred years. If the Jovian planets formed in this way, they could have formed before the solar nebula disappeared, even if the nebula was eroded quickly by neighboring massive hot stars.

This new insight into the formation of the outer planets may also help explain a puzzle about the formation of Uranus and Neptune. Those planets are so far from the sun that accretion could not have built them rapidly. The gas and dust of the solar nebula must have been sparse out there, and Uranus and Neptune orbit so slowly they would not have swept up material very rapidly. The conventional view is that they grew by accretion so slowly that they never became quite massive enough to begin accelerated growth by gravitational collapse. In fact, it is hard to understand how they could have reached even their present sizes if they started growing by accretion so far from the sun. Theoretical calculations show that they might instead have formed closer to the sun, in the region of Jupiter and Saturn, and then could have been shifted outward by gravitational interactions with the bigger planets. In any case, the formation of Uranus and Neptune is part of the Jovian problem.

The traditional solar nebula theory proposes that the planets formed by accreting a core and then, if they became massive enough, accelerated growth by gravitational collapse. The proposed modification to the theory suggests that the outer planets could have skipped the core accretion phase.

Explaining the Characteristics of the Solar System

Now you have learned enough to put all the pieces of the puzzle together and explain the distinguishing characteristics of the solar system in Table 19-1.

The disk shape of the solar system is inherited from the motion of material in the solar nebula. The sun and planets and moons mostly revolve and rotate in the same direction because they formed from the same rotating gas cloud. The orbits of the planets lie in the same plane because the rotating solar nebula collapsed into a disk, and the planets formed in that disk.

The solar nebula hypothesis is evolutionary in that it calls on continuing processes to gradually build the planets. To explain the odd rotations of Venus and Uranus, however, you may need to consider catastrophic events. Uranus rotates on its side. This might have been caused by an off-center collision with a massive planetesimal when the planet was nearly formed. Two hypotheses have been proposed to explain the backward rotation of Venus. Theoretical models suggest that the sun can produce tides in the thick atmosphere of Venus that could have eventually reversed the planet's rotation—an evolutionary hypothesis. It is also possible that the rotation of Venus was altered by an off-center impact late in the planet's formation, and that is a catastrophic hypothesis. Both may be true.

The second item in Table 19-1, the division of the planets into Terrestrial and Jovian worlds, can be understood through the condensation sequence. The Terrestrial planets formed in the inner part of the solar nebula, where the temperature was high and only compounds such as the metals and silicates could condense to form solid particles. That produced the small, dense Terrestrial planets. In contrast, the Jovian planets formed in the outer solar nebula, where the lower temperature allowed the gas to form large amounts of ices, perhaps three times more ices than silicates. That allowed the Jovian planets to grow rapidly and became massive, low-density worlds. Also, Jupiter and Saturn are so massive they were able to grow by drawing in cool gas by gravitational collapse from the solar nebula. The Terrestrial planets could not do this because they never became massive enough.

The heat of formation (the energy released by in-falling matter) was tremendous for these massive planets. Jupiter must have grown hot enough to glow with a luminosity of about 1 percent that of the present sun, although it never got hot enough to generate nuclear energy as a star would. Nevertheless, Jupiter is still hot inside. In fact, both Jupiter and Saturn radiate more heat than they absorb from the sun, so they are evidently still cooling.

A glance at the solar system suggests that you should expect to find a planet between Mars and Jupiter at the present location of the asteroid belt. Mathematical models indicate that the reason asteroids are there rather than a planet is that Jupiter grew into such a massive body that it was able to gravitationally disturb the motion of nearby planetesimals. The bodies that could have formed a planet just inward from Jupiter's orbit instead collided at high speeds and shattered rather than combining, were thrown into the sun, or were ejected from the solar system. The asteroids seen today are the last remains of those rocky planetesimals.

The comets, in contrast, are evidently the last of the icy planetesimals. Some may have formed in the outer solar nebula beyond Neptune and Pluto, but many probably formed among the Jovian planets where ices could condense easily. Mathematical models show that the massive Jovian planets could have ejected some of these icy planetesimals into the far outer solar system. In a later chapter, you will see evidence that some comets are icy bodies coming from those distant locations, falling back into the inner solar system.

The icy Kuiper belt objects appear to be ancient planetesimals that formed in the outer solar system but were never incorporated into a planet. They orbit slowly far from the light and warmth of the sun and, except for occasional collisions, have not changed much since the solar system was young. The gravitational influence of the planets deflects Kuiper belt objects into the inner solar system where they also are seen as comets.

The large satellite systems of the Jovian worlds may contain two kinds of moons. Some moons may have formed in orbit around forming planets in a miniature version of the solar nebula. Some of the smaller moons, in contrast, may be captured planetesimals, asteroids, and comets. The large masses of the Jovian planets would have made it easier for them to capture satellites.

In Table 19-1, you noted that all four Jovian worlds have ring systems, and you can understand this by considering the large mass of these worlds and their remote location in the solar system. A large mass makes it easier for a planet to hold onto orbiting ring particles; and, being farther from the sun, the ring particles are not as quickly swept away by the pressure of sunlight and the solar wind. It is hardly surprising, then, that the Terrestrial planets, low-mass worlds located near the sun, have no planetary rings.

The last entry in Table 19-1 is the common ages of solar system bodies, and the solar nebula theory has no difficulty explaining that characteristic. If the theory is correct, then the planets formed at the same time as the sun and should have roughly the same age.

The solar nebula theory can account for all of the distinguishing characteristics of the solar system, but there is yet another test you should apply to the theory. What about the problem that troubled Laplace and his nebular hypothesis—the angular momentum problem? If the sun and planets formed from a contracting nebula, the sun should have been left spinning very rapidly. That is, the sun should have most of the angular momentum in the solar system, and instead it has very little.

To study this problem, astronomers used the Spitzer Space Telescope to examine 500 young stars in the Orion Nebula. Those that rotate slowly are five times more likely to have a surrounding disk of gas and dust than the faster rotators. This confirms astronomer's expectations that the strong magnetic fields of young stars extend out into their disks. This allows the transfer of angular momentum, speeding the disk's rotation and slowing the star's rotation. Thus, the angular momentum problem is no longer an objection to the solar nebula theory.

Your general understanding of the origin of the solar system gives you a new way of thinking about asteroids, meteors, and comets. They are the last of the debris left behind by the solar nebula. These objects are such important sources of information about the history of our solar system that they will be discussed in detail in Chapter 25. But for now you can consider how the sun blew away the last of the gas and dust in the solar nebula.

Clearing the Nebula

The sun probably formed along with many other stars in a swirling nebula. Observations of young stars in Orion (Figure 19-3) suggest that radiation from nearby hot stars would have evaporated the disk of gas and dust around the sun and that the gravitational influence of nearby stars would have pulled gas away. Even without the external effects, four internal processes would have gradually destroyed the solar nebula.

The most important of these internal processes was radiation pressure (see Chapter 11). When the sun became a luminous object, light streaming from its photosphere pushed against the particles of the solar nebula. Large bits of matter like planetesimals and planets were not affected, but low-mass specks of dust and individual atoms and molecules were pushed outward and eventually driven from the system.

The second effect that helped clear the nebula was the solar wind, the flow of ionized hydrogen and other atoms away from the sun's upper atmosphere. This flow is a steady breeze that rushes past Earth at about 400 km/s (250 mi/s). Young stars have even stronger winds than stars of the sun's age and irregular fluctuations in luminosity, like those observed in young stars such as T Tauri stars, which can accelerate the wind. The strong surging wind from the young sun may have helped push dust and gas out of the nebula.

The third effect that helped clear the nebula was the sweeping up of space debris by the planets. All of the old, solid surfaces in the solar system are heavily cratered by meteorite impacts (■ Figure 19-11). Earth's moon, Mercury, Venus, Mars, and most of the moons in the solar system are covered with craters. A few of these craters have been formed recently by the steady rain of meteorites that falls on all the planets in the solar system, but most of the craters appear to have been formed before roughly 4 billion years ago in what is called the **heavy bombardment,** as the last of the debris in the solar nebula were swept up by the planets.

The fourth effect was the ejection of material from the solar system by close encounters with planets. If a small object such as a planetesimal passes close to a planet, the small object's path will be affected by the planet's gravity field. In some cases, the small object can gain energy from the planet's motion and be thrown out of the solar system. Ejection is most probable in encounters with massive planets, so the Jovian planets were probably very efficient at ejecting the icy planetesimals that formed in their region of the nebula.

Attacked by the radiation and gravity of nearby stars and racked by internal processes, the solar nebula could not survive very long. Once the gas and dust were gone and most of the planetesimals were swept up, the planets could no longer gain significant mass, and the era of planet building ended.

■ Figure 19-11

Every old, solid surface in the solar system is scarred by craters. (a) Earth's moon has craters ranging from basins hundreds of kilometers in diameter down to microscopic pits. (b) The surface of Mercury, as photographed by a passing spacecraft, shows vast numbers of overlapping craters. (NASA)

SCIENTIFIC ARGUMENT

Why are there two kinds of planets in our solar system?

This is an opportunity for you to build an argument that closely analyzes the solar nebula theory. Planets begin forming from solid bits of matter, not from gas. Consequently, the kind of planet that forms at a given distance from the sun depends on the kind of substances that can condense out of the gas there to form solid particles. In the inner parts of the solar nebula, the temperature was so high that most of the gas could not condense to form solids. Only metals and silicates could form solid grains, and the innermost planets grew from this dense material. Much of the mass of the solar nebula consisted of hydrogen, helium, water vapor, and other gases, and they were present in the inner solar nebula but couldn't form solid grains. The Terrestrial planets could grow only from the solids in their zone, not from the gases, so the Terrestrial planets are small and dense.

In the outer solar nebula, the composition of the gas was the same, but it was cold enough for water vapor, and other simple molecules containing hydrogen, to condense to form ice grains. Because hydrogen was so abundant, there was lots of ice available. The outer planets grew from large amounts of ice combined with small amounts of metals and silicates. Eventually the outer planets grew massive enough that they could begin to capture gas directly from the nebula, and they became the hydrogen- and helium-rich Jovian worlds.

The condensation sequence combined with the solar nebula theory gives you a way to understand the difference between the Terrestrial and Jovian planets. Now expand your argument: **Why do some astronomers argue that the formation of the Jovian planets is a problem that needs further explanation?**

19-4 19-4 Planets Orbiting Other Stars

ARE THERE OTHER planetary systems? The evidence says yes. Do they contain planets like Earth? The evidence so far is incomplete.

Planet-Forming Disks

Both visible- and radio-wavelength observations detect dense disks of gas and dust orbiting young stars. For example, at least 50 percent of the stars in the Orion nebula are surrounded by such disks (Figure 19-3). A young star is detectable at the center of most disks, and astronomers can measure that the disks contain many Earth masses of material in a region a few times larger in diameter than our solar system. The Orion star-forming region is only a few million years old, so planets may not have formed in these disks yet. Furthermore, the intense radiation from nearby hot stars is evaporating the disks so quickly that planets may never have a chance to grow large. The important point for astronomers is that so many young stars have disks. Evidently, disks of gas and dust are a common feature around stars that are forming.

The Hubble Space Telescope can detect dense disks around young stars in a slightly different way. The disks show up in silhouette against the nebulae that surround the newborn stars (■ Figure 19-12). These disks are related to the formation of

DG Tau B

Haro 6-5B

500 AU

IRAS 04248+2612

IRAS 04302+2247

Infrared images

■ Figure 19-12

Dark bands (indicated by arrows) are edge-on disks of gas and dust around young stars seen in Hubble Space Telescope near-infrared images. Planets may eventually form in these disks. These systems are so young that material is still falling inward and being illuminated by light from the stars. (D. Padgett, IPAC/Caltech; W. Brandner, IPAC; K. Stapelfeldt, JPL; and NASA).

comets, and Kuiper belt objects, and astronomers have evidence that the solar system's Kuiper belt extending beyond the orbit of Neptune is an example of an old debris disk.

Some examples of debris disks are around the stars Beta Pictoris, HD 107146, and Epsilon Eridani (■ Figure 19-13). The dust disk around Beta Pictoris, an A-type star more massive and luminous than the sun, is about 20 times the diameter of our solar system. The dust disk around Epsilon Eridani, which is a K-type star somewhat smaller than the sun, is similar in size to the solar system's Kuiper belt. Like most of the other known low-density disks, both of these examples have central zones with even lower density. Those inner regions are understood to be places where planets have finished forming and swept up most of the construction material.

Few examples of planets orbiting stars with debris disks have been detected, but the presence of dust with short lifetimes around old stars assures you that small bodies such as asteroids and comets must be present as sources of the dust. If those small objects are there, then it is likely that there are also planets orbiting those stars.

Infrared observations reveal that the star Vega, easily visible in the northern hemisphere summer sky, also has a debris disk, and detailed studies show that much of the dust in that disk is tiny. The pressure of the light from Vega should blow away small dust particles quickly, so astronomers conclude that the dust being observed now must have been produced by a big event like the collision of two large planetesimals within the last million years (■ Figure 19-14). Fragments from that collision are still smashing into each other now and then and producing more dust, continuing to enhance the debris disk. This effect has also been found in the disk around the faint star known as HIP 8920. Such smashups probably happen rarely in a dust disk, but when they happen, they make the disk very easy to detect.

Notice the difference between the two kinds of planet-related disks that astronomers have found. The low-density dust disks such as the ones around Beta Pictoris, Epsilon Eridani, and Vega are produced by dust from collisions among comets, asteroids, and Kuiper belt objects. Such disks are evidence that planetary systems have already formed (■ Figure 19-15). In comparison, the dense disks of gas and dust such as those seen round the stars in Orion are sites where planets could be forming right now.

bipolar flows (page 223) in that they focus the gas flowing way from a young star into two jets shooting in opposite directions.

In addition to these dense, hot planet-forming disks around young stars, infrared astronomers have found cold, low-density dust disks around stars much older than the newborn stars in Orion, old enough to have finished forming. These tenuous dust disks are sometimes called **debris disks** because they are evidently made of dusty debris produced in collisions among small bodies such as comets, asteroids, and Kuiper belt objects, rather than dust left over from an original protostellar disk. That conclusion is based on calculations showing that the observed dust would be removed by radiation pressure in a much shorter time than the ages of those stars, meaning the dust there now must have been created relatively recently. Our own solar system contains such "second-generation" dust produced by asteroids,

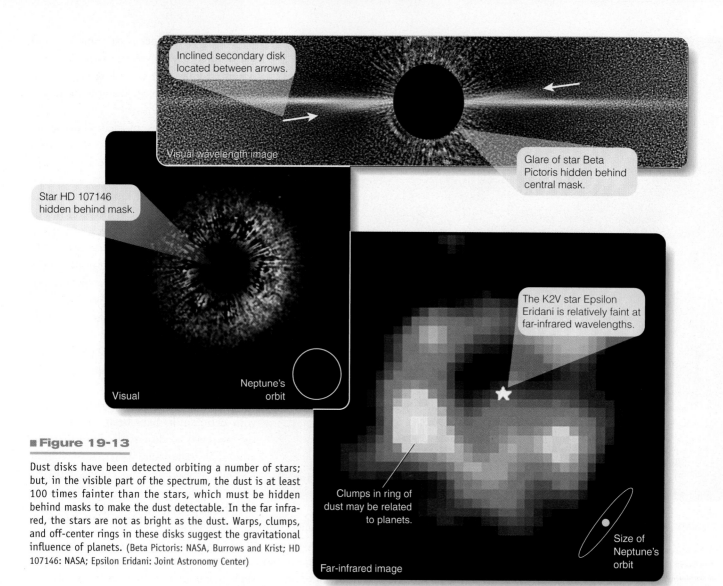

Inclined secondary disk located between arrows.

Visual wavelength image

Glare of star Beta Pictoris hidden behind central mask.

Star HD 107146 hidden behind mask.

Visual

Neptune's orbit

The K2V star Epsilon Eridani is relatively faint at far-infrared wavelengths.

Clumps in ring of dust may be related to planets.

Far-infrared image

Size of Neptune's orbit

■ **Figure 19-13**

Dust disks have been detected orbiting a number of stars; but, in the visible part of the spectrum, the dust is at least 100 times fainter than the stars, which must be hidden behind masks to make the dust detectable. In the far infra- red, the stars are not as bright as the dust. Warps, clumps, and off-center rings in these disks suggest the gravitational influence of planets. (Beta Pictoris: NASA, Burrows and Krist; HD 107146: NASA; Epsilon Eridani: Joint Astronomy Center)

■ **Figure 19-14**

Collisions between asteroids are rare events, but they generate lots of dust and huge numbers of fragments, as in this artist's conception. Further collisions between fragments can continue to produce dust. Because such dust is blown away quickly, astrono- mers treat the presence of dust as evidence that objects of asteroid size are also present. (J. Lomberg/ Gemini Observatory)

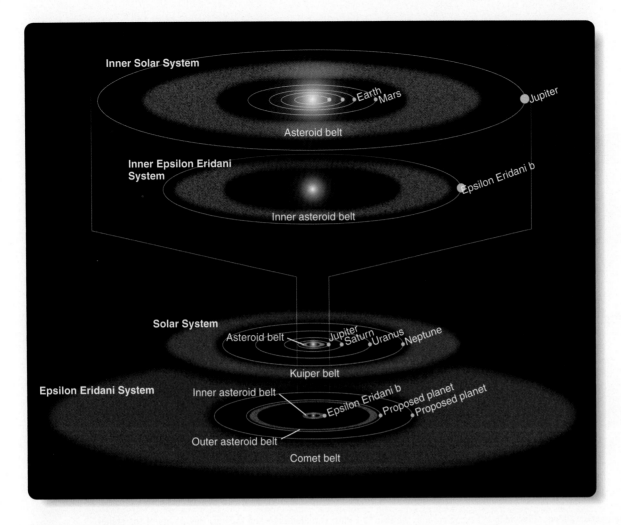

■ Figure 19-15

Dust in debris belts around older main-sequence stars indicates ongoing collisions of asteroids and comets. Such activity in our solar system is ultimately driven by the gravitational influence of planets. The locations of debris belt edges may be defined by orbits of adjacent planets. The inferred architecture of the Epsilon Eridani planetary system is shown in comparison with our solar system. (Artist's conception based on Spitzer Space Telescope and Caltech Submillimeter Observatory observations by D. Backman et al.; NASA/JPL-Caltech/R. Hurt)

Observing Extrasolar Planets

A planet orbiting another star is called an **extrasolar planet.** Such a planet would be quite faint and difficult to see so close to the glare of its star. But there are ways to find these planets. To understand one important way, all you have to do is imagine walking a dog.

You will remember that Earth and the moon orbit around their common center of mass, and two stars in a binary system orbit around their center of mass. When a planet orbits a star, the star moves very slightly as it orbits the center of mass of the planet–star system. Think of someone walking a poorly trained

dog on a leash; the dog runs around pulling on the leash, and even if it were an invisible dog, you could plot its path by watching how its owner was jerked back and forth. Astronomers can detect a planet orbiting another star by watching how the star moves as the planet tugs on it.

The first planet detected this way was discovered in 1995 orbiting the sun-like star 51 Pegasi. As the planet circles the star, the star wobbles slightly, and that very small motion of the star is detectable by Doppler shifts in the star's spectrum (■ Figure 19-16a) (see Chapters 7 and 9). From the motion of the star and estimates of the star's mass, astronomers can deduce that the planet has at least half the mass of Jupiter and orbits only 0.05 AU from the star. Half the mass of Jupiter amounts to 160 Earth masses, so this is a large planet. Note also that it orbits very close to its star, much closer than Mercury orbits around our sun.

Astronomers were not surprised by the announcement that a planet had been found orbiting a sun-like star; for years astronomers had assumed that many stars had planets. Nevertheless, they greeted the details of this discovery with professional skepticism (**How Do We Know? 19-2**). That skepticism led to careful tests of the data and further observations that confirmed

■ Figure 19-16

Just as someone walking a lively dog is tugged around, the star 51 Pegasi is pulled back and forth by the gravity of the planet that orbits it every 4.2 days. The wobble is detectable in precision observations of the star's Doppler shift. Someone walking three dogs is pulled about in a more complicated pattern, and you can see something similar in the Doppler shifts of Upsilon Andromedae, which is orbited by three planets detected so far. The influence of its shortest-period planet has been removed in this graph to reveal the orbital influences of the other two planets.

the discovery. In fact, almost 400 planets have been discovered in this way, including at least three planets orbiting the star Upsilon Andromedae (Figure 19-16b) and five orbiting 55 Cancri—true planetary systems. Over 25 such multiple-planet systems have been found.

Another way to search for planets is to look for changes in the brightness of the star when the orbiting planet crosses in front of the star, called a **transit.** The decrease in light during a planet transit is very small, but it is detectable, and astronomers have used this technique to find many planets. From the amount of light lost, astronomers can tell that these planets with Jovian masses have Jovian diameters, and thus Jovian densities and compositions.

The Spitzer Space Telescope has detected infrared radiation from two large hot planets already known from star wobble Doppler shifts. As these planets orbit their parent stars, the amount of infrared radiation from each system varies. When the planets pass behind their parent stars, the total infrared brightness of the systems noticeably decreases. These measurements confirm the existence of the planets and indicate their temperatures and sizes.

Notice how the techniques used to detect these planets resemble techniques used to study binary stars (see Chapter 9). Most of the planets were discovered using the same observational methods used to study spectroscopic binaries, but some were found by observing the stars as if they were eclipsing binaries. In contrast, a few extrasolar planets have been found by a technique called **microlensing**, in which an extrasolar planet passes precisely between Earth and a background star, briefly magnifying the distant star's brightness by gravitational lensing.

The planets discovered so far tend to be massive and have short orbital periods because lower-mass planets or longer-period

Scientists: Courteous Skeptics

What does it mean to be skeptical yet also open to new ideas? "Scientists are just a bunch of skeptics who don't believe in anything." That is a **Common Misconception** among people who don't understand the methods and goals of science. Yes, scientists are skeptical about new ideas and discoveries, but they do hold strong beliefs about how nature works. Scientists are skeptical not because they want to disprove everything but because they are searching for the truth and want to be sure that a new description of nature is reliable before it is accepted.

Another **Common Misconception** is that scientists automatically accept the work of other scientists. On the contrary, scientists skeptically question every aspect of a new discovery. They may wonder if another scientist's instruments were properly calibrated or whether the scientist's mathematical models are correct. Other scientists will want to repeat the work themselves using their own instruments to see if they can obtain the same results. Every observation is tested, every discovery is confirmed, and only an idea that survives many of these tests begins to be accepted as a scientific truth.

Scientists are prepared for this kind of treatment at the hands of other scientists. In fact, they expect it. Among scientists it is not bad manners to say, "Really, how do you know that?" or "Why do you think that?" or "Show me the evidence!" And it is not just new or surprising claims that are subject to such scrutiny. Even though astronomers had long expected to discover planets orbiting other stars, when a planet was finally discovered circling 51 Pegasi, astronomers were skeptical. This was not because they thought the observations were necessarily flawed but because that is how science works.

The goal of science is to tell stories about nature. Some people use the phrase "telling a story" to describe someone who is telling a fib. But the stories that scientists tell are exactly the opposite; perhaps you could call them "antifibs" because they are as true as scientists can make them. Skepticism eliminates stories with logical errors, flawed observations, or misunderstood evidence and eventually leaves only the stories that best describe nature.

Skepticism is not a refusal to hold beliefs. Rather, it is a way for scientists to find and keep those natural principles that are worthy of acceptance.

A laboratory cell for the investigation of cold fusion claims that were thereby found to be false. (Photo by Steven Krivit of a device at the U.S. Navy SPAWAR Systems Center in San Diego)

planets are harder to detect. Low-mass planets don't tug on their stars very much, and present-day spectrographs can't detect the very small velocity changes that these gentle tugs produce. Planets with longer periods are harder to detect because astronomers have not been making high-precision observations for a long enough time. Jupiter takes 11 years to circle the sun once, so it will take years for astronomers to see the longer-period wobbles produced by planets lying farther from their stars. You should not be surprised that the first planets discovered are massive and have short orbital periods.

The new planets may seem odd for another reason. As you have learned for our solar system, the large planets formed farther from the sun where the solar nebula was colder and ices could condense. How could big planets near their stars (called "**hot Jupiters**") have formed? Theoretical calculations indicate that planets forming in an especially dense disk of matter could spiral inward as they sweep up gas and planetesimals. That means it is possible for a few planets to become the massive, short-period planets that are detected most easily.

Many of the newly discovered extrasolar planets have elliptical orbits, and that seems odd when compared with our solar system, in which the planetary orbits are nearly circular. Theorists point out, however, that planets in some young planetary systems can interact with each other and can be thrown into elliptical orbits. This effect is probably rare in planetary systems, but astronomers find these extreme systems more easily because they tend to produce easily detected wobbles.

The preceding paragraphs should reassure you that massive planets in small or elliptical orbits do not fundamentally contradict the solar nebula theory. In fact, as astronomers continue to refine their instruments to detect smaller velocity shifts in stars, they find lower-mass planets. A planet with only about 5 times the mass of Earth, less than $\frac{1}{3}$ the mass of Uranus or Neptune, was found by the Doppler shift technique in 2007. This small extrasolar planet orbits its red dwarf parent star in only 13 Earth-days at a distance of 0.07 AU. With a diameter estimated to be 1.5 times larger than Earth and a

■ Figure 19-17

(a) Visible-wavelength images of 3 planets at apparent distances of 25, 40, and 70 AU from the star HR 8799. (C. Marois et al./ National Research Council of Canada/AURA/Keck Observatories) (b) Near-infrared image of a planet orbiting about 120 AU from the star Fomalhaut (alpha Piscis Austrinus), at the inside edge of that star's previously known debris ring. The inset shows motion of the object between 2004 and 2006, at the correct rate for a planet at that position orbiting a star of that mass. (P. Kalas et al./ STScI/NASA)

surface temperature that would permit liquid water, it is clearly not a Jovian planet.

Among the planets found so far, most are orbiting stars that are metal rich rather than metal poor. This supports the scenario of planet formation by the accretion of a core of solids and the later accumulation of gas. It is evidence against formation by direct collapse, which does not require the presence of solids such as metals and silicates to start planet formation.

Actually getting an image of a planet orbiting another star is about as easy as photographing a bug crawling on the bulb of a searchlight miles away. Planets are small and dim and get lost in the glare of the stars they orbit. Nevertheless, during 2008, astronomers managed to image three planets around the A-type star HR 8799,

using adaptive optics and coronagraph instruments mounted on the Gemini and Keck telescopes atop Mauna Kea, and 1 planet around the A-type star Fomalhaut (alpha Piscis Austrinis), using the Hubble Space Telescope's near-infrared camera (■ Figure 19-17).

Searches for more extrasolar planets are being conducted. The Kepler space telescope mission, launched in 2009, will be sensitive enough to detect transits of planets as small as Earth. Space observatories will be able eventually to image Jovian and even Terrestrial planets directly around sunlike stars. The discovery of extrasolar planets gives astronomers added confidence in the solar nebula theory. The theory predicts that planets are common, and astronomers are finding them orbiting many stars.

SCIENTIFIC ARGUMENT

Why are debris disks evidence that planets have already formed?

Sometimes a good scientific argument combines evidence, theory, and an astronomer's past experience, a kind of scientific common sense. Certainly the cold debris disks seen around stars like Vega are not places where planets are forming. They are not hot enough or dense enough to be young disks. Rather, the debris disks must be older, and the dust is being produced by collisions among comets, asteroids, and Kuiper belt objects. Small dust particles would be blown away or destroyed relatively quickly, so these collisions must be a continuing process. The successful solar nebula theory gives astronomers reason to believe that where you find comets, asteroids, and Kuiper belt objects, you should also find planets, so the dust disks seem to be evidence that planets have already formed in such systems.

Now build a new argument. **What direct evidence can you cite that planets orbit other stars?**

The matter you are made of came from the big bang, and it has been cooked into a wide variety of atoms inside stars. Now you can see how those atoms came to be part of Earth. Your atoms were in the cloud of gas that formed the solar system 4.6 billion years ago, and nearly all of that matter contracted to form the sun, but a small amount left behind in a disk formed planets. In the process, your atoms became part of Earth.

You are a planet-walker, and you have evolved to live on the surface of Earth. Are there other beings like you in the universe? Now you know that planets are common, and you can reasonably suppose that there are more planets in the universe than there are stars. However complicated the formation of the solar system was, it is a common process, so there may indeed be more planet-walkers living on other worlds.

But what are those distant planets like? Before you can go very far in your search for life beyond Earth, you need to explore the range of planetary types. It is time to pack your spacesuit and voyage out among the planets of our solar system, visit them one by one, and search for the natural principles that relate planets to each other. That journey begins in the next chapter.

Study and Review

Summary

▶ Descartes proposed that the solar system formed from a contracting vortex of matter—an **evolutionary hypothesis (p. 398)**. Buffon later suggested that a passing comet pulled matter out of the sun to form the planets—a **catastrophic hypothesis (p. 398)**. Later astronomers replaced the comet with a star to produce the **passing star hypothesis (p. 398)**.

▶ Laplace's **nebular hypothesis (p. 398)** required a contracting nebula to leave behind rings that formed each planet, but it could not explain the sun's low angular momentum, a puzzle known as the **angular momentum problem (p. 399)**.

▶ Hypotheses for the origin of the solar system have been either catastrophic or evolutionary. Catastrophic hypotheses depend on a rare event such as the collision of the sun with another star. Evolutionary hypotheses propose that the planets formed by gradual, natural processes. The evidence now strongly favors the **solar nebula theory (p. 399)**, an evolutionary scenario.

▶ Modern astronomy reveals that all the matter in the universe, including our solar system, was originally formed as hydrogen and helium in the big bang. Atoms heavier than helium were cooked up in nuclear reactions in later generations of stars. The sun and planets evidently formed from a cloud of gas and dust in the interstellar medium.

▶ The solar nebula theory proposes that the planets formed in a disk of gas and dust around the protostar that became the sun. Observations show that these disks are common.

▶ The solar system is disk shaped, with all the planets orbiting nearly in the same plane. The orbital revolution of all the planets, the rotation of most of the planets on their axes, and the revolution of most of their moons are all in the same direction, counterclockwise as seen from the north.

▶ The planets are divided into two groups. The inner four planets are **Terrestrial planets (p. 402)**—small, rocky, dense Earth-like worlds. The next four outward are Jupiter-like **Jovian planets (p. 402)** that are large and low density.

▶ All four of the Jovian worlds have ring systems and large families of moons. The Terrestrial planets have no rings and few moons.

▶ Most of the **asteroids (p. 401)**, small, irregular, rocky bodies, are located between the orbits of Mars and Jupiter.

▶ The **Kuiper belt (p. 404)** is composed of small, icy bodies that orbit the sun beyond the orbit of Neptune.

▶ **Comets (p. 404)** are icy bodies that pass through the inner solar system along long elliptical orbits. As the ices vaporize and release dust, the comet develops a tail that points approximately away from the sun.

▶ **Meteoroids (p. 405)** that fall into Earth's atmosphere are vaporized by friction and are visible as streaks of light called **meteors (p. 404)**. Larger and stronger meteoroids may survive to reach the ground, where they are called **meteorites (p. 405)**.

▶ The age of a rocky body can be found by radioactive dating, based on the decay **half-life (p. 405)** of radioactive atoms. The oldest rocks from Earth, the moon, and Mars have ages over 4 billion years. The oldest objects in our solar system are some meteorites that have ages of 4.6 billion years. This is taken to be the age of the solar system.

▶ **Condensation (p. 409)** in the solar nebula converted some of the gas into solid bits of matter, which grow by **accretion (p. 409)** to form billions of **planetesimals (p. 409)**.

▶ Planets begin growing by accretion of solid material into **protoplanets (p. 409)**. Once a protoplanet approaches about 15 Earth masses, it can begin growing by **gravitational collapse (p. 410)** as it pulls in gas from the solar nebula.

- According to the **condensation sequence (p. 408)**, the inner part of the solar nebula was so hot that only metals and rocky materials could form solid grains. The dense Terrestrial planets grew from those solid particles and did not include many ices or low-density gases.

- The outer solar nebula, beyond the **ice line (p. 408)**, was cold enough for ices as well as metals and rocky minerals to form solid particles. The Jovian planets grew rapidly and incorporated large amounts of low-density ices and gases.

- Evidence that the condensation sequence was important in the solar nebula can be found in the high densities of the Terrestrial planets relative to the Jovian planets. Comparing the **uncompressed densities (p. 408)** of the Terrestrial planets shows that the innermost Terrestrial planets have the highest densities.

- The Terrestrial planets may have formed slowly from the accretion of planetesimals of similar composition. Later, radioactive decay plus **heat of formation (p. 410)** melted each planet's interior to cause **differentiation (p. 410)** into layers of differing density. In that scenario, Earth's early atmosphere was probably supplied by a combination of **outgassing (p. 411)** from Earth's interior and planetesimal impacts.

- Disks of gas and dust around protostars may not last long enough to form Jovian planets by accretion and then by gravitational collapse. Some models suggest the Jovian planets could have formed more rapidly by **direct collapse (p. 412)**, skipping the condensation and accretion steps.

- In addition to intense light from hot nearby stars and the gravitational influence of passing stars, the solar nebula was eventually cleared away by radiation pressure, the solar wind, and the sweeping up or ejection of debris by the planets.

- All of the old surfaces in the solar system were heavily cratered during the **heavy bombardment (p. 413)** by debris that filled the solar system when it was young.

- Hot disks of gas and dust have been detected in early stages of star formation and are believed to be the kind of disk in which planets could form.

- Cold dust disks, also known as **debris disks (p. 415)**, appear to be composed of dust released by collisions among comets, asteroids, and Kuiper belt objects. Such disks may be signs that planets have already formed in those systems.

- Planets orbiting other stars, called **extrasolar planets (p. 417)**, have been detected by the way they tug their stars about, creating small Doppler shifts in the stars' spectra. Planets have also been detected in **transits (p. 418)** as they cross in front of their star and partly block the star's light. A few planets have been detected when they orbited behind their star and their infrared radiation was cut off. A few more have been detected by gravitational **microlensing (p. 418)**.

- Nearly all extrasolar planets found so far are massive, Jovian worlds orbiting close to their parent stars, called **hot Jupiters (p. 419)**. Lower-mass Terrestrial planets are harder to detect but may be common.

Review Questions

1. What produced the helium now present in the sun's atmosphere? In Jupiter's atmosphere? In the sun's core?

2. What produced the iron and heavier elements like gold and silver in Earth's core and crust?

3. What evidence can you cite that disks of gas and dust are common around young stars?

4. According to the solar nebula theory, why is the sun's equator nearly in the plane of the planets' orbits?

5. Why does the solar nebula theory predict that planetary systems are common?

6. Why do astronomers think the solar system formed about 4.6 billion years ago?

7. If you visited another planetary system, would you be surprised to find planets older than Earth? Why or why not?

8. Why is almost every solid surface in our solar system scarred by craters?

9. What is the difference between condensation and accretion?

10. Why don't Terrestrial planets have rings like the Jovian planets?

11. How does the solar nebula theory help you understand the location of asteroids?

12. How does the solar nebula theory explain the dramatic density difference between the Terrestrial and Jovian planets?

13. What does the term *differentiated* mean when applied to a planet? Would you expect to find that planets are usually differentiated? Why?

14. What processes cleared the nebula away and ended planet building?

15. What is the difference between the dense hot disks seen around some stars and the low-density cold disks seen around some other stars?

16. What evidence can you cite that planets orbit other stars?

17. **How Do We Know?** The evidence is overwhelming in support of the idea that the Grand Canyon was dug over a span of millions of years by the erosive power of the Colorado River and its tributary streams. Is that a catastrophic theory or an evolutionary theory?

18. **How Do We Know?** Why must scientists be skeptical of new discoveries even when they think that the discoveries are correct?

Discussion Questions

1. If you visited some other planetary system in the act of building planets, would you expect to see the condensation sequence at work, or was it probably unique to our solar system? How do the properties of the extrasolar planets discovered so far affect your answer?

2. In your opinion, do most planetary systems have asteroid belts? Would all planetary systems show evidence of an age of heavy bombardment?

3. If the solar nebula hypothesis is correct, then there are probably more planets in the universe than stars. Do you agree? Why or why not?

4. The human race has intelligence and consequently has both the ability and the responsibility to wonder about its origins. Do you agree?

Problems

1. If you observed the solar system from the nearest star (distance = 1.3 parsecs), what would the maximum angular separation be between Earth and the sun? (*Hints:* Use the small-angle formula, Chapter 3, and see the definition of parallax on page 169.)

2. The brightest planet in our sky is Venus, which is sometimes as bright as apparent magnitude −4 when it is at a distance of about 1 AU. How many times fainter would it look from a distance of 1 parsec (2.06×10^5 AU)? What would its apparent magnitude be? (*Hints:* Remember the inverse square law from Chapter 9; also, review the definition of magnitudes in Chapter 2.)

3. What is the smallest-diameter crater you can identify in the photo of Mercury on page 402? (*Hint:* See Appendix A, "Properties of the Planets," to find the diameter of Mercury in kilometers.)

4. A sample of a meteorite has been analyzed, and the result shows that out of every 1000 nuclei of potassium-40 originally in the meteorite, only 250 have not decayed. How old is the meteorite? (*Hint:* See Figure 19-6.)

5. In Table 19-2, which object's observed density differs least from its uncompressed density? Why?

6. What composition might you expect for a planet that formed in a region of the solar nebula where the temperature was about 100 K?

7. Suppose that Earth grew to its present size in 1 million years through the accretion of particles averaging 100 grams each. On the average, how many particles did Earth capture per second? (*Hint:* See Appendix A to find Earth's mass.)

8. If you stood on Earth during its formation, as described in Problem 7, and watched a region covering 100 m², how many impacts would you expect to see in an hour? (*Hint:* Assume that Earth had its present radius. The surface area of a sphere is $4\pi r^2$.)

9. The velocity of the solar wind is roughly 400 km/s. How long does it take to travel from the sun to Earth?

Learning to Look

1. What do you see in the image at the right that indicates this planet formed far from the sun?

NASA

2. Why do astronomers conclude that the surface of Mercury, shown at right, is old? When did the majority of those craters form?

NASA

3. In the mineral specimen represented to the right, radioactive atoms (red) have decayed to form daughter atoms (blue). How old is this specimen in half-lives? (See Figure 19-7).

20 | Earth: The Standard of Comparative Planetology

Guidepost

In the preceding chapter, you learned how our solar system formed as a by-product of the formation of the sun. You also saw how distance from the sun determined the general composition of each planet. In this chapter, you begin your study of individual planets with Earth. You will come to see Earth not only as your home, but as a planet among other planets. On the way, you will answer four essential questions:

How does Earth fit among the Terrestrial planets?

How has Earth changed since it formed?

What is the inside of Earth like?

How has Earth's atmosphere formed and evolved?

Like a mountain climber establishing a base camp before attempting the summit, you will, in this chapter, establish your basis of comparison on Earth. In the following chapters you will visit worlds that are un-Earthly but, in some ways, familiar.

The beauty of planet Earth can be deceptive. It was not always as it is now, and it will not survive unchanged forever. It was born in the solar nebula, and its end will come when the sun dies. (Jean-Bernard Carillet/Getty Images)

Nature evolves. The world was different yesterday.

— PRESTON CLOUD, *COSMOS, EARTH AND MAN*

PLANETS, LIKE PEOPLE, ARE MORE ALIKE than they are different. They are described by the same basic principles, and their differences arise mostly because of small differences in background. To understand the planets, you can compare and contrast them to identify those principles, an approach called **comparative planetology.**

Earth is the ideal starting point for your study because it is the planet you know best. It is also a complex planet. Earth's interior is molten and generates a magnetic field. Its crust is active, with moving continents, earthquakes, volcanoes, and mountain building. Earth's oxygen-rich atmosphere is unique in the solar system. The properties of Earth will give you perspective on the other planets in our solar system.

■ **Figure 20-1**

Planets in comparison. Earth and Venus are similar in size, but their atmospheres and surfaces are very different. The moon and Mercury are much smaller, and Mars is intermediate in size. (Moon: UCO/Lick Observatory: All planets: NASA)

20-1) A Travel Guide to the Terrestrial Planets

IF YOU VISIT THE CITY OF GRANADA in Spain, you will probably consult a travel guide. If it is a good guide, it will do more than tell you where to find museums and restrooms. It will give you a preview of what to expect. You are beginning a journey to the Earth-like worlds, so you should consult a travel guide and see what is in store.

Five Worlds

You are about to visit Mercury, Venus, Earth, Earth's moon, and Mars. It may surprise you that the moon is included in your itinerary. It is, after all, just a natural satellite orbiting Earth and isn't one of the planets. But the moon is a fascinating world of its own, it makes a striking comparison with the other worlds on your list, and its history gives you important information about the history of Earth and the other planets.

■ Figure 20-1 compares the five worlds. The first feature you might notice is diameter. The moon is small, and Mercury is not much bigger. Earth and Venus are large and quite similar in size,

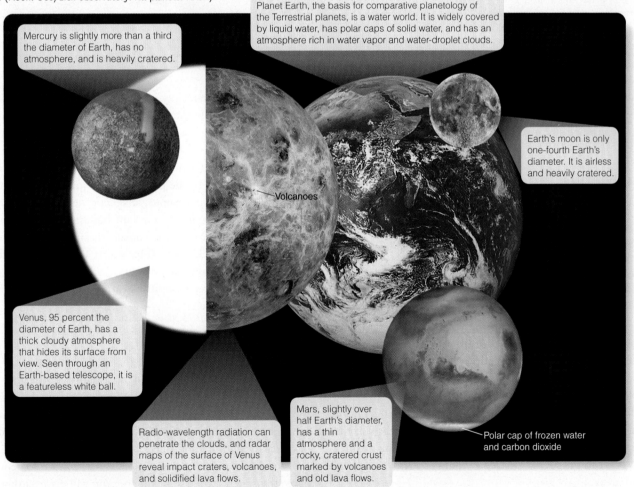

Mercury is slightly more than a third the diameter of Earth, has no atmosphere, and is heavily cratered.

Planet Earth, the basis for comparative planetology of the Terrestrial planets, is a water world. It is widely covered by liquid water, has polar caps of solid water, and has an atmosphere rich in water vapor and water-droplet clouds.

Volcanoes

Earth's moon is only one-fourth Earth's diameter. It is airless and heavily cratered.

Venus, 95 percent the diameter of Earth, has a thick cloudy atmosphere that hides its surface from view. Seen through an Earth-based telescope, it is a featureless white ball.

Radio-wavelength radiation can penetrate the clouds, and radar maps of the surface of Venus reveal impact craters, volcanoes, and solidified lava flows.

Mars, slightly over half Earth's diameter, has a thin atmosphere and a rocky, cratered crust marked by volcanoes and old lava flows.

Polar cap of frozen water and carbon dioxide

Understanding Planets: Follow the Energy

What causes change? One of the best ways to think about a scientific problem is to follow the energy. According to the principle of cause and effect, every effect must have a cause, and every cause must involve energy. Energy moves from regions of high concentration to regions of low concentration and, in doing so, produces changes. For example, coal burns to make steam in a power plant, and the steam passes through a turbine and then escapes into the air. In flowing from the burning coal to the atmosphere, the heat spins the turbine and makes electricity.

Scientists commonly use energy as a key to understanding nature. A biologist might ask where certain birds get the energy to fly thousands of miles, and a geologist might ask where the energy comes from to power a volcano. Energy is everywhere, and when it moves, whether it is in birds or molten magma, it causes change. Energy is the "cause" in "cause and effect."

In earlier chapters, the flow of energy from the inside of a star to its surface helped you understand how stars, including the sun, work. You saw that the outward flow of energy supports the star against its own weight, drives convection currents that produce magnetic fields, and causes surface activity such as spots, prominences, and flares. You were able to understand stars because you could follow the flow of energy outward from their interiors.

You can also think of a planet by following the energy. The heat in the interior of a planet may be left over from the formation of the planet, or it may be heat generated by radioactive decay, but it must flow outward toward the cooler surface, where it is radiated into space. In flowing outward, the heat can cause convection currents in the mantle, magnetic fields, plate motions, quakes, faults, volcanism, mountain building, and more.

When you think about any world, be it a small asteroid or a giant planet, think of it as a source of heat that flows outward through the planet's surface into space. If

Heat flowing out of Earth's interior generates geological activity such as that at Yellowstone National Park. (M. Seeds)

you can follow that energy flow, you can understand a great deal about the world. A planetary astronomer once said, "The most interesting thing about any planet is how its heat gets out."

---

but Mars is a medium-sized world. You will discover that size is a critical factor in determining a world's personality. Small worlds tend to be geologically inactive, while larger worlds tend to be active.

Core, Mantle, and Crust

The Terrestrial worlds are made up of rock and metal. They are all differentiated, which means they are each separated into layers of different density, with a dense metallic core surrounded by a less-dense rocky **mantle,** and a low-density crust on the outside.

As you learned in Chapter 19, when the planets formed, their surfaces were subjected to heavy bombardment by left-over planetesimals and debris in the young solar system. You will see lots of craters on these worlds, especially on Mercury and the moon, many of them dating back to the heavy bombardment era. Notice that cratered surfaces are old. For example, if a lava flow covered up some cratered landscape after the end of the heavy bombardment, few craters could be formed later on that surface because most of the debris in the solar system was gone. When you see a smooth plain on a planet, you can guess that surface is younger than the heavily cratered areas.

Another important way you can study a planet is by following the energy flow. In the preceding chapter you learned that the heat in the interior of a planet may be partly from radioactive decay and partly left over from the planet's formation, but in any case it must flow outward toward the cooler surface where it is radiated into space. In the process of flowing outward, the heat can cause convection currents, magnetic fields, plate motions, quakes, faults, volcanism, mountain building, and more. Heat flowing outward through the cooler crust makes a large world like Earth geologically active (**How Do We Know? 20-1**). In contrast, the moon and Mercury, both small worlds, cooled quickly inside, so they have little heat flowing outward now and are relatively inactive.

Atmospheres

When you look at Mercury and the moon in Figure 20-1, you can see their craters, plains, and mountains clearly; they each have little or no atmosphere to obscure your view. In comparison, the surface of Venus is completely hidden by a cloudy atmosphere even thicker than Earth's. Mars, the medium-sized planet, has a relatively thin atmosphere.

You might ponder two questions. First, why do some worlds have atmospheres while some do not? You will discover that both size and temperature are important. The second question is more complex. Where did those atmospheres come from? To answer that question in later chapters, you will have to study the geological history of these worlds.

SCIENTIFIC ARGUMENT

Why do you expect the inner planets to be high-density worlds?
In Chapter 19, you saw how the inner planets formed from hot inner parts of the solar nebula. No ice solidified there, so the inner planets could grow only from particles of rock and metal able to condense from hot gas. So, you expect the inner planets to be made mostly of rock and metal, which are dense materials.

As you visit the Terrestrial planets, you will find craters almost everywhere. **What made all of those craters?**

20-2 Earth as a Planet

LIKE ALL THE TERRESTRIAL PLANETS, Earth formed from the inner solar nebula about 4.6 billion years ago. Even as it took form, it began to change.

Four Stages of Planetary Development

There is evidence that Earth and the other Terrestrial planets, plus Earth's moon, passed through four developmental stages (■ Figure 20-2).

The first stage of planetary evolution is *differentiation,* the separation of material according to density. As you have already learned, Earth is differentiated, meaning, separated into layers of different density. That differentiation is understood to have occurred due to melting of Earth's interior caused by heat from a combination of radioactive decay plus energy released by infalling matter during the planet's formation. Once the interior of Earth melted, the densest materials were able to sink to the core.

The second stage, *cratering,* could not begin until a solid surface formed. The heavy bombardment of the early solar system made craters on Earth just as it did on the moon and other planets. As the debris in the young solar system cleared away, the rate of cratering impacts fell gradually to its present low rate. You will learn in the next chapter that evidence provided by lunar crater counts and rock samples indicates there was a temporary large increase in the impact cratering rate near the end of the heavy bombardment, and this violent event likely would have affected all the planets.

The third stage, *flooding,* began as radioactive decay continued to heat Earth's interior and caused rock to melt in the upper mantle, where the pressure was lower than in the deep interior. Some of that molten rock welled up through cracks in the crust

and flooded the deeper impact basins. Later, as the environment cooled, water fell as rain and flooded the basins to form the first oceans. Note that on Earth, basin flooding was first by lava and later by water.

The fourth stage, *slow surface evolution,* has continued for at least the past 3.5 billion years. Earth's surface is constantly changing as sections of crust slide over and against each other, push up mountains, and shift continents. In addition, moving air and water erode the surface and wear away geological features. Almost all traces of the first billion years of Earth's history have been destroyed by the active crust and erosion.

Terrestrial planets pass through these four stages, but differences in mass, temperature, and composition among the planets

Four Stages of Planetary Development

Differentiation produces a dense core, thick mantle, and low-density crust.

The young Earth was heavily bombarded in the debris-filled early solar system.

Flooding by molten rock and later by water can fill lowlands.

Slow surface evolution continues due to geological processes, including erosion.

■ **Figure 20-2**

The four stages of Terrestrial planetary development are illustrated for Earth.

can emphasize some of those stages over others and produce surprisingly different worlds.

Exceptional Earth

Earth is a good standard for comparative planetology (**Celestial Profile 2**). Every major process on any rocky world in our solar system is represented in some form on Earth. Nevertheless, Earth is unusual, if not unique, among the planets in our solar system, in two ways: the presence of abundant liquid water and the presence of life.

First, 75 percent of Earth's surface is covered by liquid water. No other planet in our solar system has liquid water on its surface, although, as you will learn in later chapters, Mars had surface water long ago, Venus probably did, and some moons in the outer solar system show evidence of having liquid water under their surfaces. Water fills Earth's oceans, evaporates into the atmosphere, forms clouds, and then falls as rain. Water falling on the continents flows downhill to form rivers that flow back to the sea and, in doing so, produces intense erosion. Entire mountain ranges can literally dissolve and wash away in only a few tens of millions of years, less than 1 percent of Earth's total age. You will not see such rapid erosion on most worlds. Liquid water is, in fact, a rare material on most planets.

Your home planet is special in a second way. Some of the matter on the surface of this world is alive, and a small part of that living matter, including you, is aware. No one is sure how the presence of living matter has affected the evolution of Earth, but this process seems to be totally missing from other worlds in our solar system. Furthermore, as you will learn later in this chapter, the thinking part of the life on Earth, humankind, is actively altering our planet.

Earth's surface is marked by high continents and low seafloors, but the crust is only 10 to 60 km thick. Below that lie a deep mantle and an iron core. (NGDC)

Celestial Profile 2: Earth

Motion:

Average distance from the sun	1.00 AU (1.50×10^8 km)
Eccentricity of orbit	0.017
Maximum distance from the sun	1.017 AU (1.52×10^8 km)
Minimum distance from the sun	0.983 AU (1.47×10^8 km)
Inclination of orbit to ecliptic	0° (by definition)
Average orbital velocity	29.8 km/s
Orbital period	1.0000 y (365.25 days)
Period of rotation	24.00 h (with respect to the sun)
Period of rotation	23.93 h (with respect to the stars)
Inclination of equator to orbit	23.4°

Characteristics:

Equatorial diameter	1.28×10^8 km
Mass	5.97×10^{24} kg
Average density	5.50 g/cm³ (4.07 g/cm³ uncompressed)
Surface gravity	1.00 Earth gravity
Escape velocity	11.2 km/s
Surface temperature	−90° to 60°C (−130° to 140°F)
Average albedo	0.39
Oblateness	0.0034

Personality Point:

Earth comes, through Old English *eorthe* and Greek *Eraze,* from the Hebrew *erez,* which means ground. *Terra* comes from the Roman goddess of fertility and growth; thus, *Terra Mater,* Mother Earth.

SCIENTIFIC ARGUMENT

Why should you think Earth went through an early stage of cratering?

When you build a scientific argument, take great care to distinguish between theory and evidence. Recall from the previous chapter that the planets formed by the accretion of planetesimals from the solar nebula. The proto-Earth may have been molten as it formed, but as soon as it grew cool enough to form a solid crust, the remaining planetesimal impacts would have formed craters. So you can reason from the solar nebula hypothesis that Earth should have been cratered. But you can't use a theory as evidence to support some other theory. To find real observational evidence, you need only look at the moon. The moon has craters, and so does every other old surface in our solar system. There must have been a time, when the solar system was young, during which there were large numbers of objects striking all the planets and moons and blasting out craters. If it happened to other worlds in our solar system, it must have happened to Earth, too.

The best evidence to support your argument would be lots of craters on Earth, but, of course, there are few craters on Earth. Extend your argument. **How has the presence of liquid water on Earth affected the appearance of Earth's crust?**

20-3 The Solid Earth

ALTHOUGH YOU MIGHT THINK of earth as solid rock, it is in fact neither entirely solid nor entirely rock. The thin crust seems solid, but it floats and shifts on a semiliquid layer of molten rock just below the crust. Below that lies a deep, rocky mantle surrounding a core of liquid metal. Much of what you see on Earth's surface is determined by conditions and processes in its interior.

Earth's Interior

The theory of the origin of planets from the solar nebula predicts that Earth should have melted and differentiated into a dense metallic core and a dense mantle with a low-density silicate crust. But did it? Where's the evidence? Earth's average density can be calculated easily from its known mass and density. Clearly, the silicate rocks on Earth's surface have lower density than material inside the planet. But, what more can be determined about Earth's interior?

High temperature and tremendous pressure in Earth's interior make any direct exploration impossible. Even the deepest oil wells extend only a few kilometers down and don't reach through the crust. It is impossible to drill far enough to sample Earth's core. Yet Earth scientists have studied the interior and found clear evidence that Earth did differentiate (**How Do We Know? 20-2**).

This exploration of Earth's interior is possible because earthquakes produce vibrations called **seismic waves** that travel through the crust and interior and eventually register on sensitive detectors called **seismographs** all over the world (■ Figure 20-3). Two kinds of seismic waves are important to this discussion. The **pressure (P) waves** are much like sound waves in that they travel as a sequence of compressions and decompressions. As a *P* wave passes, particles of matter vibrate back and forth parallel to the direction of wave travel (■ Figure 20-4a). In contrast, the **shear (S) waves** move as displacements of particles perpendicular to

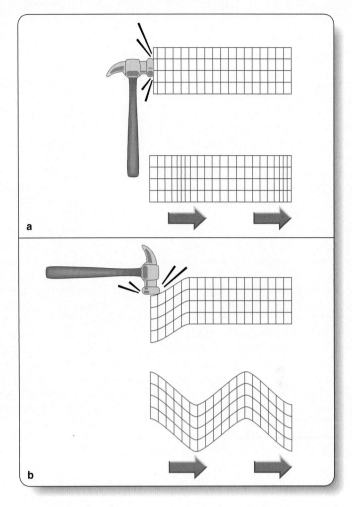

■ **Figure 20-4**

(a) *P*, or pressure, waves, like sound waves in air, travel as a region of compression. (b) *S*, or shear, waves, like vibrations in a bowl of jelly, travel as displacements perpendicular to the direction of travel. *S* waves tend to travel more slowly than *P* waves and cannot travel through liquids.

the waves' direction of travel (Figure 20-4b). That means that *S* waves distort the material but do not compress it. Normal sound waves are pressure waves, whereas the water waves you can surf on, and vibrations you see in a bowl of jelly, are shear waves. Because *P* waves are compression waves, they can move through a liquid. *S* waves can move along the surface of a liquid, but not through it. A glass of water can't shimmy like jelly because a liquid does not have the rigidity required to transmit *S* waves.

The *P* and *S* waves caused by an earthquake do not travel in straight lines or at constant speed within Earth. The waves may reflect off boundaries between layers of different density, or they may be refracted as they pass through a boundary. In addition, the gradual increase in temperature and density toward Earth's center means the speed of sound increases as

■ **Figure 20-3**

A seismograph in northern Canada made this record of seismic waves from an earthquake in Mexico. The first vibrations, *P* waves, arrived 11 minutes after the quake, but the slower *S* waves took 20 minutes to make the journey.

Studying an Unseen World

How can studying what can't be seen save your life? Science tells us how nature works, and the basis for scientific knowledge is evidence gathered through observation. But much of the natural world can't be observed directly because it is too small, or far away, or deep underground. Yet geologists describe molten rock deep inside Earth, and biologists discuss the structure of genetic molecules. So how can these scientists know about things they can't observe directly?

A virus, which can be as common as a cold or as deadly as Ebola, contains a tiny bit of genetic information in the form of a DNA molecule. You have surely had a virus, but you've never seen one. Even under the best electron microscopes, a virus can be seen only as a hazy pattern of shadows. Nevertheless scientists know enough about them to devise ingenious ways to protect us from viral disease.

A virus is DNA hidden inside a protective coat of protein molecules, which is a rigid molecular lattice almost like a mineral. In fact, a culture of viruses can be crystallized, and the shapes of the crystals reveal the shape and structure of the virus. Unlike a crystal of calcite, however, a crystal of viruses also contains genetic information.

Scientists can make a vaccine to protect against a certain virus if they can identify a unique molecular pattern on the protein coat. The vaccine is harmless but contains that same pattern and trains your body's immune system to recognize the pattern and attack it. Vaccines significantly reduce the danger of common illness such as chicken pox and influenza, and they have virtually wiped out devastating diseases like polio and smallpox in the developed world. Researchers are currently working on a vaccine for HIV/AIDS that would potentially save millions of lives.

Even though viruses are too small to see, scientists can use chains of inference and the interaction of theory and evidence to deduce the structure of a virus. Whether it is a virus or the roots of a volcano, science takes us into realms beyond human experience and allows us to see the unseen.

The electron microscope allows biologists to deduce the elegant structure of the virus that causes the common infection called pink eye. (From *Virus Ultrastructure: Electron Micrograph Images.* Copyright 1995 by Linda M. Stannard. Reprinted with permission from Linda M. Stannard. Found at: www.web.uct.ac.za/depts/mmi/stannard/adeno.html)

---

well. These changes cause sound waves to be refracted as they travel through Earth's interior, meaning that, instead of following straight lines, seismic waves curve away from the denser, hotter central regions. Geoscientists can use the arrival times of reflected and refracted seismic waves from distant earthquakes to construct a model of Earth's interior.

Such studies confirm that the interior consists of three parts: a central core, a thick mantle, and a thin crust. S waves provide an important clue to the nature of the core. When an earthquake occurs, no direct S waves pass through the core to register on seismographs on the opposite side of Earth, as if the core were casting a shadow (■ Figure 20-5). The absence of S waves shows that the core is mostly liquid, and the size of the S-wave shadow fixes the size of the core at about 55 percent of Earth's radius. Mathematical models predict that the core is also hot (about 6000 K), dense (about 14 g/cm^3), and composed of iron and nickel.

Earth's core is as hot as the surface of the sun, but it is under such tremendous pressure that the material cannot vaporize. Because of its high temperature, most of the core is a liquid. Nearer the center the material is under even higher pressure,

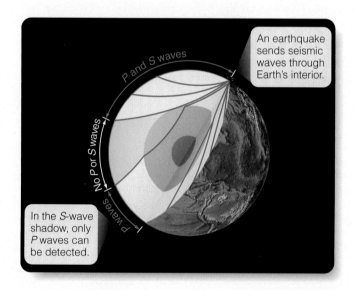

■ Figure 20-5

P and *S* waves give you clues to the structure of Earth's interior. No direct *S* waves from an earthquake reach the side of Earth opposite their source, indicating that Earth's core is liquid. The size of the *S* wave "shadow" tells you the size of the liquid outer part of the core.

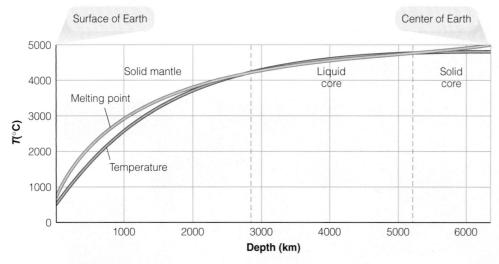

■ Figure 20-6

Theoretical models combined with observations of the velocity of seismic waves reveal the temperature inside Earth (blue line). The melting point of the material (red line) is determined by its composition and by the pressure. In the mantle and in the inner core, the melting point is higher than the existing temperature, and the material is not molten.

alloy, an even better electrical conductor than copper, the material commonly used for electrical wiring. The rotation of this convecting, conducting liquid generates Earth's magnetic field in a process called the dynamo effect (■ Figure 20-7). That is the same process that generates the solar magnetic field in the convective layers of the sun (see Chapter 8), and you will see it again when you explore other planets.

Earth's magnetic field protects it from the solar wind. Blowing outward from the sun at about 400 km/s, the solar wind consists of ionized gases carrying a small part of the sun's magnetic field. When the solar wind encounters Earth's magnetic field, it is deflected like water flowing around a boulder in a stream. The surface where the solar wind is first deflected is called the **bow shock**, and the cavity dominated by Earth's magnetic field is called the **magnetosphere** (■ Figure 20-8a). High-energy particles from the solar wind leak into the magnetosphere and become trapped within Earth's magnetic field to produce the **Van Allen belts** of radiation. You will see in later chapters that all planets that have magnetic fields have bow shocks, magnetospheres, and radiation belts.

which in turn raises the melting point so high that the material cannot melt (■ Figure 20-6). That is why there is an inner core of solid iron and nickel. Estimates suggest the inner core's radius is about 22 percent that of Earth.

The paths of seismic waves in the mantle, the layer of dense rock that lies between the molten core and the crust, show that it is not molten, but it is not precisely solid either. Mantle material behaves like a **plastic,** a material with the properties of a solid but capable of flowing under pressure. The asphalt used in paving roads is a common example of a plastic. It shatters if struck with a sledgehammer, but it bends under the steady weight of a heavy truck. Just below Earth's crust, where the pressure is less than at greater depths, the mantle is most plastic.

Earth's rocky crust is made up of low-density rocks and floats on the denser mantle. The crust is thickest under the continents, up to 60 km thick, and thinnest under the oceans, where it is only about 10 km thick. Unlike the mantle, the crust is brittle and can break when it is stressed.

Although Earth's core is only 2000 miles from you, it is completely inaccessible. Earth's seismic activity reveals some of Earth's innermost secrets. But there is another source of evidence about Earth's interior—its magnetic field.

The Magnetic Field

Apparently, Earth's magnetic field is a direct result of its rapid rotation and its molten metallic core. Internal heat forces the liquid core to circulate with convection while Earth's rotation turns it about an axis. The core is a highly conductive iron–nickel

■ Figure 20-7

The dynamo effect couples convection in the liquid core with Earth's rotation to produce electric currents that are believed to be responsible for Earth's magnetic field.

Magnetosphere: the region controlled by the planet's magnetic field

Bow shock

Solar wind

Radiation belts

a

Dark clouds silhouetted against the much higher aurora

Rays follow Earth's magnetic field.

b

■ **Figure 20-8**

(a) Earth's magnetic field dominates space around Earth by deflecting the solar wind and trapping high-energy particles in radiation belts. The magnetic field lines enter Earth's atmosphere around the north and south magnetic poles. (b) Powerful currents flow down along the magnetic field lines near the poles and excite gas atoms to emit photons, creating auroras. Colors are produced as different atoms are excited. Note the meteor (shooting star). (Jimmy Westlake)

Earth's magnetic field produces the dramatic and beautiful auroras, glowing rays and curtains of light in the upper atmosphere (Figure 20-8b). The solar wind carries charged particles past Earth's extended magnetic field, and this generates tremendous electrical currents that flow into Earth's atmosphere near the north and south magnetic poles (see Chapter 8). The currents ionize gas atoms in Earth's atmosphere, and when the ionized atoms capture electrons and recombine, they produce an emission spectrum as if they were part of a vast "neon" sign (see Chapter 7).

Although you can be confident that Earth's magnetic field is generated within its molten core, many mysteries remain. For example, rocks retain traces of the magnetic field in which they solidify, and some contain fields that point backward. That is, they imply that Earth's magnetic field was reversed at the time they solidified. Careful analysis of such rocks indicates that Earth's field has reversed itself in a very irregular pattern, on average every 700,000 years or so during the past 30 million years, with the north magnetic pole becoming the south magnetic pole and vice versa. The reversals are poorly understood, but they may be related to changes in the core's convection.

Convection in Earth's core is important because it generates the magnetic field. As you will see in the next section, convection in the mantle constantly remakes Earth's surface.

Earth's Active Crust

Earth's crust is composed of low-density rock that floats on the mantle. The image of a rock floating may seem odd, but recall that the rock of the mantle is very dense. Also, just below the crust, the mantle rock tends to be highly plastic, so great sections of low-density crust do indeed float on the semi-liquid mantle like great lily pads floating on a pond.

The motion of the crust and the erosive action of water make Earth's crust highly active. Read **The Active Earth** on pages 434–435 and notice three important points and six new terms:

❶ *Plate tectonics*, the motion of crustal plates, produces much of the geological activity on Earth. Plates spreading apart can form *rift valleys*, or, on the ocean floor, *midocean rises* where molten rock solidifies to form *basalt*. A plate sliding into a *subduction zone* can trigger volcanism, and the collision of plates can produce *folded mountain ranges*. Chains of volcanoes such as the Hawaiian islands can result when a plate moves horizontally across a hot spot.

❷ Notice how the continents on Earth's surface have moved and changed over periods of hundreds of millions of years. A hundred million years is only 0.1 billion years, so sections of Earth's crust are in rapid motion relative to the 4.6 billion-year age of the planet.

3 Most of the geological features you know—mountain ranges, the Grand Canyon, and even the familiar outline of the continents—are recent products of Earth's active surface. Earth's surface is constantly renewed. The oldest rocks on Earth, small crystals of the mineral zircon from western Australia, are 4.4 billion years old. Most of the crust is much younger than that. Most of the mountains and valleys you see around you are no more than a few tens of millions of years old.

The average speed of plate movement is slow, but sudden movements do occur. Plate margins can stick, accumulate stress, and then release it suddenly. For example, that's what happened in 2004 along a major subduction zone in the Indian Ocean. The total motion was as much as 15 meters, and the resulting earthquake caused devastating tsunamis (tidal waves). Every day, minor earthquakes occur on moving faults, and the stress that builds in those faults that are sticking will eventually be released in major earthquakes.

Earth's active crust explains why Earth contains so few impact craters. The moon is richly cratered, but Earth's surface has only about 150 impact craters. Plate tectonics and erosion have destroyed all but the most recent craters on Earth.

You can see that Earth's geology is dominated by two dramatic forces. Heat rising from the interior drives plate tectonics. Just below the thin crust of solid rock lies a churning molten layer that rips the crust to fragments and pushes the pieces about like rafts of wood on a pond. The second force modifying the crust is water. It falls as rain and snow and tears down mountains, erodes river valleys, and washes any raised ground into the sea. Tectonics builds up mountains and continents, and then erosion rips them down.

SCIENTIFIC ARGUMENT

What evidence indicates that Earth has a liquid metal core?
A good scientific argument focuses on evidence. In this case, the evidence is indirect because you can never visit Earth's core. Seismic waves from distant earthquakes pass through Earth, but a certain kind of wave, the *S* type, does not pass through the core. Because the *S* waves cannot move through a liquid, scientists conclude that Earth's core is partly liquid. Earth's magnetic field is further evidence of a liquid metallic core. The theory for the generation of magnetic fields, the dynamo effect, requires a moving, conducting liquid (for a planet) or gas (for a star) in the interior. If Earth's core were not partly a liquid metal, it would not be able to generate a magnetic field.

Two different kinds of evidence tell you that our planet has a liquid core. Can you build a new argument? **What evidence can you cite to support the theory of plate tectonics?**

20-4 Earth's Atmosphere

YOU CAN'T TELL THE STORY of Earth without mentioning its atmosphere. Not only is it necessary for life, but it is also intimately related to the crust. It affects the surface through erosion by wind and water, and in turn the chemistry of Earth's surface affects the composition of the atmosphere.

Origin of the Atmosphere

Until a few decades ago, planetary scientists thought the early Earth might have attracted small amounts of gases such as hydrogen, helium, and methane from the solar nebula to form a **primeval atmosphere.** According to that old hypothesis, slow decay of radioactive elements eventually heated Earth's interior; melted it; caused it to differentiate into core, mantle, and crust; and triggered widespread volcanism.

When a volcano erupts, 50 to 80 percent of the gas released is water vapor. The rest is mostly carbon dioxide, nitrogen, and smaller amounts of sulfur gases such as hydrogen sulfide—the rotten-egg gas that you smell if you visit geothermal pools and geysers such as those at Yellowstone National Park. These gases could have diluted the primeval atmosphere and eventually produced a **secondary atmosphere** rich in carbon dioxide, nitrogen, and water vapor.

In contrast, a modern understanding of planet building shows that Earth formed so rapidly that it was substantially heated by the impacts of infalling material, as well as by radioactive decay. If Earth's surface was molten as it formed, then outgassing would have been continuous, and the early atmosphere would have been rich in carbon dioxide, nitrogen, and water vapor from the beginning. In other words, planetary scientists now think Earth went straight to the volcanic "secondary atmosphere" and never had a hydrogen-rich primeval atmosphere. You will find in Chapter 26 that the lack of hydrogen in Earth's original atmosphere has important implications for how life began on our planet.

Astronomers also have suspected that some of the abundant water on Earth arrived late in the formation process as a bombardment of volatile-rich planetesimals. These icy bodies, the theory goes, were scattered by the growing mass of the outer planets and by the outward migration of Saturn, Uranus, and Neptune. The inner solar system, including Earth, would then have been bombarded by a storm of comets, some of which could have supplied some or all of Earth's water. That hypothesis once faced a serious objection. Spectroscopic studies of a few comets revealed that the ratio of deuterium to hydrogen in comets does not match the ratio in the water on Earth. Some astronomers thought this meant that the water now on Earth could not have arrived in cometlike planetesimals. However, studies of Comet LINEAR, which broke up in 1999 as it passed near the sun, show that the water in that comet had a ratio of isotopes

The Active Earth

1 Our world is an astonishingly active planet. Not only is it rich in water and therefore subject to rapid erosion, but its crust is divided into moving sections called plates. Where plates spread apart, lava wells up to form new crust; where plates push against each other, they crumple the crust to form mountains. Where one plate slides over another, you see volcanism. This process is called **plate tectonics,** referring to the Greek word for "builder." (An architect is literally an arch builder.)

A typical view of planet Earth

Mountains are common on Earth, but they erode away rapidly because of the abundant water.

William K. Hartmann

Janet Seeds

A **rift valley** forms where continental plates begin to pull apart. The Red Sea has formed where Africa has begun to pull away from the Arabian peninsula.

Midocean rise

Red Sea

Midocean rise

National Geophysical Data Center

1a Evidence of plate tectonics was first found in ocean floors, where plates spread apart and magma rises to form **midocean rises** made of rock called **basalt,** a rock typical of solidified lava. Radioactive dating shows that the basalt is younger near the midocean rise. Also, the ocean floor carries less sediment near the midocean rise. As Earth's magnetic field reverses back and forth, it is recorded in the magnetic fields frozen into the basalt. This produces a magnetic pattern in the basalt that shows that the seafloor is spreading away from the midocean rise.

1b A **subduction zone** is a deep trench where one plate slides under another. Melting releases low-density magma that rises to form volcanoes such as those along the northwest coast of North America, including Mount St. Helens.

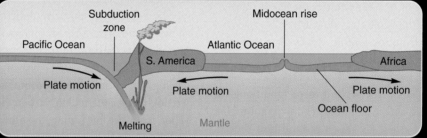

Subduction zone

Midocean rise

Pacific Ocean

Atlantic Ocean

S. America

Africa

Plate motion

Plate motion

Plate motion

Ocean floor

Melting

Mantle

Subduction zone

Hawaiian-Emperor chain

Subduction zone

Hawaii

Appalachian Mountains

Midocean rise

Ural Mountains

Himalaya Mountains

Red Sea

Midocean rise

Andes Mountains

Midocean rise

Subduction zone

1c Hot spots caused by rising magma in the mantle can poke through a plate and cause volcanism such as that in Hawaii. As the Pacific plate has moved northwestward, the hot spot has punched through to form a chain of volcanic islands, now mostly worn below sea level. **Folded mountain ranges** can form where plates push against each other. For example, the Ural Mountains lie between Europe and Asia, and the Himalaya Mountains are formed by India pushing north into Asia. The Appalachian Mountains are the remains of a mountain range thrust up when North America was pushed against Africa.

1d The floor of the Pacific Ocean is sliding into subduction zones in many places around its perimeter. This pushes up mountains such as the Andes and triggers earthquakes and active volcanism all around the Pacific in what is called the Ring of Fire. In places such as southern California, the plates slide past each other, causing frequent earthquakes.

National Geophysical Data Center

Hawaii

Yellow lines on this globe mark plate boundaries. Red dots mark earthquakes since 1980. Earthquakes within the plate, such as those at Hawaii, are related to volcanism over hot spots in the mantle.

Continental Drift

Not long ago, Earth's continents came together to form one continent.

Pangaea

200 million years ago

Pangaea broke into a northern and a southern continent.

Laurasia

Gondwanalan

135 million years ago

Notice India moving north toward Asia.

65 million years ago

The continents are still drifting on the "plastic" upper mantle.

Today

2 The floor of the Atlantic Ocean is not being subducted. It is locked to the continents and is pushing North and South America away from Europe and Africa at about 3 cm per year, a motion called *continental drift*. Radio astronomers can measure this motion by timing and comparing radio signals from pulsars using European and American radio telescopes. Roughly 200 million years ago, North and South America were joined to Europe and Africa. Evidence of that lies in similar fossils and similar rocks and minerals found in the matching parts of the continents. Notice how North and South America fit against Europe and Africa like a puzzle.

Mike Seeds

Formation of Grand Canyon
Age of dinosaurs
Formation of Earth
Heavy bombardment
Breakup of Pangaea
? Oldest fossil life
First animals emerge on land

4.6   4   3   2   1   Now

Billions of years ago

3 Plate tectonics pushes up mountain ranges and causes bulges in the crust, and water erosion wears the rock away. The Colorado River began cutting the Grand Canyon only about 10 million years ago when the Colorado plateau warped upward under the pressure of moving plates. That sounds like a long time ago, but it is only 0.01 billion years. A mile down, at the bottom of the canyon, lie rocks 0.57 billion years old, the roots of an earlier mountain range that stood as high as the Himalayas. It was pushed up, worn away to nothing, and covered with sediment long ago. Many of the geological features we know on Earth have been produced by relatively recent events.

similar to water on Earth. Those data suggest that there may be major differences in composition among comets. Icy planetesimals that formed far from the sun may be richer in deuterium, while those that formed closer to the orbit of Jupiter may contain water with isotope ratios more like those in Earth's water. This is a subject of continuing research, and it shows that the origin of Earth's atmosphere and oceans is yet to be fully understood.

In whatever way Earth's atmosphere originated, the mix of gases must have changed over time. The young atmosphere would have been rich in water vapor, carbon dioxide, and other gases. As it cooled, the water condensed to form the first oceans. Carbon dioxide is easily soluble in water—which is why carbonated beverages are so easy to manufacture—and the first oceans began to absorb atmospheric carbon dioxide. Once in solution, the carbon dioxide reacted with dissolved substances in the seawater to form silicon dioxide, limestone, and other mineral sediments in the ocean floor, freeing the seawater to absorb more carbon dioxide. Thanks to those chemical reactions in the oceans, the carbon dioxide was transferred from the atmosphere to seafloor sediments.

When Earth was young, its atmosphere had no free oxygen, that is, oxygen not combined with other elements. Oxygen is very reactive and quickly forms oxides in the soil or combines with iron and other substances dissolved in water. Only the action of plant life keeps a steady supply of oxygen in Earth's atmosphere via photosynthesis, which makes energy for plants by absorbing carbon dioxide and releasing oxygen. Beginning about 2 to 2.5 billion years ago, photosynthetic plants in the oceans had multiplied to the point where they made oxygen at a rate faster than chemical reactions could remove it from the atmosphere. After that time, atmospheric oxygen increased rapidly. (This topic will be discussed again in Chapter 26.) It is a **Common Misconception** that there is life on Earth because of oxygen. The truth is exactly the opposite: There is oxygen in Earth's atmosphere because of life. Most life forms on Earth do not need oxygen (except the minority of creatures that are animals, including us), and some are even poisoned by it.

An ozone molecule consists of three oxygen atoms linked together (O_3). Ozone molecules are very good at absorbing ultraviolet photons. Earth's lower atmosphere is now protected from ultraviolet radiation by an **ozone layer** about 15 to 30 km above the surface that exists because the atmosphere contains abundant ordinary oxygen (O_2) from which ozone is made. Because the atmosphere of the young Earth did not contain oxygen, an ozone layer could not form, and the sun's ultraviolet radiation was able to penetrate deep into the atmosphere. There the energetic ultraviolet photons would have broken up weaker molecules such as water (H_2O). The hydrogen from the water then escaped to space, and the oxygen formed oxides in the crust. Earth's atmosphere could not reach its present composition (■ Table 20-1) until it was protected by an ozone layer, and that required oxygen.

■ Table 20-1 | **Earth's Atmosphere**

Gas	Percent by Weight
N_2	75.5
O_2	23.1
Ar	1.29
CO_2	0.05
Ne	0.0013
He	0.00007
CH_4	0.0001
Kr	0.0003
H_2O (vapor)	1.7–0.06

Climate and Human Effects on the Atmosphere

If you climb to the top of a high mountain, you will find the temperature to be much lower than at sea level (■ Figure 20-9). Most clouds form at such altitudes. Higher still, you would find the air much colder, and so thin it could not protect you from the intense ultraviolet radiation in sunlight.

You can live on Earth's surface in safety because of Earth's atmosphere, but modern civilization is altering Earth's atmosphere in at least two serious ways, by adding carbon dioxide (CO_2) and by destroying ozone.

The concentration of CO_2 in Earth's atmosphere is important because CO_2 can trap heat in a process called the

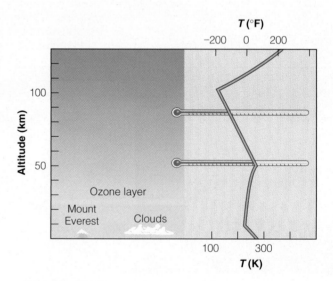

■ Figure 20-9

Thermometers placed in Earth's atmosphere at different levels would register the temperatures shown in the graph at the right. The lower few kilometers where you live are comfortable, but higher in the atmosphere the temperature is quite low. The ozone layer lies about 15 to 30 km above Earth's surface.

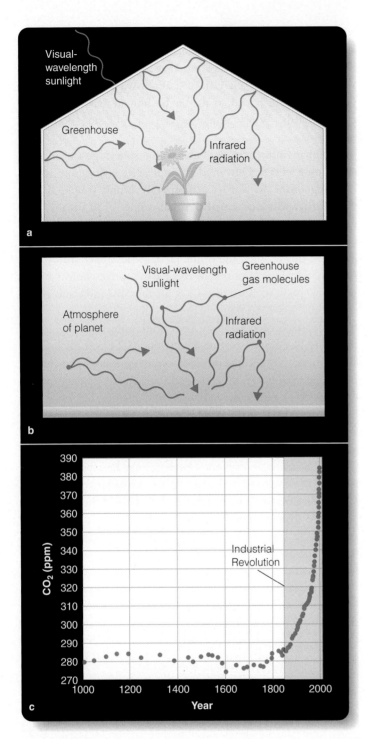

■ Figure 20-10

The greenhouse effect: (a) Visual-wavelength sunlight can enter a greenhouse and heat its contents, but the longer-wavelength infrared radiation cannot get out. (b) The same process can heat a planet's surface if its atmosphere contains greenhouse gases such as CO_2. (c) The concentration of CO_2 in Earth's atmosphere as measured in Antarctic ice cores remained roughly constant for thousands of years until the beginning of the Industrial Revolution around the year 1800. Since then it has increased by more than 30 percent. Evidence from proportions of carbon isotopes and oxygen in the atmosphere proves that most of the added CO_2 is the result of burning fossil fuels. (Graph adapted from a figure by Etheridge, Steele, Langenfelds, Francey, Barnola, and Morgan)

greenhouse effect (■ Figure 20-10a). When sunlight shines through the glass roof of a greenhouse, it heats the benches and plants inside. The warmed interior radiates infrared radiation, but the glass is opaque to infrared. Warm air in the greenhouse cannot mix with cooler air outside, so heat is trapped within the greenhouse, and the temperature climbs until the glass itself grows warm enough to radiate heat away as fast as the sunlight enters. This is the same process that heats a car when it is parked in the sun with the windows rolled up.

Earth's atmosphere is transparent to sunlight, and when the ground absorbs the sunlight, it grows warmer and radiates at infrared wavelengths. However, CO_2 makes the atmosphere less transparent to infrared radiation, so infrared radiation from the warm surface is absorbed by the atmosphere and cannot escape back into space. That traps heat and makes Earth warmer (Figure 20-10b).

It is a **Common Misconception** that the greenhouse effect is only bad. Evidence indicates that Earth has had a greenhouse effect for its entire history. Without the greenhouse effect, Earth presently would be at least 30°C (54°F) colder and uninhabitable for humans. The problem is that human civilization is adding CO_2 to the atmosphere more rapidly than it can be naturally removed, thereby increasing the intensity of the greenhouse effect.

CO_2 is not the only greenhouse gas. Water vapor, methane, and other gases also help warm Earth, but CO_2 is the most important. For 4 billion years, natural processes on Earth have removed CO_2 from the atmosphere and buried the carbon in the form of limestone, coal, oil, and natural gas. Since the beginning of the Industrial Revolution in the late 18th century, humans have been digging up lots of carbon-rich fuels, burning them to get energy, and releasing CO_2 back into the atmosphere. It is a **Common Misconception** that human output of CO_2 is minor compared to natural sources such as volcanoes. Careful measurements of carbon isotope ratios and relative amounts of CO_2 versus O_2 in the atmosphere show that the CO_2 added to the atmosphere since the year 1800 is mostly or entirely due to human burning of fossil fuels. Estimates are that the amount of CO_2 in Earth's atmosphere could double during the 21st century. The increased concentration of CO_2 is increasing the greenhouse effect and warming Earth in what is known as **global warming.** Studies of the growth rings in very old trees show that the average Earth climate had been cooling for most of the last 1000 years, but the 20th century reversed that trend with a rise of 0.56 to 0.92°C (1.01 to 1.66°F). The amount of warming to expect in the future is difficult to predict because Earth's climate is critically sensitive to a number of different factors, not just the abundance of greenhouse gases. For example, a planet's **albedo** is the fraction of the sunlight hitting it that gets reflected away. A planet with an albedo of 1 would be perfectly white, and a planet with an albedo of 0 would be perfectly black. Earth's overall albedo is 0.39, meaning it reflects back into space 39 percent of the sunlight that hits it. Much of that reflection is caused by clouds, and the formation of clouds depends critically on the presence of water vapor in the upper atmosphere, the temperature of the upper atmosphere, and the patterns of atmospheric circulation. Even a small change in any of these factors could change Earth's albedo and thus its climate. For example, a slight warming should increase water vapor in the atmosphere, and water vapor is another greenhouse gas that would enhance the warming. But increased water vapor could increase cloud cover, increase Earth's albedo, and partially reduce the warming. On the other hand, high icy clouds tend to enhance the greenhouse effect. The situation is complex, and therefore precise calculations of future warming are not easy to make. Also, even small changes in temperature can alter circulation patterns in the atmosphere and in the oceans, and the consequences of such changes are very difficult to model.

Even though the future is uncertain, general trends now point to substantial continued warming. Mountain glaciers have melted back dramatically since the 19th century. Measurements show that polar ice in the form of permafrost, ice shelves, and ice on the open Arctic Ocean is melting. It is a **Common Misconception** that the observed warming of the Earth is due to natural causes rather than the greenhouse effect. Regular and predictable changes in Earth's axis inclination and orientation and in the shape of its orbit, called Milankovitch cycles (see Chapter 3), currently would be driving Earth's climate toward lower, not higher, temperatures. Also, careful observations during recent decades by space probes indicate the sun has not been increasing measurably in luminosity. The observed warming must be strong to be occurring in the face of opposing astronomical effects.

Although changes are small now, it is a serious issue for the future. Even a small rise in temperatures will dramatically affect agriculture, not only through rising temperatures but also through changes in rainfall. It is a **Common Misconception** that all of Earth will warm at the same rate if there is global warming. Models predict that although most of North American will grow warmer and drier, Europe initially will become cooler and wetter. Also, the melting of ice on polar landmasses such as Greenland can cause a rise in sea levels that will flood coastal regions and alter shore environments. A modest rise will cover huge low-lying areas such as the entire state of Florida.

There is no doubt that civilization is warming Earth through an enhanced greenhouse effect, but a remedy is difficult to imagine. Reducing the amount of CO_2 and other greenhouse gases released to the atmosphere is difficult because modern society depends on burning fossil fuels for energy. Conserving forests is difficult because growing populations, especially in developing countries with large forest reserves, demand the wood and the agricultural land produced when forests are cut. Political, business, and economic leaders argue that the issue is uncertain, but all around the world scientists of stature have reached agreement: Global warming is real, is driven by human activity, and will change Earth. What humanity can or will do about it is uncertain.

Human influences on Earth's atmosphere go beyond the greenhouse effect. Our modern industrial civilization is also reducing ozone in Earth's atmosphere. Many people have a **Common Misconception** that ozone is bad because they hear it mentioned as a pollutant of city air, produced by auto emissions. Breathing ozone is bad for you, but, as you learned earlier in this chapter, the ozone layer in the upper atmosphere protects the lower atmosphere and Earth's surface from harmful solar UV photons. Ozone (O_3) is an unstable molecule and is chemically active. Certain chemicals called chlorofluorocarbons (CFCs), used for refrigeration, air conditioning, and some industrial processes, can destroy ozone. As these CFCs escape into the atmosphere, they become mixed into the ozone layer and convert the ozone back into normal oxygen molecules. Ordinary oxygen does not block ultraviolet radiation, so depleting the ozone layer causes an increase in ultraviolet radiation at Earth's surface. In small doses, ultraviolet radiation can produce a suntan, but in larger doses it can cause skin cancers.

The ozone layer over the Antarctic may be especially sensitive to CFCs. Starting in the late 1970s, the ozone concentration fell significantly over the Antarctic, and a hole in the ozone layer developed over the continent each October at the time of the Antarctic spring (■ Figure 20-11). Satellite and ground-based measurements showed the same thing beginning to happen at higher northern latitudes, with the amount of ultraviolet radiation reaching the ground increasing. This was an early warning that human activity is modifying Earth's atmosphere in a potentially dangerous way. Fortunately, as a result of that warning, international agreements banned most uses of CFCs, and the trend of ozone hole expansion seems to have slowed and may be reversing.

There is yet another **Common Misconception** that global warming and ozone depletion are two names for the same thing. Take careful note that the ozone hole is a second Earth environmental issue that is basically separate from global warming. The CO_2 and ozone problems in Earth's atmosphere are paralleled on Venus and Mars. When you study Venus in Chapter 22, you will discover a runaway greenhouse effect that has made the surface of the planet hot enough to melt lead. On Mars you will discover an atmosphere without an ozone layer. A few minutes of sunbathing on Mars would kill you. Once again, you can learn more about your own planet by studying the extreme conditions on other planets.

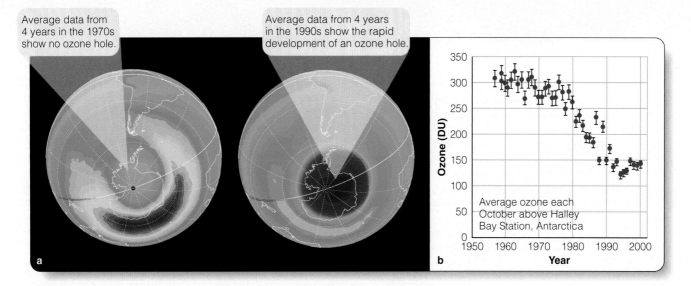

■ **Figure 20-11**

(a) Satellite observations of ozone concentrations over Antarctica are shown here as red for highest concentration and violet for lowest. Since the 1970s, a hole in the ozone layer has developed over the South Pole. (b) Although ozone depletion is most dramatic above the South Pole, ozone concentrations have declined at all latitudes. (NASA/GSFC/TOMS and Glenn Carver)

SCIENTIFIC ARGUMENT

Why does Earth's atmosphere contain little carbon dioxide and lots of oxygen?

Sometimes as you build a scientific argument, you must contradict what seems, at first glance, a simple truth. In this case, because volcanic outgassing releases mostly CO_2, N_2, and water vapor, you might expect Earth's atmosphere to be very rich in CO_2. Luckily for the human race, CO_2 is highly soluble in water, and Earth's surface temperature allows it to be covered with liquid water. The CO_2 dissolves in the oceans and combines with minerals in seawater to form deposits of silicon dioxide, limestone, and other mineral deposits. In this way, the CO_2 is removed from the atmosphere and buried in Earth's crust. Oxygen, in contrast, is highly reactive and forms oxides so easily you might expect it to be rare in the atmosphere. Happily for us animals, it is continually replenished as green plants release oxygen into Earth's atmosphere faster than chemical reactions can remove it. Were it not for liquid-water oceans and plant life, Earth would have a thick CO_2 atmosphere with no free oxygen.

Now follow up on your argument. **Why would an excess of CO_2 and a deficiency of free oxygen be harmful to all life on Earth in ways that go beyond mere respiration?**

What Are We? Scientific Imagineers

One of the most fascinating aspects of science is its power to reveal the unseen. That is, it reveals regions you can never visit. You saw this in earlier chapters when you studied the inside of the sun and stars, the surface of neutron stars, the event horizon around black holes, the cores of active galaxies, and more. In this chapter, you have "seen" Earth's core.

An engineer is a person who builds things, so you can call a person who imagines things an imagineer. Most creatures on Earth cannot imagine situations that do not exist, but humans have evolved the ability to say, "What if?" Our ancient ancestors could imagine what would happen if a tiger was hiding in the grass, and we can imagine the inside of Earth.

A poet can imagine the heart of Earth, and a great writer can imagine a journey to the center of Earth. In contrast, scientists use their imagination in a carefully controlled way. Guided by evidence and theory, they can imagine the molten core of our planet. As you read this chapter you saw the yellow-orange glow and felt the heat of the liquid iron, and you were a scientific imagineer.

Human imagination makes science possible and provides one of the great thrills of science—exploring beyond the limits of normal human experience.

Summary

- Earth is the standard of **comparative planetology (p. 425)** in the study of the Terrestrial planets because we know it best and because it contains all of the phenomena found on the other Terrestrial planets.

- Our discussion of the Terrestrial planets considers Earth, the moon, Mercury, Venus, and Mars. Earth's moon is included because it is a complex world and makes a striking comparison with Earth.

- The Terrestrial worlds differ mainly in size, but they all have low-density crusts, **mantles (p. 426)** of dense rock, and metallic cores.

- Comparative planetology warns you to expect that cratered surfaces are old, that heat flowing out of a planet drives geological activity, and that the nature of a planet's atmosphere depends on the size of the planet and its temperature.

- At some point early in its history Earth was hot enough to be completely molten, which caused it to differentiate into layers of different density.

- Earth has passed through four stages as it has evolved: (1) differentiation, (2) cratering, (3) flooding by lava and water, and (4) slow surface evolution. The other Terrestrial planets and the moon also passed through the same stages, which had different effects and durations depending on the specific properties of each body.

- Earth is peculiar in that it has large amounts of liquid water on its surface, and that water drives strong erosion that alters the surface geology.

- Earth is also peculiar in that it is the only known home for life.

- **Seismic waves (p. 429)** generated by earthquakes can be detected by **seismographs (p. 429)** all over the world and can reveal Earth's internal structure.

- **Pressure (P) waves (p. 429)** can travel through a liquid, but **shear (S) waves (p. 429)** cannot. Observations show that S waves cannot pass through Earth's core, and that is evidence that the core is liquid. Measurements of heat flowing outward from the interior, combined with mathematical models, reveal that the core is very hot and composed of iron and nickel.

- Although Earth's crust is brittle and breaks under stress, the mantle is **plastic (p. 431)** and can deform and flow under pressure.

- Earth's magnetic field is generated by the dynamo effect in the liquid, convecting, rotating, conducting core. The magnetic field shields Earth from the solar wind by producing a **bow shock (p. 431)** and a **magnetosphere (p. 431)** around the planet. Radiation belts called the **Van Allen belts (p. 431)**, as well as aurora displays, are also produced by the magnetic field.

- Earth is dominated by **plate tectonics (p. 434)**, which breaks the crust into moving sections. Plate tectonics is driven by heat flowing upward from the interior.

- Tectonic plates are made of low-density, brittle rock that floats on the hotter plastic upper layers of the mantle. **Rift valleys (p. 434)** can be produced where plates begin pulling away from each other.

- New crust is formed along **midocean rises (p. 434)** where molten rock solidifies to form **basalt (p. 434)**. Crust is destroyed where it sinks into the mantle along **subduction zones (p. 434)**. Volcanism and earthquakes are common along the edge of the plates.

- The motion of a plate across a hot spot can produce a chain of volcanic islands such as the Hawaiian island chain. Hot-spot volcanism is not related to subduction zones.

- The continents are drifting slowly on the plastic mantle, and their arrangement changes with time. Where they collide, they can form **folded mountain ranges (p. 434)**.

- Most geological features on Earth, such as mountain ranges and the Grand Canyon, have been formed recently. The first billion years of Earth's geology are almost entirely erased by plate tectonics and erosion.

- Because Earth formed hot, it never had a **primeval atmosphere (p. 433)** rich in hydrogen and helium that was later replaced by a **secondary atmosphere (p. 433)** baked out of the interior.

- Because Earth formed in a molten state, its first atmosphere was probably mostly carbon dioxide, nitrogen, and water vapor. Most of the carbon dioxide eventually dissolved in seawater and was added to ocean sediments. Plant life has added oxygen to the atmosphere.

- Ultraviolet photons can break up water molecules in a planet's atmosphere, but as soon as Earth had enough oxygen, an **ozone layer (p. 436)** could form high in Earth's atmosphere. The ozone absorbs ultraviolet photons and protects water molecules.

- The **albedo (p. 437)** of a planet is the fraction of sunlight hitting it that it reflects into space. Small changes in the albedo of Earth caused by changes in clouds and atmospheric currents can have a dramatic effect on climate.

- The **greenhouse effect (p. 437)** can warm a planet if gases such as carbon dioxide in the atmosphere are transparent to light but opaque to infrared. The natural greenhouse effect warms Earth and makes it comfortable for life, but greenhouse gases added by industrial civilization are responsible for **global warming (p. 437)**.

- Measurement of carbon isotope ratios and carbon dioxide versus oxygen abundances make it clear that the CO_2 added to the atmosphere since 1800 is predominantly from burning of fossil fuels. Observations and model calculations have eliminated other candidate causes for the current warming such as natural climate cycles or variations in the sun's output.

- The ozone layer high in Earth's atmosphere protects the surface from ultraviolet radiation, but certain chemicals called chlorofluorocarbons released in industrial processes attack the ozone layer and thin it. This is allowing more harmful ultraviolet radiation to reach Earth's surface.

Review Questions

1. Why would you include the moon in a comparison of the Terrestrial planets?
2. In what ways is Earth peculiar among the Terrestrial planets?
3. What are the four stages of planetary development?
4. How do you know that Earth differentiated?
5. What evidence can you cite that Earth's metallic core is liquid?
6. How are earthquakes in Hawaii different from those in Southern California?
7. What characteristics must Earth's core have in order to generate a magnetic field?
8. How do island chains located in the centers of tectonic plates such as the Hawaiian islands help you understand plate tectonics?
9. What evidence can you cite that the Atlantic Ocean is growing wider?
10. How is your concept of Earth's first atmosphere related to the speed with which Earth formed from the solar nebula?
11. What has produced the oxygen in Earth's atmosphere?
12. How does the increasing abundance of CO_2 in Earth's atmosphere cause a rise in Earth's temperature?
13. Why would a decrease in the density of the ozone layer cause public health problems?
14. **How Do We Know?** How is deducing the structure of a virus like finding the composition of Earth's core?

Discussion Questions

1. If you orbited a planet in another solar system and discovered oxygen in its atmosphere, what might you expect to find on its surface?

2. If liquid water is rare on the surface of planets, then most Terrestrial planets must have CO_2-rich atmospheres. Correct? Why?

Problems

1. In Figure 20-3, the earthquake occurred 7440 km from the seismograph. How fast did the *P* waves travel in km/s? How fast did the *S* waves travel?

2. What percentage of Earth's volume is taken up by its metallic core?

3. If the Atlantic seafloor is spreading at 3 cm/year and is now 6400 km wide, how long ago were the continents in contact?

4. The Hawaiian-Emperor chain of undersea volcanoes is about 7500 km long, and the Pacific plate is moving 9.2 cm a year. How old is the oldest detectable volcano in the chain? What has happened to older volcanoes in the chain?

5. From Hawaii to the bend in the Hawaiian-Emperor chain is about 4000 km. Use the speed of plate motion given in Problem 4 to estimate how long ago the direction of plate motion changed. (Note that the San Andreas fault in southern California became active at about the same time!)

6. Calculate the age of the Grand Canyon as a percent of Earth's age.

Learning to Look

1. Look at the globe of Earth shown on page 435 and look for volcanoes scattered over the Pacific Ocean. What is producing these volcanoes?

2. In what ways is the photo at the right a typical view of the surface of planet Earth? How is it unusual among planets in general?

William K. Hartmann

3. What do you see in this photo that suggests heat is flowing out of Earth's interior?

USGS

21 | The Moon and Mercury: Comparing Airless Worlds

Guidepost

Want to fly to the moon? You will need to pack more than your lunch. There is no air and no water, and the sunlight is strong enough to kill you. Mercury is the same kind of world. Take shelter in the shade, and you will freeze to death in moments. Earth seems normal to you, and other worlds are, well, unearthly, but they are related to Earth in surprising ways. Exploring these two airless worlds will answer five essential questions:

— **Why is the moon airless and cratered?**

— **How did the moon form and evolve?**

— **In what ways is Mercury similar to, and different from, the moon?**

— **How did Mercury form and evolve?**

— **How are the histories of the moon and Mercury connected to Earth?**

You are beginning your detailed study of planets by exploring airless worlds; in the next chapter you will move on to bigger planets with atmospheres. They are not necessarily more interesting places, but they are just a bit less unearthly.

When astronauts stepped onto the surface of the moon, they found an unearthly world with no air, no water, weak gravity, and a dusty, cratered surface. Through comparative planetology, the moon reveals a great deal about our own beautiful Earth. (JSC/NASA)

> *That's one small step for [a] man . . .*
> *one giant leap for mankind.*
>
> — NEIL ARMSTRONG, ON THE MOON

> *Beautiful, beautiful. Magnificent desolation.*
>
> — EDWIN E. (BUZZ) ALDRIN JR., ON THE MOON

IF YOU HAD BEEN THE FIRST PERSON to step onto the surface of the moon, what would you have said? Neil Armstrong responded to the historic significance of being the first human to step onto the surface of another world. Buzz Aldrin was second, and he responded to the moon itself. It *is* desolate, and it *is* magnificent. But it is not unusual. Many planets in the universe probably look like Earth's moon, and astronauts may someday walk on such worlds and compare them with our moon.

In this chapter, you will use comparative planetology to study the moon and Mercury, and you will continue following three important themes of planetary astronomy: impact cratering, internal heat flow, and giant impact-induced volcanism. These three themes will help you organize the flood of details astronomers have learned about the moon and Mercury.

21-1 The Moon

ONLY 12 PEOPLE HAVE STOOD on the moon, but planetary astronomers know it well. The photographs, measurements, and samples brought back to Earth paint a picture of an airless, ancient, battered crust, and a world created by a planetary catastrophe.

The View from Earth

A few billion years ago, the moon must have rotated faster than it does today, but Earth is over 80 times more massive than the moon (**Celestial Profile 3**), and its tidal forces on the moon are strong. Earth's gravity raised tidal bulges on the moon, and friction in the bulges has slowed the moon until it now rotates once each orbit, keeping the same side facing Earth. A moon whose rotation is locked to its planet is said to be **tidally coupled.** That is why we always see the same side of the moon; the back of the moon is never visible from Earth. The moon's familiar face has shone down on Earth since long before there were humans (■ Figure 21-1).

Based on what you already know, you can predict that the moon should have no atmosphere. It is a small world with an escape velocity too low to keep gas atoms and molecules from escaping into space. You can confirm your theory with even a small telescope. You see no clouds or other obvious traces of an atmosphere, and shadows near the **terminator,** the dividing line between

Earth's moon is about one-fourth the diameter of Earth. Its low density indicates that it contains little iron, but the size of its iron core and the amount of remaining heat are unknown. (NASA)

Celestial Profile 3: The Moon

Motion:

Average distance from Earth	3.84×10^5 km (center to center)
Eccentricity of orbit	0.055
Inclination of orbit to ecliptic	5.1°
Average orbital velocity	1.02 km/s
Orbital period (sidereal)	27.3 d
Orbital period (synodic)	29.5 d
Inclination of equator to orbit	6.7°

Characteristics:

Equatorial diameter	3.48×10^3 km
Mass	7.35×10^{22} kg (0.0123 $M_\oplus$)
Average density	3.36 g/cm³ (3.3 g/cm³ uncompressed)
Surface gravity	0.17 Earth gravity
Escape velocity	2.4 km/s (0.21 $V_\oplus$)
Surface temperature	−170° to 130°C (−275° to 265°F)
Average albedo	0.07

Personality Point:

Lunar superstitions are common. The words *lunatic* and *lunacy* come from *luna*, the moon. Someone who is *moonstruck* is supposed to be a bit nutty. Because the moon affects the ocean tides, many superstitions link the moon to water, to weather, and to women's cycle of fertility. According to legend, moonlight is supposed to be harmful to unborn children; but, on the plus side, moonlight rituals are said to remove warts.

The dark, smooth areas of the moon are called seas (*maria* in Latin).

Plato

Mare Imbrium

Mare Serenitatis

Kepler

Mare Crisium

Mare Tranquillitatis

Copernicus

Oceanus Procellarum

Mare Foecunditatis

Mare Nectaris

Mare Humorum

Mare Nubium

Tycho

Visual-wavelength image

Much of the surface is covered with craters on top of craters.

■ Figure 21-1

The side of the moon that faces Earth is a familiar sight. Craters have been named for famous scientists and philosophers, and the so-called seas have been given romantic names. Mare Imbrium is the Sea of Rains, and Mare Tranquillitatis is the Sea of Tranquillity. There is, in fact, no water on the moon. (Photo © UC Regents/Lick Observatory)

daylight and darkness, are sharp and black. There is no air on the moon to scatter light and soften shadows. Also, with even a small telescope you could watch stars disappear behind the **limb** of the moon—the edge of its disk—without dimming. Clearly, the moon is an airless (and, therefore, soundless) world.

The surface of the moon is divided into two dramatically different kinds of terrain. The lunar highlands are filled with jumbled mountains, but there are no folded mountain ranges like the ones on Earth. This shows that the moon has no plate tectonics. The mountains are pushed up by millions of impact craters one on top of the other. In fact, the highlands are saturated with craters, meaning that it would be impossible to form a new crater without destroying the equivalent of one old crater. In contrast the lowlands, about 3 km (2 mi) lower than the highlands, are smooth, dark plains called **maria,** Latin for "seas." (The singular of *maria* is **mare,** pronounced MAH-ray.) The first telescope observers thought these were bodies of water, but further examination showed that the maria are marked by ridges, faults, smudges, and scattered craters and can't be water. Rather, the maria are ancient lava flows that have apparently covered the older, cratered lowlands.

Those lava flows suggest volcanism, but only small traces of past volcanic activity are visible from Earth. No major volcanic peaks are visible on the moon, and no active volcanism has ever been detected. The lava flows that created the maria happened long ago and were much too fluid to build peaks. With a good telescope and some diligent searching you could see a few small domes pushed up by lava below the surface, and you could see long, winding channels called **sinuous rilles** (■ Figure 21-2). These channels are often found near the edges of the maria and were evidently cut by flowing lava. In some cases, such a channel may once have had a roof of solid rock, forming a lava tube. After the lava drained away, meteorite impacts collapsed the roof to form a sinuous rille. The view from Earth provides only hints of ancient volcanic activity associated with the maria.

Lava flows and impact cratering have dominated the history of the moon. Study **Impact Cratering** on pages 446–447 and notice three important points and five new terms:

1 Impact craters have certain distinguishing characteristics, such as their shape and the *ejecta, rays,* and *secondary craters* around them.

2 Lunar impact craters range from tiny pits formed by *micrometeorites* to giant *multiringed basins.*

3 Most of the craters on the moon are old; they were formed long ago when the solar system was young.

Meteorites strike the moon all the time, but large impacts are rare today. Astronomers estimate that meteorites with diameters of tens of meters strike the moon every few decades, but no one has ever seen such an impact with certainty. Small flashes of light have been seen on the dark side of the moon during showers of meteors, but those impacts must have been made by very small objects, perhaps only centimeters in size. No significant change has been seen on the moon since the invention of the telescope. As you will learn in Chapter 25, large impacts do happen on the moon and Earth, but they are quite rare, and nearly all of the lunar craters seen through telescopes date from the solar system's youth.

The lunar features visible from Earth allow you to begin constructing a tentative hypothesis to explain the history of the moon. Such a hypothesis provides a framework that will help you organize all of the details and observations (**How Do We Know? 21-1**). As the moon formed, its crust would have been heavily cratered by debris left over from the formation of the planets. Sometime after the cratering subsided, lava welled up from below the crust and flooded the lowlands, covering the craters there and forming the smooth maria. You can locate a few large craters on the maria such as Kepler and Copernicus in Figure 21-1, but note that the bright rays around them show that they are relatively young, because rays are darkened and erased by exposure to sunlight, solar wind, and micrometeorite bombardment. The maria are only

Hadley Rille is a sinuous rille near the edge of Mare Imbrium.

Faults where the crust has broken

The lunar highlands are saturated with craters on top of craters.

Apollo 15 found Hadley Rille to be a 1200-foot-deep lava channel.

The smooth maria are generally circular with faults and wrinkles in the old lava surface.

Visual-wavelength images

Ancient craters partly flooded by lava

■ **Figure 21-2**

Details visible in photographs show that meteorite impacts long ago covered the moon with craters, but that lava flooded out and filled the largest basins covering the craters there with smooth plains. (Hadley: NASA; Moon disk, highlands, and mare: © UC Regents/Lick Observatory)

lightly scarred by impacts and must be younger than the cratered highlands.

It is difficult to estimate the true age of any specific crater. In some cases, you can find **relative ages** by noting that a crater or its rays partially covers other craters. Clearly the crater on top must be younger than the craters on the bottom. Relative ages can be calibrated using radioactive ages of lunar samples, which indicate how the cratering rate decreased when the moon was young. Combining all this information, astronomers can study the size and number of craters on a section of the moon's surface and estimate that section's **absolute age** in years. The maria, containing few craters, appear to be 3 to 4 billion years old, and the highlands are older.

Earth-based observations allowed astronomers to begin telling the story of the moon's surface, but the view from Earth does not provide enough evidence. To really understand the history of the lunar surface, humans had to go there and bring back samples.

The Apollo Missions

On May 25, 1961, President John Kennedy committed the United States to landing a human being on the moon by 1970. Although the reasons for that decision related more to economics, international politics, and the stimulation of technology than to science, the Apollo program became a fantastic scientific adventure, including six expeditions to the surface of the moon that changed how we all think about Earth.

Flying to the moon is not particularly difficult. With powerful enough rockets and enough food, water, and air, it is a straightforward trip. Landing on the moon is more difficult but not impossible. The moon's gravity is only one-sixth that of Earth, and there is no atmosphere to disturb the trajectory of the spaceship. Getting to the moon isn't too hard, and landing is possible; the difficulty is doing both on one trip. The spaceship must carry food, water, and air for a number of days in space plus fuel and rockets for mid-course corrections and for a return to Earth. All of this adds up to a ship that is too massive to make a safe landing on the lunar surface. The solution was to take two spaceships to the moon, one to make the round-trip in and one to land in (■ Figure 21-3).

The command module was the long-term living space and command center for the trip. Three astronauts had to live in it for a week, and it had to carry all the life-support equipment, navigation instruments, computers, power packs, and so on for a week's jaunt in space. The lunar landing module (LM for short)

Impact Cratering

1 The craters that cover the moon and many other bodies in the solar system were produced by the high-speed impact of meteorites of all sizes. Meteorites striking the moon travel 10 to 70 km/s and can hit with the energy of many nuclear bombs.

A meteorite striking the moon's surface can deliver tremendous energy and can produce an impact crater 10 or more times larger in diameter than the meteorite. The vertical scale is exaggerated at right for clarity.

Impact Cratering

A meteorite approaches the lunar surface at high velocity.

On impact, the meteorite is deformed, heated, and vaporized.

The resulting explosion blasts out a round crater.

Slumping produces terraces in crater walls, and rebound can raise a central peak.

1a Lunar craters such as Euler, 27 km (17 mi) in diameter, look deep when you see them near the terminator where shadows are long, but a typical crater is only a fifth to a tenth as deep as its diameter, and large craters are even shallower.

Because craters are formed by shock waves rushing outward, by the rebound of the rock, and by the expansion of hot vapors, craters are almost always round, even when the meteorite strikes at a steep angle.

Debris blasted out of a crater is called ejecta, and it falls back to blanket the surface around the crater. Ejecta shot out along specific directions can form bright rays.

Euler

NASA

Visual-wavelength image

Rays

Tycho

Visual

Visual

NASA

NASA

1b Rock ejected from distant impacts can fall back to the surface and form smaller craters called **secondary craters**. The chain of craters here is a 45-km-long chain of secondary craters produced by ejecta from the large crater Copernicus 200 km out of the frame to the lower right.

Bright ejecta blankets and rays gradually darken as sunlight alters minerals and small meteorites stir the dusty surface. Bright rays are signs of youth. Rays from the crater Tycho, perhaps only 100 million years old, extend halfway around the moon.

2 Plum Crater (right), 40 m (130 ft) in diameter, was visited by Apollo 16 astronauts. Note the many smaller craters visible. Lunar craters range from giant impact basins to tiny pits in rocks struck by **micrometeorites,** meteorites of microscopic size.

Lunar rover

Sun glare in camera lens

NASA

Visual-wavelength images

Mare Orientale

Solidified lava

2a In larger craters, the deformation of the rock can form one or more inner rings concentric with the outer rim. The largest of these craters are called **multiringed basins.** In Mare Orientale on the west edge of the visible moon, the outermost ring is almost 900 km (550 mi) in diameter.

2b The energy of an impact can melt rock, some of which falls back into the crater and solidifies. When the moon was young, craters could also be flooded by lava welling up from below the crust.

A few meteorites found on Earth have been identified chemically as fragments of the moon's surface blasted into space by cratering impacts. The fragmented nature of these meteorites indicates that the moon's surface has been battered by impact craters.

NASA

3 Most of the craters on the moon were produced long ago when the solar system was filled with debris from planet building. As that debris was swept up, the cratering rate fell rapidly, as shown schematically below.

Meteorite from moon

Rate of Crater Formation

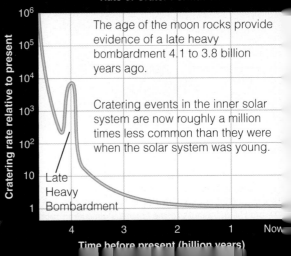

The age of the moon rocks provide evidence of a late heavy bombardment 4.1 to 3.8 billion years ago.

Cratering events in the inner solar system are now roughly a million times less common than they were when the solar system was young.

Cratering rate relative to present

10^6
10^5
10^4
10^3
10^2
10
1

Late Heavy Bombardment

4   3   2   1   Now

Time before present (billion years)

How Hypotheses and Theories Unify the Details

Why is playing catch more than just looking at the ball? Like any technical subject, science includes a mass of details, facts, figures, measurements, and observations. The flood of details can be overwhelming, but one of the most important characteristics of science comes to your rescue. The goal of science is not to discover more details but to explain the details with a unifying hypothesis or theory. A good theory is like a basket that makes it easier for you to carry a large assortment of details.

For example, when a psychologist begins studying the way the human eye and brain respond to moving objects, the data are a sea of detailed measurements and observations. Infants look at a moving ball for only moments, but older children look longer. Adults can concentrate longer on the moving ball, but their eyes move differently if they are given a stick to point with. Scans of brain activity show that different areas of the brain are active in different age subjects and under different circumstances.

From the data, the psychologist might form the hypothesis that the human brain processes visual information differently depending on its intended use. If you look at a baseball being rubbed in the hands of a pitcher, your brain processes the visual information one way. If you see a baseball flying at you and you have to catch it, your brain processes the information in a different way. The psychologist's theory brings all of the details into place as parts of a logical theory about the ability and necessity of action. Babies don't catch balls. Sometimes a ball is an object that might be rough or smooth, but sometimes it is an object to be caught. The brain responds appropriately.

The goal of science is to understand nature, not to memorize details. Whether scientists

When scientists create a hypothesis, it draws together a great many observations and measurements. (Phyllis Leber)

are psychologists studying brain functions or astronomers studying the formation of other worlds, they are trying to unify their data and explain it with a single hypothesis or theory.

Visual-wavelength image

■ **Figure 21-3**

Inside the lunar module, the two astronauts stood in a space hardly bigger than two telephone booths. The metal skin was so thin it was easily flexible, like metal foil, and the legs of the module, designed specifically for the moon's weak gravity, could not support the lander's weight on Earth. Only the upper half of the lander blasted off from the surface to return the astronauts to the command module in orbit around the moon. (NASA) was tacked to the front of the command module like a bicycle strapped to the front of the family camper. It carried only enough fuel and supplies for the short trip to the lunar surface, and it was built to minimize weight and maximize maneuverability.

The weaker gravity of the moon made the design of the LM simpler. Landing on Earth requires reclining couches for the astronauts, but the trip to the lunar surface involved smaller accelerations. In an early version of the LM, the astronauts sat on what looked like bicycle seats, but these were later scrapped to save weight. The astronauts had no seats at all in the LM, and once they began their descent and acquired weight, they stood at the controls held by straps, riding the LM like daredevils on a rocket surfboard.

When it lifted off from the lunar surface, the LM saved weight by leaving the larger descent rocket and support stage behind. Only the compartment containing the two astronauts, their instruments, and their cargo of rocks returned to the command module orbiting above. The astronauts in the LM blasting up from the lunar surface were again standing at the controls. The rocket engine that lifted them back into orbit around the moon was not much bigger than a dishwasher.

The most complicated part of the trip was the rendezvous and docking between the tiny remains of the LM and the command module. Aided by radar systems and computers, the two astronauts docked with the command module, transferred their moon rocks, and jettisoned the remains of the LM. Only the command module returned to Earth.

The first human-piloted lunar landing was made on July 20, 1969. While Michael Collins waited in orbit around the moon, Neil Armstrong and Edwin Aldrin Jr. took the LM down to the surface. Although much of the descent was controlled by computers, the astronauts had to override a number of computer alarms and take control of the LM to avoid a boulder-strewn crater bigger than a football field.

Between July 1969 and December 1972, 12 people reached the lunar surface and collected 380 kg (840 lb) of rocks and soil (■ Table 21-1). The flights were carefully planned to visit different regions and develop a comprehensive understanding of the lunar surface.

The first flights went to relatively safe landing sites (■ Figure 21-4)—Mare Tranquillitatis for Apollo 11 and Oceanus Procellarum for Apollo 12. Apollo 13 was aimed at a more complicated site, but an explosion in an oxygen tank on the way to the moon ended all chances of a landing and nearly cost the astronauts their lives. They succeeded in using the life support in the LM to survive the trip around the moon, and they eventually returned to Earth safely in the crippled command module.

The last four Apollo missions, 14 through 17, sampled geologically important places on the moon. Apollo 14 visited the Fra Mauro region, which is covered by ejecta from the impact that dug the multiringed basin now filled by Mare Imbrium. Apollo 15 visited the edge of Mare Imbrium at the foot of the Apennine

■ Table 21-1 | Apollo Lunar Landings

Apollo Mission*	Astronauts: Commander LM Pilot CM Pilot	Date	Mission Goals	Sample Weight (kg)	Typical Samples	Ages (10^9 y)
11	Armstrong Aldrin Collins	July 1969	First human landing; Mare Tranquillitatis	21.7	Mare basalts	3.48–3.72
12	Conrad Bean Gordon	Nov. 1969	Visit Surveyor 3; sample Oceanus Procellarum (mare)	34.4	Mare basalts	3.15–3.37
14	Shepard Mitchell Roosa	Feb. 1971	Fra Mauro, Imbrium ejecta sheet	42.9	Breccia	3.85–3.96
15	Scott Irwin Worden	July 1971	Edge of Mare Imbrium and Apennine Mountains, Hadley Rille	76.8	Mare basalts; highland anorthosite	3.28–3.44 4.09
16	Young Duke Mattingly	April 1972	Sample highland crust; Cayley formation (ejecta); Descartes	94.7	Highland basalt; breccia	3.84 3.92
17	Cernan Schmitt Evans	Dec, 1972	Sample highland crust; dark halo craters; Taurus–Littrow	110.5	Mare basalt; highland breccia fractured dunite	3.77 3.86 4.48

*The Apollo 13 mission suffered an explosion on the way to the moon and did not land.

Apollo 17, the last Apollo mission to the moon, landed in the highlands in December 1972.

Apollo 11 landed in the lunar lowlands in July 1969.

■ Figure 21-4

Apollo 11, the first mission to the moon, landed on the smooth surface of Mare Tranquillitatis in the lunar lowlands, and the horizon was straight and level. When Apollo 17 landed at Taurus–Littrow in the lunar highlands, the astronauts found the horizon mountainous and the terrain rugged. Landing sites for the other Apollo missions are shown on the photo of the moon. (Moon: © UC Regents/Lick Observatory; Astronauts: NASA)

Mountains and examined Hadley Rille (see Figure 21-2). Apollo missions 16 and 17 visited highland regions to sample older parts of the lunar crust (look again at Figure 21-4). Almost all of the lunar samples from these six landings are now held at the Planetary Materials Laboratory at the Johnson Space Center in Houston, although one has been embedded in a stained glass window in the National Cathedral in Washington, DC. These lunar samples are a national treasure containing clues to the beginnings of our solar system.

Moon Rocks

Many scientific measurements were made on the moon, but the most exciting prospect was the return of moon rocks to Earth. Analysis could reveal clues to the chemical and physical history of the moon, the origin and evolution of Earth, and the conditions in the solar nebula under which the planets formed.

Of the many rock samples that the Apollo astronauts carried back to Earth, every one is igneous. That is, they formed by the cooling and solidification of molten rock. No sedimentary rocks were found, consistent with the understanding that the moon has never had liquid water on its surface. In addition, the rocks were extremely dry. Almost all Earth rocks contain 1 to 2 percent water, either as free water trapped in the rock or as water molecules chemically bonded with certain minerals. But moon rocks contain no water at all.

Rocks from the lunar maria are dark-colored, dense basalts much like the solidified lava produced by the Hawaiian volcanoes (■ Figure 21-5). These rocks are rich in heavy elements such as iron, manganese, and titanium, which give them their dark color. Some of the basalts are **vesicular,** meaning that they contain holes caused by bubbles of gas in the molten rock. Like bubbles in a carbonated beverage, these bubbles do not form while the magma is under pressure. Only when the molten rock flows out onto the surface, where the pressure is low, do bubbles appear. The vesicular nature of some of the basalts shows that these rocks formed in lava flows that reached the surface and did not solidify underground.

Absolute ages of the mare basalts can be found from the radioactive atoms they contain (see Chapter 19), and these ages range from about 2 to 4 billion years. These ages confirm that the lava flows happened after the end of the heavy bombardment.

The highlands are composed of low-density rock containing calcium-, aluminum-, and oxygen-rich minerals that would have been among the first to solidify and float to the top of molten rock.

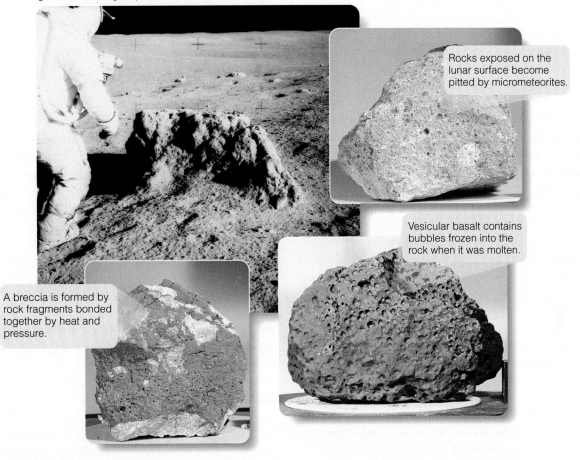

The Apollo astronauts found that all moon rocks are igneous, meaning they solidified from molten rock.

Rocks exposed on the lunar surface become pitted by micrometeorites.

Vesicular basalt contains bubbles frozen into the rock when it was molten.

A breccia is formed by rock fragments bonded together by heat and pressure.

■ **Figure 21-5**

Rocks returned from the moon show that the moon formed in a molten state, that it was heavily fractured by cratering when it was young, and that it is now affected mainly by micrometeorites grinding away at surface rock. (NASA)

Some of this rock is **anorthosite,** a light-colored rock that contributes to the highlands' bright contrast with the dark, iron-rich basalts of the lowlands. The rocks of the highlands, although badly shattered by impacts, represent the moon's original low-density crust, whereas the mare basalts rose as molten rock from the deep crust and upper mantle. The highland crustal rocks range in age from 4.0 to 4.5 billion years old, significantly older than the mare basalts.

Moon rocks are igneous, but many are classified as **breccias,** rocks that are made up of fragments of earlier rocks cemented together by heat and pressure. Evidently, after the molten rock solidified, meteorite impacts broke up the rocks and fused them together time after time.

If you went to the moon, you would get your spacesuit dirty. Both the highlands and the lowlands of the moon are covered by a layer of powdered rock and crushed fragments called the **regolith.** It is about 10 m deep on the maria but over 100 m deep in certain places in the highlands. About 1 percent of the regolith is meteoric fragments; the rest is the smashed remains of moon rocks that have been pulverized by the constant rain of meteorites. The smallest meteorites, the micrometeorites, do the most damage by constantly sandblasting the lunar surface, grinding the rock down to fine dust. The Apollo astronauts found that the dust coated their spacesuits and equipment, and then the interior of the Lunar Module after they climbed back inside. Impact cratering, a theme of this chapter, dominates the lunar surface and is responsible for the lunar regolith.

The moon rocks are old, dry, igneous, and badly shattered by impacts. You can use these facts, combined with what you know about lunar features, to tell the story of the moon.

The History of the Moon

Evidence preserved in the Apollo moon rocks shows that the moon must have formed in a molten state. Planetary geologists now refer to the newborn moon as a magma ocean. Evidently, denser materials sank to form a small core, and, as the magma ocean cooled, low-density minerals crystallized and floated to the top to form a low-density crust. In this way the moon differentiated into core, mantle, and crust. This corresponds to the first of the four stages of Terrestrial planet development displayed in Figure 20-2. The radioactive ages of the moon rocks show that the surface solidified between 4.6 and 4.1 billion years ago. The moon has a low average density and no magnetic field, so its dense core must be small. The core may still retain enough heat to be partially molten, but it can't contain much molten iron, or the dynamo effect would produce a magnetic field.

The second stage, cratering, began as soon as the crust solidified, and the older highlands show that the cratering was intense during the first 0.5 billion years or so—during the heavy bombardment at the end of planet building. The cratering rate should have fallen rapidly as the solar system was cleared of debris. However, there is evidence from lunar crater counts and rock sample ages that there was a temporary surge in impact rate, called the **late heavy bombardment**, about 4 billion years ago, near the end of the heavy bombardment era. Models of the solar system's evolution mentioned in Chapter 19 and 23 indicate that the late heavy bombardment could have been caused by an episode of Jovian planet migration that would have scattered remnant planetesimals into collisions with all the solar system's planets and moons.

The moon's crust was shattered to a depth of 10 kilometers or so, and the largest impacts during the heavy bombardment and late heavy bombardment formed giant multiringed crater basins hundreds of kilometers in diameter, such as Mare Imbrium and Mare Orientale. This led to the third stage—flooding. Although Earth's moon cooled rapidly after its formation, radioactive decay heated material deep in the crust, and part of it melted. Molten rock followed the cracks up to the surface and flooded the giant basins with successive lava flows of dark basalts from about 4 to

about 2 billion years ago. This formed the maria (■ Figure 21-6).

It is a **Common Misconception** that the lava that floods out on the surfaces of Earth and other planets comes from the molten core. The lava comes from the lower crust and upper mantle. The pressure is lower there, and that lowers the melting point of the rock enough that radioactive decay can melt portions of the rock. If there are faults and cracks, the magma can reach the surface and form volcanoes and lava flows. Whenever you see lava flows on a planet, you can be sure heat is flowing out of the interior, but the lava did not come all the way from the core.

Some maria on the moon, such as Mare Imbrium, Mare Serenitatis, Mare Humorum, and Mare Crisium, retain their round shapes, but others are irregular because the lava overflowed the edges of the basin or because the shape of the basin was modified by further cratering. The floods of lava left other characteristic features frozen into the maria. In places, the lava formed channels that are seen from Earth as sinuous rilles. Also, the weight of the maria pressed the crater basins downward, and the solidified lava was compressed and formed wrinkle ridges visible even in small telescopes. The tension at the edges of the maria broke the hard lava to produce straight fractures and faults. All of these features are visible in Figure 21-2. As time passed, further cratering and overlapping lava floods modified the maria. Consequently, you should think of the maria as accumulations of features reflecting multiple events during the moon's complex history.

Mare Imbrium is a dramatic example of how the great basins became the maria. Its story can be told in detail partly because of evidence gathered by Apollo 14 astronauts, who landed on ejecta

Near Side

Mare Imbrium

Mare Serenitatis

Mare Crisium

Far Side

Major impacts broke the crust, and lava welled up to flood the largest basins, forming maria.

├──── 200 km ────┤

Aitken Basin

■ **Figure 21-6**

Much of the near side of the moon is marked by great, generally circular lava plains called maria. The crust on the far side is thicker, and there is much less flooding. Even the huge Aitken Basin contains little lava flooding. In these maps, color marks elevation, with red the highest regions and purple the lowest. (Adapted from a diagram by William Hartmann; NASA/Clementine) from the Imbrium impact (■ Figure 21-7), and by the Apollo 15 astronauts, who landed at the edge of the mare itself. Near the end of the heavy bombardment, roughly 4 billion years ago, a planetesimal estimated to have been at least 60 km (40 mi) across (about the size of Rhode Island) struck the moon and blasted out a giant multiringed basin. The impact was so violent the ejecta blanketed 16 percent of the moon's surface. After the cratering rate fell at the end of the heavy bombardment, lava flows welled up time after time and flooded the Imbrium Basin, burying all but the highest parts of the giant multiringed basin. The Imbrium Basin is now a large, generally round mare marked by only a few craters that have formed since the last of the lava flows (■ Figure 21-8).

This story of the moon might suggest that it was a violent place during the cratering phase, but large impacts were in fact rare; the moon was, for the most part, a peaceful place even during the heavy bombardment. Had you stood on the moon at that time you would have experienced a continuous rain of micrometeorites and much less common pebble-size impacts. Centuries might pass between major impacts. Of course, when a large impact did occur far beyond the horizon, it might have buried you under ejecta or jolted you by seismic shocks. You could have felt the Imbrium impact anywhere on the moon, but had you been standing on the side of the moon directly opposite that impact, you would have been at the focus of seismic waves traveling around the moon from different directions. When the waves met under your feet, the surface would have jerked up and down by as much as 10 m. The place on the moon opposite the Imbrium Basin is a strangely disturbed landscape called **jumbled terrain.** You will see similar effects of large impacts on other worlds.

Studies of our moon show that its crust is thinner on the side facing Earth, perhaps due to tidal effects. Consequently, while lava flooded the basins on the Earth-ward side, it was unable to rise through the thicker crust to flood the lowlands on the far side. The largest known impact basin in the solar system is the Aitken Basin near the moon's south pole (Figure 21-6b). It is about 2500 ki (1500 mi) in diameter and as deep as 13 kilometers (8 mi) in places, but flooding has never filled it with smooth lava flows.

Origin of Mare Imbrium

Four billion years ago, an impact forms a multiringed basin over 1000 km (700 mi) in diameter.

Continuing impacts crater the surface but do not erase the high walls of the multiringed basin.

Archimedes

Impacts form a few large craters, and, starting about 3.8 billion years ago, lava floods low regions.

Repeated lava flows cover most of the inner rings and overflow the basin to merge with other flows.

Kepler   Copernicus

Impacts continue, including those that formed the relatively young craters Copernicus and Kepler.

■ **Figure 21-7**

Apollo 14 landed on rugged terrain suspected of being ejecta from the Imbrium impact. The large boulder here is ejecta that, at some time in the past, fell here from an impact far beyond the horizon. (NASA)

■ **Figure 21-8**

Lava flooding after the end of the heavy bombardment filled a giant multiringed basin and formed Mare Imbrium. (Don Davis)

The moon is small, and small worlds cool rapidly because they have a large ratio of surface area to volume. The rate of heat loss is proportional to the surface area, and the amount of heat in a world is proportional to the volume. The smaller a world is, the easier it is for the heat to escape. That is why a small cupcake fresh from the oven cools more rapidly than a large cake. The moon lost much of its internal heat when it was young, and it is the outward flow of heat that drives geological activity, so the moon is mostly inactive today. The crust of the moon rapidly grew thick and never divided into moving plates. There are no rift valleys or folded mountain chains on the moon. The last lava flows on the moon ended about 2 billion years ago when the moon's internal temperature fell too low to maintain subsurface lava.

The overall terrain on the moon is almost fixed. On Earth a billion years from now, plate tectonics will have totally changed the shapes of the continents, and erosion will have long ago worn away the mountain ranges you see today. On the moon, with no atmosphere and no water, there is no Earth-like erosion. Over the next billion years, impacts will have formed only a few more large craters, and nearly all of the lunar scenery will be unchanged. Micrometeorites are the biggest influence; they will have blasted the soil, erasing the footprints left by the Apollo astronauts and reducing the equipment they left behind to peculiar chemical contamination in the regolith at the six Apollo landing sites.

You have studied the story of the moon's evolution in detail for later comparison with other planets and moons in our solar system, but the story has skipped one important question: Where did Earth get such a large satellite?

The Origin of Earth's Moon

Over the last two centuries, astronomers developed three different hypotheses for the origin of Earth's moon. The *fission hypothesis* proposed that the moon broke from a rapidly spinning young Earth. The *condensation hypothesis* suggested that Earth and its moon condensed together from the same cloud of matter in the solar nebula. The *capture hypothesis* suggested that the moon formed elsewhere in the solar nebula and was later captured by Earth. Each of these older ideas had problems and failed to survive comparison with all the evidence.

In the 1970s, after moon rocks were returned to Earth and studied in detail, a new hypothesis originated that combined some aspects of the three older hypotheses. The **large-impact hypothesis** proposes that the moon formed when a very large planetesimal, estimated to have been at least as massive as Mars, smashed into the proto-Earth. Model calculations indicate that this collision would have ejected a disk of debris into orbit around Earth that would have quickly formed the moon (■ Figure 21-9).

This hypothesis explains several phenomena. If the proto-Earth and impactor had each already differentiated, the ejected material would have been mostly iron-poor mantle and crust, which would explain the moon's low overall density and iron-poor composition. Furthermore, the material would have lost its volatile

components while it was in space, so the moon would have formed lacking volatiles. Such an impact would have melted the proto-Earth, and the material falling together to form the moon would also have been heated hot enough to melt completely. This fits the evidence that the highland anorthosite in the moon's oldest rocks formed by differentiation of large quantities of molten material.

The Large-Impact Hypothesis

A protoplanet nearly the size of Earth differentiates to form an iron core.

Another body that has also formed an iron core strikes the larger body and merges, trapping most of the iron inside.

Iron-poor rock from the mantles of the two bodies forms a ring of debris.

Volatiles are lost to space as the particles in the ring begin to accrete into larger bodies.

Eventually the moon forms from the iron-poor and volatile-poor matter in the disk.

■ Figure 21-9

Sometime before the solar system was 50 million years old, a collision produced Earth and the moon in its orbit inclined to Earth's equator.

The large-impact hypothesis is consistent with the known evidence and is now considered likely to be correct.

This hypothesis would explain other things. The collision must have occurred at a steep angle to eject enough matter to make the moon, so the objects could not have collided head-on. A glancing collision would have spun the material rapidly enough to explain the observed angular momentum in the Earth–moon system. And, as mentioned above, if the two colliding planetesimals had already differentiated, the ejected material would be mostly iron-poor mantle and crust. Calculations indicate that the iron core of the impacting body would have fallen into the larger body that became Earth. This would explain why the moon is so poor in iron and why the abundances of other elements are so similar to those in Earth's mantle. Finally, the collision-heated material that eventually became the moon would have remained in a disk long enough for water and other volatile elements, which the moon lacks, to be outgassed and lost to space.

The moon is evidently the result of a giant impact. Until recently, astronomers have been reluctant to consider such catastrophic events, but a number of lines of evidence suggest that other planets also may have been affected by giant impacts. Consequently, the third theme identified in the introduction to this chapter, giant impacts, has the potential to help you understand other worlds. Catastrophic events are rare, but they can occur.

Mercury is a bit over one-third the diameter of Earth, but its high density must mean it has a large iron core. The amount of heat it retains is unknown. (NASA)

SCIENTIFIC ARGUMENT

If the moon was intensely cratered by the heavy bombardment and then formed great lava plains, why didn't the same thing happen on Earth?

Is this argument obvious? It is still worth reviewing as a way to test your understanding. In fact, the same thing did happen on Earth. Although the moon has more craters than Earth, the moon and Earth are the same age, and both were battered by meteorites during the heavy bombardment. Some of those impacts on Earth must have been large and dug giant multiringed basins. Lava flows must have welled up through Earth's crust and flooded the lowlands to form great lava plains much like the lunar maria.

Earth, however, is a larger world and has more internal heat, which escapes more slowly than the moon's heat did. The moon is now geologically dead, but Earth is very active, with heat flowing outward from the interior to drive plate tectonics. The moving plates long ago erased all evidence of the cratering and lava flows dating from Earth's youth.

Comparative planetology is a powerful tool in that it allows you to see similar processes occurring under different circumstances. For example, expand your argument to explain a different phenomenon. **Why doesn't the moon have a magnetic field?**

21-2 Mercury

EARTH'S MOON AND MERCURY are good subjects for comparative planetology. They are similar in a number of ways. Most important, they are small worlds (**Celestial Profile 4**); the moon

Celestial Profile 4: Mercury

Motion:

Average distance from the sun	0.387 AU (5.79×10^7 km)
Eccentricity of orbit	0.206
Inclination of orbit to ecliptic	7.0°
Average orbital velocity	47.9 km/s
Orbital period	0.241 y (88.0 days)
Period of rotation	58.6 d (direct)
Inclination of equator to orbit	0°

Characteristics:

Equatorial diameter	4.89×10^3 km (0.382 $D_\oplus$)
Mass	3.31×10^{23} kg (0.0558 $M_\oplus$)
Average density	5.44 g/cm³ (5.4 g/cm³ uncompressed)
Surface gravity	0.38 Earth gravity
Escape velocity	4.3 km/s (0.38 $V_\oplus$)
Surface temperature	−170° to 430°C (−275° to 805°F)
Average albedo	0.1
Oblateness	0

Personality Point:

Mercury lies very close to the sun and completes an orbit in only 88 days. For this reason, the ancients named the planet after Mercury, the fleet-footed messenger of the gods. The name is also applied to the element mercury, which is also known as quicksilver because it is a heavy, quickly flowing silvery liquid at room temperatures.

is only a fourth of Earth's diameter, and Mercury is just over a third of Earth's diameter. Their rotation has been altered by tides, their surfaces are heavily cratered, their lowlands are flooded in places by ancient lava flows, and both are airless and have ancient, inactive surfaces. The impressive differences between them also will help you understand the nature of these airless worlds.

Mercury is the innermost planet in the solar system, and thus its orbit keeps it near the sun in the sky, viewed from Earth. It is sometimes visible near the horizon in the evening sky after sunset or in the dawn sky just before sunrise. Earth-based telescopes show the small disk of Mercury passing through phases like the moon and Venus. The Mariner 10 spacecraft looped through the inner solar system in 1974 and 1975, taking photographs and other measurements during three flybys of Mercury. Astronomers managed in 2007 to make impressively high-resolution images from Earth of the parts of Mercury not covered by Mariner 10's images (■ Figure 21-10). A new spacecraft called MESSENGER (MErcury Surface, Space ENvironment, GEochemistry, and Ranging mission) has made two flybys of Mercury at the time of this writing and will make one more before it goes into orbit around the planet in 2011 and begins a yearlong close-up study (■ Figure 21-11).

Rotation and Revolution

During the 1880s, the Italian astronomer Giovanni Schiaparelli sketched the faint features he thought he saw on the disk of Mercury and concluded that the planet was tidally locked to the sun and kept the same side facing the sun throughout its orbit. This was actually a very good guess because, as you will see, tidal coupling between rotation and revolution is common in the solar system. You have already seen that the moon is tidally locked to Earth. But the rotation of Mercury is more complex than Schiaparelli thought.

■ Figure 21-11

The MESSENGER spacecraft will make three flybys and then spend a year orbiting Mercury, observing from behind a fabric sunscreen. (NASA/Johns Hopkins University Applied Physics Lab/Carnegie Institute of Washington)

In 1962, radio astronomers detected blackbody emissions from the planet and concluded that the dark side was not as cold as it should have been if the planet kept one side in perpetual darkness. In 1965, radio astronomers made radar contact with Mercury by using the 305-m Arecibo dish (see Figure 6-21) to transmit a pulse of radio energy at Mercury and then waiting for the reflected signal to return. Doppler shifts in the reflected radio pulse showed that the planet was rotating with a period of only about 59 days, noticeably shorter than the orbital period of 88 days.

Mercury is tidally coupled to the sun but in a different way than the moon is coupled to Earth. Mercury rotates not once per orbit but 1.5 times per orbit. That is, its period of rotation is two-thirds its orbital period. This means that a mountain on Mercury directly facing the sun at one place in its orbit will point away from the sun one orbit later and toward the sun after the next orbit (■ Figure 21-12).

■ Figure 21-10

Using the 4.1-meter SOAR telescope in Chile by remote control from their offices in North Carolina, astronomer Gerald Cecil and undergraduate student Dmitry Rashkeev resolved details on Mercury as small as 150 km during March and April 2007, the highest-quality images of that planet ever made from Earth. The observations were timed to view mostly the side of Mercury that had not been previously imaged by the Mariner 10 probe. The telescope aperture was masked down to 1.35 meters in diameter to reduce the effect of Earth atmosphere "seeing." A series of very rapid exposures were taken with a digital camera, with most images being discarded, saving only the highest-resolution data. (G. Cecil/University of North Carolina)

The Rotation of Mercury

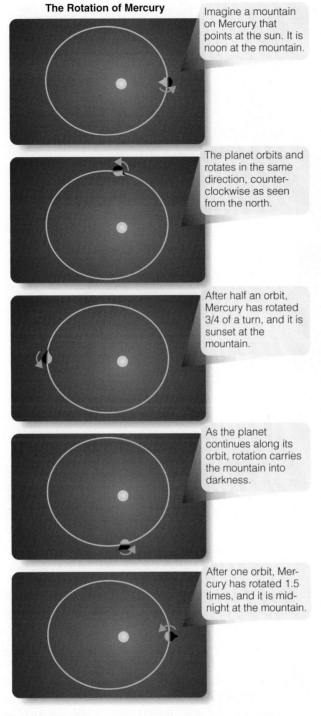

Imagine a mountain on Mercury that points at the sun. It is noon at the mountain.

The planet orbits and rotates in the same direction, counter-clockwise as seen from the north.

After half an orbit, Mercury has rotated 3/4 of a turn, and it is sunset at the mountain.

As the planet continues along its orbit, rotation carries the mountain into darkness.

After one orbit, Mercury has rotated 1.5 times, and it is midnight at the mountain.

■ **Figure 21-12**

Mercury's rotation is in resonance with its orbital motion. It orbits the sun in 88 days and rotates on its axis in two-thirds of that time. One full day on Mercury from noon to noon takes two orbits.

If you flew to Mercury and landed your spaceship in the middle of the day side, the sun would be high overhead, and it would be noon. Your watch would show almost 44 Earth days passing before the sun set in the west, and a total of 88 Earth days would pass before the sun reached the midnight position. In those 88 Earth days, Mercury would have completed one orbit around the sun (Figure 21-12). It would require another entire orbit of Mercury for the sun to return to the noon position overhead. So a full day on Mercury is two Mercury years long!

The complex tidal coupling between the rotation and revolution of Mercury is an important illustration of the power of tides. Just as the tides in the Earth–moon system have slowed the moon's rotation and locked it to Earth, so have the sun–Mercury tides slowed the rotation of Mercury and coupled its rotation to its revolution. Astronomers refer to such a relationship as a **resonance.** You will see other such resonances as you continue to explore the solar system.

Like its rotation, Mercury's orbital motion is complex. Recall from Chapter 5 that Mercury's orbit is modestly eccentric and precesses faster than can be explained by Newton's laws but at just the rate predicted by Einstein's theory of general relativity. The orbital motion of Mercury is taken as strong confirmation of the curvature of space-time as predicted by general relativity.

The Surface of Mercury

Because Mercury is close to the sun, the temperatures on Mercury are extreme. If you stood in direct sunlight on Mercury, you would hear your spacesuit's cooling system cranking up to top speed as it tried to keep you cool. Daytime temperatures can exceed 700 K (800°F), although about 500 K is a more usual high temperature. If you stepped into shadow on Mercury or took a walk at night, with no atmosphere to distribute heat, your spacesuit heaters would struggle to keep you warm. The surface can cool to 100 K (-280°F). Nights on Mercury are bitter cold. Don't go to Mercury in a cheap spacesuit.

Nights are cold on Mercury because it has almost no atmosphere. It borrows hydrogen and helium atoms from the solar wind, and atoms such as oxygen, sodium, potassium, and calcium have been detected in a cloud above the planet's surface that has such a low density that the atoms do not collide with each other. They just bounce from place to place on the surface and, because of the low escape velocity, eventually disappear into space. Some of these atoms are probably baked out of the crust, or possibly produced by very low-level remnant volcanic venting.

In photographs, Mercury looks much like Earth's moon (■ Figure 21-13). It is heavily battered, with craters of all sizes, including some large basins. Some craters are obviously old and degraded; others seem quite young and have bright rays of ejecta. However, a quick glance at photos of Mercury shows no large, dark maria like the moon's flooded basins.

When planetary scientists began looking at Mercury flyby photographs in detail, they discovered something not seen on the moon. Mercury is marked by great curved cliffs called **lobate scarps** (■ Figure 21-14). These seem to have formed when the planet cooled and shrank in diameter by a few kilometers, wrinkling its crust as a drying apple wrinkles its skin. Some of these scarps are as high as 3 km and reach hundreds of kilometers across the surface. Other faults in Mercury's crust are straight and

The impact that formed the multiringed basin Caloris pushed up mountain ranges as high as 3 km.

The surface of Mercury is heavily cratered.

Formation nicknamed "the spider" on the floor of Caloris basin.

Visual and near-infrared wavelength images

■ Figure 21-13

(a) This 2008 MESSENGER spacecraft flyby image in false-color highlights differences in composition between different parts of Mercury's surface. (NASA/JHU/APL) (b) The Caloris ringed basin, photographed by the Mariner 10 spacecraft as it flew past the planet in 1975. (NASA) (c) The origin of the spider formation photographed by MESSENGER is a puzzle. (NASA/JHU/APL)

may have been produced by tidal stresses generated when the sun slowed Mercury's rotation.

The largest basin on Mercury is called Caloris Basin after the Latin word for "heat," recognition of its location at one of the two "hot poles" that face the sun at alternate perihelions. At the times of the Mariner encounters, the Caloris Basin was half in shadow (■ Figure 21-15a). Although half cannot be seen, the low angle of illumination was ideal for the study of the lighted half because it produced dramatic shadows.

Caloris is a gigantic multiringed impact basin 1300 km (800 mi) in diameter with concentric mountain rings up to 3 km high. The impact threw ejecta 600 to 800 km across the planet, and the focusing of seismic waves on the far side produced peculiar terrain that looks much like the jumbled area on the moon's surface that lies opposite the Imbrium basin (Figure 21-15b and c). The Caloris Basin is partially filled with lava flows. Some of this lava may be material melted by the energy of the impact, but some may be lava from below the crust that leaked up through cracks. The weight

of this lava and the sagging of the crust have produced deep cracks in the central lava plains. The geophysics of such large, multiringed crater basins is not well understood at present, but Caloris Basin seems to be the same kind of structure as the Imbrium Basin on the moon, although it has not been as deeply flooded with lava.

When the MESSENGER spacecraft begins orbiting Mercury in 2011, it will photograph nearly all the planet's surface at a much higher resolution than did Mariner 10. Those new photographs will help planetary scientists build a much more complete understanding of Mercury's surface.

The Plains of Mercury

The most striking difference between Mercury and the moon is that Mercury lacks the great dark lava plains so obvious on the moon. Under careful examination, the Mariner 10 photographs show that Mercury has plains, two different kinds, in fact, but they are different from the moon's. Understanding these differences is the key to understanding the history of Mercury.

A lobate scarp (arrow) crosses craters, indicating that Mercury cooled and shrank, wrinkling its crust, after many of its craters had formed. (NASA)

Visual-wavelength image

Much of Mercury's surface is old, cratered terrain (■ Figure 21-16), but other areas called **intercrater plains** are less heavily cratered. Those plains are marked by meteorite craters less than 15 km in diameter and secondary craters produced by chunks of ejecta from larger impacts. Unlike the heavily cratered regions, the intercrater plains are not totally saturated with craters. As an expert in comparative planetology, you can recognize that this means that the intercrater plains were produced by later lava flows that buried older terrain.

Smaller regions called **smooth plains** appear to be even younger than the intercrater plains. They have fewer craters and appear to be lava flows that occurred after most cratering had ended. Much of the region around the Caloris Basin is composed of these smooth plains (Figure 21-16), and they appear to have formed soon after the Caloris impact.

Given the available evidence, planetary astronomers conclude that the plains of Mercury are solidified lava flows much like the maria on the moon. Unlike the maria, Mercury's lava plains are not significantly darker than the rest of the crust. This may be due to a compositional difference between Mercury's lava flows and the moon's. Except for a few bright crater rays, Mercury's surface is a uniform gray with an albedo of only about 0.1. That means Mercury's lava plains are not as dramatically obvious on photographs as the much darker maria on our own moon, which show up in contrast to the lighter highlands.

The Interior of Mercury

One of the most striking differences between Mercury and the moon is the composition of their interiors. You have seen that the moon is a low-density world that contains no more than a small core of metals. In contrast, evidence suggests that Mercury has a large metallic core.

Mercury is over 60 percent denser than the moon. Yet Mercury's surface appears to be normal rock, so you can conclude that its interior contains a large core of dense metals, mostly iron. In proportion to its size, Mercury must have a larger metallic core than Earth (see the diagram in Celestial Profile 4).

If Mercury had a large metallic core that remained molten, then the dynamo effect would generate a magnetic field (see Chapter 20). The Mariner 10 spacecraft found a magnetic field only about 0.5 percent as strong as Earth's, and this weak field made it difficult to understand the interior. Because Mercury is a small world, it should have lost most of its internal heat long ago and should not have a molten core. Nevertheless, radar observations of Mercury's rotation show that the surface of the planet is shifting back and forth slightly in response to the sun's gravity. That must mean that at least the outer core is molten. If Mercury's iron core contains a higher-than-Earthly concentration of sulfur, the melting point would be lowered, and the outer core, where the pressure is lower, could be molten. It is not clear, however, why a planet that formed so close to the sun could contain so much sulfur, which is a volatile material. The

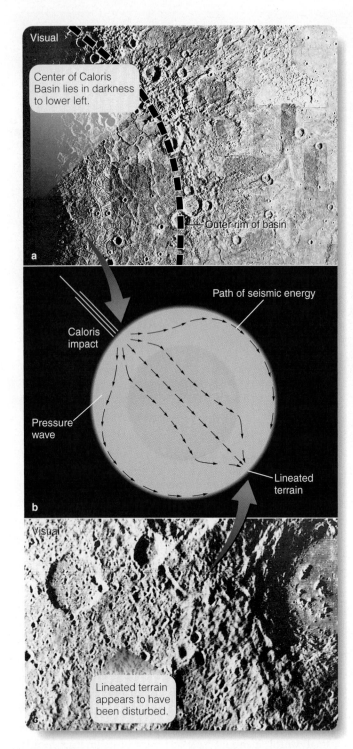

Visual

Center of Caloris Basin lies in darkness to lower left.

Outer rim of basin

a

Path of seismic energy

Caloris impact

Pressure wave

Lineated terrain

b

Visual

Lineated terrain appears to have been disturbed.

■ Figure 21-15

The huge impact that formed the Caloris Basin on Mercury sent seismic waves through the planet. Where the waves came together on the far side, they produced this lineated terrain, which resembles the jumbled terrain on Earth's moon opposite the Imbrium impact. (NASA)

MESSENGER spacecraft will make measurements of Mercury's gravitational and magnetic fields that will help planetary astronomers understand its core.

■ Figure 21-16

Study this region of Mercury carefully, and you will notice the plains between the craters. This surface is not saturated as are the lunar highlands, but it contains more craters than the surface of the maria on Earth's moon. This shows that these plains formed after the heaviest of the cratering in the early solar system. (NASA)

It is also difficult to explain the proportionally large size of the metallic core inside Mercury. In Chapter 19, you saw that planets forming near the sun should incorporate more metals, but some models suggest that this effect alone cannot account for the size of Mercury's very large metallic core. One hypothesis is that heat from the sun vaporized and drove away some of the rock-forming elements in the inner solar nebula. Another theory involves a giant impact when Mercury was young, an impact much like the planet-shattering impact proposed to explain the origin of Earth's moon. If the forming planet had differentiated and was then struck by a large planetesimal, the impact could have shattered the crust and mantle and blasted much of the lower-density material into space. The denser core could have survived, re-formed, and then swept up some of the lower-density debris to form a thin mantle and crust. This scenario would leave Mercury with a deficiency of low-density crustal rock. It is possible that both Mercury and the moon may be products of giant impacts.

The MESSENGER spacecraft will be able to test this hypothesis when it goes into orbit around Mercury in 2011. The probe will analyze the composition of the crust by remote measurements from orbit, and the chemical composition of the rock will reveal its history.

A History of Mercury

Can you combine evidence and theory to tell the story of Mercury? It formed in the innermost part of the solar nebula, and, as you have seen, a giant impact may have robbed it of some of its lower-density rock and left it a small, dense world with a surprisingly large metallic core.

Like the moon, Mercury suffered heavy cratering by debris in the young solar system. Planetary scientists don't know accurate ages for features on Mercury, but you can assume that cratering, the second stage of planetary development, occurred over the same period as the cratering on the moon. This intense cratering declined rapidly as the planets swept up the last of the debris left over from planet building.

The cratered surface of Mercury is not exactly like that of the moon. Because of Mercury's stronger gravity, the ejecta from an impact on Mercury is thrown only about 65 percent as far as on the moon, and that means the ejecta from an impact on Mercury does not blanket as much of the surface. Also, the intercrater plains appear to have formed when lava flows occurred during the heavy bombardment, burying the older surface, and then accumulated more craters. Sometime near the end of cratering, a planetesimal over 100 km in diameter smashed into the planet and blasted out the great multiringed Caloris Basin. Only parts of that basin have been flooded by lava flows.

The smooth plains contain fewer craters and may date from the time of the Caloris impact. The impact may have been so big

it fractured the crust and allowed lava flows to resurface wide areas. Because this happened near the end of cratering, the smooth plains have few craters.

Finally, the cooling interior contracted, and the crust broke to form the lobate scarps. Lava flooding ended quickly, perhaps because the shrinking planet squeezed off the lava channels to the surface. Mercury lacks a true atmosphere, so you would not expect flooding by water, but radar images show a bright spot at the planet's north pole that may be caused by ice trapped in perpetually shaded crater floors where the temperature never exceeds 60 K (–350°F). This may be water from comets that occasionally collide with Mercury and deliver a burst of water vapor. Similar water deposits may exist at the poles of Earth's moon.

The fourth stage in the story of Mercury, slow surface evolution, is now limited to micrometeorites, which grind the surface to dust; rare larger meteorites, which leave bright-rayed craters; and the slow but intense cycle of heat and cold, which weakens the rock at the surface. The planet's crust is now thick, and although its core may be partially molten, the heat flowing outward is unable to drive plate tectonics that would actively erase craters and build folded mountain ranges.

SCIENTIFIC ARGUMENT

Why don't Earth and the moon have lobate scarps?

Of course, this calls for a scientific argument based on comparative planetology. You might expect that any world with a large metallic interior should have lobate scarps. When the metallic core cools and contracts, the world should shrink, and the contraction should wrinkle and fracture the brittle crust to form lobate scarps. But there are other factors to consider. Earth has a fairly large metallic core; but it has not cooled very much, and the crust is thin, flexible, and active. If any lobate scarps ever did form on Earth, they would have been quickly destroyed by plate tectonics.

The moon does not have a large metal core. It may be that the rocky interior did contract slightly as the moon lost its internal heat, but that smaller contraction may not have produced major lobate scarps. Also, any surface features that formed early in the moon's history would have been destroyed by the heavy bombardment.

You can, in a general way, understand lobate scarps, but now add timing to your argument. **How do you know the lobate scarps on Mercury formed after most of the heavy bombardment was over?**

What Are We? Comfortable

Many planets in the universe probably look like the moon and Mercury. They are small, airless, and cratered. Some are made of stone; and some, because they formed farther from their star, are made mostly of ices. If you randomly visited a planet anywhere in the universe, you might find yourself standing on a cratered moonscape.

Earth-like worlds are unusual, but perhaps not rare. The Milky Way Galaxy contains over 100 billion stars, and over

100 billion galaxies are visible with existing telescopes. Most of those stars probably have planets, and although many planets look like Earth's moon and Mercury, there are also probably plenty of Earth-like worlds.

As you look around your planet, you should feel comfortable living on such a beautiful planet, but it was not always such a nice place. The craters on the moon and the moon rocks returned by astronauts show that the moon formed as a sea of magma.

Mercury seems to have had a similar history, so the Earth likely formed the same way. It was once a seething ocean of liquid rock swathed in a hot, thick atmosphere, torn by eruptions of more rock, explosions of gas from the interior, and occasional impacts from space. The moon and Mercury show that that is the way Terrestrial planets begin. Earth has evolved to become your home world, but mother Earth has had a violent past.

Summary

▶ The moon is **tidally coupled (p. 443)** to Earth and rotates on its axis once each orbit, keeping the same side facing Earth.

▶ The moon is small and has only one-sixth the gravity of Earth. It has such a low escape velocity that it is unable to retain an atmosphere. Observers on Earth see sharp shadows on the moon's surface, especially near the **terminator (p. 443)**, and stars disappear behind the **limb (p. 444)** of the moon without dimming. Both observations are evidence of the lack of an atmosphere. Astronauts visiting the moon verified that the moon has no measurable atmosphere.

▶ Large, smooth, dark plains on the moon called **maria** (singular, **mare**) **(p. 444)** are old lava flows that fill the lowlands. Evidence of lava is seen as **sinuous rilles (p. 444)** that once carried flowing lava, faults where the lava plain cracked, and wrinkles in the surface.

▶ When a meteorite strikes the moon, it digs a large round impact crater and throws out debris that falls back as **ejecta (p. 446)** and can form **rays (p. 446)** and **secondary craters (p. 446)**.

▶ The largest impacts on the moon dug huge **multiringed basins (p. 447)**.

▶ The highlands on the moon are saturated with craters. Rare meteorite impacts continue to form new craters, and **micrometeorites (p. 447)** constantly grind the surface down to dust, but most of the craters on the moon are very old.

▶ Astronomers can find **relative ages (p. 445)** for lunar features by looking to see which lies on top and which lies below. **Absolute ages (p. 445)** in years can be found by counting craters on surfaces and comparing the results with an estimate of the rate of crater formation calibrated using radioactive ages of lunar rock samples.

▶ Most of the craters on the moon were formed during the heavy bombardment at the end of planet building about 4 billion years ago. No crater is known with certainty to have been formed on the moon in historic times.

▶ Between 1969 and 1972, 12 astronauts set foot on the moon and returned specimens to Earth.

▶ The moon rocks are all igneous, showing that they solidified from molten rock. Some are **vesicular (p. 450)** basalts, showing that they formed in lava flows on the surface. Light-colored **anorthosite (p. 451)** is part of the old crust and helps make the highlands brighter than the maria in the lowlands. Many of the rocks are **breccias (p. 451),** which shows that much of the lunar crust was fractured by meteorite impacts.

▶ The surface of the moon is covered by rock crushed and powdered by meteorite impacts to form a soil called **regolith (p. 451)**.

▶ There is evidence from lunar crater counts and rock sample ages of an episode of increased impact rate, labeled the **late heavy bombardment (p. 452)**, about 4 billion years ago near the end of the heavy bombardment era. Many of the giant impact basins containing mare were formed during this time. That event may have been caused by Jovian planets migrating and scattering remnant planetesimals across the solar system.

▶ The Imbrium basin was formed about 4 billion years ago by the impact of a planetesimal at least 60 km (40 mi) in diameter. Seismic waves traveling through the moon were focused to the far side and produced **jumbled terrain (p. 453)**. Later flooding has nearly buried the original basin.

▶ The fission, condensation, and capture hypotheses for the origin of the moon have all been abandoned. The commonly accepted explanation is called the **large-impact hypothesis (p. 454)**. The moon appears to have formed from a ring of debris ejected into space when a large planetesimal struck the proto-Earth after it had differentiated. This would explain, for example, the moon's low density and lack of volatiles.

▶ The moon rocks show that the moon formed in a molten state.

▶ The moon differentiated but contains little iron. Its low-density crust was heavily cratered and shattered to great depth.

▶ Lava, flowing up from below the crust, filled the lowlands to form the smooth maria plains. The maria formed after the end of the heavy bombardment and contain few craters.

▶ The near side of the moon has a thin crust, possibly due to tidal forces. The back side has a thicker crust and little lava flooding.

▶ Because the moon is small, it has lost its internal heat and is geologically dead. The only slow surface evolution occurring now is the blasting of micrometeorites.

▶ Mercury is tidally locked to the sun and rotates 1.5 times per orbit in a **resonance (p. 457)** relationship between its rotation and its revolution.

▶ Mercury is a small world that has been unable to retain a true atmosphere and has lost most of its internal heat. It is cratered and geologically inactive.

▶ As the metallic core cooled and contracted, the brittle crust broke to form **lobate scarps (p. 457)**, like wrinkles in the skin of a drying apple.

▶ The Caloris Basin is a large, multiringed basin on Mercury that has been partially flooded by lava flows.

▶ The **intercrater plains (p. 459)** on Mercury appear to be later lava flows that covered older craters and then accumulated more craters. The **smooth plains (p. 459)** seem to be more recent lava flows that contain few craters. All of these plains are a similar shade of gray, so dark lava flows are not visible on Mercury as they are in the moon's maria.

▶ Mercury formed in the inner solar system and contains a larger proportion of dense metals. It is possible that a large impact shattered and drove off some of the planet's crust. This could explain why it has a larger metallic core even than would be predicted by the condensation sequence.

▶ It is not clear how much heat remains in Mercury. It is not geologically active, and it does not have a strong magnetic field. Nevertheless it has a weak magnetic field, and radar observations of its rotation suggest that the outer layers of its large iron core remain molten.

▶ Mercury was heavily cratered during the heavy bombardment, but lava flows covered some of those craters, and new craters formed the intercrater plains. Fractures produced by the Caloris impact may have triggered later lava flows that formed the smooth plains.

▶ The MESSENGER spacecraft will go into orbit around Mercury in 2011 and provide more extensive photography of its surface and detailed measurements of its physical properties.

Review Questions

1. How could you find the relative ages of the moon's maria and highlands?
2. How can you tell that Copernicus is a young crater?
3. Why did the first Apollo missions land on the maria? Why were the other areas of more scientific interest?
4. Why do astronomers suppose that the moon formed with a molten surface?

5. Why are so many lunar samples breccias?

6. What do the vesicular basalts tell you about the evolution of the lunar surface?

7. What evidence would you expect to find on the moon if it had been subjected to plate tectonics? Do you find such evidence?

8. How does the large-impact hypothesis explain the moon's lack of iron? Of volatiles?

9. How does the tidal coupling between Mercury and the sun differ from that between the moon and Earth?

10. What is the difference between the intercrater plains and the smooth plains in terms of time of formation?

11. What evidence can you cite that Mercury has a partially molten, metallic core?

12. How were the histories of the moon and Mercury similar? How were they different?

13. What is the main reason that the surface evolution of both the moon and Mercury has essentially come to a stop, but the Earth's surface evolution continues?

14. **How Do We Know?** How is a hypothesis or theory like a container in which you can carry an assortment of ideas, observations, facts, and measurements?

Discussion Questions

1. Old science-fiction paintings and drawings of colonies on the moon often showed very steep, jagged mountains. Why did the artists assume that the mountains would be more jagged than mountains on Earth? Why are lunar mountains actually less jagged than mountains on Earth?

2. From your knowledge of comparative planetology, propose a description of the view that astronauts would have if they landed on the surface of Mercury.

Problems

1. Calculate the escape velocity of the moon from its mass and diameter. (*Hint:* See Chapter 5.)

2. Why do small planets cool faster than large planets? Compare surface area to volume. Why is that comparison important?

3. The smallest detail visible through Earth-based telescopes is about 1 arc second in diameter. What linear size is this on the moon? (*Hint:* Use the small-angle formula, Chapter 3.)

4. The trenches where Earth's seafloor slips downward are 1 km or less wide. Could Earth-based telescopes resolve such features on the moon? Why can you be sure that such features are not present on the moon?

5. The Apollo command module orbited the moon about 100 km above the surface. What was its orbital period? (*Hint:* See Chapter 5.)

6. From a distance of 100 km above the surface of the moon, what is the angular diameter of an astronaut in a spacesuit? Could someone have seen the astronauts from the command module? (*Hint:* Use the small-angle formula, Chapter 3.)

7. If you transmitted radio signals to Mercury when it was closest to Earth and waited to hear the radar echo, how long would you wait?

8. Suppose you sent a spacecraft to land on Mercury, and it transmitted radio signals to Earth at a wavelength of 10 cm. If you saw Mercury at its greatest angular distance west of the sun, to what wavelength would you have to tune your radio telescope to detect the signals? (*Hints:* See Celestial Profile 4 and the section on the Doppler shift in Chapter 7.)

9. What would the wavelength of maximum output be for infrared radiation from the surface of Mercury? How would that differ for the moon?

10. Calculate the escape velocity from Mercury. How does that compare with the escape velocity from the moon and from Earth?

Learning to Look

1. Examine the mountains at the Apollo 17 landing site (Figure 21-4). What processes shape mountains on Earth that have not affected mountains on the moon?

2. The rock shown in Figure 21-7 was thrown from beyond the horizon and landed where the astronauts found it. It must have formed a small impact crater, but the astronauts didn't find traces from that impact. Why not? (*Hint:* When did the rock fall?)

3. In this photo, astronaut Alan Bean works at the Apollo 12 lander. Describe the surface you see. What kind of terrain did they land on for this, the second human moon landing?

NASA

Comparative Planetology of Venus and Mars

Mars rover Spirit, about the size of a riding lawnmower, could not take its own picture. It has been digitally added to this photo of the Martian surface. Rovers carry instruments to analyze rocks and are controlled from Earth.
(NASA/JPL-Caltech/Cornell)

Guidepost

You have been to the moon and to Mercury, and now you are going to find Venus and Mars dramatically different from those small, inactive and airless worlds. Venus and Mars have internal heat and atmospheres. The internal heat means they are geologically active, and the atmospheres mean they have weather. As you explore, you will discover answers to six essential questions:

— **Why is the atmosphere of Venus so thick?**

— **What is the hidden surface of Venus really like?**

— **How did Venus form and evolve?**

— **Why is the atmosphere of Mars so thin?**

— **What is the evidence that Mars once had water on its surface?**

— **How did Mars form and evolve?**

The comparative planetology questions that need to always be on your mind when you explore another world are these: How and why is this world similar to Earth? How and why is this world different from Earth? You will see that small initial differences can have big effects.

You are a planet-walker, and you are becoming an expert on the kind of planets you can imagine walking on. But there are other worlds beyond Mars in our solar system so peculiar they have no surfaces to walk on, even in your imagination. You will explore them in the next two chapters.

There wasn't a breath in that land of death…

— ROBERT SERVICE, "THE CREMATION OF SAM McGEE"

Tʜᴇ ᴛᴇᴍᴩᴇʀᴀᴛᴜʀᴇ ᴏɴ Mᴀʀꜱ on a hot summer day at noon might feel pretty pleasant at around 20°C (68°F). But without a spacesuit, you could live only about 30 seconds because the air is mostly carbon dioxide with almost no oxygen and is deadly dry. Even more important, the air pressure is less than 1 percent that at the surface of Earth, so your exposed body fluids such as tears and saliva would boil if you stepped outside your spaceship unprotected.

Not even a spacesuit would save you on Venus. The air pressure there is 90 times Earth's, and the air is almost entirely carbon dioxide, with traces of various acids. Worse yet, the surface is hot enough to melt lead.

Venus and Mars resemble Earth in some ways, so why are they such unfriendly places to visit? Comparative planetology will give you some clues.

22-1) Venus

Aɴ ᴀꜱᴛʀᴏɴᴏᴍᴇʀ ᴏɴᴄᴇ ʙᴇᴄᴀᴍᴇ ᴀɴɴᴏʏᴇᴅ when someone referred to Venus as a planet gone wrong. "No," she argued, "Venus is probably a fairly normal planet. It is Earth that is peculiar. The universe probably contains more planets like Venus than like Earth." To understand how unusual Earth is, you need only to compare it with Venus.

In many ways, Venus is a twin of Earth, and you might expect surface conditions on the two planets to be quite similar. Venus and Earth are almost exactly the same size and mass, with Venus having 95 percent the diameter of Earth (**Celestial Profile 5**). Venus and Earth have similar average densities, and they formed in the same part of the solar nebula—Venus's orbit is the closest to Earth's of all the planets, so Venus's overall composition is similar to Earth's (see Chapter 19). Also, planets the size of Earth and Venus cool slowly, so you might expect Venus, like Earth, to have a molten metallic core and an active crust with plate tectonics.

Unfortunately, the surface of Venus is perpetually hidden by thick clouds that completely envelop the planet, preventing us from easily observing conditions there. From the time of Galileo until the early 1960s, astronomers could only speculate about Earth's twin. Some science fiction writers imagined that Venus was a steamy swamp planet inhabited by strange creatures, while others imagined that it was completely covered by an ocean or by a planetwide dusty desert.

Starting in the 1960s, astronomers have used microwave blackbody emission from Venus to measure its surface temperature, and radar to penetrate the clouds, image the surface, and measure the planet's rotation. At least 23 spacecraft have flown

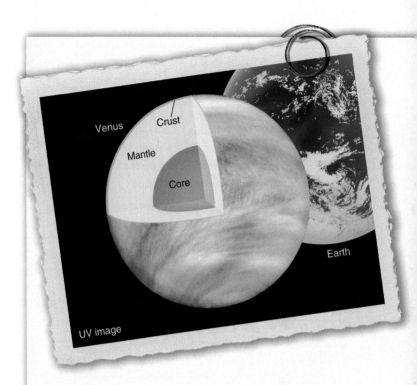

Venus is only 5 percent smaller than Earth, but its atmosphere is perpetually cloudy, and its surface is hot enough to melt lead. It may have a hot core about the size of Earth's.

Celestial Profile 5: Venus

Motion:

Average distance from the sun	0.723 AU (1.08 × 10⁸ km)
Eccentricity of orbit	0.007
Inclination of orbit to ecliptic	3.4°
Average orbital velocity	35.0 km/s
Orbital period	0.6152 y (224.7days)
Period of rotation	243.0 days (retrograde)
Inclination of equator to orbit	177°

Characteristics:

Equatorial diameter	1.21×10^4 km (0.949 $D_\oplus$)
Mass	4.87×10^{24} kg (0.815 $M_\oplus$)
Average density	5.24 g/cm³ (4.2 g/cm³ uncompressed)
Surface gravity	0.90 Earth gravity
Escape velocity	10.3 km/s (0.92 $V_\oplus$)
Surface temperature	470°C (880°F)
Albedo (cloud tops)	0.76
Oblateness	0

Personality Point:

Venus is named for the Roman goddess of love, perhaps because the planet often shines so beautifully in the evening or dawn sky. In contrast, the ancient Maya identified Venus as their war god Kukulkan and sacrificed human victims to the planet when it rose in the dawn sky.

past or orbited Venus, and over a dozen have landed on its surface. The resulting picture of Venus is dramatically different from the murky swamps of fiction. In fact, the surface of Venus is drier than any desert on Earth and twice as hot as a kitchen oven set to its highest temperature. Another startling contrast to Earth is that Venus rotates very slowly, once in 243 Earth days, in the retrograde (backward) direction.

If Venus is not a planet gone wrong, it is certainly a planet gone down a different evolutionary path than your home planet. How did Earth's twin become so different?

The Atmosphere of Venus

Although Venus is Earth's twin in size, its atmosphere is truly unearthly. The composition, temperature, and density of Venus' atmosphere make the planet's surface entirely inhospitable. About 96 percent of its atmosphere is carbon dioxide, and 3.5 percent is nitrogen. The remaining 0.5 percent is water vapor, sulfuric acid (H_2SO_4), hydrochloric acid (HCl), and hydrofluoric acid (HF). In fact, the thick clouds that hide the surface are composed of sulfuric acid droplets and microscopic sulfur crystals.

Soviet and U.S. spacecraft dropped probes into the atmosphere of Venus, and those probes radioed data back to Earth as they fell toward the surface. These studies show that Venus's cloud layers are much higher and more stable than those on Earth. The highest layer of clouds, the layer visible from Earth, extends from about 60 to 70 km (about 40 to 45 mi) above the surface (■ Figure 22-1). For comparison, the clouds on Earth normally do not extend higher than about 16 km (10 mi).

These cloud layers are highly stable because the atmospheric circulation on Venus is much more regular than that on Earth. The heated atmosphere at the **subsolar point,** the point on the planet where the sun is directly overhead, rises and spreads out in the upper atmosphere. Convection circulates this gas toward the dark side of the planet and the poles, where it cools and sinks. This circulation produces 300 km/hour jet streams in the upper atmosphere, which move from east to west (the same direction the planet rotates) so rapidly that the entire atmosphere rotates with a period of only four days.

The details of this atmospheric circulation are not well understood, but it seems that the slow rotation of the planet is an important factor. On Earth, large-scale circulation patterns are broken into smaller cyclonic disturbances by Earth's rapid rotation. Because Venus rotates more slowly, its atmospheric circulation is not broken up into cyclonic storms but instead is organized as a planetwide wind pattern.

Although Venus's upper atmosphere is cool, the lower atmosphere is quite hot (Figure 22-1b). Instrumented probes that have reached the surface report that the temperature is 470°C (880°F), and the atmospheric pressure is 90 times that of Earth. Earth's atmosphere is 1000 times less dense than water, but on Venus the air is only 10 times less dense than water. If you could survive the unpleasant atmospheric composition, intense heat, and high pressure, you could strap wings to your arms and fly.

The present atmosphere of Venus is extremely dry, but there is evidence that it once had significant amounts of water. As one of the Pioneer Venus probes descended through the

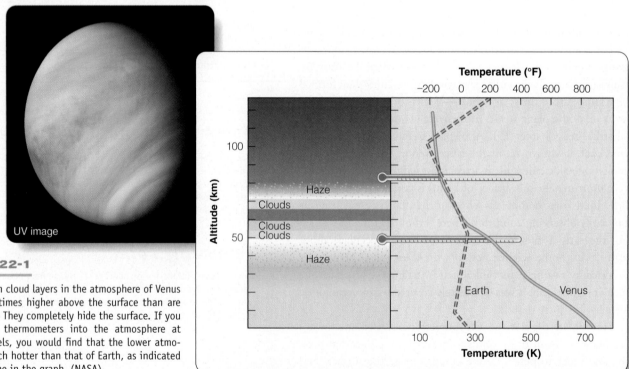

■ **Figure 22-1**

The four main cloud layers in the atmosphere of Venus are over 10 times higher above the surface than are Earth clouds. They completely hide the surface. If you could insert thermometers into the atmosphere at different levels, you would find that the lower atmosphere is much hotter than that of Earth, as indicated by the red line in the graph. (NASA) atmosphere of Venus in 1978, it discovered that deuterium is about 150 times more abundant compared to normal hydrogen atoms than it is on Earth. This abundance of deuterium, the heavy isotope of hydrogen, could have developed because Venus has no ozone layer to absorb the ultraviolet radiation in sunlight. These UV photons broke water molecules into hydrogen and oxygen. The oxygen would have formed oxides in the soil, and the hydrogen would have leaked away into space. The heavier deuterium atoms would leak away more slowly than normal hydrogen atoms, which would increase the ratio of deuterium to normal hydrogen.

Venus has essentially no water now, but the amount of deuterium in the atmosphere suggests that it may have once had enough water to make a planetwide ocean at least 25 meters deep. (For comparison, the water on Earth would make a uniform ocean about 3000 meters deep.) Venus is now a deadly dry world with only enough water vapor in its atmosphere to make a planet-wide ocean 0.3 meter (1 foot) deep. Venus's present lack of water is one of the biggest differences between that planet and Earth.

The Venusian Greenhouse

You saw in Chapter 20 how the greenhouse effect warms Earth. Carbon dioxide (CO_2) is transparent to light but opaque to infrared (heat) radiation. That means energy can enter the atmosphere as light and warm the surface, but the surface cannot radiate the energy back to space easily because the atmospheric CO_2 is opaque to infrared radiation. Venus also has a greenhouse effect, but on Venus the effect is fearsomely strong; that is the explanation for why Venus, although it is farther from the sun than Mercury, is actually hotter. Whereas Earth's atmosphere contains only about 0.04 percent CO_2, the atmosphere of Venus contains 96 percent CO_2, and as a result temperatures on the surface of Venus are more than hot enough to melt lead. The thick atmosphere and its high winds carry heat around the planet efficiently enough to make surface temperatures on Venus nearly the same everywhere. This evidently offsets the effect of the planet's slow rotation that should cause a large temperature difference between the day side and the night side.

Planetary astronomers think they know how Venus got into such a jam. When Venus was young, it may have been cooler than it is now; but, because it formed 30 percent closer to the sun than did Earth, it was always warmer than Earth, and that unleashed processes that made it even hotter. Calculations indicate that Venus and Earth should have outgassed about the same amount of CO_2, but Earth's oceans have dissolved most of Earth's CO_2 and converted it to sediments such as limestone. If all of Earth's carbon were dug up and converted back to CO_2, our atmosphere would be about as dense as the air on Venus and composed mostly of CO_2, like Venus's atmosphere.

As you saw in the previous section, Venus may once have had water on its surface, but that water would have begun to evaporate at the temperatures of early Venus. Carbon dioxide is highly soluble in water, but as surface water disappeared on Venus, the ability to dissolve CO_2 and remove it from the atmosphere also would have disappeared. The surface of Venus is now so hot that even sulfur, chlorine, and fluorine have baked out of the rock and formed sulfuric, hydrochloric, and hydrofluoric acid vapors.

The Surface of Venus

Given that the surface of Venus is perpetually hidden by clouds, is hot enough to melt lead, and suffers under crushing atmospheric pressure, it is surprising how much planetary scientists know about the geology of Venus. Early radar maps made from Earth penetrated the clouds and showed that it had mountains, plains, and some craters. The Soviet Union launched a number of spacecraft that landed on Venus, and although the surface conditions caused the spacecraft to fail within an hour or so of landing, they did analyze the rock and transmit a few images back to Earth. The rock seems to be basalt, a typical product of volcanism. The images revealed dark-gray rocky plains bathed in a deep-orange glow caused by sunlight filtering down through the thick atmosphere (■ Figure 22-2).

The U.S. Pioneer Venus main probe orbited Venus in 1978 and made radar maps showing features as small as 25 km in diameter. Later, two Soviet Venera spacecraft mapped the north polar region with a resolution of 2 km. From 1992 to 1994, the U.S. Magellan spacecraft orbited Venus and created radar maps showing details as small as 100 m. These radar maps provide a comprehensive look below the clouds.

The color of Venus radar maps is mostly arbitrary. Human eyes can't see radio waves, so the radar maps must be given some false colors to distinguish height or roughness or composition. Some maps use blues and greens for lowlands and yellows and reds for highlands. Remember when you look at these maps that there is no liquid water on Venus. Magellan scientists chose to use yellows and oranges for their radar maps in an effort to mimic the orange color of daylight caused by the thick atmosphere (■ Figure 22-3). When you look at these orange images, you need to remind yourself that the true color of the rock is dark gray (**How Do We Know? 22-1**).

Radar maps of Venus reveal a number of things about the surface. If you transmit a radio signal down through the clouds and measure the time until you hear the echo coming back up, you can measure the altitude of the surface. As a result, part of the Magellan data is a detailed altitude map of the surface. You can also measure the amount of the signal that is reflected from each spot on the surface. Much of the surface of Venus is made up of old smooth lava flows that do not look bright in radar maps, but faults and uneven terrain look brighter. Some young, rough lava flows are very rough and contain billions of tiny crevices

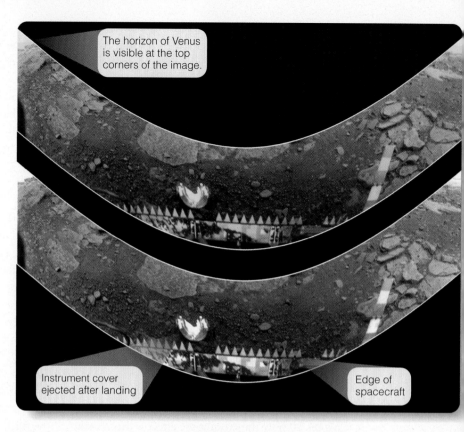

■ Figure 22-2

The Venera lander touched down on Venus in 1982 and carried a camera that swiveled from side to side to photograph the surface. The orange glow is produced by the thick atmosphere; when that is corrected to produce the view as it would be under white light, you can see that the rocks are dark gray. Isotopic analysis suggests they are basalts.

(■ Figure 22-4) that bounce the radar signal around and shoot it back the way it came. These rough lava flows look very bright in radar maps. Certain mineral deposits are also bright. Radar maps do not show how the surface would look to human eyes but rather provide information about altitude, roughness, and, in some cases, chemical composition.

The big map in ■ Figure 22-5 is a map of all of Venus except the polar regions. (Note that this map has been color coded by altitude.) By international agreement, the names of celestial bodies and features on celestial bodies are assigned by the International Astronomical Union, which has decided that all names on Venus should be feminine. There are only a few exceptions, such as the mountain Maxwell Montes, 50 percent higher than Mount Everest. It was discovered during early Earth-based radar mapping and named for James Clark Maxwell, the 19th-century physicist who first described electromagnetic radiation. Alpha Regio and Beta Regio, later found to be volcanic peaks, were also discovered by radar before the naming convention was adopted. Other names on Venus are feminine, such as the highland regions Ishtar Terra and Aphrodite Terra, named for the Babylonian and Greek goddesses of love. The insets in Figure 22-5 show roughness and composition of the surface in maps made by different satellites and color coded in different ways. All of these radar maps paint a picture of a hot, violent, desert world.

Radar maps show that the surface of Venus consists of low, rolling plains and highland regions. The rolling plains appear to be large-scale smooth lava flows, and the highlands are regions of deformed crust.

Just as in the case of the lunar landscape, craters are the key to figuring out the age of the surface. With nearly 1000 impact craters on its surface, Venus has more craters than

■ Figure 22-3

Venus without its clouds: This mosaic of Magellan radar maps has been given an orange color to mimic the sunset coloration of daylight at the surface of the planet. The image shows scattered impact craters and volcanic regions such as Beta Regio and Atla Regio. (NASA)

Data Manipulation

Why do scientists think it is OK to visually enhance their data? Planetary astronomers studying Venus change the colors of radar maps and stretch the height of mountains. If they were making political TV commercials and were caught digitally enhancing a politician's voice, they would be called dishonest, but scientists often manipulate and enhance their data. It's not dishonest because the scientists are their own audience.

Research physiologists studying knee injuries, for instance, can use magnetic resonance imaging (MRI) data to study both healthy and damaged knees. By placing a patient in a powerful magnetic field and irradiating his or her knee with precisely tuned radio frequency pulses, the MRI machine can force one in a million hydrogen atoms to emit radio frequency photons. The intensity and frequency of the emitted photons depends on how the hydrogen atoms are bonded to other atoms, so bone, muscle, and cartilage emit different signals. An antenna in the machine picks up the emitted signals and stores huge masses of data in computer memory as tables of numbers.

The tables of numbers are meaningless in that form to the physiologists, but by manipulating the data, they can produce images that reveal the anatomy of a knee. By enhancing the data, they can distinguish between bone and cartilage and see how tendons are attached. They can filter the data to see fine detail or smooth the data to eliminate distracting textures. Because the physiologists are their own audience, they know how they are manipulating the data and can use it to devise better ways to treat knee injuries.

When scientists say they are "massaging the data," they mean they are filtering, enhancing, and manipulating it to bring out the features they need to study. If they were presenting that data to a television audience to promote a cause or sell a product, it would be dishonest, but scientists' manipulation of the data allows them to better understand how nature works.

You are accustomed to seeing data manipulated and presented in convenient ways. (PhotoDisc/Getty Images)

■ **Figure 22-4**

Although it is nearly 1000 years old, this lava flow near Flagstaff, Arizona, is still such a rough jumble of sharp rock that it is dangerous to venture onto its surface. Rough surfaces are very good reflectors of radio waves and look bright in radar maps. Solidified lava flows on Venus show up as bright regions in the radar maps because they are rough. (Mike Seeds)

Earth but not nearly as many as the moon. The craters are uniformly scattered over the surface and look sharp and fresh (■ Figure 22-6). With no water and a thick, slow-moving lower atmosphere, there is little erosion on Venus, and the thick atmosphere protects the surface from small meteorites. Consequently, there are no small craters. Planetary scientists conclude that the surface of Venus is older than Earth's surface but not as old as the moon's. Unlike the moon, there are no very old, cratered highlands. Lava flows seem to have covered the entire surface of Venus within approximately the last half-billion years.

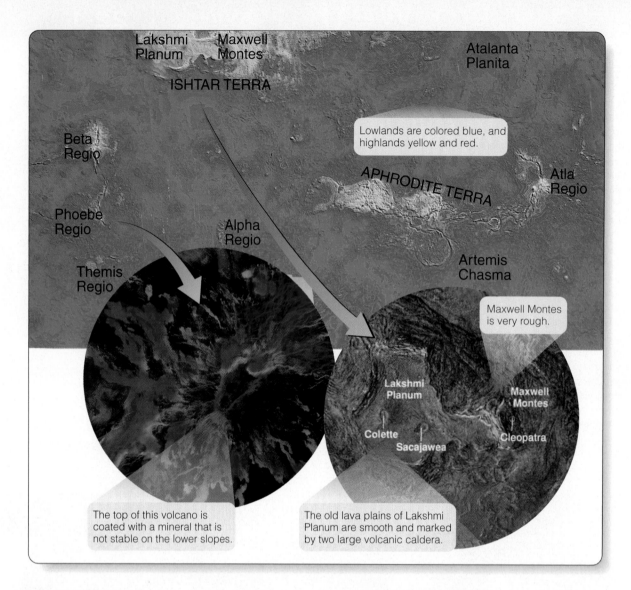

Lakshmi Planum Maxwell Montes

Atalanta Planita

ISHTAR TERRA

Beta Regio

Lowlands are colored blue, and highlands yellow and red.

APHRODITE TERRA

Atla Regio

Phoebe Regio

Alpha Regio

Themis Regio

Artemis Chasma

Maxwell Montes is very rough.

Lakshmi Planum

Maxwell Montes

Colette

Cleopatra

Sacajawea

The top of this volcano is coated with a mineral that is not stable on the lower slopes.

The old lava plains of Lakshmi Planum are smooth and marked by two large volcanic caldera.

■ **Figure 22-5**

Notice how these three radar maps show different things. The main map here shows elevation over most of the surface of Venus. Only the polar areas are not shown. The inset map at left shows an electrical property of surface minerals related to chemical composition. The detailed map of Maxwell Montes and Lakshmi Planum at right is color coded to show degree of roughness, with purple smooth and orange rough. (Maxwell and Lakshmi Planum map: USGS; other maps: NASA)

Volcanism on Venus

Volcanism seems to dominate the surface of Venus. Much of Venus is covered by lava flows such as those photographed by the Venera landers (Figure 22-2). Also, volcanic peaks and other volcanic features are evident in radar maps.

As usual, you can learn more about other worlds by comparing them with each other and with Earth. Read **Volcanoes** on pages 472–473 and notice three important ideas and two new terms:

1 There are two main types of volcanoes found on Earth. *Composite volcanoes* tend to be associated with plate motion and located near the edges of plates, whereas *shield volcanoes*

are associated with hot spots caused by columns of magma rising from deep in the mantle, and not by plate motion.

2 Notice that you can recognize the volcanoes on Venus and Mars by their shapes, even when the images are manipulated in computer mapping. The volcanoes found on Venus and Mars are shield volcanoes, produced by hot-spot volcanism and not by plate tectonics.

3 Also notice the large size of volcanoes on Venus and Mars. They have grown very large because of repeated eruptions at the same place in the crust. This is also evidence that, unlike Earth, neither Venus nor Mars has been dominated by plate tectonics and horizontal crust motions.

■ Figure 22-6

Impact crater Howe in the foreground of this Magellan radar image is 37 km (23 mi) in diameter. Craters in the background are 47 km (29 mi) and 63 km (39 mi) in diameter. This radar map has been digitally modified to represent the view as if from a spacecraft flying over the craters. (NASA)

The radar image of Sapas Mons in ■ Figure 22-7 shows a dramatic overhead view of this volcano, which is 400 km (250 mi) in diameter at its base and 1.5 km (0.9 mi) high. Many bright, young lava flows radiate outward, covering older, darker flows.

Remember that the colors in this image are artificial; if you could walk across these lava flows and shine your spacesuit's white headlight on them, you would find them solid, dark gray stone. Sapas Mons and other nearby volcanoes are located along a system of faults where rising magma evidently broke through the crust.

In addition to the volcanoes, radar images reveal other volcanic features on the surface of Venus. Lava channels are common, and they appear similar to the sinuous rilles visible on Earth's moon. The longest channel on Venus is also the longest known lava channel in the solar system. It stretches 6800 km (4200 mi), roughly twice the distance from Chicago to Los Angeles. These channels are 1 to 2 km wide and can sometimes be traced back to collapsed areas where lava appears to have drained from beneath the crust.

For further evidence of volcanism on Venus, you can look at features called **coronae,** circular bulges up to 2100 km in diameter containing volcanic peaks and lava flows. The coronae appear to be caused by rising currents of molten magma below the crust that create an uplifted dome and then withdraw to allow the surface to subside and fracture. Coronae are sometimes accompanied by circular outpourings of viscous lava called pancake domes, and by domes and hills pushed up by molten

■ Figure 22-7

(a) Volcano Sapas Mons, lying along a major fracture zone, is topped by two lava-filled calderas and flanked by rough lava flows. The orange color of this radar map mimics the orange light that filters through the thick atmosphere. (NASA) (b) Seen by light typical of Earth's surface, Sapas Mons might look more like this computer-generated landscape. Volcano Maat Mons rises in the background. The vertical scale has been exaggerated by a factor of 15 to reveal the shape of the volcanoes and lava flows. (Copyright © 1992, David P. Anderson, Southern Methodist University)

Volcanoes

1 Molten rock (magma) is less dense than the surrounding rock and tends to rise. Where it bursts through Earth's crust, you see volcanism. The two main types of volcanoes on Earth provide good examples for comparison with those on Venus and Mars.

On Earth, **composite volcanoes** form above subduction zones where the descending crust melts and the magma rises to the surface. This forms chains of volcanoes along the subduction zone, such as the Andes along the west coast of South America.

Magma rising above subduction zones is not very fluid, and it produces explosive volcanoes with sides as steep as 30°.

Oceanic plate
Upper mantle
Subduction zone
Composite volcanoes
Continental crust
Upper mantle

Chains of composite volcanoes are not found on Venus or Mars, which is evidence that subduction and plate motion does not occur on those worlds.

Based on *Physical Geology*, 4th edition, James S. Monroe and Reed Wicander, Wadsworth Publishing Company. Used with permission.

Mount St. Helens exploded northward on May 18, 1980, killing 63 people and destroying 600 km² (230 mi²) of forest with a blast of winds and suspended rock fragments that moved as fast as 480 km/hr (300 mph) and had temperatures as hot as 350°C (660°F). Note the steep slope of this composite volcano.

USGS

Shield volcano
Lava flow
Magma chamber
Oceanic crust

1a A shield volcano is formed by highly fluid lava (basalt) that flows easily and creates low-profile volcanic peaks with slopes of 3° to 10°. The volcanoes of Hawaii are shield volcanoes that occur over a hot spot in the middle of the Pacific plate.

Magma collects in a chamber in the crust and finds its way to the surface through cracks.

Magma forces its way upward through cracks in the upper mantle and causes small, deep earthquakes.

A hot spot is formed by a rising convection current of magma moving upward through the hot, deformable (plastic) rock of the mantle.

The Cascade Range composite volcanoes are produced by an oceanic plate being subducted below North America and partially melting.

Seattle
Washington
St Helens
Rainier
Pacific Ocean
Portland
Hood
Oregon
Shasta
Nevada
California
Lassen

Volcano Gula Mons

Volcano Sif Mons

Radar map

NASA

Mike Seeds

2 Volcanoes on Venus are shield volcanoes. They appear to be steep sided in some images created from Magellan radar maps, but that is because the vertical scale has been exaggerated to enhance detail. The volcanoes of Venus are actually shallow-sloped shield volcanoes.

3 Volcanism over a hot spot results in repeated eruptions that build up a shield volcano of many layers. Such volcanoes can grow very large.

Vertical scale exaggerated

Hot spot

2a This computer model of a mountain with the vertical scale magnified 10 times appears to have steep slopes such as those of a composite volcano.

A true profile of the computer model shows the mountain has very shallow slopes typical of shield volcanoes.

Old volcanic island eroded below sea level

Plate motion

Hot spot

If the crustal plate is moving, magma generated by the hot spot can repeatedly penetrate the crust to build a chain of volcanoes. Only the volcanoes over the hot spot are active. Older volcanoes slowly erode away. Such volcanoes cannot grow large because the moving plate carries them away from the hot spot.

Time since last eruption (million years)

5   3   1.5   1   0

Kauai   Oahu   Molokai   Maui   Hawaii   Active volcanoes

Plate motion

Newborn underwater volcano

3a The volcanoes that make up the Hawaiian Islands as shown at left have been produced by a hot spot poking upward through the middle of the moving Pacific plate.

NASA

3b The plate moves about 9 cm/yr and carries older volcanic islands northwest, away from the hot spot. The volcanoes cannot grow extremely large because they are carried away from the hot spot. New islands form to the southeast over the hot spot.

Olympus Mons at right is the largest volcano on Mars. It is a shield volcano 25 km (16 mi) high and 700 km (440 mi) in diameter at its base. Its vast size is evidence that the crustal plate must have remained stationary over the hot spot. This is evidence that Mars has not had plate tectonics.

Olympus Mons contains 95 times more volume than the largest volcano on Earth, Mauna Loa in Hawaii.

Caldera from repeated eruptions

Digital elevation map

■ Figure 22-8

Volcanic features on Venus: (a) Arrows point to a 600-km (400-mi) segment of Baltis Vallis, the longest lava-flow channel in the solar system. It is at least 6800 km long. (b) Aine Corona, about 200 km (120 mi) in diameter, is marked by faults, lava flows, small volcanic domes, and pancake domes of solidified lava. (c) This perspective view shows a hill typical of those associated with a corona. Molten lava below the surface appears to have pushed up the hill, causing the network of radial faults. (d) Other regions of the crust appear to have collapsed as subsurface magma drained away. (NASA)

rock below the surface. All of these volcanic features are shown in ■ Figure 22-8.

There is no reason to suppose that all of the volcanoes found on Venus are extinct, so volcanoes may be erupting on Venus right now. However, the radar maps caught no evidence of actual eruptions in progress.

If you want to learn more of the secrets of Venus, you will want to visit the big land mass called Ishtar Terra. Western Ishtar consists of a high volcanic plateau called Lakshmi Planum. It rises 4 km (2.5 mi) above the rolling plains and appears to have formed from lava flows originating in volcanic vents such as Collette and Sacajawea (see Figure 22-5). Although folded mountain ranges showing widespread plate tectonics do not

occur on Venus as they do on Earth, the areas north and west of Lakshmi Planum appear to be ranges of wrinkled mountains where some type of horizontal crust motion has pushed up against Ishtar Terra. Furthermore, faults and deep chasms are widespread over the surface of Venus, and that suggests stretching of the crust in those areas. So, although no direct evidence of plate motion is visible, there has certainly been compression and wrinkling of the crust in some areas and stretching and faulting in other areas, suggesting some limited crustal motion.

While Earth's crust has broken into rigid moving plates, the surface of Venus seems more pliable and does not break easily into plates. The history of Venus has been a fiery tale, dominated by volcanism.

The Rotation of Venus

Nearly all of the planets in our solar system rotate counterclockwise as seen from the north. Uranus is an exception, and so is Venus.

In 1962, radio astronomers were able to transmit a radio pulse of precise wavelength toward Venus and detect the echo returning some minutes later. That is, they detected Venus by radar. But the echo was not at one precise wavelength. Part of the reflected signal had a longer wavelength, and part had a shorter wavelength. Evidently the planet was rotating; radio energy reflected from the receding edge was redshifted, and radio energy reflected from the approaching edge was blueshifted. From this Doppler effect, the radio astronomers could tell that Venus was rotating once every 243.0 Earth days. Furthermore, because the western edge of Venus produced the blueshift, the planet had to be rotating in the backward direction.

Why does Venus rotate backward, and very slowly? For decades, textbooks have suggested that proto-Venus was set spinning backward when it was struck off-center by a large planetesimal. That is a reasonable possibility; you have seen that a similar collision probably gave birth to Earth's moon. But there is an alternative. Mathematical models suggest that the rotation of a Terrestrial planet with a molten core and a dense atmosphere can be gradually reversed by solar tides in its atmosphere. Notice the contrast between the catastrophic theory of a giant impact and the evolutionary theory of atmospheric tides. It is possible that both mechanisms played a role in causing Venus's peculiar rotation. Perhaps Venus's very slow rotation is the explanation for why there is no dynamo effect to produce a magnetic field.

A History of Venus

Earth passed through four major stages in its history (see Chapter 20), and you have seen how the moon and Mercury were affected by their own versions of the same stages. Venus, however, has had a peculiar passage through planetary development, and its history is difficult to understand. Planetary scientists are not sure of all the details about how the planet formed and differentiated, how it was cratered and flooded, or how its surface has evolved.

Venus is only slightly closer to the sun than Earth, so you might expect from the condensation sequence that it should have a similar over-all composition with perhaps slightly higher metal content than Earth. Instead, Venus's uncompressed density is slightly *less* than Earth's (look back to Table 19-2). The density and size of Venus still require that it have a dense metallic interior much like Earth's. However, if the metal in Venus's core is molten, then you would expect the dynamo effect to generate a magnetic field. But, no spacecraft has detected a magnetic field around Venus; its magnetic field must be at least 25,000 times weaker than Earth's. Some theorists wonder if the

core of the planet is solid. If it is solid, scientists are puzzled by how Venus got rid of its internal heat faster than Earth did.

Because the planet lacks a magnetic field, it is not protected from the solar wind. The solar wind slams into the uppermost layers of Venus' atmosphere, forming a bow shock where the wind is slowed and deflected (■ Figure 22-9). Planetary scientists know little about the differentiation of the planet into core and mantle, so the size of the core shown in Figure 22-9 is estimated by analogy with Earth's. The magnetic field carried by the solar wind drapes over Venus like seaweed over a fishhook, forming a long tail within which ions flow away from the planet. You will see in Chapter 25 that comets, which also lack magnetic fields, interact with the solar wind in the same way.

Studies of moon rocks show that the moon formed as a sea of magma; and, presumably, Venus and Earth formed in the same way and never had primeval atmospheres rich in hydrogen. Instead, they outgassed carbon dioxide atmospheres as they formed. Calculations show that Venus and Earth have outgassed about the same amount of CO_2, but Earth's oceans have dissolved that CO_2 and converted it to sediments such as limestone. The main cause of the difference between surface conditions on Earth and Venus is the lack of water on Venus. Venus may have had oceans when it was young; but, because Venus is closer to the sun than Earth, it was initially warmer, and the CO_2 in the atmosphere created a greenhouse effect that made the planet even warmer. That process could have dried up any oceans that did exist and reduced the ability of the planet to clear its atmosphere of CO_2. As more CO_2 was outgassed, the greenhouse effect grew even more severe. Venus became trapped in a runaway greenhouse effect.

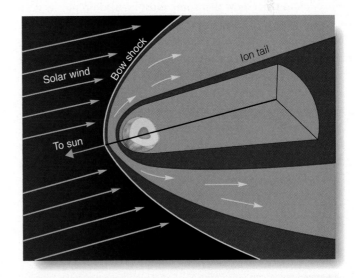

■ **Figure 22-9**

By analogy with Earth, the interior of Venus should contain a molten core (size estimated here), but no spacecraft has detected a planetary magnetic field. Thus, Venus is unprotected from the solar wind, which strikes the planet's upper atmosphere and is deflected into an ion tail.

In comparison, Earth avoided a runaway greenhouse effect because it was farther from the sun and always cooler than Venus. Consequently, it could form and preserve liquid-water oceans, which absorbed the CO_2 and left an atmosphere of nitrogen that was relatively transparent in some parts of the infrared. As you learned earlier, if all of the carbon in Earth's sediments was put back into the atmosphere as CO_2, our air would be as dense as that of Venus, and Earth would suffer from a tremendous greenhouse effect. Recall also from Chapter 20 how the use of fossil fuels and the destruction of forests are increasing the CO_2 concentration in our atmosphere and warming the planet. Venus warns us of what a greenhouse effect can do.

Fully 70 percent of the heat from Earth's interior flows outward through volcanism along midocean ridges. But Venus lacks crustal rifts, and even its numerous volcanoes cannot carry much heat out of the interior. Rather, Venus seems to get rid of its interior heat through large currents of hot magma that rise beneath the crust. Coronae, lava flows, and volcanism occur above such currents. The surface rock on Venus is the same kind of dark-gray basalt found in ocean crust on Earth.

True plate tectonics is not important on Venus. For one thing, the crust is very dry and is consequently about 12 percent less dense than Earth's crust. This low-density crust is more buoyant than Earth's crust and resists being pushed into the interior. Also, the crust is so hot that it is halfway to its melting point. Such hot rock is not very stiff, so it cannot form the rigid plates typical of plate tectonics on Earth.

There is no sign of plate tectonics on Venus, but there is evidence that convection currents below the crust are deforming the crust to create coronae and push up mountains such as Maxwell. Detailed measurements of the strength of gravity over Venus's mountains show that some must be held up not by deep roots like mountains on Earth but by rising currents of magma. Other mountains, like those around Ishtar Terra, appear to be folded mountains caused by limited horizontal motions in the crust, driven perhaps by convection currents in the mantle.

The small number of craters on the surface of Venus hints that the entire crust has been replaced within the last half-billion years or so. This may have occurred in a planetwide overturning as the old crust broke up and sank and lava flows created a new crust. This could happen periodically on Venus, or the planet may have had geological processes more like Earth's until a single resurfacing geologically recently. In either case, unearthly Venus may eventually reveal more about how our own world works.

SCIENTIFIC ARGUMENT

What evidence can you point to that Venus does not have plate tectonics?

Sometimes a scientific argument can be helpful by eliminating a possibility. On Earth, plate tectonics is identifiable by the worldwide network of faults, subduction zones, volcanism, and folded mountain chains that outline the plates. Although some of these features are visible on Venus, they do not occur in a planetwide network of plate boundaries. Volcanism is widespread, but folded mountain ranges occur in only a few places, such as near Lakshmi Planum and Maxwell Montes, and, unlike on Earth, they do not make up long mountain chains. Also, the large size of the shield volcanoes on Venus shows that the crust is not moving over the hot spots in the way the Pacific seafloor is moving over the Hawaiian hot spot.

At first glance, you might think that Earth and Venus should be as similar as siblings, but comparative planetology reveals that they are more like cousins. You can blame the thick atmosphere of Venus for altering its geology, but that calls for a new scientific argument: **Why isn't Earth's atmosphere similar to that of Venus?**

22-2 Mars

MERCURY AND THE MOON ARE SMALL. Venus and Earth are the largest of the Terrestrial planets. Mars has an intermediate size. It is twice the diameter of the moon but only a little more than half of Earth's diameter (**Celestial Profile 6**). Mars's small size has allowed it to cool faster than Earth, and much of its atmosphere has leaked away. Its present carbon-dioxide atmosphere is a bit less than 1 percent as dense as Earth's.

No Canals on Mars

Long before the space age, the planet Mars was a mysterious landscape in the public mind. In the century following Galileo's first astronomical use of the telescope, astronomers discovered dark markings on Mars as well as bright polar caps. Timing the motions of the markings, they concluded that a Martian day was about 24 hours 40 minutes long. Its axis is tipped 25.2° to its orbit, almost exactly the same as Earth's 23.4° tilt, so Mars has seasons with about the same winter/summer contrast as Earth. Mars's year is about 1.88 Earth years long. These similarities with Earth encouraged the belief that Mars might be inhabited.

In 1858, the Jesuit astronomer Angelo Secchi referred to a region on Mars as *Atlantic Canale*. This is the first use of the Italian word *canale* (channel) to refer to a feature on Mars. Then, in the late summer of 1877, the Italian astronomer Giovanni Schiaparelli, using a telescope only 8.75 in. in diameter, thought he glimpsed fine, straight lines on Mars. He too used the Italian word *canali* (plural) for these lines, and the word was translated into English not as "channel," a narrow body of water that is a natural geological feature, but as "canal," an artificially dug channel. Thus the "canals of Mars" were born. Many astronomers could not see the canals at all, but others drew maps showing hundreds (■ Figure 22-10).

In the decades that followed Schiaparelli's "discovery," many people assumed that the canals were watercourses built by an intelligent race to carry water from the polar caps to the lower latitudes. Much of this excitement was generated by Percival Lowell, a wealthy Bostonian who, in 1894, founded Lowell Observatory in Flagstaff, Arizona, principally for the study of Mars. He not only mapped hundreds of canals but also popularized his results in books and lectures. Although some astronomers claimed the canals were merely illusions, by 1907 the general public was so sure that life existed on Mars that the *Wall Street Journal* suggested that the most extraordinary event of the previous year had been "the proof by astronomical observations…that conscious, intelligent human life exists upon the planet Mars." Further sightings of bright clouds and flashes of light on Mars strengthened this belief, and some urged that gigantic geometrical diagrams be traced in the Sahara Desert to signal to the Martians that Earth, too, is inhabited. All seemed to agree that the Martians were older and wiser than humans.

This fascination with men from Mars was not a passing fancy. Beginning in 1912, Edgar Rice Burroughs (author of the Tarzan stories) wrote a series of 11 novels about the adventures of the Earthman John Carter, lost on Mars. Burroughs made the geography of Mars, named by Schiaparelli after Mediterranean lands both real and mythical, into household words. He also made his Martians small and gave them green skin.

By Halloween night of 1938, people were so familiar with life on Mars that they were ready to believe that Earth could be invaded. When a radio announcer repeatedly interrupted dance music to report the landing of a spaceship in New Jersey, the emergence of monstrous creatures, and their destruction of whole cities, thousands of otherwise sensible people fled in panic, not knowing that Orson Welles and other actors were dramatizing H. G. Wells's book *The War of the Worlds.*

Public fascination with Mars, its canals, and its little green men lasted right up until July 15, 1965, when Mariner 4, the first spacecraft to fly past Mars, radioed back photos of a dry, cratered surface and proved that there are no canals and no Martians. The canals are optical illusions produced by the human brain's powerful ability to assemble a field of disconnected marks into a coherent image. If your brain could not do this, the photos on these pages would be nothing but swarms of dots, and the images on a TV screen would never make sense. The downside of this is that the brain of an astronomer looking for something at the edge of visibility is capable of connecting faint, random markings on Mars into the straight lines of canals.

Even today, Mars holds some fascination for the general public. Grocery store tabloids regularly run stories about a giant face carved on Mars by an ancient race. Although planetary scientists recognize it as nothing more than chance shadows in a photograph and dismiss the issue as a silly hoax, the stories persist.

Mars is only half the diameter of Earth and probably retains some internal heat, but the size and composition of its core are not well known. (NASA)

Celestial Profile 6: Mars

Motion:

Average distance from the sun	1.52 AU (2.28 × 10⁸ km)
Eccentricity of orbit	0.093
Inclination of orbit to ecliptic	1.9°
Average orbital velocity	24.1 km/s
Orbital period	1.881 y (687.0 days)
Period of rotation	24.62 h
Inclination of equator to orbit	25.2°

Characteristics:

Equatorial diameter	6.79 × 10³ km (0.531 $D_\oplus$)
Mass	6.42 × 10²⁵ kg (0.108 $M_\oplus$)
Average density	3.94 g/cm³ (3.3 g/cm³ uncompressed)
Surface gravity	0.38 Earth gravity
Escape velocity	5.0 km/s (0.45 $V_\oplus$)
Surface temperature	–140° to 15°C (–220° to 60°F)
Average albedo	0.16
Oblateness	0.009

Personality Point:

Mars is named for the god of war. Minerva was the goddess of defensive war, but Bullfinch's *Mythology* refers to Mars's "savage love of violence and bloodshed." You can see how the planet glows blood red in the evening sky because of iron oxides in its soil.

■ Figure 22-10

(a) Early in the 20th century, Percival Lowell mapped canals over the face of Mars and concluded that intelligent life resided there. (Lowell Observatory) (b) Modern images recorded by spacecraft reveal a globe of Mars with no canals. Instead, the planet is marked by craters and, in some places, volcanoes. Both of these images are reproduced with south at the top, as they appear in telescopes. Lowell's globe is inclined more nearly vertically and is rotated slightly to the right compared with the modern globe. (U.S. Geological Survey)

A hundred years of speculation have raised high expectations for Mars. If there were intelligent life on Mars and its representatives came to Earth, they would probably be a big disappointment to the readers of the tabloids.

The Atmosphere of Mars

If you visited Mars, your first concern, even before you opened the door of your spaceship, would be the atmosphere. Is it breathable? Even for the astronomer observing safely from Earth, the atmosphere of Mars is of major interest. The gases that cloak Mars are critical to understanding the history of the planet.

The air on Mars is 95 percent carbon dioxide, with a few percent each of nitrogen and argon. You probably noticed that this is quite similar to the composition of Venus's atmosphere. The reddish color of the Martian soil is caused by iron oxides (rusts), and this is a warning that the oxygen humans would prefer to find in the atmosphere is locked in chemical compounds in the soil. The Martian atmosphere contains almost no water vapor or oxygen, and its density at the surface of the planet is only about 1 percent that of Earth's atmosphere. This does not provide enough pressure to prevent liquid water from boiling into vapor. Water can exist at the Martian surface only as ice or vapor.

Although the air is thin, it is dense enough to be visible in photographs (■ Figure 22-11). Haze and clouds come and go, and occasional weather patterns are visible. Winds on Mars can be strong enough to produce dust storms that envelop the entire planet. The polar caps visible in photos are also related to the Martian atmosphere. The ices in the polar caps are frozen carbon dioxide ("dry ice") with frozen water underneath.

Visual-wavelength image

■ Figure 22-11

The atmosphere of Mars is evident in this image made by the Hubble Space Telescope. The haze is made up of high, water-ice crystals in the thin CO_2 atmosphere. The spot at extreme left is the volcano Ascraeus Mons, 25 km (16 mi) high, poking up through the morning clouds. Note the north polar cap at the top. (Philip James, University of Toledo; Steven Lee, University of Colorado, Boulder; and NASA)

Visual-wavelength image

■ **Figure 22-12**

Mars is a red desert planet, as shown in this true-color photo made by the Rover Opportunity. The rock outcrop is a meter-high crater wall. After taking this photo, Opportunity descended into the crater to study the wall. Dust suspended in the atmosphere colors the sky red-orange. (NASA © 1995–2007 by Calvin J. Hamilton)

If you could visit Mars you would find it a reddish, airless, bone-dry desert (■ Figure 22-12). To understand Mars, you can ask why its atmosphere is so thin and dry and why the surface is rich in oxides. To find those answers you need to consider the origin and evolution of the Martian atmosphere.

Presumably, the gases in the Martian atmosphere were mostly outgassed from its interior. Volcanism on Terrestrial planets typically releases carbon dioxide and water vapor, plus other gases. Because Mars formed farther from the sun, you might expect that it would have incorporated more volatiles when it formed. But Mars is smaller than Earth, so it has had less internal heat to drive geological activity, and that would lead you to suspect that it has not outgassed as much as Earth. In any case, whatever outgassing took place occurred early in the planet's history, and Mars, being small, cooled rapidly and now releases little gas.

How much atmosphere a planet has depends on how rapidly it loses gas to space, and that depends on the planet's mass and temperature. The more massive the planet, the higher its escape velocity (see Chapter 5), and the more difficult it is for gas atoms to leak into space. Mars has a mass less than 11 percent that of Earth, and its escape velocity is only 5 km/s, less than half Earth's. Consequently, gas atoms can escape from it much more easily than they can escape from Earth.

The temperature of a planet's atmosphere is also important. If a gas is hot, its molecules have a higher average velocity and are more likely to exceed escape velocity. That means a planet near the sun is less likely to retain an atmosphere than a more distant, cooler planet. The velocity of a gas molecule, however, also depends on the mass of the molecule. On average, a low-mass molecule travels faster than a massive molecule. For that reason, a planet loses its lowest-mass gases more easily because those molecules travel fastest.

You can see this principle of comparative planetology if you plot a diagram such as that in ■ Figure 22-13. The data points show the escape velocity versus temperature for the larger objects in our solar system. The temperature used in the diagram is the temperature of the gas that is in a position to escape. For the moon, which has essentially no atmosphere, this is the temperature of the sunlit surface. For Mars, the temperature that is important is that at the top of the atmosphere.

The lines in Figure 22-13 show the typical velocities of the fastest-traveling examples of various molecules. At any given temperature, some water molecules, for example, travel faster than others, and it is the highest-velocity molecules that escape from a planet. The diagram shows that the Jovian planets have escape velocities so high that very few molecules can escape. Earth and Venus can't hold hydrogen, and Mars can hold only the more massive molecules. Earth's moon is too small to keep any gases from leaking away. You can refer back to this diagram when you study the atmospheres of other worlds in later chapters.

Over the 4.6 billion years since Mars formed, it has lost some of its lower-mass gases. Water molecules are massive enough for Mars to keep, but ultraviolet radiation can break them up. The hydrogen escapes, and the oxygen, a very reactive element, forms more oxides in the soil—the oxides that make Mars the red planet. Recall that on Earth the ozone layer protects water vapor from ultraviolet radiation, but Mars never had an oxygen-rich atmosphere, so it never had an ozone layer. Ultraviolet photons from the sun can penetrate deep into the atmosphere and break up molecules. In this way, molecules too massive to leak into space can be lost if they break into lower-mass fragments.

The argon in the Martian atmosphere is evidence that there once was a denser blanket of air. Argon atoms are massive, almost

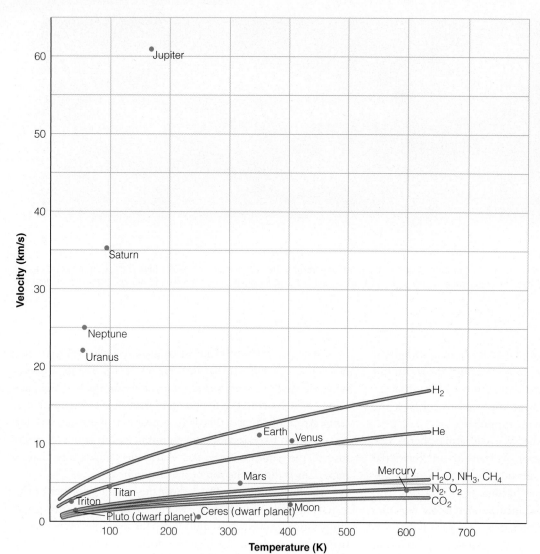

■ **Figure 22-13**

Loss of planetary atmosphere gases. Dots represent the escape velocity and temperature of various solar-system bodies. The lines represent the typical highest velocities of molecules of various masses. The Jovian planets have high escape velocities and can hold onto even the lowest-mass molecules. Mars can hold only the more massive molecules, and the moon has such a low escape velocity that even the most massive molecules can escape.

as massive as a carbon dioxide molecule, and would not be lost easily. In addition, argon is inert and cannot form compounds in the soil. The 1.6 percent argon in the atmosphere of Mars is evidently left over from an ancient atmosphere that may have been 10 to 100 times denser than the present Martian air.

Finally, you should consider the interaction of the solar wind with the atmosphere of Mars. This is not an important process for Earth because Earth has a magnetic field that deflects the solar wind. In contrast, Mars has no magnetic field, and the solar wind interacts directly with the Martian atmosphere. Detailed calculations show that significant amounts of carbon dioxide could have been carried away by the solar wind over the history of the planet. This process would have been most efficient long ago when the sun was more active and the solar wind was stronger. However, you should also keep in mind that Mars probably had a magnetic field when it was younger and still retained significant internal heat. A magnetic field would have protected its atmosphere from the solar wind.

The polar caps contain large amounts of carbon dioxide ice; and, as spring comes to a hemisphere, that ice begins to vaporize and returns to the atmosphere. Meanwhile, at the other pole, carbon dioxide is freezing out and adding to the polar cap there. Dramatic evidence of this cycle appeared when the camera aboard the Mars Odyssey probe sent back images of dark markings on the south polar cap. Evidently as spring comes to the polar cap and the sun begins to peek above the horizon, sunlight penetrates the meter-thick ice and vaporizes carbon dioxide, which bursts out in geysers a few tens of meters high carrying dust and sand. Local winds push the debris downwind to form the fan-shaped dark markings (■ Figure 22-14). These dark markings appear each spring but last only a few months as frozen carbon dioxide returns to the atmosphere.

Although planetary scientists remain uncertain as to how much of an atmosphere Mars has had in its past and how much it has lost, it is a good example for your study of comparative planetology. When you look at Mars, you see what can happen

a Visual-wavelength image

(a) Each spring, spots and fans appear on the ice of the south polar cap on Mars. (b) Studies show the ice is frozen carbon dioxide in a nearly clear layer about a meter thick. High-pressure carbon dioxide gas vaporized by spring sunlight bursts out of the ice in geysers. The gas carries sand and dust hundreds of meters into the air. (NASA; Arizona State University/Ron Miller)

b

to the atmosphere of a medium-size world. Like its atmosphere, the geology of Mars is probably typical of medium-size worlds.

The Geology of Mars

If you ever decide to visit another world, Mars may be your best choice. Mars is much more friendly than the moon, Mercury, or Venus. The nights on Mars are deadly cold, but a hot summer day would be comfortable **(Celestial Profile 6)**. Mars has weather, complex geology, and signs that water once flowed over its surface. You might even hope to find traces of ancient life hidden in the rocks.

Spacecraft have been visiting Mars for almost 40 years, but the pace has picked up recently. A small armada of spacecraft has gone into orbit around Mars to photograph and analyze its surface, and six spacecraft have landed. Two Viking landers touched down in 1976, and three rovers have landed in recent years. Rovers have an advantage because they are wheeled robots that can be controlled from Earth and directed to travel from feature to feature and make detailed measurements. Pathfinder and its rover, Sojourner, landed in 1997. Rovers Spirit and Opportunity

landed in 2004, carrying sophisticated instruments to explore the rocky surface. The Phoenix probe landed in the north polar region of Mars in 2008.

Photographs made by rovers and landers on the surface of Mars, such as Figure 22-12, show reddish deserts of broken rock. These appear to be rocky plains fractured by meteorite impacts, but they don't look much like the surface of Earth's moon. The atmosphere of Mars, thin though it is, protects the surface from the blast of micrometeorites that grinds moon rocks to dust. Also, Martian dust storms may sweep fine dust away from some areas, leaving larger rocks exposed.

Spacecraft orbiting Mars have imaged the surface and measured elevations to reveal that all of Mars is divided into two parts. The southern highlands are heavily cratered, and the number of craters there shows that they must be old. In contrast, the northern lowlands are smooth (■ Figure 22-15) and so remarkably free of craters that they must have been resurfaced no more than a billion years ago. Some astronomers have suggested that volcanic floods filled the northern lowlands and buried the craters there. Growing evidence, however, suggests that the northern

■ Figure 22-15

These globes of Mars are color coded to show elevation. The northern lowlands lie about 4 km (2.5 mi) below the southern highlands. Volcanoes are very high (white), and the giant impact basins, Hellas and Argyre, are low. Note the depth of the canyon Valles Marineris. The two Viking spacecraft landed on Mars in 1976. Pathfinder landed in 1997. Rovers Spirit and Opportunity landed in 2004. (NASA)

lowlands were once filled by an ocean of liquid water. This is an exciting hypothesis and will be mentioned again later in this chapter when you consider the history of water on Mars.

The cratering and volcanism on Mars fit with what you already know of comparative planetology. Mars is larger than Earth's moon, so it cooled more slowly, and its volcanism has continued longer. But Mars is smaller than Earth and less geologically active, so some of its ancient cratered terrain has survived undamaged by volcanism and plate tectonics.

The Martian volcanoes are shield volcanoes with shallow slopes, showing that the lava flowed easily. As you learned from Earth and Venus, shield volcanoes occur over hot spots of rising magma below the crust and are not related to plate tectonics. The largest volcano in the solar system is Olympus Mons on Mars (see page 483). The shield volcano Mauna Loa in Hawaii is so heavy it has sunk into Earth's crust to form an undersea depression like a moat around a castle. Olympus Mons is much larger than Mauna Loa but has not sunk into the crust of Mars, which shows that the crust of Mars is much thicker than the crust of Earth. You can see the evidence in ■ Figure 22-16.

Other evidence indicates that the Martian crust has been thinner and more active than the moon's. Valles Marineris is a network of canyons 4000 km (2500 mi) long and up to 600 km (400 mi) wide (Figure 22-16). At its deepest, it is four times deeper than the Grand Canyon on Earth, and it is long enough to stretch from New York to Los Angeles. The canyon has been produced by faults that allowed great blocks of crust to sink. Later landslides and erosion modified the canyon further. Although Valles Marineris is an old feature, it does show that the crust of Mars has been more active than the crusts of the moon or Mercury, worlds that lack such dramatic canyons.

The faults that created Valles Marineris seem to be linked at the western end to a great volcanic bulge in the crust of Mars called the Tharsis rise. Nearly as large as the United States, the Tharsis rise extends 10 km (6 mi) above the mean radius of Mars. Tharsis is home to many smaller volcanoes, but on its summit lie three giants, and just off of its northwest edge lies huge Olympus Mons (Figure 22-16). The origin of the Tharsis rise is not well understood, but it appears that magma rising from below the crust has pushed the crust up and broken through repeatedly to build a giant bulge of volcanic deposits. This bulge is large enough to have modified the climate and seasons on Mars and may be critical in understanding the history of the planet.

A similar uplifted volcanic bulge, the Elysium region, visible in Figure 22-15, lies halfway around the planet. It appears to be similar to the Tharsis rise, but it is more heavily cratered and so must be older.

The vast sizes of features like the Tharsis rise and Olympus Mons show that the crust of Mars has not been broken into horizontally mobile plates. If a plate were moving over a hot spot, the rising magma would produce a long chain of shield volcanoes and not a single large peak. On Earth, the hot spot that creates the volcanic Hawaiian Islands has punched through the moving Pacific plate repeatedly to produce the Hawaiian-Emperor island chain extending 7500 km (4700 mi) northwest across the Pacific seafloor (page 473). No such chains of volcanoes are evident on Mars, so you can conclude that the crust is not divided into moving plates.

No spacecraft has ever photographed an erupting volcano on Mars, but it is possible that some of the volcanoes are still active. Lack of impact craters in the youngest lava flows in the Tharsis region and the Elysium region show that the volcanoes may have been active as recently as a few million years ago, which,

Olympus Mons

Ascraeus Mons

Pavonis Mons

Arsia Mons

Elevation (meters)

27,000

-1,000

Olympus Mons is about 100 times larger in volume than Mauna Loa, the largest volcano on Earth.

10 km
100 km

Olympus Mons

Sea level   Moat

Mauna Loa

Green area: The Tharsis rise is a 10-km-thick dome of lava flows.

■ **Figure 22-16**

High volcanoes and deep canyons mark the surface of Mars. Olympus Mons, a shield volcano, is much larger than the largest volcano on Earth. In this false-color image, three other volcanoes are visible. Those three volcanoes are also visible in the photo, along with the canyon Valles Marineris, which stretches as far as the distance from New York to Los Angeles. (Four volcanoes: © Calvin J. Hamilton, Columbia, Maryland; photo: NASA/ USGS)

geologically speaking, is only yesterday. Mars may still retain enough heat to trigger an eruption, but the interval between eruptions could be very long.

Finding the Water on Mars

The quest for water on Mars is exciting because water has been deeply involved in the evolution of the planet, but it is also exciting because life depends on water. If life managed to begin on Mars, then the planet must have had water, and if life survives there, water must be hidden somewhere on the desert planet.

The two Viking spacecraft reached orbit around Mars in 1976 and photographed exciting hints that water once flowed over the surface. As you have learned, liquid water cannot exist on the surface now because it would boil away under the extremely low atmospheric pressure, so the Viking photos were evidence that water once flowed on Mars and that conditions

there must have been quite different long ago. More recent missions to Mars such as Mars Global Surveyor, which reached Mars in 1997; Mars Odyssey (2001); Mars Express (2003); and Mars Reconnaissance Orbiter (2005) have identified numerous additional features related to water.

Two kinds of formations hint at water flowing over the surface. **Outflow channels** appear to have been cut by massive floods carrying as much as 10,000 times the volume of water flowing down the Mississippi River (■ Figure 22-17a). In a matter of hours or days, such floods swept away landscape features and left outflow channels. The number of craters formed on top of the outflow channels show that they are billions of years old. The **valley networks** look like meandering riverbeds that may have formed over long periods (Figure 22-17b). The valley networks are also located in the old, cratered, southern hemisphere, and they are also very old.

a Visual-wavelength image

b Visual-wavelength image

■ Figure 22-17

These visual-wavelength images made by the Viking orbiters show some of the features that suggest liquid water on Mars. (a) Outflow channels are broad and shallow and deflect around obstructions such as craters. They appear to have been produced by sudden floods. (a) Valley networks resemble drainage patterns and suggest water flowing over long periods. Crater counts show that both formations are old, but valley networks are older than outflow channels. (NASA © Calvin J. Hamilton)

northern lowlands were filled by an ocean when Mars was younger. Large, generally circular depressions such as Hellas and Argyre appear to be impact basins that also may once have been flooded by water.

Mars Orbiter photographed the eroded remains of a river delta in an unnamed crater in the old highlands (■ Figure 22-18). Details show that the river flowed for long periods of time, shifting its channel to form meanders and braided channels as rivers on Earth do. The shape of the delta suggests it formed when the river flowed into deeper water and dropped its sediment, much as the Mississippi drops its sediment and builds its delta in the Gulf of Mexico.

Did Mars once have that much water? Deuterium is 5.5 times more abundant than normal (light) hydrogen in the Martian atmosphere, and that suggests that Mars once had about 20 times more water than it has now. Presumably, much of the water was broken up and the normal hydrogen mostly lost to space.

The remaining water on Mars could survive if it were frozen in the crust. High-resolution images and measurements made

Visual-wavelength image

■ Figure 22-18

This distributary fan was formed where an ancient stream flowed into a flooded crater. Sediment in the moving water was deposited in the still water to form a lobed delta that later became sedimentary rock. Detailed analysis reveals that the stream changed course time after time, and this shows that the stream flowed for an extended period and was not just a short-term flood. Also, the shape of the fan is evidence that a lake persisted in the crater while the fan developed. (NASA/JPL/Malin/Space Science Systems)

Many flow features lead into the northern lowlands, and the smooth terrain there has been interpreted as ancient ocean floor. Features along the edges of the lowlands have been compared to shorelines, and many planetary scientists conclude that the from orbit reveal features that suggest subsurface ice. Gullies leading downhill appear to have been eroded recently, judging from their lack of craters; these may have been formed by water seeping from below the surface. Some regions of collapsed terrain appear to be places where subsurface water has drained away. Photos taken over a period of years reveal the appearance of recent landslides that may have been caused by water gushing from crater walls and carrying debris downhill before vaporizing completely. Instruments aboard the Mars Odyssey spacecraft detected water frozen in the soil over large areas of the planet. At latitudes farther than 60 degrees from the equator, water ice may make up more than 50 percent of the surface soil.

If you added a polar bear, changed the colors, and hid the craters in ■ Figure 22-19a, it would look like the broken pack ice on Earth's Arctic Ocean. Mars Express photographed these dust-covered formations near the Martian equator, and the shallow depth of the craters suggests that the ice is still there, just below the surface.

Much of the ice on Mars may be hidden below the polar caps. Radar aboard the Mars Express orbiter was able to penetrate 3.7 km (2.3 mi) below the surface and map ice deposits hidden below the south polar region (Figure 22-19b). There is enough water there, at least 90 percent pure, to cover the entire planet to a depth of 11 meters. The Phoenix probe, which landed in 2008 near Mars's north pole, found water ice not only mixed with the soil as permafrost, but also as small chunks of pure ice, indicating that there once was standing water that had frozen in place.

Rovers Spirit and Opportunity were targeted to land in areas suspected of having had water on their surfaces. Images made from orbit showed flow features at the Spirit landing site, and hematite, a mineral that forms in water, was detected from orbit at the Opportunity landing site. Both rovers reported exciting discoveries, including evidence of past water. Using its analytic instruments, Opportunity found small spherical concretions of hematite (dubbed blueberries) that must have formed in abundant water. Later, Spirit found similar concretions in its area. In other rocks, Opportunity found layers of sediments with ripple marks and crossed layers showing they were deposited in moving water (■ Figure 22-20). Chemical analysis of the rocks at the Opportunity site showed the presence of sulfates much like Epsom salts plus bromides and chlorides. On Earth, these compounds are left behind when bodies of water dry up. Halfway

a Visual wavelength image

b Radar image

Outline of south polar cap

c

■ **Figure 22-19**

(a) Like broken pack ice, these formations near the equator of Mars suggest floating ice that broke up and drifted apart. Scientists propose that the ice was covered by a protective layer of dust and volcanic ash and may still be present. (ESA/DLR/F. U. Berlin/G. Neukum) (b) Radar aboard the Mars Express satellite probed beneath the surface to image water ice below the south polar cap. The black circle is the area that could not be studied from the satellite's orbit. (NASA/JPL/ESA/Univ. of Rome/MOLA Science Team/USGS) (c) This view from the Phoenix lander shows the landscape of Mars's north polar plain, including polygonal cracks understood to result from seasonal expansion and contraction of ice under the surface. (NASA/JPL-Caltech/University of Arizona.)

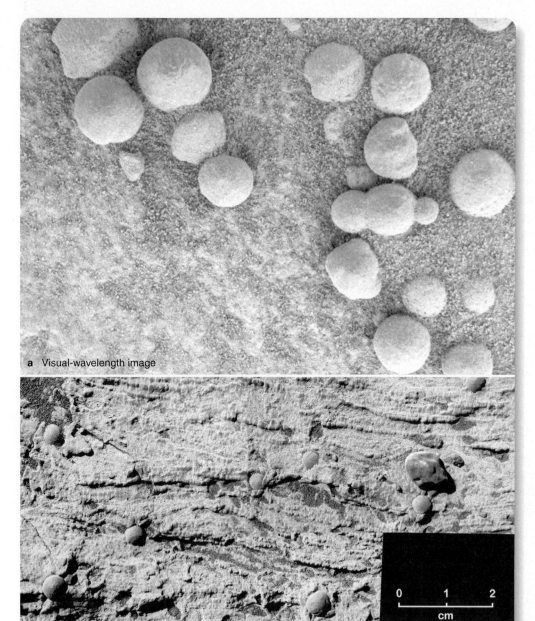

a Visual-wavelength image

b Visual-wavelength image

(a) Rover Opportunity photographed these hematite concretions ("blueberries") in a rock near its landing site. The spheres appear to have grown as minerals collected around small crystals in the presence of water. Similar concretions are found on Earth. (b) The layers in this rock were deposited as sand and silt in rapidly flowing water. From the way the layers curve and cross each other, geologists can estimate that the water was at least ten centimeters deep. A few "blueberries" and one small pebble are also visible in this image. (NASA.JPL/Cornell/USGS)

around Mars, Spirit found the mineral goethite, which only forms in the presence of water.

One amazing bit of evidence of water on Mars is the analysis of rock samples from the planet. Of course, no astronaut has ever visited Mars and brought back a rock, but over the history of the solar system occasional impacts by asteroids have blasted giant craters on Mars and ejected bits of rock into space. A few of those bits of rock have fallen to Earth as meteorites, and over 30 have been found and identified (■ Figure 22-21). These meteorites include basalts, as you might expect from a planet so heavily covered by lava flows. They also contain small traces of water and minerals that are deposited by water. Chemical analysis shows

that the magma from which the rocks solidified must have contained up to 1.8 percent water. If all of the lava flows on Mars contained that much water and it was all outgassed, it could create a planetwide ocean 20 m deep. That isn't quite enough to explain all the flood features on Mars, but it does show that the planet once had abundant water on its surface.

Mars has water, but it is hidden. When humans reach Mars, they will not need to dig far to find water in the form of ice. They can use solar power to break the water into hydrogen and oxygen. Hydrogen is fuel, and oxygen is the breath of life, so the water on Mars may prove to be buried treasure. Even more exciting is the realization that Mars once had bodies of liquid water

Visual-wavelength image

ALH84001,
,0

■ Figure 22-21

(a) The impact crater Galle, known for obvious reasons as the Happy Face Crater, is 210 km (130 mi) in diameter. Such large impacts may occasionally eject fragments of the crust into space. A few fragments from Mars have fallen to Earth as meteorites. (Malin Space Science Systems/NASA) (b) Meteorite ALH84001, found in Antarctica, has been identified as an ancient rock from Mars. Minerals found in the meteorite were deposited in water and thus suggest that the Martian crust was once richer in water than it is now. (NASA)

on its surface. It is a desert world now, but someday an astronaut may scramble down an ancient Martian streambed, turn over a rock, and find a fossil. It is even possible that life started on Mars and has managed to persist as the planet gradually became less hospitable. For example, life may have hung on by retreating to limited warm and wet oases underground. You will learn in Chapter 26 about possible evidence of ancient life in Mars meteorite ALH84001 and, even more intriguing, indications in spectra of Mars's atmosphere of current methane production that could be biological.

A History of Mars

The history of Mars is like a play where all the exciting stuff happens in the first act. After the first two billion years on Mars, most of the activity was over, and it has gone downhill ever since.

Planetary scientists have good evidence that Mars differentiated when it formed and had a hot, molten core. Some of the evidence comes from exquisitely sensitive Doppler-shift measurements of radio signals coming from spacecraft orbiting Mars. Measuring the shifts allowed scientists to map the gravitational field and study the shape of Mars in such detail that they could detect tides on Mars caused by the sun's gravity. Those tides are less than a centimeter high; but, by comparing them with models of the interior of Mars, the scientists can show that Mars has a very dense core, a less dense mantle, and a low-density crust.

Observations made from orbit show that Mars has no overall magnetic field, but it does have traces of magnetism frozen into

some sections of old crust. This shows that soon after Mars formed, it had a hot metallic core in which the dynamo effect generated a magnetic field. Because Mars is small, it lost its heat rapidly, and most of its core gradually froze solid. That may be why the dynamo finally shut down. Today Mars probably has a large solid core surrounded by a thin shell of liquid core material in which the dynamo effect is unable to generate a magnetic field.

No one is sure what produced the dramatic difference between the southern highlands and northern lowlands. Powerful convection in the planet's mantle may have pushed crust together to form the southern highlands. The suggestion that a catastrophic impact produced the northern lowlands does not seem to fit with the structure of the highlands, but it is not impossible.

Planetary scientists divide the history of Mars into three periods. The first, the **Noachian period,** extended from the formation of the crust about 4.3 billion years ago until roughly 3.7 billion years ago. During this time the crust was battered by the heavy bombardment as the last of the debris in the young solar system was swept up. The old southern hemisphere survives from this period. The largest impacts blasted out the great basins like Hellas and Argyre very late in the cratering, and there is no trace of magnetic field in those basins. Evidently the dynamo had shut down by then.

The Noachian period included flooding by great lava flows that smoothed some regions. Volcanism in the Tharsis and Elysium regions was very active, and the Tharsis rise grew into a

■ Figure 22-22

The Tharsis rise is a bulge on the side of Mars consisting of stacked lava flows extending up to 10 km (6 mi) high and over a third the diameter of Mars. It dominates this image of Mars, with a few clouds clinging to the four largest volcanoes. This image was recorded in late winter for the southern hemisphere. Notice the size of the southern polar cap. (NASA/JPL/Malin Space Science Systems)

huge bulge on the side of Mars (■ Figure 22-22). Some of the oldest lava flows on Mars are in the Tharsis rise, but it also contains some of the most recent lava flows. It has evidently been a major volcanic area for most of the planet's history.

The valley networks found in the southern highlands were formed during the Noachian period when water fell as rain or snow and drained down slopes. To keep the water liquid required a higher temperature and higher atmospheric pressure than is present on Mars today. Violent volcanism could have vented gases, including more water vapor that kept the air pressure high. This may have produced episodes in which water flowed over the surface and collected in the northern lowlands and in the deep basins to form oceans and lakes, but it's not known how long those bodies of water survived. A planetwide magnetic field may have protected the atmosphere from the solar wind.

Because Mars is small, it lost its internal heat quickly, and atmospheric gases escaped into space. The **Hesperian period** extended from roughly 3.7 billion years ago to about 3 billion years ago. During this time massive lava flows covered some sections of the surface. Most of the outflow channels date from this period, which suggests that the loss of atmosphere drove Mars to become a deadly cold desert world with its water frozen in the crust. When volcanic heat or large impacts melted subsurface ice, the water could have produced violent floods and shaped the outflow channels.

The history of Mars may hinge on climate variations. Models calculated by planetary scientists suggest that Mars may have once rotated at a much steeper angle to its orbit, as much as 45°. This could have resulted in a generally warmer climate and kept more of the carbon dioxide from freezing out at the poles. The rise of the Tharsis bulge could have tipped the axis to its present 25° and cooled the climate. Some calculations suggest that Mars goes through cycles similar to Earth's Milankovitch cycles (see Chapter 20) as its rotational inclination fluctuates, and this may cause short-term variations in climate, much like the ice ages on Earth.

The third period in the history of Mars, the **Amazonian period,** extended from about 3 billion years ago to the present and was mostly uneventful. The planet has lost much of its internal heat, and the core no longer generates a global magnetic field. The crust of Mars is too thick to be active with plate tectonics, and consequently there are no folded mountain ranges on Mars resembling the ones on Earth. The huge size of the Martian volcanoes clearly shows that crustal plates have not moved on Mars. Volcanism may still occur occasionally on Mars, but the crust has grown too thick for much geological activity beyond slow erosion by wind-borne dust and the occasional meteorite impact.

Planetary scientists cannot tell the story of Mars in great detail, but it is clear that the size of Mars has influenced both its atmosphere and its geology. Neither small nor large, Mars is a medium-sized world, with characteristics intermediate between small Mercury and Earth's moon on one hand, and large Venus and Earth on the other.

SCIENTIFIC ARGUMENT

Why doesn't Mars have coronae like those on Venus?
This argument is a good opportunity to apply the principles of comparative planetology. The coronae on Venus are caused by rising currents of molten magma in the mantle pushing upward under the crust and then withdrawing to leave the circular scars called coronae. Earth, Venus, and Mars have had significant amounts of internal heat, and there is plenty of evidence that they have had rising convection currents of magma under their crusts. Of course, you wouldn't expect to see coronae on Earth; its surface is rapidly modified by erosion and plate tectonics. Furthermore, the mantle convection on Earth seems to produce plate tectonics rather than coronae. Mars, however, is a smaller world and must have cooled faster. There is no evidence of plate tectonics on Mars, and giant volcanoes suggest rising plumes of magma erupting up through the crust at the same point over and over. Perhaps there are no coronae on Mars because the crust of Mars rapidly grew too thick to deform easily over a rising plume. On the other hand, perhaps you could think of the entire Tharsis bulge as a single giant corona.

Planetary scientists haven't explored enough planets yet to see all the fascinating combinations nature has in store. But it does seem likely that the geology of Mars is typical of medium-size worlds. Of course, Mars is not medium in terms of its location. Of the Terrestrial planets, Mars is the farthest from the sun. Build a scientific argument to analyze that factor. **How has the location of Mars affected the evolution of its atmosphere?**

22-3 The Moons of Mars

IF YOU COULD CAMP OVERNIGHT on Mars, you might notice its two small moons, Phobos and Deimos. Phobos, shaped like a flattened loaf of bread measuring 20 km × 23 km × 28 km in size, would appear less than half as large in angular diameter as Earth's full moon. Deimos, only 12 km in diameter and three times farther from Mars, would look only $\frac{1}{15}$ the diameter of Earth's moon.

Both moons are tidally locked to Mars, keeping the same side facing the planet as they orbit. Also, both moons revolve around Mars in the same direction that Mars rotates, but Phobos follows such a small orbit that it revolves faster than Mars rotates. If you camped overnight on Mars, you would see Phobos rise in the west, drift eastward across the sky, and set in the east 6 hours later.

Origin and Evolution

Deimos and Phobos are typical of the small, rocky moons in our solar system (■ Figure 22-23). Their albedos are only about 0.06, making them look as dark as coal. They have low densities, about 2 g/cm³.

Many of the properties of these moons suggest that they are captured asteroids. In the outer parts of the asteroid belt, almost all asteroids are dark, low-density objects like Phobos and Deimos. Massive Jupiter, orbiting just outside the asteroid belt, can scatter such bodies throughout the solar system, so you should not be surprised if a number of them have encountered Mars, the closest Terrestrial planet to the asteroid belt.

However, capturing a passing asteroid into a closed orbit is not so easy that it can be expected to happen often. An asteroid approaches a planet along a hyperbolic (open) orbit and, if it is unimpeded, swings around the planet and disappears back into space. To change the hyperbolic orbit into a closed orbit, the asteroid must somehow be slowed down as it passes. Tidal forces might do this, but in the case of Mars they would be rather weak. Interactions with other moons or grazing collisions with a thick atmosphere might also slow the asteroid enough so it could be captured.

Both Phobos and Deimos have been photographed by nearby spacecraft, and those photos show that the satellites are heavily cratered. Such cratering could have occurred either while the moons were still in the asteroid belt or while they were in orbit around Mars. In any case, the heavy battering has broken the satellites into irregular chunks of rock, and they cannot pull themselves into smooth spheres because their gravity is too weak to overcome the structural strength of the rock. You will

■ Figure 22-23

The moons of Mars are too small to pull themselves into spherical shape. Deimos is about half the size of Phobos. The two moons were named for the mythical attendants of Mars, the god of war. Phobos was the god of fear, and Deimos was the god of dread. (Phobos: Damon Simonelli and Joseph Ververka, Cornell University/NASA; Deimos: NASA)

Phobos is marked by the large crater Stickney, which is 10 km in diameter.

Deimos looks smoother because it has more dust and debris on its surface.

Visual-wavelength images

discover in the next chapters that low-mass moons are typically irregular in shape, whereas more massive moons are more spherical.

Images of Phobos reveal a unique set of narrow, parallel grooves (see Figure 22-23). Averaging 150 m wide and 25 m deep, the grooves run from Stickney, the largest crater, to an oddly featureless region on the opposite side of the satellite. One theory suggests that the grooves are deep fractures produced by the impact that formed Stickney. The featureless region opposite Stickney may be similar to the jumbled terrains found on Earth's moon and on Mercury. All these regions were produced by the focusing of seismic waves from a major impact on the far side of the body. High-resolution photographs show that the grooves are lines of pits, suggesting that the pulverized rock material on the surface has drained into the fractures or that gas, liberated by the heat of impact, escaped through the fractures and blew away the dusty soil.

Observations made with the Mars Global Surveyor's infrared spectrometer show that Phobos's surface cools quickly from –4°C to –112°C (from 25°F to –170°F) as it passes from sunlight into the shadow of Mars. Solid rock would retain heat and cool more slowly. To cool as quickly as it does, the dust must be at least a meter deep and very fine. In most photos made by the spacecraft camera, the dust blankets the terrain, but some photos show boulders a few meters in diameter that are thought to be ejecta from impacts.

Deimos looks even smoother than Phobos because of an even thicker layer of dust on its surface (Figure 22-23). This material partially fills craters and covers minor surface irregularities. It seems certain that Deimos experienced collisions in its past, so fractures may be hidden below the debris.

The debris on the surfaces of the moons raises an interesting question. How can the weak gravity of small bodies hold on to fragments from meteorite impacts? Escape velocity on Phobos is only 12 m/s. An athletic astronaut could almost jump into space. Certainly, most fragments from impacts should escape, but some do fall back and accumulate on the surface.

Deimos, smaller than Phobos, has a smaller escape velocity, but it has more debris on its surface because it is farther from Mars. Phobos is close enough to Mars that most ejecta from impacts on Phobos will be drawn into Mars. Deimos, being farther from Mars, is able to keep a larger fraction of its ejecta. Phobos is so close to Mars that tides are making its orbit shrink, and it will fall into Mars or be ripped apart by tidal forces within about 100 million years.

Deimos and Phobos illustrate three principles of comparative planetology that you will find helpful as you explore farther from the sun. First, some satellites are probably captured asteroids. Second, small satellites tend to be irregular in shape and heavily cratered. And third, tidal forces can affect small moons and gradually change their orbits. You will find even stronger tidal effects in Jupiter's satellite system in the next chapter.

SCIENTIFIC ARGUMENT

Why would you be surprised if you found volcanism on Phobos or Deimos?

This is another obvious argument, isn't it? But remember, the purpose of a scientific argument is to test your own understanding, so it is a good way to review. In discussing Earth's moon, Mercury, Venus, Earth, and Mars, you have seen illustrations of the principle that the larger a world is, the more slowly it loses its internal heat. It is the flow of that heat from the interior through the surface into space that drives geological activity such as volcanism and plate motion. A small world, like Earth's moon, cools quickly and remains geologically active for a shorter time than a larger world like Earth. Phobos and Deimos are not just small, they are tiny. However they formed, any interior heat would have leaked away very quickly; with no energy flowing outward, there can be no volcanism.

Some futurists suggest that the first human missions to Mars will not land on the surface of the planet but will build a colony on Phobos or Deimos. These plans are based on speculation that there may be water deep inside the moons that colonists could use. Build an argument based on what you know about water on Mars. **What would happen to water released in the sunlight on the surface of such small worlds?**

What Are We? Earth-Folk

Space travel isn't easy. We humans made it to the moon, but it took everything we had in the late 1960s. Going back to the moon will be easier next time because the technology will be better, but it will still be expensive and will require people with heroic talent to design, build, and fly the spaceships. Going beyond the moon will be even more difficult.

Going to Mercury or Venus doesn't seem worth the effort. Mercury is barren and dangerous, and the heat and air pressure on Venus may prevent any astronaut from ever visiting its surface. In the next two chapters, you will discover that the Jovian planets and their moons also are not places humans are likely to visit soon. The stars are so far away they may be forever beyond the reach of human spaceships. But Earth has a neighbor.

Astronomically Mars is just up the street, and it isn't such a bad place. You would need a good spacesuit and a pressurized colony to live there, but it isn't impossible. Solar energy and water are abundant. It seems inevitable not only that humans will walk on Mars but that they will someday live there. We Earth-folk have an exciting future. Eventually we will be the Martians.

Summary

- Venus is Earth's twin in size but is slightly closer to the sun.

- Venus rotates so slowly that solar heat at the **subsolar point (p. 466)** produces strong atmospheric circulation that circles the planet in only four days.

- The atmosphere of Venus is 95 times thicker than Earth's and composed almost entirely of carbon dioxide.

- Venus is heated by a runaway greenhouse effect. The temperature at the surface of Venus is about 470°C (880°F), hotter than Mercury even though it is farther from the sun.

- The surface of Venus is so hot that compounds have cooked out of the crust to form traces of sulfuric, hydrochloric, and hydrofluoric acids in the atmosphere. The very high clouds on Venus are composed of small droplets of sulfuric acid and sulfur crystals.

- Although it is perpetually hidden below thick clouds, the surface of Venus can be studied by radar mapping, which reveals higher uplands and low rolling plains. Volcanoes, lava flows and channels, and impact craters are detectable. Volcanism is apparently common on Venus, and much of the surface is solidified lava flows. Volcanoes are probably still active on Venus.

- Radar maps can measure altitude, roughness, and in some cases, composition of the surface.

- Landers have analyzed the surface rock and found it to be similar to basalts on Earth.

- **Composite volcanoes (p. 472)** on Earth have steep slopes and are associated with subduction zones. **Shield volcanoes (p. 472)** have shallow slopes and are associated with hot spots. The volcanoes on Venus are shield volcanoes.

- Plate motion across a hot spot produces chains of volcanic peaks. The large size of the volcanic peaks on Venus, and the fact that they are shield volcanoes, shows that the crust is not made of moving plates.

- **Coronae (p. 471)** form where rising currents of magma push the crust up and then withdraw, forming circular faults with associated volcanoes and lava flows.

- Because Venus formed closer to the sun than Earth, it was initially warmer, and whatever oceans it may originally have had were not able to persist and remove carbon dioxide from the atmosphere. The accumulating carbon dioxide produced an intense greenhouse effect, made the planet very hot, and evaporated the remaining water in a runaway greenhouse effect.

- The surface of Venus appears to be about half a billion years old. Planetary scientists suspect that the entire planet was resurfaced by an outpouring of lava.

- Venus has no detectable magnetic field, so its core does not support the dynamo effect, which is a puzzle.

- Venus rotates retrograde (backward). This may have been caused by an off-center impact by a very large planetesimal as the planet was forming or by solar tides raised in its thick atmosphere.

- Mars is smaller than Earth but larger than the moon. It has lost the lower-mass atoms from its atmosphere because of its low escape velocity.

- The atmosphere on Mars is very low-density, consisting mostly of carbon dioxide, and the pressure at the surface is too low to prevent water from boiling away.

- Mars has no magnetic field to protect it from the solar wind, and some of its atmosphere probably has been blasted away over its history by the pressure of the solar wind.

- Although 19th-century astronomers thought they saw networks of canals on Mars, images from spacecraft show that Mars is a dry, desert world on which liquid water does not currently exist.

- The southern hemisphere of Mars is old and heavily cratered, but the northern lowlands are smooth and mostly free of craters.

- Images from spacecraft orbiting Mars reveal **outflow channels (p. 483)** that appear to have been cut by massive floods and **valley networks (p. 483)** that resemble dry riverbeds. Crater counts show that these features are in very old terrain.

- The smooth lowlands of Mars's northern hemisphere may have once contained a liquid-water ocean. Some outflow channels lead into the lowlands, and features resembling shorelines have been found.

- Evidence suggests that whatever water Mars retains is now frozen in the crust as permafrost and as large deposits under the polar caps. Where it seeps out, it can cut gullies and form similar flow features, but rivers, lakes, and oceans cannot now exist on Mars because of the low atmospheric pressure.

- There is evidence that Mars once had a molten core that generated a magnetic field, but it has no detectable magnetic field now. Planetary scientists hypothesize that most of the core has solidified, and the molten outer layer of the core is too small to generate a magnetic field.

- The **Noachian period (p. 487)** extended from the formation of the crust to the end of heavy cratering about 3.7 billion years ago. The valley networks formed during this period, which suggests that the atmosphere was denser then, and water fell as rain or snow.

- The **Hesperian period (p. 488)** began as cratering declined and massive lava flows resurfaced some regions. The climate was colder and the atmosphere thinner, with water frozen in the crust. Massive floods and outflow channels seem to have been produced by sudden melting of subsurface ice.

- The **Amazonian period (p. 488)** extended from about 3 billion years ago to the present and is marked by continued low-rate cratering and erosion by wind, and by small amounts of water seeping from subsurface ice.

- Volcanism has been important throughout the history of Mars, and the Tharsis rise is a huge volcanic uplift. Volcanoes were active in the Noachian period and probably still erupt on Mars.

- Olympus Mons is a very large volcano, but it has not sunk into the crust, and that shows that the crust of Mars is now quite thick.

- The development of the Tharsis rise may have altered the rotation of Mars and changed its climate.

- Mars has captured two asteroids into orbit as moons. Phobos and Deimos are small, irregularly shaped, and cratered. Both are tidally locked to Mars.

Review Questions

1. Why might you expect Venus and Earth conditions to be similar?

2. What evidence can you cite that Venus and Mars once had more water than at present? Where did that water come from? Where did it go?

3. What features would you look for in high-resolution radar maps of Venus to search for plate tectonics?

4. What evidence shows that Venus has been resurfaced within the last billion years?

5. Why doesn't Mars have mountain ranges like those on Earth? Why doesn't Earth have large volcanoes like those on Mars?

6. What were the canals on Mars? How do they differ from the outflow channels and valley networks on Mars?

7. Propose an explanation for the nearly pure carbon dioxide atmospheres of Venus and Mars. Why is Earth's atmosphere different?

8. What evidence can you cite that the climate on Mars has changed?

9. How can planetary scientists estimate the ages of the outflow channels and valley networks on Mars?

10. Why are Phobos and Deimos nonspherical? Why is Earth's moon much more spherical?

11. **How Do We Know?** How are a weather radar map and an image of a mountain on Venus related?

Discussion Questions

1. From what you know of Earth, Venus, and Mars, do you expect the volcanoes on Venus and Mars to be active or extinct? Why?

2. If you had a time machine, plus superpowers sufficient to modify or move entire planets, what would you change about Mars, as it was forming, to make its surface environment remain more Earth-like to the present day? How about Venus?

3. Can you make a hypothesis about a single event that might explain both Venus's slow rotation and its geologically recent resurfacing?

4. If humans someday colonize Mars, the biggest problem may be finding water and oxygen. With plenty of solar energy beating down through the thin atmosphere, how might colonizers extract water and oxygen from the Martian environment?

Problems

1. How long would it take radio signals to travel from Earth to Venus and back if Venus were at its nearest point to Earth? At its farthest point from Earth? (*Hint:* The speed of light is 3.00×10^8 meters per second.)

2. The Pioneer Venus orbiter circled Venus with a period of 24 hours. What was its average distance above the *surface* of Venus? (*Hint:* See Chapter 5.)

3. Calculate the velocity of Venus in its orbit around the sun. (*Hint:* See Chapter 5.)

4. What is the maximum angular diameter of Venus as seen from Earth? (*Hint:* Use the small-angle formula, Chapter 3.)

5. If the Magellan spacecraft transmitted radio signals down through the clouds on Venus and heard an echo from a certain spot 0.000133 second before the main echo, how high is the spot above the average surface of Venus? (*Hint:* The speed of light is 3.00×10^8 meters per second.)

6. The smallest feature visible through an Earth-based telescope has an angular diameter of about 1 arc second. If a canal on Mars was just visible when Mars was at its closest to Earth, how wide was the canal? (*Hint:* Use the small-angle formula, Chapter 3.)

7. What is the maximum angular diameter of Phobos as seen from Earth? What surface features should you expect to see from Earth? From the surface of Mars? (*Hints:* Use the small-angle formula, Chapter 3, and use information in the Appendix tables to derive the distances between the objects in question.)

8. What is the maximum angular diameter of Deimos as seen from the surface of Mars? (*Hints:* Use the small-angle formula, Chapter 3, and use information in the Appendix tables to derive the distances between the objects in question.)

9. Deimos is about 12 km in diameter and has a density of 2 g/cm³. What is its mass? (*Hint:* The volume of a sphere is $\frac{4}{3}\pi r^3$.)

Learning to Look

1. Volcano Sif Mons on Venus is shown in this radar image. What kind of volcano is it, and why is it orange in this image? What color would the rock be if you could see it with your own eyes?

NASA

2. Olympus Mons on Mars is a very large volcano. In this image you can see multiple caldera at the top. What do those caldera and the immense size of the volcano indicate about the geology of Mars?

NASA

23 | Comparative Planetology of Jupiter and Saturn

Infrared + visual-wavelength images

Guidepost

As you begin this chapter, you leave behind the psychological security of planetary surfaces. You can imagine standing on the moon, on Mars, or even on Venus, but Jupiter and Saturn have no surfaces. Here you face a new challenge—to use comparative planetology to study worlds so unearthly you cannot imagine really being there. On the other hand, Jupiter and Saturn also have extensive systems of moons and rings. Someday humans may walk on some of the moons and watch erupting volcanoes or stroll through methane rain storms, and then journey to the rings and float among the ring particles. As you study these worlds you will find answers to four essential questions:

— **How do the outer planets compare with the inner planets?**

— **How did Jupiter and Saturn form and evolve?**

— **How is Saturn different from Jupiter?**

— **How did Jupiter's and Saturn's systems of moons and rings form and evolve?**

After learning about the two largest Jovian planets, in the next chapter you will continue your trip away from the sun and visit their two smaller, and in some ways even stranger, siblings, Uranus and Neptune. It will be interesting, but there is no place like home.

A montage of images of Jupiter and its volcanic moon Io taken in 2007 by the New Horizons spacecraft during its Jupiter flyby on the way to Pluto and the Kuiper belt. The prominent bluish-white oval in the near infrared image of Jupiter is the Great Red Spot. The Io image combines visual and near infrared data, showing a major eruption in progress on Io's night side at the northern volcano Tvashtar. Incandescent lava glows red beneath a 330-kilometer-high volcanic plume, whose uppermost portions are illuminated by sunlight. The plume appears blue due to scattering of sunlight by small particles in the plume. (NASA/Johns Hopkins University Applied Physics Laboratory/Southwest Research Institute)

There is something fascinating about science. One gets such wholesale returns of conjecture out of such a trifling investment of fact.

— MARK TWAIN, *LIFE ON THE MISSISSIPPI*

WHEN MARK TWAIN WROTE THE SENTENCES that open this chapter, he was poking gentle fun at science, but he was right. The exciting thing about science isn't the so-called facts, the observations in which scientists have greatest confidence. Rather, the excitement lies in the understanding that scientists get by rubbing a few facts together. Science can take you to strange new worlds such as Jupiter and Saturn, and you can get to know them by combining the available observations with known principles of comparative planetology.

23-1 A Travel Guide to the Outer Planets

IF YOU TRAVEL MUCH, you know that some cities make you feel at home, and some do not. In this and the next chapter, you will visit worlds that are truly un-Earthly. This travel guide will warn you what to expect.

The Outer Planets

The outermost planets in our solar system are Jupiter, Saturn, Uranus, and Neptune—the Jovian planets, meaning they resemble Jupiter. ■ Figure 23-1 compares the four outer worlds, and one striking feature, of course, is their sizes. Figure 23-1 shows Earth in scale to the Jovian planets, and it seems tiny in comparison. You can also see that the four Jovian planets can be divided into two pairs, with Jupiter and Saturn being large and nearly the same size, whereas Uranus and Neptune are smaller but very similar in size to each other.

The other feature you will notice immediately when you look at Figure 23-1 is Saturn's rings. They are bright and beautiful and composed of billions of ice particles, each particle following its own orbit around the planet. Astronomers have discovered that Jupiter, Uranus, and Neptune also have rings, but they are not easily detected from Earth and are not visible in this figure. As you visit these worlds in this chapter and the next, you will be able to compare and contrast four giant planets, four moon systems, and four different sets of planetary rings.

■ Figure 23-1

The principal worlds of the outer solar system are the four massive but low-density Jovian planets, each much larger than Earth. (NASA/JPL/Space Science Institute/University of Arizona)

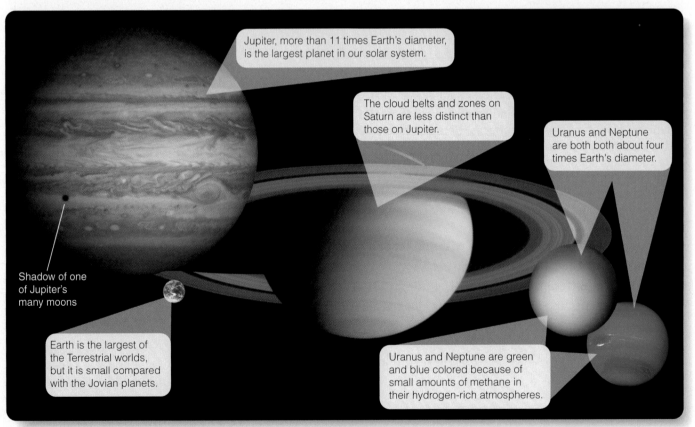

Jupiter, more than 11 times Earth's diameter, is the largest planet in our solar system.

The cloud belts and zones on Saturn are less distinct than those on Jupiter.

Uranus and Neptune are both both about four times Earth's diameter.

Shadow of one of Jupiter's many moons

Earth is the largest of the Terrestrial worlds, but it is small compared with the Jovian planets.

Uranus and Neptune are green and blue colored because of small amounts of methane in their hydrogen-rich atmospheres.

Atmospheres and Interiors

All the Jovian worlds have hydrogen-rich atmospheres filled with clouds. On Jupiter and Saturn, you can see that the clouds form dark belts and light zones that circle the planets like the stripes on a child's ball. This form of atmospheric circulation is called **belt–zone circulation.** You will find traces of belts and zones on Uranus and Neptune, but they are not very distinct. All the Jovian worlds also have giant circulating storms, the primary example of which is Jupiter's Great Red Spot, which is more than twice the size of Earth. These Jovian storms are comparable to Terrestrial hurricanes, but they can last for centuries. The Great Red Spot storm has been going strong at least since the first telescope observations of Jupiter 400 years ago.

The gaseous atmospheres of the Jovian planets are not very deep. Jupiter's atmosphere makes up only about one percent of its radius. Below that, Jupiter and Saturn are composed of liquid hydrogen, so an older term for these planets, the *gas giants*, reflects a **Common Misconception.** In fact they are made mostly of liquid rather than gas and could more correctly be called the *liquid giants*. Only near their centers could these worlds contain dense material with the composition of rock and metal, but the sizes of these cores are not well known.

Uranus and Neptune are sometimes called the ice giants because they contain a great deal of water, much of which is probably in a solid form. Like Jupiter and Saturn, Uranus and Neptune contain denser material in their cores.

On your visits to the Jovian planets, notice that they are low-density worlds that are rich in hydrogen. Jupiter and Saturn are mostly liquid hydrogen, and even Uranus and Neptune contain a much larger proportion of hydrogen than does Earth. Recall from Chapter 19 that these worlds are hydrogen-rich and low density because they formed in the outer solar nebula where water vapor could freeze to form tremendous amounts of tiny ice particles. These hydrogen-rich ice particles accreted to begin forming the planets; and, once the growing planets became massive enough, they could draw in more hydrogen gas directly by gravitational collapse.

Satellite Systems

All of the Jovian worlds have large satellite systems. Around each Jovian planet, the moons can be classified into two groups: (1) the **regular satellites,** which tend to be large and orbit in the prograde direction, relatively close to their parent planet, with low inclinations to the planet's equator; versus (2) the **irregular satellites,** which tend to be smaller than the regular satellites, sometimes have retrograde and/or highly inclined orbits, and are generally far from their parent planet. Astronomers have evidence that the regular satellites formed approximately where they are now as the planets formed but that the irregular satellites are mostly, if not all, captured objects.

As you focus on the moons of the Jovian worlds, look for evidence of two processes. The orbits of some moons may have been modified by interactions with other moons, so that they now revolve around their planet in mutual resonances. The same process may allow moons to affect the orbital motions of particles in planetary rings.

The second process allows tides to heat the interiors of some moons and produce geological activity on their surfaces, including volcanoes and lava flows. You have learned that the entire solar system received a heavy bombardment after the planets formed, and heavily cratered surfaces are old, so when you see a section of a moon's surface, or an entire moon, that has few craters, you know that moon must have been geologically active since the end of the heavy bombardment.

SCIENTIFIC ARGUMENT

Why do you expect the outer planets to be low-density worlds?
To build this scientific argument, you need to think about how the planets formed from the solar nebula. In Chapter 19, you discovered that the inner planets could not incorporate ice when they formed because it was too hot near the sun; but, in the outer solar nebula, the growing planets could accumulate lots of ice. Eventually they grew massive enough to grow by gravitational collapse, and that pulled in hydrogen and helium gas. That makes the outer planets low-density worlds.

The outer planets may be unearthly, but they are understandable. For example, extend your argument. **Why do you expect the outer planets to have rings and moons?**

23-2 Jupiter

JUPITER IS THE MOST MASSIVE of the Jovian planets, containing more material than all of the other planets combined. This high mass accentuates some processes that are less obvious or nearly absent on the other Jovian worlds. Just as you used Earth as the basis of comparison for your study of the Terrestrial planets, you can examine Jupiter in detail and use it as a standard in your comparative study of the other Jovian planets.

Surveying Jupiter

Jupiter is extreme because it is big, massive, mostly liquid hydrogen, and very hot inside. The preceding facts are common knowledge among astronomers, but you should demand an explanation of how they know these facts. Often the most interesting thing about a fact isn't the fact itself but how it is known.

At its closest point to Earth, Jupiter is about eight times farther away than Mars, but even a small telescope will reveal that the disk of Jupiter appears more than twice as big as the disk of Mars. If you use the small-angle formula (see Chapter 3), you can compute the diameter of Jupiter—1.4×10^5 km, which is about 11 times Earth's diameter (**Celestial Profile 7**).

You can see that Jupiter is massive by watching its moons race around it at high speed. Io is the innermost of the four Galilean moons, and its orbit is just a bit larger than the orbit of our moon around Earth. Io streaks around its orbit in less than two days, whereas Earth's moon takes a month. Jupiter has to be a very massive world to hold on to such a rapidly moving moon (■ Figure 23-2). In fact, you can use the radius of Io's orbit and its orbital period in Newton's version of Kepler's third law (see Chapter 5) to calculate the mass of Jupiter, which is 1.9×10^{27} kg, 318 times Earth's mass.

Learning the size and mass of Jupiter is relatively easy, but you might wonder how astronomers know that it is made mostly of hydrogen. The first step is to divide mass by volume to find Jupiter's average density, 1.34 g/cm³. Of course, it is denser at the center and less dense near the surface, but this average density reveals that it can't contain much rock. Rock has a density of 2.5 to 4 g/cm³, so Jupiter must contain material mostly of lower density, such as hydrogen.

Spectra recorded from Earth and from spacecraft visiting Jupiter show that the composition of Jupiter is much like that of the sun—it is mostly hydrogen and helium. This fact was confirmed in 1995 when a probe from the Galileo spacecraft parachuted into the atmosphere and radioed its results back to Earth. Jupiter is mostly hydrogen and helium, with traces of heavier atoms that form molecules such as methane (CH_4), ammonia (NH_3), and water (■ Table 23-1).

Just as astronomers can build mathematical models of the interiors of stars, they can use the equations that describe gravity, energy, and the compressibility of matter to build mathematical models of the interior of Jupiter. These models reveal that the interior of the planet is mostly liquid hydrogen containing small amounts of heavier elements. The pressure and temperature are higher than the **critical point** for hydrogen, and that means there is no difference between gaseous hydrogen and liquid hydrogen. If you parachuted into Jupiter, you would fall through the gaseous atmosphere and notice the density of the surrounding fluid gradually increasing until you were in a liquid, but you would never splash into a liquid surface.

Roughly a quarter of the way to the center, the pressure is high enough to force the hydrogen to change into **liquid metallic hydrogen,** which is a very good electrical conductor. Because liquid metallic hydrogen has been very difficult to create and study in the laboratory so far, its properties are poorly understood. That is the reason why the models are uncertain about the depth of the transition from normal to metallic liquid hydrogen.

The models are also uncertain about the presence of a heavy element core in Jupiter. The planet contains about 30 Earth masses of elements heavier than helium, but much of that may be suspended in the convectively stirred liquid hydrogen. Measurements by orbiting spacecraft indicate that no more than 10 Earth masses are included in a heavy element core. Some astronomy books refer to this as a rocky core, but, if it exists, it

Jupiter is mostly a liquid planet. It may have a small core of heavy elements not much bigger than Earth. (NASA/JPL/University of Arizona)

Celestial Profile 7: Jupiter

Motion:

Average distance from the sun	5.20 AU (7.78×10^8 km)
Eccentricity of orbit	0.048
Inclination of orbit to ecliptic	1.3°
Average orbital velocity	13.1 km/s
Orbital period	11.87 y
Period of rotation	9.92 h
Inclination of equator to orbit	3.1°

Characteristics:

Equatorial diameter	1.43×10^5 km (11.2 $D_\oplus$)
Mass	1.90×10^{27} kg (318 $M_\oplus$)
Average density	1.34 g/cm³
Gravity at base of clouds	2.54 Earth gravities
Escape velocity	61 km/s (5.4 $V_\oplus$)
Temperature at cloud tops	−130°C (−200°F)
Albedo	0.51
Oblateness	0.064

Personality Point:

Jupiter is named for the Roman king of the gods, and it is the largest planet in our solar system. It can be very bright in the night sky, and its cloud belts and four largest moons can be seen through even a small telescope. Its moons are visible even with a good pair of binoculars mounted on a tripod or braced against a wall.

It is obvious that Jupiter is a very massive planet when you compare the motion of Jupiter's moon Io with Earth's moon. Although Io is 10 percent farther from Jupiter, it travels 17 times faster in its orbit than does Earth's moon around Earth. Clearly, Jupiter's gravitational field is much stronger than Earth's, and that means Jupiter must be very massive.

■ **Table 23-1** | **Composition of Jupiter and Saturn (by Number of Molecules)**

Molecule	Jupiter (%)	Saturn (%)
H_2	86	93
He	13	5
H_2O	0.1	0.1
CH_4	0.1	0.2
NH_3	0.02	0.01

cannot be anything like the rock you know on Earth. The center of Jupiter is five or six times hotter than the surface of the sun and is prevented from exploding into vapor only by the tremendous pressure. If there is a core, it is "rocky" only in the sense that it contains heavy elements.

How do astronomers know Jupiter is hot inside? Infrared observations show that Jupiter is glowing strongly in the infrared, radiating 1.7 times more energy than it receives from the sun. That observation, combined with models of its interior, provides an estimate of its internal temperature. You will learn later in this chapter that Saturn resembles Jupiter in this respect.

You can tell that Jupiter is mostly a liquid just by looking at it. If you measure a photograph of Jupiter, you will discover that it is slightly flattened; it is a bit over 6 percent larger in diameter through its equator than through its poles. This is referred to as Jupiter's **oblateness.** The amount of flattening depends on the speed of rotation and on the rigidity of the planet. Jupiter's flattened shape shows that the planet cannot be as rigid as a Terrestrial planet and must have a liquid interior.

Basic observations and the known laws of physics can tell you a great deal about Jupiter's interior. Its vast magnetic field can tell you even more.

Jupiter's Magnetic Field

As early as the 1950s, astronomers detected radio noise coming from Jupiter and recognized it as synchrotron radiation. That form of radio energy is produced by fast electrons spiraling in a magnetic field, so it was obvious that Jupiter had a magnetic field.

In 1973 and 1974, two Pioneer spacecraft flew past Jupiter, followed in 1979 by two Voyager spacecraft. Those probes found that Jupiter has a magnetic field about 14 times stronger than the Earth's field. Evidently the field is produced by the dynamo effect operating in the highly conductive liquid metallic hydrogen as it is circulated by convection and spun by the rapid rotation of the planet. This powerful magnetic field dominates a huge magnetosphere around the planet. Compare the size of Jupiter's field with that of Earth in ■ Figure 23-3.

Jupiter's magnetic field deflects the solar wind and traps high-energy particles in radiation belts much more intense than Earth's. The radiation is more intense because Jupiter's magnetic field is stronger and can trap and hold more particles, and higher-energy particles, than Earth's field can. The spacecraft passing through the radiation belts received radiation doses equivalent to a billion chest X-rays—at least 100 times the lethal dose for a human. Some of the electronics on the spacecraft were damaged by the radiation.

You will recall that Earth's magnetosphere interacts with the solar wind to produce auroras, and the same process occurs on Jupiter. Charged particles in the magnetosphere leak downward along the magnetic field, and, where they enter the atmosphere,

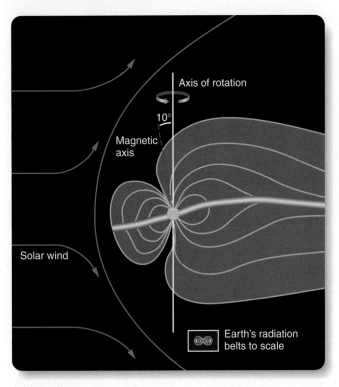

■ Figure 23-3

Jupiter's magnetic field is large and powerful. It traps particles from the solar wind to form powerful radiation belts. The rapid rotation of the planet forces the slightly inclined magnetic field to wobble up and down as the planet rotates. Earth's magnetosphere and radiation belts are shown to scale.

they produce auroras 1000 times more luminous than those on Earth. The auroras on Jupiter, like those on Earth, occur in rings around the magnetic poles (■ Figure 23-4).

The four Galilean moons of Jupiter orbit inside the magnetosphere, and some of the heavier ions in the radiation belts come from the innermost moon, Io. As you will see later in this chapter, Io has active volcanoes that spew gas and ash. Because Io orbits with a period of 1.8 days, and Jupiter's magnetic field rotates in only 10 hours, the wobbling magnetic field rushes past Io at high speed, sweeping up stray particles, accelerating them to high energy, and spreading them around Io's orbit in a doughnut of ionized gas called the **Io plasma torus.**

Jupiter's magnetic field interacts with Io to produce a powerful electric current (about a million amperes) that flows through a curving path called the **Io flux tube** from Jupiter out to Io and back to Jupiter. Small spots of bright auroras lie at the two points where the Io flux tube enters Jupiter's atmosphere (Figure 23-4).

Fluctuations in the auroras reveal that the solar wind buffets Jupiter's magnetosphere, but some of the fluctuations seem to be caused by changes in the magnetic dynamo deep inside the planet. In this way, studies of the auroras on Jupiter may help astronomers learn more about its liquid depths.

Jupiter's powerful magnetic field is invisible to your eyes, but the swirling cloud belts are beautifully visible in their complexity.

Jupiter's Atmosphere

As you learned earlier, Jupiter is a liquid world that has no surface. The gaseous atmosphere blends gradually with the liquid hydrogen interior. Below the clouds of Jupiter lies the largest ocean in the solar system—an ocean that has no surface and no waves.

When you look at Jupiter, all you see are clouds. You can detect a nearly transparent hydrogen and helium atmosphere above the cloud tops by noticing that Jupiter has limb darkening, just as the sun does (see Chapter 8). When you look near the limb of Jupiter (the edge of its disk), the clouds are much dimmer (look back at Figure 23-1) because it is nearly sunset or sunrise along the limb. If you were on Jupiter at that location, you would see the sun just above the horizon, and sunlight arriving there would be dimmed by passing through the planet's atmosphere. In addition, sunlight reflected from the clouds must travel back out through the atmosphere at a steep angle to reach Earth, dimming the light further. Jupiter is brighter near the center of the disk because the sunlight shines nearly straight down on the clouds.

Study **Jupiter's Atmosphere** on pages 500–501 and notice four important ideas:

1 The atmosphere is hydrogen-rich, and the clouds are confined to a shallow layer.

2 The cloud layers lie at certain temperatures within the atmosphere where ammonia (NH_3), ammonium hydrosulfide (NH_4SH), and water (H_2O) can condense to form ice particles.

3 The belt–zone circulation is driven by high- and low-pressure areas related to those on Earth.

4 Finally, the major spots on Jupiter, although they are only circulating storms, can remain stable for decades or even centuries.

Circulation in Jupiter's atmosphere is not totally understood. Observations made by the Cassini spacecraft as it raced past Jupiter on its way to Saturn revealed that the dark belts, which were thought to be entirely regions of sinking gas, contain small rising storm systems too small to have been seen in images by previous probes. Evidently, the general circulation usually attributed to the belts and zones is much more complex when it is observed in more detail. Further understanding of the small-scale motions in Jupiter's atmosphere may have to await future planetary probes.

The highly complex spacecraft that have visited Jupiter are examples of how technology can give scientists the raw data they need to form their understanding of nature. Science is about understanding nature, and Jupiter is an entirely new kind of planet in your study. In fact, Jupiter has another feature that you did not find anywhere among the Terrestrial planets. Jupiter has a ring.

Jupiter's huge magnetic field funnels energy from the solar wind down to form rings of auroras around its magnetic poles, which are tipped relative to its rotational poles. The same aurora phenomenon happens on Earth. The Io flux tube connects the small moon Io to the planet and carries a powerful electric current that creates spots of auroras where it touches the planet's atmosphere. (Jupiter: John Clarke, University of Michigan, NASA; Flux tube: NASA)

Visual-wavelength image

Auroral ring

Base of the Io flux tube

UV image

Rotation

UV image

Jupiter's rotation carries the atmosphere past the base of the Io flux tube.

Auroral ring

a

The Io flux tube is an electric circuit connecting Io to Jupiter's magnetic field.

Visual

Io

UV

b

Jupiter's Ring

Astronomers have known for centuries that Saturn has rings, but it was not until 1979 when the Voyager 1 spacecraft sent back photos that Jupiter's ring was discovered. The discovery was confirmed later by difficult ground-based measurements. Less than one percent as bright as Saturn's rings, the ghostly ring around Jupiter is a puzzle. What is it made of? Why is it there? A few simple observations will help you solve some of these puzzles.

Saturn's rings are made of bright ice chunks, but the particles in Jupiter's ring are very dark and reddish. This is evidence that its ring is rocky rather than icy. You can also conclude that the ring particles are mostly microscopic. Photos show that Jupiter's ring is very bright when illuminated from behind (■ Figure 23-5). In other words, it is scattering light forward. Efficient **forward scattering** occurs when particles have diameters roughly the same as the wavelength of light, a few millionths of a meter. Large particles do not scatter light forward, so a ring filled with basketball-size particles would look dark when illuminated from

behind. The forward scattering tells you that Jupiter's ring is made mostly of particles about the size of those in smoke.

Larger particles are not entirely ruled out. A sparse component of rocky objects ranging from pieces of gravel to boulders is possible, but objects larger than 1 km would have been detected in spacecraft photos. The vast majority of the ring particles are microscopic dust.

The size of the ring particles is a clue to their origin, and so is their location. They orbit inside the **Roche limit,** the distance from a planet within which a moon cannot hold itself together by its own gravity. If a moon orbits relatively far from its planet, then the moon's gravity will be much greater than the tidal forces caused by the planet, and the moon will be able to hold itself together. If, however, a planet's moon comes inside the Roche limit, the tidal forces can overcome its gravity and pull the moon apart. The International Space Station can orbit inside Earth's Roche limit because it is held together by bolts and welds, and a single large rock can survive inside the Roche limit if it is strong

Jupiter's Atmosphere

1 Humans will probably never visit Jupiter's atmosphere. Its cloud layers are deathly cold, and the deeper layers that are warmer have a crushingly high pressure. There is no free oxygen to breathe; the gases are roughly three-quarters hydrogen and a quarter helium, plus small amounts of water vapor, methane, ammonia, and similar molecules. Traces of sulfur and molecules containing sulfur probably make it smell bad. Of course, Jupiter has no surface, so there isn't even a place to stand.

Belts are dark bands of clouds.

Zones are bright bands of clouds.

Shadow of Europa

NASA

Jupiter's moon Europa

NASA/JPL/Univ. of AZ

Lightning bolts are common in Jupiter's turbulent clouds.

Artist Concept

Hughes Aircraft Co

1a The only spacecraft to enter Jupiter's atmosphere was the Galileo probe. Released from the Galileo spacecraft, the probe entered Jupiter's atmosphere in 1995. It parachuted through the upper atmosphere of clear hydrogen, released its heat shield, and then fell through Jupiter's stormy atmosphere until it was crushed by the increasing pressure.

Jupiter's atmosphere is a very thin layer of turbulent gas above the liquid interior. It makes up only about 1 percent of the radius of the planet.

The Great Red Spot at right is a giant circulating storm in one of the southern zones. It has lasted at least 300 years since astronomers first noticed it after the invention of the telescope. Smaller spots are also circulating storms.

NASA/JPL, Univ. of AZ

...ayers of clouds contain ammonia hydrosulfide crystals, ...nd deeper still lies a cloud layer of water droplets. ...hese compounds are normally white, so planetary ...cientists think the colors arise from small amounts of ...ther molecules formed in reactions powered by ...ghtning or sunlight.

...you could put thermometers in Jupiter's atmosphere at ...ifferent levels, you would discover that the temperature ...ses below the uppermost clouds.

...ar below the clouds, the temperature and pressure ...imb so high the gaseous atmosphere merges ...radually with the liquid hydrogen interior and there is ...o surface.

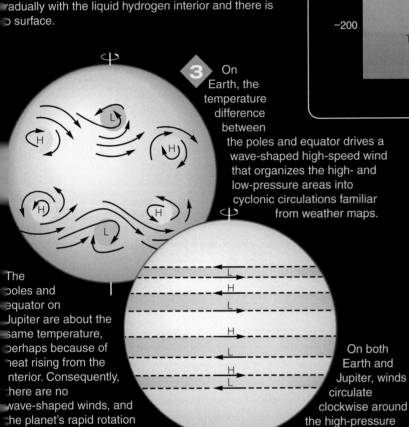

3 On Earth, the temperature difference between the poles and equator drives a wave-shaped high-speed wind that organizes the high- and low-pressure areas into cyclonic circulations familiar from weather maps.

...The ...poles and ...equator on ...Jupiter are about the ...same temperature, ...perhaps because of ...heat rising from the ...nterior. Consequently, ...here are no ...wave-shaped winds, and ...the planet's rapid rotation ...stretches the high- and ...ow-pressure areas into belts and ...zones that circle the planet.

On both Earth and Jupiter, winds circulate clockwise around the high-pressure areas in the northern hemisphere and counterclockwise south of the equator.

Zones are brighter than belts because rising gas forms clouds high in the atmosphere, where sunlight is strong.

North   Equator

4 Three circulating storms visible as white ovals since the 1930s ...merged in 1998 to form a single white ...oval. In 2006, the storm intensified and ...urned red like the Great Red Spot. The ...reason for the red color is unknown, but it ...may show that the storm is bringing material ...up from lower in the atmosphere.

...Storms in Jupiter's atmosphere may be stable ...or decades or centuries, but astronomers had ...never before witnessed the appearance of a new ...red spot. It may eventually vanish or develop further. ...Even the Great Red Spot may someday vanish.

Great Red Spot

Red Jr.

Enhanced visible + infrared

Visual-wavelength images

■ Figure 23-5

(a) The main ring of Jupiter, illuminated from behind, glows brightly in this visual-wavelength image made by the Galileo spacecraft while it was within Jupiter's shadow. (b) Digital enhancement and false color reveal the halo of ring particles that extends above and below the main ring. The halo is just visible in panel a. (c) Structure in the ring is probably caused by the gravitational influence of Jupiter's inner moons. (a. and b.: NASA; c. NASA/Johns Hopkins University Applied Physics Lab/Southwest Research Institute)

enough not to break. However, a moon composed of separate rocks and particles held together by their mutual gravity could not survive inside a planet's Roche limit. Tidal forces would destroy such a moon. If a planet and its moon have the same average densities, the Roche limit is at 2.44 times the planet's radius. Jupiter's main ring has an outer radius of 130,000 km (1.8 Jupiter radii) and lies inside Jupiter's Roche limit. The rings of Saturn, Uranus, and Neptune also lie within those planets' respective Roche limits.

Now you can understand the dust in Jupiter's ring. If a dust speck gets knocked loose from a larger rock orbiting inside the Roche limit, the rock's gravity cannot hold the dust speck. And the billions of dust specks in the ring can't pull themselves together to make a larger body—a moon—because of the tidal forces inside the Roche limit.

You can also be sure that the ring particles are not old. The pressure of sunlight and Jupiter's powerful magnetic field alter the orbits of the particles, and they gradually spiral into the planet. Images show faint ring material extending down toward Jupiter's cloud tops, and this is evidently dust specks spiraling inward. Dust is also lost from the ring as electromagnetic effects

force it out of the plane of the ring to form a low-density halo above and below the ring (Figure 23-5b). Yet another reason the ring particles can't be old is that the intense radiation around Jupiter can grind dust specks down to nothing in a century or so. For all these reasons, the rings seen today can't be made up of material that has been in the form of small particles for the entire time since the formation of Jupiter.

Obviously, the rings of Jupiter must be continuously resupplied with new material. Dust particles can be chipped off rocks ranging in size from gravel to boulders within the ring, and small moons that orbit near the outer edge of the rings lose particles as they are hit by meteorite impacts. Observations made by the Galileo spacecraft show that the main ring is densest at its outer edge, where the small moon Adrastea orbits, and that another small moon, Metis, orbits inside the ring. Clearly these moons must be structurally strong to withstand Jupiter's tidal forces. Images from the Voyager and Galileo probes also reveal much fainter rings, called the **gossamer rings,** extending twice as far from the planet as the main ring. These gossamer rings are most dense at the orbits of two small moons, Amalthea and Thebe, more evidence that ring particles are being blasted into space by impacts on the moons.

Besides supplying the rings with particles, the moons help confine the ring particles and keep them from spreading outward. You will find that this is an important process in planetary rings when you study the rings of Saturn later in this chapter.

Your exploration of Jupiter reveals that it is much more than just a big planet. It is the gravitational and magnetic center of an entire community of objects. Occasionally the community suffers an intruder.

Giant Impacts in the Outer Solar System

Comets are very common in the solar system, and Jupiter probably is hit by comets more often than most planets due to its strong gravity. No one had ever seen it happen until 1994, when fragments from a comet disrupted by Jupiter's tidal forces a few years earlier looped back and smashed into the planet. Those impacts are covered more fully, including images, in Chapter 25 within the context of a discussion of the effects on Earth of comet and asteroid impacts.

The comet collision with Jupiter was an astonishing spectacle, but what can it tell you about Jupiter? In fact, the separate impacts were revealing in two ways. First, astronomers used the impacts as probes of Jupiter's atmosphere. By making assumptions about the nature of Jupiter's atmosphere and by using supercomputers, astronomers created models of a high-velocity projectile penetrating into Jupiter's upper atmosphere. By comparing the observed impacts with the models, astronomers were able to fine-tune the models to better represent Jupiter's atmosphere. This method of comparing models with reality is a critical part of science.

Second, the spectacle is a reminder that asteroids and comets, the leftover construction debris from the formation of the solar system, are expected to hit all the planets and their moons occasionally. In 2009, Australian amateur astronomer Anthony Wesley discovered a dark spot that appeared suddenly on Jupiter, and alerted the world scientific community. The spot is apparently the scar of a new impact by an asteroid or comet. Astronomers estimate that Jupiter probably is hit by an object larger than 1 km several times per century. With no solid surface, Jupiter itself does not display its history of impacts, but its moons do. The fact that Jupiter's moons are observed to have radically different crater counts is a clue that their geologic histories have differed.

The History of Jupiter

Your goal in studying any planet is to be able to tell its story—to describe how it got to be the way it is. While you can understand part of the story of Jupiter, there is still much to learn.

If the solar nebula theory for the origin of the solar system is correct, then Jupiter formed from the colder gases of the outer solar nebula, where ices of water and other molecules were able to condense. Thus, Jupiter grew rapidly and became massive enough to capture hydrogen and helium gas from the solar nebula and form a deep liquid hydrogen envelope. Models are uncertain as to whether a heavy element core survives; it may have been mixed in with the convecting liquid hydrogen envelope, and astronomers estimate that the mass of Jupiter's heavy element core is between 0 and 10 Earth masses.

In the interior of Jupiter, hydrogen exists as liquid metallic hydrogen, a very good electrical conductor. The planet's rapid

rotation, coupled with the outward flow of heat from its hot interior, drives a dynamo effect that produces a powerful magnetic field. That vast magnetic field traps high-energy particles from the solar wind to form intense radiation belts and auroras.

The rapid rotation and large size of Jupiter cause belt–zone circulation in its atmosphere. Heat flowing upward from the interior causes rising currents in the bright zones, and cooler gas sinks in the dark belts. As on Earth, winds blow at the margins of these regions, and large spots appear to be cyclonic disturbances. Internal heat has been escaping since Jupiter formed, so you can guess that Jupiter's atmospheric circulation and storms were stronger in the distant past and will diminish in the future.

Although the age of planet building is long past, debris in the form of meteorites and occasional comets continue to hit Jupiter, as it does all the planets. Any debris left over from the formation of Jupiter would have been blown away by sunlight and the solar wind or destroyed by other processes long ago, so the dust trapped in Jupiter's thin ring must be young. It probably comes from meteorites hitting and eroding the innermost moons.

Your study of Jupiter has been challenging because it is so unlike Earth. Most of the features and processes you found on the Terrestrial planets are missing on Jupiter, but, as the prototype of the Jovian worlds, it earns its place as the ruler of the solar system.

SCIENTIFIC ARGUMENT

How do astronomers know Jupiter is hot inside?
A scientific argument is a way to test ideas, and sometimes it is helpful to test even the most basic ideas. You know that something is hot if you touch it and it burns your fingers, but you can't touch Jupiter. You also know something is hot if it is glowing bright red—it is red hot. But Jupiter is not glowing red hot. You can tell that something is hot if you can feel heat when you hold your hand near it. That is, you can detect infrared radiation with your skin. In the case of Jupiter, you would need greater sensitivity than the back of your hand, but infrared telescopes reveal that Jupiter is a source of infrared radiation; it is glowing in the infrared. Sunlight would warm Jupiter a little bit, but it is emitting 70 percent more infrared than it should. That means it must be hot inside. From models of the interior, astronomers conclude that the center must be five or six times hotter than the surface of the sun to make the surface of the planet glow as much as it does in the infrared.

Astronomical understanding is usually based on simple observations, so build an argument to answer the following simple question. **How do astronomers know that Jupiter has a low density?**

23-3 Jupiter's Family of Moons

HOW MANY MOONS DOES JUPITER HAVE? Astronomers are finding many small moons, and the count is now over 60. (You will have to check the Internet to get the latest figure because more moons are discovered every year.) Most of these moons are small and

■ **Figure 23-6**

The Gallilean satellites of Jupiter from left to right are Io, Europa, Ganymede, and Callisto. The circle shows the size of Earth's moon. (NASA)

rocky, and many are probably captured asteroids. Four of the moons, those discovered by Galileo and now called the **Galilean satellites,** are large and have interesting geologies (■ Figure 23-6).

Your study of the moons of Jupiter will illustrate three important principles in comparative planetology. First, a body's composition depends on the temperature of the material from which it formed. This is illustrated by the prevalence of ice as a building material in the outer solar system, where sunlight is weak. You are already familiar with the second principle: that cratering can reveal the age of a surface. Also, as you have seen in your study of the Terrestrial planets, internal heat has a powerful influence over the geology of these larger moons.

Callisto: An Ancient Surface

The outermost of Jupiter's four large moons, Callisto, is half again as large in diameter as Earth's moon. Like all of Jupiter's larger satellites, Callisto is tidally locked to its planet, keeping the same side forever facing Jupiter. From its gravitational influence on passing spacecraft, astronomers can calculate Callisto's mass, and dividing that mass by its volume shows that its density is 1.8 g/cm³. Ice has a density of about 1 and rock 2.5 to 4 g/cm³, so Callisto must be a mixture of rock and ice.

Images from the Voyager and Galileo spacecraft show that the surface of Callisto is dark, dirty ice heavily pocked with craters (■ Figure 23-7). Old, icy surfaces in the solar system become dark because of dust added by meteorites and because meteorite impacts vaporize water, leaving any dust and rock in the ice behind to form a dirty crust. You may have seen the same thing happen to a city snowbank. As the snow evaporates over a few days, the crud in the snow is left behind to form a dirty rind. Break through that dirty surface, and the snow is much cleaner underneath.

Spectra of Callisto's surface show that in most places it is a 50:50 mix of ice and rock, but some areas are ice free. Nevertheless, the slumped shapes of craters suggests that the outer 10 km of

this moon is mostly frozen water; ice isn't very strong, so big piles of it tend to slump under their own weight. The disagreement between the spectra and the shapes of craters can be understood when you recall that the spectra contain information about only the outer 1 mm of the surface, which can be quite dirty, while the shapes of craters tell you about the outermost 10 km, which appear to be rich in ice.

Delicate measurements of the shape of Callisto's gravitational field were made by the Galileo spacecraft as it flew by. Those measurements show that Callisto has never fully differentiated to form a dense core and a lower-density mantle. Its interior is a mixture of rock and ice rather than having distinct layers of different composition. This is consistent with the observation that Callisto has only a weak magnetic field of its own. A strong magnetic field could be generated by the dynamo effect in a liquid convecting core, and Callisto has no core. It does, however,

Visual-wavelength images

■ **Figure 23-7**

The dark surface of Callisto is dirty ice marked by craters in these images. The youngest craters look bright because they have dug down to cleaner ice. Valhalla is the 4000 km (2500 mi) diameter scar of a giant impact feature, one of the largest in the solar system. Valhalla is so large and old that the icy crust has flowed back to partially heal itself, and the outer rings of Valhalla are shallow troughs marking fractures in the crust. (NASA) interact with Jupiter's magnetic field in a way that suggests it has a layer of liquid water roughly 10 km thick about 100 km below its icy surface. Slow radioactive decay in Callisto's interior may produce enough heat to keep this layer of water from freezing.

Ganymede: An Obscure Past

The next Galilean moon inward is Ganymede, larger than Mercury, and over three-quarters the diameter of Mars. In fact, Ganymede is the largest moon in the solar system. Its density is 1.9 g/cm³, and its influence on the Galileo spacecraft reveals that it is differentiated into a rocky core, an ice-rich mantle, and a crust of ice 500 km thick. It may even have a small inner iron core. Ganymede is large enough for radioactive decay to have melted its interior when it formed, allowing rock and iron to sink to its center.

Ganymede's surface hints at an active past. Although a third of the surface is old, dark, and cratered like Callisto's, the rest is marked by bright parallel grooves. Because this bright **grooved terrain** (■ Figure 23-8a) contains fewer craters, it must be younger.

Observations show that the bright terrain was produced when the icy crust broke and water flooded up from below and froze. As the surface broke over and over, sets of parallel groves were formed. Some low-lying regions are smooth and appear to have been flooded by water. Spectra reveal concentrations of salts such as those that would be left behind by the evaporation of mineral-rich water. Also, some features in or near the bright terrain appear to be caldera formed when subsurface water drained away and the surface collapsed (Figure 23-8b).

The Galileo spacecraft found that Ganymede has a magnetic field about 10 percent as strong as Earth's. It even has its own magnetosphere inside the larger magnetosphere of Jupiter. Mathematical models calculated by planetary scientists do not predict that a magnetic field this strong should arise from the dynamo effect in a liquid water mantle layer with the size and location of the one in Ganymede, and there does not appear to be enough heat in Ganymede for it to have a molten metallic core. Thus, the cause of Ganymede's unique magnetic field remains a puzzle. One hypothesis is that the magnetic field is left over and frozen into the rock from a time when Ganymede was hotter and more active.

Ganymede's magnetic field fluctuates with the 10-hour period of Jupiter's rotation. The rotation of the planet sweeps its tilted magnetic field past the moon, and the two fields interact. That interaction reveals that the moon has a layer of liquid water about 170 km (110 mi) below its surface. The data indicate that the water layer is about 5 km (3 mi) thick. It is possible that the water layer was thicker and closer to the surface long ago when the interior of the moon was warmer. That might explain the flooding that appears to have formed the bright grooved terrain.

Ganymede orbits rather close to massive Jupiter, and that exposes it to two unusual processes that many worlds never experience. **Tidal heating,** the frictional heating of a body by changing tides (■ Figure 23-9a), could have heated Ganymede's interior and added to the heat generated by radioactive decay. In its current nearly circular orbit, this moon experiences little or no tidal heating. But, at some point in the past, interactions with the

Visual-wavelength images

■ Figure 23-8

(a) This color-enhanced image of Ganymede shows the frosty poles at top and bottom, the old dark terrain, and the brighter grooved terrain. (b) A band of bright terrain runs from lower left to upper right, and a collapsed area, a possible caldera, lies at the center in this visual-wavelength image. Calderas form where subsurface liquid has drained away, and the bright areas do contain other features probably due to flooding by water. (NASA)

■ **Figure 23-9**

Two effects on planetary satellites. (a) Tidal heating occurs when changing tides cause friction within a moon. (b) The focusing of meteoroids exposes satellites in inner orbits to more impacts than satellites in outer orbits receive.

other moons could have pushed Ganymede into a more eccentric orbit. Tidal forces due to Jupiter's gravity would have deformed the moon, and as Ganymede followed its orbit, varying in distance from Jupiter, tides would have flexed it, and friction would have heated it. Such an episode of tidal heating might have been enough to drive a dynamo to produce a magnetic field and break the crust to make the bright terrain.

The second process that affects Ganymede is the inward focusing of meteorites. Because massive planets like Jupiter draw debris inward, the closer a moon orbits to the planet, the more often it will be struck by meteorites (Figure 23-9b). You should expect such a moon to have lots of craters, but the bright terrain on Ganymede has few craters. That part of Ganymede's surface must be only about 1 billion years old, and this should alert you that the Galilean moons are not just dead lumps of rock and ice. The closer you get to Jupiter, the more active the moons are.

Europa: A Hidden Ocean

The next Galilean moon inward is Europa, which is a bit smaller than Earth's moon (Figure 23-6). Europa has a density of 3.0 g/cm³, so it must be mostly rock and metal. Yet its surface is ice.

Europa lies closer to Jupiter than Ganymede, so it should be exposed to more meteorite impacts than Callisto or Ganymede, yet the icy crust of

Europa is almost free of craters. Recent craters such as Pwyll are bright, but most are hardly more than blemishes in the ice (■ Figures 23-10). Evidently the surface of Europa is active and erases craters almost as fast as they form. The number of impact scars on Europa suggests that the average age of its surface is only 10 million years. Other signs of activity include long cracks in the icy crust and regions where the crust has broken into sections that have moved apart as if they were icebergs floating on water (Figure 23-10c).

Europa's clean, bright face also tells you its surface is young. The albedo of the surface is 0.69, meaning that it reflects 69 percent of the light that hits it. This high albedo is produced by clean ice. You have discovered that old, icy surfaces tend to be very dark, so Europa's high albedo means the surface is active, covering older surfaces with fresh ice.

Europa is too small to have retained much heat from its formation or from radioactive decay, and the Galileo spacecraft

■ **Figure 23-10**

(a) The icy surface of Europa is shown here in natural color. Many faults are visible on its surface, but very few craters. The bright crater is Pwyll, a young impact feature. (b) This circular bull's-eye is 140 km (90 mi) in diameter. It is the remains of an impact by an object estimated to have been about 10 km in diameter. Notice the younger cracks and faults that cross the older impact feature. (c) Like icebergs on the Arctic Ocean, blocks of crust on Europa appear to have floated apart. Spectra show that the blue ice is stained by salts such as those that would be left behind by mineral-rich water welling up from below and evaporating. White areas are ejecta from the impact that formed crater Pwyll. (NASA)

Pwyll

Visual-wavelength images

found that Europa has no magnetic field of its own. It cannot have a molten conducting core. Tidal heating, however, is important for Europa and apparently provides enough heat to keep the little moon active. In fact, the curving cracks in its crust reveal the shape of the tidal forces that flex it as Europa orbits Jupiter.

If you hiked on Europa with a compass in your hand, you would detect a magnetic field, but not from Europa itself. Jupiter rotates rapidly and drags its strong magnetic field past the little moon. That induces a fluctuating magnetic field at Europa that would make your compass wander uselessly. Europa's interaction with Jupiter's magnetic field reveals the presence of a liquid-water ocean lying just 15 km (10 mi) below the icy surface. The ocean may be as deep as 150 km (100 mi) (■ Figure 23-11) and could contain twice as much water as all the oceans on Earth. It is likely to be rich in dissolved minerals, which make the water a good electrical conductor and allow it to interact with Jupiter's magnetic field. No one knows what might be swimming through such an ocean, and many scientists hope for a future mission to Europa to drill through the ice crust and sample the ocean below for signs of life.

Tidal heating makes Europa geologically active. Apparently, rising currents of water can break through the icy crust or melt surface patches. Many of the cracks show evidence that they have spread apart and that fresh water has welled up and frozen between the walls of the crack. In other regions, compression of Europa's crust is revealed by networks of faults and low ridges. Compression on Earth pushes up mountain ranges, but no such ranges appear on Europa. The icy crust isn't strong enough to support ridges higher than a kilometer or so.

Orbiting deep inside Jupiter's radiation belts, Europa is bombarded by high-energy particles that damage the icy surface. Water molecules are freed and broken up, then dispersed into a doughnut-shaped cloud spread round Jupiter and enclosing Europa's orbit. Flying past Jupiter in 2002 on its way to Saturn, the Cassini spacecraft was able to image this cloud of glowing gas. Europa's gas cloud is evidence that moons orbiting deep inside a massive planet's radiation belts are exposed to a form of erosion that is entirely lacking on Earth's moon.

Io: Roaring Volcanoes

Geological activity is driven by heat flowing out of a planet's interior, and nothing could illustrate this principle better than Io, the innermost of Jupiter's Galilean moons. Photographs from the Voyager and Galileo spacecraft show no impact craters at all—surprising considering Jupiter's power to focus meteoroids inward (Figure 23-11b). There is no difficulty explaining the missing craters. Over 150 active volcanoes are visible on Io's surface, blasting enough ash out over the surface to bury any newly formed craters (■ Figure 23-12). Io is more geologically active than any other object in the solar system, even more than Earth.

Spectra reveal that Io has a tenuous atmosphere of gaseous sulfur and oxygen, but those gases can't be permanent. Even though the erupting volcanoes pour out about one ton of gases per second, the gases leak into space easily because of Io's low escape velocity. Also, any gas atoms that become ionized are swept away by Jupiter's rapidly rotating magnetic field. The ions produce a cloud of sulfur and sodium ions in a torus (a doughnut shape) enclosing Io's orbit (■ Figure 23-13).

The temperature at the surface averages 130 K (−225°F) and the atmospheric pressure is very low. Because of the continuous volcanism and the sulfurous gases, Io's thin atmosphere is smelly with sulfur. In fact, the reddish color of Jupiter's small inner

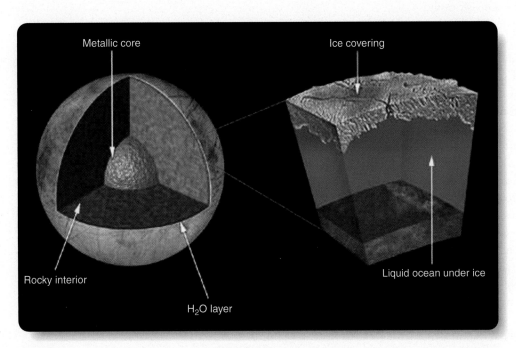

■ **Figure 23-11**

The gravitational influence of Europa on the passing Galileo spacecraft shows that this moon has differentiated into a dense core and rocky mantle. Magnetic interactions with Jupiter show that it has a liquid-water ocean below its icy crust. Heat produced by tidal heating could flow outward as convection in such an ocean and drive geological activity in the icy crust. (NASA)

Metallic core

Ice covering

Rocky interior

H_2O layer

Liquid ocean under ice

Plume from volcano Pillan Patera rises 140 km.

Plume from volcano Prometheus

Shadow of plume

Visual + infrared images

Volcano Pele

Debris ejected from Pele

Five months after the previous image, a new volcano has emerged.

Volcano Pillan Patera

Hot lava at front of advancing lava flows

Volcanic caldera

Lava curtain erupting through a fault

50 km

Caldera Culann Patera has produced multiple lava flows.

■ **Figure 23-12**

These enhanced-color images of volcanic features on Io were produced by combining visual and near-infrared images and digitally enhancing the color. To human eyes, most of Io would look pale yellow and light orange. (NASA)

moon Amalthea may be caused by sulfur pollution escaping from Io. The main problem for you to consider before walking across the surface of Io would be radiation. Io is deep inside Jupiter's magnetosphere and radiation belts. Unless your spacesuit had impressive shielding, the radiation would be lethal. Io, like Venus, may be a place that humans will not visit easily.

You can use basic observations to deduce the nature of Io's interior. From its density, 3.5 g/cm³, you can conclude that it is rocky. Spectra reveal no trace of water at all, so there is no ice on Io. In fact, it is the driest world in our solar system. The oblateness of Io caused by its rotation and by the slight distortion produced by Jupiter's gravity gives astronomers more clues to its interior. Model calculations suggest it contains a modest core of iron or iron mixed with sulfur, a deep rocky mantle that is partially molten, and a thin, rocky crust.

The colors of Io have been compared to those of a badly made pizza. The reds, oranges, and browns of Io are caused by sulfur and sulfur compounds, and an early hypothesis proposed that the crust is mostly sulfur. New evidence says otherwise. Infrared measurements show that volcanoes on Io erupt lava with a temperature over 1500°C (2700°F), about 300°C hotter than lavas on Earth. Sulfur on Io would boil at only 550°C, so the volcanoes must be erupting molten rock and not just liquid sulfur. Also, a few isolated mountains exist that are as high as 18 km, twice the height of Mount Everest. Sulfur is not strong

enough to support such high mountains. These are all indications that the crust of Io is probably silicate rock.

Volcanism is continuous on Io. Plumes come and go over periods of months, but some volcanic vents, such as Pele, have been active since the Voyager spacecraft first visited Io in 1979 (Figure 23-12). Earth's explosive volcanoes eject lava and ash because of water dissolved in the lava. As rising lava reaches Earth's surface, the sudden decrease in pressure allows the water to come out of solution in the lava, like popping the cork on a bottle of champagne: The water flashes into vapor and blasts material out of the volcano, the process that was responsible for the Mount St. Helens explosion in 1980. But Io is dry. Instead, its volcanoes appear to be powered by sulfur dioxide dissolved in the magma. When the pressure on the magma is released, the sulfur dioxide boils out of solution and blasts gas and ash high above the surface in plumes up to 500 km high. Ash falling back to the surface produces debris layers around the volcanoes, such as that around Pele in Figure 23-12. Whitish areas on the surface are frosts of sulfur dioxide.

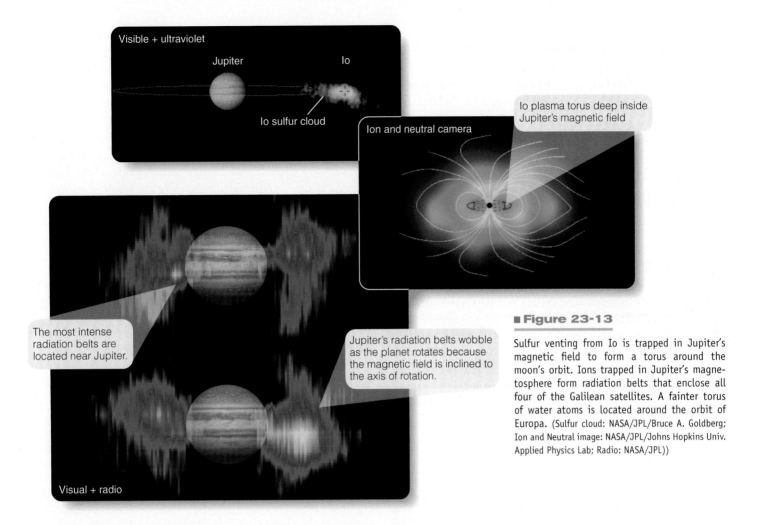

Visible + ultraviolet

Jupiter

Io

Io sulfur cloud

Ion and neutral camera

Io plasma torus deep inside Jupiter's magnetic field

The most intense radiation belts are located near Jupiter.

Jupiter's radiation belts wobble as the planet rotates because the magnetic field is inclined to the axis of rotation.

Visual + radio

■ **Figure 23-13**

Sulfur venting from Io is trapped in Jupiter's magnetic field to form a torus around the moon's orbit. Ions trapped in Jupiter's magnetosphere form radiation belts that enclose all four of the Galilean satellites. A fainter torus of water atoms is located around the orbit of Europa. (Sulfur cloud: NASA/JPL/Bruce A. Goldberg; Ion and Neutral image: NASA/JPL/Johns Hopkins Univ. Applied Physics Lab; Radio: NASA/JPL))

Great lava flows can be detected carrying molten material downhill, burying the surface under layer after layer. Sometimes lava bursts upward through faults to form long lava curtains, a form of eruption seen in Hawaii. Both of these processes are shown in Figure 23-12.

What powers Io? It has abundant internal heat, but it is only 5 percent bigger than Earth's moon, which is cold and dead. Io is too small to have retained heat from its formation or to remain hot from radioactive decay. In fact, the energy blasting out of its volcanoes adds up to about three times more energy than it could make by radioactive decay in its interior.

The answer is that Io is heated by a stronger version of the kind of tidal heating that has affected Ganymede and Europa. Because Io is so close to Jupiter, the tides it experiences are powerful and should have forced Io's orbit to become circular long ago. Io, however, is strongly influenced by its neighboring moons. Io, Europa, and Ganymede are locked in an orbital resonance; in the time it takes Ganymede to orbit once, Europa orbits twice and Io four times. This gravitational interaction keeps the orbits, especially Io's, slightly eccentric; and Io, also being closest to Jupiter, suffers dramatic tides, with its surface rising and falling by about 100 m. For comparison, tides on Earth move the solid ground by

only a few centimeters. The resulting friction in Io is enough to melt the interior and drive volcanism. In fact, there is enough energy flowing outward to continually recycle Io's crust. Deep layers melt, are spewed out through the volcanoes to cover the surface, and are later covered themselves until they are buried so deeply that they are again melted.

The four Galilean moons show a clear sequence of more and more tidal heating the nearer they are to Jupiter. The more distant moons have geologies dominated by impacts, while the closer moons are dominated by heat flow from inside and have few craters. What a difference a few hundred thousand miles makes!

The History of the Galilean Moons

Each time you have finished studying a world, you have tried to summarize its history. Now you have studied a system of four small worlds. Can you tell their story? To do that you need to draw on what you have learned about the moons and on what you have learned about Jupiter and the origin of the solar system (Chapter 19).

The minor, irregular moons of Jupiter are probably captured asteroids, but the regular Galilean satellites seem to be primordial. That is, they formed with Jupiter. Also, they seem to be

Table 23-2 | The Galilean Satellites*

Name	Radius (km)	Density (g/cm³)	Orbital Period (days)
Io	1821	3.528	1.769
Europa	1561	3.014	3.551
Ganymede	2631	1.942	7.155
Callisto	2410	1.8344	16.689

*For comparison, the radius of Earth's moon is 1738 km, and its density is 3.36 g/cm³

interrelated in that their densities are related to their distance from Jupiter (■ Table 23-2).

From all the evidence, astronomers propose that the four moons formed in a disk-shaped nebula around Jupiter—a mini-solar nebula—in much the same way the planets formed from the solar nebula around the sun. As Jupiter grew massive, it would have formed a hot, dense disk of matter around its equator. The moons could have condensed inside that disk with the innermost moons, Io and Europa, forming from rocky material and the outer moons, Ganymede and Callisto, incorporating more ice. This hypothesis follows the same condensation sequence that led to rocky planets forming near the sun and ice-rich worlds forming farther away.

There are objections to this hypothesis. The disk around Jupiter would have been dense and hot, and moons would have formed rapidly, perhaps in only 1000 years. If the moons formed quickly, the heat of formation released as material fell into the moons would not have leaked away quickly, and they would have grown so hot they would have lost their water. Ganymede and Callisto are rich in water. Furthermore, Callisto has never been hot enough to differentiate and form a core. Also, mathematical models show that moons orbiting in the dense disk would have swept up debris and lost orbital momentum; they would have spiraled into Jupiter within a century.

A newer hypothesis proposes that Jupiter's early disk was indeed dense and hot and may have created moons, but those moons spiraled into the planet and were lost. Only later, as the disk grew thinner and cooler, did the present Galilean moons begin to form. Additional material may have dribbled slowly into the disk, and the moons could have formed slowly enough to retain their water and avoid spiraling into Jupiter. In this scenario, many large moons may have accreted around Jupiter. The Galilean satellites you observe now would thus be only the last batch, formed when the disk of construction material around Jupiter had become thin enough that they did not fall into Jupiter and disappear. The same migration and destruction process may apply, on a larger scale, to planets forming in extrasolar planetary systems (see Chapter 19).

You can combine this hypothesis with what you know about tidal heating to understand the interiors of the moons. The moons formed slowly, over perhaps 100,000 years, and were not heated severely by in-falling material. The inner moons, however, were cooked by tidal heating—possibly enhanced when an orbital resonance developed between Ganymede, Europa, and Io. The innermost moon, Io, was heated so much it lost all of its water, and Europa retained only a small amount. Ganymede was heated enough to differentiate but retained much of its water. Callisto, orbiting far from Jupiter and avoiding orbital resonances, was never heated enough to differentiate. The Galilean moons as they appear today seem to be the result of a combination of slow formation and tidal heating.

The Galilean satellite system is full of clues to the history of the solar system. Understanding that history prepares you to explore farther from the sun.

SCIENTIFIC ARGUMENT

What produces Io's internal heat?
Scientific arguments commonly draw on basic principles that are well understood. In this case, you understand that small worlds lose their internal heat quickly and become geologically inactive. Io is only slightly larger than Earth's moon, which is cold and dead, but Io is full of energy flowing outward.

Clearly, Io must have a powerful source of heat inside, and that heat source is tides. Io's orbit is slightly eccentric (noncircular), so it is sometimes closer to Jupiter and sometimes farther away. This means that Jupiter's powerful gravity sometimes squeezes Io more than at other times, and the flexing of the little moon's interior produces heat through friction. Such tides would rapidly force Io's orbit to become circular, and then tidal heating would end and the planet would become inactive—except that the gravitational tugs of the other moons keep Io's orbit eccentric. Thus, it is the influence of its companions that keeps Io in such an active state.

Io has almost no impact craters, but Callisto has many. Build a new scientific argument drawing on a different principle. **What does the difference in crater distributions on the Galilean satellites tell you about their history?**

23-4) Saturn

SATURN HAS PLAYED SECOND FIDDLE to its own rings since Galileo first saw it in 1610. He didn't recognize the rings for what they are, but today they are instantly recognizable as one of the wonders of the solar system. Nevertheless, Saturn itself, not quite 10 times Earth's diameter (**Celestial Profile 8**), is a fascinating planet with a few mysteries of its own. Your exploration of Saturn and its rings can make use of the principles you have learned from Jupiter.

Surveying Saturn

The basic characteristics of Saturn reveal its composition and interior. Only about a third of the mass of Jupiter and 16 percent smaller in radius, Saturn has an average density of 0.69 g/cm³. It is less dense than water—it would float! Spectra show that its atmosphere is rich in hydrogen and helium (see Table 23-1), and models predict that it is mostly liquid hydrogen with a core of heavy elements.

Infrared observations show that Saturn is radiating 1.8 times as much energy as it receives from the sun, showing that heat is flowing out of its interior. It must be very hot inside Saturn, as is also true for Jupiter. In fact, Saturn's interior is too hot. It should have lost more heat since it formed. Astronomers have calculated models indicating that helium in the liquid hydrogen interior is condensing into droplets and falling inward. The falling droplets, releasing energy as they pick up speed, heat the planet. This heating is similar to the heating produced when a star contracts and may also occur to some extent in the atmospheres of Jupiter, Uranus, and Neptune.

Just as for Jupiter, you can learn more about Saturn's interior from its magnetic field. Spacecraft have found that Saturn's magnetic field is about 20 times weaker than Jupiter's. It also has correspondingly weaker radiation belts. Models comparing Saturn with Jupiter predict that the lower pressure inside Saturn produces a smaller mass of liquid metallic hydrogen. Heat flowing outward causes convection in this conducting layer, and the rapid rotation drives a dynamo effect that produces the magnetic field. Unlike most magnetic fields, Saturn's is not inclined to its axis of rotation, something you can see in ultraviolet images that show rings of auroras around Saturn's poles (■ Figure 23-14). This perfect alignment between Saturn's magnetic axis and the axis of rotation is peculiar, isn't seen in any other planet, and isn't understood.

Saturn's atmosphere blends gradually into its liquid interior. The size of its core is uncertain. (NASA/STScI)

Celestial Profile 8: Saturn

Motion:

Average distance from the sun	9.54 AU (1.43 × 10⁹ km)
Eccentricity of orbit	0.056
Inclination of orbit to ecliptic	2.5°
Average orbital velocity	9.64 km/s
Orbital period	29.46 y
Period of rotation	10.66 h
Inclination of equator to orbit	26.4°

Average distance from the sun 9.54 AU (1.43×10^9 km)
Eccentricity of orbit 0.056
Inclination of orbit to ecliptic 2.5°
Average orbital velocity 9.64 km/s
Orbital period 29.46 y
Period of rotation 10.66 h
Inclination of equator to orbit 26.4°

Characteristics:

Equatorial diameter 1.21×10^5 km (9.42 $D_\oplus$)
Mass 5.69×10^{26} kg (95.1 $M_\oplus$)
Average density 0.69 g/cm³
Gravity at base of clouds 1.16 Earth gravities
Escape velocity 35.6 km/s (3.2 $V_\oplus$)
Temperature at cloud tops −180°C (−290°F)
Albedo 0.61
Oblateness 0.102

Personality Point:

The Greek god Cronus was forced to flee when his son Zeus took power. Cronus fled to Italy, where the Romans called him Saturn, protector of the sowing of seed. He was celebrated in a weeklong wild party called the Saturnalia at the time of the winter solstice. Early Christians took over the holiday to celebrate Christmas.

Visual + ultraviolet

Auroras vary day to day because of changes in the solar wind.

■ Figure 23-14

Auroras on Saturn occur in rings around the planet's magnetic poles. Because the magnetic field is not inclined very much to the axis of rotation, the rings occur nearly at the planet's geometrical poles. (Compare with Figure 23-4.) (NASA, ESA, J. Clarke, Boston Univ. and X. Levay, STScI)

Like Jupiter, Saturn's atmosphere is rich in hydrogen and displays belt–zone circulation, which appears to arise in the same way as the circulation patterns on Jupiter. The light-colored zones are higher clouds formed by rising gas, and the darker belts are lower clouds formed by sinking gas.

Notice, however, that the zones and belt clouds are not very distinct on Saturn compared with Jupiter (■ Figure 23-15a). Measurements from the Voyager and Cassini spacecraft indicate that Saturn's atmosphere is much colder than Jupiter's—something you would expect because Saturn is twice as far from the sun and receives only one-fourth as much solar energy per square meter. The clouds on Saturn form at about the same temperature as the clouds on Jupiter, but those temperature levels are deeper in Saturn's cold atmosphere. Compare the cloud layers in Figure 23-15b with those shown in the diagram on page 501. Because they are deeper in the atmosphere, the cloud layers look dimmer from your viewpoint outside, and a high layer of haze formed by methane crystals makes the cloud layers even more indistinct. The atmospheres of Jupiter and Saturn are actually very similar once you account for the fact that Saturn is colder.

One dramatic difference between Jupiter and Saturn concerns the winds. On Jupiter, winds form the boundaries for each of the belts and zones, but on Saturn the pattern is not the same. Saturn has fewer such winds, but they are much stronger. The eastward wind at the equator of Saturn, for example, blows at 500 m/s (1100 mph), roughly five times faster than the eastward wind at Jupiter's equator. The reason for this difference is not clear.

Saturn's Rings

Looking at the beauty and complexity of Saturn's rings, an astronomer once said, "The rings are made of beautiful physics." You could add that the physics is actually rather simple, but the result is one of the most amazing sights in our solar system.

In 1609, Galileo became the first to see the rings of Saturn; but perhaps because of the poor optics in his telescopes, he did not recognize the rings as a disk. He drew Saturn as three objects—a central body and two smaller ones on either side. In 1659, Christian Huygens (pronounced approximately, *Howk-gins*) realized that the rings form a disk surrounding but not touching the planet.

Understanding Saturn's rings has required human ingenuity continuing to the present day. In 1859, James Clerk Maxwell (for whom the large mountain on Venus is named)

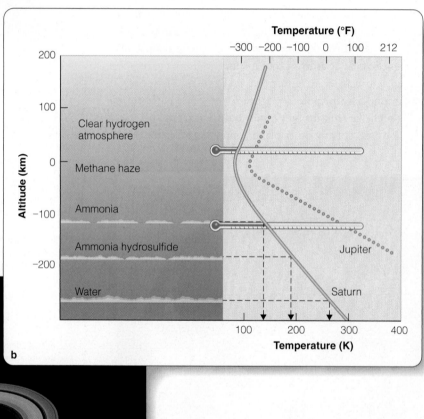

■ Figure 23-15

(a) Saturn's belt–zone circulation is not very distinct at visible wavelengths. These images were recorded when Saturn's southern hemisphere was tipped toward Earth. (NASA and E. Karkoschka) (b) Because Saturn is colder than Jupiter, the clouds form deeper in the hazy atmosphere. Notice that the three cloud layers on Saturn form at about the same temperatures as do the three cloud layers on Jupiter.

proved mathematically that solid rings would be unstable. Saturn's rings, he concluded, had to be made of separated particles. In 1867, Daniel Kirkwood demonstrated that gaps in the rings were caused by resonances with some of Saturn's moons. Spectra of the rings eventually showed that the particles were mostly water ice.

Study **The Rings of Saturn** on pages 514–515 and notice three points and a new term:

1 The rings are made up of billions of ice particles, each in its own orbit around the planet. But, just as for Jupiter's rings, the particles observed now in Saturn's rings can't have been there since the planet formed. The rings must be replenished now and then by impacts on Saturn's icy moons or by the disruption of a small moon that moves too close to the planet.

2 The gravitational effects of small moons called *shepherd satellites* can confine some rings in narrow strands or keep the edges of rings sharp. Moons can also produce waves in the rings that are visible as tightly wound ringlets.

3 The ring particles are confined to a thin layer in Saturn's equatorial plane by the gravity of small moons. The small moons in turn are controlled by gravitational interactions with larger, more distant moons. The rings of Saturn, and the rings of the other Jovian worlds, are created from and controlled by the planet's moons. Without the moons, there would be no rings.

Modern astronomers find simple gravitational interactions producing even more complex processes in the rings. Where particles orbit in resonance with a moon, the moon's gravity triggers spiral density waves in much the same way that spiral arms are produced in galaxies. The spiral density waves spread outward through the rings. If the moon follows an orbit that is inclined to the ring plane, the moon's gravity causes a different kind of wave—spiral bending waves—ripples extending above and below the ring plane, which spread inward. Both of these kinds of processes are shown in the inset ring image on page 515.

Many other processes occur in the rings. Specks of dust become electrically charged by sunlight, and Saturn's magnetic field lifts them out of the ring plane. Small moonlets embedded in the rings produce gaps, waves, and scallops in the rings. The Cassini spacecraft has recorded dramatic images (■ Figure 23-16) of the Saturn ring system, including two faint outer rings (E and G) that are rarely detectable from Earth, and these also appear to be related to moons.

The word "particle" in colloquial language connotes tiny specks, but in the context of Saturn's rings, astronomers use that term to refer to any object from snowlike powder grains up to building-sized icy mini-moons (look again at page 514). The larger objects are understood to be aggregates of the smaller ones. The subtle colors of

■ Figure 23-16

The Cassini spacecraft recorded this image as it passed through Saturn's shadow. Earth is visible as a faint blue dot just inside the G ring, and jets of ice particles vented from the moon Enceladus are visible at the left extreme of the larger E ring. Two faint rings associated with small moons were discovered in this image. (NASA/JPL/Space Science Institute)

The Ice Rings of Saturn

1 The brilliant rings of Saturn are made up of billions of ice particles ranging from microscopic specks to chunks bigger than a house. Each particle orbits Saturn in its own circular orbit. Much of what astronomers know about the rings was learned when the Voyager 1 spacecraft flew past Saturn in 1980, followed by the Voyager 2 spacecraft in 1981. The Cassini Spacecraft reached orbit around Saturn in 2004. From Earth, astronomers see three rings labeled A, B, and C. Voyager and Cassini images reveal over a thousand ringlets within the rings.

Saturn's rings can't be leftover material from the formation of Saturn. The rings are made of ice particles, and the planet would have been so hot when it formed that it would have vaporized and driven away any icy material. Rather, the rings must be debris from collisions between passing comets, or other objects, and Saturn's icy moons. Such impacts should occur every 100 million years or so, and they would scatter ice throughout Saturn's system of moons. The ice would quickly settle into the equatorial plane, and some would become trapped in rings. Although the ice may waste away due to meteorite impacts and damage from radiation in Saturn's magnetosphere, new impacts could replenish the rings with fresh ice. The bright, beautiful rings you see today may be only a temporary enhancement caused by an impact that occurred since the extinction of the dinosaurs.

Encke Gap

Cassini Division

A ring

B ring

C ring

As in the case of Jupiter's ring, Saturn's rings lie inside the planet's Roché limit where the ring particles cannot pull themselves together to form a moon.

Because it is so dark, the C ring was once called the crepe ring.

Earth to scale

Visual-wavelength image

1a An astronaut could swim through the rings. Although the particles orbit Saturn at high velocity, all particles at the same distance from the planet orbit at about the same speed, so they collide gently at low velocities. If you could visit the rings, you could push your way from one icy particle to the next. This artwork is based on a model of particle sizes in the A ring.

The C ring contains boulder-size chunks of ice, whereas most particles in the A and B rings are more like golf balls, down to dust-size ice crystals. Further, C ring particles are less than half as bright as particles in the A and B rings. Cassini observations show that the C ring particles contain less ice and more minerals.

NASA

2 Because of collisions among ring particles, planetary rings should spread outward. The sharp outer edge of the A ring and the narrow F ring are confined by **shepherd satellites** that gravitationally usher straying particles back into the rings.

Some gaps in the rings, such as the Cassini Division, are caused by resonances with moons. A particle in the Cassini Division orbits Saturn twice for each orbit of the moon Mimas. On every other orbit, the particle feels a gravitational tug from Mimas. These tugs always occur at the same places in the orbit and force the orbit to become slightly elliptical. Such an orbit crosses the orbits of other particles, which results in collisions, and that removes the particle from the gap.

This image was recorded by the Cassini spacecraft looking up at the rings as they were illuminated by sunlight from below. Saturn's shadow falls across the upper side of the rings.

Pandora

Visual-wavelength image

The F ring is clumpy and sometimes appears braided because of two shepherd satellites.

F ring

Visual-wavelength images

Waves in the A ring

F ring close up

Prometheus

The Encke Gap is not empty. Note the ripples at the inner edge. A small moon orbits inside the gap.

Encke Gap

Saturn does not have enough moons to produce all of its ringlets by resonances. Many are produced by tightly wound waves, much like the spiral arms found in disk galaxies.

Cassini Division

Encke Gap

A ring

3 How do moons happen to be at just the right places to confine the rings? That puts the cosmic cart before the horse. The ring particles get caught in the most stable orbits among Saturn's innermost moons. The rings push against the inner moons, but those moons are locked in place by resonances with larger, outer moons. Without the moons, the rings would spread and dissipate.

This combination of UV images has been given false color to show the ratio of mineral material to pure ice. Blue regions such as the A ring are the purest ice, and red regions such as the Cassini Division are the dirtiest ice. How the particles become sorted by composition is unknown.

Saturn's rings are a very thin layer of particles and nearly vanish when the rings turn edge-on to Earth. Although ripples in the rings caused by waves may be hundreds of meters high, the sheet of particles may be only about ten meters thick.

Ultraviolet image

Who Pays for Science?

Why shouldn't you plan for a career as an industrial paleontologist? Searching out scientific knowledge can be expensive, and that raises the question of funding. Some science has direct applications, and industry supports such research. For example, pharmaceutical companies have large budgets for scientific research leading to the creation of new drugs. But some basic science is of no immediate practical value. Who pays the bill?

A paleontologist is a scientist who studies ancient life forms by examining fossils of plant and animal remains, and such research does not have commercial applications. Except for the rare Hollywood producer about to release a dinosaur movie, corporations can't make a profit from the discovery of a new dinosaur. The practical-minded stockholders of a company will not approve major investments in such research.

Consequently, digging up dinosaurs, like astronomy, is poorly funded by industry.

It falls to government institutions and private foundations to pay the bill for this kind of research. The Keck Foundation has built two giant telescopes with no expectation of financial return, and the National Science Foundation has funded thousands of astronomy research projects for the benefit of society.

The discovery of a new dinosaur or a new galaxy is of no great financial value, but such scientific knowledge is not worthless. Its value lies in what it tells us about the world we live in. Such scientific research enriches our lives by helping us understand what we are. Ultimately, funding basic scientific research is a public responsibility that society must balance against other needs. There isn't anyone else to pick up the tab.

Sending the Cassini spacecraft to Saturn costs each U.S. citizen 56¢ per year over the life of the project.

---

the rings arise from contamination in the ice, and some areas have unusual compositions. The Cassini Division, for instance, contains particles that are richer in rock than most of the ring. No one knows how these differences in composition arise, but they must be related to the way the rings are formed and replenished.

Like a beautiful flower, the rings of Saturn are controlled by many different natural processes. Observations from spacecraft such as Voyager and Cassini will continue to reveal even more about the rings. Such missions are expensive, of course, but they are helping us understand what we are (**How Do We Know? 23-1**).

The History of Saturn

The farther you journey from the sun, the more difficult it is to understand the history of the planets. Any fully successful history of Saturn should explain its low density, its peculiar magnetic field, and its beautiful rings. Planetary scientists can't tell a complete story yet, but you can understand a few of the principles that affected the formation of Saturn and its rings.

Most of Saturn's story parallels that of Jupiter. Saturn formed in the outer solar nebula, where ice particles were stable. It grew rapidly, becoming massive enough to capture hydrogen and helium gas directly from the nebula. The heavier elements probably form a denser core, and the hydrogen forms a liquid mantle containing liquid metallic hydrogen. The outward flow of heat from the core drives convection currents in this mantle that,

coupled with the rapid rotation of the planet, produces its magnetic field. Because Saturn is smaller than Jupiter, it has less liquid metallic hydrogen, and its magnetic field is weaker.

The rings of Saturn definitely are not primordial, meaning, the material in them now has not been in its current form since the formation of the planet. Saturn, like Jupiter, would have been very hot when it formed, and that heat would have vaporized and driven off any nearby small icy particles of leftover material. Also, such a hot Saturn would have had a very distended atmosphere, which would have slowed ring particles by friction and caused the particles to fall into the planet. Finally, the processes that tend to destroy Jupiter's ring particles also apply to Saturn's rings.

Planetary rings do not seem to be stable over 4.6 billion years, so the ring material must have been produced more recently. Saturn's beautiful rings may have been created within just the last 100 million years, an astronomically short time. One suggestion is that a small moon or an icy planetesimal came within Saturn's Roche limit, and tides pulled it apart. At least some of the resulting debris would have settled into the ring plane. Another possibility is that a comet struck one of Saturn's moons. Because both comets and moons in the outer solar system are icy, such a collision would produce icy debris. Bright planetary rings such as Saturn's may be temporary phenomena, forming when violent events produce fresh ice debris and then wasting away as the ice is gradually lost.

SCIENTIFIC ARGUMENT

Why do the belts and zones on Saturn look so faint?
One of the most powerful tools of critical thought is simple comparing and contrasting. You can make that the theme of this scientific argument by comparing and contrasting Saturn with Jupiter. In the atmosphere of Jupiter, the dark belts form in regions where gas sinks, and zones form where gas rises. The rising gas cools and condenses to form icy crystals of ammonia, which are visible as bright clouds. Clouds of ammonia hydrosulfide and water form deeper, below the ammonia clouds, and are not as visible. Saturn is twice as far from the sun as Jupiter, so sunlight is four times dimmer. The atmosphere is colder, and gas currents do not have to rise as far to reach cold levels and form clouds. That means the clouds are deeper in Saturn's atmosphere than in Jupiter's atmosphere. Because the clouds are deeper, they are not as brightly illuminated by sunlight and look dimmer. Also, a layer of methane-ice-crystal haze high above the ammonia clouds makes the clouds even less distinct.

Now build a new argument comparing the ring systems. **How is Saturn's ring system similar to, and different from, Jupiter's ring system?**

C_2H_6	Ethane
C_2H_2	Acetylene
C_2H_4	Ethylene
C_3H_4	Methylacetylene
C_3H_8	Propane
C_4H_2	Diacetylene
HCN	Hydrogen cyanide
HC_3N	Cyanocetylene
C_2N_2	Cyanogen

23-5 Saturn's Moons

SATURN HAS OVER 30 KNOWN SATELLITES—far too many to examine individually—but these moons share characteristics common to icy worlds. Most of them are small and dead, but one is big enough to have an atmosphere and perhaps even oceans or lakes—but not of water.

Titan

Saturn's largest satellite is a giant ice moon with a thick atmosphere and a mysterious surface. From Earth it is only a dot of light, with no visible detail. Nevertheless, a few basic observations can tell you a great deal about this strange world.

Titan's mass can be estimated from its influence on both passing spacecraft and on other moons. Its mass divided by its volume reveals that its density is 1.9 g/cm^3. Its uncompressed density (Chapter 19) is only 1.2 g/cm^3. Although it must have a rocky core, it must also contain a large amount of ice.

Titan is a bit larger than the planet Mercury and almost as large as Jupiter's moon Ganymede. Unlike those worlds, Titan has a thick atmosphere. Its escape velocity is low, but it is so far from the sun that it is very cold, and most gas atoms don't move fast enough to escape. (Look back to Figure 22-13.) Methane was detected spectroscopically in 1944, and various hydrocarbons were found beginning in about 1970 (■ Table 23-3), but most of Titan's air is nitrogen with only 1.6 percent methane.

When the Voyager 1 and Voyager 2 spacecraft flew past Saturn in the early 1980s, their cameras could not penetrate Titan's hazy atmosphere (■ Figure 23-17). Measurements showed that the surface temperature is about 94 K ($-290°$F), and the

surface atmospheric pressure is 50 percent greater than on Earth. Model calculations show that in the conditions on Titan, methane could condense from the atmosphere and fall as rain. Some scientists hypothesized that Titan is covered by methane lakes or seas.

Sunlight converts methane (CH_4) into the gas ethane (C_2H_6) plus a collection of other organic molecules.* Some of these molecules produce the smoglike haze; and, as the smog particles gradually settle, they are predicted to deposit smelly, organic goo on the surface. This goo is important because similar organic molecules may have been the precursors of life on Earth. (You will examine this idea further in Chapter 26.)

Before you try to imagine floundering through this strange landscape, you can consider the recent observations made by the Cassini spacecraft, which began exploring Saturn and its moons in 2004.

Infrared cameras and radar instruments on Cassini have been able to see through the hazy atmosphere. The surface is not a featureless ocean of methane, nor an icy plane covered with goo. Rather, the surface consists of icy, irregular highlands and smoother dark areas. There are only a few craters, which suggests geological activity is erasing craters almost as quickly as they are formed.

The Cassini spacecraft released a probe named Huygens, which parachuted down through the atmosphere of Titan and eventually landed on the surface. Huygens radioed back images of the surface as it descended under its parachute, and those images show dark drainage networks that lead into dark smooth areas (Figure 23-17). Those dark regions, which look a lot like bodies of liquid, are actually dry or mostly dry. Precipitation may have washed the black goo off the highlands into the stream channels and lowlands, so that they look smooth and dark even

---

*Organic molecules are common in living things on Earth but do not have to be derived from living things. In other words, biological substances are organic, but organic substances are not necessarily biological. One chemist defined an organic molecule as "any molecule with a carbon backbone."

As the Huygens probe descended by parachute through Titan's smoggy atmosphere, it photographed the surface from an altitude of 8 km (5 mi). Although no liquid was present, dark drainage channels lead into the lowlands. Radar images reveal lakes of liquid methane and ethane around the poles. Once the Huygens probe landed on the surface, it radioed back photos showing a level plain and chunks of ice smoothed by a moving liquid. (ESA/NASA/JPL/USGS/University of Arizona)

Cassini radar image of methane lakes that look dark because they do not reflect radio waves.

b Visual-wavelength image

Drainage channels probably were cut by flowing liquid methane.

Possible methane fog

At visual wavelengths, Titan's dense atmosphere hides its surface.

Icy grapefruit-size "rocks" on Titan are bathed in orange light from its hazy atmosphere.

though the liquid had temporarily evaporated. If you visit Titan, you may get caught in a shower of methane rain, but it may not rain often at your landing site.

When the Huygens probe landed on Titan's frigid surface, it radioed back measurements and images. The surface is mostly frozen water ice with some methane mixed in. The sunlight is orange because it has filtered down through the orange haze. Rocks littering the ground are actually steel-hard chunks of supercold water ice smoothed by erosion. Some rest in small depressions, suggesting that a liquid has flowed around them. You can see these depressions around the rocks in Figure 23-17c.

Radar observations made as the Cassini probe orbited past Titan have revealed lakes of liquid methane in its polar regions, confirming the earlier hypotheses. Some of those lakes are as large as Lake Superior. Evaporation from the lakes can maintain the 1.6 percent methane gas in the atmosphere, but sunlight eventually destroys methane, so Titan must have a large supply of methane ice. Ice volcanoes on Titan may occasionally vent methane into the atmosphere.

By the way, before you go to Titan, check your spacesuit for leaks. Nitrogen is not a very reactive gas, but methane is used as cooking gas on Earth and is highly flammable. Of course, there is no free oxygen on Titan, so you are safe so long as your spacesuit does not leak oxygen.

■ Figure 23-18

A few of Saturn's moons compared with Earth's moon at the right. In general, larger moons are round and more likely to show signs of geological activity. Small moons such as Phoebe and Hyperion are cratered and do not have enough gravity to overcome the strength of their own material and squeeze themselves into a spherical shape.

The Smaller Moons

In addition to Titan, Saturn has a large family of smaller moons. They are mixtures of rock and ice and are heavily cratered. Some of the smallest are probably captured objects and are geologically dead, but some of the larger moons show traces of geological activity. You can compare the sizes of a few of these moons in ■ Figure 23-18.

The moon Phoebe orbits on the outer fringes of Saturn's satellite family, and it moves in the retrograde direction—it orbits backward. It is quite small, only about 210 km (130 mi) in diameter, but it is nevertheless the largest of Saturn's irregular satellites. Phoebe's surface is dark, with an albedo of only 6 percent, and heavily cratered (■ Figure 23-19). Traces of ice are detected where impacts have excavated deeper layers or where landslides have exposed fresh material. The density of Phoebe is 1.6 g/cm³, which is high enough to show that it contains a significant amount of rock. It seems unlikely that Phoebe came from the asteroid belt, where ice is relatively rare. It is more likely to be a captured Kuiper belt object that originated in an orbit beyond Neptune.

Larger regular moons such as Tethys, which has a diameter of over 1000 km (620 mi), are icy and cratered, but they show some signs of geological activity. Some smooth areas on Tethys appear to have been resurfaced by flowing water "lava," and long cracks and grooves may have formed when geological activity strained the icy crust (Figure 23-19).

■ Figure 23-19

Phoebe and Tethys have ancient cratered surfaces, but they differ in interesting ways. Phoebe is only $\frac{1}{5}$ the diameter of Tethys and shows no sign of internal heat causing surface activity. Tethys has smooth areas and long cracks on its surface, showing that it has been active. Phoebe is probably a captured Kuiper belt object, but Tethys likely formed with Saturn. (NASA/JPL/Space Science Institute)

Phoebe is a small, dark, cratered moon with no sign of geological activity.

Long cracks in the cratered surface of Tethys show the larger moon has been geologically active.

Visual-wavelength images

Plumes of icy particles vent from Enceladus's south polar region in this false-color image.

False color

Blue "tiger stripes" mark the south polar region of Enceladus.

UV + Visual + IR

IR image

50 km

■ **Figure 23-20**

The bright, clean icy surface of Enceladus does not look old. Some areas have few craters, and the numerous cracks and lanes of grooved terrain resemble the surface of Jupiter's moon Ganymede. Enceladus is venting water, ice, and organic molecules from geysers near its south pole. A thermal infrared image reveals internal heat leaking to space from the "tiger stripe" cracks where the geysers are located. (NASA/JPL/Space Science Institute)

the surface. As these ice crystals escape into space, they replenish Saturn's E ring, which is densest at the position of Enceladus. Infrared images made by Cassini show significant amounts of heat escaping to space through the same cracks from which the water is venting (Figure 23-20).

The possibility of liquid water below the icy crust of Enceladus has excited those scientists searching for life on other worlds. You will read more about this possibility in Chapter 26. Nevertheless, it will be a long time before explorers can drill through the crust and analyze the water below for signs of living things.

Of course, you are wondering how a little moon like Enceladus can have heat flowing up from its interior. With a density of 1.6 g/cm³, Enceladus must contain a significant rocky core, but radioactive decay is not enough to keep it active. A clue lies in the moon's orbit. Enceladus orbits Saturn in a resonance with the larger moon Dione. Each time Dione orbits Saturn once, Enceladus orbits twice. That means Dione's gravitational tugs on Enceladus always occur in the same places and make the orbit of the little moon slightly eccentric. As Enceladus follows that eccentric orbit around Saturn, tides flex it, and tidal heating warms the interior. You saw how resonances keep some of Jupiter's moons active, so you can add Enceladus to the list.

More complicated gravitational interactions between moons are dramatically illustrated by the two small moons that shepherd the F ring (page 515). An even more peculiar pair of moons is known as the coorbital satellites. These two irregularly shaped moonlets have orbits separated by only 100 km. Because one moon is about 200 km in diameter and the other about 100 km, they cannot pass in their orbits. Instead, the innermost moon gradually catches up with the outer moon. As the moons draw closer together, the gravity of the trailing moon slows the leading moon and makes it fall into a lower orbit. Simultaneously, the gravity of the leading moon pulls the trailing moon forward, and it rises into a higher orbit (■ Figure 23-21). The higher orbit has a longer period, so the trailing moon begins to fall behind the leading moon, which is now in a smaller, faster orbit. In this

With a diameter of 520 km (320 mi), the small moon Enceladus isn't much larger than Phoebe, but Enceladus shows dramatic signs of geological activity (■ Figure 23-20). For one thing, Enceladus has an albedo of 0.9. That is, it reflects 90 percent of the sunlight that hits it, and that makes it the most reflective object in the solar system. You know that old icy surfaces become dark, so the surface of Enceladus must be quite young. Look closely at the surface and you will see that some regions have few craters, and that grooves and cracks are common. Observations made by the Cassini spacecraft show that Enceladus has a tenuous atmosphere of water vapor and nitrogen. It is too small to keep such an atmosphere, so it must be releasing gas continuously. Cassini detected a large cloud of water vapor over the moon's south pole where water vents through cracks and produces ice-crystal jets extending hundreds of kilometers above

Coorbital Moons

The inner moon orbits faster and overtakes the outer moon.

(Not to scale)

The gravitational interaction pulls the outer moon backward and the inner moon forward.

As they approach, the inner moon moves to a higher orbit, and the outer moon sinks to a lower orbit.

The moons have changed orbits, and the inner moon begins gaining on the outer moon.

The inner moon will eventually overtake the outer moon from behind once again.

■ **Figure 23-21**

Saturn's coorbital moons follow nearly identical orbits. The moon in the lower orbit travels faster and always overtakes the other moon from behind. The moons interact and change orbits over and over again.

elegant dance, these moons exchange orbits and draw apart only to meet again and again. It seems very likely that these two moons are fragments of a larger moon destroyed by a major impact.

In addition to waltzing coorbital moons, the Voyager spacecraft discovered small moonlets trapped at the L4 and L5 Lagrangian points (see Figure 13-5) in the orbits of Dione and Tethys. These points of stability lie 60° ahead of and 60° behind the two moons, and small moonlets can become trapped in these regions. (You will see in Chapter 25 that some asteroids are trapped in the Lagrangian points of Jupiter's and Neptune's orbits around the sun.) This gravitational curiosity is not unique to the Saturn system, and it indicates that interactions between moons can dramatically alter their orbits.

Saturn has too many moons to discuss in detail here, but you should meet at least one more, Iapetus (pronounced *Ee-yap-eh-tus*). It is literally an odd ball: Iapetus is an asymmetric moon. Its trailing side, the side that always faces backward as it orbits Saturn, is old, cratered, icy, and about as bright as dirty snow. Its leading side, the side that always faces forward in its orbit, is also old and cratered, but it is much darker than you would expect. It has an albedo of only 4 percent—about as dark as fresh asphalt on a highway (■ Figure 23-22). The origin of this dark material is unknown, but theorists suspect that the little moon has swept

Visual-wavelength image

■ **Figure 23-22**

Like the windshield of a speeding car, the leading side of Saturn's moon Iapetus seems to have accumulated a coating of dark material. The poles and trailing side of the moon are much cleaner ice. The equatorial ridge is 20 km (12 mi) wide and up to 13 km (8 mi) high. It stretches roughly 1,300 km (800 mi) along the moon's equator. (NASA/JPL/Space Science Institute) up dark, silicon- and carbon-rich material on its leading side. The source of the material covering the leading side of Iapetus could be meteorites striking and eroding the carbonaceous surface of the outermost moon, Phoebe, and tossing the resulting dust into space to be scooped up eventually by Iapetus.

Another odd feature on Iapetus shows up in Cassini images—an equatorial ridge that stands as high as 13 km (8 mi) in some places. You can see the ridge clearly in Figure 23-21. The origin of this ridge is unknown, but it is not a minor feature. At that height, it is over 50 percent higher than Mount Everest, and it extends for a long distance across the surface. That is a big pile of rock and ice. The ridge sits atop an equatorial bulge, and both ridge and bulge may have formed when Iapetus was young, spun rapidly, and was still mostly molten.

Saturn's moons illustrate a number of principles of comparative planetology. Small moons are irregular in shape, and old surfaces are dark and cratered. Resonances can trigger tidal heating, and that can in turn resurface moons and outgas atmospheres. Small moons can't keep atmospheres, but big, cold moons can. You are an expert in all of this, so you are ready to wonder where the moons came from.

The Origin of Saturn's Moons

Jupiter's four Galilean satellites seem clearly related to one another, and you can safely conclude that they formed with Jupiter. No such simple relationships link Saturn's satellites. That seems to indicate that, unlike Jupiter, Saturn was not enough of a heat source during that system's formation to cause the densities of its regular moons to follow the condensation sequence. Planetary scientists also suspect that comet impacts have so badly fractured the regular moons that they no longer show much evidence of their common origin. Understanding the origin of Saturn's moons is also difficult because the moons interact gravitationally so that the orbits they now occupy may differ significantly from their earlier orbits.

The complex orbital relationships of Saturn's moons and their evidently intense cratering suggest that the moons have interacted and may have collided with each other, with comets, and with large planetesimals in the past. Nevertheless, as with Jupiter's moons, astronomers hypothesize that most or all of Saturn's regular moons formed with the planet and that the irregular moons are captured. As you continue your exploration of the outer solar system, you can be alert for the presence of more such small, icy worlds.

SCIENTIFIC ARGUMENT

What features on Enceladus suggest that it has been active?
This argument is based on comparative planetology applied, in this case, to moons. The smaller moons of Saturn are icy worlds battered by impact craters, and you can suspect that they are cold and old. Small worlds lose their heat quickly; and, with no internal heat, there is no geological activity to erase impact craters. A small, icy world covered with craters is exactly what you would expect in the outer solar system. Enceladus, however, is peculiar. Although it is small and icy, its surface is highly reflective, and some areas contain fewer craters than you would expect. In fact, some regions seem almost free of craters. Grooves and faults mark some regions of the little moon and suggest motion in the crust. These features should have been destroyed long ago by impact cratering, so you must suppose that the moon has been geologically active at some time since the end of the heavy bombardment at the conclusion of planet building. The water vents discovered at the south pole of Enceladus show the moon is still active.

If you look at Titan, Saturn's largest moon, you see quite a different world. Build an argument based on a different principle of comparative planetology. **How can such a small world as Titan keep a thick atmosphere?**

What Are We?   Basic Scientists

People often describe science that has no known practical value as basic science or basic research. The exploration of distant worlds would be called basic science, and it is easy to argue that basic science is not worth the effort and expense because it has no known practical use. Of course, the problem is that no one has any way of knowing what knowledge will be of use until that knowledge is acquired.

In the middle of the 19th century, Queen Victoria asked physicist Michael Faraday what good his experiments with electricity and magnetism were. He answered, "Madam, what good is a baby?" Of course, Faraday's experiments were the beginning of the electronic age. Many of the practical uses of scientific knowledge that fill your world—digital electronics, synthetic materials, modern vaccines— began as basic research. Basic scientific research provides the raw materials that technology and engineering use to solve problems, so to protect its future, the human race must continue its struggle to understand how nature works.

Basic scientific research has yet one more important use that is so valuable it seems an insult to refer to it as merely practical. Science is the study of nature, and as you learn more about how nature works, you learn more about what your existence in this universe means. The seemingly impractical knowledge gained from space probes visiting other worlds tells you about your own planet and your own role in the scheme of nature. Science tells us where we are and what we are, and that knowledge is beyond value.

Summary

- The outer planets, Jupiter, Saturn, Uranus, and Neptune, are much larger than Earth and lower in density. These Jovian planets are rich in hydrogen. All four of the Jovian planets have rings, large satellite systems, and shallow atmospheres above liquid hydrogen mantles.

- Jupiter and Saturn show strong **belt–zone circulation (p. 495)**, but this is harder to see on Uranus and Neptune. Belts are low-pressure areas where gas is sinking, and zones are high-pressure areas where gas is rising.

- Moons in the Jovian satellite systems interact gravitationally, and some moons have been heated by tides to produce geological activity. Most are old and cratered. **Regular satellites (p. 495)** are generally larger, are close to the parent planet, and have low orbital inclinations; **irregular satellites (p. 495)** are generally small, are far from the parent planet, and have high orbital inclinations.

- Simple observations made from Earth show that Jupiter is 11 times Earth's diameter and 318 times Earth's mass. From that you can calculate its density, which is much lower than Earth's. It is rich in hydrogen and helium and cannot contain more than a small core of heavy elements.

- Not far below Jupiter's clouds, the temperature and pressure exceed the **critical point (p. 496)**, which means there is no difference between gaseous and liquid hydrogen. Consequently, the liquid hydrogen layer has no surface; the transition from gaseous hydrogen to liquid hydrogen is gradual.

- Jupiter's atmospheric composition is much like that of the sun—mostly hydrogen and helium with smaller amounts of heavier elements.

- Infrared observations show that Jupiter radiates more heat than it receives from the sun, so its interior must be five or six times hotter than the sun's surface and is prevented from flashing into vapor by the high pressure.

- The pressure inside Jupiter converts much of its hydrogen into **liquid metallic hydrogen (p. 496)**, and the dynamo effect generates a powerful magnetic field that produces rings of auroras around the planet's magnetic poles, interacts with the small moon Io, and traps high-energy particles to form intense radiation belts.

- The **oblateness (p. 497)** of Jupiter arises because its hydrogen envelope is highly fluid and the planet rotates rapidly.

- Ionized atoms from Jupiter's inner moon Io are swept up by Jupiter's rapidly spinning magnetic field to form the **Io plasma torus (p. 498)**, which encloses the orbit of the moon. Powerful electrical currents flow through the **Io flux tube (p. 498)** and produce spots of aurora where it enters Jupiter's atmosphere.

- Jupiter's shallow atmosphere is rich in hydrogen, with three layers of clouds at the temperatures where ammonia, ammonium hydrosulfide, and water condense. High- and low-pressure areas form belt–zone circulation.

- Spots on Jupiter, such as the Great Red Spot, are long-lasting, circulating storm systems.

- **Forward scattering (p. 499)** shows that Jupiter's ring is composed of tiny dust specks orbiting inside Jupiter's **Roche limit (p. 499)**. The dust particles cannot have survived since the formation of the planet; rather, they are being produced by meteorite impacts on some of Jupiter's inner moons.

- A small moon can orbit inside a planet's Roche limit and survive if it is a solid piece of rock strong enough to endure the tidal forces trying to pull it apart.

- The dimmer **gossamer rings (p. 502)** lie near the orbits of two moons, adding evidence that the rings are sustained by particles from moons.

- Impacts on moons and planets must be common in the history of the solar system. Jupiter was hit by the fragmented head of a comet in 1994. Such impacts had not been seen before.

- At least some of Jupiter's small moons are captured asteroids.

- The four **Galilean satellites (p. 504)** appear to have formed with Jupiter. They have higher densities closer to Jupiter and lower farther from Jupiter, similar to the dependence of planet densities on distance from the sun caused by the condensation sequence.

- Callisto, the outermost Galilean satellite, is composed of ice and rock and has an old and cratered surface. Unlike the three inner moons, Callisto is not caught in an orbital resonance and has never been active.

- Ganymede, Europa, and the innermost moon, Io, are locked in an orbital resonance, and that causes **tidal heating (p. 505)**. Ganymede's surface is old and cratered in some areas, but bright **grooved terrain (p. 505)** must have been produced by a past episode of geological activity.

- The inward focusing of meteorites should expose moons near massive planets to more cratering impacts, so it is surprising that Europa and Io have almost no craters, but this is explained by geological activity caused by tidal heating.

- Europa is mostly rock with a thin icy crust that contains only a few scars of past craters. Cracks and lines show that the crust has broken repeatedly, and a subsurface ocean probably vents through the crust and deposits ice to cover craters as fast as they form. The subsurface ocean might be a place to look for life.

- Io is strongly heated by tides and has no water at all. Over 150 volcanoes erupt molten rock and throw ash high above the surface. No impact craters are visible because they are destroyed or buried as fast as they form. Sulfur compounds color the surface yellow and orange and vent into space to be caught in Jupiter's magnetic field.

- Saturn must have formed much as Jupiter did, but it is slightly smaller than Jupiter and less dense than water. It has a hot interior but contains less liquid metallic hydrogen, so its magnetic field is weaker than Jupiter's and is, for some reason, closely aligned with its axis of rotation.

- Saturn is twice as far from the sun as Jupiter and is much colder. The three cloud layers seen on Jupiter form deeper in Saturn's hazy atmosphere and are not as clearly visible.

- Saturn's rings are composed of ice particles and cannot have lasted since the formation of the planet. The rings must receive occasional additions of ice particles when a small moon wanders inside Saturn's Roche limit and is pulled apart by tides or when comets hit the planet's icy moons.

- Icy particles can become trapped in stable places among the orbits of the innermost small moons, those within the Roche limit. Resonances with outer moons can produce gaps in the rings and generate waves that move like ripples through the rings. Small **shepherd satellites (p. 515)** can confine sections of the ring to produce sharp edges, ripples, or narrow ringlets.

- Without moons to confine them, the rings would have spread outward and dissipated long ago.

- Some of Saturn's smaller moons, such as Phoebe, are probably captured asteroids or Kuiper belt objects. All of the moons are mixtures of rock and ice.

- Titan, the largest moon, is so big it can retain a dense atmosphere of nitrogen with a small amount of methane. The methane condenses from the atmosphere, falls as rain, and drains over the surface, washing dark, organic material into drainage channels and on into the lowlands.

▶ The methane in Titan's atmosphere can be destroyed by sunlight, so it must be continuously replenished. It probably vents from the icy crust and may form methane volcanoes. Lakes of liquid methane have been found in the moon's polar regions.

▶ Some of the larger moons, such as Tethys, have old, dark, cratered surfaces with cracks and smoothed areas that suggest past activity. Enceladus, a rather small moon, is the most reflective object in the solar system and has large smooth areas, so it must have been very active. It orbits in a resonance with the moon Dione, and that may cause tidal heating inside Enceladus.

▶ Water vapor has been found above the south pole of Enceladus where water vents into space and forms ice crystals, which resupply Saturn's E ring.

▶ The moon Iapetus has a bright icy surface on its trailing side, but its leading side is coated with very dark material, possibly debris from Phoebe. In addition, Iapetus has a long equatorial ridge higher than Mount Everest on Earth. The ridge and the moon's equatorial bulge may have formed when the moon was young, molten, and spinning rapidly.

▶ The origin and evolution of Saturn's moons is not as clear as for Jupiter's Galilean moons. Orbital interactions and impacts have been important to these moons.

Review Questions

1. Why is Jupiter more oblate than Earth? Do you expect all Jovian planets to be oblate? Why or why not?

2. How do the interiors of Jupiter and Saturn differ? How does this affect their magnetic fields?

3. What is the difference between a belt and a zone?

4. How can you be certain that Jupiter's ring does not date from the formation of the planet?

5. If Jupiter had a satellite the size of our own moon orbiting outside the orbit of Callisto, what would you predict for its density and surface features?

6. Why are there no craters on Io and few on Europa? Why should you expect Io to suffer more impacts per square kilometer than Callisto?

7. Why are the belts and zones on Saturn less distinct than those on Jupiter?

8. If Saturn had no moons, what do you suppose its rings would look like?

9. Where did the particles in Saturn's rings come from?

10. How can Titan keep an atmosphere when it is smaller than airless Ganymede?

11. If you piloted a spacecraft to visit Saturn's moons and wanted to land on a geologically old surface, what features would you look for? What features would you avoid?

12. Why does the leading side of some satellites differ from the trailing side?

13. **How Do We Know?** Why would you expect research in archaeology to be less well funded than research in chemistry?

Discussion Questions

1. Some astronomers argue that Jupiter and Saturn are unusual, while other astronomers argue that all solar systems should contain one or two such giant planets. What do you think? Support your argument with evidence.

2. Why don't the Terrestrial planets have rings?

Problems

1. What is the maximum angular diameter of Jupiter as seen from Earth? What is the minimum? Repeat this calculation for Saturn and Titan. (*Hint:* Use the small-angle formula, Chapter 3.)

2. The highest-speed winds on Jupiter are in the equatorial jet stream, which has a velocity of 150 m/s. How long does it take for these winds to circle Jupiter?

3. What are the orbital velocity and period of a ring particle at the outer edge of Jupiter's ring? At the outer edge of Saturn's A ring? (*Hints:* The radius of the edge of the A ring is 136,500 km. Also, see Chapter 5.)

4. What is the angular diameter of Jupiter as seen from the surface of Callisto? (*Hint:* Use the small-angle formula, Chapter 3.)

5. What is the escape velocity from the surface of Ganymede if its mass is 1.5×10^{23} kg and its radius is 2.6×10^3 km? (*Hint:* See Chapter 5.)

6. If you were to record the spectrum of Saturn and its rings, you would find light from one edge of the rings redshifted and light from the other edge blueshifted. If you observed at a wavelength of 500 nm, what difference in wavelength should you expect between the two edges of the rings? (*Hints:* See Problem 3 and Chapter 7.)

7. What is the difference in orbital velocity between particles at the outer edge of Saturn's B ring and particles at the inner edge of the B ring? (*Hint:* The outer edge of the B ring has a radius of 117,500 km, and the inner edge has a radius of 92,000 km.)

8. What is the difference in orbital velocity between the two coorbital satellites if the semimajor axes of their orbits are 151,400 km and 151,500 km? The mass of Saturn is 5.7×10^{26} kg. (*Hint:* See Chapter 5.)

Learning to Look

1. This image shows a segment of the surface of Jupiter's moon Callisto. Why is the surface dark? Why are some craters dark and some white? What does this image tell you about the history of Callisto?

NASA/JPL

2. The Cassini spacecraft recorded this image of Saturn's A ring and the Encke Gap. What do you see in this photo that tells you about processes that confined and shape planetary rings?

NASA/JPL/Space Science Institute

24 | Uranus, Neptune, and the Dwarf Planets

Guidepost

Two planets circle the sun in the twilight beyond Saturn. You will find Uranus and Neptune substantially different from Jupiter and Saturn but still recognizable as Jovian planets. As you explore further you will also discover a family of dwarf planets, including Pluto, which appear to be leftover planet construction material. This chapter will help you answer four essential questions:

How are Uranus and Neptune similar to, and different from, Jupiter and Saturn?

How did Uranus and Neptune, along with their rings and moons, form and evolve?

How is Neptune different from Uranus?

How are Pluto and the dwarf planets related to the origin of the solar system?

As you finish this chapter, you will have visited all of the major worlds in our solar system. But there is more to see. Vast numbers of small rocky and icy bodies orbit among the planets, and the next chapter will introduce you to these fragments from the age of planet building.

A good many things go around in the dark besides Santa Claus.

— HERBERT HOOVER

OUT IN THE DARKNESS BEYOND SATURN, out where sunlight is 1000 times fainter than on Earth, there are objects orbiting the sun that Aristotle, Galileo, and Newton never imagined. They knew about Mercury, Venus, Mars, Jupiter, and Saturn, but our solar system also includes worlds that were not discovered until after the invention of the telescope. The stories of those discoveries highlight the process of scientific discovery, and the characteristics of these dimly lit worlds will reveal more of nature's secrets from the birth of the solar system.

24-1 Uranus

IN MARCH 1781, Benjamin Franklin was in France raising money, troops, and arms for the American Revolution. George Washington and his colonial army were only six months away from the defeat of Cornwallis at Yorktown and the end of the war. In England, King George III was beginning to show signs of madness. And a German-speaking music teacher in the English resort city of Bath was about to discover the planet Uranus.

The Discovery of Uranus

William Herschel (■ Figure 24-1) came from a musical family in Hanover, Germany, but emigrated to England as a young man and eventually obtained a prestigious job as the organist at the Octagon Chapel in Bath.

To compose exercises for his students and choral and organ works for the chapel, Herschel studied the mathematical principles of musical harmony from a book by Professor Robert Smith of Cambridge. The mathematics in the book were so interesting that Herschel searched out other works by Smith, including a book on optics. Of course, it is not surprising that an 18th-century book on optics written by a professor in England relied heavily on Isaac Newton's discoveries and described the principles

b Enhanced infrared image

■ Figure 24-1

(a) When William Herschel discovered Uranus in 1781, he saw only a tiny green-blue dot. He never knew how interesting that planet is. Even the designer of this stamp marking the passage of Comet Halley in 1986 had to guess at the planet's appearance. (b) An image of Uranus recorded by a near-infrared camera on the Keck telescope shows banding and cloud features. Seasonal changes are observed on Uranus as spring comes to the northern hemisphere. The rings look red in this view because of image processing. (Lawrence Sromovsky, UW-Madison Space Science and Engineering Center) of Newton's reflecting telescope (see Chapter 6). William Herschel and his brother Alexander began building telescopes, and William went on to study astronomy in his spare time.

Herschel's telescopes were similar to Newton's in that they had metal mirrors, but Herschel's were much larger. Newton's telescope had a mirror about 1 in. in diameter, but Herschel developed ways of making much larger mirrors, and he soon had telescopes as long as 20 ft. One of his favorite telescopes was 7 ft long and had a mirror 6.2 in. in diameter. Using this telescope, he began the research project that led to the discovery of Uranus.

Herschel did not set out to search for a planet; he was trying to detect stellar parallax produced by Earth's motion around the sun (see Figure 9-3). No one had yet detected this effect, although by the 1700s all astronomers accepted the idea that Earth moved. Galileo had pointed out that parallax might be detected if a nearby star and a very distant star lay so nearly along the same line of sight that they looked like a very close double star through a telescope. In such a case, Earth's orbital motion would produce a parallactic shift in the position of the nearby star with respect to the more distant star (■ Figure 24-2). Herschel began to examine all stars brighter than eighth magnitude to search for double stars that might show parallax. That project alone took

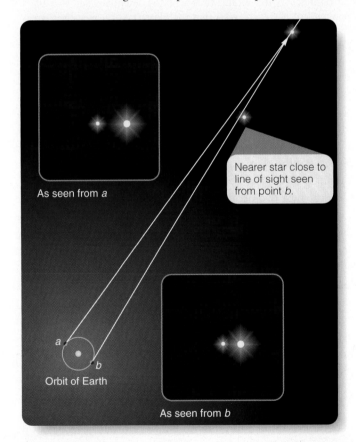

As seen from *a*

Nearer star close to line of sight seen from point *b*.

a

b

Orbit of Earth

As seen from *b*

■ **Figure 24-2**

A double star consisting of a nearby star and a more distant star could be used to detect stellar parallax. Seen from point *b* in Earth's orbit, the two stars appear closer together than from point *a*. The effect is actually much too small to detect by too small to detect by the unaided eye.

over two years. In the process, of course, he found many double stars that were binary stars that are actually close together in space and orbiting each other (see Chapter 9).

On the night of March 13, 1781, Herschel set up the 7-ft-long telescope in his back garden and continued his work. He later wrote, "In examining the small stars in the neighborhood of H Geminorum, I perceived one that appeared visibly larger than the rest." As seen from Earth, Uranus is never larger in angular diameter than 3.7 arc seconds, so Herschel's detection of the disk illustrates the quality of his telescope and his eye. At first he suspected that the object was a comet, but other astronomers quickly realized that it was a planet orbiting the sun beyond Saturn.

The discovery of Uranus made Herschel world famous. Since antiquity, astronomers had known of five planets—Mercury, Venus, Mars, Jupiter, and Saturn—and they had supposed that the list was complete. Herschel's discovery extended the classical universe by adding a new planet. The English public accepted Herschel as their astronomer-hero, and, having named the new planet *Georgium Sidus* (George's Star) after King George III, Herschel received a royal pension. The former music teacher was welcomed into court society, where he eventually met and married a wealthy widow and took his place as one of the great English astronomers. His new financial position allowed him to build large telescopes on his estate and, with his sister Caroline, also a talented astronomer, he attempted to map the extent of the universe. You read about their "star gauging" research in Chapter 15.

Continental astronomers were less than thrilled that an Englishman had made such a great discovery, and even some professional English astronomers thought Herschel a mere amateur. They called his discovery a lucky accident. Herschel defended himself by making three points. First, he had built some of the finest-quality telescopes then in existence. Second, he had been conducting a systematic research project and would have found Uranus eventually because he was inspecting all of the brighter stars visible with his telescope. And third, he had great experience seeing fine detail with his telescopes. As a musician, he knew the value of practice and applied it to the business of astronomical observing. In fact, records show that other astronomers had seen Uranus at least 17 times before Herschel, but each time they failed to notice that it was not a star. They plotted Uranus on their charts as if it were just another faint star.

This illustrates one of the ways in which scientific discoveries are made. Often, discoveries seem accidental, but on closer examination you find that the scientist has earned the right to the discovery through many years of study and preparation (**How Do We Know? 24-1**). To quote a common saying, "Luck is what happens to people who work hard."

Continental astronomers, especially the French, insisted that the new planet not be named after an English king. They, along with many other non-English astronomers, stubbornly called the planet Herschel. Years later, German astronomer Johann Bode suggested the name Uranus, one of the most senior of the Greek gods.

Scientific Discoveries

Why didn't Galileo expect to discover Jupiter's moons? In 1928, Alexander Fleming noticed that bacteria in a culture dish were avoiding a spot of mold. He went on to discover penicillin. In 1895, Conrad Roentgen noticed a fluorescent screen glowing in his laboratory when he experimented with other equipment. He discovered X-rays. In 1896, Henri Becquerel stored a uranium mineral on a photographic plate safely wrapped in black paper. The plate was later found to be fogged, and Becquerel discovered natural radioactivity. Like many discoveries in science, these seem to be accidental; but, as you have seen in this chapter, "accidental" doesn't quite describe what happened.

The most important discoveries in science are those that totally change the way people think about nature, and it is very unlikely that anyone would predict such discoveries. For the most part, scientists work within a paradigm (look back at **How Do We Know? 4-1**), a set of models, hypotheses, theories, and expectations about nature, and it is very difficult to imagine natural events that lie beyond that paradigm. Ptolemy, for example, could not have imagined galaxies because they were not part of his geocentric paradigm. That means that the most important discoveries in science are almost always unexpected.

An unexpected discovery, however, is not the same as an accidental discovery. Fleming discovered penicillin in his culture dish not because he was the first to see it, but because he had studied bacterial growth for many years; so, when he saw what many others must have seen before, he recognized it as important. Roentgen realized that the glowing screen in his lab was important, and Becquerel didn't discard that fogged photographic plate. Long years of experience prepared them to recognize the significance of what they saw.

A historical study has shown that each time astronomers build a telescope that greatly surpasses existing telescopes in capability, their most important discoveries are unexpected. Herschel didn't expect to discover Uranus with his 7-foot telescope, and modern astronomers didn't expect to discover evidence of dark energy with the Hubble Space Telescope.

The discovery of pulsars, spinning neutron stars, was totally unexpected, as important scientific discoveries often are. (NASA/McGill/V. Kaspi et al.)

Scientists pursuing basic research are rarely able to explain the potential value of their work, but that doesn't make their discoveries accidental. They earn their right to those lucky accidents.

Over the half-century following the discovery of Uranus, astronomers noted that Newton's laws did not exactly predict the observed position of the planet. Tiny variations in the orbital motion of Uranus eventually led to the discovery of Neptune, a controversial story you will read later in this chapter.

The Motion of Uranus

Uranus orbits nearly 20 AU from the sun and takes 84 years to go around once (**Celestial Profile 9**). The ancients thought of Saturn as the slowest of the planets, but Saturn orbits in a bit over 29 years. Uranus, being farther from the sun, moves even slower than Saturn and has a longer orbital period.

The rotation of Uranus is peculiar. Earth rotates approximately upright in its orbit. That is, its axis of rotation is inclined only 23.5° from the perpendicular to its orbit. The other planets have similarly moderate axial inclinations. Uranus, in contrast, rotates on an axis that is inclined 97.9° from the perpendicular to its orbit. It rotates on its side (■ Figure 24-3).

Because of its odd axial tilt, seasons on Uranus are extreme. The first good photographs of Uranus were taken in 1986, when the Voyager 2 spacecraft flew past. At that time, Uranus was in the segment of its orbit in which its south pole faced the sun. Consequently, its southern hemisphere was bathed in continuous sunlight, and a creature living on Uranus (an unlikely possibility, as you will discover later) would have seen the sun near the planet's south celestial pole. The sun was at southern solstice on Uranus in 1986, and you can see this at lower left in Figure 24-3. Over the next two decades, Uranus moved about a quarter of the way around its orbit, and, with the sun shining down from above the planet's equator, a citizen of Uranus would see the sun rise and set with the rotation of the planet. The sun reached equinox on Uranus in December 2007, and you can see that geometry by looking at the lower right in Figure 24-3. As Uranus continues along its orbit, the sun approaches the planet's north celestial pole, and the southern hemisphere of the planet experiences a lightless winter lasting 21 Earth years. In other words, the ecliptic on Uranus passes very near the planet's celestial poles, and the result is strong seasonal variation.

The Atmosphere of Uranus

Like Jupiter and Saturn, Uranus has no surface. The gases of its atmosphere—mostly hydrogen, 15 percent helium, and a few percent methane, ammonia, and water vapor—blend gradually into a fluid interior.

Seen through Earth-based telescopes, Uranus is a small, featureless greenish-blue disk. The green-blue color arises because the atmosphere contains methane, a good absorber of longer-wavelength photons. As sunlight penetrates into the atmosphere and is scattered back out, the longer-wavelength (red) photons are more likely to be absorbed. That means that the sunlight reflecting off Uranus and then entering your eye is richer in blue photons, giving the planet a blue color.

As Voyager 2 drew closer to the planet in late 1985, astronomers studied the images radioed back to Earth. Uranus was a pale green-blue ball with no obvious clouds, and only when the images were carefully computer enhanced was any banded structure detected (■ Figure 24-4). A few very high clouds of methane ice particles were detected, and their motions allowed astronomers to make the first good measurement of the planet's rotation period.

You can understand the nearly featureless appearance of the atmosphere by studying the temperature profile of Uranus shown in ■ Figure 24-5. The atmosphere of Uranus is much colder than that of Saturn or Jupiter. Consequently, the three cloud layers of ammonia, ammonia hydrosulfide, and water that form the belts and zones in the atmospheres of Jupiter and Saturn lie very deep in the atmosphere of Uranus. These cloud layers, if they exist at all in Uranus, are not visible because of the thick atmosphere of hydrogen through which an observer has to look. The clouds that are visible on Uranus are clouds of methane ice crystals, which form at such a low temperature that they occur high in the atmosphere of Uranus. Figure 24-5 shows that there can be no methane clouds on Jupiter because that planet is too warm. The coldest part of Saturn's atmosphere is just cold enough to form a thin methane haze high above its more visible cloud layers. (See Figure 23-15b.)

The clouds and atmospheric banding that are faintly visible on Uranus appear to be the result of belt–zone circulation, which is a bit surprising. Uranus rotates on its side, so solar energy strikes its surface with geometry quite different than that for Jupiter and Saturn. Evidently belt–zone circulation is dominated by the rotation of the planet and not by the direction of sunlight.

The Voyager 2 images from 1986 made some astronomers expect that Uranus was always a nearly featureless planet, but later observations have revealed that Uranus has seasons. Since 1986, Uranus has moved along its orbit, and spring has come to its northern hemisphere. The Hubble Space Telescope and giant Earth-based telescopes have detected changing clouds on Uranus, including a dark cloud that may be a vortex resembling the spots on Jupiter (■ Figure 24-6). The clouds appear to be part of a seasonal cycle on Uranus, but its year lasts 84 Earth years, so you will have to be patient to see summer come to its northern hemisphere.

The Interior of Uranus

Astronomers cannot describe the interiors of Uranus and Neptune as accurately as they can the interiors of Jupiter and Saturn. Observational data are sparse, and the materials inside these planets are not as easy to model as simple liquid hydrogen.

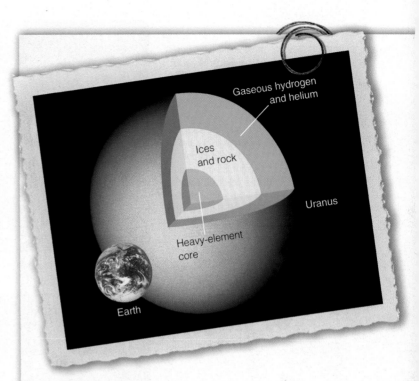

Uranus rotates on its side. When Voyager 2 flew past in 1986, the planet's south pole was pointed almost directly at the sun. (NASA)

Celestial Profile 9: Uranus

Motion:

Average distance from the sun	19.2 AU (2.87×10^9 km)
Eccentricity of orbit	0.046
Inclination of orbit to ecliptic	0.8°
Average orbital velocity	6.8 km/s
Orbital period	84.0 y
Period of rotation	17.23 h
Inclination of equator to orbit	97.9° (retrograde rotation)

Characteristics:

Equatorial diameter	5.11×10^4 km (4.01 $D_\oplus$)
Mass	8.69×10^{25} kg (14.5 $M_\oplus$)
Average density	1.29 g/cm³
Gravity	0.9 Earth gravity
Escape velocity	22 km/s (2.0 $V_\oplus$)
Temperature above cloud tops	−220°C (−365°F)
Albedo	0.35
Oblateness	0.023

Personality Point:

Most creation stories begin with a separation of opposites, and Greek mythology is no different. Uranus (the sky) separated from Gaia (Earth) who was born from the void, Chaos. They gave birth to the giant Cyclops, Cronos (Saturn, father of Zeus), and his fellow Titans. Uranus is sometimes called the starry sky, but the sun (Helios), moon (Selene), and the stars were born later, so Uranus, one of the most ancient gods, began as the empty, dark sky.

■ Figure 24-3

Uranus rotates on an axis that is tipped 97.9° from the perpendicular to its orbit, so its seasons are extreme. When one of its poles is pointed nearly at the sun (a solstice), an inhabitant of Uranus would see the sun near a celestial pole, and it would never rise or set. As it orbits the sun, the planet maintains the direction of its axis in space, and thus the sun moves from pole to pole. At the time of an equinox on Uranus, the sun would be on the celestial equator and would rise and set with each rotation of the planet. Compare with similar diagrams for Earth on page 24.

■ Figure 24-4

(a) This Voyager 2 image of Uranus was made in 1986 and shows no clouds. Only when the image is computer enhanced, as in (b), is a banded structure visible. At the time, the axis of rotation was pointed nearly at the sun. (c) Under extreme computer enhancement, small methane clouds were visible. The geometry of the banding and the clouds suggests belt–zone circulation analogous to that on Saturn and Jupiter. (NASA)

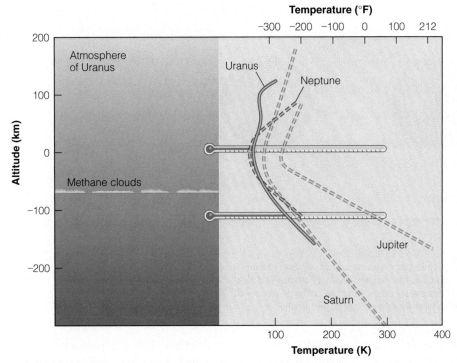

Temperature (°F)

■ Figure 24-5

The atmosphere of Uranus is much colder than that of Jupiter or Saturn, and the only visible cloud layer is one formed of methane ice crystals deep in the hydrogen atmosphere. Other cloud layers would be much deeper in the atmosphere and are not visible. The temperature profile of Neptune is similar to that of Uranus, and it has methane clouds at about the same place in its atmosphere.

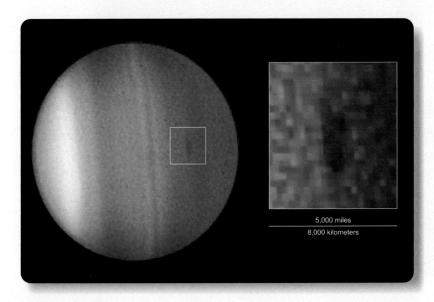

■ Figure 24-6

A dark cloud, possibly a circulating storm, is visible in this Hubble Space Telescope image of Uranus. (NASA, ESA, Sromovsky, Fry, Hallel, and Rages)

The average density of Uranus, 1.3 g/cm^3, tells you that the planet must contain a larger share of dense materials than Saturn. Nearly all models of the interior of Uranus contain three layers. The uppermost layer, the atmosphere, is rich in hydrogen and helium. Below the atmosphere, a deep mantle must contain large amounts of water, methane, and ammonia in a solid or slushy state, mixed with hydrogen and silicate matter. This mantle is sometimes described as "ice," but, because of high pressure and a temperature of a few thousand degrees, it is quite unlike the earthly material that word suggests. The third layer in the three-layer models is a small heavy-element core. Many books refer to the core as "rocky," but, again, because of the high pressure and high temperature, the material is not very rock-like. The term *rock* refers to its chemical composition and not to its other properties.

It is a **Common Misconception** to imagine that the four Jovian planets are gas giants. As you have learned, Jupiter and Saturn are mostly liquid. Uranus and Neptune are sometimes described as "ice giant" planets, in recognition of the large proportion of solid water in their interiors.

Because Uranus has a much lower mass than Jupiter, its internal pressure is not high enough to produce liquid metallic hydrogen. Consequently, you might expect it to lack a strong magnetic field, but the Voyager 2 spacecraft found that Uranus has a magnetic field about 75 percent as strong as Earth's. Uranus's field is tipped 60° to the axis of rotation and is offset from the center of the planet by about 30 percent of the planet's radius (■ Figure 24-7). Theorists suggest that this unexpectedly oddly oriented magnetic field is produced by a dynamo effect operating not at the center but nearer the surface in a layer of liquid water with dissolved ammonia and methane. Such a material would be a good conductor of electricity, and the rotation of the planet coupled with convection in the fluid could generate the magnetic field.

As it made its closest approach to Uranus, Voyager 2 observed effects of the planet's magnetic field. This allowed a more precise measurement of Uranus's rotation period than was possible from motions of difficult-to-detect cloud features. The magnetic field deflects the

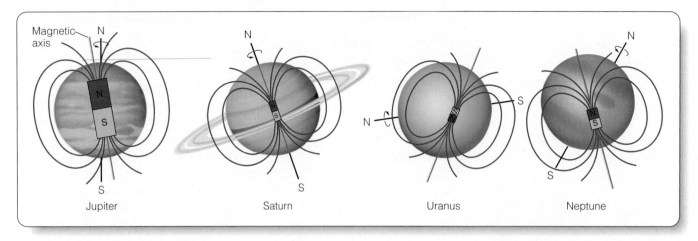

■ Figure 24-7

The magnetic fields of Uranus and Neptune are peculiar. While the magnetic axis of Jupiter is tipped only 10° from its axis of rotation, and the magnetic axis of Saturn is not tipped at all, the magnetic axes of Uranus and Neptune are tipped at large angles. Furthermore, the magnetic fields of Uranus and Neptune are offset from the center of the planet. This suggests that the dynamo effect operates differently in Uranus and Neptune than in Jupiter, Saturn, and Earth.

solar wind and traps some charged particles to create weak radiation belts in the planet's magnetosphere. High-speed electrons spiraling along the magnetic field produce synchrotron radio emission just as around Jupiter, and the Voyager 2 spacecraft recorded this radiation fluctuating with a period of 17.2 hours—the period of rotation of the magnetic field and, presumably, the planetary interior.

The magnetic field and the high inclination of the planet produce some peculiar effects. As is the case for all planets with magnetic fields, the solar wind deforms the magnetosphere and draws it out into a long tail extending away from the planet in the direction opposite the sun. The rapid rotation of Uranus and its high inclination give the magnetosphere and its long extension a corkscrew shape. At the time Voyager 2 flew past in 1986, the south pole of Uranus was pointed nearly at the sun, and once during each rotation the solar wind poured down into the south magnetic pole. The resulting interaction produced strong auroras that Voyager 2 detected in the ultraviolet at both magnetic poles (■ Figure 24-8). In the years since, Uranus has moved farther

■ Figure 24-8

Auroras on Uranus were detected in the ultraviolet by the Voyager 2 spacecraft when it flew by in 1986. These maps of opposite sides of Uranus show the location of auroras near the magnetic poles. Recall that the magnetic field is highly inclined and offset from the planet's center, so the magnetic poles do not lie near the poles defined by rotation. The white dashed line marks zero longitude. (Courtesy Floyd Herbert, LPL) around its orbit, so the geometry of its interaction with the solar wind is now different. Unfortunately, no spacecraft orbit Uranus at present, and there is no way to observe effects of these changes in detail.

Like the magnetic field, the temperature of Uranus can reveal something about its interior. Jupiter and Saturn are warmer than you would expect, given the amount of energy they receive from the sun, and this means that heat is leaking out from their hot interiors. Uranus, in contrast, is about the temperature you would expect for a world at its distance from the sun. Apparently, it has lost much of its interior heat. Yet, it must have some internal heat to cause convection in the fluid mantle and drive the dynamo effect. The temperature in its core is estimated from models to be about 8000 K. The decay of natural radioactive elements would generate heat, but some astronomers have suggested that the slow settling of heavier elements through the fluid mantle could also release energy to warm the interior.

Laboratory studies of methane show that it can break down under the temperature and pressure found inside Uranus and form various compounds plus pure carbon in the form of diamonds. If this happens in Uranus, the diamond crystals would fall inward, warming the interior through friction. Determining for sure whether a planetwide rain of diamonds actually exists inside Uranus is probably forever beyond human reach.

For a Jovian world, Uranus seems small and mostly featureless. But now you are ready to visit one of its best attractions—its rings.

The Rings of Uranus

Both Uranus and Neptune have rings that are more like those of Jupiter than those of Saturn. They are dark, faint, not easily visible from Earth, and confined by shepherd satellites.

Study **The Rings of Uranus and Neptune** on pages 534–535 and notice three important points about the rings of Uranus and one new term:

1 The rings of Uranus were discovered during an *occultation* when Uranus crossed in front of a star.

2 The rings are made up of a thin layer of very dark boulders. They are confined by small moons, and except for the outermost rings, they contain little dust.

3 Like the rings of Jupiter and Saturn, the rings around Uranus and Neptune cannot survive for long periods. All the Jovian rings need to be resupplied with material from impacts on moons.

When you read about Neptune's rings later in this chapter, you will return to this artwork and see how closely the two ring systems compare.

Images made with the Hubble space telescope in 2003 and 2005 have revealed two larger, fainter, dustier rings lying outside the previously known ring system (■ Figure 24-9). The larger of

■ **Figure 24-9**

Two newly discovered rings orbit Uranus far outside the previously known rings. The outermost ring follows the orbit of the small moon Mab, only 12 km (7 mi) in diameter. The short bright arcs in this photo were caused by moons moving along their orbits during the long time exposure. (NASA, ESA, M. Showalter, SETI Institute)

these rings coincides with the orbit of the small moon Mab and is probably replenished by particles blasted off of the moon by meteorite impacts. The smaller of the rings is confined between the orbits of the moons Portia and Rosalind.

As you read about planetary rings, notice their close relationship with moons. Because of collisions among ring particles, planetary rings tend to spread outward, almost like an expanding

1 The rings of Uranus were discovered in 1977, when Uranus crossed in front of a star. During this **occultation**, astronomers saw the star dim a number of times before and again after the planet crossed over the star. The dips in brightness were caused by rings circling Uranus.

More rings were discovered by Voyager 2. The rings are identified in different ways depending on when and how they were discovered.

Notice the eccentricity of the ε ring. It lies at different distances on opposite sides of the planet.

2 The albedo of the ring particles is only about 0.015, darker than lumps of coal. If the ring particles are made of methane-rich ices, radiation from the planet's radiation belts could break the methane down to release carbon and darken the ices. The same process may darken the icy surface of Uranian moons.

The narrowness of the rings suggests they are shepherded by small moons. Voyager 2 found Ophelia and Cordelia shepherding the ε ring. Other small moons must be shepherding the other narrow rings. Such moons must be structurally strong to hold themselves together inside the planet's Roche limit.

Ophelia

Cordelia

The eccentricity of the ε ring is apparently caused by the eccentric orbits of Ophelia and Cordelia.

λ
η
γ
δ
β
α
6
5
4
1986
U2R

2a When the Voyager 2 spacecraft looked back at the rings illuminated from behind by the sun, the rings were not bright. That is, the rings are not bright in forward-scattered light. That means they must not contain small dust particles. The nine main rings contain particles no smaller than meter-sized boulders.

Uranus

3 Ring particles don't last forever as they collide with each other and are exposed to radiation. The rings of Uranus may be resupplied with fresh particles occasionally as impacts on icy moons scatter icy debris.

Collisions among the large particles in the ring produce small dust grains. Friction with Uranus's tenuous upper atmosphere plus sunlight pressure act to slow the dust grains and make them fall into the planet. The Uranian rings actually contain very little dust.

Disk of Neptune

Visual-wavelength image

The rings of Neptune are bright in forward-scattered light, as in the image above, and that indicates that the rings contain significant amounts of dust. The ring particles are as dark as those that circle Uranus, so they probably also contain methane-rich ice darkened by radiation.

4 The brightness of Neptune is hidden behind the black bar in this Voyager 2 image. Two narrow rings are visible, and a wider, fainter ring lies closer to the planet. More ring material is visible between the two narrow rings.

Arc

Arc

5 When Neptune occulted stars, astronomers sometimes detected rings and sometimes did not. From that they concluded that Neptune might have ring arcs. Computer enhancement of this Voyager 2 visual-wavelength image shows arcs, regions of higher density, in the outer ring.

The ring arcs visible in the outer ring appear to be generated by the gravitational influence of the moon Galatea, but other moons must also be present to confine the rings.

Enhanced visual image

4a Neptune's rings lie in the plane of the planet's equator and inside the Roche limit. The narrowness of the rings suggests that shepherd moons must confine them, and a few such moons have been found among the rings. There must be more undiscovered small moons to confine the rings completely.

Naiad

Galatea

Thalassa

Adams

LeVerrier

Despina

Galle

4c Like the rings of the other Jovian planets, the ring particles that orbit Neptune cannot have survived since the formation of the planet. Occasional impacts on Neptune's moons must scatter debris and resupply the rings with fresh particles.

4b Neptune's rings have been given names associated with the planet's history. English astronomer Adams and French astronomer LeVerrier predicted the existence of Neptune from the motion of Uranus. The German astronomer Galle discovered the planet in 1846 based on LeVerrier's prediction.

Neptune

gas. If a planet had no moons, its rings would spread out into a more and more tenuous sheet until they were gone. The spreading rings can be anchored by small shepherd moons, which interact gravitationally with wandering ring particles, absorb orbital energy, and cause the particles to remain within the rings. As they gain orbital energy, these small moons move slowly outward, but they can be anchored in turn by orbital resonances with larger, more distant moons that are so massive they do not get pushed outward significantly. In this way, a system of moons can confine and preserve a system of planetary rings.

The Moons of Uranus

Uranus has five large regular moons that were discovered from Earth-based observations (■ Figure 24-10). Those five moons, from the outermost inward, are Oberon, Titania, Umbriel, Ariel, and Miranda. The names Umbriel and Ariel are names from Alexander Pope's *The Rape of the Lock,* and the rest are from Shakespeare's *A Midsummer Night's Dream* and *The Tempest* (an Ariel also appears in *The Tempest*). Spectra show that the moons contain frozen water, although their surfaces are dark. Planetary scientists assumed they were made of dirty ices, but little more was known of the moons before Voyager 2 flew through the system.

In addition to imaging the known moons, the Voyager 2 cameras discovered ten more moons too small to have been seen from Earth. Since then, the construction of new-generation telescopes and the development of new imaging techniques (see Chapter 6) have allowed astronomers to find even more small

moons orbiting Uranus. Roughly 30 are currently known, but there are almost certainly more to be found.

The smaller moons are all as dark as coal. They are icy worlds with surfaces that have been darkened by impacts vaporizing ice and concentrating embedded dirt. In addition, they orbit inside the radiation belts, and that radiation can convert methane trapped in their ices into dark carbon deposits to further darken their surfaces.

More is known about the five larger moons. They are all tidally locked to Uranus, and that means their south poles were pointed toward the sun in 1986. Voyager could not photograph their northern hemispheres, so the analysis of their geology must depend on images of only half their surfaces. The densities of the moons suggest that they contain relatively large rock cores surrounded by icy mantles, as shown in Figure 24-10.

Oberon, the outermost of the large moons, has a cratered surface, but there is visible evidence that it was once geologically active (■ Figure 24-11). A large fault crosses the sunlit hemisphere, and dark material, perhaps dirty water "lava," appears to have flooded the floors of some craters.

Titania is the largest of the five moons and has a heavily cratered surface, but it has no very large craters (Figure 24-11). This suggests that after the end of the heavy bombardment, the young Titania underwent an active phase in which its surface was flooded with water that covered early craters with fresh ice. Since then, the craters that have formed are not as large as the largest of those that were erased. The network of faults that crosses Titania's surface is another sign of past activity.

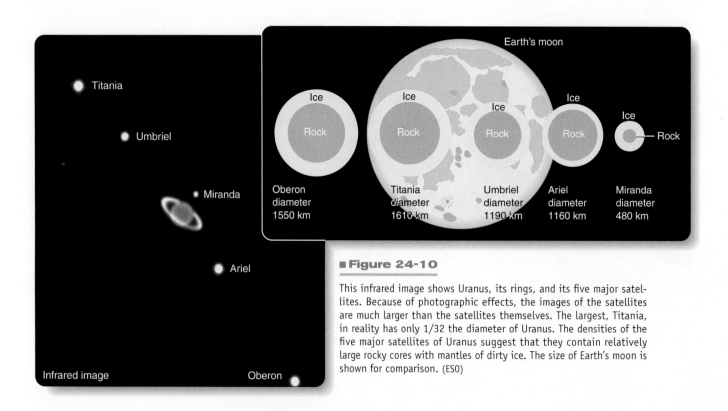

■ Figure 24-10

This infrared image shows Uranus, its rings, and its five major satellites. Because of photographic effects, the images of the satellites are much larger than the satellites themselves. The largest, Titania, in reality has only 1/32 the diameter of Uranus. The densities of the five major satellites of Uranus suggest that they contain relatively large rocky cores with mantles of dirty ice. The size of Earth's moon is shown for comparison. (ESO)

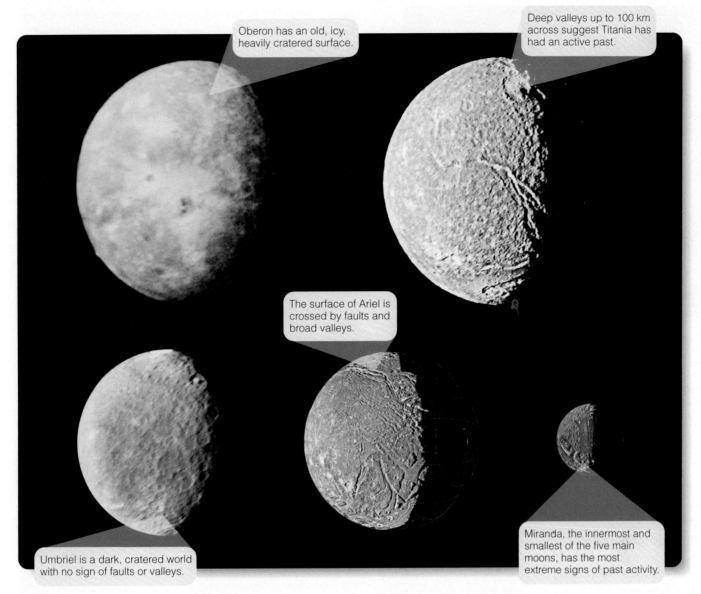

■ Figure 24-11

The five largest moons of Uranus, shown here in correct relative size scale, range from the largest, Titania, 46 percent the diameter of Earth's moon, down to Miranda, only 14 percent the diameter of Earth's moon. For a better view of Miranda, see the next figure. (Ariel and Miranda: U.S. Geological Survey, Flagstaff, Arizona; Other images: NASA)

Umbriel, the next moon inward, is a dark, cratered world with no sign of faults or surface activity (Figure 24-11). It is the darkest of the moons, with an albedo of only 0.16 compared with 0.25 to 0.45 for the other moons. Its crust is a mixture of rock and ice. A bright crater floor in one region suggests that clean ice may lie at shallow depths in some regions.

Ariel has the brightest surface of the five major Uranian satellites and shows clear signs of geological activity. It is crossed by faults over 10 km deep, and some regions appear to have been smoothed by resurfacing, as you can see in Figure 24-11. Crater counts show that the smoothed regions are in fact younger than the other regions. Ariel may have been subject to tidal heating caused by an orbital resonance with Miranda and Umbriel.

Miranda is a mysterious moon. As you can see in Figure 24-11, it is the smallest of the five large moons, but it appears to have been the most active. In fact, its active past appears to have been quite unusual. Miranda is marked by oval patterns of grooves known as **ovoids** (■ Figure 24-12). These features were originally hypothesized to have been produced when mutual gravitation pulled together fragments of an earlier moon shattered by a major impact. More recent studies of the ovoids show that they are associated with faults, ice-lava flows, and rotated blocks of crust, suggesting that a major impact was not involved. Rather, the ovoids may have been created by internal heat driving large but very slow convection currents in Miranda's icy mantle.

Certainly, Miranda has had a violent past. Near the equator, a huge cliff rises 20 km (12 mi). If you stood in your spacesuit at

■ Figure 24-12

Miranda, the smallest of the five major moons of Uranus, is only 480 km (290 mi) in diameter, but its surface shows signs of activity. This photomosaic of Voyager 2 images reveals that it is marked by great oval systems of grooves. The smallest features detected are about 1.5 km (1 mi) in diameter. (U.S. Geological Survey, Flagstaff, Arizona)

the top of the cliff and dropped a rock over the edge, it would fall for 10 minutes before hitting the bottom. Nevertheless, crater counts indicate that the cliff and the ovoids are old. Miranda is no longer geologically active, but you can read hints of its active past on its disturbed surface.

If the ovoids were caused by convection in Miranda's icy mantle, then heat rising from its interior must have been the dominant factor. Miranda is so small that its heat of formation must have been lost quickly, and there is no reason to expect it to have been strongly heated by radioactive decay. Tidal heating could have occurred if Miranda's orbit was once made slightly eccentric by a resonance with other moons. Your knowledge of tidal heating in other moons can help you understand Miranda.

A History of Uranus

The challenge of comparative astronomy is to tell the story of a world, and Uranus may present the biggest challenge of all the objects in our solar system. Not only is it so distant that it is difficult to study, but it is also peculiar in many ways.

Uranus formed from the solar nebula, as did the other Jovian planets, but calculations show that Uranus and Neptune could not have grown to their present size in the slow-moving orbits they now occupy so far from the sun. Computer models of planet formation in the solar nebula suggest that Uranus and Neptune formed closer to the sun, in the neighborhood of Jupiter and Saturn. Gravitational interactions among the Jovian planets could have gradually moved Uranus and Neptune outward to their present locations. One such model has Neptune forming closer to the sun than Uranus and the two planets later switching places as they moved out. As you will learn later in this chapter, the migration of giant planets could have triggered the late heavy bombardment episode. These are interesting hypotheses, and they illustrate how uncertain the histories of the outer planets really are.

The highly inclined axis of Uranus may have originated late in its formation when it was struck by a planetesimal that would have to have been as large as Earth. That impact also may have disturbed the interior of the world and caused it to lose much of its heat. Uranus now radiates less than 10 percent more heat than it receives from the sun. There is now just enough heat flowing outward to drive circulation in its slushy mantle and generate its magnetic field. A more recent study shows that tidal interactions with Saturn could have altered Uranus's axis of rotation as it was pushed outward. In this case, an older catastrophic hypothesis is being challenged by a newer evolutionary hypothesis (**How Do We Know? 19-1**).

Impacts have been important in the history of the moons and rings of Uranus. All of the moons are cratered, and some show signs of large impacts. Meteorites and the nuclei of comets striking the moons may create debris that becomes trapped among the orbits of the smaller moons to produce the narrow rings. The ring particles observed now could not have lasted since the formation of the planet, so they must be replenished with fresh material now and then. When the final history of Uranus is written, it will surely include some dramatic impact events.

SCIENTIFIC ARGUMENT

How do astronomers know what the interior of Uranus is like?
This argument must combine observation with theory. Obviously, you can't see inside the planet, so planetary scientists are limited to a few basic observations that they must connect with models in a chain of inference to describe the interior. First, the size of Uranus can be found from its angular diameter and distance, and you can find its mass by observing the orbital radii and orbital periods of its moons. Its mass divided by its volume equals its density, which implies that it must contain a certain proportion of dense material such as ice and rock, more than there is inside Saturn. Add to that the chemical composition obtained from spectra, and you have the data needed to build a mathematical model of the interior. Such models predict a core of heavy elements and a mantle of ices mixed with heavier material of rocky composition.

Going from observable properties to unobservable properties is the heart of astronomical research. Now use this approach to build a new argument: **What observational properties of the rings of Uranus show that small moons must orbit among the rings?**

24-2 Neptune

URANUS AND NEPTUNE are often discussed together. They are about the same size and density and are very similar planets in some ways. They do differ, however, in certain respects. Unlike Uranus, Neptune has a significant amount of heat flowing out from its interior. Also, Neptune has especially complicated ring and satellite systems. Even the discovery of Neptune differed from the discovery of Uranus.

The Discovery of Neptune

The discovery of Neptune triggered one of the greatest controversies in the history of science. For over a century people told the story and took sides, but only in the last few years has the real story become known. You can follow the story and decide which side you favor.

In 1843, the young English astronomer John Couch Adams (1819–1892) completed his degree in astronomy and immediately began the analysis of one of the great problems of 19th-century astronomy. William Herschel had discovered Uranus in 1781, but earlier astronomers had seen the planet as early as 1690 and had mistakenly plotted it on charts as a star. When 19th-century astronomers tried to combine all those data, they didn't quite fit together. No planet obeying Newton's laws of motion and controlled only by the gravity of the sun and the other known planets could follow such an orbit.

Some astronomers suggested that the gravitational attraction of an undiscovered planet was causing the discrepancies. Adams began with the observed variations from the predicted positions of Uranus, never more than 2 arc minutes, and by October 1845 he had, through a laborious and difficult calculation, computed the orbit of the undiscovered planet. He sent his prediction to the Astronomer Royal, Sir George Airy, who passed it on to an observer who began a painstaking search of the area star by star.

Meanwhile, the French astronomer Urbain Jean Leverrier (1811–1877) made the same calculations and sent his predicted position of the planet to Johann Galle at the Berlin Observatory. Galle received Leverrier's prediction on the afternoon of September 23, 1846, and, after searching for 30 minutes that evening, found Neptune. It was only 1° from the position predicted by Leverrier.

The discovery of a new planet caused a sensation, but English astronomers didn't like a Frenchman getting all the credit. After all, they said, the planet was found only 2° from the position predicted by the orbit computed by their own astronomer, Adams. When the English announced Adams's work, the French suspected that he had plagiarized the calculations, and the controversy was bitter, as controversies between England and France often are. For over a century, historians of science have repeated the story of the young English astronomer who missed his chance because the astronomers in charge of the search were careless and slow.

Original papers related to Adam's calculations were lost for decades, but when they were found in 1998, they painted a different picture. Adams did the calculations correctly, but he computed only the orbit for the new planet. He didn't actually calculate its position in the sky along the orbit; that was left to the English astronomers conducting the search. Once the new planet was discovered, the English astronomers, out of national pride, pressed Adam's case further than they should have.

For 150 years, astronomers took sides or gave both astronomers equal credit. In fact, it seems clear that Leverrier deserves credit for making an accurate, useful prediction of a position on the sky and then pressing it aggressively on an astronomer who had the right skills to make the search. You should still give both astronomers credit for solving a difficult problem that was one of the great challenges of the age. A modern analysis shows that both Leverrier and Adams made unwarranted assumptions about the undiscovered planet's distance from the sun. By good fortune their assumptions made no difference in the 19th century, and the planet was close to the positions they predicted. Do you think they deserve less credit for that reason? They tried, and the other astronomers of the world didn't.

Leverrier and Adams could have been beaten to the discovery had Galileo paid a little less attention to Jupiter and a little more attention to what he saw in the background. Modern studies of Galileo's notebooks show that he saw Neptune on December 24, 1612, and again on January 28, 1613, but he plotted it as a star in the background of drawings of Jupiter. It is interesting to speculate about the response of the Inquisition had Galileo proposed that a planet existed beyond Saturn. Unfortunately for history, but perhaps fortunately for Galileo, he did not recognize Neptune as a planet, and its discovery had to wait another 234 years.

Historians of science have recounted the discovery of Neptune as a triumph for Newtonian physics: The three laws of motion and the law of gravity had proved sufficient to predict the position and orbit of an unseen planet. Thus, the discovery of Neptune was fundamentally different from the discovery of Uranus. Uranus was discovered "accidentally" in the course of Herschel's attempt to systematically observe the entire sky, whereas the existence of Neptune was predicted by Leverrier and Adams using basic laws.

The Atmosphere and Interior of Neptune

Little was known about Neptune before the Voyager 2 spacecraft swept past it in 1989. Seen from Earth, Neptune is a tiny, blue-green dot never more than 2.3 arc seconds in diameter. Before Voyager 2, astronomers knew Neptune is almost four times the diameter of Earth, or about 4 percent smaller in diameter than Uranus (**Celestial Profile 10**), with a mass about 17 times that of Earth, 20 percent more than Uranus. Spectra revealed that, as in the case of Uranus, its blue-green color was caused by methane in its hydrogen-rich atmosphere absorbing red light. Neptune's density showed that it is a Jovian planet rich in hydrogen, but almost no detail was visible from Earth, so even its period of rotation was uncertain.

Voyager 2 passed only 4900 km (3050 mi) above Neptune's cloud tops, closer than any spacecraft had ever come to one of the Jovian planets. The images it captured revealed that Neptune is marked by dramatic belt–zone circulation parallel to the planet's equator. Voyager 2 also saw at least four cyclonic disturbances. The largest, dubbed the Great Dark Spot, looked similar to the Great Red Spot on Jupiter (■ Figure 24-13). Neptune's Great Dark Spot was located in the southern hemisphere and rotated around its center counterclockwise, with a period of about 16 days. Like the Great Red Spot, it appeared to be caused by gas rising from its planet's interior. Unexpectedly, when the Hubble Space Telescope began imaging Neptune in 1994, the Great Dark Spot was gone, and new cloud features were seen appearing and disappearing in Neptune's atmosphere (Figure 24-13). Evidently, the cyclonic disturbances on Neptune are not nearly as long lived as Jupiter's Great Red Spot, which has persisted for at least 400 years.

The Voyager 2 images reveal other cloud features standing out against the deep blue of the methane-rich atmosphere. The white clouds are made of crystals of frozen methane and range up to 50 km above the deeper layers, just where the temperature in Neptune's atmosphere is low enough for rising methane to freeze into crystals. (See Figure 24-5.) Presumably these features are related to rising convection currents that produce clouds high in Neptune's atmosphere where they catch sunlight and appear bright. Special filters can reveal these cloud belts in visual-wavelength images and at infrared wavelengths (■ Figure 24-14). Some observations made by the Hubble Space Telescope suggest that atmospheric activity on Neptune may be related to flares and other eruptions on the sun, but more data are needed to explore this connection.

As on the other Jovian worlds, winds circle Neptune parallel to its equator, but Neptune's winds blow at very high speeds and tend to blow backward—against the rotation of the planet. Why Neptune should have such high-speed retrograde winds is not understood, and it is part of the larger problem of understanding belt–zone circulation.

Now that you have seen belts and zones on all four of the Jovian planets (assuming that the very faint clouds observed on Uranus are in fact traces of belt–zone circulation), you can ask what drives this circulation. Because belts and zones remain parallel to a planet's equator even when the planet rotates at a high inclination, as in the case of Uranus, it seems reasonable to believe that the atmospheric circulation is dominated by the rotation of the planet, and perhaps also by heat flow and circulation currents in the liquid interior, but not by solar heating.

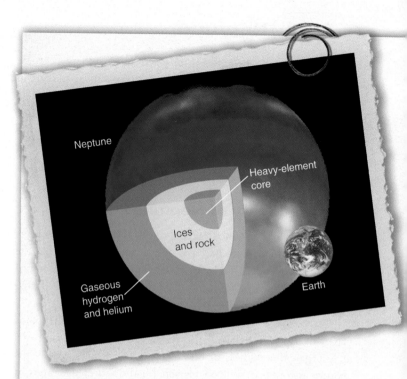

Neptune was tipped slightly away from the sun when the Hubble Space Telescope recorded this image. The interior is much like Uranus's, but there is more heat. (NASA)

Celestial Profile 10: Neptune

Motion:

Average distance from the sun	30.1 AU (4.50 × 10⁹ km)
Eccentricity of orbit	0.010
Inclination of orbit to ecliptic	1.8°
Average orbital velocity	5.4 km/s
Orbital period	164.8 y
Period of rotation	16.05 h
Inclination of equator to orbit	28.8°

Characteristics:

Equatorial diameter	4.95×10^5 km ($3.93\ D_\oplus$)
Mass	1.03×10^{26} kg ($17.2\ M_\oplus$)
Average density	1.66 g/cm³
Gravity	1.2 Earth gravities
Escape velocity	25 km/s ($2.2\ V_\oplus$)
Temperature at cloud tops	−215°C (−355°F)
Albedo	0.35
Oblateness	0.017

Personality Point:

Because the planet Neptune looked so blue, astronomers named it after the Roman god of the sea, Neptune (Poseidon to the Greeks). His wife was Amphitrite, granddaughter of Ocean, one of the Titans. Neptune controlled the storms and waves and was a powerful god, not to be trifled with. His three-pronged trident became the symbol for the planet Neptune.

Neptune in 1989

Great Dark Spot

Visual-wavelength image
from Voyager 2

1996

2002

Visual-wavelength
images from
Hubble Space Telescope

1998

■ **Figure 24-13**

Because Neptune's equator is inclined almost 29 degrees in its orbit, it experiences seasons. Because of the planet's orbital period, each season lasts about 40 years. Since Voyager 2 visited in 1989, spring has come to the southern hemisphere, and the weather has clearly changed, which is surprising because sunlight on Neptune is 900 times dimmer than on Earth. (NASA, L. Sromovsky, and P. Fry, University of Wisconsin-Madison.)

Visual

Infrared

■ **Figure 24-14**

(a) This visual-wavelength image of Neptune was made through filters that make belts of methane stand out. (NASA and Erich Karkoschka) (b) The infrared image at right was recorded using one of the Keck 10-meter telescopes and adaptive optics. The location of methane cloud belts around the planet are evident. (U. C. Berkeley/W. M. Keck Observatory)

The same observations that helped define the interior of Uranus can be applied to Neptune. Models suggest that the interior contains a small heavy-element core, surrounded by a deep mantle of slushy or solid water mixed with heavier material having a chemical composition resembling rock. Neptune's magnetic field is a bit less than half as strong as Earth's and is tipped 47° from the axis of rotation. It is also offset 55 percent of the way to the surface (Figure 24-7). As in the case of Uranus, Neptune's field is probably generated by the dynamo effect acting in the conducting fluid mantle rather than in the planet's core.

Neptune has more internal heat than Uranus, and part of that heat may be generated by radioactive decay in the minerals in its interior. Some of the energy also may be released by denser material falling inward, including, as in the case of Uranus, diamond crystals formed by the disruption of methane.

Neptune is a tantalizing world just big enough to be imaged by the Hubble Space Telescope but far enough away to make it difficult to study. The data from Voyager 2 revealed one detail that had been nearly undetectable from Earth—rings.

The Rings of Neptune

Astronomers on Earth saw hints of rings earlier when Neptune occulted stars, but the rings were not firmly recognized until Voyager 2 flew past the planet in 1989.

Look again at **The Rings of Uranus and Neptune** on pages 534–535 and compare the rings of Neptune with those of Uranus. Notice two additional points:

4 Neptune's rings, named after the astronomers involved in the discovery of the planet, are similar to those of Uranus but contain more small dust particles that forward-scatter light.

5 Also notice a new way that rings can interact with moons: One of Neptune's moons produces short arcs in the outermost ring, and a similar arc has been found in Saturn's rings.

Like the rings of Uranus, Saturn, and Jupiter, the particles observed now in Neptune's rings can't be primordial. That is, they can't have lasted in their present form since the formation of Neptune. Evidently, impacts on moons occasionally scatter debris through the satellite system, and some of it falls into the places where the orbits of ring particles are most stable among the orbits of the moons.

The Moons of Neptune

Before Voyager 2 visited Neptune, only two moons were known, but Voyager 2 discovered six more small moons, and a few more small moons have been found since, using Earth-based telescopes. Neptune has at least 13 moons. The two largest moons, Triton and Nereid, have been a puzzle for years because of their peculiar orbits.

Triton has a nearly circular orbit, but it travels retrograde—clockwise as seen from the north. This makes Triton the only large satellite in the solar system with a backward orbit; all other retrograde satellites are very small. The other Neptunian satellite visible from Earth, Nereid, moves in the prograde direction, but its orbit is highly elliptical and very large (■ Figure 24-15). Nereid takes 359.4 days to orbit Neptune once. Many astronomers have speculated that the orbits of the two moons are evidence of a violent event long ago. An encounter with a massive planetesimal may have disturbed the moons, or Triton itself may have been captured into orbit during a close encounter with Neptune.

The six moons that Voyager 2 found orbit Neptune among the rings. No new moons were found beyond the orbit of Triton, and some astronomers have suggested that Triton, in its retrograde orbit, would have consumed any moons near it.

The Voyager 2 photographs show that Triton is highly complex. Although it is only 2720 km in diameter (78 percent the size of Earth's moon), it is so cold (35 K, or –396°F) that it can hold a thin atmosphere, 10^5 times less dense than Earth's atmosphere, composed of nitrogen and some methane. Although a few wisps of haze can be seen in the photographs, the atmosphere is transparent, and the surface is easily visible (■ Figure 24-16).

The surface of Triton is evidently composed of ices. The surface ice is dominated by frozen nitrogen with some methane, carbon monoxide, and carbon dioxide. That is consistent with the nitrogen-rich atmosphere. Some regions of the surface that look dark may be slightly older terrain that darkened

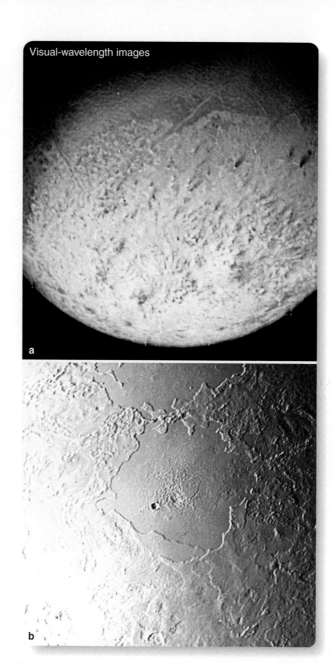

Visual-wavelength images

■ Figure 24-16

(a) Triton's south pole (bottom) had been in sunlight for 30 years when Voyager 2 flew past in 1989. The frozen nitrogen in the polar cap appears to be vaporizing, perhaps to refreeze in the darkness at the north pole. The dark smudges are produced when liquid nitrogen in the crust vaporizes and drives nitrogen geysers. (b) Roughly round basins on Triton may be old impact basins flooded repeatedly by liquids from the interior. Notice the small number of craters on Triton, a clue that it is a partially active world. (NASA)

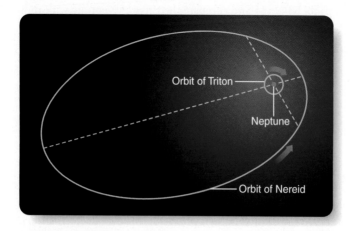

■ Figure 24-15

Nereid has a large, eccentric orbit around Neptune, but Triton follows a small, circular, retrograde orbit. At a distance of 30 AU from Earth, Triton is never seen farther than 16 arc seconds from the center of Neptune.

as sunlight converted methane into organic compounds. Triton's south pole had been turned toward the sun for 30 years when Voyager 2 flew past, and deposits of nitrogen frost in a large polar cap appeared to be vaporizing there and refreezing in the darkness of the north pole (Figure 24-16a). The cycle of nitrogen on Triton resembles in some ways the cycle of carbon dioxide on Mars.

The surface of Triton contains evidence that the icy moon has been active recently and may still be active. You would expect a moon located so close to the Kuiper belt to have lots of craters, but Triton has few. The average age of the surface is no more than 100 million years and may be even less. Some process has erased older craters. Evidence of geological activity includes long linear features that appear to be fractures in an icy crust, and some roughly round basins that appear to have been flooded time after time by liquids from the interior (Figure 24-16b). Triton is much too cold for the liquid to be molten rock or even liquid water. Rather, the floods must have been composed of water that contained agents such as ammonia, which would lower the freezing point of the liquid. It isn't possible to say at present whether Triton is still active, but 100 million years isn't very long in the history of the solar system. Triton may still suffer periodic eruptions and floods.

Another form of activity on Triton leaves dark smudges visible in the bright nitrogen ices near its south pole. These appear to be caused by nitrogen ice beneath the crust. Warmed slightly by the sun, the nitrogen ice can change from one form of solid nitrogen to another and release heat that can vaporize some of the nitrogen. Heat rising from the interior can also vaporize nitrogen. This nitrogen vapor vents through the crust, forming nitrogen gas geysers up to 8 km (5 mi) high. The venting gas may carry dark material from below the ice that falls to the surface to form the dark smudges. Another possibility is that methane is carried along with the nitrogen, and sunlight converts some of the methane into dark organic material, which falls to the surface.

Active worlds must have a source of energy, so you are probably wondering where Triton gets its energy. Triton is big enough to retain some thermal energy from low-level radioactivity in its interior. That may be enough to melt some ices and cause flooding on the surface. The nitrogen geysers may be powered partly by heat from the interior and partly by sunlight. In fact, Triton is very efficient at absorbing sunlight. Its thin atmosphere does not dim sunlight, and its crust is composed of ices that are partially transparent to light. As the light penetrates into the ice and is absorbed, it warms the ices. However, the crust is not very transparent to infrared radiation, so the heat is trapped in the ice. So, the crust of Triton appears to be heated, in part, by an icy form of the greenhouse effect.

This low-level heating would not be enough to erase nearly all of Triton's craters, so some planetary astronomers wonder if Triton might have been captured by Neptune relatively recently, meaning, within the last billion years. Tidal forces from such a capture would have caused enough tidal heating to melt Triton and totally resurface it. Enough of that heat may remain to keep Triton active to this day.

The History of Neptune

Can you tell the story of Neptune? In some ways it seems to be a simpler, smaller version of Jupiter and Saturn, but, like Uranus, Neptune's magnetic field is peculiar, and its moons and rings also deserve careful attention.

You can assume that Neptune formed from the solar nebula much as did Uranus. Like Uranus, Neptune's hazy atmosphere, marked by changing cloud patterns, hides a mantle of partially frozen ices where astronomers suspect the dynamo effect generates its off-center magnetic field. Inside that mantle is a denser core. Neptune, like Jupiter and Saturn but unlike Uranus, has significant amounts of heat flowing out to space from its interior.

Neptune's satellite system suggests a peculiar history. Triton, the largest moon, revolves around Neptune in a retrograde orbit, while Nereid's long-period orbit is highly elliptical. These orbital oddities suggest that the satellite system may have been disturbed by an encounter with a large planetesimal or during the capture of Triton. You have seen evidence in other satellite systems of impacts with large objects, so such an event is not unreasonable.

A number of smaller moons orbit Neptune near its ring system. Because the rings are bright in forward scattering, you can conclude that they contain some dust, and the shepherding of small satellites must confine their width and produce the observed arcs. As with the other Jovian planets, such rings could not have survived since the origin of the solar system, so the rings must be occasionally supplied with fresh particles probably generated by the impacts of meteorites and comets on Neptune's moons. Once again, the evidence of major impacts in the solar system's history assures you that such impacts do occur.

SCIENTIFIC ARGUMENT

Why is Neptune blue but its clouds white?

To solve this problem you must build a scientific argument that follows a process step by step. When you look at something, you really turn your eyes toward it and receive light from the object. When you look at Neptune, the light you receive is sunlight that is reflected from various layers of Neptune and journeys to your eyes. Because sunlight contains a distribution of photons of all visible wavelengths, it looks white to human eyes, but sunlight entering Neptune's atmosphere must pass through hydrogen gas that contains a small amount of methane. While hydrogen is transparent, methane is a good absorber of longer wavelengths, so red photons are more likely to be absorbed than blue photons. Once the light is scattered from deeper layers, it must run this methane gauntlet again to emerge from the atmosphere, and again red photons are more likely to be absorbed. The light that finally emerges from Neptune and eventually reaches your eyes is poor in longer wavelengths and thus looks blue.

The methane-ice-crystal clouds lie at high altitudes, so sunlight does not have to penetrate very far into Neptune's atmosphere to reflect off the clouds, and consequently it loses many fewer of its red photons. The clouds look white.

This discussion shows how a careful, step-by-step analysis of a natural process can help you better understand how nature works. For example, build a step-by-step argument to answer the following: **Where does the energy come from to power Triton's surface geysers?**

24-3 The Dwarf Planets

IN 1930, A WORLD WAS FOUND orbiting beyond Neptune. Although a solid object smaller than Earth's moon rather than a low-density Jovian planet, the public welcomed it as the ninth planet, and it was named Pluto. At the end of the 20th century, with much improved telescopes, astronomers found more such small worlds, and it became clear that Pluto was just one of a large family of similar objects.

In 2006, the International Astronomical Union voted to move Pluto out of the family of planets and make it part of a larger family of small worlds labeled "dwarf planets." To understand this controversial subject, you can start with Pluto and its discovery.

The Discovery of Pluto

Percival Lowell (1855–1916) was fascinated with the idea that an intelligent race built the canals he thought he could see on Mars (see Chapter 22). Lowell founded Lowell Observatory in Flagstaff, Arizona, primarily for the study of Mars. Later, some say motivated to improve the reputation of his observatory, he began to search for a planet beyond Neptune.

Lowell used the same method that Adams and Leverrier had used to predict the position of Neptune. Working from what were understood to be irregularities in the motion of Neptune, Lowell predicted the location of an undiscovered planet beyond Neptune. He concluded it would contain about 7 Earth masses and would look like a 13th-magnitude object in eastern Taurus. Lowell searched for the planet photographically until his death in 1916.

In the late 1920s, 22-year-old amateur astronomer Clyde Tombaugh began using a homemade 9-in. telescope to sketch Jupiter and Mars from his family's wheat farm in western Kansas. He sent his drawings to Lowell Observatory, and the observatory director Vesto Slipher (see Chapter 16) hired him without an interview. The young Tombaugh bought a one-way train ticket for Flagstaff not knowing what his new job would be like.

Slipher set Tombaugh to work photographing the sky along the ecliptic around the predicted position of the planet. The search technique was a classic method in astronomy. Tombaugh obtained pairs of 14 × 17-inch glass plates exposed two or three days apart. To search a pair of plates, he mounted them in a blink comparator, a machine that allowed him to look through a microscope at a small spot on one plate and then, at the flip of a lever, see the same spot on the other plate. As he blinked back and forth, the star images did not move, but a planet would have moved along its orbit during the two or three days that elapsed before the second plate was exposed. So Tombaugh searched the giant plates, star image by star image, looking for an image that moved. A single pair of plates could contain 400,000 star images. He searched pair after pair and found nothing.

The observatory director turned to other projects, and Tombaugh, working alone, expanded his search to cover the entire ecliptic. For almost a year, Tombaugh exposed plates by night and blinked plates by day. Then, on February 18, 1930, nearly a year after he had left Kansas, a quarter of the way through a pair of plates, he found a 15th magnitude image that moved (■ Figure 24-17). He later remembered, " 'Oh,' I thought, 'I had better look at my watch; this could be a historic moment. It was within about 2 minutes of 4 PM [MST].' " The discovery was announced on March 13, the 149th anniversary of the discovery of Uranus and the 75th anniversary of the birth of Percival Lowell. The object was named Pluto after the god of the underworld and, also in a way, after Lowell, because the first two letters in Pluto are the initials of Percival Lowell.

The discovery of Pluto seemed a triumph of discovery by prediction, but Tombaugh sensed something was wrong from the first moment he saw the image. It was moving in the right direction by the right amount, but it was 2.5 magnitudes too faint. Clearly, Pluto was not the 7-Earth-mass planet that Lowell had predicted. The faint image implied that Pluto was a small world with a mass too low to noticeably alter the motion of Neptune.

Later analysis has shown that the variations in the motion of Neptune, which Lowell used to predict the location of Pluto, were random uncertainties of observation and could not have led to a trustworthy prediction. The discovery of the new planet only 6° from Lowell's predicted position was apparently an accident.

Pluto as a World

Pluto is very difficult to observe from Earth. Only a bit larger than 0.1 arc second in diameter, it is only 65 percent the diameter of Earth's moon and shows little surface detail even when observed with the Hubble Space Telescope, although as you will learn,

■ Figure 24-17

Pluto is small and far away, so its image is indistinguishable from that of a star on most photographs. Clyde Tombaugh discovered the planet in 1930 by looking for an object that moved relative to the stars on a pair of photographs taken a few days apart. (Lowell Observatory photographs)

astronomers have used a clever trick to make low-resolution maps of Pluto and its moon Charon. If all goes well the New Horizons probe, due to arrive in 2015, will send the first close-up images of Pluto and its moons.

Most planetary orbits in our solar system are nearly circular, but Pluto's is significantly eccentric. In fact, from 1979 to 1999, Pluto was closer to the sun than Neptune. The two worlds will never collide, however, because Pluto's orbit is inclined 17° to the ecliptic and because, as you will learn later in this chapter, Pluto and Neptune orbit in resonance with each other so they never come close together.

If you land on the surface of Pluto, your spacesuit will have to work hard to keep you warm. Orbiting so far from the sun, Pluto is cold enough to freeze most compounds that you think of as gases, and spectroscopic observations have found evidence of solid nitrogen ice on its surface with traces of frozen methane and carbon monoxide. The maximum daytime temperature of about 55 K ($-360°$F) is enough to vaporize some of the nitrogen and carbon monoxide and a little of the methane to form a thin atmosphere around Pluto. This atmosphere was detected in 1988 when Pluto occulted a distant star, and the starlight was observed to fade gradually rather than winking out suddenly.

Pluto's largest moon was discovered on photographs in 1978. It is very faint and about half the diameter of Pluto (■ Figure 24-18). The moon was named Charon after the mythological ferryman who transports souls across the river Styx into the underworld. Two smaller moons, named Nix and Hydra, were found in 2005 and confirmed in 2006 by astronomers using the Hubble Space Telescope.

The discovery of Pluto's moons is important for a number of reasons. Charon, the largest and easiest to track, orbits Pluto in a nearly circular orbit in the plane of Pluto's equator. Observations show that the moon and Pluto are tidally locked to each other and that Pluto's axis of rotation is highly inclined to its orbit around the sun (■ Figure 24-19). Furthermore, tracking the orbital motion of Charon allowed calculation of the mass of Pluto. Charon orbits 19,640 km from Pluto with an orbital period of 6.387 days. Kepler's third law reveals that the mass of the system is 6.5×10^{-9} solar masses or only about 0.002 Earth mass. Most of that mass is Pluto, which seems to be about 12 times more massive than Charon.

You know that the mass of a body is important in astronomy because mass divided by volume is density. The density of Pluto is about 2 g/cm^3, and the density of Charon is just a bit less. Those densities indicate that Pluto and Charon must contain about 35 percent ice and 65 percent rock. Spectra of Charon show that the small moon has a surface that is mostly water ice with not much evidence of other volatiles that are detected in spectra of Pluto. Perhaps Charon has lost its more volatile compounds because of its lower escape velocity. Water ice at Charon's surface temperature is no more volatile than is a piece of rock on Earth, so a water ice surface could last a long time.

Another reason Pluto's moon Charon has proved important is that, as Charon and Pluto orbit the sun, occasionally their mutual orbit is seen edge-on from Earth. During those times, astronomers can watch Pluto and Charon eclipse each other; and, by carefully measuring the combined light from the two objects, they can produce crude maps (■ Figure 24-20). Those

■ **Figure 24-18**

(a) A high-quality, ground-based photo shows Pluto and its moon, Charon, badly blurred by seeing. (NASA) (b) The Hubble Space Telescope image clearly separates the planet and its moon and allows more accurate measurements of the position of the moon. (R. Albrecht, ESA/ESO Space Telescope European Coordinating Facility, NASA) (c) A long-exposure photograph made in 2006 with the Hubble Space Telescope confirmed discovery of two more moons of Pluto that were named Nix and Hydra. (NASA, ESA, H.Weaver/JHU/APL, A. Stern/SwRI) observations reveal that Pluto has a surprising amount of albedo variation on its surface, but nobody knows what the dark and light features might be. Understanding that will have to wait until the New Horizons probe flies by in 2015.

Both Pluto and Charon go through dramatic seasons much like those on Uranus as they circle the sun with their highly inclined rotation axes. This should cause large changes in Pluto's atmosphere as the planet grows warmer when it is closest to the sun, as it was in the late 1980s, and then freezes as it draws away.

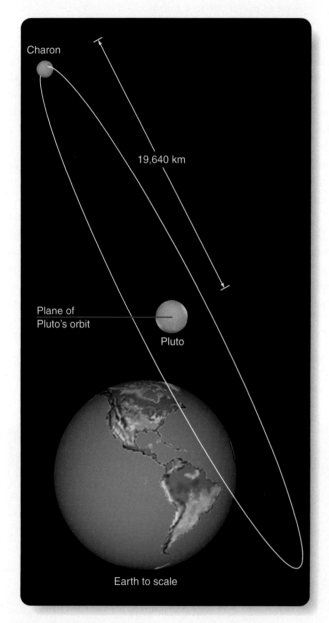

■ **Figure 24-19**

The nearly circular orbit of Charon is only a few times bigger than Earth. It is shown here nearly edge-on, and consequently it looks elliptical in this diagram. Charon's orbit and the equator of Pluto are inclined 119.6° to the plane of Pluto's orbit around the sun.

The Family of Dwarf Planets

Perhaps the most interesting thing about Pluto is that it is not alone. In Chapter 19, you read about the Kuiper belt objects that orbit beyond Neptune. There are many thousands of such objects, and some of them are quite large. At least one is larger than Pluto.

The object known as Eris, discovered in 2003, is 4 percent larger in diameter than Pluto and 27 percent more massive. It orbits about 1.7 times farther away from the sun than does Pluto. Eris's orbit is more eccentric and more highly inclined than Pluto's, but it seems to be a similar object. The discovery of Eris led the International Astronomical Union to recognize a new class of solar system objects called **dwarf planets**—objects that orbit the sun and are large enough to assume a spherical shape but not large enough to have sufficient gravitational influence to absorb or otherwise clear away remaining objects in the same region. In contrast, the major planets, including Earth, were able to do that type of regional clearing in the process of growing from protoplanets into planets. Three solar system objects are clearly dwarf planets—Pluto and Eris in the Kuiper belt, plus Ceres, the 900-km-diameter asteroid that orbits within the asteroid belt between Mars and Jupiter and is nearly twice as big as the next largest asteroids, Pallas and Vesta.

Roughly ten other Kuiper belt objects are known to have sizes approaching that of Pluto and Eris, and there are probably others yet to be discovered. Two large objects named Sedna and Orcus are each about 63 percent the size of Pluto. Another object, called Quaoar (pronounced *kwah-o-wahr*), is 50 percent the diameter of Pluto. The ten largest Kuiper belt objects are considered candidate dwarf planets, pending determination of their shape. One strange object that may complicate things is Haumea, with such a rapid spin—once every 4 hours—that it is shaped like a flattened cigar. One of its dimensions is nearly as large as Pluto's diameter. Haumea is not spherically shaped, but if it were not spinning so rapidly, it might be a sphere and meet the definition of a dwarf planet. Should the effect of Haumea's rotation be counted in considering its status, or not?

Some astronomers argue that Charon, Pluto's big spherical moon, should be a member of the dwarf planets even though it orbits another world and not the sun. Other astronomers are upset that Ceres, a rocky asteroid, is included. The classification may seem arbitrary until you begin thinking about how the dwarf planets formed. Some astronomers refer to them as oligarchs. The term *oligarch* is usually applied to business or political leaders who are the biggest, meanest dudes in town. They are not alone, but they are the bosses. The dwarf planets appear to have been bodies in the solar nebula that grew more rapidly than their neighbors and became dominant, but never got big enough to take over completely and sweep up all objects orbiting nearby. Planets such as Earth and Jupiter cleared their orbital lanes

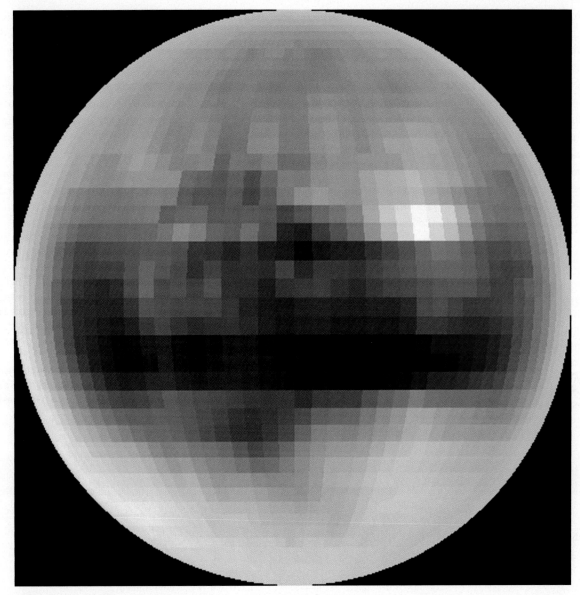

■ Figure 24-20

Observing Pluto's brightness variations as its moon Charon occasionally moves across the planet's disk allowed astronomers to make this low-resolution map of Pluto. These are approximately true colors. (E. Young/SwRI)

around the sun, but the dwarf planets never got quite big enough to do that.

Pluto and the Plutinos

No, this section is not about a 1950s rock-and-roll band. It is about the history of the dwarf planets, and it will take you back billions of years to watch the outer planets form.

You should begin by eliminating an old idea. As soon as Pluto was discovered, astronomers realized that it was much smaller than its Jovian neighbors, and some suggested that it was a moon of Neptune that had escaped. The orbits of Neptune and Pluto actually cross, although they will never collide. That escaped-moon hypothesis for Pluto has been totally abandoned. It is hard to understand how Pluto could have escaped from Neptune and reached its present orbit. And how did it get moons, if it was once a moon itself? Modern astronomers have a much better hypothesis, and it recognizes that Pluto is just one of the dwarf planets that is related to many other objects in the Kuiper belt.

Dozens, perhaps hundreds, of Kuiper belt objects are, like Pluto, caught in a 3:2 resonance with Neptune. That is, they orbit the sun twice while Neptune orbits three times. You learned about orbital resonances when you studied Jupiter's Galilean moons. A 3:2 resonance with Neptune makes the orbiting bodies immune to any disturbing gravitational influence from Neptune so their orbits are more stable. Because

Pluto is also caught in the same 3:2 resonance, these Kuiper belt objects have been named **plutinos.**

How did the plutinos get caught in resonances with Neptune? Computer models of the formation of the planets suggest that Uranus and Neptune may have formed closer to the sun, where the solar nebula was denser. Sometime later, gravitational interactions with Jupiter and Saturn gradually shifted the two ice giants outward, and, as Neptune migrated outward, its orbital resonances could have swept up small bodies like nets pushed in front of a fishing boat. Other Kuiper belt objects are caught in other stabilizing resonances, and they were apparently swept up in the same way. The plutinos in 3:2 resonance and other Kuiper belt objects in other resonances with Neptune are evidence that Neptune really did migrate outward. This planet migration could have scattered small bodies throughout the solar system and caused the apparent late heavy bombardment event during which Earth, the moon, and other solar system bodies suffered a brief but devastating increase in cratering rate.

Some astronomers are angry that the International Astronomical Union "demoted" Pluto, but it is actually a more interesting world once you realize that it is the best studied of the dwarf planets. In the inner solar system, only the asteroid Ceres was able to grow fast enough to become a dwarf planet, but in the outer solar system huge numbers of icy bodies formed, ranging from pebbles to the oligarchs now recognized as dwarf planets. As they are understood better, the dwarf planets will reveal more secrets from the age of planet building.

SCIENTIFIC ARGUMENT

Why is Earth a planet and not a dwarf planet?
This question calls for an argument based on a scientific classification. If it is to be useful, a classification must be based on real characteristics, so you need to think about the definition of the dwarf plants. According to the International Astronomical Union, a dwarf planet must orbit the sun, not be a satellite of a planet, and be spherical. Earth meets these characteristics, but there is one more requirement. By definition, a dwarf planet must not have been large enough to clear out most of the smaller objects near its orbit. As Earth grew in the solar nebula, it absorbed the small bodies that orbited the sun in similar orbits. In other words, Earth cleared its traffic lane around the sun. Pluto never became massive enough to clear its lane (the Kuiper belt), so Pluto is defined as a dwarf planet. Because Earth grew large enough to sweep its traffic lane clear, Earth is defined as a planet.

The dwarf planets are interesting for what they can reveal about the origin of the solar system. **How do the orbital resonances between the plutinos and Neptune confirm a hypothesis for the formation of the Jovian planets?**

What Are We? Trapped

No person has ever been farther from Earth than the moon. We humans have sent robotic spacecraft to explore the worlds in our solar system beyond Earth's moon, but no human has ever set foot on them. We are trapped on Earth.

We lack the technology to leave Earth easily. Getting away from Earth's gravitational field calls for very large rockets. America built huge rockets in the 1960s and early 1970s to send astronauts to the moon, but such rockets no longer exist. The best technology today can carry astronauts just a few hundred kilometers above Earth's surface to orbit above the atmosphere. We can probably reach Mars with a few decades of effort, but going beyond may take more resources than Earth can provide.

There is another reason we Earthlings are trapped on our planet. We have evolved to fit the environment on Earth. None of the planets or moons you explored beyond Earth would welcome you. Radiation belts, extreme heat or cold, and lack of air are obvious problems, but Earthlings have evolved to live with one Earth gravity. Astronauts in orbit for just a few weeks suffer biomedical problems because their muscles and bones no longer feel Earth's gravity. Could humans live for years in the weak gravity on Mars? We may be trapped on Earth not because we lack big rockets but because we need Earth's environment.

It seems likely that we need Earth more than it needs us. The human race is changing the world we live on at a terrific pace, and some of those changes are making Earth less hospitable. All of your exploring of un-Earthly worlds serves to remind you of the nurturing beauty of our home planet. It is probably the only one we will ever have.

Summary

- Uranus was discovered by William Herschel in 1781.

- Although Uranus is a Jovian planet, it is significantly smaller and less massive than Jupiter. Uranus is an ice giant planet about four times the diameter of Earth. Uranus rotates "on its side," with its pole nearly in the plane of its orbit, causing it to have extreme seasons.

- The atmosphere of Uranus is mostly hydrogen and helium with some methane, which absorbs longer-wavelength photons and gives the planet a greenish-blue color.

- The atmosphere of Uranus is so cold that only methane clouds are visible, and some traces of belt–zone circulation can be seen. As spring has come to the northern hemisphere, more cloud features have developed, suggesting that Uranus follows a seasonal cycle and is not always as bland as it was when Voyager 2 flew past in 1986.

- Model calculations indicate that Uranus has a small core of dense matter and a deep slushy mantle of ice, water, and rock. Convection in the mantle may produce its highly inclined offset magnetic field.

- Uranus emits about the predicted amount of heat for a planet at its distance from the sun, which suggests that it is not extremely hot inside.

- The rings of Uranus were discovered during an **occultation (p. 534)** as the planet crossed in front of a star.

- The rings of Uranus are composed mostly of boulder-size objects darkened by radiation and trapped among the orbits of small moons. The ring material is probably produced by impacts on icy moons.

- The five large moons of Uranus appear to be icy and old, although some show signs of geological activity. Miranda appears to have suffered from dramatic activity, as shown by **ovoids (p. 537)** on its surface. Tidal heating is a likely source of the energy that drove this activity.

- Uranus appears to have formed slowly and never became massive enough to trap large amounts of hydrogen and helium from the solar nebula. Uranus and Neptune are thought to have formed closer to the sun and were moved outward by gravitational interactions with Jupiter and Saturn.

- An impact by a large planetesimal while Uranus was forming may have caused the planet to rotate around a highly inclined axis, but it is also possible that tidal interactions with Saturn altered the rotation of Uranus as it was moved outward.

- Neptune was discovered in 1846 based on a position computed from irregularities it was causing in the orbital motion of Uranus.

- Neptune is an ice giant quite similar in size to Uranus. It has a core of denser material; a mantle of ice, water, and rock; and an atmosphere of hydrogen and helium with traces of methane, which gives the planet a blue color.

- Methane clouds come and go in Neptune's cold atmosphere and appear to follow a belt–zone circulation.

- Circulation in the liquid mantle gives rise to Neptune's magnetic field.

- Neptune has more internal heat than Uranus, and the sinking of dense material, including diamonds, may be adding to the internal heat.

- The rings of Neptune probably formed when impacts on moons scattered icy debris into stable places among the orbits of the small moons. Forward scattering shows that the rings contain more small dust particles than those of Uranus. Arcs in the rings appear to be caused by the gravitational influence of a small moon or moons.

- Triton, Neptune's largest moon, follows a retrograde orbit, and Nereid follows a long eccentric orbit. These two moons' odd orbits may have been caused by the gravitational influence of a massive planetesimal or by the capture of Triton.

- Triton has an icy surface and a thin atmosphere of nitrogen. The lack of many craters, flooded areas, and the presence of cracks and faults suggest that the moon may still be active. Sunlight and heat from the interior appear to trigger nitrogen geysers in the crust. Tidal heating during a close approach to Neptune when it was captured into orbit is another possible source of heat.

- Neptune formed slowly, as did Uranus, and never accumulated a deep atmosphere of hydrogen and helium before the solar nebula was blown away.

- Pluto was discovered in 1930 during a search for a large planet orbiting beyond Neptune and disturbing Neptune's orbital motion. That discovery was in a sense an accident, because Pluto is much too small to affect Neptune, and more observations of Neptune indicate its orbital motion is actually undisturbed.

- No spacecraft has yet visited Pluto, but the New Horizons probe is on its way for a flyby in 2015.

- Spectroscopic observations indicate Pluto has a frigid crust of solid nitrogen ice with traces of frozen methane and carbon monoxide. Its thin atmosphere is mostly nitrogen.

- Pluto's moon Charon orbits in an orbit highly inclined to their orbit around the sun. Charon and Pluto are tidally locked to face each other. That means Pluto rotates on its side much like Uranus.

- Careful measurements of the brightness of Charon and Pluto on occasions when they move in front of each other have allowed astronomers to construct low-resolution maps of both objects.

- The density of Pluto shows that it and Charon must contain about two-thirds rock and one-third ices.

- The **dwarf planets (p. 546)** are small bodies that orbit the sun and do not orbit a planet; they are spherical, like the major planets, but unlike the major planets they are not large enough to have cleared their orbital lanes of other objects.

- Pluto, another Kuiper belt object named Eris, and the asteroid Ceres are classified as dwarf planets. About 10 other Kuiper belt objects are candidate dwarf planets pending the determination of their shapes. At present more than a thousand Kuiper belt objects are known, most of which are too small to be dwarf planets.

- The dwarf planets grew large in the solar nebula but never became large enough capture or eject other objects orbiting nearby.

- Pluto and similar Kuiper belt objects called **plutinos (p. 548)** are caught in a stabilizing 3:2 resonance with Neptune. Many other Kuiper belt objects orbit in other resonances with Neptune. These objects are evidence that the Jovian planets interacted soon after formation, pushed Neptune outward in the solar system, and swept up remnant planetesimals in these resonances.

Review Questions

1. Describe the location of the equinoxes and solstices in the Uranian sky. What are seasons like on Uranus?

2. Why is belt–zone circulation difficult to detect on Uranus?

3. Discuss the origin of the rings of Uranus and Neptune. Cite evidence to support hypotheses.

4. How do the magnetic fields of Uranus and Neptune suggest that the mantles inside those planets are fluid?

5. If Neptune had no satellites at all, would you expect it to have rings? Why or why not?

6. Why might the surface brightness of ring particles and small moons orbiting Uranus and Neptune depend on whether those planets have extensive and strong magnetic fields?

7. Both Uranus and Neptune have a blue-green tint when observed through a telescope. What does that tell you about their composition?

8. How can small worlds like Triton and Pluto have atmospheres when a larger world such as Ganymede has none?

9. Why do you suspect that Triton has had an active past? What sources of energy could power such activity?

10. If you visited the surface of Pluto and found Charon as a full moon directly overhead, where would Charon be in the sky when it was new? When it was first quarter?

11. What evidence can you cite that Pluto and Charon are made of mixtures of rock and ice?

12. Why was Pluto reclassified as a dwarf planet?

13. **How Do We Know?** How was the discovery of Neptune not accidental?

Discussion Questions

1. Why might it be unfair to describe William Herschel's discovery of Uranus as accidental? Why might it be unfair to describe the discovery of the rings of Uranus as accidental?

2. Suggest a single phenomenon that could explain the inclination of the rotation axis of Uranus, the peculiar orbits of Neptune's satellites, and the existence of Pluto's moons.

Problems

1. What is the maximum angular diameter of Uranus as seen from Earth? Of Neptune? Of Pluto? (*Hint:* Use the small-angle formula, Chapter 3.)

2. One way to recognize a distant planet is by its motion along its orbit. If Uranus circles the sun in 84.0 years, how many arc seconds will it move in 24 hours? (This does not include the motion of Earth. Assume a circular orbit for Uranus.)

3. What is the orbital velocity of Miranda around Uranus? (*Hints:* See Chapter 5, and look in the Appendix tables for Oberon's orbital data.)

4. What is the escape velocity from the surface of Miranda? (*Hints:* Miranda's radius = 242 km. Assume that its density is 2.00 g/cm³. See Chapter 5.)

5. The magnetosphere of Uranus rotates with the planetary interior in 17.24 hours. What is the velocity of the outer portion of the magnetic field just beyond the orbit of Oberon? (*Hints:* The circumference of a circle is $2\pi r$; look in the Appendix tables for Oberon's orbital data.)

6. If the ϵ ring is 60.0 km wide and the orbital velocity of Uranus around the sun is 6.81 km/s, how long a blink should you expect to see when the ring crosses in front of a star? Is this consistent with the data on page 534?

7. What is the escape velocity from the surface of an icy moon with a diameter of 20 km? (*Hints:* The density of ice is 1 g/cm³. The volume of a sphere is $\frac{4}{3}\pi r^3$. See Chapter 5.)

8. What is the difference in the orbital velocities of the two shepherd satellites Cordelia and Ophelia? (*Hints:* Orbital radii = 49,800 km and 53,800 km. See Chapter 5.)

9. Repeat Problem 2 for Pluto. In other words, ignoring the motion of Earth, how far across the sky would Pluto move in 24 hours? (Assume a circular orbit for Pluto.)

10. Given the size of Triton's orbit ($r = 355,000$ km) and its orbital period ($P = 5.88$ days), calculate the mass of Neptune. (*Hint:* See Chapter 5.)

Learning to Look

1. Compare Figure 24-8 with Figure 24-7 and add labels to the aurora identifying the north and south magnetic poles on Uranus.

2. Sketch Earth's moon to scale in Figure 24-11.

3. Two images of Uranus show it as it would look to the eye and through a red filter that enhances methane clouds in the northern hemisphere. Why didn't Voyager 2 photograph the northern hemisphere? What do the visible atmospheric features tell you about circulation on Uranus?

NASA

25 | Meteorites, Asteroids, and Comets

Artist's conception

Guidepost

In Chapter 19 you began your study of planetary astronomy by considering evidence about how our solar system formed. In the five chapters that followed you surveyed the planets and found more clues about the origin of the solar system. But most traces of the early histories of the planets have been erased by geological activity or other processes. Now you can study smaller, better-preserved objects that tell more about the era of planet building.

Asteroids and comets are unevolved objects, leftover planet construction "bricks." You will find them much as they were when they formed 4.6 billion years ago. Meteors and meteorites are fragments of comets and asteroids that arrive at Earth and can give you a close look at those ancient planetesimals. As you explore, you will find answers to four important questions:

Where do meteors and meteorites come from?

What are asteroids?

What are comets?

What happens when an asteroid or comet hits Earth?

As you finish this chapter, you will have acquired real insight into your place in nature. You live on the surface of a planet. Are any other planets inhabited? That is the subject of the next, and final, chapter.

The Dawn spacecraft was launched in 2007 on a mission to explore the large asteroid Vesta and the dwarf planet Ceres that circle the sun in the asteroid belt between the orbits of Mars and Jupiter. This artist's conception shows Dawn's approach to Vesta (top right), scheduled for 2011.

ONE AFTERNOON in 1954, while Mrs. E. Hulitt Hodges of Sylacauga, Alabama, lay napping on her living room couch, an explosion and a sharp pain jolted her awake. Analysis of the brick-sized rock that smashed through the ceiling and bruised her left leg showed that it was a meteorite. Mrs. Hodges is the only person known to have been injured by a meteorite. Coincidentally, she lived right across the street from the Comet Drive-In Theater.

Meteorites arrive from space all over the Earth every day, although not as spectacularly as the one that struck Mrs. Hodges. You will learn in this chapter that meteorites are fragments of asteroids, and that asteroids, as well as their icy cousins the comets, carry precious clues about conditions in the solar nebula from which the sun and planets formed. Because you cannot easily visit comets and asteroids, you can begin by learning about the pieces of those bodies that come to you.

25-1 Meteoroids, Meteors, and Meteorites

YOU LEARNED SOME THINGS about meteorites in Chapter 19 when you studied evidence for the age of the solar system. There you saw that the solar system includes small particles called *meteoroids*. Some of them collide with Earth's atmosphere at speeds of 10 to 70 km/s. Friction with the air heats the meteoroids enough so that they glow, and you see them vaporize as streaks across the night sky. Those streaks are called *meteors* ("shooting stars"). If a meteoroid is big enough and holds together well enough, it can survive its plunge through the atmosphere and reach Earth's surface. Once the object strikes Earth's surface, it is called a *meteorite* ("-ite" being the Greek root for "rock"). As you will learn later in this chapter, the largest of those objects can blast out craters on Earth's surface, but such big impacts are extremely rare. The great majority of meteorites are too small to form craters.

What can meteorites and meteors tell you about the origin of the solar system? To answer that question, you can consider their compositions and orbits.

Composition of Meteorites and Meteors

One of the best places to look for meteorites turns out to be certain parts of Antarctica—not because more meteorites fall there but because they are easy to recognize. No Earth rocks are on top of the Antarctic ice cap; the nearest native rocks are buried under the ice. Any rock you find there must have fallen from space. (For similar reasons, another good place to find meteorites is the Sahara desert, where deep layers of sand keep Earth rocks completely out of sight.) The slow flow of the Antarctic ice cap from the center of the continent toward the ocean concentrates meteorites in areas of especially good hunting where the moving ice runs into mountain barriers, slows down, and evaporates. Teams of scientists travel to Antarctica and ride snowmobiles in systematic sweeps across the ice each South Pole summer to recover meteorites (■ Figure 25-1). A four- to eight-person team can find a thousand meteorites during a single two-month field season. After 25 years of work, more than half of the 40,000 meteorites in human hands are from Antarctica.

Meteorites that are seen to fall are called **falls;** a fall is known to have occurred at a given time and place, and thus the meteorite is well documented. A meteorite that is discovered on or in the ground, but was not seen to fall, is called a **find.** Such a meteorite could have fallen thousands of years ago. The distinction between *falls* and *finds* will be important as you analyze the different kinds of meteorites.

Meteorites can be divided into three broad composition categories. **Iron meteorites** (■ Figure 25-2a) are solid chunks of iron and nickel. **Stony meteorites** (Figure 25-2b) are silicate masses that resemble Earth rocks. **Stony-iron meteorites** (Figure 25-2c) are mixtures of iron and stone. **Carbonaceous chondrites** (pronounced *kon-drite;* Figure 25-2d) are a special type of stony meteorite.

Iron meteorites are easy to recognize because they are heavy, dense lumps of metal—a magnet will stick to them. That explains an important statistic. Iron meteorites make up 66 percent of finds (■ Table 25-1) but only 6 percent of falls. Why? Because an iron meteorite doesn't look like an ordinary rock. If you trip over one on a hike, you are more likely to recognize it as something odd, carry it home, and show it to the local museum. Also, some stony meteorites deteriorate rapidly when exposed to weather; irons are made of stronger material and generally survive longer. That means there is a **selection effect** that makes it more likely that iron meteorites will be found (**How Do We Know? 25-1**). The fact that only 6 percent of falls are irons shows that iron meteoroids, although easier to find on Earth, are relatively rare in space.

When iron meteorites are sliced open, polished, and etched with acid, they reveal regular bands called **Widmanstätten patterns** (pronounced *Veed-mahn-state-en*) (■ Figure 25-3). Those patterns are caused by certain alloys of iron and nickel that formed crystals as the molten metal cooled and solidified long ago. The size and shape of the bands indicate that the molten metal cooled very slowly, no faster than 20 degrees Kelvin per million years.

Large or small, meteorites are sealed airtight and refrigerated until they can be studied.

■ **Figure 25-1**

Braving bitter cold and high winds, teams of scientists riding snowmobiles search for meteorites that fell long ago in Antarctica and are exposed as the ice evaporates. When a meteorite is found, it is photographed where it lies, assigned a number, and placed in an airtight bag. Thousands of meteorites have been collected in this way, including rare meteorites from the moon and Mars. (Courtesy Monika Kress)

The Widmanstätten pattern tells you that the metal in iron meteorites was once molten and must have been well insulated to cool so slowly. Such slow cooling indicates a location inside bodies at least 30 km in diameter. (In comparison, a small lump of molten metal exposed in space would cool in just a few hours.) On the other hand, the iron meteorites do not show effects of the very high pressures that would exist deep inside a planet. Evidently, iron meteorite material formed in the cooling interiors of planetesimal-sized objects, not planets. You will find this is one important clue to the origin of meteorites.

A small fraction of falls are meteorites made of mixed iron and stone (Figure 25-2b). These stony-iron meteorites appear to have solidified from both molten iron and rock—the kind of environment you might expect to find deep inside a planetesimal at the boundary between a liquid metal core and a rocky mantle.

In contrast to irons and stony-irons, stony meteorites (Figure 25-2c) are common among falls (Table 25-1). Although there are many different types of stony meteorites, you can classify them into two main categories depending on their physical properties and chemical content, **chondrites** and **achondrites.**

Chondrites look like dark gray, granular rocks (Figure 25-2d). The classification of meteorites has become quite complicated, and there are many types of chondrites, but in general they contain some volatiles including water and organic (carbon) compounds. A few chondrites appear to have formed in the presence of liquid water.

Most types of chondrites also contain **chondrules,** small round bits of glassy rock only a few millimeters across. To be glassy rather than crystalline, the chondrules must have cooled from a molten state quickly, within a few hours. One hypothesis is that chondrules are bits of matter from the inner part of the solar nebula, near the sun, that were blown outward by winds or jets to cooler parts of the nebula where they condensed and were later incorporated into larger rocks. Another hypothesis is that the chondrules were once solid bits of matter that were melted by shock waves spreading through the solar nebula and then resolidified. The presence of chondrule particles inside chondrite meteorites indicates that those rocks have never been melted since they formed because melting would have destroyed the chondrules.

Among the chondrites, the carbonaceous chondrites are rare but quite important. These dark gray, rocky meteorites are

Iron meteorites are very heavy for their size and have a dark, irregular surface.

A stony-iron meteorite cut and polished reveals a mixture of iron and rock.

Stony meteorites tend to have a fusion crust caused by melting in Earth's atmosphere.

Chondrules are small, glassy spheres found in chondrites.

a

b

c

d

■ Figure 25-2

The three main types of meteorites—(a) irons, (b) stony-irons, and (c) stones—have distinctive characteristics. (d) Carbonaceous chondrite meteorites are a rare type of stony meteorite that is rich in carbon, making the rock very dark. (Lab photos courtesy of Russell Kempton, New England Meteoritical)

■ Table 25-1	Proportions of Meteorites	
Type	Falls (%)	Finds (%)
Iron	6	66
Stony-iron	2	8
Stony	92	26

■ Figure 25-3

Sliced, polished, and etched with acid, iron meteorites show what is called a Widmanstätten pattern of large crystals, indicating that this material cooled very slowly from a molten state and must have been inside a fairly large object. (Photo courtesy of Russell Kempton, New England Meteoritical Services)

especially rich in water, other volatiles, and organic compounds. Those substances all would have been lost if the meteoroid had been heated even to room temperature.

One of the most important meteorites ever studied was a carbonaceous chondrite seen falling in 1969 near the little Mexican village of Allende (pronounced *ah-yen-day*). About 2 tons of fragments were recovered. Studies of the Allende meteorite disclosed that it contained chondrules, water, complex organic compounds including amino acids, and a number of small, irregular inclusions

Selection Effects

How is a red insect like a red car? Scientists must plan ahead and design their research projects with great care. Biologists studying insects in the rain forest, for example, must choose which ones to catch. They can't catch every insect they see, so they might decide to catch and study any insect that is red. If they are not careful, a selection effect could bias their data and lead them to incorrect conclusions without their ever knowing it.

For example, suppose you needed to measure the speed of cars on a highway. There are too many cars to measure every one, so you might reduce the workload and measure only red cars. It is quite possible that this selection criterion will mislead you because people who buy red cars may be more likely to be younger and drive faster. Should you instead measure only brown cars? No, because older, more sedate people might tend to buy brown cars. Only by very carefully designing your experiment can you be certain that the cars you measure are traveling at typical speeds.

Astronomers understand that what you see through a telescope depends on what you notice, and that is powerfully influenced by what are called **selection effects**. The biologists in the rain forest, for example, should not catch and study only red insects. Often, the most brightly colored insects are poisonous or at least taste bad to predators. Catching only red insects could produce a result highly biased by a selection effect.

Visual-wavelength image

Things that are bright and beautiful, such as spiral galaxies, may attract a disproportionate amount of attention. Scientists must be aware of such selection effects. (Hubble Heritage Team/STScI/ AURA/NASA)

rich in calcium, aluminum, and titanium (■ Figure 25-4). Now called **CAIs,** for calcium–aluminum-rich inclusions, these bits of matter are highly refractory; that is, they vaporize or condense only at very high temperatures.

If you could scoop out a portion of the sun's photosphere and cool it, the first particles to solidify would have the chemical composition of CAIs. As the temperature fell, other materials would become solid in accord with the condensation sequence described in Chapter 19. When the material finally reached room temperature, you would find that almost all of the hydrogen, helium, and some other gases such as argon and neon had escaped and that the remaining lump would have almost exactly the same overall chemical composition as the Allende meteorite. You can understand this is evidence that the Allende meteorite is a very old sample of the solar nebula, confirmed by the fact that the CAIs have radioactive ages equal to the oldest of any other solar system material.

Another large load of carbonaceous chondrite material arrived on Earth in the year 2000 at Tagish Lake in the Canadian Arctic. Analysis of that meteorite produced a surprise: It has noticeably less complex organics than Allende. Scientists are not sure whether this means that the Tagish organics formed so early in the solar system's history that chemical reactions had not yet advanced to the stage of making Allende's complex compounds, or whether the Tagish material was once heated just enough to break down big molecules into smaller ones.

The condensing solar nebula should have incorporated volatiles and organics into solid particles as they formed. If that material had later been heated it would have lost the volatiles, and many of the organic compounds would have been destroyed. The chondrites show properties ranging from

Chondrule

CAIs

■ Figure 25-4

A sliced portion of the Allende carbonaceous chondrite meteorite, showing irregularly shaped white inclusions called CAIs that were probably the first solid material to condense as the solar system formed. (NASA)

carbonaceous chondrites, most of which have avoided being heated or modified, to other chondrites in which the material was slightly heated and somewhat altered from the form in which it first solidified. Chondrites in general offer us the best direct information about conditions and processes occurring in the earliest days of the solar nebula when planetesimals and planets were forming.

Stony meteorites called achondrites contain no chondrules and also lack volatiles. These rocks appear to have been subjected to intense heat that melted the chondrules and completely drove off the volatiles, leaving behind rock with composition similar to Earth's basalts.

The different types of meteorites evidently had a wide variety of histories. Some achondrites seem like pieces of lava flows, whereas stony-iron and iron meteorites apparently were once deep inside the molten interiors of differentiated objects. The differences between various chondrites are thought to result from: (1) meteoritic material solidifying at different distances from the sun with different chemical compositions due to the temperature-dependent condensation sequence, (2) each location in the nebula having some material transported and mixed in from other locations, and (3) processes that altered meteoritic material after condensation. Meteorites provide evidence that the early history of the solar system was complex.

Orbits of Meteors and Meteorites

Meteoroids are much too small to be visible through even the largest telescope. They are visible only when they fall into Earth's atmosphere and are heated by friction with the air. A typical meteoroid has roughly the mass of a paper clip and vaporizes at an altitude of about 80 km (50 mi) above Earth's surface. The meteor trail points back along the path of the meteoroid, so if you study the direction and speed of meteors, you can get clues to their orbits in the solar system before they encountered Earth.

One way to backtrack meteor trails is to observe **meteor showers.** On any clear night, you can see 3 to 15 meteors per hour, but on some nights you can see a shower of hundreds of meteors per hour that are obviously related to each other. To confirm this, try observing a meteor shower. Pick a shower from ■ Table 25-2 and on the appropriate night stretch out in a lawn chair and watch a large area of the sky. When you see a meteor, sketch its path on the appropriate sky chart from the back of this book. In just an hour or so you will discover that all or almost all of the meteors you see seem to come from a single area of the sky, called the **radiant** of the shower (■ Figure 25-5a). Meteor showers are named after the constellation from which they seem to radiate; for example, the Perseid shower seen in mid-August radiates from the constellation Perseus.

Observing a meteor shower is a natural fireworks show, but it is even more exciting when you understand what a meteor shower tells you. The fact that the meteors in a shower appear to come from a single point in the sky means that the meteoroids were traveling through space along parallel paths. When they encounter Earth and are vaporized in the upper atmosphere, you see their fiery tracks in perspective, so they appear to come from a single radiant point, just as railroad tracks seem to come from a single point on the horizon (Figure 25-5b).

			Radiant*		
Shower	Dates	Hourly Rate	R. A.	Dec.	Associated Comet
Quadrantids	Jan. 2–4	30	15h 24m	50°	
Lyrids	April 20–22	8	18h 4m	33°	1861 I
η Aquarids	May 2–7	10	22h 24m	0°	Halley?
δ Aquarids	July 26–31	15	22h 36m	−10°	
Perseids	Aug. 10–14	40	3h 4m	58°	Swift-Tuttle
Orionids	Oct. 18–23	15	6h 20m	15°	Halley?
Taurids	Nov. 1–7	8	3h 40m	17°	Encke
Leonids	Nov. 14–19	6	10h 12m	22°	1866 I Temp
Geminids	Dec. 10–13	50	7h 28m	32°	

■Table 25-2 | **Meteor Showers**

*R. A. and Dec. give the celestial coordinates (right ascension and declination) of the radiant for each shower.

■ Figure 25-5

(a) Meteors in a meteor shower enter Earth's atmosphere along parallel paths, but perspective makes them appear to diverge from a single point in the sky. (b) Similarly, parallel railroad tracks appear to diverge from a point on the horizon.

Studies of meteor shower radiants reveal that those meteoroids are orbiting the sun along the paths of comets. As you learned in Chapter 19, the vaporizing head of a comet releases bits of rock that become spread along its entire orbit (■ Figure 25-6). When Earth passes through this stream of material, you see a meteor shower. In some cases the comet has wasted away and is no longer visible, but in other cases the comet is still prominent, although located somewhere else along its orbit. For example, each May, Earth comes near the orbit of Comet Halley, and you can see the Eta Aquarid shower. Each October, Earth passes near the other side of the orbit of Comet Halley, and the Orionid shower appears.

Even when there is no shower, you still can occasionally see meteors, which are called **sporadic meteors** because they are not part of specific showers. Many of these are produced by stray bits of matter that were released long ago by comets. Such comet debris gradually get spread throughout the inner solar system, away from their original tracks, and bits collide with Earth even when there is no shower.

Another way to backtrack meteor trails is to photograph the same meteor from two locations on Earth a few miles apart.

■ Figure 25-6

(a) Meteors in a shower are debris left behind as a comet's icy nucleus vaporizes. The rocky and metallic bits of matter spread along the comet's orbit. If Earth passes through such material, you can see a meteor shower. (b) In this infrared image of Comet Encke, the millimeter-sized bits of rock along its orbit glow as they are warmed by sunlight. The Taurid meteor shower occurs every October when Earth crosses Encke's orbit. (NASA/JPL-Caltech/M. Kelley, Univ. of Minnesota)

Then, you can use triangulation to find the altitude, speed, and direction of the meteor as it moves through the atmosphere, and work backward to calculate its orbit before it entered Earth's atmosphere. These studies confirm that meteors belonging to showers, as well as some sporadic meteors, have orbits that are similar to the orbits of comets. In contrast, a few sporadic meteors, including *all* observed meteorite falls, have orbits that lead back to the asteroid belt between Mars and Jupiter. From this you can conclude that meteors have a dual source: Many come from comets, but a few come from the asteroid belt. Meteors that are big and durable enough to become meteorites on the ground appear always to come from the asteroid belt.

It is a **Common Misconception** that a bright meteor disappearing behind a distant hill or line of trees probably landed just a mile or two away. This has triggered hilarious "wild goose chases" as police, fire companies, and TV crews try to find the impact site. Almost every meteor you see vaporizes high above Earth's surface. Only rarely does a meteor become a meteorite by reaching the ground, and it can land as much as 100 miles from where you are standing when you see it.

Origin of Meteoroids and Meteorites

Evidence you have already encountered suggests that many meteorites are fragments of parent bodies that were large enough to grow hot from radioactive decay or other processes. They then melted and differentiated to form iron-nickel cores and rocky mantles. The molten iron cores would have been well insulated by the thick rocky mantles, so that the iron would have cooled slowly enough to produce big crystals that result in Widmanstätten patterns. Some stony meteorites that have been strongly heated appear instead to have come from the mantles or surfaces of such bodies. Stony-iron meteorites apparently come from boundaries between stony mantles and iron cores. Collisions could break up such differentiated bodies and produce different kinds of meteorites (■ Figure 25-7). In contrast, many chondrites are probably fragments of smaller bodies that never melted, and carbonaceous chondrites may be from unaltered bodies that formed especially far from the sun.

These hypotheses trace the origin of meteorites to planetesimal-like parent bodies, but they leave you with a puzzle. The small meteoroids now flying through the solar system cannot have existed in their present form since the formation of the solar system because they would have been swept up by the planets in a billion years or less. They could not have survived traveling in their current orbits for the full 4.6 billion years that the solar system has existed. Nevertheless, when the orbits of meteorite falls are determined, those orbits lead back into the asteroid belt. Thus, all the evidence together indicates that the meteorites now in museums around the world were produced

The Origin of Meteorites

A large planetesimal can keep its internal heat long enough to differentiate.

Collisions break up the layers of different composition.

Silicates

Cratering collisions

Iron

Meteorites from deeper in the planetesimal were heated to higher temperatures.

Fragments from near the core might have been melted entirely.

Fragments of the iron core would fall to Earth as iron meteorites.

■ **Figure 25-7**

Some of the planetesimals that formed early in the solar system's history may have differentiated—that is, melted and separated into layers of different density and composition, as did the Terrestrial planets. The fragmentation of such a planetesimal could produce different types of meteorites. (Adapted from a diagram by Clark Chapman)

by asteroid collisions within the last billion years. Astronomers conclude that nearly all meteors are material from comets, but meteorites are pieces of shattered asteroids.

How can you say that meteors come from comets, but meteorites come from asteroids?

To begin with, remember the distinction between meteors and meteorites. A meteor is the streak of light seen in the sky when a particle from space is heated by friction with Earth's atmosphere. A meteorite is a piece of space material that actually reaches the ground.

The distinction between comet and asteroid sources must take into account two very strong effects that prevent you from finding meteorites that originated in comets. First, evidence that you will learn more about later in this chapter indicates that cometary material is physically weak, so comet particles vaporize in Earth's atmosphere easily. Very few ever reach the ground. Second, even if a comet particle reached the ground, it would be so fragile that it would weather away rapidly, and you would be unlikely to find it before it disappeared. Asteroidal particles, however, are made from rock and metal and are stronger. They are more likely to survive their plunge through the atmosphere and, afterward, more likely to survive erosion on the ground. Every known meteorite is from the asteroids—not a single meteorite is known to be cometary. In contrast, meteor tracks show that most meteors you see come from comets, and very few are from the asteroid belt.

Now build a new argument. **What evidence suggests that meteorites were once part of larger bodies broken up by impacts?**

The Asteroid Belt

The first asteroid was discovered on January 1, 1801 (the first night of the 19th century) by the Sicilian monk Giuseppe Piazzi. It was later named Ceres after the Roman goddess of the harvest (and source of our word *cereal*).

Astronomers were excited by Piazzi's discovery because there seemed to be a pattern to the location of planet orbits, except for a wide gap between Mars and Jupiter where the pattern implied a planet "ought" to exist at an average distance from the sun of 2.8 AU. Ceres fit the pattern: Its average distance from the sun is 2.77 AU. But Ceres is much smaller than the planets, and three even smaller objects—Pallas, Juno, and Vesta—were discovered within a few years, all orbiting between Mars and Jupiter, so astronomers decided that Ceres and the other asteroids should not be considered true planets. As you learned in Chapter 24, Ceres has now been re-classified as a dwarf planet because it has enough gravitational strength to squeeze itself into a spherical shape but not enough to have absorbed or cleared away the rest of the asteroids.

Today over 100,000 asteroids have well-charted orbits. Only three are larger than 400 km in diameter (■ Figure 25-8), and most are much smaller. Astronomers are sure that all the large

25-2 Asteroids

ASTEROIDS ARE DISTANT OBJECTS too small to study in detail with Earth-based telescopes. Astronomers nevertheless have learned a surprising amount about those little worlds, using spacecraft and space telescopes.

Properties of Asteroids

Evidence from meteorites shows that the asteroids are the last remains of the rocky planetesimals that built the Terrestrial planets 4.6 billion years ago.

Study **Observations of Asteroids** on pages 560–561 and notice four important points:

1. Most asteroids are irregular in shape and battered by impact cratering. Many asteroids seem to be rubble piles of broken fragments.

2. Some asteroids are double objects or have small moons in orbit around them. This is further evidence that asteroids have suffered collisions.

3. A few asteroids show signs of geological activity that probably happened on their surfaces when those asteroids were young.

4. Asteroids can be classified by their albedos, colors, and spectra to reveal clues to their compositions. This also allows them to be compared to meteorites in labs on Earth.

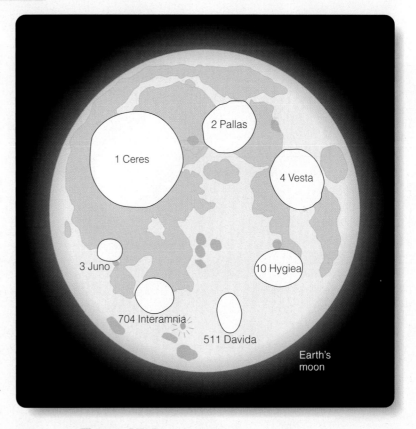

■ Figure 25-8

The relative size and approximate shape of the larger asteroids are shown here compared with the size of Earth's moon. Smaller asteroids can be highly irregular in shape.

Observations of Asteroids

1 Seen from Earth, asteroids look like faint points of light moving in front of distant stars. Not many years ago they were known mostly for drifting slowly through the field of view and spoiling long time exposures. Some astronomers referred to them as "the vermin of the sky." Spacecraft have now visited asteroids, and the images radioed back to Earth show that the asteroids are mostly small, gray, irregular worlds heavily cratered by impacts.

The Near Earth Asteroid Rendezvous (NEAR) spacecraft visited the asteroid Eros in 2000 and found it to be heavily cratered by collisions and covered by a layer of crushed rock ranging from dust to large boulders. The NEAR spacecraft eventually landed on Eros.

Eros appears to be a solid fragment of rock.

Visual-wavelength image

NASA

10 km

Visual-wavelength image

NASA

5 meters

Most asteroids are too small for their gravity to pull them into a spherical shape. Impacts break them into irregularly shaped fragments.

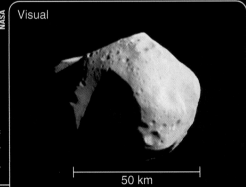

NASA

Visual

The surface of Mathilde is very dark rock.

50 km

1a The mass of an asteroid can be found from its gravitational influence on passing spacecraft. Its volume can be measured using images made from a range of perspectives. The density is mass divided by volume. Mathilde, at left, has such a low density that it cannot be solid rock. Like many asteroids, Mathilde may be a rubble pile of broken fragments with large empty spaces between fragments.

If you walked across the surface of an irregularly shaped asteroid such as Eros, you would find gravity very weak; and in many places, it would not be perpendicular to the surface.

Enhanced visual image

Like most asteroids, Gaspra would look gray to your eyes; but, in this enhanced image at left, color differences probably indicate difference in mineralogy.

5 km

NASA

Radar image

NASA

2 Asteroids that pass near Earth can be imaged by radar. The asteroid Toutatis is revealed to be a double object—two objects orbiting close to each other or actually in contact.

Ida

NASA

30 km

Enhanced visual + infrared

Dactyl

Double asteroids are more common than was once thought, reflecting a history of collisions and fragmentation. The asteroid Ida is orbited by a moon Dactyl only about 1.5 km in diameter.

Occasional collisions among the asteroids release fragments, and Jupiter's gravity scatters them into the inner solar system as a continuous supply of meteorites.

3 The large asteroid Vesta, as shown at right, provides evidence that some asteroids once had geological activity. No spacecraft has visited it, but its spectrum resembles that of solidified lava. Images made by the Hubble Space Telescope allow the creation of a model of its shape. It has a huge crater at its south pole. A family of small asteroids is evidently composed of fragments from Vesta, and a certain class of meteorites, spectroscopically identical to Vesta, are believed to be fragments from the asteroid. The meteorites appear to be solidified basalt.

NASA

Vesta

Visual-wavelength image

500 km

Model

Elevation map

13-km-deep crater

Elevation

-12km   +12km

3a Vesta appears to have had internal heat at some point in its history, perhaps due to the decay of radioactive minerals. Lava flows have covered at least some of its surface.

Meteorite from Vesta

5 cm
2 in.

Courtesy of Russell Kemton, New England Meteoritical

4 Although asteroids would look gray to your eyes, they can be classified according to their albedos (reflected brightness) and spectroscopic colors. As shown at left, S-types are brighter and tend to be reddish. They are the most common kind of asteroid and appear to be the source of the most common chondrites.

M-type asteroids are not too dark but are also not very red. They may be mostly iron-nickel alloys.

C-type asteroids are as dark as lumps of sooty coal and appear to

Bright

0.4

0.3

0.2

Albedo (reflected brightness)

0.1

0.06

0.04

Dark

M

S

C

Common in the inner asteroid belt

Common in the outer asteroid belt

Grayer ← → Redder

0.8   1.0   1.2   1.4   1.6

asteroids in the asteroid belt have been discovered but are also sure that many small asteroids remain undiscovered.

Movies and TV have created a **Common Misconception** that flying through an asteroid belt is a hair-raising plunge requiring constant dodging left and right. The asteroid belt between Mars and Jupiter is actually mostly empty space. In fact, if you were standing on an asteroid, it would be many months or years between sightings of other asteroids.

If you discover an asteroid you are allowed to choose a name for it, and asteroids have been named for spouses, lovers, dogs, politicians, and others.* Once an orbit has been calculated, the asteroid is assigned a number listing its order in the catalog known as the *Ephemerides of Minor Planets*. Thus, Ceres is officially known as 1 Ceres, Pallas as 2 Pallas, and so on.

The distribution of asteroids in the belt is strongly affected by Jupiter's gravitation. Certain orbits in the belt that are almost free of asteroids are called **Kirkwood gaps** after their discoverer, Daniel Kirkwood (■ Figure 25-9). These missing orbits are at certain distances from the sun where an asteroid would find itself in a resonance with Jupiter. For example, an asteroid with an average distance from the sun of 3.28 AU will go exactly twice around the sun in the time it takes Jupiter to go once. Such an asteroid would pass Jupiter at the same place in space every second orbit and be tugged outward. The cumulative perturbations would rapidly change the asteroid's orbit until it was no longer in resonance with Jupiter. Thus, Jupiter effectively eliminates objects from the orbit resonance. The example given represents a 2:1 resonance, but gaps occur in the asteroid belt at many other resonances, including 3:1, 5:2, and 7:3. You will recognize that Kirkwood gaps in the asteroid belt are produced in the same way as some of the gaps in Saturn's rings (see Chapter 23) that were also discovered by Kirkwood.

Computer models show that the motion of asteroids in Kirkwood gaps is described by a theory in mathematics that deals with chaotic behavior. As an example, consider how the smooth motion of water sliding over the edge of a waterfall decays rapidly into a chaotic jumble. The same theory of chaos that describes the motion of the water shows how the slowly changing orbit of an asteroid within one of the Kirkwood gaps can suddenly (astronomically speaking) become a long, eccentric orbit that carries the asteroid into the inner solar system.

Asteroids Outside the Main Belt

You don't have to go all the way to the asteroid belt if you want to visit an asteroid; some follow orbits that cross the orbits of the Terrestrial planets and come near Earth. Others wander far away, among the Jovian worlds. There are also asteroids that share orbits with the planets (■ Figure 25-10).

Apollo-Amor objects are asteroids with orbits that carry them into the inner solar system. Amor objects follow orbits that cross the orbit of Mars but don't reach the orbit of Earth, whereas Apollo objects have Earth-crossing orbits. About 3000 Apollo and Amor objects have been found so far. The influences of Jupiter and other planets act to continually change their orbits. Astronomers calculate that about one-third of Apollo-Amors will be thrown into the sun, a few will be ejected from the solar system, and, as you will discover later in this chapter, some are doomed to collide with a planet—perhaps ours.

Several research teams are now intent on identifying **Near-Earth Objects (NEOs),** including Apollo-Amor objects. For example, LONEOS (Lowell Observatory Near-Earth Object Search) is searching the entire sky visible from Lowell Observatory in northern Arizona once a month. The LINEAR (Lincoln Near-Earth Asteroid Research) telescope in New Mexico (■ Figure 25-11) and the NEAT (Near-Earth Asteroids Tracking) facilities in California and Hawaii also have been successful in finding NEOs, as well as new main-belt asteroids and Kuiper belt objects. The combined searches are expected to be able to locate at least 90 percent of the NEOs larger than 1 km in diameter by 2011.

It is easy to hypothesize that the Apollo-Amor objects are rocky asteroids that have been sent into their unusual orbits by collisions in the main asteroid belt or by planetary perturbations,

---

*Some sample asteroid names: Chicago, Vaticana, Noel, Ohio, Tea, Gaby, Fidelio, Hagar, Geisha, Tata, Mimi, Dulu, Tito, Zulu, Zappafrank, and Garcia (after the late musicians Frank Zappa and Jerry Garcia, respectively).

■ **Figure 25-9**

The red curve in this plot shows the number of asteroids at different distances from the sun. Purple bars mark Kirkwood gaps, where there are few asteroids. Note that these gaps match resonances with the orbital motion of Jupiter.

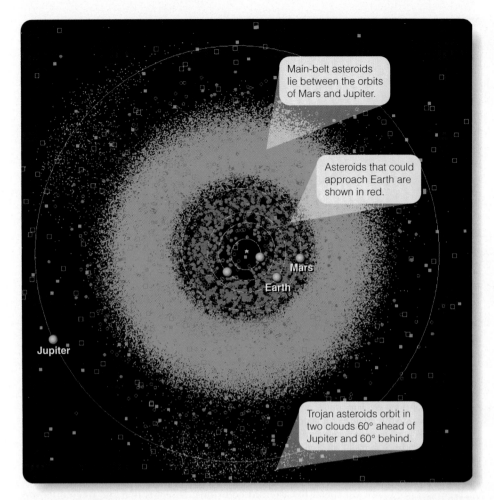

Main-belt asteroids lie between the orbits of Mars and Jupiter.

Asteroids that could approach Earth are shown in red.

Mars

Earth

Jupiter

Trojan asteroids orbit in two clouds 60° ahead of Jupiter and 60° behind.

■ **Figure 25-10**

This diagram plots the position of known asteroids between the sun and the orbit of Jupiter on a specific day. Most asteroids are in the main belt. Squares, filled or empty, show the location of known comets. Although asteroids and comets are small bodies and lie far apart, there are a great many of them in the inner solar system. (Minor Planet Center)

for example Jupiter's Kirkwood gap-clearing effect that you learned about in the previous section. There is evidence that a few of these objects instead may be comets that became trapped in short orbits that kept them in the inner solar system so they have exhausted their volatiles. You can see from this that the distinction between comets and asteroids is not sharply defined.

Jupiter ushers two groups of nonbelt asteroids around its own orbit. These objects have become trapped in the Lagrangian points along Jupiter's orbit that are 60° ahead of and 60° behind the planet. Lagrangian points are regions like cosmic sinkholes where gravitational effects of the two larger bodies, in this case the sun and Jupiter, combine to trap small bodies (Figure 25-10). (For an example of Lagrangian points in a stellar context, see the positions labeled L_4 and L_5 in Figure 13-5.) The Jupiter Lagrangian-point objects are called **Trojan asteroids** because individual asteroids have been named after the heroes of the Trojan War (588 Achilles, 624 Hektor, 659 Nestor, and 1143

Odysseus, for example). Almost 2000 Trojan asteroids are known, but only the brightest have been given names. Some astronomers speculate that there may be as many Trojan asteroids as asteroids in the main belt. Astronomers have also found a few objects in the Lagrangian points of the orbits of Mars and Neptune. Other planets, including Earth, may have undiscovered Lagrangian-point asteroids trapped in their orbits.

There are other nonbelt asteroids beyond the main belt. The object Chiron, found in 1977, is about 170 km (110 mi) in diameter. Its orbit carries it from the orbit of Uranus to just inside the orbit of Saturn. Although it was first classified as an asteroid, Chiron surprised astronomers ten years after its discovery by suddenly brightening as it released jets of vapor and dust. Old photographs were found showing that Chiron had done this before. Astronomers now suspect Chiron has a rocky crust covering deposits of ices such as solid nitrogen, methane, and carbon monoxide. You will learn in the next section that this more resembles the characteristics of comets than asteroids. Objects like Chiron with orbits between, or crossing, orbits of the Jovian planets are called **centaurs.** The characteristics of centaurs show you yet again that the distinction between asteroids and comets is not clear cut.

As technology allows astronomers to detect smaller and more distant objects, they are learning that our solar system contains large numbers of these small bodies. The challenge is to explain their origin.

Origin and History of the Asteroids

An old hypothesis proposed that asteroids are the remains of a planet that exploded. Planet-shattering death rays may make for exciting science-fiction movies, but in reality planets do not explode. The gravitational field of a planet holds the mass together so tightly that completely disrupting the planet would take tremendous energy. In addition, the present-day total mass of the asteroids is only about one-twentieth the mass of Earth's moon, hardly enough to be the remains of a planet.

Astronomers have evidence that the asteroids are the remains of material lying 2 to 4 AU from the sun that was unable to form a planet because of the gravitational influence of Jupiter, the next planet outward. Over the 4.6-billion-year history of the solar system, most of the objects originally in the asteroid belt have

The LINEAR telescope is 1 meter in diameter.

■ **Figure 25-11**

(a) The LINEAR telescope searches for asteroids every clear night when the moon is not bright. A diagram showing color codes for the thoroughness of the LINEAR search over the entire sky for one year. The green (poorly searched) region is the plane of the Milky Way, where asteroids are difficult to discover against a dense starry background. (MIT/Lincoln Labs)

collided, fragmented, and been covered with craters. Some asteroids were perturbed by the gravity of Jupiter and other planets into orbits that collided with planets or the sun, caused them to be captured as planetary satellites, or ejected them from the solar system. The present-day asteroids are understood to be a very minor remnant of the original mass in that zone.

Collisions among asteroids must have been occurring since the formation of the solar system (look again at Figure 25-7 and page 560). Astronomers have found evidence of catastrophic impacts powerful enough to shatter an asteroid. Early in the 20th century, astronomer Kiyotsugu Hirayama discovered that some groups of asteroids share similar orbits. Each group is distinct from other groups, but asteroids within a given group have the same average distance from the sun, the same eccentricity, and the same inclination. Up to 20 of these **Hirayama families** are known. Modern observations show that the asteroids in a family typically share similar spectroscopic characteristics. Apparently, each family was produced by a catastrophic collision that broke a single asteroid into fragments that continue traveling along similar orbits around the sun. Evidence shows that one family

was produced only 5.8 million years ago in a collision between asteroids estimated to have been 3 km and 16 km in diameter, traveling at relative speeds of about 5 km/s (11,000 mph), a typical speed for asteroid collisions. It seems that the fragmentation of asteroids is a continuing process.

In 1983, the Infrared Astronomy Satellite detected the infrared glow of sun-warmed dust scattered in bands throughout the asteroid belt. These dust bands appear to be the products of past collisions. The dust will eventually be destroyed, but because collisions occur constantly in the asteroid belt, new dust bands will presumably be produced as the present bands dissipate. The interplanetary dust in our solar system is analogous to dust in extrasolar planetary debris disks, produced astronomically recently by collisions of remnant plantesimals (see Chapter 19).

Even though most of the planetesimals originally in the main belt have been lost or destroyed, the objects left behind carry clues to their origin in their albedos and spectroscopic colors (p. 561). **C-type asteroids** have albedos less than 0.06 and would look very dark to your eyes. They are probably made of carbon-rich material similar to that in carbonaceous chondrite meteorites. C-type asteroids are more common in the outer asteroid belt. It is cooler there, and the condensation sequence (see Chapter 19) predicts that carbonaceous material would form more easily in the outer belt than in the inner belt.

S-type asteroids have albedos of 0.1 to 0.2, so they would look brighter as well as redder than C-types; S-types may be composed of rocky material. **M-type** asteroids are also bright but not as red as the S-types; they seem to be metal-rich and may be fragments from iron cores of differentiated asteroids. A few other types of asteroids are known, and a number of individual asteroids have been found that are unique, but these three classes include most of the known asteroids.

Although S-type asteroids are very common in the inner asteroid belt, their colors and albedos are different from those of chondrites, the most common kind of meteorite. This represented a puzzle to astronomers; shouldn't the common type of asteroid nearest Earth be the source of the most common type of meteorite that hit Earth? New evidence from the analysis of moon rocks and from observations of Eros, an S-type asteroid, shows that bombardment by micrometeorites and solar wind particles can redden and darken rocky materials until they have the colors and albedos of S-type asteroids. It therefore seems likely that chondrite meteorites are in fact fragments of S-type asteroids.

In March 2009 a small asteroid (2–3 meters in diameter, about the size of a small truck) was spotted by the NEO detection network on a collision course with Earth. Astronomers were able to observe it in space before impact and discovered that its colors and albedo matched the fairly rare F-type asteroids that are mostly in the outer belt. The asteroid entered Earth's atmosphere over the desert of northern Sudan and was witnessed exploding. Scientists Peter Jenniskens from the SETI Institute and Muawia Shaddad of the University of Khartoum organized a team of local faculty and students to search for pieces of the object. They ultimately found about 4 kilograms (9 pounds) of fragments corresponding to the rate ureilite meteorite type. For the first time, planetary scientists were able to make a definite connection between an asteroid observed in space and meteorites with properties measured in an Earth laboratory.

As you saw in the case of Vesta, a few asteroids may once have been geologically active, with lava flowing on their surfaces when they were young. Perhaps they incorporated especially large amounts of short-lived radioactive elements such as aluminum-26. Those radioactive elements were probably produced by a supernova explosion that could also have been the trigger for the formation of the sun and planets while seeding the young solar system with its nucleosynthesis products (see Chapter 13 and Figure 11-2).

Not all large asteroids have been active. Ceres, 900 km in diameter, is almost twice as big as Vesta, but it shows no spectroscopic sign of past activity and evidently has an ice-rich mantle. The puzzling differences between those two large asteroids will be investigated by the Dawn spacecraft that is on its way to orbit Vesta in 2011 and Ceres in 2015.

Although there are still mysteries to solve, you can understand the story of the asteroids. They are fragments of planetesimals, some of which differentiated, developed molten metal cores, in a few cases even had lava flows on their surfaces, and then cooled slowly. The largest asteroids astronomers see today may be nearly unbroken examples of original planetesimals, but the smaller asteroids are fragments produced by 4.6 billion years of collisions.

SCIENTIFIC ARGUMENT

What is the evidence that asteroids have been fragmented?
First, your argument might note that the solar nebula theory predicts that planetesimals collided and either stuck together or fragmented. This is suggestive, but it is not evidence. A theory can never be used as evidence to support some other theory or hypothesis. Evidence means observations or the results of experiments, so your argument must cite observations. The spacecraft photographs of asteroids show irregularly shaped little worlds heavily scarred by impact craters. Further evidence indicates some asteroids may be pairs of bodies split apart but still in contact, and images of asteroid Ida reveal a small satellite, Dactyl. Other asteroids with moons have been found. These double asteroids and asteroids with moons probably reveal the results of fragmenting collisions between asteroids. Furthermore, meteorites appear to have come from the asteroid belt astronomically recently, so fragmentation must be a continuing process there.

Now build an argument to combine what you know of meteorites with your experience with asteroids. **What evidence could you cite to show what the first planetesimals were like?**

25-3 Comets

FEW SIGHTS IN ASTRONOMY are more beautiful than a bright comet hanging in the night sky (■ Figure 25-12). It is a **Common Misconception** that comets whiz rapidly across the sky like meteors. Actually, comets move with the stately grace of great ships at sea, their motion hardly apparent; night by night they shift position slightly against the background stars, and they may remain visible for weeks.

Throughout history, comets have been considered omens of doom. Comets may be beautiful, but are also so strange in appearance that they can create some instinctive alarm. Even recent appearances of bright comets have caused predictions of the end of the world. In 1910, Comet Halley was spectacular, and it was frightening to some people. Comet Kohoutek in 1973, Comet Halley returning in 1986, and Comet Hale–Bopp in 1997 also caused concern among the superstitious.*

Faint comets are common; several dozen are discovered each year. Truly bright comets appear about once per decade. Comet McNaught in 2007 was bright enough to be classed

---

*Comets are now named after the person or persons who discover them. Comet Halley, in contrast, which has been seen occasionally for at least the last 2,250 years, has no known "discoverer." It is named after Edmund Halley, an English astronomer who was a friend of Isaac Newton and who was the first to realize that certain comets appearing at 76-year intervals were actually the same comet on a repeating orbit. Halley correctly predicted that the comet would be seen again in a certain year.

■ Figure 25-12

Comet McNaught swept through the inner solar system in 2007 and was a dramatic sight in the southern sky. Seen here from Australia, the comet was on its way back into deep space after making its closest approach to the sun ten days earlier. Comet McNaught began this passage with a period of about 300,000 years, but gravitational perturbations by the planets changed its orbit shape from elliptical to hyperbolic, so it will never return but instead is leaving the solar system to journey forever in interstellar space. (© John White)

with other great comet appearances such as Comet Halley in 1910. An average person might see five or ten bright comets in a lifetime. While everyone can enjoy the beauty of comets, astronomers study them because they are messengers from the past carrying cargos of information about the origin of our solar system.

Properties of Comets

As always, you should begin your study of a new kind of object by summarizing its observational properties. What do comets look like, and how do they behave?

Study **Observations of Comets** on pages 568–569 and notice three important properties of comets plus three new terms:

1 Comets have two kinds of tails, shaped by the solar wind and solar radiation. Gas and dust released by a comet's icy nucleus produces a head or *coma* and are then blown outward, away from the sun. The gas produces a *type I*, or *gas, tail*, and the dust produces a *type II*, or *dust, tail*.

2 Comet dust produces not only one of the two types of comet tails but also spreads throughout the solar system. Some of those comet dust particles later encounter the Earth and are seen as meteors.

3 Evidence shows that comet nuclei are fragile and can break into pieces easily.

Astronomers can put these and other observations together to study the structure of comet nuclei.

The Geology of Comet Nuclei

The nuclei of comets are quite small and cannot be studied in detail using Earth-based telescopes. Nevertheless, when a comet nucleus approaches the sun, it emits material that forms into a coma (head) and tail that can be millions of kilometers in size and is easily observed.

Spectra of comet comae (plural of *coma*) and tails indicate the nuclei must contain ices of water and other volatile compounds such as carbon dioxide, carbon monoxide, methane, ammonia, and so on. These are the kinds of compounds that would have condensed in cold regions of the solar nebula. This convinces astronomers that comets are ancient samples of the gases and dust from which the outer planets formed. As the ices absorb energy from sunlight, they sublime—change from a solid directly into a gas. The gases break down and combine chemically, producing other substances found in comet spectra. For example, vast clouds of hydrogen gas observed around the heads of comets are understood to derive from the breakup of ice molecules.

Five spacecraft flew past the nucleus of Comet Halley when it visited the inner solar system in 1985 and 1986. Other spacecraft flew past the nuclei of Comet Borrelly in 2001, Comet Wild 2 (pronounced *vildt-two*) in 2004, and Comet Tempel 1 in 2005. Images show that all these comet nuclei are 1 to 10 km across, similar in size to many asteroids, and irregular in shape (■ Figure 25-13). In general, these nuclei are darker than a lump of coal, which suggests composition similar to carbon-rich carbonaceous chondrite meteorites described earlier in this chapter.

The mass and density of comet nuclei can be calculated from their gravitational influence on passing spacecraft. Comet nuclei appear to have densities between 0.1 and 0.25 g/cm³, much less than the density of ice. Also, as you will learn later in this chapter, comets subjected to tidal stresses from Jupiter or the sun come apart very easily. Comet nuclei have been described as dirty snowballs or icy mudballs, but that seems to be incorrect; their shapes, low densities, and lack of material strength suggest that comets are not solid objects. The evidence leads astronomers to conclude that most comet nuclei must be fluffy mixtures of ices and dust with significant amounts of empty space. On the other hand, images of the nucleus of Comet Wild 2 revealed cliffs, pinnacles, and other features that show the material has enough strength to stand against the weak gravity of the comet.

Photographs of comet comae (Figure 25-13) often show jets springing from the nucleus into the coma and being swept back by the pressures of sunlight and the solar wind to form the tail. Studies of the motions of these jets as the nucleus rotates reveal that they originate from small active regions that may be similar

■ **Figure 25-13**

Visual-wavelength images made by spacecraft and by the Hubble Space Telescope show how the nuclei of comets produce jets of gases from regions where sunlight vaporizes ices. (Halley nucleus: © 1986 Max-Planck Institute; Halley coma: Steven Larson; Comets Borrelly, Hale–Bopp, and Wild 2: NASA)

The nucleus of Comet Halley is irregular and emitting jets from active regions.

Jets from the nucleus of Comet Halley form a pinwheel in the coma because of the rotation of the nucleus.

Debris ejected from the nucleus

Hubble Space Telescope image of coma of Comet Hale–Bopp.

Nucleus

a   10 km

b

c

Enhanced visual images

The nucleus of Comet Wild 2 is highly irregular.

Jets vent from active regions

d   5 km

Jet

Jet

5 km

Active regions on the nucleus of Comet Borrelly emit jets when they rotate into sunlight.

e

Observations of Comets

1 A **type I** or **gas tail** is produced by ionized gas carried away from the nucleus by the solar wind. The spectrum of a gas tail is an emission spectrum. The atoms are ionized by the ultraviolet light in sunlight. The wisps and kinks in gas tails are produced by the magnetic field embedded in the solar wind.

Spectra of gas tails reveal atoms and ions such as H_2O, CO_2, CO, H, OH, O, S, C, and so on. These are released by the vaporizing ices or produced by the breakdown of those molecules. Some gases, such as hydrogen cyanide (HCN), must be formed by chemical reactions.

Gas tail (Type I)

Dust tail (Type II)

1a A **type II** or **dust tail** is produced by dust that was contained in the vaporizing ices of the nucleus. The dust is pushed gently outward by the pressure of sunlight, and it reflects an absorption spectrum, the spectrum of sunlight. The dust is not affected by the magnetic field of the solar wind, so dust tails are more uniform than gas tails. Dust tails are often curved because the dust particles follow their individual orbits around the sun once they leave the nucleus. Because of the forces acting on them, both gas and dust tails extend away from the sun.

Nucleus ——————

1b The nucleus of a comet (not visible here) is a small, fragile lump of porous rock containing ices of water, carbon dioxide, ammonia, and so on. Comet nuclei can be to 100 km in diameter.

Coma

The **coma** of a comet is the cloud of gas and dust that surrounds the nucleus. It can be over 1,000,000 km in diameter, bigger than the sun.

1c Comet Mrkos in 1957 shows how the gas tail can change from night to night due to changes in the magnetic field in the solar wind.

Caltech

2 As the ices in a comet nucleus vaporize, they release dust particles that not only form the dust tail but also spread throughout the solar system.

The Deep Impact spacecraft released an instrumented probe into the path of Comet Tempel 1. When the comet slammed into the probe at 10.2 km/s as shown at right, huge amounts of gas and dust were released. From the results, scientists conclude that the nucleus of the comet is rich in dust finer than the particles of talcum powder. The nucleus is marked by craters, but it is not solid rock. It is about the density of fresh-fallen snow.

Visual-wavelength images

Only seconds before impact, craters are visible on the dark surface.

Dust particles (arrows) were embedded in the collector when they struck at high velocity.

Direction of travel

A microscopic mineral crystal from Comet Wild 2

Images of Comet Tempel 1 from the flyby probe 13 seconds after the impact probe hit. Gas and dust are thrown out of the impact crater.

2a The Stardust spacecraft flew past the nucleus of Comet Wild 2 and collected dust particles (as shown above) in an exposed target that was later parachuted back to Earth. The dust particles hit the collector at high velocity and became embedded, but they can be extracted for study.

Some of the collected dust is made of high-temperature minerals that could only have formed near the sun. This suggests that material from the inner solar nebula was mixed outward and became part of the forming comets in the outer solar system. Other minerals found include olivine, a very common mineral on Earth but not one that scientists expected to find in a comet.

This dust particle was collected by spacecraft above Earth's atmosphere. It is almost certainly from a comet.

Comet 73P/Schwassmann-Wachmann3 Fragment B

Fragments

3 The nuclei of comets are not strong and can break up. In 2006, Comet Schwassmann-Wachmann 3 broke into a number of fragments that themselves fragmented. Fragment B is shown at the right breaking into smaller pieces. The gas and dust released by the breakup made the comet fragments bright in the night sky, and some were visible with binoculars. As its ices vaporize and its dust spreads, the comet may totally disintegrate and leave nothing but a stream of debris along its previous orbit.

Comets most often break up as they pass close to the sun or close to a massive planet like Jupiter. Comet LINEAR broke up in 2000 as it passed by the sun. The comet that hit Jupiter in 1994 was first ripped to pieces by tidal stresses from Jupiter's gravity. Comets can also fragment far from planets, perhaps because of the vaporization of critical structural areas of ice.

Visual

■ **Figure 25-14**

The crusts of comets are evidently delicate mixtures of rock, ice, and dust. The dust is ejected along with gases as the ices in a comet vaporize in sunlight, as shown in this artist's conception. (NASA/NSSDC; Tom Herbst, Max-Planck-Institut für Astronomie, Heidelberg; Doug Hamilton, Max-Planck-Institut für Kernphysik, Heidelberg; Hermann Böehnhardt, Universitäts-Sternwarte, München; and Jose Luis Ortiz Moreno, Instituto de Astrofisica)

to volcanic faults or vents (■ Figure 25-14). As the rotation of a comet nucleus carries an active region into sunlight, it begins venting gas and dust, and as it rotates into darkness it shuts down.

The nuclei of comets appear to have a crust of rocky dust left behind as the ices vaporize. Breaks in that crust can expose ices to sunlight, and vents can occur in those regions. It also seems that some comets have large pockets of volatiles buried below the crust. When one of those pockets is exposed and begins to vaporize, the comet can suffer a dramatic outburst, as Comet Holmes did in 2007 (■ Figure 25-15).

Astronomers have devised ways to study comet material more directly. The Stardust spacecraft passed through the tail of Comet Wild 2 in 2004, collected dust particles that had been ejected from the comet's nucleus, and returned the samples in a sealed capsule to Earth in 2006 for analysis. In 2005, the Deep Impact spacecraft released an instrumented impactor probe into the path of comet Tempel 1. As planned, the nucleus of the comet ran into the impactor at almost 10 km/s (22,000 mph). The probe broke through the crust of the nucleus and blasted vapor and dust out into space where the Deep Impact "mother ship," as well as the Spitzer and Hubble space telescopes and observatories on Earth, could analyze it (page 569). Those

missions produced the surprising discovery that some comet dust is crystalline and must have formed originally in very warm environments close to the sun, but then was incorporated somehow into comet nuclei in the cold outer solar system.

The Solar and Heliospheric Observatory (SOHO) spacecraft was put into space to observe the sun, but it has also discovered over a thousand comets, called "sun grazers," that come very close to the sun, in some cases 70 times closer to the sun's surface than the planet Mercury (■ Figure 25-16). As many as three comets per week plunge into the sun and are destroyed. Most sun grazers belong to one of four groups, and the comets in each group have very similar orbits. Like the Hirayama families of asteroids, these comet groups appear to be made up of fragments of larger comet nuclei. The original comet may have been ripped apart by the violence of gases superheated near the sun and bursting through the crust, or by solar tidal forces, or both.

■ **Figure 25-15**

Composite of 19 snapshots of Comet Holmes, showing its changing brightness and position spanning the period from October 2007 until March 2008. During its outburst in late October 2007, the comet brightened by a factor of about 500,000 as a large pocket of volatile material exploded through its crust and spread into space. (John Pane)

Sun hidden behind mask

Comets

Visual-wavelength image

Sun-grazing comets can be destroyed quickly by the sun, but even normal comets suffer from the effects of solar heating. Each passage around the sun vaporizes many millions of tons of ices, so the nucleus slowly loses its ices until there is nothing left but dust and rock moving along an orbit around the sun. The eventual fate of a comet is clear, but a more important question is its origin.

The Origin and History of Comets

Family relationships among the comets can give you clues to their origin. Most comets have long, elliptical orbits with periods greater than 200 years and are known as long-period comets. The long-period comet orbits are randomly inclined to the plane of the solar system, so those comets approach the inner solar system from all directions. Long-period comets revolve around the sun in about equal numbers in prograde orbits (the same direction in which the planets move) and retrograde orbits.

In contrast, about 100 or so of the 600 well-studied comets have orbits with periods less than 200 years. These short-period comets usually follow orbits that lie within 30° of the plane of the solar system, and most revolve around the sun prograde. Comet Halley, with a period of 76 years, is an unusual short-period comet with a retrograde orbit.

A comet cannot survive long in an orbit that brings it into the inner solar system. The heat of the sun vaporizes ices and reduces comets to inactive bodies of rock and dust; such comets can last at most 100 to 1000 orbits around the sun. Astronomers calculate that even before a comet completely vaporizes from solar heating, it can't survive more than about half a million years crossing the orbits of the planets, especially Jupiter, without having its path rerouted into the sun or out of the solar system or colliding with one of the planets. Therefore, comets visible in our skies now can't have survived in their present orbits for 4.6 billion years since the formation of the solar system, and that means there must be a continuous supply of new comets. Where do they come from?

In the 1950s, astronomer Jan Oort proposed that the long-period comets are objects that fall inward from what has become known as the **Oort cloud,** a spherical cloud of icy bodies that extends from about 10,000 to 100,000 AU from the sun (■ Figure 25-17). Astronomers estimate that the cloud contains several trillion (10^{12}) icy bodies. Far from the sun, they are very cold, lack comae and tails, and are invisible from Earth. The gravitational influence of occasional passing stars can perturb a few of these objects and cause them to fall into the inner solar system, where the heat of the sun warms their ices and transforms them into comets. The fact that long-period comets are observed to fall inward from all directions is explained by their Oort cloud reservoir being spherically symmetric around the sun and inner solar system.

It is not surprising that stars pass close enough to affect the Oort cloud. For example, data from the Hipparcos satellite show

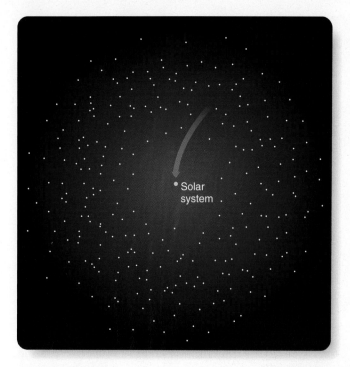

■ Figure 25-17

Long-period comets appear to originate in the spherical Oort cloud. Objects that fall into the inner solar system from that cloud arrive from all directions.

that the star Gliese 710 will pass within 1 light-year (about 63,000 AU) of the sun, crossing through the Oort cloud, in about a million years. The result may be a shower of Oort cloud objects perturbed into the inner solar system, where, warmed by the sun, they will become comets.

Saying that comets come from the Oort cloud only pushes the mystery back one step. How did those icy bodies get there? In preceding chapters, you have studied the origin and evolution of our solar system so carefully that the answer may leap out at you. Those Oort cloud comets are some of the icy planetesimals that formed in the outer solar nebula. The bodies in the Oort cloud, however, could not have formed at their present location because the solar nebula would not have been dense enough so far from the sun. And, if they had formed from the solar nebula, they would be distributed in a disk and not in a sphere. Astronomers think the Oort cloud planetesimals formed in the outer solar system near the present orbits of the giant planets. As those planets grew, they swept up many of these planetesimals, but they also would have ejected some out of the solar system. Most of those ejected objects vanished into space, but perhaps 10 percent had their orbits modified by the gravity of stars passing nearby and became part of the Oort cloud. Some of those later became the long-period comets.

Long-period comets originate in the Oort cloud, and some of the short-period comets do also. A few short-period comets, including Comet Halley, appear to have begun as long-period

comets from the Oort cloud and had their orbits altered by a close encounter with Jupiter. However, that process can't explain all of the short-period comets: Some follow orbits that could not have been produced by Oort cloud objects interacting with Jupiter or the other planets. There must be another source of icy bodies in our solar system. To find the answer, you need only look beyond the orbit of Neptune and study the icy Kuiper belt objects.

Comets from the Kuiper Belt

You first met the Kuiper belt in Chapter 19 when you studied the origin of the solar system. In Chapter 24, you learned about the largest Kuiper belt objects as examples of dwarf planets. In this chapter, it is important to study the smaller bodies of the Kuiper belt because they are one of the sources of comets.

In 1951, astronomer Gerard Kuiper proposed that the formation of the solar system should have left behind a belt of small, icy planetesimals beyond the Jovian planets and in the plane of the solar system. Such objects were first discovered in 1992 and are now known as Kuiper belt objects (KBOs).*

The Kuiper belt objects are small, icy bodies (■ Figure 25-18) that orbit in the plane of the solar system extending from the orbit of Neptune out to about 50 AU from the sun. Some objects are known to loop out as far as 1000 AU, but those may have been scattered into those orbits by gravitational interactions with passing stars. The entire Kuiper belt, containing as many as 100,000 objects 100 km or larger in diameter and hundreds of millions of smaller bodies, would be hidden behind the yellow dot representing the solar system in Figure 25-17. Some Kuiper belt objects are as large, or larger than, Pluto, but most are quite small.

Can this belt of ancient, icy worlds generate short-period comets? Because Kuiper belt objects orbit in the same direction as the planets and in the plane of the solar system, it is possible for an object perturbed inward by the influence of the giant planets to move into an orbit resembling those of the short-period comets. Rare collisions and interactions among the KBOs could also add to a continuous supply of small, icy bodies from the Kuiper belt sent into the inner solar system.

Comets vary in brightness and orbit. Nevertheless, there are two basic types of comets in our solar system. Some originate in the Oort cloud far from the sun. Others come from the Kuiper belt just beyond Neptune. They all share one characteristic—they are ancient icy bodies that were born when the solar system was young.

---

*In 1943 and 1949, astronomer Kenneth Edgeworth published papers that included a paragraph speculating about objects beyond Pluto. Consequently, you may occasionally see the Kuiper belt referred to as the Edgeworth–Kuiper belt, but most astronomers refer to this part of the solar system as the Kuiper belt.

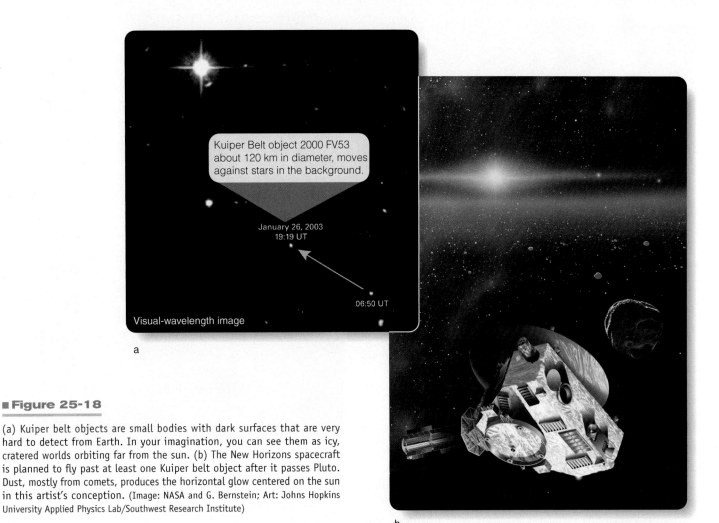

Figure 25-18

(a) Kuiper belt objects are small bodies with dark surfaces that are very hard to detect from Earth. In your imagination, you can see them as icy, cratered worlds orbiting far from the sun. (b) The New Horizons spacecraft is planned to fly past at least one Kuiper belt object after it passes Pluto. Dust, mostly from comets, produces the horizontal glow centered on the sun in this artist's conception. (Image: NASA and G. Bernstein; Art: Johns Hopkins University Applied Physics Lab/Southwest Research Institute)

SCIENTIFIC ARGUMENT

How do comets help explain the formation of the planets?
This argument must refer to the solar nebula hypothesis. The planetesimals that formed in the inner solar nebula were warm and could not incorporate much ice. The asteroids are understood to be the last remains of such rocky bodies. On the other hand, planetesimals in the outer solar system contained large amounts of ices. Many of them were destroyed by being accreted together to make the Jovian planets, but some survived intact. The icy bodies of the Oort cloud and the Kuiper belt may be the solar system's last surviving icy planetesimals. When those icy objects have their orbits perturbed by the gravity of the planets or passing stars, some are redirected into the inner solar system where you see them as comets. The gases released by comets indicate that they are rich in volatile materials such as water and carbon dioxide. These are the ices you would expect to find in the icy planetesimals. Comets also contain dust with rocklike chemical composition, and the planetesimals must have included large amounts of such dust frozen into the ices when they formed. Thus, the nuclei of comets seem to be frozen samples of the original outer solar nebula.

Nearly all of the mass of a comet is in the nucleus, but the light you see comes from the coma and the tail. Build a new argument to discuss observations. **What do spectra of comets tell you about the process that converts dirty ice into a comet?**

25-4 Asteroid and Comet Impacts

METEORITE IMPACTS ON HOMES of the type described at the start of this chapter are not common. Most meteors are small particles ranging from a few centimeters down to microscopic dust. Astronomers estimate that Earth gains about 40,000 tons of mass per year from meteorites of all sizes. (That may seem to you like a lot, but it is less than a hundred-thousandth of a trillionth of Earth's total mass.) Statistical calculations indicate that a meteorite large enough to cause some damage, like the one that hit Mrs. Hodges and her house in 1954, strikes a building somewhere in the world about once every 16 months.

Objects a few tens of meters or less in diameter are likely to fragment and explode in Earth's atmosphere without reaching the surface, but the shock waves from their explosions could still cause serious damage on Earth's surface. Declassified data from military satellites show that Earth is hit about once a week by meter-size asteroids. What happens when even larger solar system objects collide with Earth?

■ **Figure 25-19**

(a) The Barringer Meteorite Crater (near Flagstaff, Arizona) is nearly a mile in diameter and was formed about 50,000 years ago by the impact of an iron meteorite estimated to have been roughly 50 meters in diameter. Notice the raised and deformed rock layers all around the crater. The brick museum building visible on the far rim at right provides some idea of scale. (M. A. Seeds) (b) Like all larger-impact features, the Barringer Meteorite Crater has a raised rim and scattered ejecta. (USGS)

Barringer Crater

Barringer Crater near Flagstaff, Arizona, is 1.2 km ($\frac{3}{4}$ of a mile) in diameter and 200 m (650 ft) deep. It seems quite large when you stand on the edge, and the hike around it, though beautiful, is long and dry (■ Figure 25-19). Barringer Crater was the subject of controversy among geologists for years as to whether it was caused by a volcanic event or a large meteorite impact. Finally, in 1963, Eugene Shoemaker proved in his doctoral thesis that the crater must be the result of an impact because quartz crystals in and around it had been subjected to pressures much higher than can be produced by a volcano.

Further studies showed Barringer Crater was created approximately 50,000 years ago by a meteorite estimated to have been about 50 m (160 ft) in diameter, as large as a good-sized building, that hit at a speed of 11 km/s, releasing as much energy as a large thermonuclear bomb. An object of that size could be called either a large meteorite or a small asteroid. Debris at the site shows that the impactor was composed of iron.

The Tunguska Event

On a summer morning in 1908, reindeer herders and homesteaders in central Siberia were startled to see a brilliant blue-white fireball brighter than the sun streak across the sky. Still descending, it exploded with a blinding flash and an intense pulse of heat. One eyewitness account states:

The whole northern part of the sky appeared to be covered with fire....I felt great heat as if my shirt had caught fire...there was a...mighty crash....I was thrown

on the ground about [7 meters] from the porch....A hot wind, as from a cannon, blew past the huts from the north.

The blast was heard up to 1000 km away, and the resulting pulse of air pressure circled Earth twice. For a number of nights following the blast, European astronomers, who knew nothing of the explosion, observed a glowing reddish haze high in the atmosphere.

When members of a scientific expedition arrived at the site in 1927, they found that the blast had occurred above the Stony Tunguska River valley and had flattened trees in an irregular pattern extending out 30 km (20 mi) (■ Figure 25-20). The trees were knocked down pointing away from the center of the blast, and limbs and leaves had been stripped away. The trunks of trees at the very center of the area were still standing, although they had lost all their limbs. No crater has been found, so it seems that the explosion, estimated to have equaled 12 megatons (12 million tons) of TNT, occurred at least a few kilometers above the ground.

In the early 1980s, a detailed analysis of all the Tunguska evidence suggested that the impactor's speed and direction resembled the orbits of Apollo objects. In 1993, astronomers produced computer models of objects entering Earth's atmosphere at various speeds and concluded that the fragile icy head of a comet would have exploded much too high in the atmosphere. On the other hand, a dense iron-rich meteorite would be so strong that it would have survived to reach the ground and would have formed a large crater. Therefore, the most likely candidate for the Tunguska object seems to be a stony

asteroid about 30 m in diameter, perhaps one-tenth the mass of the Barringer impactor. The models indicate that an object of this size with moderate material strength would have fragmented and exploded at just about the right height to produce the observed blast. This conclusion is consistent with modern studies of the Tunguska area showing that thousands of tons of powdered material with a composition resembling carbonaceous chondrites are scattered in the soil.

Big Impacts

There are some very big craters in the solar system, for example on the moon (page 446), that show what can happen when a full-sized asteroid or comet collides with a planet. Also, Earthlings watched in awe in 1994 as fragments from the nucleus of Comet Shoemaker–Levy 9 (abbreviated SL-9) slammed into Jupiter and produced impacts equaling millions of megatons (that is, trillions of tons) of TNT (■ Figure 25-21). Note that the Shoemaker in Shoemaker–Levy refers to Carolyn and Eugene Shoemaker who co-discovered the comet with David Levy. Eugene Shoemaker is the person whose analysis showed that Barringer Crater in Arizona is an impact crater.

As you know, Jupiter does not have a solid surface, so SL-9 did not leave any permanent craters, but astronomers have found chains of craters on other solar system objects that seem to have been formed by fragmented comets (■ Figure 25-22). Evidently events like the SL-9 collision with Jupiter have occurred many times in the history of the solar system.

What would happen if an object the size of SL-9, or even larger, were to hit Earth? Sixty-five million years ago, at the end of the Cretaceous period, over 75 percent of the species on Earth, including the dinosaurs, became extinct. Scientists have found a thin layer of clay all over the world that was laid down at that time, and it is rich in the element iridium—common in meteorites but rare in Earth's crust. This suggests that an impact occurred that was large enough to have altered Earth's climate and caused the worldwide extinction.

■ Figure 25-20

The 1908 Tunguska event in Siberia destroyed an area the size of a large city. Here the area of destruction is superimposed on a map of Washington, D.C., and its surrounding beltway. In the central area, trees were burned; in the outer area, trees were blown down in a pattern away from the path of the impactor.

■ **Figure 25-21**

In 1992 Comet Shoemaker–Levy 9 passed within 1.3 planetary radii of Jupiter's center, well within its Roche limit, and tidal forces ripped the nucleus into more than 20 pieces. The fragmented pieces were as large as a few kilometers in diameter and spread into a long string of objects that looped away from Jupiter and then fell back to strike the planet, producing massive impacts over a period of six days in July 1994. Note that the impact flash in panel (c) is larger than Earth. (NASA)

Mathematical models combined with observations create a plausible scenario of a major impact on Earth. Of course, creatures living near the site of the impact would die in the initial shock, but then things would get bad elsewhere. An impact at sea would create tsunamis (tidal waves) many hundreds of meters high that would sweep around the world, devastating regions far inland from coasts. On land or sea, a major impact would eject huge amounts of pulverized rock high above the atmosphere. As this material fell back, Earth's atmosphere would be turned into a glowing oven of red-hot meteorites streaming through the air, and the heat would trigger massive forest fires around the world. Soot from such fires has been found in the layers of clay laid down at the end of the Cretaceous period. Once the firestorms cooled, the remaining dust in the atmosphere would block sunlight and produce deep darkness for a year or more, killing off most plant life. At the same time, if the impact site were at or near limestone deposits, large amounts of carbon dioxide could be released into the atmosphere and produce intense acid rain.

Geologists have located a crater at least 180 km (110 mi) in diameter centered near the village of **Chicxulub** (pronounced *cheek-shoe-lube*) in the northern Yucatán region of Mexico (■ Figure 25-23). Although the crater is now completely covered by sediments, mineral samples show that it contains shocked quartz typical of impact sites and that it is the right age. The impact of an object 10 to 14 km in diameter formed the crater about 65 million years ago, just when the dinosaurs and many other species died out. Most scientists now conclude that this is the scar of the impact that ended the Cretaceous period.

There are a number of major extinctions in the fossil record, and at least some of these were probably caused by large impacts. Large asteroid impacts on Earth happen very rarely from a human perspective, but they happen often relative to geological

Visual-wavelength image

a

b

c

■ **Figure 25-22**

(a) Closeup image of the Comet Shoemaker–Levy 9 fragment train on the way to colliding with Jupiter. (b) A 40-km-long crater chain on Earth's moon, and (c) a 140-km-long crater chain on Jupiter's moon Callisto, probably formed by the impact of fragmented comet nuclei similar to Shoemaker–Levy 9. (NASA)

and astronomical time scales. For example, astronomers estimate an Apollo object hits Earth once every 250,000 years on average. A typical Apollo with a diameter of 1 km would strike with the power of a 100,000-megaton bomb and dig a crater more than 10 km in diameter. The good news is that we are certain that no known Apollo object will hit Earth in the foreseeable future; the bad news is that there are about 1000 of them 1 km in size or larger.

Asteroid 2004 MN4 was initially predicted to have a 2.6 percent chance of striking Earth in 2029. That object is about 400 m ($\frac{1}{4}$ mile) in diameter, large enough to do significant damage over a wide area but not large enough to alter Earth's global climate. Fortunately, further observations and calculations revealed that the object will not hit Earth. There will be no impact by 2004 MN4 in 2029, but there are plenty more asteroids in Earth-crossing orbits to be discovered. For example, a rock designated 2009 DD45, estimated to have been 30 m (100 ft) in diameter, about the size of the Tunguska impactor, passed only 64,000 km (40,000 mi) from Earth in March 2009. That is only twice the distance of humanity's geosynchronous communications and weather satellites, a

United States

Mexico

Chicxulub crater

Yucatán

(b)

300 km

(a)

■ **Figure 25-23**

The giant impact scar buried in Earth's crust near the village of Chicxulub in the northern Yucatán peninsula was formed about 65 million years ago by the impact of a large asteroid or comet. This gravity map shows the extent of the crater hidden below limestone deposited long after the impact. (Virgil L. Sharpton, University of Alaska, Fairbanks) very near miss indeed, yet DD45 was first spotted only three days before its closest approach.

Some people have argued that the danger from asteroid and comet impacts is so great that governments should develop massive nuclear-tipped missiles, ready to blast a meteoroid to pieces long before it can reach Earth. Other experts respond that lots of small fragments slamming into Earth may be even worse than one big impact. Astronomers point out that the biggest objects are so rare they can be ignored. The real danger lies in the more common smaller, yet still substantial, meteoroids, which are difficult to detect with current telescopes. The future of our civilization on Earth may depend on our doing an increasingly careful job of tracking both large and small objects that cross our path with surprising frequency.

What Are We? Sitting Ducks

Human civilization is spread out over Earth's surface and exposed to anything that falls out of the sky. Meteorites, asteroids, and comets bombard Earth, producing impacts that vary from dust settling gently on rooftops to disasters capable of destroying all life. In this case, the scientific evidence is conclusive and highly unwelcome.

Statistically we are quite safe. The chance that a major impact will occur during your lifetime is so small it is hard to estimate. But the consequences of such an impact are so severe that humanity should be preparing. One way to prepare is to find those objects that could hit us, map their orbits, and identify any that are dangerous.

What we do next isn't clear. Blowing up a dangerous asteroid in space might make a good movie, but converting one big projectile into a thousand small ones might not be very smart. Changing an asteroid's orbit could be difficult without a few decades' advance warning. Unlikely or not, large impacts demand consideration and preparation.

Throughout the universe there may be two kinds of inhabited worlds. On one type of world, intelligent creatures have developed ways to prevent asteroid and comet impacts from altering their climates and destroying their civilizations. But on other worlds, including Earth, intelligent races have not yet found ways to protect themselves. Some of those civilizations survive. Some don't.

Study and Review

Summary

► Review from Chapter 19: The term *meteoroid* refers to small solid particles orbiting in the solar system. The term *meteor* refers to a visible streak of light from a meteoroid heated and glowing as it enters Earth's atmosphere. The term *meteorite* refers to space material that has reached Earth's surface.

► Meteorites that are seen to hit Earth are called **falls (p. 552)**. **Finds (p. 552)** are meteorites discovered on the ground that fell unobserved, perhaps thousands of years ago.

► **Iron meteorites (p. 552)** are mostly iron and nickel; when sliced open, polished, and etched, they show **Widmanstätten patterns (p. 552)**. These reveal that the metal cooled from a molten state very slowly.

► **Stony meteorites (p. 552)** include **chondrites (p. 553)**, which contain small, glassy particles called **chondrules (p. 553)**, solidified droplets of once-molten material that formed in the solar nebula by an as-yet unknown mechanism.

► **Stony-iron meteorites (p. 552)** are quite rare and, as the name implies, consist of a mixture of stony and metallic material.

► **Selection effects (p. 552, 555)** cause iron meteorites to be the most common finds, even though stony meteorites are the most common falls.

► Stony meteorites that are rich in volatiles and carbon are called **carbonaceous chondrites (p. 552)**. They are among the least modified meteorites. Some carbonaceous chondrites contain **CAIs (p. 555)**, calcium–aluminum-rich inclusions, which are understood to be the very first solid particles to condense in the cooling solar nebula.

► An **achondrite (p. 553)** is a stony meteorite that contains no chondrules and no volatiles. Achondrites appear to have been melted after they formed and, in some cases, resemble solidified lavas.

► Evidence from the orbits of meteorites seen to fall, and from the composition of the meteorites, suggests that meteorites are fragments of asteroids. Other evidence, including orbital paths indicated by the **radiant (p. 556)** points of **meteor showers (p. 556)**, indicates in contrast that the vast majority of meteors, including both meteors in meteor showers and isolated **sporadic meteors (p. 557)**, appear to be low-density, fragile bits of debris from comets.

► Many meteorites appear to have formed as part of larger bodies that melted, differentiated, and cooled very slowly. Later these bodies were broken up, and fragments from the core became iron meteorites, fragments from the outer layers became stony meteorites, and fragments from intermediate layers became stony-irons.

► Asteroids are irregular in shape and heavily cratered from collisions. Their surfaces are covered by gray, pulverized rock, and some asteroids have such low densities they must be fragmented rubble piles.

- Most asteroids lie in a belt between Mars and Jupiter. **Kirkwood gaps (p. 562)** in asteroid belt orbits are caused by orbital resonances with Jupiter.

- Two groups of asteroids called the **Trojan asteroids (p. 563)** are caught in the Lagrangian points along Jupiter's orbit 60° ahead and 60° behind the planet. **Apollo-Amor objects (p. 562)** have orbits that cross into the inner solar system. If they pass near Earth, they are called **Near-Earth Objects (NEOs) (p. 562)**. **Centaurs (p. 563)** are asteroids that orbit among the planets of the outer solar system.

- The asteroids formed as rocky planetesimals between Mars and Jupiter, but Jupiter prevented them from accumulating into a planet. Collisions have fragmented all but the largest of the asteroids. Most of the material inferred to have been originally in the asteroid belt has been gravitationally perturbed and swept up by the planets or tossed out of the solar system.

- **Hirayama families (p. 564)** of asteroids follow very similar orbits and have similar spectra. They appear to be fragments produced in past collisions of asteroids.

- **C-type (p. 564)** asteroids are more common in the outer asteroid belt where the solar nebula was cooler. They are darker and may be carbonaceous. **S-type (p. 564)** asteroids are the most common and may be the source of the more common kind of meteorites, the chondrites. S-type asteroids are more frequently found in the inner belt. **M-type (p. 564)** asteroids appear to have nickel-iron compositions and may be the cores of differentiated asteroids shattered by collisions.

- A visible comet is produced by a lump of ices and rock usually between 1 and 100 km in diameter, referred to as the comet nucleus. In long, elliptical orbits, the icy nucleus stays frozen until it nears the sun. Then, some of the ices vaporize and release dust and gas that is blown away to form a prominent head and tail.

- A **type I (gas) (p. 568)** comet tail is ionized gas carried away by the solar wind. A **type II (dust) (p. 568)** tail is solid debris released from the nucleus and blown outward by the pressure of sunlight. A comet's tail always points away from the sun, no matter in what direction the comet is moving.

- The **coma (p. 568)**, or head, of a comet can be up to a million kilometers in diameter.

- Spacecraft flying past comets have revealed that they have very dark, rocky crusts. Jets of vapor and dust issue from active regions on the sunlit side.

- The low density of comet nuclei shows that they are irregular mixtures of ices and silicates, probably containing large voids. At least one comet nucleus has surface features showing the material has a surprising amount of strength.

- Comets are believed to have formed as icy planetesimals in the outer solar system, and some were ejected to form the **Oort cloud (p. 571)**. Comets perturbed inward from the Oort cloud become long-period comets.

- Other icy bodies formed in the outer solar system and now make up the Kuiper belt beyond Neptune. Objects from the Kuiper belt that are perturbed into the inner solar system can become short-period comets.

- A major impact on Earth can trigger extinctions. These are due to global fires caused by heated material falling back into the atmosphere, tsunamis inundating coastal regions around the world, acid rain resulting from large amounts of carbon dioxide released into the atmosphere, and climate change caused by the atmosphere filling with dust, plunging the entire Earth into darkness for years.

- An impact at **Chicxulub (p. 576)** in Mexico's Yucatán region 65 million years ago appears to have triggered the extinction of 75 percent of the species then on Earth, including the dinosaurs.

Review Questions

1. What do Widmanstätten patterns indicate about the history of iron meteorites?
2. What do chondrules tell you about the history of chondrites?
3. Why are there no chondrules in achondritic meteorites?
4. Why do astronomers refer to carbonaceous chondrites as unmodified or "primitive" material?
5. How do observations of meteor showers reveal one of the sources of meteoroids?
6. How can most meteors be cometary if all meteorites are asteroidal?
7. Why do astronomers think the asteroids were never part of a full-sized planet?
8. What evidence indicates that the asteroids are mostly fragments of larger bodies?
9. What evidence indicates that some asteroids have differentiated?
10. What evidence indicates that some asteroids have had geologically active surfaces?
11. How is the composition of meteorites related to the formation and evolution of asteroids?
12. What is the difference between a type I comet tail and a type II tail?
13. What evidence indicates that cometary nuclei are rich in ices?
14. Why do short-period comets tend to have orbits near the plane of the solar system?
15. What are the hypotheses for how the bodies in the Kuiper belt and the Oort cloud formed?
16. **How Do We Know?** How would studying the chemical composition of only the largest, brightest, and most easily observed asteroids possibly yield misleading information about asteroids in general?

Discussion Questions

1. It has been suggested that humans may someday mine the asteroids for materials to build and supply space colonies. What kinds of materials could Earthlings get from asteroids? (Hint: What are S-, M-, and C-type asteroids made of, respectively?)
2. If cometary nuclei were heated during the formation of the solar system by internal radioactive decay rather than by solar radiation, how would comets differ from what is observed?
3. Do you think the government should spend money to find near-Earth asteroids? How serious is the risk?

Problems

1. Large meteorites are hardly slowed by Earth's atmosphere. Assuming the atmosphere is 100 km thick and that a large meteorite falls perpendicular to the surface, how long does it take to reach the ground? (Hint: Refer to the text for typical speeds of meteoroids.)
2. If a single asteroid 1 km in diameter were to be fragmented into meteoroids 1 m in diameter, how many would it yield? (Hint: The volume of a sphere $= \frac{4}{3}\pi r^3$.)
3. If a trillion (10^{12}) asteroids, each 1 km in diameter, were assembled into one body, how large would it be? (Hint: The volume of a sphere $= \frac{4}{3}\pi r^3$.) Compare that to the size of Earth.
4. The asteroid Vesta has a mass of 2×10^{20} kg and a radius of about 250 km. What is its escape velocity? Could you jump off the asteroid? (Hint: See Chapter 5.)
5. What is the maximum angular diameter of the largest asteroid, Ceres, as seen from Earth? Could Earth-based telescopes detect surface features? Could the Hubble Space Telescope? (Hints: Use the small-angle formula, Chapter 3. The angular resolution of Earth-based

telescopes is about 1 arc second and of Hubble about 0.1 arc second. Ceres's average distance from the sun is 2.8 AU.)

6. What is the orbital period of Ceres? *(Hints:* Use Kepler's third law and refer to the previous problem for Ceres's average distance from the sun.)

7. At what distances from the sun would you expect to find Kirkwood gaps where the orbital period of asteroids is one-half of, and one-third of, the orbital period of Jupiter? Compare your results with Figure 25-9. *(Hint:* Use Kepler's third law.)

8. If the velocity of the solar wind is about 400 km/s and the visible tail of a comet is 1×10^8 km long, how long does it take a solar wind atom to travel from the nucleus to the end of the visible tail?

9. If you saw Comet Halley when it was 0.7 AU from Earth and it had a visible tail 5° long, how long was the tail in kilometers? Suppose that the tail was not perpendicular to your line of sight. Is your first answer too large or too small? *(Hint:* Use the small-angle formula, Chapter 3.)

10. What is the orbital period of a comet nucleus in the Oort cloud? What is its orbital velocity? *(Hints:* Use Kepler's third law. The circumference of a circular orbit $= 2\pi r$. Refer to the text for typical Oort cloud object distances from the sun.)

11. The mass of an average comet's nucleus is about 10^{12} kg. If the Oort cloud contains 2×10^{11} comet nuclei, what is the mass of the cloud in Earth masses? Compare that with Jupiter's mass. *(Hint:* See Appendix Table A-10.)

Learning to Look

1. What do you see in the image to the right that tells you the size of planetesimals when the solar system was forming?

Russell Kempton, New England Meteoritical Services

2. Discuss the surface of the asteroid Mathilde, pictured to the right. What do you see that tells you something about the history of the asteroids?

Visual

NASA

3. What do you see in this image of the nucleus of Comet Borrelly that tells you how comets produce their comae and tails?

Visual

NASA

26 | Astrobiology: Life on Other Worlds

Guidepost

This chapter is either unnecessary or vital. If you believe that astronomy is the study of the physical universe above the clouds, then you are done; the previous 25 chapters completed your study of astronomy. But, if you believe that astronomy is the study not only of the physical universe but also of your role as a living being in the evolution of the universe, then everything you have learned so far from this book has been preparation for this final chapter.

As you read this chapter, you will ask four important, related questions:

- **What is life?**
- **How did life originate on Earth?**
- **Could life begin on other worlds?**
- **Can humans on Earth communicate with civilizations on other worlds?**

You won't get more than the beginnings of answers to those questions here, but often in science asking a question is more important than getting an immediate answer.

You have explored the universe from the phases of the moon to the big bang, from the origin of Earth to the death of the sun. Astronomy is meaningful, not just because it is about the universe but because it is also about you. Now that you know astronomy, you see yourself and your world in a different way. Astronomy has changed you.

Single amino acids can be assembled into long proteinlike molecules. When such material cools in water, it often forms microspheres, tiny globules with double-layered boundaries similar to cell membranes. Microspheres may have been an intermediate stage in the evolution of life between complex but nonliving molecules and living cells holding molecules reproducing genetic information.
(Sidney Fox and Randall Grubbs)

Did I solicit thee from darkness to promote me?

— ADAM, TO GOD, IN JOHN MILTON'S *PARADISE LOST*

As a living thing, you have been promoted from darkness. The atoms of carbon, oxygen, and other heavy elements that are necessary components of your body did not exist at the beginning of the universe but were built up by successive generations of stars.

The elements from which you are made are common everywhere in the observable universe, so it is possible that life began on other worlds and evolved to intelligence. If so, perhaps those other civilizations will be detected from Earth. Future astronomers may discover distant alien species completely different from any life on Earth.

Your goal in this chapter is to try to understand truly intriguing puzzles—the origin and evolution of life on Earth and what that tells you about whether there is life on other worlds (**How Do We Know? 26-1**). This new hybrid field of study is called **astrobiology.**

26-1) The Nature of Life

WHAT IS LIFE? Philosophers have struggled with that question for thousands of years, and it is not possible to answer it completely in one chapter or even one book. An attempt at a general definition of what living things do, distinguishing them from nonliving things, might be: Life is a *process* by which an organism extracts energy from the surroundings, maintains itself, and modifies the surroundings to foster its own survival and reproduction.

One very important observation is that all living things on Earth, no matter how apparently different, share certain characteristics in how they perform the process of life.

The Physical Basis of Life

The physical basis of life on Earth is the element carbon (■ Figure 26-1). Because of the way carbon atoms bond to each other and to other atoms, they can join into long, complex, stable chains that are capable, among many other feats, of storing and transmitting information. A large amount of information is necessary to control the activities and maintain the forms of living things.

It is possible that life on other worlds could use silicon instead of carbon. Silicon is right below carbon in the periodic table (Appendix Table A-16), which means that it shares many of carbon's chemical properties. But life based on silicon rather than carbon seems unlikely because silicon chains are harder to assemble and disassemble than their carbon counterparts and can't be as lengthy. Science fiction has proposed even stranger life forms based on, for example, electromagnetic fields and ionized gas, and none of these possibilities can be ruled out. Those hypothetical life forms make for fascinating speculation, but for now they can't be studied systematically in the way that life on Earth can.

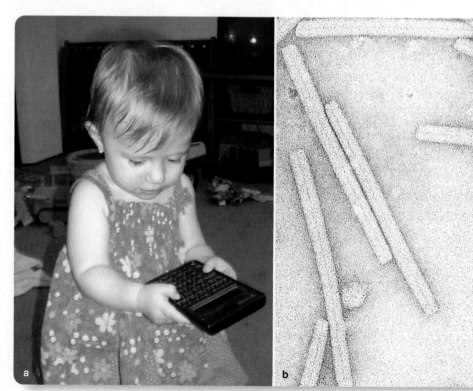

■ Figure 26-1

All living things on Earth are based on carbon chemistry. Even the long molecules that carry genetic information, DNA and RNA, have a framework defined by chains of carbon atoms. (a) Ana, a complex mammal, contains about 60 AU of DNA. (Jamie Backman) (b) Each rod-like tobacco mosaic virus contains a single spiral strand of RNA about 0.01 mm long as its genetic material. (L. D. Simon)

The Nature of Scientific Explanation

Must science and religion be in conflict?
Science is a way of understanding the world around you, and at the heart of that understanding are explanations that science gives for natural phenomena. Whether you call these explanations stories, histories, hypotheses, or theories, they are attempts to describe how nature works based on evidence and intellectual honesty. While you may take these explanations as factual truth, you can understand that they are not the only explanations that describe the universe.

A separate class of explanations involves religion. For example, the Old Testament description of creation does not fit well with scientific observations, but it is a way of understanding the universe nonetheless. Religious explanations are based partly on faith rather than on strict rules of logic and evidence, and it is wrong to demand that they follow the same rules as scientific explanations. In the same way, it is wrong to demand that scientific explanations take into account religious beliefs. The so-called conflict between science and religion arises when people fail to recognize that science and religion are different ways of knowing about the universe.

Scientific explanations are very compelling because science has been very successful at producing technological innovations that have changed the world you live in. From new vaccines, to digital music players, to telescopes that can observe the most distant galaxies, the products of the scientific process are all around you. Scientific explanations have provided tremendous insights into the workings of nature. Many people are attracted to the suggestion, made by evolutionary biologist Stephen Jay Gould and others, that religious explanations and scientific explanations should be considered as "separate magisteria." In other words, religion and science are devoted to different realms of the mystery of existence.

Science and religion offer differing ways of explaining the universe, but the two ways follow separate rules and cannot be judged by each other's standards. The trial of Galileo can be understood as a conflict between these two ways of knowing.

Galileo's telescope gave him a new way to know about the universe.

This chapter is concerned with the origin and evolution of life as it is on Earth, based on carbon, not because of lack of imagination but because it is the only form of life about which we know anything.

Even carbon-based life has its mysteries. What makes a lump of carbon-based molecules a living thing? An important part of the answer lies in the transmission of information from one molecule to another.

Information Storage and Duplication

Most actions performed by living cells are carried out by molecules that are built within the cells. Cells must store recipes for making all those molecules, as well as how and when to use them, and then somehow pass the recipes on to their offspring.

Study **DNA: The Code of Life** on pages 584–585 and notice four important points and seven new terms:

1 The chemical recipes of life are stored in each cell as information on *DNA (deoxyribonucleic acid)* molecules that resemble a ladder with rungs that are composed of chemical bases. The recipe information is expressed by the sequence of the rungs, providing instructions to guide specific chemical reactions within the cell.

2 The instructions stored in DNA are genetic information passed along to offspring. DNA instructions normally are expressed by being copied into a messenger molecule called *RNA (ribonucleic acid)*. The RNA molecule travels to a location in the cell where its message causes a sequence of molecular units called *amino acids* to be connected into large molecules called *proteins*. Proteins serve as the cell's basic structural molecule or as *enzymes* that control chemical reactions.

3 The DNA molecule reproduces itself when a cell divides so that each new cell contains a copy of the original information. A sequence of DNA that composes one instruction is called a *gene*. Genes are organized into long coiled chains called *chromosomes*. The genes linked on one chromosome are normally passed on to offspring together.

To produce viable offspring, a cell must be able to make copies of its DNA. Surprisingly, it is important for the continued existence of all life that the copying process includes mistakes.

DNA: The Code of Life

1 The key to understanding life is information — the information that guides all of the processes in an organism. In most living things on Earth, that information is stored on a long spiral molecule called **DNA (deoxyribonucleic acid).**

1a The DNA molecule looks like a spiral ladder with rails made of phosphates and sugars. The rungs of the ladder are made of four chemical bases arranged in pairs. The bases always pair the same way. That is, base A always pairs with base T, and base G always pairs with base C.

1b Information is coded on the DNA molecule by the order in which the base pairs occur. To read that code, molecular biologists have to "sequence the DNA." That is, they must determine the order in which the base pairs occur along the DNA ladder.

The Four Bases

- **A** Adenine
- **C** Cytosine
- **G** Guanine
- **T** Thymine

2 DNA automatically combines raw materials to form important chemical compounds. The building blocks of these compounds are relatively simple **amino acids.** Segments of DNA act as templates that guide the amino acids to join together in the correct order to build specific **proteins,** chemical compounds important to the structure and function of organisms. Some proteins called **enzymes** regulate metabolic processes. In this way, DNA recipes regulate the production of the compounds of life.

The traits you inherit from your parents, the chemical processes that animate you, and the structure of your body are all encoded in your DNA. When people say "you have your mother's eyes," they are talking about DNA codes.

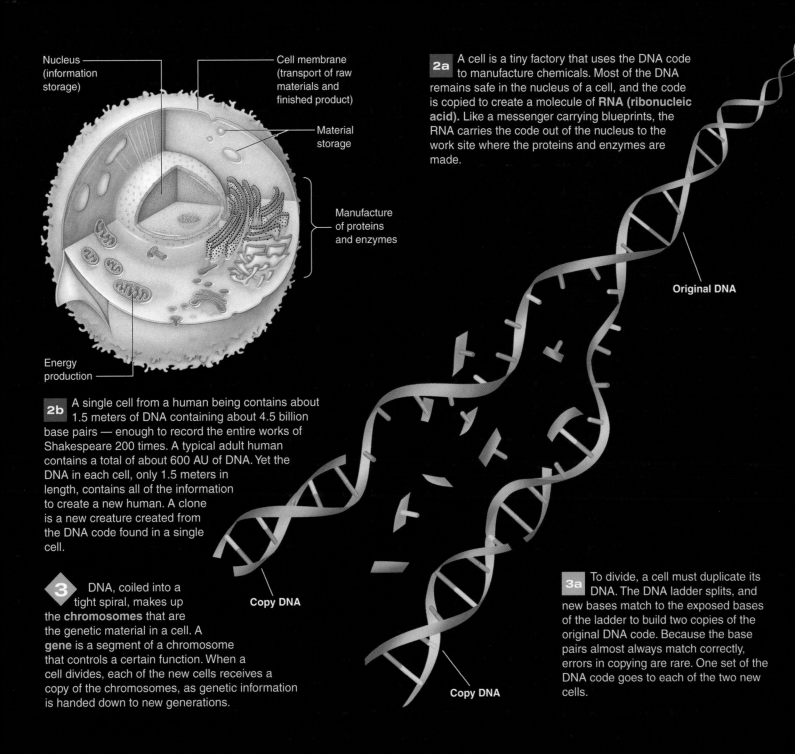

Nucleus
(information
storage)

Cell membrane
(transport of raw
materials and
finished product)

Material
storage

Manufacture
of proteins
and enzymes

Energy
production

2a A cell is a tiny factory that uses the DNA code to manufacture chemicals. Most of the DNA remains safe in the nucleus of a cell, and the code is copied to create a molecule of **RNA (ribonucleic acid).** Like a messenger carrying blueprints, the RNA carries the code out of the nucleus to the work site where the proteins and enzymes are made.

Original DNA

2b A single cell from a human being contains about 1.5 meters of DNA containing about 4.5 billion base pairs — enough to record the entire works of Shakespeare 200 times. A typical adult human contains a total of about 600 AU of DNA. Yet the DNA in each cell, only 1.5 meters in length, contains all of the information to create a new human. A clone is a new creature created from the DNA code found in a single cell.

Copy DNA

3 DNA, coiled into a tight spiral, makes up the **chromosomes** that are the genetic material in a cell. A **gene** is a segment of a chromosome that controls a certain function. When a cell divides, each of the new cells receives a copy of the chromosomes, as genetic information is handed down to new generations.

3a To divide, a cell must duplicate its DNA. The DNA ladder splits, and new bases match to the exposed bases of the ladder to build two copies of the original DNA code. Because the base pairs almost always match correctly, errors in copying are rare. One set of the DNA code goes to each of the two new cells.

Copy DNA

Cell Reproduction by Division

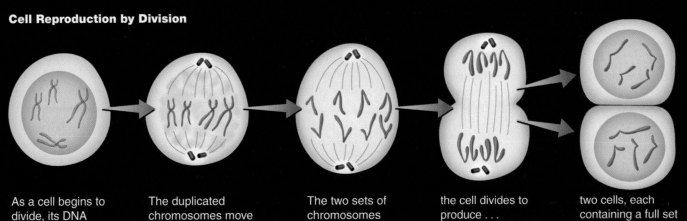

As a cell begins to divide, its DNA duplicates itself.

The duplicated chromosomes move to the middle.

The two sets of chromosomes separate, and . . .

the cell divides to produce . . .

two cells, each containing a full set of the DNA code.

Modifying the Information

Earth's environment changes continuously. To survive, species must change as their food supply, climate, or home terrain changes. If the information stored in DNA could not change, then life would go extinct quickly. The process by which life adjusts itself to changing environments is called **biological evolution.**

When an organism reproduces, its offspring receive a copy of its DNA. Sometimes external effects such as natural radiation alter the DNA during the parent organism's lifetime, and sometimes mistakes are made in the copying process, so that occasionally the copy is slightly different from the original. Offspring born with random alterations to their DNA are called **mutants.** Most mutations make no difference, but some mutations are fatal, killing the afflicted organisms before they can reproduce. In rare but vitally important cases, a mutation can actually help an organism survive.

These changes produce variation among the members of a species. All of the squirrels in the park may look the same, but they carry a range of genetic variation. Some may have slightly longer tails or faster-growing claws. These variations make almost no difference until the environment changes. For example, if the environment becomes colder, a squirrel with a heavier coat of fur will, on average, survive longer and produce more offspring than its normal contemporaries. Likewise, the offspring that inherit this beneficial variation will also live longer and have more off-spring of their own. In contrast, squirrels containing DNA recipes for thin fur coats will gradually decrease in number. These differing rates of survival and reproduction are examples of **natural selection.** Over time, the beneficial variation increases in frequency, and a species can evolve until the entire population shares the trait. In this way, natural selection adapts species to their changing environments by selecting, from the huge array of random variations, those that would most benefit the survival of the species.

It is a **Common Misconception** that evolution is random, but that is not true. The underlying mechanisms creating variation within each species may be random, but natural selection is not random because progressive changes in a species are directed by changes in the environment.

SCIENTIFIC ARGUMENT

Why is it important that errors occur in copying DNA?
Sometimes the most valuable scientific arguments are those that challenge what seems like common sense. It appears obvious that mistakes shouldn't be made in copying DNA, but in fact variation is necessary for long-term survival of a species. For example, the DNA in a starfish contains all the information the starfish needs to grow, develop, survive, and reproduce. The information must be passed on to the starfish's offspring for them to survive. That

information must change, however, if the environment changes. A change in the ocean's temperature may kill the specific shellfish that the starfish eat. If none of the starfish are able to digest another kind of food—if all the starfish have exactly the same DNA—they all will die. But if a few starfish are born with the ability to make enzymes that can digest a different kind of shellfish, the species may be able to carry on.

Variations in DNA are caused both by external factors such as natural radiation and by occasional mistakes in the copying process. The survival of life depends on this delicate balance between mostly reliable reproduction and the introduction of small variations in DNA. Now build a new argument. **Why does the DNA copying process need to be mostly reliable?**

26-2 Life in the Universe

LIFE AS WE KNOW IT consists of just the single example of life on Earth. It is OK to think of all life on Earth as being just a single type of life, because, as you learned in the previous section, all living things on Earth have the same physical basis: the same chemistry and the same genetic code alphabet. How life began on Earth and then developed and evolved into its present variety is the only solid information you have to work with, when considering what might be possible on other worlds.

Everything currently known about life on Earth indicates that the same natural processes should lead to the origin of life on some fraction of other planets with liquid water. If there is life on other worlds, does it use DNA and RNA to carry the information for life processes, or different molecules playing the same role, or some radically different scheme? There is no way to know unless another example of life is found on another world. If and when that day comes, even if the non-Earthly life is a simple one-celled organism, the discovery will be one of the most important in the history of science. It will complete the journey of human understanding, begun in the Copernican revolution, of progressive realizations that Earth is not unique.

Origin of Life on Earth

It is obvious that the 4.5 billion chemical bases that make up human DNA did not come together in the right order just by chance. The key to understanding the origin of life lies in picturing the processes of evolution running "backward." The complex interplay of environmental factors with the DNA of generation after generation of organisms drove some life forms to become more sophisticated over time, until they became the unique and specialized creatures alive today. Imagining this process in reverse leads to the idea that life on Earth began with very simple forms.

Biologists hypothesize that the first living things would have been carbon-chain molecules able to copy themselves. Of course, this is a scientific hypothesis for which you can seek evidence. What evidence exists regarding the origin of life on Earth?

The oldest fossils are the remains of sea creatures, and this indicates that life began in the sea. Identifying the oldest fossils is not easy, however. Ancient rocks from western Australia that are at least 3.4 billion years old contain features that biologists identify as **stromatolites,** fossilized remains of colonies of single-celled organisms (■ Figure 26-2). Fossils this old are difficult to recognize because the earliest living things did not contain easily preserved hard parts like bones or shells and because the individual organisms were microscopic. Thus the evidence, though scarce, indicates that simple organisms lived in Earth's oceans less than 1.2 billion years after Earth formed. Stromatolite colonies of microorganisms are more complex than individual cells, so

you can imagine there probably were earlier, simpler organisms. Where did those first simplest organisms come from?

An important experiment performed by Stanley Miller and Harold Urey in 1952 sought to re-create the conditions in which life on Earth began. The **Miller experiment** consisted of a sterile, sealed glass container holding water, hydrogen, ammonia, and methane. An electric arc inside the apparatus made sparks to simulate the effects of lightning in Earth's early atmosphere (■ Figure 26-3).

Miller and Urey let the experiment run for a week and then analyzed the material inside. They found that the interaction between the electric arc and the simulated atmosphere had produced many organic molecules from the raw material of the experiment, including such important building blocks of life as amino acids. (Recall that an organic molecule is simply a molecule with a carbon-chain structure and need not be derived from a living thing: "Organic" does not necessarily imply "biological.")

When the experiment was run again using different energy sources such as hot silica to represent molten lava spilling into the ocean, similar molecules were produced. Even a source of ultraviolet radiation representing the small amount of UV in sunlight was sufficient to produce complex organic molecules.

■ **Figure 26-2**

(a) A fossil stromatolite from western Australia that is more than 3 billion years old, constituting some of the oldest evidence of life on Earth. Stromatolites are formed, layer upon layer, by mats of bacteria living in shallow water where they are covered repeatedly by sediments. (Chip Clark, National Museum of Natural History) (b) Artist's conception of a scene on the young Earth, 3 billion years ago, with stromatolite bacterial mats growing near the shores of an ocean. (Mural by Peter Sawyer)

■ Figure 26-3

(a) The Miller experiment circulated gases through water in the presence of an electric arc. This simulation of primitive conditions on Earth produced many complex organic molecules, including amino acids, the building blocks of proteins. (b) Stanley Miller with a Miller apparatus. (Stanley Miller)

Scientists are professionally skeptical about scientific findings (see "How Do We Know?" 19-2), and they have reevaluated the Miller–Urey experiment in light of new information. According to updated models of the formation of the solar system and Earth (see Chapters 19 and 20), Earth's early atmosphere probably consisted mostly of carbon dioxide, nitrogen, and water vapor instead of the mix of hydrogen, ammonia, methane, and water vapor assumed by Miller and Urey. When gases corresponding to the newer understanding of the early Earth atmosphere are processed in a Miller apparatus, lesser, but still significant, amounts of organic molecules are produced.

The Miller experiment is important because it shows that complex organic molecules form naturally in a wide variety of circumstances. Lightning, sunlight, and hot lava are just some of the energy sources that can naturally rearrange common simple molecules into the complex molecules that make life possible. If you could travel back in time, you would expect to find Earth's early oceans filled with a rich mixture of organic compounds called the **primordial soup.**

Many of these organic compounds would have been able to link up to form larger molecules. Amino acids, for example, can link together to form proteins by joining ends and releasing a water molecule (■ Figure 26-4). That reaction, however, does not

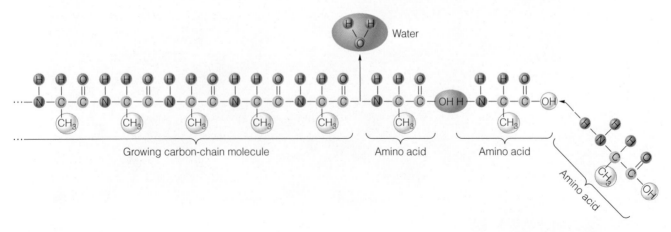

■ Figure 26-4

Amino acids can link together via the release of a water molecule to form long carbon-chain molecules. The amino acid in this hypothetical example is alanine, one of the simplest.

proceed easily in a water solution. Scientists hypothesize that this step may have been more likely to happen on shorelines or in sun-warmed tidal pools where organic molecules from the primordial soup could have been concentrated by water evaporation. The production of large organic molecules may have been aided in such semidry environments by clay crystals acting as templates to hold the organic subunits close together.

These complex organic molecules were still not living things. Even though some proteins may have contained hundreds of amino acids, they did not reproduce but rather linked and broke apart at random. Because some molecules are more stable than others, and some bond together more easily than others, scientists hypothesize that a process of **chemical evolution** eventually concentrated the various smaller molecules into the most stable larger forms. Eventually, according to the hypothesis, somewhere in the oceans, after sufficient time, a molecule formed that could copy itself. At that point, the natural selection and chemical evolution of molecules became the biological evolution of living things.

An alternate theory for the origin of life holds that reproducing molecules may have arrived here from space. Astronomers have found a wide variety of organic molecules in the interstellar medium, and similar compounds have been found inside meteorites (■ Figure 26-5). The Miller experiment showed how easy it is for complex organic molecules to form naturally from simpler compounds, so it is not surprising to find them in space. Although speculation is fun, the hypothesis that life arrived on Earth from space is presently more difficult to test than the hypothesis that Earth's life originated on Earth.

Whether the first reproducing molecules formed here on Earth or in space, the important thing is that they could have formed by natural processes. Scientists know enough about those processes to feel confident about them, even though some of the steps remain unknown.

The details of the origin of the first cells are unknown. The structure of cells may have arisen automatically because of the way molecules interact during chemical evolution. If a dry mixture of amino acids is heated, the acids form long, proteinlike molecules that, when poured into water, collect to form microscopic spheres that behave in ways similar to cells (pictured in the image on the opening page to this chapter). They have a thin membrane surface, they absorb material from their surroundings, they grow in size, and they divide and bud just as cells do. However, they contain no large molecule that copies itself, so they are not alive. The first reproducing molecule to be surrounded by a protective membrane, resulting in the first cell, would have gained an important survival advantage over other reproducing molecules.

Geologic Time and the Evolution of Life

Biologists infer that the first cells must have been simple single-celled organisms similar to modern bacteria. As you learned earlier, these kinds of cells are preserved in stromatolites (Figure 26-2), mineral formations produced by layers of bacteria and shallow ocean sediments. Stromatolite fossils are found in rocks with radioactive ages of 3.4 billion years, and living stromatolites still form in some places today.

Stromatolites and other photosynthetic organisms would have begun adding oxygen, a product of photosynthesis, to Earth's early atmosphere. An oxygen abundance of only 0.1 percent would have created an ozone screen, protecting organisms from the sun's ultraviolet radiation and later allowing life to colonize the land.

Over the course of eons, the natural processes of evolution gave rise to stunningly complex **multicellular** life forms with their own widely differing ways of life. It is a **Common Misconception** to imagine that life is too complex to have evolved from such simple beginnings. It is possible because small variations can accumulate, although that accumulation requires great amounts of time.

There is little evidence of anything more than simple organisms on Earth until about 540 million years ago, almost 3 billion years after the earliest signs of life, at which time fossils indicate life suddenly developing into a wide variety of complex forms such as the trilobites (■ Figure 26-6). This sudden increase in complexity is known as the **Cambrian explosion** and marks the beginning of the Cambrian period.

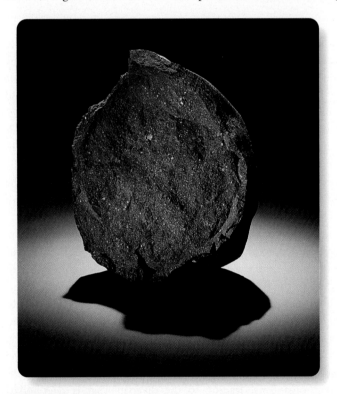

■ **Figure 26-5**

A piece of the Murchison meteorite, a carbonaceous chondrite (see Chapter 25) that fell near Murchison, Australia, in 1969. Analysis of the interior of the meteorite revealed the presence of amino acids. Whether the first chemical building blocks of life on Earth originated in space is a matter of debate, but the amino acids found in meteorites illustrate how commonly amino acids and other complex organic molecules occur in the universe, even in the absence of living things. (Chip Clark, National Museum of Natural History)

■ **Figure 26-6**

(a) Trilobites made their first appearance in the Cambrian oceans. The smallest were almost microscopic, and the largest were bigger than dinner plates. This example, about the size of your hand, lived 400 million years ago in an ocean floor that is now a limestone deposit in Pennsylvania. (Franklin & Marshall College/ Grundy Observatory/Michael Seeds) (b) In this artist's conception of a Cambrian sea bottom, Anomalocaris (near at right center and looming at upper right), about human-hand-sized, had specialized organs including eyes, coordinated fins, gripping mandibles, and a powerful, toothed maw. Notice Opabinia at center right with its long snout. (Smithsonian and D. W. Miller)

If you represented the entire history of Earth on a scale diagram, the Cambrian explosion would be near the top of the column, as shown at the left of ■ Figure 26-7. The emergence of most animals familiar to you today, including fishes, amphibians, reptiles, birds, and mammals, would be crammed into the topmost part of the chart, above the Cambrian explosion.

If you magnify that portion of the diagram, as shown on the right side of Figure 26-7, you can get a better idea of when these events occurred in the history of life. Humanoid creatures have walked on Earth for about 4 million years. This is a long time by the standard of a human lifetime, but it makes only a narrow red line at the top of the diagram. All of recorded history would be a microscopically thin line at the very top of the column.

To understand just how thin that line is, imagine that the entire 4.6-billion-year history of the Earth has been compressed onto a yearlong video and that you began watching this video on January 1. You would not see any signs of life until March or early April, and the slow evolution of the first simple forms would take the next six or seven months. Suddenly, in mid-November, you would see the trilobites and other complex organisms of the Cambrian explosion.

You would see no life of any kind on land until November 28, but once life appeared it would diversify quickly, and by December 12 you would see dinosaurs walking the continents. By the day after Christmas they would be gone, and mammals and birds would be on the rise.

If you watched closely, you might see the first humanoid forms by late afternoon on New Year's Eve, and by late evening you could see humans making the first stone tools. The Stone Age would last until 11:59 PM, after which the first towns, and then cities, would appear. Suddenly things would begin to happen at lightning speed. Babylon would flourish, the pyramids would rise, and Troy would fall. The Christian era would begin 14 seconds before the New Year. Rome would fall, then the Middle Ages and the Renaissance would flicker past. The American and French revolutions would occur one-and-a-half seconds before the end of the video.

By imagining the history of Earth as a yearlong video, you have gained some perspective on the rise of life. Tremendous amounts of time were needed for the first simple living things to evolve in the oceans. As life became more complex, new forms arose more and more quickly as the hardest problems—how to reproduce, how to take energy efficiently from the environment, how to move around—were "solved" by the process of biological evolution. The easier problems, like what to eat, where to live, and how to raise young, were managed in different ways by different organisms, leading to the diversity that is seen today. Intelligence—that which appears to set humans apart from other animals—may be a unique solution to an evolutionary problem posed to humanity's ancient ancestors. A smart animal is better able to escape predators, outwit its prey, and feed and shelter itself and its offspring, so under certain conditions evolution is likely to naturally select for intelligence.

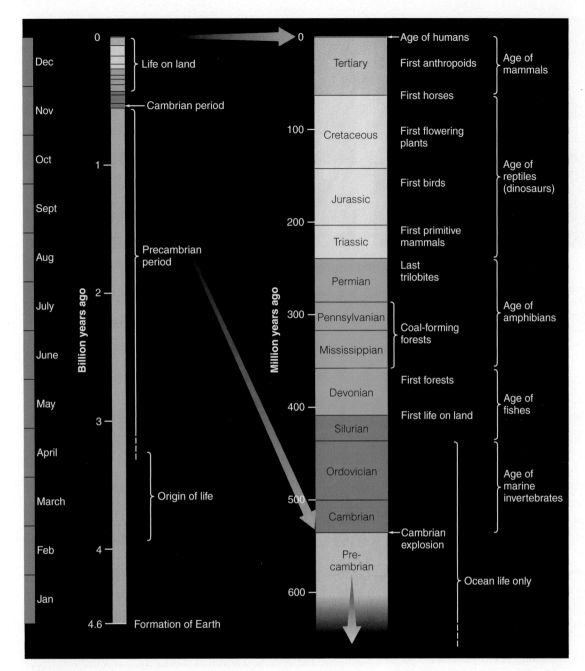

■ Figure 26-7

Complex life has developed on Earth only recently. If the entire history of Earth were represented in a time line (left), you have to examine the end of the line closely to see details such as life leaving the oceans and dinosaurs appearing. The age of humans would still be only a thin line at the top of your diagram. If the history of Earth were a year-long videotape, humans would not appear until the last hours of December 31.

Extremophiles

Scientists on Earth are finding life in places previously judged inhospitable, such as the bottoms of ice-covered lakes in Antarctica, far underground inside solid rock, and among the cinders at the summits of extinct volcanoes (■ Figure 26-8a). An organism that can survive and even thrive in an extreme environment is called an **extremophile.** Maybe you have friends like that.

Linguists can figure out the vocabulary of the long-vanished Indo-European language by comparing words in modern languages such as English, Spanish, Russian, Greek, and Hindi that evolved from it. In much the same way, biologists can work out the DNA sequences of ancient species by comparing the sequences of their present-day descendants. This type of analysis indicates that the creature that was ancestor to all life on Earth today resembled present-day single-celled organisms known as **archaea,** especially the extremophile types of archaea that are tolerant of high temperatures, called **thermophiles** (Figure 26-8b). Some biologists think this is evidence that life began near volcanic vents on the sea

■ **Figure 26-8**

Every life form on Earth has evolved to survive in some ecological niche. (a) Wekiu bugs live with the astronomers at an altitude of 13,800 feet atop the Hawaiian volcano Mauna Kea. The bugs inhabit spaces between the icy cinders and eat insects carried up by ocean breezes. (Kris Koenig/Coast Learning Systems) (b) Grand Prismatic Spring in Yellowstone National Park is about 90 meters (300 feet) across. Colonies of thermophilic (heat-loving) single-celled organisms thrive around the edge of the pool at temperatures up to 72°C (162°F) and produce the yellow, orange, and red pigments. The water in the center of the pool is too hot even for thermophiles. (S. Leach/U. Colorado Denver)

floor or in hot rock deep underground. Others suggest that the heavy bombardment during the end of the solar system's formation (see Chapter 19) would have repeatedly boiled much of Earth's oceans away. If life had already begun by then, the only organisms that survived this phase of the planet's history to become our ancestors by natural selection would have been heat resistant.

Life may have required special circumstances to start, but once it started, biological evolution allowed life to spread across Earth and adapt to a wide range of conditions. Eventually all niches—even extreme environments—became occupied. This means that, if life begins on a planet, even if most of the environment of the planet later becomes inhospitable as seems to have happened on Mars (see Chapter 22), some life could continue to survive.

It is difficult to pin down a range of environments and be sure that life cannot exist outside those conditions, so long as there is even occasionally some liquid water present. Scientists searching for life on other worlds must keep in mind Earth's extremophiles and the harsh conditions in which they thrive.

Life in Our Solar System

Could there be carbon-based life elsewhere in our solar system? Liquid water seems to be a requirement of carbon-based life, necessary both as the medium for vital chemical reactions and to transport nutrients and wastes. It is not surprising that life developed in Earth's oceans and stayed there for billions of years before it was able to colonize the land.

Scientists are in general agreement that any world harboring living things must have significant quantities of some type of

liquid as the medium in which the processes of life can occur. Water is a cosmically abundant substance with properties such as high heat capacity that set it apart from other common molecules that are liquid at the temperatures of planetary surfaces. Maybe there are other liquids that can support the processes of life on other planets, but water, aside from being common in the universe, has characteristics that cause Earth scientists to regard it as special, and not just because they are made of water themselves.

Many worlds in the solar system can be eliminated immediately as hosts for water-based life because liquid water is not possible there. The moon and Mercury are airless, and water would boil away into space immediately. Venus has traces of water vapor in its atmosphere, but it is too hot for liquid water to survive on the surface. The Jovian planets have deep atmospheres, and at certain altitudes it is likely that water condenses into liquid droplets. However, it seems unlikely that life could have originated there. The Jovian planets do not have solid surfaces (see Chapters 23 and 24), so isolated water droplets cannot mingle to mimic the rich primordial oceans of Earth, where organic molecules grew and interacted. Additionally, powerful downdraft currents in the atmospheres of the giant planets would quickly carry any reproducing molecules that did form there into inhospitably hot lower regions.

As you learned in Chapter 23, at least one of the Jovian satellites could potentially support life. Jupiter's moon Europa appears to have a liquid-water ocean below its icy crust, and minerals dissolved in the water could provide a source of raw material for chemical evolution. Europa's ocean is kept warm and liquid now by tidal heating. There also may be liquid water layers under the surfaces of Ganymede and Callisto. That can change as the moons interact gravitationally and their orbits vary; Europa, Ganymede, and Callisto may have been frozen solid at other times in their histories, which would probably have destroyed any living organism that had developed there.

Saturn's moon Titan is rich in organic molecules. You learned in Chapter 23 that sunlight converts the methane in Titan's atmosphere into organic smog particles that settle to the surface. The chemistry of life that could have evolved from those molecules and survived in Titan's lakes of methane is unknown. It is fascinating to consider possibilities, but Titan's extremely low temperature of −180°C (−290°F) would make chemical reactions so slow that life processes seem unlikely.

Water containing organic molecules has been observed venting from the south polar region of Saturn's moon Enceladus (see Chapter 23). It is possible that life could exist in that water under Enceladus's crust, but the moon is very small, and its tidal heating might operate only occasionally. Enceladus may not have had plentiful liquid water for the extended time necessary for the rise of life.

Mars is the most likely place for life to exist in the solar system because, as you learned in Chapter 22, there is a great deal of evidence that liquid water once flowed on its surface. Even so, results from searches for signs of life on Mars are not encouraging. The robotic spacecraft Viking 1 and Viking 2 landed on Mars in 1976 and tested soil samples for living organisms. Some of the tests had puzzling semipositive results that scientists hypothesize were caused by nonbiological chemical reactions in the soil. No evidence clearly indicates the presence of life or even of organic molecules currently in the Martian soil. If life survives on Mars, it may be hidden below ground where there may be liquid water and where UV radiation from the sun cannot penetrate.

There was a splash of news stories in the 1990s regarding supposed chemical and physical traces of life on Mars discovered inside a Martian meteorite found in Antarctica (■ Figure 26-9). Scientists were excited by the announcement, but they employed professional skepticism and immediately began testing the evidence. Their results suggest that the unusual chemical signatures in the rock may have formed by processes that did not involve life. Tiny features in the rock that were originally thought to be

■ **Figure 26-9**

(a) Meteorite ALH84001 is one of a dozen meteorites known to have originated on Mars. Its name means this meteorite was the first one found in 1984 near Antarctica's Allan Hills. (b) A research group claimed that the meteorite contained chemical and physical traces of ancient life on Mars, including what appear to be fossils of microscopic organisms. That evidence has not been confirmed, and the claim continues to be tested and debated. (NASA) (c) A map of Mars color-coded to show methane concentration in the atmosphere measured by spectrographs on Earth-based telescopes. Methane is most abundant in locations apart from volcanic regions, indicating the methane may be produced biologically. (NASA / M. Mumma) fossils of ancient Martian microorganisms could possibly be non-biological mineral formations instead.

In 2009 astronomers observing the Martian atmosphere announced detection of faint traces of methane, a substance made abundantly by living things on Earth. Methane would be destroyed in the Martian environment by solar UV radiation and chemical reactions, so the methane that is present must have been produced recently. There are also geological processes that can emit methane, but those processes are connected with volcanism. The map of Martian atmospheric methane concentrations in Figure 26-9c shows methane primarily in locations that are not volcanic provinces. Perhaps organisms living in the Martian soil are making methane right now. This evidence regarding potential life on Mars remains highly controversial. Conclusive evidence of life on Mars may have to wait until a geologist from Earth can scramble down dry Martian streambeds and crack open rocks looking for fossils, or drill into the soil seeking signs of metabolizing microorganisms.

There is no strong evidence for the existence of life in the solar system other than on Earth. Now your search will take you to distant planetary systems.

Life in Other Planetary Systems

Could life exist in other planetary systems? You already know that there are many different kinds of stars and that many of these stars have planetary systems. As a first step toward answering this question, you can try to identify the kinds of stars that seem most likely to have stable planetary systems where life could evolve.

If a planet is to be a suitable home for living things, it must be in a stable orbit around its sun. That is easy in a planetary system like our own, but planet orbits in binary star systems would be unstable unless the component stars are very close together or very far apart. Astronomers can calculate that, in binary systems with stars separated by intermediate distances of a few AU, the planets should eventually be swallowed up by one of the stars or ejected from the system. Half the stars in the galaxy are members of binary systems, and many of them are unlikely to support life on planets.

Moreover, just because a star is single does not necessarily make it a good candidate for sustaining life. Earth required perhaps as much as 1 billion years to produce the first cells and 4.6 billion years for intelligence to emerge. Massive stars that shine for only a few million years do not meet this criterion. If the history of life on Earth is representative, then stars more massive and luminous than about spectral type F5 last too short a time for complex life to develop. Main-sequence stars of types G and K, and possibly some of the M stars, are the best candidates.

The temperature of a planet is also important, and that depends on the type of star it orbits and its distance from the star. Astronomers have defined a **habitable zone** around a star as a region within which orbiting planets have temperatures permitting the existence of liquid water. The sun's habitable zone extends from near the orbit of Venus to the orbit of Mars, with Earth right in the middle. A low-luminosity star has a small and narrow habitable zone, whereas a high-luminosity star has a large and wide one.

Stable planets inside the habitable zones of long-lived stars are the places where life seems most likely, but, given the tenacity and resilience of Earth's life forms, there might be other, seemingly inhospitable, places in the universe where life exists. You should also note that three of the environments considered as possible havens for life—Europa, Titan, and Enceladus—are in the outer solar system, far outside the sun's conventionally defined habitable zone.

SCIENTIFIC ARGUMENT

What evidence indicates that life is possible on other worlds?
A good scientific argument involves careful analysis of evidence. Fossils on Earth show that life originated in the oceans at least 3.4 billion years ago, and biologists have outlined likely chemical processes that, over long time intervals, could have changed simple organic compounds into reproducing molecules inside membranes, the first simple life forms. Meager fossil evidence indicates that life developed slowly at first. The pace of evolution quickened about half a billion years ago, when life took on complex forms. Later, life emerged onto the land and continued evolving rapidly into diverse forms. Intelligence is a relatively recent development: It is only a few million years old.

If this evolutionary process occurred on Earth, it seems reasonable that it could have occurred on other worlds as well. Earth-like worlds could be plentiful in the universe. Life may begin and eventually evolve to intelligence on any world where conditions are right. Now make a related argument. **What are the conditions you should expect on other worlds that host life?**

26-3 Intelligent Life in the Universe

COULD INTELLIGENT LIFE ARISE on other worlds? To try to answer this question, you can estimate the chances of any type of life arising on other worlds, then assess the likelihood of that life developing intelligence. If other civilizations exist, it is possible humans eventually may be able to communicate with them. Nature puts restrictions on the pace of such conversations, but the main problem lies in the unknown life expectancy of civilizations.

Travel Between the Stars

The distances between stars are almost beyond comprehension. The fastest human device ever launched, the *New Horizons* probe currently on its way to Pluto and the Kuiper belt (see Chapter 24), will take about 90,000 years to travel the distance to the nearest star, 4 light-years. The obvious way to overcome these huge distances is with tremendously fast spaceships, but even the closest stars are many light-years away.

Nothing can exceed the speed of light, and accelerating a spaceship close to the speed of light takes huge amounts of energy. Even if you travel slower than light, your rocket would still require massive amounts of fuel. If you wanted to pilot a spaceship with a mass of 100 tons (about the size of a fancy yacht) to the nearest star, and you traveled at half the speed of light so as to arrive in eight years, the trip would require 400 times as much energy as the entire United States consumes in a year. Don't even think about how much fuel the starship *Enterprise* needs.

These limitations not only make it difficult for humans to leave the solar system, but they would also make it difficult for aliens to visit Earth. Reputable scientists have studied "unidentified flying objects" (UFOs) and have never found any evidence that Earth is being visited or has ever been visited by aliens (**How Do We Know? 26-2**). Humans are unlikely ever to meet aliens face-to-face. However, communication by electromagnetic signals across interstellar distances takes relatively little energy.

Radio Communication

Nature puts restrictions on travel through space, and it also restricts the possibility of communicating with distant civilizations by radio. One restriction is based on simple physics: Radio signals are electromagnetic waves and travel at the speed of light. Due to the distances between the stars, the speed of radio waves would severely limit humanity's ability to carry on normal conversations with distant civilizations. Decades could elapse between asking a question and getting an answer.

So, rather than try to begin a conversation, one group of astronomers decided in 1974 to broadcast a message of greeting toward the globular cluster M13, 26,000 light years away, using the Arecibo radio telescope (see Figure 6-21b). When the signal arrives 26,000 years in the future, alien astronomers may be able to understand it because the message is **anticoded,** meaning that it is intended to be decoded by beings about whom we know nothing except that they build radio telescopes. The message is a string of 1679 pulses and gaps. Pulses represent 1s, and gaps represent 0s. The string can be arranged in two dimensions in only two possible ways: as 23 rows of 73 or as 73 rows of 23. The second arrangement forms a picture containing information about life on Earth (■ Figure 26-10).

What are the chances that a signal like the Arecibo message would be heard across interstellar distances? Surprisingly, a radio dish the size of the Arecibo telescope, located anywhere in the Milky Way Galaxy, could detect the output from "our" Arecibo. The human race's modest technical capabilities already can put us into cosmic chat rooms.

Although the 1974 Arecibo beacon was the only powerful signal sent purposely from Earth to other star systems, Earth is sending out many other signals more or less accidentally. Short-wave radio signals, including TV and FM, have been leaking into space for the last 60 years or so. Any civilization within 60 light-years could already have detected Earth's civilization. That works both ways: Alien signals, whether intentional messages of friendship or the blather of their equivalent to daytime TV, could be arriving at Earth now. Groups of astronomers from several countries are pointing radio telescopes at the most likely stars and listening for alien civilizations.

Which channels should astronomers monitor? Signals with wavelengths longer than 100 cm would get lost in the background noise of our Milky Way Galaxy, while wavelengths shorter than about 1 cm are mostly absorbed in Earth's atmosphere. Between those wavelengths is a radio window that is open for communication. Even this restricted window contains millions of possible radio-frequency bands and is too wide to monitor easily, but astronomers may have thought of a way to narrow the search. Within this broad radio window lie the 21-cm spectral line of neutral hydrogen and the 18-cm line of OH (■ Figure 26-11). The interval between those lines has low background interference and is named the **water hole** because H plus OH yields water. Any civilizations sophisticated enough to do radio astronomy would know of these lines and might appreciate their significance in the same way as do Earthlings.

A number of searches for extraterrestrial radio signals have been made, and some are now under way. This field of study is known as **SETI, Search for Extra-Terrestrial Intelligence,** and it has generated heated debate among astronomers, philosophers, theologians, and politicians. You might imagine that the discovery of real alien intelligence would cause a huge change in humanity's worldview, akin to Galileo's discovery that the moons of Jupiter do not go around the Earth. Congress funded a NASA SETI search for a short time but ended support in the early 1990s. In fact, the annual cost of a major search is only about as much as a single Air Force helicopter, but much of the reluctance to fund searches stems from issues other than cost. Segments of the population, including some members of Congress, considered the idea of extraterrestrial beings as so outlandish that continued public funding for the search became impossible.

In spite of the controversy, the search continues. The NASA SETI project canceled by Congress was renamed Project Phoenix and completed using private funds. The SETI Institute, founded in 1984, managed Project Phoenix plus several other important searches and is currently building a new radio telescope array in northern California, in collaboration with the University of California, Berkeley, and partly funded by Paul Allen of Microsoft (■ Figure 26-12).

There is even a way for you to help with searches. The Berkeley SETI team (*Note:* they are separate from the SETI Institute), with the support of the Planetary Society, has

UFOs and Space Aliens

Has Earth been visited by aliens? If you conclude that there is likely to be life on other worlds, then you might be tempted to use UFO sightings as evidence to test your hypothesis. Scientists don't do this for two reasons.

First, the reputation of UFO sightings and alien encounters does not inspire confidence that these data are reliable. Most people hear of such events in grocery store tabloids, day-time talk shows, or sensational "specials" on viewer-hungry cable networks. You should take note of the low reputation of the media that report UFOs and space aliens. Most of these reports, like the reports that Elvis is alive and well, are simply made up for the sake of sensation, and you cannot use them as reliable evidence.

Second, the few UFO sightings that are not made up do not survive careful examination. Most are mistakes and unintentional misinterpretations, committed by honest people, of natural events or human-made objects. It is very important to realize that experts have studied these incidents over many decades and found *none* that are convincing to the professional scientific community. In short, despite false claims to the contrary on TV shows, there is no dependable evidence that Earth has ever been visited by aliens.

In a way, that's too bad. A confirmed visit by intelligent creatures from beyond our solar system would answer many questions. It would be exciting, enlightening, and, like any real adventure, a bit scary. Most scientists would love to be part of such a discovery. But, scientists must professionally pay attention to what is supported by evidence rather than what might be thrilling. There is not yet any direct evidence of life on other worlds.

Flying saucers from space are fun to think about, but there is no evidence that they are real.

recruited about 4 million owners of personal computers that are connected to the Internet. You can download a screen saver that searches data files from the Arecibo radio telescope for signals whenever you are not using the computer. For information, locate the seti@home project at http://setiathome.ssl.berkeley.edu/.

The search continues, but radio astronomers struggle to hear anything against the worsening babble of radio noise from human civilization. Wider and wider sections of the electromagnetic spectrum are being used for Earthly communication, and this, combined with stray electromagnetic radiation from electronic devices including everything from computers to refrigerators, makes hearing faint radio signals difficult. It would be ironic if humans fail to detect faint radio signals from another world because our own world has become too noisy. One alternate search strategy is to look for rapid flashes of laser light at optical or near-infrared wavelengths. Such extraterrestrial signals, if they exist, would have the advantage of being easily distinguished from natural light sources but the disadvantage of being blocked by interstellar dust. Ultimately, the chance of success for any of the searches depends on the number of inhabited worlds in the galaxy.

How Many Inhabited Worlds?

Given enough time, the searches will find other worlds with civilizations, assuming that there are at least a few out there. If intelligence is common, scientists should find signals relatively soon—within the next few decades—but if intelligence is rare, it may take much longer.

Simple arithmetic can give you an estimate of the number of technological civilizations in the Milky Way Galaxy with which you might communicate, N_c. The formula proposed for discussions about N_c is named the **Drake equation** after the radio astronomer Frank Drake, a pioneer in the search for extraterrestrial intelligence. The version of the Drake equation presented here is modified slightly from its original form:

$$N_c = N_* \cdot f_P \cdot n_{HZ} \cdot f_L \cdot f_I \cdot f_S$$

N_* is the number of stars in our galaxy, and f_P represents the fraction of stars that have planets. If all single stars have planets, f_P is about 0.5. The factor n_{HZ} is the average number of planets in each planetary system suitably located in the habitable zone—meaning, for the sake of the present discussion, the number of planets per planetary system possessing substantial amounts of liquid water. The conventional habitable zone in our system

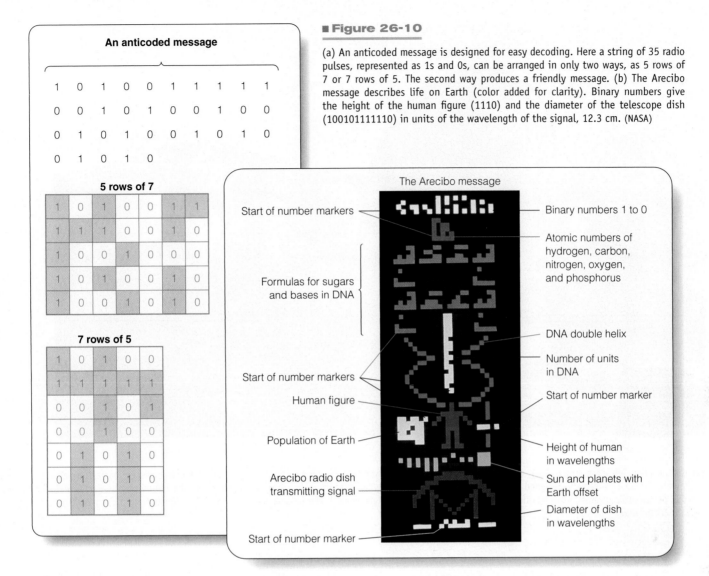

An anticoded message

1	0	1	0	0	1	1	1	1	1
0	0	1	0	1	0	0	1	0	0
0	1	0	1	0	0	1	0	1	0
0	1	0	1	0

5 rows of 7

7 rows of 5

■ **Figure 26-10**

(a) An anticoded message is designed for easy decoding. Here a string of 35 radio pulses, represented as 1s and 0s, can be arranged in only two ways, as 5 rows of 7 or 7 rows of 5. The second way produces a friendly message. (b) The Arecibo message describes life on Earth (color added for clarity). Binary numbers give the height of the human figure (1110) and the diameter of the telescope dish (100101111110) in units of the wavelength of the signal, 12.3 cm. (NASA)

The Arecibo message

- Start of number markers
- Atomic numbers of hydrogen, carbon, nitrogen, oxygen, and phosphorus
- Binary numbers 1 to 0
- Formulas for sugars and bases in DNA
- DNA double helix
- Number of units in DNA
- Start of number markers
- Human figure
- Start of number marker
- Population of Earth
- Height of human in wavelengths
- Arecibo radio dish transmitting signal
- Sun and planets with Earth offset
- Diameter of dish in wavelengths
- Start of number marker

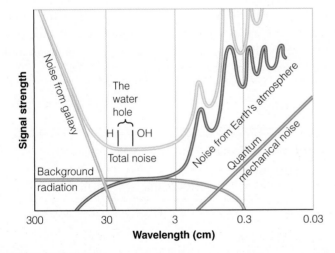

■ **Figure 26-11**

Radio noise from various astronomical sources and Earth's atmospheric opacity make it difficult to detect distant signals at wavelengths longer than 100 cm or shorter than 1 cm. In this range, wavelengths of radio emission lines from H atoms and from OH molecules mark a small wavelength range named the water hole that may be a likely channel for interstellar communication.

contains Earth's orbit, and, arguably, Venus and Mars as well. Europa and Enceladus in our solar system show that liquid water can exist due to tidal heating outside the conventional habitable zone. Thus, n_{HZ} may be larger than had been originally thought. The factor f_L is the fraction of suitable planets on which life begins, and f_I is the fraction of those planets where life evolves to intelligence.

The six factors on the right-hand side of the Drake equation can be roughly estimated, with decreasing certainty as you proceed from left to right. The final factor is extremely uncertain. That factor f_S is the fraction of a star's life during which an intelligent species is communicative. If a society survives at a technological level for only 100 years, the chances of communicating with it are small. On the other hand, a society that stabilizes and remains technologically capable for a long time is much more

■ **Figure 26-12**

Part of the Allen Telescope Array (ATA), which is now being built in California, is planned to eventually include 350 radio dishes, each 6 meters in diameter, in an arrangement designed to maximize their combined angular resolution. As radio astronomers aim the telescope at galaxies and nebulae of scientific interest, state-of-the-art computer systems will analyze stars in the field of view searching for signals from distant civilizations. (SETI Institute)

likely to be detected. For a star with a life span of 10 billion years, f_S might conceivably range from 10^{-8} for extremely short-lived societies to 10^{-4} for societies that survive for a million years. ■ Table 26-1 summarizes what many scientists consider a reasonable range of values for f_S and the other factors.

If the optimistic estimates are true, there could be a communicative civilization within a few tens of light-years from Earth. On the other hand, if the pessimistic estimates are true, Earth may be the only planet that is capable of communication within thousands of the nearest galaxies.

■ **Table 26-1** | **The Number of Technological Civilizations per Galaxy**

Estimates	Variables	Pessimistic	Optimistic
N_*	Number of stars per galaxy	2×10^{11}	2×10^{11}
f_P	Fraction of stars with planets	0.1	0.5
n_{HZ}	Number of planets per star that lie in habitable zone for longer than 4 billion years	0.01	1
f_L	Fraction of suitable planets on which life begins	0.01	1
f_I	Fraction of planets with life where life evolves to intelligence	0.01	1
f_S	Fraction of star's existence during which a technological society survives	10^{-8}	10^{-4}
N_c	Number of communicative civilizations per galaxy	2×10^{-4}	1×10^7

Why does the number of civilizations that could be detected depend on how long civilizations survive at a technological level?

This scientific argument depends on the timing of events. If you turned a radio telescope to the sky and scanned millions of frequency bands for many stars, you would be taking a snapshot of the universe at a particular time. Broadcasts from other civilizations must be arriving at that same time if they are to be detected. If most civilizations survive for a long time, there is a much greater chance that you will detect one of them in your snapshot than if

civilizations tend to disappear quickly due to, for example, nuclear war or environmental collapse. If most civilizations last only a short time, there may be none capable of transmitting during the cosmically short interval when Earthlings are capable of building radio telescopes to listen for them.

The speed at which astronomers can search for signals is limited because computers must search many frequency intervals, but not all frequencies inside Earth's radio window are subject to intensive search. Build a new argument to explain: **Why is the water hole an especially good frequency band in which to listen?**

What Are We?   Matter and Spirit

There are over 4000 religions around the world, and nearly all hold that humans have a dual nature: We are physical objects made of atoms, but we are also spiritual beings. Science is unable to examine the spiritual side of existence, but it can tell us about our physical nature.

The matter you are made of appeared in the big bang and was cooked into a wide range of elements inside stars. Your atoms may have been inside at least two or three generations of stars. Eventually, your atoms became part of a nebula that contracted to form our sun and the planets of the solar system

Your atoms have been part of Earth for the last 4.6 billion years. They have been recycled many times through dinosaurs,

stromatolites, fish, bacteria, grass, birds, worms, and other living things. You are using your atoms now, but when you are done with them, they will go back to Earth and be used again and again.

When the sun swells into a red giant star and dies in a few billion years, Earth's atmosphere and oceans will be driven away, and at least the outer few kilometers of Earth's crust will be vaporized and blown outward to become part of the nebula around the white-dwarf remains of the sun. Your atoms are destined to return to the interstellar medium and will become part of future generations of stars and planets.

The message of astronomy is that humans are not just observers: We are participants in the universe. Among all of

the galaxies, stars, planets, planetesimals, and bits of matter, humans are objects that can think, and that means we can understand what we are.

Is the human race the only thinking species? If so, we bear the sole responsibility to understand and admire the universe. The detection of signals from another civilization would demonstrate that we are not alone, and such communication would end the self-centered isolation of humanity and stimulate a reevaluation of the meaning of human existence. We may never realize our full potential as humans until we communicate with non-human intelligent life.

Study and Review

Summary

▶ Consideration of the possibility that life exists elsewhere in the universe, and the study of life and its origin on Earth as it relates to life on other worlds, is called **astrobiology (p. 582)**.

▶ Life can be defined as a process that extracts energy from the surroundings, maintains an organism, and modifies the surroundings to promote the organism's survival.

▶ Living things have a physical basis—the arrangement of matter and energy that makes life possible. Life on Earth is based on carbon chemistry occurring in bags of water (cells).

▶ Living things must have a controlling unit of information that can be passed to successive generations.

▶ Genetic information for life on Earth is stored in long carbon-chain molecules such as **DNA (deoxyribonucleic acid) (p. 584)**.

▶ The DNA molecule stores information in the form of chemical bases linked together like the rungs of a ladder. Copied by the **RNA (ribonucleic acid) (p. 585)** molecule, the patterns of bases act as recipes for connecting together **amino acid (p. 584)** subunits to construct **proteins (p. 584)**, including **enzymes (p. 584)** that are respectively the main structural and control components of the life process.

- The unit of heredity is a **gene (p. 585)**, a piece or several pieces of DNA that in most cases specifies the construction of one particular type of protein molecule. Genes are connected together in structures called **chromosomes (p. 585)**, that are essentially single long DNA molecules.

- When a cell divides, the chromosomes split lengthwise and duplicate themselves so that each of the new cells can receive a copy of the genetic information.

- **Biological evolution (p. 586)** is the process by which life adjusts itself to changing environments.

- Errors in duplication or damage to the DNA molecule can produce **mutants (p. 586)**, organisms that contain new DNA information and therefore have new properties. Variation in genetic codes can become widespread among individuals in a species. **Natural selection (p. 586)** determines which of these variations are best suited to survive, and the species evolves to fit its environment.

- Evolution is not random. Genetic variation is random, but natural selection is controlled by the environment.

- The oldest definitely identified fossils on Earth, structures called **stromatolites (p. 587)** that are composed of stacks of bacterial mats and sediment layers, are at least 3.4 billion years old. Those fossils provide evidence that life began in the oceans.

- Fossil evidence indicates that life began on Earth as simple single-celled organisms like bacteria and much later evolved into more complex, **multicellular (p. 589)** creatures.

- The **Miller experiment (p. 587)** shows that the chemical building blocks of life form naturally under a wide range of circumstances.

- Scientists hypothesize that **chemical evolution (p. 589)** occurred before biological evolution. Chemical evolution concentrated simple molecules into a diversity of larger stable organic molecules dissolved in the young Earth's oceans, but those molecules did not reproduce copies of themselves. The hypothetical organic-rich water is sometimes referred to as the **primordial soup (p. 588)**. Biological evolution began when molecules developed the ability to make copies of themselves.

- Life forms did not become large and complex until about 0.5 billion years ago, during what is called the **Cambrian explosion (p. 589)**.

- Life emerged from the oceans only about 0.4 billion years ago, and human intelligence developed over the last 4 million (0.004 billion) years.

- Life as it is known on Earth requires liquid water and thus a specific range of temperatures.

- Organisms that thrive in extreme environments are called **extremophiles (p. 591)**. Genetic evidence indicates that the common ancestor of all Earth life was a **thermophile (p. 591)**, a heat-tolerant version of present-day single-celled organisms called **archaea (p. 591)**.

- No other planet in our solar system appears to harbor life at present. Most are too hot or too cold, although life might have begun on Mars before the planet became too cold and dry. If so, life conceivably could persist today on Mars in limited hospitable environments.

- Liquid water exists, and therefore Earth-like life is at least possible, under the surfaces of Jupiter's moons Europa and Ganymede and Saturn's moon Enceladus. Saturn's moon Titan has abundant organic compounds but does not have liquid water.

- Because the origin of life and its evolution into intelligent creatures took so long on Earth, scientists do not consider middle- and upper-main-sequence stars, which shine for astronomically short time spans, as likely hosts for life-bearing planets.

- Main-sequence G and K stars are thought to be likely candidates to host planets with life. Scientists are not sure whether the M stars are also good candidates.

- The **habitable zone (p. 594)** around a star, within which planets can have liquid water on their surfaces, may be larger than scientists had

expected, given the wide variety of living things now found in extreme environments on Earth. Tidally heated moons orbiting large planets could have liquid water at any distance from a star.

- Because of distance, speed, and fuel, travel between the stars seems almost impossible for humans or for aliens who might visit Earth.

- Communication between planetary systems using electromagnetic signals such as radio waves or laser beams may be possible, but a real conversation would be difficult because of long travel times for such signals.

- Broadcasting a radio (or light) beacon of pulses would distinguish the signal from naturally occurring emission and identify the source as a technological civilization. The signal can be **anticoded (p. 595)** in the hope it would be possible for another civilization to decode.

- One good part of the radio spectrum for communication is called the **water hole (p. 595)**, the wavelength range from the 21-cm spectral line of hydrogen to the 18-cm line of OH. Even so, millions of radio wavelengths need to be tested to fully survey the water hole for a given target star.

- Sophisticated searches are now underway to detect radio transmissions from civilizations on other worlds, but such **SETI (Search for Extra-Terrestrial Intelligence) (p. 595)** programs are hampered by limited computer power and radio noise pollution from human civilization.

- The number of civilizations in our galaxy that are at a technological level and able to communicate while humans are listening can be estimated by the **Drake equation (p. 596)**. This number is limited primarily by the lifetimes of their and our civilizations.

Review Questions

1. If life is based on information, what is that information?
2. How does the DNA molecule produce a copy of itself?
3. What would happen to a life form if the genetic information handed down to offspring was copied extremely inaccurately? How would that endanger the future of the life form?
4. What would happen to a life form if the information handed down to offspring was always the same? How would that endanger the future of the life form?
5. Give an example of natural selection acting on new DNA patterns to select the most advantageous characteristics.
6. What evidence do scientists have that life on Earth began in the sea?
7. Why do scientists generally think that liquid water is necessary for the origin of life?
8. What is the difference between chemical evolution and biological evolution?
9. What is the significance of the Miller experiment?
10. How does intelligence make a creature more likely to survive?
11. Why are upper-main-sequence (high-luminosity) stars unlikely sites for intelligent civilizations?
12. Why is it reasonable to suspect that travel between stars is nearly impossible?
13. How does the stability of technological civilizations affect the probability that Earth can communicate with them?
14. What is the water hole, and why is it a good "place" to search for extraterrestrial civilizations?
15. Why is it difficult to anticode a message? In other words, why is it hard to make a message that potentially can be understood by completely unknown recipients?
16. **How Do We Know?** How do science and religion have complementary explanations of the world?
17. **How Do We Know?** Why are scientists sure Earth has never been visited by aliens?

Discussion Questions

1. Do you expect that hypothetical alien recipients of the Arecibo message will be able to decode it? Why or why not?

2. How do you think the detection of extraterrestrial intelligence would be received by the public? Would it be likelier to upset, or confirm, human's beliefs about themselves and the world?

3. What do you think it would mean if decades of careful searches for radio signals for extraterrestrial intelligence turn up nothing?

Problems

1. A single human cell encloses about 1.5 m of DNA, containing 4.5 billion base pairs. What is the spacing between these base pairs in nanometers? That is, how far apart are the rungs on the DNA ladder?

2. If you represent Earth's history by a line 1 m long, how long a segment would represent the 400 million years since life moved onto the land? How long a segment would represent the 4-million-year history of human life?

3. If a human generation, the average time from birth to childbearing, has been 20 years long, how many generations have passed in the last 1 million years?

4. If a star must remain on the main sequence for at least 4 billion years for life to evolve to intelligence, what is the most massive a star can be and still possibly harbor intelligent life on one of its planets? (*Hints:* See Chapter 12 and Appendix Table A-7.)

5. If there are about 1.4×10^{-4} stars like the sun per cubic light-year, how many lie within 100 light-years of Earth? (*Hint:* The volume of a sphere is $\frac{4}{3} \pi r^3$.)

6. Mathematician Karl Gauss suggested planting forests and fields in gigantic geometric figures as signals to possible Martians that intelligent life exists on Earth. If Martians had telescopes that could resolve details no smaller than 1 arc second, how large would the smallest element of Gauss's signal have to be for it to be visible at Mars's closest approach to Earth? (*Hints:* See Appendix Table A-10 and use the small-angle formula, Chapter 3.)

7. If you detected radio signals with an average wavelength of 20 cm and suspected that they came from a civilization on a distant Earth-like planet, roughly how much of a change in wavelength should you expect to see because of the orbital motion of the distant planet? (*Hints:* See the equation for the Doppler effect in Chapter 7; the Earth's orbital velocity is 30 km/s.)

8. Calculate the number of communicative civilizations per galaxy using your own estimates of the factors in Table 26-1.

Learning to Look

1. The star cluster shown in the image to the right contains cool red giants and main-sequence stars from hot blue stars all the way down to red dwarfs. Discuss the likelihood that planets orbiting any of these stars might be home to life. (*Hint:* Estimate the age of the cluster.)

Visual — NASA

2. If you could search for life in the galaxy shown in the image to the right, would you look among disk stars or halo stars? Discuss the factors that influence your decision.

Visual — ESO

Afterword

The aggregate of all our joys and sufferings, thousands of confident religions, ideologies and economic doctrines, every hunter and forager, every hero and coward, every creator and destroyer of civilizations, every king and peasant, every young couple in love, every hopeful child, every mother and father, every inventor and explorer, every teacher of morals, every corrupt politician, every superstar, every supreme leader, every saint and sinner in the history of our species, lived there on a mote of dust, suspended in a sunbeam.

CARL SAGAN (1934–1996)

Earth photographed by Voyager 1 from the edge of the solar system. (NASA)

OUR JOURNEY TOGETHER IS OVER; but, before we part company, let's ponder one final time the primary theme of this book—humanity's place in the physical universe. Astronomy gives us some comprehension of the workings of stars, galaxies, and planets, but its greatest value lies in what it teaches us about ourselves. Now that you have surveyed astronomical knowledge, you can better understand your own position in nature.

To some, the word *nature* conjures up visions of furry rabbits hopping about in a forest glade. To others, nature is the blue-green ocean depths, and still others think of nature as windswept mountaintops. As diverse as these images are, they are all Earth-bound. Having studied astronomy, you can see nature as a beautiful mechanism composed of matter and energy, interacting according to simple rules, forming galaxies, stars, planets, mountaintops, ocean depths, forest glades, and people.

Perhaps the most important astronomical lesson is that humanity is a small but important part of the universe. Most of the universe is probably lifeless. The vast reaches between the galaxies appear to be empty of all but the thinnest gas, and stars are much too hot to preserve the chemical bonds that seem necessary for life to survive and develop. It seems that only on the surfaces of a few planets, where temperatures are moderate, can atoms link together in special ways to form living matter.

If life is special, then intelligence is precious. The universe must contain many planets devoid of life, planets where sunlight has shined unfelt for billions of years. There may also exist planets on which life has developed but has not become complex, planets where the wind stirs wide plains of grass and rustles through dark forests. On some planets, creatures resembling Earth's insects, fish, birds, and animals may watch the passing days only dimly aware of their own existence. It is intelligence, human or alien, that gives meaning to the landscape.

Science is the process by which Earth's intelligence has tried to understand the physical universe. Science is not the invention of new devices or processes. It does not create home computers, cure the mumps, or manufacture plastic spoons—those are engineering and technology, the adaptation of scientific understanding for practical purposes. Science is the understanding of nature, and astronomy is that understanding on the grandest scale. Astronomy is the science by which the universe, through its intelligent lumps of matter, tries to understand its own existence.

As the primary intelligent species on this planet, we are the custodians of a priceless gift—a planet filled with living things. This is especially true if life is rare in the universe. In fact, if Earth is the only inhabited planet, our responsibility is overwhelming. We are the only creatures who can take action to preserve the existence of life on Earth; ironically, our own actions are the most serious hazards.

The future of humanity is not secure. We are trapped on a tiny planet with limited resources and a population growing faster than our ability to produce food. We have already driven some creatures to extinction and now threaten others. We are changing the climate of our planet in ways we do not fully understand. Even if we reshape our civilization to preserve our world, the sun's evolution will eventually destroy Earth.

This may be a sad prospect, but a few factors are comforting. First, everything in the universe is temporary. Stars die, galaxies die; perhaps the entire universe will someday end. Our distant future is limited, and this assures us that we are a part of a much larger whole. Second, we have a few billion years to prepare, and a billion years is a very long time. Only a few million years ago, our ancestors were starting to walk upright and communicate. A billion years ago, our ancestors were microscopic organisms living in the oceans. To suppose that a billion years hence there will be beings resembling today's humans, or that humans will still be the dominant intelligence on Earth, or that humans will even exist, are ultimately conceits.

Our responsibility is not to save our race for all eternity but to behave as dependable custodians of our planet, preserving it, admiring it, and trying to understand it. That calls for drastic changes in our behavior toward other living things and a revolution in our attitude toward our planet's resources. Whether we can change our ways is debatable—humanity is far from perfect in its understanding, abilities, or intentions. However, you must not imagine that we, and our civilization, are less than precious. We have the gift of intelligence, and that is the finest thing this planet has ever produced.

We shall not cease from exploration
And the end of all our exploring
Will be to arrive where we started
And know the place for the first time.
                              —*T. S. Eliot, "Little Gidding"*

Excerpt from "Little Gidding" in *Four Quartets,* copyright 1942 by T. S. Eliot and renewed 1970 by Esme Valerie Eliot, reprinted by permission of Harcourt, Inc. and Faber & Faber, Ltd.

Appendix A
Units and Astronomical Data

Introduction

THE METRIC SYSTEM IS USED WORLDWIDE as the system of units, not only in science but also in engineering, business, sports, and daily life. Developed in 18th-century France, the metric system has gained acceptance in almost every country in the world because it simplifies computations.

A system of units is based on the three fundamental units for length, mass, and time. Other quantities, such as density and force, are derived from these fundamental units. In the English (or British) system of units (commonly used only in the United States, Tonga, and Southern Yemen, but, ironically, not in Great Britain) the fundamental unit of length is the foot, composed of 12 inches. The metric system is based on the decimal system of numbers, and the fundamental unit of length is the meter, composed of 100 centimeters.

Because the metric system is a decimal system, it is easy to express quantities in larger or smaller units as is convenient. You can give distances in centimeters, meters, kilometers, and so on. The prefixes specify the relation of the unit to the meter. Just as a cent is 1/100 of a dollar, so a centimeter is 1/100 of a meter. A kilometer is 1000 m, and a kilogram is 1000 g. The meanings of the commonly used prefixes are given in ▣ Table A-1.

■ Table A-1 | Metric Prefixes

Prefix	Symbol	Factor
Mega	M	10^6
Kilo	k	10^3
Centi	c	10^{-2}
Milli	m	10^{-3}
Micro	μ	10^{-6}
Nano	n	10^{-9}

■ Table A-2 SI *(Système International)* Metric Units

Quantity	SI Unit
Length	Meter (m)
Mass	Kilogram (kg)
Time	Second (s)
Force	Newton (N)
Energy	Joule (J)

The SI Units

ANY SYSTEM OF UNITS based on the decimal system would be easy to use; but, by international agreement, the preferred set of units, known as the *Système International d'Unités* (SI units) is based on the meter, kilogram, and second. These three fundamental units define the rest of the units, as given in ▣ Table A-2.

The SI unit of force is the newton (N), named after Isaac Newton. It is the force needed to accelerate a 1 kg mass by 1 m/s², or the force roughly equivalent to the weight of an apple at Earth's surface. The SI unit of energy is the joule (J), the energy produced by a force of 1 N acting through a distance of 1 m. A joule is roughly the energy in the impact of an apple falling off a table.

Exceptions

Units can help you in two ways. They make it possible to make calculations, and they can help you to conceive of certain quantities. For calculations, the metric system is far superior, and it is used for calculations throughout this book.

Americans commonly use the English system of units, so for conceptual purposes this book also expresses quantities in English units. Instead of saying the average person would weigh 133 N on the moon, it might be more helpful to some readers for that weight to be expressed as 30 lb. Consequently, this text commonly gives quantities in metric form followed by the English form in parentheses: The radius of the moon is 1738 km (1080 mi).

In SI units, density should be expressed as kilograms per cubic meter, but no human hand can enclose a cubic meter, so that unit does not help you grasp the significance of a given density. This book refers to density in grams per cubic centimeter. A gram is roughly the mass of a paperclip, and a cubic centimeter is the size of a small sugar cube, so you can easily conceive of a density of 1 g/cm³, roughly the density of water. This is not a bothersome departure from SI units because you will not have to make complex calculations using density.

Conversions

TO CONVERT FROM ONE METRIC UNIT to another (from meters to kilometers, for example), you have only to look at the prefix. However, converting from metric to English or English to metric is more complicated. The conversion factors are given in ▣ Table A-3.

1 inch = 2.54 centimeters	1 meter = 39.36 inches = 3.28 feet
1 foot = 0.3048 meter	1 kilometer = 0.6214 mile
1 mile = 1.609 kilometers	1 kilogram = 0.0685 slug
1 slug = 14.59 kilograms	1 Newton = 0.2248 pound
1 pound = 4.448 Newtons	1 Joule = 0.7376 foot-pound
1 foot-pound = 1.356 Joules	1 Joule/s = 0.001341 horsepower
1 horsepower = 745.7 Joules/s	1 Joule/s = 1 Watt
1 centimeter = 0.394 inch	

■ Table A-4 **Temperature Scales and Conversion Formulas**

	Kelvin (K)	Centigrade (°C)	Fahrenheit (°F)
Absolute zero	0 K	−273°C	−459°F
Freezing point of water	273 K	0°C	32°F
Boiling point of water	373 K	100°C	212°F

Conversions:

$$K = °C + 273$$
$$°C = \left(\frac{5}{9}\right)(°F - 32)$$
$$°F = \left(\frac{9}{5}\right)(°C) + 32$$

Example: The radius of the moon is 1738 km. What is this in miles? Table A-3 indicates that 1.000 mile equals 1.609 km, so

$$1738 \text{ km} \times \frac{(1.000 \text{ mi})}{(1.609 \text{ km})} = 1080 \text{ mi}$$

Temperature Scales

IN ASTRONOMY, as in most other sciences, temperatures are expressed on the Kelvin scale, although the centigrade (or Celsius) scale is also used. The Fahrenheit scale commonly used in the United States is not used in scientific work.

Temperatures on the Kelvin scale are measured from absolute zero, the temperature of an object that contains no extractable heat. In practice, no object can be as cold as absolute zero, although laboratory apparatuses have reached temperatures lower than 10^{-6} K. The Kelvin scale is named after the Scottish mathematical physicist William Thomson, Lord Kelvin (1824–1907).

The centigrade scale refers temperatures to the freezing point of water (0°C) and to the boiling point of water (100°C). One degree centigrade is $\frac{1}{100}$ of the temperature difference between the freezing and boiling points of water, thus the prefix *centi*. The centigrade scale is also called the Celsius scale after its inventor, the Swedish astronomer Anders Celsius (1701–1744).

The Fahrenheit scale fixes the freezing point of water at 32°F and the boiling point at 212°F. Named after the German physicist Gabriel Daniel Fahrenheit (1686–1736), who made the first successful mercury thermometer in 1720, the Fahrenheit scale is used routinely only in the United States.

It is easy to convert temperatures from one scale to another using the information given in ■Table A-4.

Powers of 10 Notation

POWERS OF 10 make writing very large numbers much simpler. For example, the nearest star is about 43,000,000,000,000 km from the sun. Writing this number as 4.3×10^{13} km is much easier.

Very small numbers can also be written with powers of 10. For example, the wavelength of visible light is about 0.0000005 m. In powers of 10 this becomes 5×10^{-7} m.

The powers of 10 used in this notation appear below. The exponent tells you how to move the decimal point. If the exponent is positive, move the decimal point to the right. If the exponent is negative, move the decimal point to the left. For example, 2.0000×10^3 equals 2000, and 2×10^{-3} equals 0.002.

$$10^5 = 100,000$$
$$10^4 = 10,000$$
$$10^3 = 1,000$$
$$10^2 = 100$$
$$10^1 = 10$$
$$10^0 = 1$$
$$10^{-1} = 0.1$$
$$10^{-2} = 0.01$$
$$10^{-3} = 0.001$$
$$10^{-4} = 0.0001$$

If you use scientific notation in calculations, be sure you correctly enter the numbers into your calculator. Not all calculators accept scientific notation, but those that can have a key labeled EXP, EEX, or perhaps EE that allows you to enter the exponent of ten. To enter a number such as 3×10^8, press the keys 3 EXP 8. To enter a number with a negative exponent, you must use the change-sign key, usually labeled +/− or CHS. To enter the number 5.2×10^{-3}, press the keys 5.2 EXP +/− 3. Try a few examples.

To read a number in scientific notation from a calculator you must read the exponent separately. The number 3.1×10^{25} may appear in a calculator display as 3.1 25 or on some calculators as 3.1 10^{25}. Examine your calculator to determine how such numbers are displayed.

Astronomy Units and Constants

ASTRONOMY, AND SCIENCE IN GENERAL, is a way of learning about nature and understanding the universe. To test hypotheses about how nature works, scientists use observations of nature. The tables that follow contain some of the basic observations that support science's best understanding of the astronomical universe. Of course, these data are expressed in the form of numbers, not because science reduces all understanding to mere numbers but because the struggle to understand nature is so demanding that science must use every valid means available. Quantitative thinking—reasoning mathematically—is one of the most powerful techniques ever invented by the human brain. Thus, these tables are not nature reduced to mere numbers but numbers supporting humanity's growing understanding of the natural world around us.

■ Table A-5 | Astronomical Constants

Velocity of light (c)	$= 3.00 \times 10^8$ m/s
Gravitational constant (G)	$= 6.67 \times 10^{-11}$ m^3/s^{2}kg
Mass of H atom	$= 1.67 \times 10^{-27}$ kg
Mass of Earth $(M_\oplus)$	$= 5.98 \times 10^{24}$ kg
Earth equatorial radius $(R_\oplus)$	$= 6.38 \times 10^3$ km
Mass of sun $(M_\odot)$	$= 1.99 \times 10^{30}$ kg
Radius of sun $(R_\odot)$	$= 6.96 \times 10^8$ m
Solar luminosity $(L_\odot)$	$= 3.83 \times 10^{26}$ J/s
Mass of moon	$= 7.35 \times 10^{22}$ kg
Radius of moon	$= 1.74 \times 10^3$ km

■ Table A-6 | Units Used in Astronomy

1 Angstrom (Å)	$= 10^{-8}$ cm
	$= 10^{-10}$ m
	$= 10$ nm
1 astronomical unit (AU)	$= 1.50 \times 10^{11}$ m
	$= 93.0 \times 10^6$ mi
1 light-year (ly)	$= 6.32 \times 10^4$ AU
	$= 9.46 \times 10^{15}$ m
	$= 5.88 \times 10^{12}$ mi
1 parsec (pc)	$= 2.06 \times 10^5$ AU
	$= 3.09 \times 10^{16}$ m
	$= 3.26$ ly
1 kiloparsec (kpc)	$= 1000$ pc
1 megaparsec (Mpc)	$= 1,000,000$ pc

Spectral Type	Absolute Visual Magnitude (M_v)	Luminosity*	Temp. (K)	λ_{max} (nm)	Mass*	Radius*	Average Density (g/cm^3)
O5	−5.8	501,000	40,000	72.4	40	17.8	0.01
B0	−4.1	20,000	28,000	100	18	7.4	0.1
B5	−1.1	790	15,000	190	6.4	3.8	0.2
A0	+0.7	79	9900	290	3.2	2.5	0.3
A5	+2.0	20	8500	340	2.1	1.7	0.6
F0	+2.6	6.3	7400	390	1.7	1.4	1.0
F5	+3.4	2.5	6600	440	1.3	1.2	1.1
G0	+4.4	1.3	6000	480	1.1	1.0	1.4
G5	+5.1	0.8	5500	520	0.9	0.9	1.6
K0	+5.9	0.4	4900	590	0.8	0.8	1.8
K5	+7.3	0.2	4100	700	0.7	0.7	2.4
M0	+9.0	0.1	3500	830	0.5	0.6	2.5
M5	+11.8	0.01	2800	1000	0.2	0.3	10.0
M8	+16	0.001	2400	1200	0.1	0.1	63

*Luminosity, mass, and radius are given in terms of the sun's luminosity, mass, and radius.

■ Table A-8 | **The 15 Brightest Stars**

Star	Name	Apparent Visual Magnitude (m_v)	Spectral Type	Absolute Visual Magnitude (m_v)	Distance (ly)
α CMa A	Sirius	−1.47	A1	1.4	8.7
α Car	Canopus	−0.72	F0	−3.1	98
α Cen	Rigil Kentaurus	−0.01	G2	4.4	4.3
V Boo	Arcturus	−0.06	K2	−0.3	36
α Lyr	Vega	0.04	A0	0.5	26.5
α Aur	Capella	0.05	G8	−0.6	45
β Ori A	Rigel	0.14	B8	−7.1	900
α CMi A	Procyon	0.37	F5	2.7	11.3
α Ori	Betelgeuse	0.41	M2	−5.6	520
α Eri	Achernar	0.51	B3	−2.3	118
β Cen AB	Hadar	0.63	B1	−5.2	490
α Aql	Altair	0.77	A7	2.2	16.5
α Tau A	Aldebaran	0.86	K5	−0.7	68
α Cru	Acrux	0.90	B2	3.5	260
α Vir	Spica	0.91	B1	−3.3	220

■ Table A-9 | The 15 Nearest Stars

Name	Absolute Magnitude (M_v)	Distance (ly)	Spectral Type	Apparent Visual Magnitude (m_v)
Sun	4.83		G2	−26.8
Proxima Cen	15.45	4.28	M5	11.05
α Cen A	4.38	4.3	G2	0.1
α Cen B	5.76	4.3	K5	1.5
Barnard's Star	13.21	5.9	M5	9.5
Wolf 359	16.80	7.6	M6	13.5
Lalande 21185	10.42	8.1	M2	7.5
Sirius A	1.41	8.6	A1	−1.5
Sirius B	11.54	8.6	white dwarf	7.2
Luyten 726-8A	15.27	8.9	M5	12.5
Luyten 726-8B (UV Cet)	15.8	8.9	M6	13.0
Ross 154	13.3	9.4	M5	10.6
Ross 248	14.8	10.3	M6	12.2
ε Eri	6.13	10.7	K2	3.7
Luyten 789-6	14.6	10.8	M7	12.2

■ Table A-10 | Properties of the Planets

Physical Properties (Earth = ⊕)

Planet	Equatorial Radius (km)	Equatorial Radius (⊕ = 1)	Mass (⊕ = 1)	Average Density (g/cm³)	Surface Gravity (⊕ = 1)	Escape Velocity (km/s)	Sidereal Period of Rotation	Inclination of Equator to Orbit
Mercury	2439	0.38	0.056	5.44	0.38	4.3	58.65d	0°
Venus	6052	0.95	0.815	5.24	0.90	10.3	243.02d	177°
Earth	6378	1.00	1.000	5.50	1.00	11.2	23.93h	23°.5
Mars	3396	0.53	0.108	3.94	0.38	5.0	24.62h	25°.3
Jupiter	71,494	11.20	317.8	1.34	2.54	61	9.92h	3°.1
Saturn	60,330	9.42	95.2	0.69	1.16	35.6	10.23h	26°.4
Uranus	25,559	4.01	14.5	1.19	0.92	22	17.23h	97°.9
Neptune	24,750	3.93	17.2	1.66	1.19	25	16.05h	28°.8

Orbital Properties

Planet	Semimajor Axis (a) (AU)	Semimajor Axis (a) (10⁶ km)	Orbital Period (P) (y)	Orbital Period (P) (days)	Average Orbital Velocity (km/s)	Orbital Eccentricity	Inclination to Ecliptic
Mercury	0.39	57.9	0.24	87.97	47.89	0.206	7°.0
Venus	0.72	108.2	0.62	224.68	35.03	0.007	3°.4
Earth	1.00	149.6	1.00	365.26	29.79	0.017	0° *
Mars	1.52	227.9	1.88	686.95	24.13	0.093	1°.9
Jupiter	5.20	778.3	11.87	4334.3	13.06	0.048	1°.3
Saturn	9.54	1427.0	29.46	10,760	9.64	0.056	2°.5
Uranus	19.18	2869.0	84.01	30,685	6.81	0.046	0°.8
Neptune	30.06	4497.1	164.79	60,189	5.43	0.010	1°.8

* By definition.

Planet	Satellite	Radius (km)	Distance from Planet (10^3 km)	Orbital Period (days)	Orbital Eccentricity	Orbital Inclination
Earth	Moon	1738	384.4	27.32	0.055	5°.1
Mars	Phobos	$14 \times 12 \times 10$	9.4	0.32	0.018	1°.0
	Deimos	$8 \times 6 \times 5$	23.5	1.26	0.002	2°.8
Jupiter	Amalthea	$135 \times 100 \times 78$	182	0.50	0.003	0°.4
	Io	1820	422	1.77	0.000	0°.3
	Europa	1565	671	3.55	0.000	0°.5
	Ganymede	2640	1071	7.16	0.002	0°.2
	Callisto	2420	1884	16.69	0.008	0°.2
	Himalia	~ 85	11,470	250.6	0.158	27°.6
Saturn	Janus	$110 \times 80 \times 100$	151.5	0.70	0.007	0°.1
	Mimas	196	185.5	0.94	0.020	1°.5
	Enceladus	250	238.0	1.37	0.004	0°.0
	Tethys	530	294.7	1.89	0.000	1°.1
	Dione	560	377	2.74	0.002	0°.0
	Rhea	765	527	4.52	0.001	0°.4
	Titan	2575	1222	15.94	0.029	0°.3
	Hyperion	$205 \times 130 \times 110$	1484	21.28	0.104	~0°.5
	Iapetus	720	3562	79.33	0.028	14°.7
	Phoebe	110	12,930	550.4	0.163	150°
Uranus	Miranda	242	129.9	1.41	0.017	3°.4
	Ariel	580	190.9	2.52	0.003	0°
	Umbriel	595	266.0	4.14	0.003	0°
	Titania	805	436.3	8.71	0.002	0°
	Oberon	775	583.4	13.46	0.001	0°
Neptune	Proteus	205	117.6	1.12	~0	~0°
	Triton	1352	354.59	5.88	0.00	160°
	Nereid	170	5588.6	360.12	0.76	27.7°

Shower	Dates	Hourly Rate	Radiant of shower R.A.	Dec.	Associated Comet
Quadrantids	Jan. 2–4	30	15^h24^m	50°	
Lyrids	April 20–22	8	18^h4^m	33°	1861 I
η Aquarids	May 2–7	10	22^h24^m	0°	Halley?
δ Aquarids	July 26–31	15	22^h36^m	−10°	
Perseids	Aug. 10–14	40	3^h4^m	58°	1982 III
Orionids	Oct. 18–23	15	6^h20^m	15°	Halley?
Taurids	Nov. 1–7	8	3^h40^m	17°	Encke
Leonids	Nov. 14–19	6	10^h12^m	22°	1866 I Temp
Geminids	Dec. 10–13	50	7^h28^m	32°	

■ Table A-13 | Greatest Elongations of Mercury*

Evening Sky	Morning Sky
Dec. 18, 2009	Jan. 27, 2010
Apr. 8, 2010**	May 26, 2010
Aug. 7, 2010	Sept. 19, 2010**
Dec. 1, 2010	Jan. 9, 2011
March 23, 2011**	May 7, 2011
July 20, 2011	Sept. 3, 2011**
Nov. 14, 2011	Dec. 23, 2011
March 5, 2012**	April 18, 2012
July 1, 2012	Aug. 16, 2012
Oct. 26, 2012	Dec. 4, 2012
Feb. 16, 2013	March 31, 2013
June 12, 2013	July 30, 2013
Oct. 9, 2013	Nov. 18, 2013

*Elongation is the angular distance from the sun to a planet.
**Most favorable elongations.

■ Table A-14 | Greatest Elongations of Venus

Evening Sky	Morning Sky
Aug. 20, 2010	Jan. 8, 2011
March 27, 2012	Aug. 15, 2012
Nov. 1, 2013	March 22, 2014
June 6, 2015	Oct. 26, 2015
Jan. 12, 2017	June 3, 2017
Aug. 17, 2018	Jan. 6, 2019
March 24, 2020	Aug. 12, 2020

■ Table A-15 | The Greek Alphabet

A, α alpha	H, η eta	N, ν nu	T, τ tau
B, β beta	Θ, θ theta	Ξ, ξ xi	Υ, υ upsilon
Γ, γ gamma	I, ι iota	O, o omicron	Φ, φ phi
Δ, δ delta	K, κ kappa	Π, π pi	X, χ chi
E, δ epsilon	Λ, λ lambda	P, ρ rho	Ψ, ψ psi
Z, δ zeta	M, μ mu	Σ, σ sigma	Ω, ω omega

Group

Noble Gases
(18)

Atomic masses are based on carbon-12. Numbers in parentheses are mass numbers of most stable or best-known isotopes of radioactive elements.

Atomic number → 11
Symbol → Na
Atomic mass → 22.99

Transition Elements

Period	IA(1)	IIA(2)	IIIB(3)	IVB(4)	VB(5)	VIB(6)	VIIB(7)	VIII (8)	VIII (9)	VIII (10)	IB(11)	IIB(12)	IIIA(13)	IVA(14)	VA(15)	VIA(16)	VIIA(17)	(18)
1	1 H 1.008																	2 He 4.003
2	3 Li 6.941	4 Be 9.012											5 B 10.81	6 C 12.01	7 N 14.01	8 O 16.00	9 F 19.00	10 Ne 20.18
3	11 Na 22.99	12 Mg 24.31											13 Al 26.98	14 Si 28.09	15 P 30.97	16 S 32.06	17 Cl 35.45	18 Ar 39.95
4	19 K 39.10	20 Ca 40.08	21 Sc 44.96	22 Ti 47.90	23 V 50.94	24 Cr 52.00	25 Mn 54.94	26 Fe 55.85	27 Co 58.93	28 Ni 58.7	29 Cu 63.55	30 Zn 65.38	31 Ga 69.72	32 Ge 72.59	33 As 74.92	34 Se 78.96	35 Br 79.90	36 Kr 83.80
5	37 Rb 85.47	38 Sr 87.62	39 Y 88.91	40 Zr 91.22	41 Nb 92.91	42 Mo 95.94	43 Tc 98.91	44 Ru 101.1	45 Rh 102.9	46 Pd 106.4	47 Ag 107.9	48 Cd 112.4	49 In 114.8	50 Sn 118.7	51 Sb 121.8	52 Te 127.6	53 I 126.9	54 Xe 131.3
6	55 Cs 132.9	56 Ba 137.3	57* La 138.9	72 Hf 178.5	73 Ta 180.9	74 W 183.9	75 Re 186.2	76 Os 190.2	77 Ir 192.2	78 Pt 195.1	79 Au 197.0	80 Hg 200.6	81 Tl 204.4	82 Pb 207.2	83 Bi 209.0	84 Po (210)	85 At (210)	86 Rn (222)
7	87 Fr (223)	88 Ra 226.0	89** Ac (227)	104 Rf (261)	105 Db (262)	106 Sg (263)	107 Bh (262)	108 Hs (265)	109 Mt (266)	110 Ds (269)	111 Uuu (272)	112 Uub (277)	113 Uub (284)	114 Uuq (285)	115 Uub (288)	116 Uuh (289)		

Inner Transition Elements

Lanthanide Series 6*	58 Ce 140.1	59 Pr 140.9	60 Nd 144.2	61 Pm (145)	62 Sm 150.4	63 Eu 152.0	64 Gd 157.3	65 Tb 158.9	66 Dy 162.5	67 Ho 164.9	68 Er 167.3	69 Tm 168.9	70 Yb 173.0	71 Lu 175.0
Actinide Series 7**	90 Th 232.0	91 Pa 231.0	92 U 238.0	93 Np 237.0	94 Pu (244)	95 Am (243)	96 Cm (247)	97 Bk (247)	98 Cf (251)	99 Es (252)	100 Fm (257)	101 Md (258)	102 No (259)	103 Lr (260)

The Elements and Their Symbols

Actinium	Ac	Cesium	Cs	Hafnium	Hf	Mercury	Hg	Protactinium	Pa	Tellurium	Te
Aluminum	Al	Chlorine	Cl	Hassium	Hs	Molybdenum	Mo	Radium	Ra	Terbium	Tb
Americium	Am	Chromium	Cr	Helium	He	Neodymium	Nd	Radon	Rn	Thallium	Tl
Antimony	Sb	Cobalt	Co	Holmium	Ho	Neon	Ne	Rhenium	Re	Thorium	Th
Argon	Ar	Copper	Cu	Hydrogen	H	Neptunium	Np	Rhodium	Rh	Thulium	Tm
Arsenic	As	Curium	Cm	Indium	In	Nickel	Ni	Rubidium	Rb	Tin	Sn
Astatine	At	Darmstadtium	Ds	Iodine	I	Niobium	Nb	Ruthenium	Ru	Titanium	Ti
Barium	Ba	Dubnium	Db	Iridium	Ir	Nitrogen	N	Rutherfordium	Rf	Tungsten	W
Berkelium	Bk	Dysprosium	Dy	Iron	Fe	Nobelium	No	Samarium	Sm	Uranium	U
Beryllium	Be	Einsteinium	Es	Krypton	Kr	Osmium	Os	Scandium	Sc	Vanadium	V
Bismuth	Bi	Erbium	Er	Lanthanum	La	Oxygen	O	Seaborgium	Sg	Xenon	Xe
Bohrium	Bh	Europium	Eu	Lawrencium	Lr	Palladium	Pd	Selenium	Se	Ytterbium	Yb
Boron	B	Fermium	Fm	Lead	Pb	Phosphorous	P	Silicon	Si	Yttrium	Y
Bromine	Br	Fluorine	F	Lithium	Li	Platinum	Pt	Silver	Ag	Zinc	Zn
Cadmium	Cd	Francium	Fr	Lutetium	Lu	Plutonium	Pu	Sodium	Na	Zirconium	Zr
Calcium	Ca	Gadolinium	Gd	Magnesium	Mg	Polonium	Po	Strontium	Sr		
Californium	Cf	Gallium	Ga	Manganese	Mn	Potassium	K	Sulfur	S		
Carbon	C	Germanium	Ge	Meitnerium	Mt	Praseodymium	Pr	Tantalum	Ta		
Cerium	Ce	Gold	Au	Mendelevium	Md	Promethium	Pm	Technetium	Tc		

Appendix B
Observing the Sky

OBSERVING THE SKY WITH THE NAKED EYE is as important to modern astronomy as picking up pretty pebbles is to modern geology. Nevertheless, the sky is inspiring—a natural wonder unimaginably bigger than the Grand Canyon, the Rocky Mountains, or any other site that tourists visit every year. To neglect the beauty of the sky is equivalent to geologists neglecting the beauty of the minerals they study. This supplement is meant to act as a tourist's guide to the sky. You analyzed the universe in the textbook's chapters; here you can admire it.

The brighter stars in the sky are visible even from the centers of cities with their air and light pollution. But in the countryside, only a few miles beyond the cities, the night sky is a velvety blackness strewn with thousands of glittering stars. From a wilderness location, far from the city's glare, and especially from high mountains, the night sky is spectacular.

Using Star Charts

THE CONSTELLATIONS ARE A FASCINATING CULTURAL HERITAGE of our planet, but they are sometimes a bit difficult to learn because of Earth's motion. The constellations above the horizon change with the time of night and the seasons.

Because Earth rotates eastward, the sky appears to rotate westward around Earth. A constellation visible overhead soon after sunset will appear to move westward, and in a few hours it will disappear below the horizon. Other constellations will rise in the east, so the sky changes gradually through the night.

In addition, Earth's orbital motion makes the sun appear to move eastward among the stars. Each day the sun moves about twice its own diameter, or about one degree, eastward along the ecliptic; consequently, each night at sunset, the constellations are shifted about one degree farther toward the west.

Orion, for instance, is visible in the evening sky in January; but, as the days pass, the sun moves closer to Orion. By March, Orion is difficult to see in the western sky soon after sunset. By June, the sun is so close to Orion it sets with the sun and is invisible. Not until late July is the sun far enough past Orion for the constellation to become visible rising in the eastern sky just before dawn.

Because of the rotation and orbital motion of Earth, you need more than one star chart to map the sky. Which chart you select depends on the month and the time of night.

Two sets of charts are included for two typical locations on Earth. The Northern Hemisphere star charts show the sky as seen from a northern latitude typical for the United States and Central Europe. The Southern Hemisphere star charts are appropriate for readers in Earth's Southern Hemisphere, including Australia, southern South America, and southern Africa.

To use the charts, select the appropriate chart and hold it overhead as shown in ■Figure B-1. If you face south, turn the chart until the words *Southern Horizon* are at the bottom of the chart. If you face other directions, turn the chart appropriately.

■**Figure B-1**

To use the star charts in this book, select the appropriate chart for the season and time. Hold it overhead and turn it until the direction at the bottom of the chart is the same as the direction you are facing.

Northern Hemisphere Sky

JANUARY
Early in Month	9 P.M.
Midmonth	8 P.M.
End of Month	7 P.M.

Months along the ecliptic show the location of the sun during the year.

Numbers along the celestial equator show right ascension.

Northern Hemisphere Sky

FEBRUARY
Early in Month	9 P.M.
Midmonth	8 P.M.
End of Month	7 P.M.

Months along the ecliptic show the location of the sun during the year.

Numbers along the celestial equator show right ascension.

Northern Hemisphere Sky

MARCH

Early in Month	9 P.M.
Midmonth	8 P.M.
End of Month	7 P.M.

Months along the ecliptic show the location of the sun during the year.

Numbers along the celestial equator show right ascension.

Northern Hemisphere Sky

APRIL

Early in Month	9 P.M.
Midmonth	8 P.M.
End of Month	7 P.M.

Months along the ecliptic show the location of the sun during the year.

Numbers along the celestial equator show right ascension.

Northern Hemisphere Sky

MAY

Early in Month	9 P.M.
Midmonth	8 P.M.
End of Month	7 P.M.

Months along the ecliptic show the location of the sun during the year.

Numbers along the celestial equator show right ascension.

Northern Hemisphere Sky

JUNE

Early in Month	9 P.M.
Midmonth	8 P.M.
End of Month	7 P.M.

Months along the ecliptic show the location of the sun during the year.

Numbers along the celestial equator show right ascension.

Northern Hemisphere Sky

JULY

Early in Month	9 P.M.
Midmonth	8 P.M.
End of Month	7 P.M.

Months along the ecliptic show the location of the sun during the year.

Numbers along the celestial equator show right ascension.

Northern Hemisphere Sky

AUGUST

Early in Month	9 P.M.
Midmonth	8 P.M.
End of Month	7 P.M.

Months along the ecliptic show the location of the sun during the year.

Numbers along the celestial equator show right ascension.

Northern Hemisphere Sky

SEPTEMBER

Early in Month	9 P.M.
Midmonth	8 P.M.
End of Month	7 P.M.

Months along the ecliptic show the location of the sun during the year.

Numbers along the celestial equator show right ascension.

Northern Hemisphere Sky

OCTOBER

Early in Month	9 P.M.
Midmonth	8 P.M.
End of Month	7 P.M.

Months along the ecliptic show the location of the sun during the year.

Numbers along the celestial equator show right ascension.

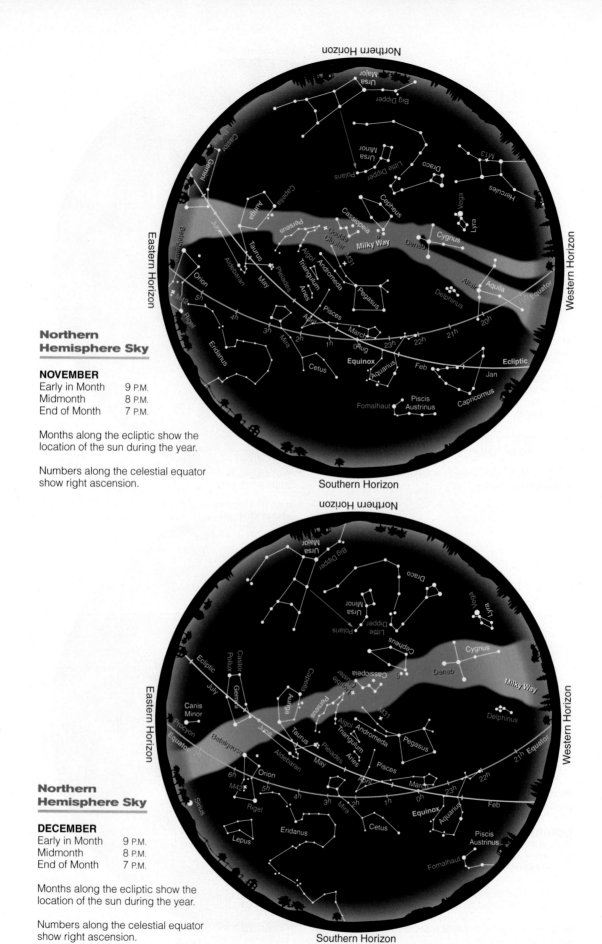

Northern Hemisphere Sky

NOVEMBER

Early in Month	9 P.M.
Midmonth	8 P.M.
End of Month	7 P.M.

Months along the ecliptic show the location of the sun during the year.

Numbers along the celestial equator show right ascension.

Northern Hemisphere Sky

DECEMBER

Early in Month	9 P.M.
Midmonth	8 P.M.
End of Month	7 P.M.

Months along the ecliptic show the location of the sun during the year.

Numbers along the celestial equator show right ascension.

Southern Hemisphere Sky

JANUARY

Early in Month	9 P.M.
Midmonth	8 P.M.
End of Month	7 P.M.

Months along the ecliptic show the location of the sun during the year.

Numbers along the celestial equator show right ascension.

Southern Hemisphere Sky

FEBRUARY

Early in Month	9 P.M.
Midmonth	8 P.M.
End of Month	7 P.M.

Months along the ecliptic show the location of the sun during the year.

Numbers along the celestial equator show right ascension.

Southern Hemisphere Sky

MARCH

Early in Month	9 P.M.
Midmonth	8 P.M.
End of Month	7 P.M.

Months along the ecliptic show the location of the sun during the year.

Numbers along the celestial equator show right ascension.

Northern Horizon

Southern Horizon

Southern Hemisphere Sky

APRIL

Early in Month	9 P.M.
Midmonth	8 P.M.
End of Month	7 P.M.

Months along the ecliptic show the location of the sun during the year.

Numbers along the celestial equator show right ascension.

Northern Horizon

Southern Hemisphere Sky

MAY

Early in Month	9 P.M.
Midmonth	8 P.M.
End of Month	7 P.M.

Months along the ecliptic show the location of the sun during the year.

Numbers along the celestial equator show right ascension.

Southern Hemisphere Sky

JUNE

Early in Month	9 P.M.
Midmonth	8 P.M.
End of Month	7 P.M.

Months along the ecliptic show the location of the sun during the year.

Numbers along the celestial equator show right ascension.

Southern Hemisphere Sky

JULY

Early in Month	9 P.M.
Midmonth	8 P.M.
End of Month	7 P.M.

Months along the ecliptic show the location of the sun during the year.

Numbers along the celestial equator show right ascension.

Southern Hemisphere Sky

AUGUST

Early in Month	9 P.M.
Midmonth	8 P.M.
End of Month	7 P.M.

Months along the ecliptic show the location of the sun during the year.

Numbers along the celestial equator show right ascension.

Southern Horizon

Musca
Chamaeleon
Mensa
LMC
Crux
Apus
Octans
Hydrus
SMC
Achernar
β
SCP
α
Circinus
Triangulum
Australe
Pavo
Tucana
Phoenix
Norma
Ara
Lupus
Indus
Grus
Telescopium
Alnair
Sculptor
Corona
Australis
Fomalhaut
Libra
Scorpius
Microscopium
Piscis Austrinus
Antares
Sagittarius
Aquarius
Dec.
Ecliptic
Capricornus
Jan.
Equator
Feb.
Ophiuchus
Milky Way
Scutum
21ʰ
22ʰ
Pisces
17ʰ
Serpens
18ʰ
19ʰ
Equuleus
Pegasus
Hercules
Aquila
Altair
Sagitta
Delphinus
Vulpecula
Vega
Lyra
Cygnus

**Southern
Hemisphere Sky**

SEPTEMBER

Early in Month	9 P.M.
Midmonth	8 P.M.
End of Month	7 P.M.

Months along the ecliptic show the location of the sun during the year.

Numbers along the celestial equator show right ascension.

Western Horizon

Eastern Horizon

Northern Horizon

Southern Horizon

Musca
Chamaeleon
Mensa
LMC
Dorado
Circinus
Apus
SCP
Hydrus
Reticulum
Centaurus
Triangulum
Australe
Octans
SMC
Horologium
Norma
Ara
Pavo
Achernar
Eridanus
Lupus
Milky Way
Telescopium
Tucana
Phoenix
Scorpius
Indus
Alnair
Grus
Dec.
Corona
Australis
Microscopium
Sculptor
Ophiuchus
Sagittarius
Piscis Austrinus
Fomalhaut
Diphda
Cetus
Scutum
Jan.
Capricornus
Aquarius
Feb.
Ecliptic
March
Equator
0ʰ
1ʰ
Aquila
21ʰ
22ʰ
23ʰ
Pisces
Altair
Delphinus
Equuleus
Sagitta
Vulpecula
Pegasus
Cygnus

**Southern
Hemisphere Sky**

OCTOBER

Early in Month	9 P.M.
Midmonth	8 P.M.
End of Month	7 P.M.

Months along the ecliptic show the location of the sun during the year.

Numbers along the celestial equator show right ascension.

Western Horizon

Eastern Horizon

Northern Horizon

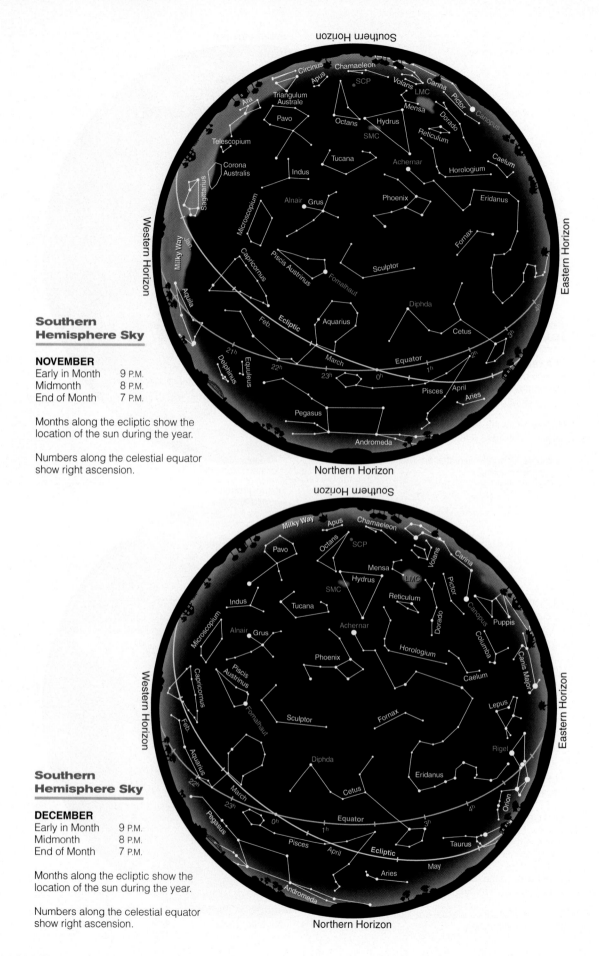

Southern Hemisphere Sky

NOVEMBER

Early in Month	9 P.M.
Midmonth	8 P.M.
End of Month	7 P.M.

Months along the ecliptic show the location of the sun during the year.

Numbers along the celestial equator show right ascension.

Southern Hemisphere Sky

DECEMBER

Early in Month	9 P.M.
Midmonth	8 P.M.
End of Month	7 P.M.

Months along the ecliptic show the location of the sun during the year.

Numbers along the celestial equator show right ascension.

Glossary

Numbers in parentheses refer to the page where the term is first discussed in the text.

absolute age (445) An age determined in years, as from radioactive dating (see also *relative age*).

absolute bolometric magnitude (172) The absolute magnitude you would observe if you could detect all wavelengths.

absolute visual magnitude (M_V) (171) Intrinsic brightness of a star; the apparent visual magnitude the star would have if it were 10 pc away.

absolute zero (127) The lowest possible temperature; the temperature at which the particles in a material, atoms or molecules, contain no energy of motion that can be extracted from the body.

absorption line (132) A dark line in a spectrum; produced by the absence of photons absorbed by atoms or molecules.

absorption (dark-line) spectrum (132) A spectrum that contains absorption lines.

acceleration (79) A change in a velocity; a change in either speed or direction. (See *velocity*.)

acceleration of gravity (77) A measure of the strength of gravity at a planet's surface.

accretion (409) The sticking together of solid particles to produce a larger particle.

accretion disk (264) The whirling disk of gas that forms around a compact object such as a white dwarf, neutron star, or black hole as matter is drawn in.

achondrite (553) Stony meteorite containing no chondrules or volatiles.

achromatic lens (102) A telescope lens composed of two lenses ground from different kinds of glass and designed to bring two selected colors to the same focus and correct for chromatic aberration.

active galactic nucleus (AGN) (356) The central energy source of an active galaxy.

active galaxy (356) A galaxy that is a source of excess radiation, usually radio waves, X-rays, gamma rays, or some combination.

active optics (111) Optical elements whose position or shape is continuously controlled by computers.

active region (155) An area on the sun where sunspots, prominences, flares, and the like occur.

adaptive optics (109) Computer-controlled telescope mirrors that can at least partially compensate for seeing.

albedo (437) The fraction of the light hitting an object that is reflected.

alt-azimuth mounting (111) A telescope mounting capable of motion parallel to and perpendicular to the horizon.

Amazonian period (488) On Mars, the geological era from about 3 billion years ago to the present marked by low-level cratering, wind erosion, and small amounts of water seeping from subsurface ice.

amino acid (584) One of the carbon-chain molecules that are the building blocks of protein.

Angstrom (Å) (100) A unit of distance; 1 Å = 10^{-10} m; often used to measure the wavelength of light.

angular diameter (19) A measure of the size of an object in the sky; numerically equal to the angle in degrees between two lines extending from the observer's eye to opposite edges of the object.

angular distance (19) A measure of the separation between two objects in the sky; numerically equal to the angle in degrees between two lines extending from the observer's eye to the two objects.

angular momentum (83) The tendency of a rotating body to continue rotating; mathematically, the product of mass, velocity, and radius.

angular momentum problem (399) An objection to Laplace's nebular hypothesis that cited the slow rotation of the sun.

annular eclipse (39) A solar eclipse in which the solar photosphere appears around the edge of the moon in a bright ring, or annulus. The corona, chromosphere, and prominences cannot be seen.

anorthosite (451) Rock of aluminum and calcium silicates found in the lunar highlands.

anticoded (595) Message designed to be understood by a recipient about whom the sender knows little or nothing, for example an interstellar broadcast aimed at possible inhabitants of another planet.

antimatter (376) Matter composed of antiparticles, which on colliding with a matching particle of normal matter annihilate and convert the mass of both particles into energy. The antiproton is the antiparticle of the proton, and the positron is the antiparticle of the electron.

aphelion (23) The orbital point of greatest distance from the sun.

apogee (39) The orbital point of greatest distance from Earth.

Apollo–Amor object (562) Asteroid whose orbit crosses that of Earth (Apollo) and Mars (Amor).

apparent visual magnitude (m_V) (15) The brightness of a star as seen by human eyes on Earth.

archaea (591) A biological kingdom of microorganisms similar to, but distinct from, bacteria, with characteristics most closely resembling those inferred for the common ancestor of all present-day Earth life.

arc minute (19) An angular measure; each degree is divided into 60 arc minutes.

arc second (19) An angular measure; each arc minute is divided into 60 arc seconds.

archaeoastronomy (50) The study of the astronomy of ancient cultures.

association (224) Group of widely scattered stars (10 to 1000) moving together through space; not gravitationally bound into a cluster.

asterism (13) A named group of stars not identified as a constellation, e.g., the Big Dipper.

asteroid (401) Small rocky world; most asteroids lie between Mars and Jupiter in the asteroid belt.

astrobiology (582) The field of study involving searches for life on other worlds and investigation of possible habitats for such life. Also known as "exobiology."

astronomical unit (AU) (4) Average distance from Earth to the sun; 1.5×10^8 km, or 93×10^6 miles.

atmospheric window (101) Wavelength region in which Earth's atmosphere is transparent—at visual, infrared, and radio wavelengths.

aurora (163) The glowing light display that results when a planet's magnetic field guides charged particles toward the north and south magnetic poles, where they strike the upper atmosphere and excite atoms to emit photons.

autumnal equinox (22) The point on the celestial sphere where the sun crosses the celestial equator going southward. Also, the time when the sun reaches this point and autumn begins in the Northern Hemisphere—about September 22.

Babcock model (158) A model of the sun's magnetic cycle in which the differential rotation of the sun winds up and tangles the solar magnetic field in a 22-year cycle. This is thought to be responsible for the 11-year sunspot cycle.

Balmer series (133) Spectral lines in the visible and near-ultraviolet spectrum of hydrogen produced by transitions whose lowest orbit is the second.

barred spiral galaxy (334) A spiral galaxy with an elongated nucleus resembling a bar from which the arms originate.

basalt (434) Dark, igneous rock characteristic of solidified lava.

belt–zone circulation (495) The atmospheric circulation typical of Jovian planets. Dark belts and bright zones encircle the planet parallel to its equator.

big bang (373) The theory that the universe began with a violent explosion from which the expanding universe of galaxies eventually formed.

big rip (388) The possible fate of the universe if dark energy increases rapidly and the expansion of space-time pulls galaxies, stars, and ultimately atoms apart.

binary star (178) One of a pair of stars that orbit around their common center of mass.

binding energy (124) The energy needed to pull an electron away from its atom.

biological evolution (586) The combined effect of variation and natural selection resulting in new species arising and existing species adapting to the environment or becoming extinct. Also called Darwinian evolution.

bipolar flow (223) Oppositely directed jets of gas ejected by some protostellar objects.

birth line (220) In the H–R diagram, the line above the main sequence where protostars first become visible.

blackbody radiation (127) Radiation emitted by a hypothetical perfect radiator; the spectrum is continuous, and the wavelength of maximum emission depends only on the body's temperature.

black dwarf (259) The end state of a white dwarf that has cooled to low temperature.

black hole (291) A mass that has collapsed to such a small volume that its gravity prevents the escape of all radiation; also, the volume of space from which radiation may not escape.

blueshift (138) The shortening of the wavelengths of light observed when the source and observer are approaching each other.

Bok globule (216) Small, dark, and dense interstellar cloud only about 1 ly in diameter that contains 10 to 1000 $M_\odot$ of gas and dust; thought to be related to star formation.

bow shock (431) The boundary between the undisturbed solar wind and the region being deflected around a planet or comet.

breccia (451) A rock composed of fragments of earlier rocks bonded together.

bright-line spectrum (132) See *emission spectrum*.

brown dwarf (237) A very cool, low-luminosity star whose mass is not sufficient to ignite nuclear fusion.

butterfly diagram (155) See *Maunder butterfly diagram*.

CAI (555) Calcium–aluminum-rich inclusions found in some meteorites.

calibrate (306) To make observations of reference objects, checks on instrument performance, calculations of units conversions, etc. needed to completely understand measurements of unknown quantities.

Cambrian explosion (589) The sudden appearance of complex life forms at the beginning of the Cambrian period 0.6 to 0.5 billion years ago. Cambrian rocks contain the oldest easily identifiable fossils.

carbonaceous chondrite (552) Stony meteorite that contains both chondrules and volatiles. These may be the least altered remains of the solar nebula still present in the solar system.

carbon deflagration (271) The process in which the carbon in a white dwarf is completely consumed by nuclear fusion, producing a type Ia supernova explosion.

carbon–nitrogen–oxygen (CNO) cycle (226) A series of nuclear reactions that use carbon as a catalyst to combine four hydrogen atoms to make one helium atom plus energy; effective in stars more massive than the sun.

Cassegrain focus (110) The optical design of a reflecting telescope in which the secondary mirror reflects light back down the tube through a hole in the center of the objective mirror.

catastrophic hypothesis (398) Explanation for natural processes that depends on dramatic and unlikely events, such as the collision of two stars to produce our solar system.

celestial equator (17) The imaginary line around the sky directly above Earth's equator.

celestial sphere (18) An imaginary sphere of very large radius surrounding Earth to which the planets, stars, sun, and moon seem to be attached.

centaur (563) An outer solar system body with an orbit entirely within the region of the Jovian planets, for example Chiron, that orbits between Saturn and Uranus.

center of mass (85) The balance point of a body or system of bodies.

central bulge (309) The spheroidal cloud of stars at the center of most spiral galaxies including our Milky Way Galaxy.

Cepheid variable star (247) Variable star with a period of 1 to 60 days; the period of variation is related to luminosity.

Chandrasekhar limit (262) The maximum mass of a white dwarf, about 1.4 $M_\odot$; a white dwarf of greater mass cannot support itself and will collapse.

charge-coupled device (CCD) (113) An electronic device consisting of a large array of light-sensitive elements used to record very faint images.

chemical evolution (589) The chemical process that led to the growth of complex molecules on the primitive Earth. This did not involve the reproduction of molecules.

Chicxulub (576) The buried crater associated with the mass extinction event at the end of the age of dinosaurs, named after the town in the coastal region of Mexico's Yucatan peninsula near the center of the crater.

chondrite (553) A stony meteorite that contains chondrules.

chondrule (553) Round, glassy body in some stony meteorites; thought to have solidified very quickly from molten drops of silicate material.

chromatic aberration (102) A distortion found in refracting telescopes because lenses focus different colors at slightly different distances. Images are consequently surrounded by color fringes.

chromosome (585) One of the bodies in a cell that contains the DNA carrying genetic information.

chromosphere (41) Bright gases just above the photosphere of the sun.

circular velocity (84) The velocity required to remain in a circular orbit about a body.

circumpolar constellation (19) Any of the constellations so close to the celestial pole that they never set (or never rise) as seen from a given latitude.

closed orbit (85) An orbit that returns to its starting point; a circular or elliptical orbit. (See *open orbit*.)

closed universe (381) A model universe in which the average density is great enough to stop the expansion and make the universe contract.

cluster method (340) The method of determining the masses of galaxies based on the motions of galaxies in a cluster.

CNO cycle (226) See *carbon–nitrogen–oxygen cycle*.

cocoon (214) The cloud of gas and dust around a contracting protostar that conceals it at visible wavelengths.

cold dark matter (383) Invisible matter in the universe composed by heavy, slow-moving particles such as WIMPs.

coma (568) The glowing head of a comet.

comet (404) One of the small, icy bodies that orbit the sun and produce tails of gas and dust when they near the sun.

compact object (259) A star that has collapsed to form a white dwarf, neutron star, or black hole.

comparative planetology (425) The study of planets by comparing the characteristics of different examples.

comparison spectrum (113) A spectrum of known spectral lines used to identify unknown wavelengths in an object's spectrum.

composite volcano (472) A volcano built up of layers of lava flows and ash falls. These are steep sided and typically associated with subduction zones.

condensation (409) The growth of a particle by addition of material from surrounding gas, one atom or molecule at a time.

condensation sequence (408) The sequence in which different materials condense from the solar nebula at increasing distances from the sun.

conservation of energy law (233) One of the basic laws of stellar structure. The amount of energy flowing out of the top of a shell must equal the amount coming in at the bottom plus whatever energy is generated within the shell.

conservation of mass law (233) One of the basic laws of stellar structure. The total mass of the star must equal the sum of the masses of the shells, and the mass must be distributed smoothly throughout the star.

constellation (12) One of the stellar patterns identified by name, usually of mythological gods, people, animals, or objects; also, the region of the sky containing that star pattern.

continuous spectrum (132) A spectrum in which there are no absorption or emission lines.

convection (145) Circulation in a fluid driven by heat; hot material rises, and cool material sinks.

convective zone (152) The region inside a star where energy is carried outward as rising hot gas and sinking cool gas.

cooling line (214) A far-infrared spectral emission line that releases energy from the insides of contracting protostellar clouds, allowing rapid contraction to continue.

corona (41) The faint outer atmosphere of the sun; composed of low-density, very hot, ionized gas. On Venus, round networks of fractures and ridges up to 1000 km in diameter.

coronae (471) On Venus, large, round geological faults in the crust caused by the intrusion of magma below the crust.

coronagraph (146) A telescope designed to photograph the inner corona of the sun.

coronal gas (204) Extremely high-temperature, low-density gas in the interstellar medium.

coronal hole (163) An area of the solar surface that is dark at X-ray wavelengths; thought to be associated with divergent magnetic fields and the source of the solar wind.

coronal mass ejection (CME) (163) Gas trapped in the sun's magnetic field.

cosmic microwave background radiation (375) Radiation from the hot clouds of the big bang explosion. Because of its large redshift, it appears to come from a body whose temperature is only 2.7 K.

cosmic ray (119) A subatomic particle traveling at tremendous velocity that strikes Earth's atmosphere from space.

cosmological constant (Λ) (387) Einstein's constant that represents a repulsion in space to oppose gravity.

cosmological principle (380) The assumption that any observer in any galaxy sees the same general features of the universe.

cosmologist (371) An astronomer or physicist whose research focuses on the overall properties of the universe and its origin.

cosmology (370) The study of the nature, origin, and evolution of the universe.

Coulomb barrier (152) The electrostatic force of repulsion between bodies of like charge; commonly applied to atomic nuclei.

Coulomb force (124) The repulsive force between particles with like electrostatic charge.

critical density (382) The average density of the universe needed to make its curvature flat.

critical point (496) The temperature and pressure at which the vapor and liquid phases of a material have the same density.

C-type asteroid (564) A type of asteroid common in the outer asteroid belt, with very low reflectivity and grayish color, probably composed of carbonaceous material.

dark age (378) The period of a few hundred million years during which the universe expanded in darkness. Extends from soon after the big bang glow faded into the infrared to the formation of the first stars.

dark energy (387) The energy of empty space that drives the acceleration of the expanding universe.

dark-line spectrum (132) See *absorption spectrum.*

dark matter (311) Nonluminous material that is detected only by its gravitational influence.

dark nebula (195) A nonluminous cloud of gas and dust visible because it blocks light from more distant stars and nebulae.

debris disk (415) A disk of dust found by infrared observations around some stars. The dust is debris from collisions among asteroids, comets, and Kuiper belt objects.

deferent (57) In the Ptolemaic theory, the large circle around Earth along which the center of the epicycle moved.

degenerate matter (241) Extremely high-density matter in which pressure no longer depends on temperature, due to quantum mechanical effects.

density (137) The amount of matter per unit volume in a material; measured in grams per cubic centimeter, for example.

density wave theory (315) Theory proposed to account for spiral arms as compressions of the interstellar medium in the disk of the galaxy.

deuterium (151) An isotope of hydrogen in which the nucleus contains a proton and a neutron.

diamond ring effect (41) A momentary phenomenon seen during some total solar eclipses when the ring of the corona and a bright spot of photosphere resemble a large diamond set in a silvery ring.

differential rotation (158) The rotation of a body in which different parts of the body have different periods of rotation; this is true of the sun, the Jovian planets, and the disk of the galaxy.

differentiation (410) The separation of planetary material according to density.

diffraction fringe (104) Blurred fringe surrounding any image caused by the wave properties of light. Because of this, no image detail smaller than the fringe can be seen.

direct collapse (412) The hypothetical process by which a Jovian planet might skip the accretion of a solid core, instead forming quickly and directly from the gases of the solar nebula.

disk component (308) All material confined to the plane of the galaxy.

distance indicator (337) Object whose luminosity or diameter is known; used to find the distance to a star cluster or galaxy.

distance modulus ($m_V - M_V$) (172) The difference between the apparent and absolute magnitude of a star; a measure of how far away the star is.

distance scale (338) The combined calibration of distance indicators used by astronomers to find the distances to remote galaxies.

DNA (deoxyribonucleic acid) (584) The long carbon-chain molecule that records information to govern the biological activity of the organism. DNA carries the genetic data passed to offspring.

Doppler effect (137) The change in the wavelength of radiation due to relative radial motion of source and observer.

double-exhaust model (360) The theory that double radio lobes are produced by pairs of jets emitted in opposite directions from the centers of active galaxies.

double-lobed radio galaxy (358) A galaxy that emits radio energy from two regions (lobes) located on opposite sides of the galaxy.

Drake equation (596) A formula for the number of communicative civilizations in our galaxy.

dust (type II) tail (568) The tail of a comet formed of dust blown outward by the pressure of sunlight. (See *gas tail.*)

dwarf planet (546) An object that orbits the sun and has pulled itself into a spherical shape but has not cleared its orbital lane of other objects. Pluto is a dwarf planet.

dynamo effect (158) The process by which a rotating, convecting body of conducting matter, such as Earth's core, can generate a magnetic field.

east point (18) The point on the eastern horizon exactly halfway between the north point and the south point; exactly east.

eccentric (55) (noun) An off-center circular path. (Note that the *adjective* "eccentric" refers instead to an ellipse that is not a perfect circle.)

eccentricity (e) (64) A measure of the flattening of an ellipse. An ellipse of $e = 0$ is circular. The closer to 1 e becomes, the more flattened the ellipse.

eclipse season (43) That period when the sun is near a node of the moon's orbit and eclipses are possible.

eclipse year (44) The time the sun takes to circle the sky and return to a node of the moon's orbit; 346.62 days.

eclipsing binary (183) A binary star system in which the stars eclipse each other.

ecliptic (21) The apparent path of the sun around the sky.

ejecta (446) Pulverized rock scattered by meteorite impacts on a planetary surface.

electromagnetic radiation (99) Changing electric and magnetic fields that travel through space and transfer energy from one place to another—for example, light, radio waves, and the like.

electron (123) Low-mass atomic particle carrying a negative charge.

ellipse (64) A closed curve enclosing two points (foci) such that the total distance from one focus to any point on the curve back to the other focus equals a constant.

elliptical galaxy (334) A galaxy that is round or elliptical in outline; it contains little gas and dust, no disk or spiral arms, and few hot, bright stars.

emission line (132) A bright line in a spectrum caused by the emission of photons from atoms.

emission nebula (194) A cloud of glowing gas excited by ultraviolet radiation from hot stars.

emission (bright-line) spectrum (132) A spectrum containing emission lines.

energy (86) The capacity of a natural system to perform work—for example, thermal energy.

energy level (126) One of a number of states an electron may occupy in an atom, depending on its binding energy.

energy transport (225) The law of energy transport states that energy must flow from hot regions to cool regions by conduction, convection, or radiation.

enzyme (584) Special protein that controls processes in an organism.

epicycle (57) The small circle followed by a planet in the Ptolemaic theory. The center of the epicycle follows a larger circle (deferent) around Earth.

equant (57) The point off-center in the deferent from which the center of the epicycle appears to move uniformly.

equatorial mounting (111) A telescope mounting that allows motion parallel to and perpendicular to the celestial equator.

escape velocity (V_e) (85) The initial velocity an object needs to escape from the surface of a celestial body.

evening star (24) Any planet visible in the sky just after sunset.

event horizon (292) The boundary of the region of a black hole from which no radiation may escape. No event that occurs within the event horizon is visible to a distant observer.

evolutionary hypothesis (398) Explanation for natural events that involves gradual changes as opposed to sudden catastrophic changes—for example, the formation of the planets in the gas cloud around the forming sun.

excited atom (126) An atom in which an electron has moved from a lower to a higher orbit.

expanding universe (372) The idea, supported by observed redshifts of galaxies, that space is stretching, carrying galaxies and galaxy clusters away from each other.

extrasolar planet (417) A planet orbiting a star other than the sun.

extremophile (591) An organism that can survive in an extreme environment, for example, very low or high temperatures, high acidity, extreme dryness, etc.

eyepiece (102) A short-focal-length lens used to enlarge the image in a telescope; the lens nearest the eye.

fall (552) A meteorite seen to fall. (See *find*.)

false-color image (113) A representation of graphical data in which the colors are altered or added to reveal details.

field (81) A way of explaining action at a distance; a particle produces a field of influence (gravitational, electric, or magnetic) to which another particle in the field responds.

field of view (2) The area visible in an image; usually given as the diameter of the region.

filament (162, 389) (1) On the sun, a prominence seen silhouetted against the solar surface. (2) A linear region containing many galaxies and galaxy clusters, part of the large-scale structure of the universe.

filtergram (146) An image (usually of the sun) taken in the light of a specific region of the spectrum—for example, an H-alpha filtergram.

find (552) A meteorite that is found but was not seen to fall. (See *fall*.)

flare (163) A violent eruption on the sun's surface.

flatness problem (384) In cosmology, the circumstance that the early universe must have contained almost exactly the right amount of matter to close space-time (to make space-time flat).

flat universe (381) A model of the universe in which space-time is not curved.

flocculent (316) Woolly, fluffy; used to refer to certain galaxies that have a woolly appearance.

flux (15, 171) A measure of the flow of energy onto or through a surface. Usually applied to light.

focal length (102) The distance from a lens to the point where it focuses parallel rays of light.

folded mountain range (434) A long range of mountains formed by the compression of a planet's crust—for example, the Andes on Earth.

forbidden line (196) A spectral line that does not occur in the laboratory because it depends on an atomic transition that is highly unlikely.

forward scattering (499) The optical property of finely divided particles to preferentially direct light in the original direction of the light's travel.

free-fall collapse (213) The early contraction of a gas cloud to form a star during which internal pressure is too low to resist contraction.

frequency (99) The number of times a given event occurs in a given time; for a wave, the number of cycles that pass the observer in 1 second.

galactic cannibalism (348) The theory that large galaxies absorb smaller galaxies.

galactic corona (311) The low-density extension of the halo of a galaxy; now suspected to extend many times the visible diameter of the galaxy.

galactic fountain (323–324) A region of the galaxy's disk in which gas heated by supernova explosions throws gas out of the disk where it can fall back and spread metals through the disk.

galaxy (5) A very large collection of gas, dust, and stars orbiting a common center of mass. The sun and Earth are located in the Milky Way Galaxy.

Galilean moons, Galilean satellites (68, 504) The four largest satellites of Jupiter, named after their discoverer, Galileo.

gamma-ray burst (297) A sudden burst of gamma rays thought to be associated with neutron stars and black holes.

gas (type I) tail (568) The tail of a comet produced by gas blown outward by the solar wind. (See *dust tail*.)

gene (585) A unit of DNA containing genetic information that influences a particular inherited trait.

general theory of relativity (92) Einstein's more sophisticated theory of space and time, which describes gravity as a curvature of space-time.

geocentric universe (54) A model universe with Earth at the center, such as the Ptolemaic universe.

geosynchronous satellite (84) An Earth satellite in an eastward orbit whose period is 24 hours. A satellite in such an orbit remains above the same spot on Earth's surface.

giant (175) Large, cool, highly luminous star in the upper right of the H–R diagram, typically 10 to 100 times the diameter of the sun.

giant molecular cloud (204) Very large, cool cloud of dense gas in which stars form.

global warming (437) The gradual increase in the surface temperature of Earth caused by human modifications to Earth's atmosphere.

globular cluster (248) A star cluster containing 50,000 to 1 million stars in a sphere about 75 ly in diameter; generally old, metal-poor, and found in the spherical component of the galaxy.

gossamer ring (502) The dimmest part of Jupiter's ring produced by dust particles orbiting near small moons.

grand design (316) Galaxy with a high-contrast simple 2-arm spiral pattern.

grand unified theory (GUT) (385) Theory that attempts to unify (describe in a similar way) the electromagnetic, weak, and strong forces of nature.

granulation (144) The fine structure visible on the solar surface caused by rising currents of hot gas and sinking currents of cool gas below the surface.

grating (113) A piece of material in which numerous microscopic parallel lines are scribed; light encountering a grating is dispersed to form a spectrum.

gravitational collapse (410) The stage in the formation of a massive planet when it grows massive enough to begin capturing gas directly from the nebula around it.

gravitational lensing (343) The effect of the focusing of light from a distant galaxy or quasar by an intervening galaxy to produce multiple images of the distant body.

gravitational radiation (286) As predicted by general relativity, expanding waves in a gravitational field that transport energy through space.

gravitational redshift (293) The lengthening of the wavelength of a photon due to its escape from a gravitational field.

greenhouse effect (437) The process by which a carbon dioxide atmosphere traps heat and raises the temperature of a planetary surface.

grooved terrain (505) Region of the surface of Ganymede consisting of bright, parallel grooves.

ground state (126) The lowest permitted electron orbit in an atom.

habitable zone (594) The region around a star within which an orbiting planet can have surface temperatures allowing liquid water.

half-life (405) The time required for half of the atoms in a radioactive sample to decay.

halo (309) The spherical region of a spiral galaxy containing a thin scattering of stars, star clusters, and small amounts of gas.

heat (127) Energy flowing from a warm body to a cool body by the agitation of particles such as atoms or molecules.

heat of formation (410) In planetology, the heat released by the infall of matter during the formation of a planetary body.

heavy bombardment (413) The period of intense meteorite impacts early in the formation of the planets, when the solar system was filled with debris.

heliocentric universe (58) A model of the universe with the sun at the center, such as the Copernican universe.

helioseismology (148) The study of the interior of the sun by the analysis of its modes of vibration.

helium flash (242) The explosive ignition of helium burning that takes place in some giant stars.

Herbig–Haro object (223) A small nebula associated with star formation that varies irregularly in brightness.

Hertzsprung–Russell (H–R) diagram (174) A plot of the intrinsic brightness versus the surface temperature of stars; it separates the effects of temperature and surface area on stellar luminosity; commonly absolute magnitude versus spectral type but also luminosity versus surface temperature or color.

Hesperian period (488) On Mars, the geological era from the decline of heavy cratering and lava flows and the melting of subsurface ice to form the outflow channels.

HI cloud (202) An interstellar cloud of neutral hydrogen.

HII region (194) A region of ionized hydrogen around a hot star.

Hirayama family (564) Family of asteroids with orbits of similar size, shape, and orientation; thought to be fragments of larger bodies.

homogeneous (380) The property of being uniform. In cosmology, the characteristic of the universe in which, on the large scale, matter is uniformly spread through the universe.

horizon (18) The line that marks the apparent intersection of Earth and the sky.

horizon problem (384) In cosmology, the circumstance that the primordial background radiation seems much more isotropic than could be explained by the standard big bang theory.

horizontal branch (249) In the H–R diagram of a globular cluster, the sequence of stars extending from the red giants toward the blue side of the diagram; includes RR Lyrae stars.

horoscope (25) A chart showing the positions of the sun, moon, planets, and constellations at the time of a person's birth; used in astrology to attempt to read character or foretell the future.

hot dark matter (383) Invisible matter in the universe composed of low-mass, high-velocity particles such as neutrinos.

hot Jupiter (419) A massive and presumably Jovian planet that orbits close to its star and consequently has a high temperature.

hot spot (360) In radio astronomy, a bright spot in a radio lobe.

H–R diagram (174) See *Hertzsprung–Russell diagram*.

Hubble constant (H) (339) A measure of the rate of expansion of the universe; the average value of dvelocity of recession divided by distance; about 70 km/s/megaparsec.

Hubble law (339) The linear relation between the distance to a galaxy and its radial velocity.

Hubble time (374) An upper limit on the age of the universe derived from the Hubble constant.

hydrostatic equilibrium (225) The balance between the weight of the material pressing downward on a layer in a star and the pressure in that layer.

hypernova (297) The explosion produced as a very massive star collapses into a black hole; thought to be responsible for at least some gamma-ray bursts.

hypothesis (66) A conjecture, subject to further tests, that accounts for a set of facts.

ice line (408) In the solar nebula, the boundary beyond which water vapor and other compounds could form ice particles.

inflationary universe (385) A version of the big bang theory that includes a rapid expansion when the universe was very young.

infrared radiation (100) Electromagnetic radiation with wavelengths intermediate between visible light and radio waves.

inner Lagrangian point (263) The point of gravitational equilibrium between two orbiting stars through which matter can flow from one star to the other.

instability strip (250) The region of the H–R diagram in which stars are unstable to pulsation; a star passing through this strip becomes a variable star.

intercloud medium (202) The hot, low-density gas between cooler clouds in the interstellar medium.

intercrater plain (459) The relatively smooth terrain on Mercury.

interferometry (112) The observing technique in which separated telescopes combine to produce a virtual telescope with the resolution of a much-larger-diameter telescope.

interstellar absorption line (197) One of the dark lines in some stellar spectra that are formed by interstellar gas.

interstellar dust (196) Microscopic solid grains in the interstellar medium.

interstellar extinction (196) The dimming of starlight by gas and dust in the interstellar medium.

interstellar medium (ISM) (193) The gas and dust distributed between the stars.

interstellar reddening (196) The process in which dust scatters blue light out of starlight and makes the stars look redder.

intrinsic brightness (171) The true brightness of an object independent of its distance. Also referred to as luminosity.

intrinsic variable star (247) A variable star driven to pulsate by processes in its interior.

inverse square law (81) The rule that the strength of an effect (such as gravity) decreases in proportion as the distance squared increases.

Io flux tube (498) A tube of magnetic lines and electric currents connecting Io and Jupiter.

Io plasma torus (498) The doughnut-shaped cloud of ionized gas that encloses the orbit of Jupiter's moon Io.

ion (124) An atom that has lost or gained one or more electrons.

ionization (124) The process in which atoms lose or gain electrons.

iron meteorite (552) A meteorite composed mainly of iron–nickel alloy.

irregular galaxy (335) A galaxy with a chaotic appearance, large clouds of gas and dust, and both population I and population II stars, but without spiral arms.

irregular satellite (495) A moon with an orbit that has large eccentricity and/or high inclination to the equator of its parent planet and/or is retrograde. Irregular moons are thought to been captured.

island universe (332) An older term for a galaxy.

isotopes (124) Atoms that have the same number of protons but a different number of neutrons.

isotropic (380) The conditions of being uniform in all directions. In cosmology, the characteristic of the universe by which, in its general properties, looks the same in every direction.

joule (J) (86) A unit of energy equivalent to a force of 1 newton acting over a distance of 1 meter; 1 joule per second equals 1 watt of power.

Jovian planet (402) Jupiter-like planet with large diameter and low density.

jumbled terrain (453) Disturbed regions of the moon's surface opposite the locations of the Imbrium Basin and Mare Orientale, possibly due to focusing of seismic waves from the large impacts that formed those basins.

Kelvin temperature scale (127) The temperature, in Celsius (centigrade) degrees, measured above absolute zero.

Keplerian motion (311) Orbital motion in accord with Kepler's laws of planetary motion.

kiloparsec (kpc) (303) A unit of distance equal to 1000 pc, or 3260 ly.

kinetic energy (86) Energy of motion. Depends on mass and velocity of a moving body.

Kirchhoff's laws (132) A set of laws that describe the absorption and emission of light by matter.

Kirkwood's gaps (562) Regions in the asteroid belt in which there are very few asteroids; caused by orbital resonances with Jupiter.

Kuiper belt (404) The collection of icy planetesimals that orbit in a region from just beyond Neptune out to about 50 AU.

Lagrangian point (263) Point of stability in the orbital plane of a binary star system, planet, or moon. One is located 60° ahead and one 60° behind the orbiting bodies; another is located between the orbiting bodies.

large-impact hypothesis (454) The hypothesis that the moon formed from debris ejected during a collision between Earth and a large planetesimal.

large-scale structure (389) The distribution of galaxy clusters and superclusters in walls and filaments surrounding voids mostly empty of galaxies.

late heavy bombardment (452) The surge in cratering impacts in the solar system that occurred about 3.8 billion years ago.

L dwarf (135) A type of star that is even cooler than the M stars.

light curve (183) A graph of brightness versus time commonly used in analyzing variable stars and eclipsing binaries.

light-gathering power (103) The ability of a telescope to collect light; proportional to the area of the telescope objective lens or mirror.

lighthouse model (282) The explanation of a pulsar as a spinning neutron star sweeping beams of radio radiation around the sky.

light pollution (106) The illumination of the night sky by waste light from cities and outdoor lighting, which prevents the observation of faint objects.

light-year (ly) (4) The distance light travels in one year.

limb (145, 444) The edge of the apparent disk of a body, as in "the limb of the moon."

limb darkening (145) The decrease in brightness of the sun or other body from its center to its limb.

line of nodes (44) The line across an orbit connecting the nodes; commonly applied to the orbit of the moon.

liquid metallic hydrogen (496) A form of hydrogen under high pressure that is a good electrical conductor.

lobate scarp (457) A curved cliff such as those found on Mercury.

local bubble or void (205) A region of high-temperature, low-density gas in the interstellar medium in which the sun happens to be located.

look-back time (338) The amount by which you look into the past when you look at a distant galaxy; a time equal to the distance to the galaxy in light-years.

luminosity (L) (172) The total amount of energy a star radiates in 1 second.

luminosity class (176) A category of stars of similar luminosity; determined by the widths of lines in their spectra.

lunar eclipse (33) The darkening of the moon when it moves through Earth's shadow.

Lyman series (133) Spectral lines in the ultraviolet spectrum of hydrogen produced by transitions whose lowest orbit is the ground state.

magnetar (297) A class of neutron stars that have exceedingly strong magnetic fields; thought to be responsible for soft gamma-ray repeaters.

magnetic carpet (147) The widely distributed, low-level magnetic field extending up through the sun's visible surface.

magnetosphere (431) The volume of space around a planet within which the motion of charged particles is dominated by the planetary magnetic field rather than the solar wind.

magnifying power (105) The ability of a telescope to make an image larger.

magnitude–distance formula (172) The mathematical formula that relates the apparent magnitude and absolute magnitude of a star to its distance.

magnitude scale (14) The astronomical brightness scale; the larger the number, the fainter the star.

main sequence (175) The region of the H–R diagram running from upper left to lower right, which includes roughly 90 percent of all stars.

mantle (426) The layer of dense rock and metal oxides that lies between the molten core and Earth's surface; also, similar layers in other planets.

mare (mä´rā) (442) (plural: **maria**) One of the lunar lowlands filled by successive flows of dark lava; from the Latin word for sea.

mass (79) A measure of the amount of matter making up an object.

mass–luminosity relation (188) The more massive a star is, the more luminous it is.

Maunder butterfly diagram (155) A graph showing the latitude of sunspots versus time; first plotted by W. W. Maunder in 1904.

Maunder minimum (155) A period of less numerous sunspots and other solar activity from 1645 to 1715.

megaparsec (Mpc) (336) A unit of distance equal to 1 million pc.

metal (319) In astronomical usage, any atom heavier than helium.

metastable level (196) An atomic energy level from which an electron takes a long time to decay; responsible for producing forbidden lines.

meteor (404) A small bit of matter heated by friction to incandescent vapor as it falls into Earth's atmosphere.

meteorite (405) A meteor that has survived its passage through the atmosphere and strikes the ground.

meteoroid (405) A meteor in space before it enters Earth's atmosphere.

meteor shower (556) An event lasting for hours or days in which the number of meteors entering Earth's atmosphere suddenly increases. The meteors in a shower have a common origin and are traveling through space on nearly parallel paths.

microlensing (418) Brightening of a background star due to focusing of its light by the gravity of a foreground extrasolar planet, allowing the planet to be detected and some of its characteristics measured.

micrometeorite (447) Meteorite of microscopic size.

midocean rise (434) One of the undersea mountain ranges that push up from the seafloor in the center of the oceans.

Milankovitch hypothesis (26) The hypothesis that small changes in Earth's orbital and rotational motions cause the ice ages.

Milky Way (6) The hazy band of light that circles the sky, produced by the combined light of billions of stars in our Milky Way Galaxy.

Milky Way Galaxy (6) The spiral galaxy containing the sun; visible at night as the Milky Way.

Miller experiment (587) An experiment that reproduced the conditions under which life began on Earth and amino acids and other organic compounds were manufactured.

millisecond pulsar (288) A pulsar with a period of approximately a millisecond, a thousandth of a second.

molecular cloud (203) An interstellar gas cloud that is dense enough for the formation of molecules; discovered and studied through the radio emissions of such molecules.

molecule (124) Two or more atoms bonded together.

momentum (79) The tendency of a moving object to continue moving; mathematically, the product of mass and velocity.

monolithic collapse hypothesis (325) The hypothesis that the Milky Way Galaxy formed by gravitational collapse of a single large spinning cloud of gas. This hypothesis is now considered inadequate to explain many observed characteristics of the Galaxy.

morning star (24) Any planet visible in the sky just before sunrise.

M-type asteroid (564) A type of asteroid with relatively high reflectivity and grayish color, probably composed primarily of metal.

multicellular (589) An organism composed of many cells.

multiringed basin (447) Very large impact basin in which there are concentric rings of mountains.

mutant (586) Offspring born with altered DNA.

nadir (18) The point on the bottom of the sky directly under your feet.

nanometer (nm) (100) A unit of length equal to 10-9 m.

natural law (66) A conjecture about how nature works in which scientists have overwhelming confidence.

natural motion (77) In Aristotelian physics, the motion of objects toward their natural places—fire and air upward and earth and water downward.

natural selection (586) The process by which the best traits are passed on, allowing the most able to survive.

neap tide (87) Ocean tide of low amplitude occurring at first- and third-quarter moon.

Near-Earth Object (NEO) (562) An asteroid or comet in an orbit that passes near or intersects Earth's orbit, that could potentially collide with Earth.

nebula (193) A cloud of gas and dust in space.

nebular hypothesis (398) The proposal that the solar system formed from a rotating cloud of gas.

neutrino (151) A neutral, massless atomic particle that travels at or nearly at the speed of light.

neutron (123) An atomic particle with no charge and about the same mass as a proton.

neutron star (280) A small, highly dense star composed almost entirely of tightly packed neutrons; radius about 10 km.

Newtonian focus (110) The focal arrangement of a reflecting telescope in which a diagonal mirror reflects light out the side of the telescope tube for easier access.

Noachian period (487) On Mars, the era that extends from the formation of the crust to the end of heavy cratering and includes the formation of the valley networks.

node (43) A point where an object's orbit passes through the plane of Earth's orbit.

nonbaryonic matter (383) In cosmology, a suspected component of the dark matter composed of matter that does not contain protons and neutrons.

north celestial pole (18) The point on the celestial sphere directly above Earth's North Pole.

north point (18) The point on the horizon directly below the north celestial pole; exactly north.

nova (264) From the Latin "new," a sudden brightening of a star, making it appear as a "new" star in the sky; thought to be associated with eruptions on white dwarfs in binary systems.

nuclear fission (150) Reaction that splits nuclei into less massive fragments.

nuclear fusion (150) Reaction that joins the nuclei of atoms to form more massive nuclei.

nucleosynthesis (322) The production of elements heavier than helium by the fusion of atomic nuclei in stars and during supernovae explosions.

nucleus (of an atom) (123) The central core of an atom containing protons and neutrons; carries a net positive charge.

OB association (224) A loosely bound cluster of young stars having spectral types O and B, indicating a region of relatively recent star formation.

objective lens or mirror (101-102) The main optical element in an astronomical telescope. The large lens at the top of the telescope or large mirror at the bottom.

oblateness (497) The flattening of a spherical body, usually caused by rotation.

observable universe (372) The part of the universe that is visible from Earth's location in space and time.

occultation (534) The passage of a larger body in front of a smaller body.

Olbers's paradox (371) The conflict between observation and theory as to why the night sky should or should not be dark.

Oort cloud (571) The cloud of icy bodies—extending from the outer part of our solar system out to roughly 100,000 AU from the sun—that acts as the source of most comets.

opacity (226) The resistance of a gas to the passage of radiation.

open cluster (248) A cluster of 10 to 10,000 stars with an open, transparent appearance and stars not tightly grouped; usually relatively young and located in the disk of the galaxy.

open orbit (85) An orbit that does not return to its starting point; an escape orbit. (See *closed orbit.*)

open universe (381) A model universe in which the average density is less than the critical density needed to halt the expansion.

outflow channel (483) Geological feature on Mars that appears to have been caused by sudden flooding.

outgassing (411) The release of gases from a planet's interior.

ovoid (537) Geological feature on Uranus's moon Miranda thought to be produced by circulation in the solid icy mantle and crust.

ozone layer (436) In Earth's atmosphere, a layer of oxygen ions (O_3) lying 15 to 30 km high that protects the surface by absorbing ultraviolet radiation.

paradigm (61) A commonly accepted set of scientific ideas and assumptions.

parallax (56) The apparent change in the position of an object due to a change in the location of the observer. Astronomical parallax is measured in seconds of arc.

parsec (pc) (169) The distance to a hypothetical star whose parallax is one second of arc; 1 pc = 206,265 AU = 3.26 ly.

partial lunar eclipse (36) A lunar eclipse in which the moon does not completely enter Earth's shadow.

partial solar eclipse (38) A solar eclipse in which the moon does not completely cover the sun.

Paschen series (133) Spectral lines in the infrared spectrum of hydrogen produced by transitions whose lowest orbit is the third.

passing star hypothesis (398) The proposal that our solar system formed when two stars passed near each other and material was pulled out of one to form the planets.

path of totality (39) The track of the moon's umbral shadow over Earth's surface. The sun is totally eclipsed as seen from within this path.

penumbra (33) The portion of a shadow that is only partially shaded.

penumbral lunar eclipse (37) A lunar eclipse in which the moon enters the penumbra of Earth's shadow but does not reach the umbra.

perigee (39) The orbital point of closest approach to Earth.

perihelion (23) The orbital point of closest approach to the sun.

period–luminosity relation (247) The relation between period of pulsation and intrinsic brightness among Cepheid variable stars.

permitted orbit (124) One of the energy levels in an atom that an electron may occupy.

photon (100) A quantum of electromagnetic energy; carries an amount of energy that depends inversely on its wavelength.

photosphere (41) The bright visible surface of the sun.

planet (3) A nonluminous object, larger than a comet or asteroid, that orbits a star.

planetary nebula (257) An expanding shell of gas ejected from a star during the latter stages of its evolution.

planetesimal (409) One of the small bodies that formed from the solar nebula and eventually grew into protoplanets.

plastic (431) A material with the properties of a solid but capable of flowing under pressure.

plate tectonics (434) The constant destruction and renewal of Earth's surface by the motion of sections of crust.

plutino (548) One of the icy Kuiper belt objects that, like Pluto, are caught in a 3:2 orbital resonance with Neptune.

polar axis (111) In an equatorial telescope mounting, the axis which is parallel to Earth's axis of rotation.

poor cluster (345) An irregularly shaped cluster that contains fewer than 1000 galaxies, many spiral, and no giant ellipticals.

population I star (319) Star rich in atoms heavier than helium; nearly always a relatively young star found in the disk of the galaxy.

population II star (319) Star poor in atoms heavier than helium; nearly always a relatively old star found in the halo, globular clusters, or the nuclear bulge.

positron (151) The antiparticle of the electron.

potential energy (86) The energy a body has by virtue of its position. A weight on a high shelf has more potential energy than a weight on a low shelf.

precession (17) The slow change in the direction of Earth's axis of rotation; one cycle takes nearly 26,000 years.

pressure (203) A force exerted over a surface; expressed as force per unit area.

pressure (P) wave (429) In geophysics, a mechanical wave of compression and rarefaction that travels through Earth's interior.

primary lens or mirror (101-102) The main optical element in an astronomical telescope. The large lens at the top of the telescope tube or the large mirror at the bottom.

prime focus (110) The point at which the objective mirror forms an image in a reflecting telescope.

primeval atmosphere (433) Earth's first air, composed of gases from the solar nebula.

primordial soup (588) The rich solution of organic molecules in Earth's first oceans.

prominence (41, 162) Eruption on the solar surface; visible during total solar eclipses.

proper motion (170) The rate at which a star moves across the sky; measured in seconds of arc per year.

protein (584) Complex molecule composed of amino acid units.

proton (123) A positively charged atomic particle contained in the nucleus of an atom; the nucleus of a hydrogen atom.

proton–proton chain (151) A series of three nuclear reactions that build a helium atom by adding together protons; the main energy source in the sun.

protoplanet (409) Massive object resulting from the coalescence of planetesimals in the solar nebula and destined to become a planet.

protostar (214) A collapsing cloud of gas and dust destined to become a star.

protostellar disk (220) A gas cloud around a forming star flattened by its rotation.

pseudoscience (25) A subject that claims to obey the rules of scientific reasoning but does not. Examples include astrology, crystal power, and pyramid power.

pulsar (282) A source of short, precisely timed radio bursts; thought to be a spinning neutron star.

pulsar wind (282) The flow of high-energy particles that carries most of the energy away from a spinning neutron star.

quantum mechanics (124) The study of the behavior of atoms and atomic particles.

quasar (quasi-stellar object, or QSO) (358) Small, powerful source of energy thought to be the active core of a very distant galaxy.

quintessence (387) The proposed energy of empty space that causes the acceleration of the expanding universe.

radial velocity (V_r) (139) That component of an object's velocity directed away from or toward Earth.

radiant (556) The point in the sky from which meteors in a shower seem to come.

radiation pressure (224) The force exerted on the surface of a body by its absorption of light. Small particles floating in the solar system can be blown outward by the pressure of the sunlight.

radiative zone (152) The region inside a star where energy is carried outward as photons.

radio galaxy (356) A galaxy that is a strong source of radio signals.

radio interferometer (115) Two or more radio telescopes that combine their signals to achieve the resolving power of a larger telescope.

ray (446) Ejecta from a meteorite impact, forming white streamers radiating from some lunar craters.

recombination (378) The stage within a million years of the big bang when the gas became transparent to radiation.

reconnection (163) The process in the sun's atmosphere by which opposing magnetic fields combine and release energy to power solar flares.

red dwarf (175) Cool, low-mass star on the lower main sequence.

redshift (138) The lengthening of the wavelengths of light seen when the source and observer are receding from each other.

reflecting telescope (101) A telescope that uses a concave mirror to focus light into an image.

reflection nebula (194) A nebula produced by starlight reflecting off dust particles in the interstellar medium.

refracting telescope (101) A telescope that forms images by bending (refracting) light with a lens.

regolith (451) A soil made up of crushed rock fragments.

regular satellite (495) A moon with an orbit that has small eccentricity, low inclination to the equator of its parent planet, and is prograde. Regular moons are thought to have formed with their respective planets rather than having been captured.

reionization (378) The stage in the early history of the universe when ultraviolet photons from the first stars ionized the gas filling space.

relative age (445) The age of a geological feature referred to other features. For example, relative ages reveal that the lunar maria are younger than the highlands.

resolving power (104) The ability of a telescope to reveal fine detail; depends on the diameter of the telescope objective.

resonance (457) The coincidental agreement between two periodic phenomena; commonly applied to agreements between orbital periods, which can make orbits more stable or less stable.

retrograde motion (56) The apparent backward (westward) motion of planets as seen against the background of stars.

revolution (20) The motion of an object in a closed path about a point outside its volume; Earth revolves around the sun.

rich cluster (344) A cluster containing over 1000 galaxies, mostly elliptical, scattered over a volume about 3 Mpc in diameter.

rift valley (434) A long, straight, deep valley produced by the separation of crustal plates.

ring galaxy (349) A galaxy that resembles a ring around a bright nucleus; thought to be the result of a head-on collision of two galaxies.

RNA (ribonucleic acid) (585) A long carbon-chain molecule that uses the information stored in DNA to manufacture complex molecules necessary to the organism.

Roche limit (499) The minimum distance between a planet and a satellite that holds itself together by its own gravity. If a satellite's orbit brings it within its planet's Roche limit, tidal forces will pull the satellite apart.

Roche lobe (263) In a system with two bodies orbiting each other, the volume of space dominated by the gravitation of one of the bodies.

Roche surface (263) In a system with two bodies orbiting each other, the outer boundary of the volume of space dominated by the gravitation of one of the bodies.

rotation (20) The turning of a body about an axis that passes through its volume; Earth rotates on its axis.

rotation curve (311, 340) A graph of orbital velocity versus radius in the disk of a galaxy.

rotation curve method (340) The procedure for finding the mass of a galaxy from its rotation curve.

RR Lyrae variable star (247) Variable star with a period of 12 to 24 hours; common in some globular clusters.

Sagittarius A* (318) The powerful radio source located at the core of the Milky Way Galaxy.

saros cycle (44) An 18-year $11\frac{1}{3}$-day period after which the pattern of lunar and solar eclipses repeats.

Schmidt-Cassegrain focus (110) The optical design of a reflecting telescope in which a thin correcting lens is placed at the top of a Cassegrain telescope.

Schwarzschild radius (R_s) (292) The radius of the event horizon around a black hole.

scientific argument (27) An honest, logical discussion of observations and theories intended to reach a valid conclusion.

scientific method (8) The reasoning style by which scientists test theories against evidence to understand how nature works.

scientific model (17) An intellectual concept designed to help you think about a natural process without necessarily being a conjecture of truth.

scientific notation (3) The system of recording very large or very small numbers by using powers of 10.

secondary atmosphere (433) The gases outgassed from a planet's interior; rich in carbon dioxide.

secondary crater (446) A crater formed by the impact of debris ejected from a larger crater.

secondary mirror (110) In a reflecting telescope, the mirror that reflects the light to a point of easy observation.

seeing (104) Atmospheric conditions on a given night. When the atmosphere is unsteady, producing blurred images, the seeing is said to be poor.

seismic wave (429) A mechanical vibration that travels through Earth; usually caused by an earthquake.

seismograph (429) An instrument that records seismic waves.

selection effect (552, 555) An influence on the probability that certain phenomena will be detected or selected, which can alter the outcome of a survey.

self-sustaining star formation (316) The process by which the birth of stars compresses the surrounding gas clouds and triggers the formation of more stars; proposed to explain spiral arms.

semimajor axis (*a*) (64) Half of the longest axis of an ellipse.

SETI (595) Search for Extra-Terrestrial Intelligence.

Seyfert galaxy (356) An otherwise normal spiral galaxy with an unusually bright, small core that fluctuates in brightness; thought to indicate the core is erupting.

Shapley–Curtis Debate (332) The 1920 debate between Harlow Shapley and Heber Curtis over the nature of the spiral nebulae.

shear (*S*) wave (429) A mechanical wave that travels through Earth's interior by the vibration of particles perpendicular to the direction of wave travel.

shepherd satellite (515) A satellite that, by its gravitational field, confines particles to a planetary ring.

shield volcano (472) Wide, low-profile volcanic cone produced by highly liquid lava.

shock wave, or shock (205, 212) A sudden change in pressure that travels as an intense sound wave.

sidereal drive (111) The motor and gears on a telescope that turn it westward to keep it pointed at a star.

sidereal period (35) The period of rotation or revolution of an astronomical body relative to the stars.

singularity (291) The object of zero radius into which the matter in a black hole is thought to fall.

sinuous rille (444) A narrow, winding valley on the moon caused by ancient lava flows along narrow channels.

small-angle formula (39) The mathematical formula that relates an object's linear diameter and distance to its angular diameter.

smooth plain (459) Apparently young plain on Mercury formed by lava flows at or soon after the formation of the Caloris Basin.

solar constant (161) A measure of the energy output of the sun; the total solar energy striking 1 m² just above Earth's atmosphere in 1 second.

solar eclipse (38) The event that occurs when the moon passes directly between Earth and the sun, blocking your view of the sun.

solar nebula theory (399) The proposal that the planets formed from the same cloud of gas and dust that formed the sun.

solar system (3) The sun and the nonluminous objects that orbit it, including the planets, comets, and asteroids.

solar wind (147) Rapidly moving atoms and ions that escape from the solar corona and blow outward through the solar system.

south celestial pole (18) The point of the celestial sphere directly above Earth's South Pole.

south point (18) The point on the horizon directly above the south celestial pole; exactly south.

special theory of relativity (91) The first of Einstein's theories of relativity, which deals with uniform motion.

spectral class or type (131) A star's position in the temperature classification system O, B, A F, G, K, and M. Based on the appearance of the star's spectrum.

spectral line (113) A dark or bright line that crosses a spectrum at a specific wavelength.

spectral sequence (131) The arrangement of spectral classes (O, B, A, F, G, K, M) ranging from hot to cool.

spectrograph (113) A device that separates light by wavelength to produce a spectrum.

spectroscopic binary (180) A star system in which the stars are too close together to be visible separately. You see a single point of light, and only by taking a spectrum can you determine that there are two stars.

spectroscopic parallax (178) The method of determining a star's distance by comparing its apparent magnitude with its absolute magnitude, as estimated from its spectrum.

spectrum (100) An arrangment of electromagnetic radiation in order of wavelength or frequency.

spherical component (309) The part of the galaxy including all matter in a spherical distribution around the center (the halo and nuclear bulge).

spicule (146) Small, flamelike projection in the chromosphere of the sun.

spiral arm (6) Long, spiral pattern of bright stars, star clusters, gas, and dust that extends from the center to the edge of the disk of spiral galaxies.

spiral galaxy (334) A galaxy with an obvious disk component containing gas; dust; hot, bright stars; and spiral arms.

spiral nebula (332) Nebulous object with a spiral appearance observed in early telescopes; later recognized as a spiral galaxy.

spiral tracer (313) Object used to map the spiral arms, for example O and B associations, open clusters, clouds of ionized hydrogen, and some types of variable stars.

sporadic meteor (557) A meteor not part of a meteor shower.

spring tide (87) Ocean tide of high amplitude that occurs at full and new moon.

standard candle (337) Object of known brightness that astronomers use to find distance—for example, Cepheid variable stars and supernovae.

star (3) A celestial object composed of gas held together by its own gravity and supported by nuclear fusion occurring in its interior.

starburst galaxy (350) A bright blue galaxy in which many new stars are forming, thought to be caused by collisions between galaxies.

star-formation pillar (218) The column of gas produced when a dense core of gas protects the nebula behind it from the energy of a nearby hot star that is evaporating and driving away a star-forming nebula.

static (371) Unchanging in overall properties; opposite of evolving.

stellar model (234) A table of numbers representing the conditions in various layers within a star.

stellar parallax (*p*) (169) A measure of stellar distance. (*See* parallax.)

stellar wind (224) Hot gases blowing outward from the surface of a star. The equivalent for another star of the solar wind.

stony-iron meteorite (552) A meteorite that is a mixture of stone and iron.

stony meteorite (552) A meteorite composed of silicate (rocky) material.

stromatolite (587) A layered fossil formation caused by ancient mats of algae or bacteria that build up mineral deposits season after season.

strong force (150) One of the four forces of nature; the strong force binds protons and neutrons together in atomic nuclei.

S-type asteroid (564) A type of asteroid common in the inner asteroid belt, with relatively high reflectivity and reddish color, probably composed of rocky material.

subduction zone (434) A region of a planetary crust where a tectonic plate slides downward.

subsolar point (466) The point on a planet that is directly below the sun.

summer solstice (22) The point on the celestial sphere where the sun is at its most northerly point; also, the time when the sun passes this point, about June 22, and summer begins in the Northern Hemisphere.

sunspot (143) Relatively dark spot on the sun that contains intense magnetic fields.

supercluster (389) A cluster of galaxy clusters.

supergiant (175) Exceptionally luminous star, 10 to 1000 times the sun's diameter.

supergranule (145) A large granule on the sun's surface including many smaller granules.

supernova (268) A "new" star appearing in Earth's sky and lasting for a year or so before fading. Caused by the violent explosion of a star.

supernova remnant (273) The expanding shell of gas marking the site of a supernova explosion.

supernova (type Ia) (271) The explosion of a star caused by the collapse of a white dwarf that has gained mass from its binary companion and exceeds the Chandrasekhar limit.

supernova (type Ib) (271) The explosion of a massive star that develops an iron core and collapses after it has lost its outer layers of hydrogen.

supernova (type I) (271) The violent explosion of a star in which the spectrum contains no hydrogen lines.

supernova (type II) (271) The explosion of a massive star that develops an iron core and collapses.

synchrotron radiation (272) Radiation emitted when high-speed electrons move through a magnetic field.

synodic period (35) The period of rotation or revolution of a celestial body with respect to the sun.

T association (224) A large, loosely bound group of T Tauri stars.

T dwarf (135) A very-low-mass star at the bottom end of the main sequence with a cool surface and a low luminosity.

temperature (127) A measure of the velocity of random motions among the atoms or molecules in a material.

terminator (443) The dividing line between daylight and darkness on a planet or moon.

Terrestrial planet (402) Earth-like planet—small, dense, rocky.

theory (66) A system of assumptions and principles applicable to a wide range of phenomena that have been repeatedly verified.

thermal energy (127) The energy stored in an object as agitation among its atoms and molecules.

thermal pulse (257) Periodic eruptions in the helium fusion shell in an aging giant star; thought to aid in ejecting the surface layers of the stars to form planetary nebulae.

thermophile (591) A type of microorganism that thrives in high-temperature environments.

tidal coupling (443) The locking of the rotation of a body to its revolution around another body.

tidal heating (505) The heating of a planet or satellite because of friction caused by tides.

tidal tail (348) A long strand of gas, dust, and stars drawn out of a galaxy interacting gravitationally with another galaxy.

time dilation (293) The slowing of moving clocks or clocks in strong gravitational fields.

total lunar eclipse (36) A lunar eclipse in which the moon completely enters Earth's dark shadow.

total solar eclipse (38) A solar eclipse in which the moon completely covers the bright surface of the sun.

totality (36) The period during a solar eclipse when the sun's photosphere is completely hidden by the moon, or the period during a lunar eclipse when the moon is completely inside the umbra of Earth's shadow.

transit (418) The passage of an extrasolar planet across the disk of its parent star as observed from Earth, partially blocking the light from the star and allowing detection and study of the planet.

transition (133) The movement of an electron from one atomic orbit to another.

triple alpha process (242) The nuclear fusion process that combines three helium nuclei (alpha particles) to make one carbon nucleus.

Trojan asteroid (563) Small, rocky body caught in Jupiter's orbit at the Lagrangian points, 60° ahead of and behind the planet.

T Tauri star (222) Young star surrounded by gas and dust contracting toward the main sequence.

turnoff point (248) The point in an H–R diagram where a cluster's stars turn off the main sequence and move toward the red giant region, revealing the approximate age of the cluster.

21-cm radiation (198) Radio emission produced by cold, low-density hydrogen in interstellar space.

ultraluminous infrared galaxy (ULIRG) (350) A highly luminous galaxy so filled with dust that most of its energy escapes as infrared photons emitted by warmed dust.

ultraviolet radiation (100) Electromagnetic radiation with wavelengths shorter than visible light but longer than X-rays.

umbra (33) The region of a shadow that is totally shaded.

uncompressed density (408) The density a planet would have if its gravity did not compress it.

unified model (363) The attempt to explain the different kinds of active galaxies and quasars by a single model.

uniform circular motion (53) The classical belief that the perfect heavens could move only by the combination of constant motion along circular orbits.

valley networks (483) Dry drainage channels resembling streambeds found on Mars.

Van Allen belt (431) One of the radiation belts of high-energy particles trapped in Earth's magnetosphere.

variable star (247) A star whose brightness changes periodically.

velocity (79) A rate of travel that specifies both speed and direction.

velocity dispersion method (341) A method of finding a galaxy's mass by observing the range of velocities within the galaxy.

vernal equinox (22) The place on the celestial sphere where the sun crosses the celestial equator moving northward; also, the time of year when the sun crosses this point, about March 21, and spring begins in the Northern Hemisphere.

vesicular (450) A porous basalt rock formed by solidified lava with trapped bubbles.

violent motion (77) In Aristotelian physics, motion other than natural motion. (See *natural motion.*)

visual binary (180) A binary star system in which the two stars are separately visible in the telescope.

void (339) A region containing relatively few galaxies, part of the large-scale structure of the universe.

water hole (595) The interval of the radio spectrum between the 21-cm hydrogen radiation and the 18-cm OH radiation, likely wavelengths to use in the search for extraterrestrial life.

wavelength (99) The distance between successive peaks or troughs of a wave; usually represented by λ.

wavelength of maximum intensity (λ_{max}) (128) The wavelength at which a perfect radiator emits the maximum amount of energy; depends only on the object's temperature.

weak force (150) One of the four forces of nature; the weak force is responsible for some forms of radioactive decay.

west point (18) The point on the western horizon exactly halfway between the north point and the south point; exactly west.

white dwarf (175) The remains of a dying star that has collapsed to the size of Earth and is slowly cooling off; at the lower left of the H–R diagram.

Widmanstätten pattern (552) Bands in iron meteorites due to large crystals of nickel–iron alloys.

WIMP (383) Weakly Interacting Massive Particle, a hypothetical type of subatomic particle of which dark matter could be composed.

winter solstice (22) The point on the celestial sphere where the sun is farthest south; also, the time of year when the sun passes this point, about December 22, and winter begins in the Northern Hemisphere.

X-ray burster (288) An object that produces occasional X-ray flares. Thought to be caused by mass transfer in a closed binary star system.

Young Stellar Object (YSO) (220) A forming star in a late protostellar evolutionary stage that has lost its obscuring cocoon of gas and but is still contracting toward the main sequence.

Zeeman effect (155) The splitting of spectral lines into multiple components when the atoms are in a magnetic field.

zenith (18) The point directly overhead on the sky.

zero-age main sequence (ZAMS) (238) The locus in the H–R diagram where stars first reach stability as hydrogen-burning stars.

zodiac (25) The band around the sky centered on the ecliptic within which the planets move.

Answers to Even-Numbered Problems

Chapter 1:
2. 3475 km; **4.** 1.1×10^8 km; **6.** about 1.2 seconds; **8.** 75,000 years; **10.** about 27

Chapter 2:
2. 2; **4.** 631; **6.** A is brighter than B by a factor of 170; **8.** 66.5°; 113.5°

Chapter 3:
2. (a) full; (b) first quarter; (c) waxing gibbous; (d) waxing crescent; **4.** 29.5 days later on about March 30th; 27.3 days later on about March 24th; **6.** 6850 arc seconds or about 1.9°; **8.** (a) The moon won't be full until Oct. 17; (b) The moon will no longer be near the node of its orbit; **10.** August 12, 2026 [July 10, 1972 + 3 × (6585 ⅓ days)]. In order to get August 12 instead of August 11, you must take into account the number of leap days in the interval.

Chapter 4:
2. Retrograde motion: Jupiter, Saturn, Uranus, Neptune; Never seen as crescents: Jupiter, Saturn, Uranus, Neptune; **4.** $\sqrt{27} = 5.2$ years; **6.** No. The ratio in the diagram is about 1.5.

Chapter 5:
2. The force of gravity on the moon is about ⅙ the force of gravity on Earth; **4.** 7350 m/s; **6.** 5070 s (1 hr and 25 min); **8.** The cannonball would move in an elliptical orbit with Earth's center at one focus of the ellipse; **10.** 6320 s (1 hr and 45 min)

Chapter 6:
2. 3m; **4.** Either Keck telescope has a light-gathering power that is 1.56 million times greater than the human eye; **6.** No, his resolving power should have been about 5.8 seconds of arc at best; **8.** 0.013 m (1.3 cm or about 0.5 in.); **10.** about 50 cm (From 400 km above, a human is about 0.25 second of arc from shoulder to shoulder.)

Chapter 7:
2. 150 nm; **4.** by a factor of 16; **6.** 250 nm; **8.** (a) B; (b) F; (c) M; (d) K; **10.** about 0.58 nm

Chapter 8:
2. 730 km; **4.** 9×10^{16} J; **6.** 0.222 kg; **8.** 400,000 years; **10.** about 3.6 times

Chapter 9:
2. 63 pc; absolute magnitude is 2; **4.** about B7; **6.** about 1580 solar luminosities; **8.** 160 pc; **10.** a, c, c, d (use Figure 9-13 to determine the absolute magnitudes); **12.** 3.69 days or 0.010 year; about 1.2 solar masses; about 0.67 and 0.53 solar mass; **14.** 1.38×10^6 km, about the size of the sun

Chapter 10:
2. 60,000 nm; **4.** 0.0001; **6.** 1.5×10^6 years; **8.** 4.2×10^{35} kg or 210,000 solar masses (*Note*: Each hydrogen molecule contains two H atoms.)

Chapter 11:
2. 25 km/s; **4.** 3.0 km/s; **6.** 9.5×10^{10} s (about 3000 years); **8.** There are four ^{1}H nuclei in the figure. They are used in a series of reactions to build up nuclei from ^{12}C to ^{15}N. In the last reaction (with the ^{15}N) a ^{12}C and a ^{4}He are produced. Because the ^{12}C can be used in the next cycle, the net is four ^{1}H nuclei in with one ^{4}He nucleus out; **10.** 7.9×10^{33} kg

Chapter 12:
2. about 9.8×10^6 years for a 16-solar-mass star; about 5.7×10^5 years for a 50-solar-mass star; **4.** about 1×10^6 times less than present or about 1.4×10^{-6} g/cm³; **6.** 2.4×10^{-9} or 1/420,000,000; **8.** about 3pc; **10.** 3.04 minutes early after 1 year; 30.4 minutes early after 10 years

Chapter 13:
2. about 1.8 ly; **4.** about 16,000 years old; **6.** about 940 years ago (approximately AD 1060); **8.** 2400 pc

Chapter 14:
2. 7.1×10^{25} J/s or about 0.19 solar luminosity; **4.** 820 km/s (assuming mass is one solar mass); **6.** about 11 seconds of arc; **8.** about 490 seconds

Chapter 15:
2. about 16 percent; **4.** 1.2×10^{14} s (3.9×10^6 yr); **6.** overestimate by a factor of 1.58; **8.** about 21 kpc; **10.** 7.9×10^{10} solar masses; **12.** about 1500 K

Chapter 16:
2. 2.6 Mpc; **4.** 90 km/s, using the mass of the galaxy inside the sun's orbit from p. 308, or about 230 km/s, extrapolating to r = 50 pc the rotation curve on p. 309 that includes the observed effects of dark matter; **6.** 29 Mpc; **8.** 5.2×10^{15} s (1.6×10^8 yr); **10.** 4.5×10^{41} kg (2.3×10^{11} solar masses)

Chapter 17:
2. 7.8×10^6 years; **4.** 0.024 pc; **6.** −28.5; **8.** about 16th magnitude; **10.** 0.16

Chapter 18:
2. 57 km/s/Mpc; 17.3 billion years; acceleration would decrease the age; **4.** 1.6×10^{-27} kg/m³; **6.** 76 km/s/Mpc

Chapter 19:
2. It will look $206,265^2 =$ about 4.3×10^{10} times fainter, which is 26.6 magnitudes fainter; +22.6 mag; **4.** about 2.3 half-lives, or 3.0 billion years; **6.** large amounts of methane and water ices; **8.** about 1300 impacts per hour

Chapter 20:
2. about 17 percent; **4.** about 8.2×10^7 yr (82 million yr); they have been subducted; **6.** 0.22 percent

Chapter 21:
2. The rate at which an object radiates energy and cools depends on its surface area, proportional to its radius squared (r^2). The energy an object contains as heat depends on its mass and therefore its volume, and that is proportional to its radius cubed (r^3). So, the cooling time depends on the amount of stored energy divided by the rate of cooling, which is proportional to the radius cubed divided by the radius squared (r^3/r^2), that equals the radius (r). This means that the bigger an object is, the longer it takes to cool; **4.** No. Their angular width would be only about 0.5 arc seconds. They would be easily visible, but are not seen, in photos taken from orbit around the moon; **6.** about 0.5 arc seconds (assuming an astronaut seen from above is about 0.5 meter in diameter); no, because that is smaller than the angular resolution of the human eye; **8.** 10.0016 cm (at western elongation the planet will be moving away from Earth, so the signal will be redshifted); **10.** Mercury, $V_e = 4250$ m/s; moon, $V_e = 2370$ m/s; Earth, $V_e = 11,200$ m/s

Chapter 22:
2. 33,400 km (39,500 km from the center of Venus); **4.** 61 arc seconds; **6.** 380 km; **8.** 120 arc seconds (corresponding to 12 km)

Chapter 23:
2. 3.0×10^5 sec (about 35 Earth days); **4.** 1.57×10^4 arc seconds (about 4.3°); **6.** about 0.056 nm; **8.** 5.2 m/s

Chapter 24:
2. 42 arc seconds; **4.** 256 m/s; **6.** 8.8 s; yes; **8.** about 410 m/s (0.41 km/s); **10.** 1.03×10^{26} kg (17.2 Earth masses)

Chapter 25:
2. 1×10^9 (one billion); **4.** about 330 m/s; no; **6.** About 4.7 yr; **8.** 2.5×10^5 s (about 2.9 days); **10.** 300 m/s at r = 10,000 AU, about 100 m/s at r = 100,000 AU

Chapter 26:
2. 8.8 cm; 0.88 mm; **4.** approximately 1.5 solar masses, spectral type F2; **6.** 380 km; **8.** No correct answer; perhaps somewhere between pessimistic and optimistic estimates in Table 26-1, 2×10^{-5} and 10^7, respectively

Index

A

Absolute bolometric magnitude, **172**
Absolute visual magnitude, **171**–172
Absolute zero, **127**
Absorption lines, 130, **132**, 197–198
Absorption spectra, 130, **132**
Absorption spectrum, photosphere, 144
Acceleration, **79**
    confirmation of, 390–392
    dark energy and, 387–388
    large-scale structure and, 390
    supernova and, 387
    of universe, 385–386
Acceleration of gravity, **77**
Accidental discovery, 528
Accretion, **409**
Accretion disk, **264**, 363–364
Achondrites, **553**, 556
Achromatic lenses, **102**, 103
Active galactic nuclei (AGN), **356**
    double-lobed radio sources and, 358, 360–361
    quasars and, 358–359, 362
    Seyfert galaxies and, 356–357
    time and, 364–366
    triggering eruptions regarding, 364
    unified model of, 363–364
Active galaxies, **356**
Active optics, 108, **111**
Active regions, 155, **157**
Adams, John Couch, 539
Adaptive optics, **108**, 112
AGN. *See* Active galactic nuclei
Airy, George, 539
Albedo, **437**–438
    Earth, 428, 437–438
    Jupiter, 496
    Mars, 477
    Mercury, 455
    moon, 443
    Neptune, 540
    Saturn, 511
    Uranus, 529
    Venus, 465
Alfonsine Tables, 55, 60, 62, 63
Algol, 184
Algol binary system, 263–264
Algol paradox, 263
Aliens, 596. *See also* Intelligent life
Allen, Paul, 596

Allende meteorite, 555
Allen Telescope Array, 115
Alpher, Ralph, 375
Altazimuth mountings, 108, **111**
Amazonian period, **488**
Amino acids, 583, **584**
Analogy, reasoning by, 372
Anaximander, 53
Andromeda Galaxy
    galaxy collisions with, 347
    Milky Way Galaxy and, 303
Angstrom, **100**
Angular diameter, **18**
    moon's, 38–39
    sun's, 39
Angular momentum, **83**
Angular momentum problem, **399**, 413
Annular eclipse, **39**–41
Anorthosite, 450–**451**
Antarctica, 552
Anticoded, **595**
Antimatter, **376**
Aphelion, **24**
Apogee, **39**
Apollo-Amor objects, **562**–563, 578
Apollo missions
    landing locations of, 449–450
    list of, 449
    LM and, 445, 448–449
    motivations for, 445
Apparent visual magnitude (m_v), **15**
Archaea, **591**–592
Archaeoastronomy, **50**
    Mayans and, 52
    Stonehenge/Newgrange and, 50, 51
    Sun Dagger and, 50, 52
    Temple of Isis/hogans and, 50
Arc minutes/seconds, **18**
Arecibo radio telescope, 595
Ariel, 537
Ariel 1, 118
Aristarchus, 54
Aristotle, 54, 77
Association, **224**
Asterisms, 13
Asteroids
    Barringer Crater and, 574
    belt, 559, 562
    classification of, 561
    cratering on, 559, 560
    double objects and, 559, 561
    families of, 564
    geological activity and, 561, 565

    impacts of, 574–578
    Jupiter's gravitation and, 562, 563
    misconceptions about, 401
    origin/history of, 563–565
    outside main belt, 562–563
    properties of, 559, 560–561
    size/shape regarding, 559
    solar system and, 401, 404
    Trojan, 563
    Tunguska event and, 574–575
    2004 MN4, 578
    types of, 564–565
Astrobiology, **582**. *See also* Biological evolution
    life on earth and, 586–592
    nature of life and, 582–586
    other planetary systems and, 594
    solar system and, 593
Astronomer's triangulation method, 169–170
Astronomia Nova (Kepler), 64
Astronomical unit (AU), **4**
Astronomy
    Archaeoastronomy, 50–52
    Copernican revolution influencing, 58–61
    of Greece, 52–55
    modern, 71–72
    Ptolemaic universe and, 55, 57
    roots of, 50–57
    why study, 7–8
Atmosphere
    Io and, 507–508
    Jovian planets and, 495
    of Jupiter, 498, 500–501
    of Mars, 478–481
    moon and, 443–444
    of Neptune, 539–540
    primeval/secondary, 433
    of Saturn, 512
    stars, 147–148
    sun, 143–148
    Terrestrial planets and, 426–427
    of Uranus, 528–529
    of Venus, 466–467
Atmosphere, Earth
    albedo and, 437–438
    climate/human effects on, 436–439
    gases in, 436
    global warming and, 437–438
    misconceptions about, 436, 437, 438
    origin of, 433, 436
    ozone and, 436, 438–439

Atmospheric windows, **101**
Atom(s). *See also* Nuclear fusion; Particles
  atomic spectra and, 130, 132–133
  Balmer thermometer and, 130–131
  carbon, 582–583
  electron shells, 124–125
  excitation of, 126–127
  kinds of, 124
  model of, 123–124
  origins of, 397
  quantum mechanics and, 124, 125
  white dwarf and, 258–259
AU. *See* Astronomical unit
Auroras, 160, **163**
Autumnal equinox, **23**

B

Baade, Walter, 280
Babcock model, **158**–159
Balmer spectral lines, 130, **133**, 134–135
Balmer thermometer, 130–131
Barringer Crater, 574
Basalt, 432, **434**
Basic scientific data, 185
Becklin, Eric, 318
Bell, Jocelyn, 281
Belt-zone circulation, **495**, 498, 501
Betelgeuse, 13
Big bang, **373**
  antimatter and, 376
  atoms and, 397
  conceptualization of, 374
  cosmic background radiation from,
    375–376
  element building and, 376–379
  energy/matter equality era and,
    377–378
  flatness/horizon problems of, 384–385
  look-back time and, 374–375
  misconceptions about, 374
  necessity of, 373–375
  nucleosynthesis during, 377
  photon/particle soup during, 376–377
  recombination era and, 378–379
  reionization era and, 378
  sound of, 391
  theory, 373–379
  universe age and, 373–374
Big rip, **388**
Binary pulsars
  gravitational radiation and, 286–287
  jets/disks and, 296
  nature of, 286–288
  star interactions and, 287–288
  violent matter interactions and, 287
  X-ray bursters and, 288

Binary stars/systems, **178**
  accretion disks and, 264
  eclipsing, 182–184
  evolution of, 262–265
  jets/disks and, 296
  masses of, 179
  mass transfer in, 263–264
  nova and, 264–265
  overview of, 178–179
  spectroscopic, 180–182
  visual, 180, 181
Binding energy, **124**
Biological evolution, **586**
  Cambrian explosion of, 589–590, 591
  carbon-chain molecules and, 586–587
  cell division and, 585
  chemical compounds and, 584
  DNA regarding, 583–586
  on Earth, 586–592
  extremophiles and, 591–592
  geologic time and, 589–592
  humanoids and, 589–590
  intelligent life and, 595–599
  Miller experiment regarding, 587–588
  nature of life and, 582–586
  origin of life and, 586–589
  in other planetary systems, 594
  our solar system and, 593
  physical basis of, 582–583
  primordial soup and, 588–589
  RNA and, 583, 585
  space hypothesis of, 589
  stromatolites and, 587, 589
  timeline representation of, 591
Bipolar flows, **221**
Blackbody radiation, **127**
  commonality of, 127–128
  cosmic background radiation and,
    375–376
  features of, 128
  human body and, 129
  wavelength and, 128–129
Black dwarf, **259**
Black hole(s), **291**
  candidates, 295
  Cygnus X-1, 294
  escape velocity regarding, 291
  event horizons confirming, 295–296
  general relativity and, 291–292
  GRBs and, 299
  jets/disks and, 296, 362–363
  leaping into, 293
  mass regarding, 365
  misconceptions about, 292–293
  quasars and, 365–366
  Schwarzschild, 291–293

  search for, 293–296
  X-ray binaries and, 293–295
Black holes, supermassive
  disks/jets and, 362–363
  double-lobed radio sources and, 358, 361
  in galaxies, 342
  mass regarding, 365
  Sagittarius A*, 319, 321
  time and, 364–366
  triggering eruptions of, 364
Blue shift, **138**–139
Bode, Johann, 527
Bok globules, 217, **218**
Bombardment, late heavy, **452**
Bow shock, **431**
Brahe, Tycho
  background on, 62
  Kepler and, 64, 65–66
  legacy of, 63
  observations of, 62–63
Breccias, **451**
Bright-line spectra, 130, **132**
Brightness, 170–172
Brown dwarfs, **237**
Bruno, Giordano, 70
de Buffon, Georges-Louis, 398
Burroughs, Edgar Rice, 477
Butterfly diagram, Maunder, 155, **156**,
  158–159

C

CAIs. *See* Calcium-aluminum-rich inclu-
  sions
Calcium-aluminum-rich inclusions (CAIs),
  555
Calibrated, **306**
Callisto
  characteristics of, 504–505
  history of, 509–510
  life regarding, 593
Caloris Basin, 458, 459
Cambrian explosion, **589**–590, 591
Cannon, Annie J., 131
Capture hypothesis, 454
Carbonaceous chondrites, **552**, 554–556
Carbon atoms, 582–583
Carbon deflagration, **271**
Carbon fusion, 245
Cassegrain focus, 108, **110**
Cassini, Giovanni, 503
Catastrophic hypothesis, **398**, 400
Cause, **80**, 259
CCDs. *See* Charge-coupled devices
Celestial equator, **17**
Celestial sphere, 16–19, **17**
Cell division, 585

Centaurs, **563**
Center of mass, 82, **85**
Central bulge, **309**
Cepheid variable stars, **247**, 306, 337–338
Ceres, 546, 547, 559
Chains of inference, 180
Chandrasekhar, Subrahmanyan, 119
Chandrasekhar limit, **262**
Chandra X-ray Observatory, 119
CHARA array, 112
Charge-coupled devices (CCDs), **113**
Charon, 545–546, 547
Chemicals
    compounds of life and, 584
    evolution and, 589
    solar nebula and, 407–408
Chicxulub, **576**
Chondrites, **553**–556
Chondrules, **553**–554
Chromatic aberration, **102**, 103
Chromosomes, 583, **585**
Chromosphere, **41**, 42
    magnetic phenomena, 160, 162
    sun's, 145–146
    temperature, 147
Circular velocity, 82, **84**
Circumpolar constellations, 16, **18**
Classification
    galaxy, 332–336
    luminosity, 176–178
    in science, 336
    stellar spectra, 131, 134–136
Climate
    Earth's, 25–27, 436–439
    human effects on, 436–439
    Milankovitch hypothesis and, 26–27
Closed orbit, 82, **85**
Closed universe, **381**–382
Cluster method, **340**–341
Clusters, star
    evolution of, 246
    horizontal branch and, 246, 249
    H-R diagrams of, 248–249
    Milky Way and, 305
    observing, 246, 248–249
    open/globular, 246, 248
Clusters, super, 389
CMEs. *See* Coronal mass ejections
CNO cycle, **226**–228
Cocoons, **214**
Cold dark matter, **383**, 391
Cold War, 297
Columbus, Christopher, 54
Coma, **568**
Comets, **404**. *See also specific* Comet
    bright v. faint, 565–566

coma of, 568
dust of, 566, 569
ices of, 566–567
impacts of, 503, 575–576, 578
Jupiter and, 503
Kuiper belt, 412, 572–573
long-period, 570, 571
misconception about, 565
nuclei geology of, 566–567, 570
nuclei mass/density of, 567
nucleus of, 566–570
Oort cloud, 571–572
origin/history of, 570–572
properties of, 566, 568–569
short-period, 570, 571–572
tails of, 566, 568
venting and, 567, 570
Compact object, **259**
Comparative planetology, **425**, 479–480
    principles of, 504
    Saturn's moons and, 522
Comparison spectrum, **113**
Composite volcanoes, 470, **472**
Compton Gamma Ray Observatory, 119
Concerning the Two Chief World Systems
    (Galilei). *See Dialogo Sopra i Due
    Massimi del Mondo*
Condensation, **409**
Condensation hypothesis, 454
Condensation sequence, **408**, 412
Confirmation, 160
Conservation of energy, 83, 86
Conservation of energy law, **233**
Conservation of mass law, **233**, 234
Consolidation, 160
Constellations
    asterisms and, 13
    circumpolar, 16, 18
    distribution regarding, 13–14
    official, 12–13
Continuous spectra, 130, **132**
Convection, **145**
Convective zone, **152**
Cooling lines, **214**
Coorbital satellites, 520–521
Copernican revolution
    background regarding, 58
    De Revolutionibus and, 58–61
    Galileo and, 68–70
Copernicus, Nicolaus
    De Revolutionibus and, 58–61
    Kepler and, 66
    model by, 58
    retrograde motion and, 59
    scientific revolution regarding, 61
    uniform circular motion and, 59–61

Core
    Earth's, 430–431
    iron, 268
    Jupiter's, 496–497
    Terrestrial planets and, 426
Corona, **41**, 42
    coronagraphs of, 143, 146, 147
    magnetic phenomena, 160, 162–163
    solar, 146–148
    spectrum, 146
    temperature/solar wind, 147
Coronae, **471**, 474
Coronagraph, 143, **146**, 147
Coronal gas, **204**–205
Coronal holes, 160, **163**
Coronal mass ejections (CMEs), 161, **163**
Cosmic microwave background, **375**,
    391–392
Cosmic rays, **119**
Cosmological constant, **387**, 388
Cosmological principle, **380**
Cosmologists, **371**
Cosmology, **370**
Cosmology, modern
    antimatter and, 376
    big bang theory in, 373–379
    cosmic background radiation and,
        375–376, 390–392
    cosmic redshift and, 380–381
    cosmological principle in, 380
    dark matter in, 382–383
    edge-center problem in, 370–371
    element building and, 376–379
    energy/matter equality era and,
        377–378
    expansion and, 372–373
    misconceptions about, 371
    nucleosynthesis and, 377
    observable universe and, 372
    Olbers's paradox and, 371
    photon/particle soup and, 376–377
    recombination era and, 378–379
    reionization era and, 378
    time/beginning and, 371–372
    universe introduction, 370–373
    universe models in, 381–382
Cosmology, 21st-century
    acceleration of universe and, 385–386
    background radiation irregularities and,
        390–392
    dark energy and, 387–388
    inflation and, 384–385
    large-scale structure and, 389–390
    universe fate and, 388
    WMAP observations illuminating,
        391–392

Coulomb barrier, **152**
Coulomb force, **124**
Crab Nebula, 272–273, 282
Cratering, impact, 427
  by asteroids, 574–578
  on asteroids, 559, 560
  by comets, 575–576, 578
  late heavy bombardment and, 452
  on Mars, 482
  on Mercury, 402, 461
  on moon, 402, 444, 446–447, 451, 452
  overview of, 401, 402
  on Phobos/Deimos, 489
  regolith and, 451
  secondary, 444, 446
  on Venus, 468–469
Craters, Earth
  Barringer Crater, 574
  Chicxulub Crater, 577
Critical density, **382**
  acceleration of universe and, 385–386
  dark energy and, 387–388
  dark matter and, 383
  inflation and, 384–385
  universe models regarding, 382–384
Critical point, **496**
Crust, 431
  Earth's active, 431, 432–433, 434–435
  Terrestrial planets and, 426
C-type asteroids, **564**–565
Curtis, Heber D., 332
Cygnus X-1, 294

D

Dark age, **378**
Dark energy, **387**
  acceleration and, 387–388
  universe fate and, 388
Dark-line spectra, 130, **132**
Dark matter, **311**
  cold/hot, 383, 391
  in cosmology, 382–383
  critical density and, 382–384
  in galaxies, 342–344
  gravitational lensing and, 343–344
  large-scale structure and, 390
Dark nebulae, **195**, 196
Data, scientific, 185
Data manipulation, 469
Davida, 559
Davis, Raymond, Jr., 153–154
Death, star
  binary, 262–265
  lower-main-sequence, 256–262
  massive, 266–276
  red dwarf, 154–155

sun and, 265–266
sun-like, 257
white dwarf, 258–259, 262
Debris disks, **415**
Deferent, 55, **57**
Degenerate matter, **241**–242
Deimos, 489–490
Density, 136, 137
  acceleration of universe and, 385–386
  comet, 567
  Earth, 428
  Jupiter, 496
  Mars, 477
  Mercury, 455
  moon, 443
  of nebulae, 196
  Neptune, 540
  photosphere, 143–144
  Saturn, 511
  solids condensation and, 408
  spiral arms and, 315–316
  star, 189
  sun, 144
  uncompressed, 408
  universe and, 381–382
  Uranus, 529
  Venus, 465
Density wave theory, **315**–316
Deoxyribonucleic acid (DNA), **583**
  biological evolution and, 586
  cell division and, 585
  chemical compounds and, 584
  RNA and, 583, 585
De Revolutionibus Orbium Coelestium
    (Copernicus)
  acceptance of, 60–61
  diagram in, 60
  planet motion in, 59–61
  publishing of, 58–59
  retrograde motion explained in, 59
  as scientific revolution, 61
Descartes, René, 397–398
De Stella Nova (Brahe), 62
Deuterium, **151**
Dialogo Sopra i Due Massimi del Mondo
    (Galilei), 70
Diameter
  angular, 18, 38–39
  of galaxies, 339–340, 341
  star, 173, 175–178
Diamond ring effect, **41**, 42
Dicke, Robert, 375
Differential rotation, **158**
Differentiation, **410**, 427
Dione, 520
Direct collapse, **412**

Discovery, accidental, 528
Disk component, **308**
Disk population stars, 319–320
Disks
  accretion, 264, 363–364
  binary pulsars and, 296
  black holes and, 296, 362–363
  debris, 415
  Jupiter regarding, 510
  Milky Way Galaxy and, 308–309
  planet forming, 414–415
  protostellar, 220–221, 223
  solar system shape and, 407, 412
Distance indicators, **337**
Distance modulus, **172**
Distance scale, **338**
DNA. *See* Deoxyribonucleic acid
Doppler effect, **137**
  blue/redshift and, 138–139
  calculating, 139
  sound and, 138
  as wavelength shift, 137–138
Double-exhaust mode, **358**, 360
Double-lobed radio galaxies, **358**, 360–361
Double-lobed radio sources
  AGN and, 358, 360–361
  double-exhaust mode/hot spots and, 358,
    360
  supermassive black holes and, 358, 361
Drake, Frank, 598
Drake equation, **596**
Dust tail, **568**
Dwarf planets, **546**
  family of, 546–547
  history of, 548
  Pluto, 544–546, 548
Dynamo effect, **158**, 431

E

Earth
  active, 432–433, 434–435
  age of, 405–406
  Asteroid 2004 MN4 and, 578
  asteroid impacts and, 576–578
  atmosphere of, 433, 436–439
  celestial sphere and, 16–19
  Chicxulub Crater on, 577
  climate, 25–27, 436–439
  core of, 430–431
  crust of, 431, 432–433, 434–435
  Doppler effect and, 139
  ecliptic and, 21
  end of, 265–266
  Eratosthenes' measurements of, 54, 55
  evolution stages of, 427
  as exceptional, 428

expanding universe and, 372–373
in field of view, 2–4
GRBs and, 299
history, 591
interior of, 429–431
Jupiter compared with, 501
life on, 586–592
lunar eclipses and, 33, 36–37
magnetic field of, 431–432
mantle of, 431
Mars compared with, 479–480
misconceptions about, 54, 436, 437, 438
moon viewed from, 443–445, 446–447
NEOs and, 562–563
observing eclipses on, 41–43
orbit regarding, 4, 20, 26, 82, 84–85,
    139, 428
as planet, 427–428
plate margins and, 433
precession, 19–20
predicting eclipses and, 43–46
profile of, 428
Roche limit and, 499, 502
rotation/revolution regarding, 20
seasons, 21–22, 23–24
seismic waves and, 429–430
shadow, 33
solar eclipses and, 37–41
solid, 429–433
supernova and, 275–276
tidal coupling and, 443
Venus compared with, 465, 466, 469,
    475–476
volcano types on, 470, 472–473
East point, **17**
Eccentricity, **64**–65
Eccentrics, **55**
Eclipses
    annular, 39–41
    lunar, 33, 36–37
    misconceptions about, 42
    observing, 41–43
    predicting, 43–46
    solar, 37–41
Eclipse season, **43**–44, 46
Eclipse year, **44**
Eclipsing binary, 182–184, **183**
Ecliptic, **21**
Edge-center problem, 370–371
Effect, **80**
Einstein, Albert
    cosmological constant of, 387
    general relativity theory and, 92–94
    space-time curvature confirmation and,
        93–94
    special relativity and, 90–92

Ejecta, 444, **446**
Electromagnetic force, 385
Electromagnetic radiation, **99**
Electromagnetic spectrum, 100–101
Electron, **123**, 124–125
Element building, 322–323, 376–379
Ellipse, **64**–65, 67
Elliptical galaxies, **332**
    classification of, 334
    diameter/luminosity of, 339–340, 341
    evolution of, 350
    mass of, 341
    number of, 336
    shape of, 333
Emission lines, 198–200
Emission nebulae, 193, **194**, 196
Emission spectra, 130, **132**
Enceladus, 520, 593
Energy, **86**
    binding, 124
    conservation law of, 233, 234
    conservation of, 83, 86
    energy/matter equality era and, 377–378
    flow, 426
    nuclear fusion and, 150, 152–153
    stars and, 225–228
    thermal, 127, 128, 213–214
Energy, dark, **387**
    acceleration and, 387–388
    universe fate and, 388
Energy levels, **126**
Energy transport, **225**–226
Enzymes, 583, **584**
Epicycle, 55, **57**
Equant, **57**
Equatorial mounting, 108, **111**
Equivalence principle, 93
Eratosthenes, 54, 55
Eris, 546
Eros, 560
Eruptions, triggering, 364
Escape velocity, **85**
    black holes and, 291
    calculating, 82
    Earth, 428
    gravity and, 83, 85
    Jupiter, 496
    Mars, 477
    Mercury, 455
    moon, 443
    Neptune, 540
    Saturn, 511
    sun, 144
    Uranus, 529
    Venus, 465
Eta Carinae, 236

Eudoxus of Cnidus, 53
Europa
    characteristics of, 506–507
    history of, 509–510
    life regarding, 593
European Extremely Large Telescope, 108,
    109
Evening star, **22**
Event horizon, **292**, 295–296
Evidence, statistical, 357
Evolution
    of binary stars/systems, 262–265
    chemical, 589
    Earth, 427
    of elliptical galaxies, 350
    of galaxies, 344–352
    globular clusters and, 246, 248
    planetary stages of, 427
    pulsar, 282–283, 286
    slow surface, 427
    of spiral galaxies, 350–351
    terrestrial planets, 427–428
Evolution, biological, **586**
    Cambrian explosion of, 589–590, 591
    carbon-chain molecules and, 586–587
    cell division and, 585
    chemical compounds and, 584
    DNA regarding, 583–586
    on Earth, 586–592
    extremophiles and, 591–592
    geologic time and, 589–592
    humanoids and, 589–590
    intelligent life and, 595–599
    Miller experiment regarding, 587–588
    nature of life and, 582–586
    origin of life and, 586–589
    in other planetary systems, 594
    our solar system and, 593
    physical basis of, 582–583
    primordial soup and, 588–589
    RNA and, 583, 585
    space hypothesis of, 589
    stromatolites and, 587, 589
    timeline representation of, 591
Evolution, post-main sequence
    degenerate matter and, 241–242
    giant expansion and, 240–241
    heavy element fusing and, 245
    helium flash and, 242–243
    helium fusion and, 242–245
    post-helium flash and, 243–245
Evolution, stellar, **175**, 176. *See also* Star
    death; Star formation
    binary stars and, 262–265
    brown dwarfs and, 237
    degenerate matter and, 241–242

Evolution, stellar (*continued*)
    evidence of, 246–252
    giant expansion and, 240–241
    heavy element fusing and, 245
    helium flash and, 242–243
    helium fusion in, 242–245
    life expectancy and, 239
    main sequence lower end and, 236–237
    main sequence regarding, 235–239
    main sequence upper end and, 236
    mass loss and, 257
    mass transfer and, 263–264
    misconception, 247
    models and, 233–235
    post-helium flash and, 243–245
    post-main sequence in, 240–246
    red dwarf, 154–155
    star clusters and, 246, 248–249
    star life regarding, 238–239
    variable stars and, 247, 250–252
    white dwarf, 258–259, 262
    ZAMS and, 238
Evolutionary hypothesis, **398**, 400
Excited atom, **126**
Expanding universe, **372**
Extrasolar planets, **417**
    center of mass regarding, 417
    hot Jupiters as, 418–419
    microlensing and, 418
    observing, 415–420
    photographing, 419
    transit and, 417–418
Extremophiles, **591**–592
Eyepiece, **102**, 103

F

Facts, 202
Falls, **552**
False-color images, **113**
Field, **81**–82
Field of view, **2**
    clusters/filaments in, 6–7
    Earth in, 2–4
    familiar territory in, 2
    Milky Way Galaxy in, 5–6
    solar system in, 3–4
Filaments, 6–7, 160, **162**, **389**
Filtergram, **146**
Find, **552**
First Narrative (Rheticus), 59
First principles, 54
Fission hypothesis, 454
Five regular solids, 63, 64
Flares, 161, **163**
Flash. *See* Helium flash; Post-helium flash
Flatness problem, **384**–385

Flat universe, **381**–382
    confirmation of, 390–392
    dark energy and, 387–388
Flocculent galaxies, **316**
Flooding, 427, 452–453
Flux, **15**–16, **171**
Focal length, **102**
Folded mountain ranges, 432, **434**
Forbidden lines, **196**
Forces of nature
    electromagnetic force, 385
    gravitational force, 385
    GUTs of, 385
    inflation and, 385
    strong/weak force, 150, 385
Forward scattering, **499**
Fountains, galactic, 323–325, **324**
Fraud, checks on, 295
Free-fall collapse, **213**
Frequency, **99**
Fusing, heavy element, 245

G

Galactic cannibalism, **347**, 349, 351
Galactic corona, **311**
Galactic fountains, 323–325, **323**
Galaxies
    active/radio, 356
    Andromeda, 303, 347
    cannibalism regarding, 347, 349, 351
    classification/shapes of, 332–336
    clusters of, 6–7, 344–346
    colliding, 346–347, 348–349
    dark matter in, 342–344
    diameter/luminosity of, 339–340, 341
    discovery of, 332
    distance to, 336–339
    double-lobed radio, 358, 360–361
    elliptical, 332, 333–334, 336, 339–340, 341, 350
    evolution of, 344–352
    family of, 331–336
    farthest, 351–352
    flocculent/grand design, 316
    Hubble law regarding, 339
    Hubble photo plates of, 332
    interacting, 347, 348–349
    irregular, 333, 335–336, 339, 341
    large-scale structure and, 389–390
    mass of, 340–341
    measuring properties of, 336–344
    misconceptions about, 6, 347–348
    origin of, 347, 350–351
    poor clusters and, 345, 346
    quantity of, 332, 333
    rich clusters and, 344–345, 346

    ring, 347, 349
    Seyfert, 356–357
    spiral, 332, 333–336, 339, 341, 350–351, 356
    supermassive black holes in, 342
    tidal tails and, 347, 348
    ultraluminous infrared/starburst, 350
Galaxy, **5**–6
Galaxy, Milky Way, **6**
    age of, 325
    center, 307–308
    disk of, 308–309
    early discoveries regarding, 303–305
    element-building process and, 322–323
    in field of view, 5–6
    fog analogy regarding, 303, 304
    galactic fountains and, 323–325
    galaxy clusters and, 345, 346
    galaxy collisions with, 347
    history of, 325–327
    mass of, 310–311
    monolithic collapse hypothesis of, 325, 327
    nucleus of, 318–321
    orbital motions in, 309–310
    origins of, 319–327
    rotation of, 311
    spherical component of, 309
    spiral arms of, 6, 310, 312–318
    star gauging and, 303
    stellar populations and, 319–320
    structure of, 308–312
    variable stars and, 305–308
Galilean moons, **68**, 509–510
Galilean satellites, **504**
Galilei, Galileo
    Aristotle and, 77
    background on, 67–68
    controversy and, 69–70
    Copernican revolution and, 68–70
    Dialogo/trial of, 70
    discoveries of, 68–69
    Galilean moons and, 68
    Milky Way Galaxy and, 303
    misconceptions about, 67
    modern science regarding, 70–71
    motion discoveries of, 76–78
    rings of Saturn and, 512
    sunspot observation by, 155
    Two New Sciences and, 78
    Venus and, 69
Galle, Johann, 539
Gamma-ray bursts (GRBs), **297**
    Cold War regarding, 297
    Earth and, 299
    hypernova/magnetars and, 297–298
    other causes of, 298–299

Gamma-Ray Large Area Space Telescope (GLAST), 119
Gamow, George, 375
Ganymede
    characteristics of, 505–506
    history of, 509–510
    life regarding, 593
Gas
    coronal, 204–205
    Earth atmosphere, 436
    gas-star-gas cycle and, 205–207
    heating, 213–214
    outgasing and, 411
Gas tail, 566, **568**
GBT, 116, 117
Gene, 583, **585**
General theory of relativity, **92**
    black holes and, 291–292
    confirmation of, 93–94
    equivalence principle and, 93
    explained, 92–93
Geocentric universe, **54**
Georgium Sidus (George's Star), 527
Geosynchronous satellite, 82, **84**
Giant, **175**
    expansion, 240–241
    luminosity classification, 176–178
Giant Magellan Telescope, 108, 109
Giant molecular clouds, **204**
GLAST. *See* Gamma-Ray Large Area Space Telescope
Global Oscillation Network Group (GONG), 149
Global warming, **437**
    albedo and, 437–438
    greenhouse effect and, 437
    misconceptions about, 438
Globular clusters, **248**
    evolution evidence and, 246, 248
    Milky Way and, 305
GONG. *See* Global Oscillation Network Group
Goodricke, John, 247
Gossamer rings, **502**
Grand-design galaxies, **316**
Grand Maximum, 164
Grand unified theories (GUTs), 385
Gran Telescopio Canarias, 108
Granulation, **144**–145
Grating, **113**
Gravitational collapse, **410**
Gravitational lensing, **343**–344
Gravitational radiation, **286**–287
Gravitational redshift, **293**
Gravity. *See also* Motion
    acceleration of, 77

asteroids and, 562, 563
binary pulsars and, 286–287
Earth, 428
escape velocity and, 83, 85
force of, 385
gas heating and, 213–214
general relativity theory and, 92–94
inverse square law and, 81
Jupiter, 496, 562–563
Kepler's laws and, 83, 86–87
Mars, 477
Mercury, 455
misconceptions about, 82, 87
moon, 443
mutual gravitation and, 81–82
Neptune, 540
Newton and, 79–83, 86–90
orbit and, 82, 84–87
Principia and, 88–89
Saturn, 511
space-time curvature confirmation and, 93–94
special relativity and, 90–92
star formation and, 211–214
tides and, 87–88
Uranus, 529
Venus, 465
GRBs. *See* Gamma-ray bursts
Greece, astronomy of
    Aristotle influencing, 54
    logic/reason and, 52–53
    philosophers influencing, 53
    religion regarding, 52
Greenhouse effect, 436–**437**, 467, 475–476
Grindstone model, 303
Grooved terrain, **505**
Ground state, **126**
GUTs. *See* Grand unified theories

H

Habitable zone, 594
Hale-Bopp, Comet, 565
Halley, Comet, 565, 566, 567, 572
Halo, **309**
Halo population stars, 319–320
Harmonice Mundi (Kepler), 64
The Harmony of the World (Kepler), 64
Haumea, 547
Hawking, Stephen, 292
Heat, **127**, 128
Heat of formation, **410**
Heavy element fusion, 245, 266–268
Heliocentric universe, **58**
    Copernicus and, 58–61
    Galileo and, 68–70
Helioseismology, **148**–149

Helium flash, **242**–243
Helium flash, post-, 243–245
Helium fusion, 242–245
Heperian period, **488**
Herbig-Haro objects, 221, **223**
Herman, Robert, 375
Herschel, Caroline, 303
Herschel, William
    self defense by, 527
    star gauging and, 303
    telescopes of, 526–527
    Uranus discovery and, 526–528
Hertzsprung, Ejnar, 306
Hertzsprung-Russell (H-R) diagram, **174**
    of clusters, 248–249
    of main sequence aging, 238, 244
    of massive stars, 241
    of planetary nebulae, 261
    stars and, 174–175, 176, 241
Hewish, Anthony, 281
HI clouds, **202**, 205
HII regions, 193, **194**
Hinode satellite, 118
Hipparchus, 55
Hirayama, Kiyotsugu, 564
Hirayama families, **564**
Hodges, E. Hulitt, 552
Hogans, 50
Holmes, Comet, 571
Homogeneous, **380**
Horizon, **17**
Horizon problem, **384**–385
Horizontal branch, 246, **249**
Horoscope, **25**
Hot dark matter, **383**, 391
Hot Jupiters, **418**–419
Hot spots, **358**, 360
H-R diagram. *See* Hertzsprung-Russell diagram
Hubble, Edwin
    distance measurement and, 339
    galaxy photo plates of, 332
    telescope named after, 117
Hubble constant, **339**, 391
Hubble law, **339**
Hubble Space Telescope, 117–118
Hubble time, **374**
Hulse, Russell, 286
Humason, Milton, 339
Huygens, Christian, 512
Hydrogen, liquid metallic, **496**
Hydrogen fusion
    CNO cycle, 226–228
    stellar, 226
    sun, 151–152
Hydrostatic equilibrium, **225**

Hygiea, 559
Hypernova, **297**–298
Hypothesis, 8, **66**
    biological evolution space, 589
    capture/condensation/fission, 454
    catastrophic/evolutionary, 398, 400
    data unification via, 448
    facts and, 202
    Milankovitch, 26–27, 438
    monolithic collapse, 325, 327
    moon origin, 454–455
    nebular, 398–399
    passing star, 398
    testing by prediction and, 89

I

Iapetus, 521–522
Ice ages, 25, 161
Ice line, **408**
Inference, chains of, 180
Inflationary universe, 384–**385**
Infrared Astronomical Satellite (IRAS), 118
Infrared radiation, **100**
    from dust, 200–201
    human body emitting, 129
    IRAS and, 118
    Orion nebula seen via, 217–218
    telescopes, 107, 118
    ultraluminous infrared galaxies and, 350
Inhabited world probabilities, 597–599
Inner Lagrangian point, **263**
Instability strip, **250**
INTEGRAL satellite, 119
Intelligent life
    inhabited world probability and,
      597–599
    radio communication with, 595–596
    space travel and, 595
Intensity, wavelength of maximum,
    128–129
Intensity ratio, 15–16
Interamnia, 559
Intercloud medium, **202**–203, 205
Intercrater plains, **459**
Interferometry, **112**, 115, 175–176
Interior
    of Earth, 429–431
    of Jupiter, 496–497, 501–502
    of Mars, 479, 487
    of Mercury, 459–460
    of moon, 451–452
    of Neptune, 541
    of Saturn, 511
    of sun, 148–153
    of Uranus, 529, 531–533
    of Venus, 475–476

Interstellar absorption lines, **197**–198
Interstellar dust, **196**, 200–201
Interstellar emission lines, 198–200
Interstellar extinction, **196**, 197
Interstellar medium (ISM), **193**
    absorption lines, 197–198
    components of, 202–205
    coronal gas, 204–205
    dust, 196, 200–201
    emission lines, 198–200
    extinction/reddening and, 196–197,
      197
    gas-star-gas cycle of, 205–207
    HI clouds, 202, 205
    intercloud medium and, 202–203, 205
    misconceptions about, 193
    molecular clouds, 203–204, 205
    nebulae, 193–196
    star formation from, 211–215
    star formation preview and, 206–207
Interstellar reddening, **196**, 197
Intrinsic brightness, **171**
Intrinsic variables, **247**
Inverse square law, **81**
Io
    atmosphere and, 507–508
    history of, 509–510
    magnetic field and, 498
    orbit of, 496, 497
    structure of, 508
    tidal heating of, 509
    volcanoes of, 507–509
Io flux tube, **498**
Io plasma torus, **498**
IRAS. *See* Infrared Astronomical Satellite
Iron core, 268
Iron meteorites, **552**–553
Irregular galaxies, **333**
    classification of, 335
    diameter/luminosity of, 339, 341
    mass of, 341
    number of, 336
Irregular satellites, **495**
Ishtar Terra, 474
Island universes, **332**
ISM. *See* Interstellar medium
Isotropic, **380**

J

James Webb Space Telescope, 118
Jenniskens, Peter, 565
Jets
    binary pulsars and, 296
    black holes and, 296, 362–363
    YSOs and, 221, 223–224
Joules, **86**

Jovian planets, **401**. *See also* Jupiter;
    Neptune; Saturn; Uranus
    atmospheres/satellite systems of, 495
    building of, 411–412
    characteristics of, 402–403
    condensation sequence and, 412
    life regarding, 593
    misconceptions about, 495, 531
    rings around, 413
    travel guide to, 494–495
Jumbled terrain, **453**
Juno, 559
Jupiter
    asteroids regarding, 562, 563
    atmosphere of, 495, 498, 500–501
    belt-zone circulation in, 498, 501
    Callisto and, 504–505, 509–510, 593
    cloud layers in, 501
    composition of, 497
    core of, 496–497
    disk-shaped nebula and, 510
    Europa and, 506–507, 509–510, 593
    forward scattering and, 499
    Ganymede and, 505–506, 509–510, 593
    gossamer rings of, 502
    great red spot and, 500, 501
    interior of, 496–497, 501–502
    Io and, 496, 497, 498, 507–510
    life regarding, 593
    magnetic field of, 497–498
    moons of, 503–510
    Neptune compared with, 533, 535
    profile of, 496
    rings around, 499, 502
    Shoemaker-Levy 9 and, 575–576
    solar nebula and, 503
    surveying, 495–496
    Uranus compared with, 533, 535, 538

K

Kant, Immanuel, 332
Kapteyn, Jacobus, 303
Kelvin temperature scale, **127**
Kepler, Johannes
    background on, 63–64
    Brahe and, 64, 65–66
    Copernicus and, 66
    empiricism of, 65
    five regular solids of, 63, 64
    Newton and, 83, 86–87
    Rudolphine Tables and, 65–66
    three motion laws of, 64–65, 67, 83,
      86–87
Keplerian motion, **311**
Kerr, Roy, 292
Kiloparsec, **303**

Kinetic energy, **86**
Kirchhoff's laws, 130, **132**
Kirkwood, Daniel, 513, **562**
Kirkwood gaps, **562**
Kohoutek, Comet, 565
Kuiper, Gerard, 404, 572
Kuiper belt, **404**
  comets from, 412, 572–573
  dwarf planets and, 546–547
  planetesimals and, 412
  Pluto/plutinos and, 548

L

Lagrangian points, **263**
de Laplace, Pierre-Simon, 398
Large Binocular Telescope, 108, 112
Large-impact hypothesis, **454**–455
Large-scale structure, **389**–390
Late heavy bombardment, **452**
Lava, 452
Lava channels, 471
Law, 66
L dwarfs, **135**–136
Leavitt, Henrietta, 306
Leverrier, Urbain Jean, 539
Levy, David, 576
Life
  biological evolution and, 586
  Cambrian explosion of, 589–590, 591
  carbon-chain molecules and, 586–587
  cell division and, 585
  chemical compounds and, 584
  DNA building, 583–586
  on Earth, 586–592
  extremophiles and, 591–592
  geologic time evolving, 589–592
  humanoids and, 589–590
  intelligent, 595–599
  Miller experiment regarding, 587–588
  nature of, 582–586
  origin of, 586–589
  in other planetary systems, 594
  our solar system and, 593
  physical basis of, 582–583
  primordial soup and, 588–589
  RNA and, 583, 585
  space hypothesis of, 589
  star, 238–239
  stromatolites as, 587, 589
  timeline representation of, 591
Light. *See also* Radiation
  atom excitation and, 126–127
  electromagnetic spectrum and, 100–101
  as particle, 100
  visible, 99, 101
  as wave, 99–100

Light curve, **183**, 184
Light-gathering power, **103**–104, 105
Lighthouse model, **282**, 284–285
Light pollution, **106**
Light year (LY), **4**–5
Limb, **145**, **444**
Limb darkening, **145**
Line of nodes, **44**
Liquid metallic hydrogen, **496**
LM. *See* Lunar landing module
Lobate scarps, **457**
Local bubble, **205**
Long-period comets, 570, 571
Look-back time, **338**–339, 374–375
Lowell, Percival, 477, 544
Luminosity, **172**
  calculating, 172
  of galaxies, 339–340, 341
  mass relation to, 188
  period-luminosity relation and, 247, 250
  star classification, 176–178
  star diameter and, 173, 176–178
  sun, 144
  temperature and, 173
  ultraluminous infrared galaxies and, 350
Luminosity classes, **176**
Lunar eclipses, **33**
  Earth and, 33, 36–37
  partial, 36–37
  Penumbral, 37
  total, 33, 36, 37
Lunar landing module (LM), 445,
  448–449
LY. *See* Light year
Lyman spectral lines, 130, **133**

M

Mab, 533
Magnetars, **297**–298
Magnetic carpet, **147**
Magnetic field
  chromosphere and, 160, 162
  corona and, 160, 162–163
  dynamo effect creating, 431
  Earth's, 431–432
  Io and, 498
  of Jupiter, 497–498
  prominences and, 161, 162
  reversal of, 432
  stars and, 159–160, 161
  sun's, 158–159, 160, 162–162
  of Uranus, 531–532
Magnetosphere, **431**
Magnifying power, **105**
Magnitude-distance formula, **172**
Magnitude scale, **14**–15

Main sequence, **175**, 176
  brown dwarfs and, 237
  H-R diagrams of, 238, 244
  life expectancy and, 239
  lower end of, 236–237
  models and, 233–235
  star life regarding, 238–239
  upper end of, 236
  why there is, 235
  ZAMS and, 238
Mantle, **426**, 431
Mare, **442**
Mare Imbrium, 452–453
Maria, **442**
Mars
  age of, 407
  atmosphere of, 478–481
  canals and, 476–478
  cratering on, 482
  Earth compared with, 479–480
  geology of, 481–483
  Heperian/Amazonian periods on, 488
  ice deposits on, 485
  interior of, 479, 487
  life regarding, 593
  moons of, 489–490
  Noachian period on, 487–488
  outflow channels/valley networks and, 483
  profile of, 477
  rocks of, 485–486
  shield volcanoes and, 470, 473
  southern highlands/northern lowlands of,
    481–482
  volcanism on, 470, 473, 482–483
  water and, 483–487
Mass, **79**
  binary stars, 179
  black holes and, 365
  center of, 82, 85, 417
  comet, 567
  conservation law of, 233, 234
  Earth, 428
  of galaxies, 340–341
  Jupiter, 496
  loss, 257
  luminosity relation to, 188
  Mars, 477
  Mercury, 455
  of Milky Way Galaxy, 310–311
  moon, 443
  Neptune, 540
  neutron star, 280
  Saturn, 511
  of stars, 178–185, 188, 227–228
  sun, 144
  sun-like stars and, 257

Mass (*continued*)
  transfer, 263–264
  Uranus, 529
  Venus, 465
  white dwarfs and, 259, 262
Massive stars
  deaths of, 266–276
  iron core and, 268
  nuclear fusion in, 245, 266–267
  supernova deaths of, 268–270
  supernova/Earth and, 275–276
  supernova observation and, 272–273
  supernova of 1987 and, 273–275
  supernova types and, 270–272
Mass-luminosity relation, **188**
*Mathematical Discourses and Demonstrations
    Concerning Two New Sciences, Relating
    to Mechanics and to Local Motion*
    (Galilei), 78
Mathematical models, 235
*Mathematical Principles of Natural Philoso-
    phy* (Newton), 88–89
Matter
  anti, 376
  atom excitation and, 126–127
  degenerate, 241–242
  energy/matter equality era and, 377–378
  misconceptions about, 124
  violent interactions of, 287
Matter, dark, **311**
  cold/hot, 383, 391
  in cosmology, 382–383
  critical density and, 382–384
  in galaxies, 342–344
  gravitational lensing and, 343–344
  hot/cold, 383
  large-scale structure and, 390
Maunder butterfly diagram, 155, **156**,
    158–159
Maunder minimum, 155, **157**
Maxwell, James Clerk
  forces of nature and, 385
  rings of Saturn and, 512–513
  Venus and, 468
Mayans, 52
McNaught, Comet, 565–566
Megaparsec, **336**
Mendel, Gregor, 8
Mercury
  Caloris Basin on, 458, 459
  cratering on, 461
  history of, 460–461
  interior of, 459–460
  life regarding, 593
  moon compared with, 455–456,
    458–459, 461

orbit, 4, 455
plains of, 458–459
profile of, 455
surface of, 457–458
temperatures on, 457
tidal coupling of, 456–457
Metastable levels, **196**
Meteorites, **405**
  achondrites, 553, 556
  Antarctica and, 552
  Barringer Crater and, 574
  CAIs and, 555
  carbonaceous chondrite, 552, 554–556
  categories of, 552–556
  chondrites, 553–556
  chondrules, 553–554
  impacts of, 574–578
  iron, 552–553
  stony, 552, 553–556, 575
  stony-iron, 552, 553
  Tunguska event and, 574–575
  ureilite, 565
Meteoroid, **405**
Meteors, **404**–405
  composition of, 552–556
  misconception about, 558
  orbits of, 556–558
  origin of, 558–559
  radiant and, 556
  sporadic, 557
Meteor showers, **556**–558
Metric system, 2
Microlensing, **418**
Micrometeorites, 444, **447**
Midocean rises, 432, **434**
Milankovitch, Milutin, 26
Milankovitch hypothesis, **26**–27, 438
Milky Way, **6**
Milky Way Galaxy, **6**
  age of, 325
  center, 307–308
  disk of, 308–309
  early discoveries regarding, 303–305
  element-building process and, 322–323
  in field of view, 5–6
  fog analogy regarding, 303, 304
  galactic fountains and, 323–325
  galaxy clusters and, 345, 346
  galaxy collisions with, 347
  history of, 325–327
  mass of, 310–311
  monolithic collapse hypothesis of, 325, 327
  nucleus of, 318–321
  orbital motions in, 309–310
  origins of, 319–327
  rotation of, 311

spherical component of, 309
spiral arms of, 6, 310, 312–318
star gauging and, 303
stellar populations and, 319–320
structure of, 308–312
variable stars and, 305–308
Miller, Stanley, 587
Miller experiment, **587**–588
Millisecond pulsars, **288**–289
Miranda, 537–538
Misconceptions, common
  asteroid, 401, 562
  aurora, 160
  big bang, 374
  black hole, 292–293
  comet, 565
  Earth atmosphere, 436, 437, 438
  Earth size, 54
  eclipses, 42
  galaxy evolution, 347–348
  galaxy/solar system/universe, 6
  Galileo, 67
  global warming, 438
  gravity, 82, 87
  ISM, 193
  Jovian planet, 495, 531
  lava, 452
  life, 589
  LY, 4–5
  matter, 124
  meteor, 558
  moon, 32, 39, 87
  natural selection, 586
  nuclear fusion, 152
  ozone, 348
  radiation, 99
  radio wave, 100
  redshift, 381
  seasons, 22
  skepticism, 419
  solar nebula, 408
  space explosion, 269, 391
  star brightness, 19
  star evolution, 247
  star size, 5
  theory, 66
  universe, 6, 371, 372
Mitchell, John, 291
Model(s)
  AGN, 363–364
  atomic, 123–124
  Babcock, 158–159
  Copernicus', 58
  grindstone, 303
  lighthouse/pulsar, 282, 284–285
  planetary nebulae, 260

scientific, 19
stellar, 233–235
supernova, 268–269
universe, 381–384
Molecular clouds, **203**–204, 205, 215–216, 218
Momentum, **79**
Monolithic collapse hypothesis, **325**, 327
Moon
  age of, 406–407, 450–451
  angular diameter of, 38–39
  Apollo missions to, 445, 448–450
  atmosphere regarding, 443–444
  cooling of, 454
  cratering of, 444, 446–447, 451, 452
  cycle/phases of, 32–33, 34–35
  Earth view of, 443–445, 446–447
  flooding and, 452–453
  history of, 444–445, 451–454
  jumbled terrain on, 453
  late heavy bombardment of, 452
  life regarding, 593
  lunar eclipses and, 33, 36–37
  magma ocean and, 451–452
  Mercury compared with, 455–456,
    458–459, 461
  misconceptions about, 32, 39, 87
  motion of, 32, 35
  origin of, 454–455
  predicting eclipses and, 43–46
  profile, 443
  rocks of, 450–451
  solar eclipse and, 39–40
  terrain of, 444
  tides and, 87–88
Moons
  Galilean, 68, 509–510
  of Jupiter, 68, 503–510
  of Mars, 489–490
  of Neptune, 533, 536, 542–543
  of Saturn, 517–522
  of Uranus, 533, 536–538
Morning star, **22**
Motion
  Galileo and, 76–78
  Keplerian, 311
  Kepler's laws of, 64–65, 67, 83, 86–87
  Milky Way Galaxy and, 309–310
  moon's, 32, 35
  natural/violent, 77
  Newton's laws of, 79–80
  planet, 22, 55–57, 59–70
  proper, 170
  retrograde, 55, 56, 59
  sun's annual, 20–21
  uniform circular, 53, 55, 56, 59–61
  of Uranus, 528

Mrkos, Comet, 568
M-type asteroids, **564**–565
Multicellular, **589**
Multiringed basins, 444, **447**
Mutants, **586**
Mutual gravitation, 81–82
m_v. *See* Apparent visual magnitude
Mysterium Cosmographicum (Kepler), 64

N

Nadir, **17**
Nanometer, **100**
Natural law, **66**
Natural motion, **77**
Natural selection, **586**
Nature as processes, 323
Neap tides, **87**, 88
Near-Earth Objects (NEOs), **562**–563
Nebulae, **193**
  Crab Nebula, 272–273, 282
  dark, 195, 196
  density of, 196
  emission, 193, 194, 196
  forbidden lines and, 196
  Orion nebula and, 215–218, 220
  planetary, 257–258, 260–261
  reflection, 193, 194–195
  solar, 399, 407–414, 503
  spectra of, 196
  spiral, 332
Nebular hypothesis, **398**–399
NEOs. *See* Near-Earth Objects
Neptune
  atmosphere of, 539–540
  discovery of, 539
  history of, 543
  interior of, 541
  Jupiter/Saturn compared with, 533, 535
  life regarding, 593
  moons of, 533, 536, 542–543
  plutinos and, 548
  profile of, 540
  rings of, 533–534, 535, 536, 541
  Rosalind and, 533
  rotation of, 412
  shepherd moons and, 533, 536
  temperature of, 533
  Umbriel/Ariel and, 537
Nereid, 542
Neutrino, **151**
Neutrino counting, 153–154
Neutron, **123**, 124
Neutron star, **280**
  binary pulsars and, 286–288
  GRBs and, 299
  jets/disks and, 296

planets orbiting, 289–290
pulsar discovery regarding, 281–282
pulsar evolution and, 282–283, 286
pulsar model and, 282, 284–285
size of, 280, 281
spin of, 281
theoretical prediction of, 280–281
New Astronomy (Kepler), 64
Newgrange, 50, 51
Newton, Isaac
  birth date regarding, 76
  first motion law of, 79
  Kepler's laws and, 83, 86–87
  legacy of, 88–90
  mutual gravitation and, 81–82
  Principia of, 88–89
  second motion law of, 79–80
  third motion law of, 80
Newtonian focus, 108, **110**
1987 supernova, 273–275
Noachian period, **487**–488
Nodes, **43**–44
Nonbaryonic matter, **383**
North celestial pole, **17**
Northern lowlands, Mars, 481–482
North point, **17**
Nova, **264**, 264–265. *See also* Hypernova;
  Supernova
Nuclear fission, **150**
Nuclear fusion, **150**
  carbon, 245
  energy transport and, 152–153
  helium, 242–245
  hydrogen, 151–152, 226–228
  in massive stars, 245, 266–267
  misconception about, 152
  neutrino counting and, 153–154
  sun, 150–154
  theory/proof of, 215
Nuclei, active galactic, **356**
  double-lobed radio sources and, 358,
    360–361
  quasars and, 358–359, 362
  Seyfert galaxies and, 356–357
  time and, 364–366
  triggering eruptions regarding, 364
  unified model of, 363–364
Nucleosynthesis, **322**–323, 377
Nucleus, **123**
  of comets, 566–570
  Milky Way Galaxy, 318–321

O

OB association, **224**
Oberon, 536
Objective lens, **101**, 102–103

Objective mirror, 101–**102**, 103
Oblateness, **497**
  Earth, 428
  Jupiter, 496
  Mars, 477
  Mercury, 455
  Neptune, 540
  Saturn, 511
  Uranus, 529
  Venus, 465
Obscuration, 308
Observable universe, **372**
Occultation, 533, **534**
Olbers, Heinrich, 371
Olbers's paradox, **371**
Oort, Jan, 571
Oort cloud, **571**–572
Opacity, **226**
Open clusters, 246, **248**
Open orbit, 82, **85**
Open universe, **381**–382
Orbit
  closed/open, 82, 85
  coorbital satellites and, 520–521
  Earth and, 4, 20, 26, 82, 84–85, 139,
    428
  electron, 124–125
  escape velocity and, 83
  gravity and, 82, 84–87
  Io, 496, 497
  Jupiter, 496
  Kepler's laws and, 83, 86–87
  Mars, 477
  Mercury and, 4, 455
  meteors, 556–558
  Milky Way Galaxy and, 309–310
  moon, 443
  Neptune, 540
  neutron star and, 289–290
  permitted, 124–125
  planets and, 401
  Saturn, 511
  Uranus, 529
  velocity and, 82–83
  Venus, 465
Orcus, 547
Orion nebula
  appearance through history of, 218
  Bok globules and, 217, 218
  infrared/visual views of, 217–218
  molecular cloud and, 215–216, 218
  observing, 215–218
  O star within, 216, 218
  star formation in, 215–218, 220
Outflow channels, **483**
Outgasing, **411**

Ovoids, **537**–538
Ozone, 436, 438–439
Ozone layer, **436**

P

Pallas, 559
Paradigm, **61**
Parallax, 55, **56**
  Herschel, William, measuring, 527
  spectroscopic, 178
  stellar, 169–170
Parsec, **169**
Parsons, William, 332
Partial lunar eclipse, **36**–37
Partial solar eclipse, **38**
Particles. *See also* Atom(s)
  big bang soup of, 376–377
  light as, 100
  white dwarf and, 258–259
  WIMPs, 383
Paschen spectral lines, 130, **133**
Passing star hypothesis, **398**
Path of totality, **39**
Payne-Gaposchkin, Cecilia, 136–137
Penumbra, **33**
Penumbral lunar eclipse, **37**
Penzias, Arno, 375
Perigee, **39**
Perihelion, **24**
Period-luminosity relation, **247**, 250
Permitted orbits, **124**–125
Philolaus, 53
Philosophiae Naturalis Principia Mathematica (Newton), 88–89
Phobos, 489–490
Phoebe, 519, 522
Photon, **100**
  atom excitation and, 126–127
  big bang soup and, 376–377
  blackbody radiation and, 127–129
Photosphere, **41**, 42
  absorption spectrum, 144
  density of, 143–144
  granulation, 144–145
  limb darkening, 145
  sun, 143–145, 147
  temperature, 147
  thinness of, 143
Piazzi, Giuseppe, 559
Pillars, star formation, 218, 219
Planet(s), **3**. *See also* Dwarf planets; Jovian planets; Terrestrial planet(s); *specific* planet
  Brahe observations of, 62–63
  building of, 408–412
  center of mass and, 417

comparative planetology and, 425,
    479–480, 504, 522
  debris disks and, 415
  Earth, 427–439
  energy flow and, 426
  extrasolar, 415–420, 594
  heavy bombardment of, 413
  hot Jupiters and, 418–419
  Jovian problem and, 411–412
  Kepler regarding, 63–67
  microlensing and, 418
  motion of, 22, 55–57, 59–70
  neutron stars and, 289–290
  orbiting other stars, 414–420
  outgasing and, 411
  photographing extrasolar, 419
  planetesimal formation and, 408–409
  planet forming disks creating, 414–415
  protoplanet growth and, 409–411
  remembering, 4
  revolution/rotation of, 401
  solar nebula composition and, 407–408
  solar system characteristics and, 412–413
  solids condensation and, 408
  Terrestrial/Jovian, 401, 402–403
  transit regarding, 417–418
  uniform circular motion and, 59–61
Planetary nebulae, **257**
  asymmetry regarding, 261
  formation of, 260–261
  model of, 260
  overview of, 257–258
Planetesimals, 408–**409**, 412
Plastic, **431**
Plate margins, 433
Plate tectonics, 432–433, **434**–435
Plato, 53
Plutinos, **548**
Pluto
  characteristics of, 544–545
  Charon and, 545–546, 547
  discovery of, 544
  temperature on, 545
Poe, Edgar Allan, 371–372
Polar axis, 108, **111**
Poor clusters, **345**, 346
Population I/Population II stars,
    319–320
Portia, 533
Positron, **151**
Post-helium flash, 243–245
Post-main sequence evolution
  degenerate matter and, 241–242
  giant expansion and, 240–241
  heavy element fusing and, 245
  helium flash and, 242–243

helium fusion and, 242–245
    post-helium flash and, 243–245
Potential energy, **86**
Precession, **19**–20
Predicting eclipses
    conditions for, 43
    eclipse season and, 43–44, 46
    saros cycle and, 44–45, 46
    space view regarding, 44
    Thales of Miletus, 45–46
Prediction, 89
Pressure (*P*) waves, **429**
Prima Narratio (Rheticus), 59
Primary lens, **101**, 102–103
Primary mirror, **101–102**, 103
Prime focus, 108, **110**
Primeval atmosphere, **433**
Primordial soup, **588**–589
Principia (Newton), 88–89
Profiles, celestial
    Earth, 428
    Jupiter, 496
    Mars, 477
    Mercury, 455
    moon, 443
    Neptune, 540
    Saturn, 511
    sun, 144
    Uranus, 529
    Venus, 465
Prominences, **41**, 42, 161, 162
Proof, 215
Proper motion, 170, **170**
Proteins, 583, **584**
Proton, **123**, 124
Proton-proton chain, **151**, 226
Protoplanets, **409**–411
Protostar, **214**
Protostellar disks, **220**–221, 223
Prutentic Tables, 60, 62
Pseudoscience, **25**
Ptolemaeus, Claudius, 55
Ptolemaic universe, 55, 57
Pulsars, **282**
    binary, 286–288, 296
    discovery of, 281–282
    evolution of, 282–283, 286
    fastest, 288–289
    gravitational radiation and, 286–287
    model of, 282, 284–285
    planets and, 289–290
    violent matter interactions and, 287
    X-ray bursters and, 288
Pulsar wind, **282**, 283
P waves. *See* Pressure waves
Pythagoras, 53

Q

Quantum mechanics, **124**, 125
Quasars, **358**
    AGN and, 358–359, 362
    black holes/time and, 365–366
Quintessence, **387**, 388

R

Radial velocity, **139**
Radiation, **99**. *See also* Light
    Doppler effect and, 137–139
    from heated object, 127–129
    infrared, 100, 129, 200–201
    laws, 129
    misconceptions about, 99
    stellar spectra and, 130–136
    sun, 152–153
    supernova and, 275
Radiation pressure, **224**
Radiative zone, **152**
Radioactive dating, 405–406
Radio communication, 595–596
Radio galaxies, **356**
Radio interferometer, **115**
Radio telescope
    advantages of, 117
    limitations of, 115–116
    map, 114–115, 116
    operation of, 114–115
Rays, 444, **446**
Reasoning by analogy, 372
Recombination, **378**–379
Reconnection, 161, **163**
Red dwarf, 154–155, **175**, 176
Redshift, **138**
    cosmic, 380–381
    Doppler effect and, 138–139
    gravitational, 293
    misconception, 381
Reflecting telescope, **101**–102, 103
Reflection nebulae, 193, **194**–195
Refracting telescope, **101**, 102–103,
    103–106
Regolith, **451**
Regular satellites, **495**
Reionization, **378**
Relativity
    general, 92–94, 291–292
    space-time curvature confirmation and,
      93–94
    special, 90–92
Religion, 52, 583
Resolving power, **104**, 105
Resonance, **457**
Retrograde motion, 55, **56**, 59

Revolution, **20**
    Copernican, 58–61, 68–70
    scientific, 61
The Revolutions of the Celestial Spheres
    (Copernicus). *See De Revolutionibus*
    Orbium Coelestium
Ribonucleic acid (RNA), 583, **585**
Rich clusters, **344**–345, 346
Rift valleys, 432, **434**
Ring galaxies, **347**, 349
Rings
    Jovian planet, 413
    Jupiter's, 499, 502
    Neptune's, 533–534, 535, 536, 541
    Saturn's, 512–516
RNA. *See* Ribonucleic acid
Roche limit, **499**, 502
Roche lobes, **263**
Roche surface, **263**
Rocks
    of Mars, 485–486
    of moon, 450–451
Rosalind, 533
ROSAT, 118
Rotation
    Earth, 428
    Jupiter, 496
    Mars, 477
    Mercury, 455
    Neptune, 540
    Saturn, 511
    Uranus, 529
    Venus, 465
Rotation curve, **311**, **340**
Rotation curve method, **340**
RR Lyrae variable stars, **247**
R_s. *See* Schwartzschild radius
Rudolphine Tables, 63, 65–66

S

Sagittarius A*, **318**
    Becklin and, 318
    center of, 319, 320
    observation of, 319–321
    radiation and, 318–319
    supermassive black hole and, 319, 321
Saha, Meghnad, 136
Saros cycle, **44**–45, 46
Satellites
    coorbital, 520–521
    Galilean, 504
    geosynchronous, 82, 84
    Hinode/IRAS, 118
    INTEGRAL, 119
    irregular/regular, 495
    shepherd, 513, 515

Satellites (*continued*)
SOHO, 149
Solar Maximum Mission, 161
Saturn
A/B/C rings of, 514
atmosphere of, 512
coorbital satellites and, 520–521
Enceladus/Dione and, 520
history of, 516
Iapetus and, 521–522
interior of, 511
Jupiter compared with, 497
life regarding, 593
Maxwell and, 512–513
moon origins and, 522
moons of, 517–522
Neptune compared with, 533, 535
Phoebe and, 519, 522
profile, 511
ring processes and, 513, 516
rings of, 512–516
shepherd satellites of, 513, 515
surveying, 510–512
Tethys and, 519
Titan and, 517–518
Uranus compared with, 533, 535, 538
Schiaparelli Giovanni, 456, 476
Schmidt-Cassegrain focus, 108, **110**
Schwartzschild, Karl, 292
Schwartzschild radius (R$_s$), **292**
Schwarzschild black holes, 291–293
Science
accidental discovery and, 528
classification in, 336
fraud, 295
Galileo and, 70–71, 78
as knowledge system, 380
payment for, 516
pseudo, 25
religion and, 583
Scientific argument, **27–28**
Scientific confidence, 153
Scientific data, 185
Scientific method, **8**, 160
Scientific models, **19**
Scientific notation, **3**
Scientific revolutions, 61
Scott, David, 77, 78
Search for Extra-Terrestrial Intelligence
(SETI), **595**
Seasons
Earth, 21–22, 23–24
eclipse, 43–44, 46
misconceptions about, 22
Secchi, Angelo, 476
Secondary atmosphere, **433**

Secondary craters, 444, **446**
Secondary mirror, 108, **110**
Sedna, 547
Seeing, **104**–105
Seismic waves, **429**–430
Seismographs, **429**
Selection effect, **555**
Self-sustaining star formation, **316**–318
Semimajor axis, **64**–65
SETI. *See* Search for Extra-Terrestrial
Intelligence
Seyfert, Carl, 356
Seyfert galaxies, **356**–357
Shaddad, Muawia, 565
Shapley, Harlow, 332
calibration and, 306–307
galaxy center and, 307–308
globular clusters and, 305
Milky Way Galaxy and, 305–308
obscuration and, 308
variable stars and, 305–306
Shapley-Curtis debate, **332**
Shear (*S*) waves, **429**
Shepherd satellites, 513, **515**
Shield volcanoes, 470, **472**
Shock, **212**
Shock waves, **205**, 212–213
Shoemaker, Carolyn, 576
Shoemaker, Eugene, 574, 576
Shoemaker-Levy 9, Comet, 575–576
Short-period comets, 570, 571–572
Sidereal drive, 108, **111**
Sidereal period, **35**
The Sidereal Messenger (Galilei). *See Sidereus
Nuncius*
Sidereus Nuncius (Galilei), 68, 69
Singularity, **291**
Sinuous rilles, **444**
Sirius, 13
Sirius B, 258
Skepticism, 419
Sky
celestial sphere, 16–19
precession, 19–20
Slipher, Vesto, 339, 544
Sloan Digital Sky Survey, 109
Slow surface evolution, 427
Small-angle formula, **39**
Smooth plains, **459**
SOFIA. *See* Stratospheric Observatory for
Infrared Astronomy
SOHO satellite, 149
Solar constant, **161**, 164
Solar eclipse, 37–**38**
angular diameter regarding, 38–39
features of, 41

moon's shadow creating, 39–40
partial, 38
total, 38, 39, 40–41
Solar Maximum Mission satellite, 161
Solar nebula
chemical composition of, 407–408
clearing of, 413–414
Jovian problem and, 411–412
Jupiter and, 503
planetesimal formation in, 408–409
protoplanet growth from, 409–411
solids condensation in, 408
Solar nebula theory, **399**
angular momentum problem regarding, 413
solar system and, 399, 407–408,
412–413
Solar system, **3**
age of, 405–407
asteroids, 401, 404
characteristic properties of, 407,
412–413
comets, 404
disk shape of, 407, 412
in field of view, 3–4
Jovian problem and, 411–412
life in, 593
meteors, 404–405
misconceptions, 6
nebula clearing and, 413
origins of, 397–399
planetesimal formation in, 408–409
protoplanet growth and, 409–411
revolution/rotation in, 401
solar nebula composition and, 407–408
solar nebula theory of, 399, 407–408,
412–413
solids condensation and, 408
space debris, 401, 404–405
survey, 401–407
Terrestrial/Jovian planets in, 401,
402–403
Solar wind, **147**, 431–432
Solids condensation, 408
Sound
big bang, 391
Doppler effect and, 138
Soup
photon/particle, 376–377
primordial, 588–589
South celestial pole, **17**
Southern highlands, Mars, 481–482
South point, **17**
Space-time. *See also* Time
cosmic redshift and, 380–381
curved/flat, 381–382
gravity and, 93–94

Space travel, 595
Special theory of relativity, **91**
    effects of, 91–92
    first postulates of, 90–91
    second postulate of, 91
Spectra, stellar
    Balmer thermometer and, 130–131
    classification, 131, 134–136
    Doppler effect and, 137–139
    formation of, 130, 132–133
    L dwarfs/T dwarfs and, 135–136
    Nebulae and, 196
    sequence and, 131–132
    solar spectrum and, 123
    star composition and, 136–137
Spectral classes/types, **131**
Spectral lines, **113**, 130, 133
Spectral sequence, **131**–132
Spectrograph, **113**–114
Spectroscopic binary, **180**–182
Spectroscopic parallax, **178**
Spectrum, **100**
    absorption, 144
    chromosphere, 145–146
    comparison, 113
    corona, 146
    electromagnetic, 100–101
    formation of, 130, 132–133
Spherical component, **309**
Spicules, **146**
Spiral arms, **6**, 310
    density wave theory and, 315–316
    evidence regarding, 316
    radio maps of, 313–314
    star formation and, 316–318
    tracing, 312–313
Spiral galaxies, **332**, 333–336
    diameter/luminosity of, 339, 341
    evolution of, 350–351
    mass of, 341
    Seyfert galaxies and, 356
Spiral nebulae, **332**
Spiral tracers, **313**
Sporadic meteors, **557**
Spring tides, **87**, 88
Spritzer Space Telescope, 118
Square Kilometer Array, 115, 116
SS 433, 296
Stadia, 54
Standard candles, **337**
Starbust galaxies, **350**
Star death
    binary, 262–265
    lower-main-sequence, 256–262
    massive, 266–276
    red dwarf, 154–155

    sun and, 265–266
    sun-like, 257
    white dwarf, 258–259, 262
Stardust, 276
Star formation
    as contagion, 218–219
    contraction heating in, 213–214
    factors preventing, 211–212
    gas-star-gas cycle of, 205–207
    ISM, 211–215
    observing, 215–218
    Orion nebula and, 215–218, 220
    pillars, 218, 219
    preview of, 206–207
    proof regarding, 214–215
    protostars and, 214
    self-sustaining, 316–318
    shock waves and, 212–213
    YSOs and, 220–224
Star-formation pillars, **218**, 219
Star gauging, 303
Stars, **3**–4. *See also* Binary stars/systems;
    Clusters, star; Main sequence; Massive
    stars; Neutron star; Post-main
    sequence evolution; Star death; Star
    formation; Stellar evolution; Sun;
    Variable stars
    astronomer's triangulation method for,
    169–170
    atmosphere, 147–148
    binary, 178–179, 262–265
    brightness of, 13, 14–15, 170–172
    census of, 185–189
    CNO cycle in, 226–228
    composition of, 136–137
    constellations, 12–14, 16, 18
    density of, 189
    diameters of, 173–178
    Doppler effect and, 137–139
    eclipsing binary, 182–184
    energy source in, 226–228
    energy transport in, 225–226
    family of, 186–188
    favorite, 14–15
    gas-star-gas cycle of, 205–207
    giants/supergiants/dwarfs, 175, 176
    H-R diagram and, 174–175, 176
    hydrostatic equilibrium in, 225
    inside, 227–228
    interferometer observations of, 175–176
    life regarding, 594
    luminosity of, 172, 173, 176–178
    magnitude/intensity and, 15–16
    making of, 211–224
    mass of, 178–185, 188, 227–228
    measuring distance to, 168–170

    misconceptions about, 5, 19, 247
    names of, 13–14
    planet forming disks around, 414–415
    Population I/Population II, 319–320
    proper motion and, 170
    proton-proton chain and, 226
    radius of, 173–174
    spectra of, 130–136
    spectroscopic binary, 180–182
    spectroscopic parallax and, 178
    spots/magnetic cycles of, 159–160, 161
    stability regarding, 224–225, 228–229
    Stellar models and, 233–235
    structure of, 224–226, 233–234
    surveying, 185–188
    thermostat regarding, 228–229, 235
    travel between, 595
    triangulation method regarding, 168–
    169
    visual binary, 180, 181
    visual representation of, 5
Static, **371**
Statistical evidence, 357
Stefan-Bolzmann law, 129
Stellar evolution, **175**, 176. *See also* Star
    death; Star formation
    binary stars and, 262–265
    brown dwarfs and, 237
    degenerate matter and, 241–242
    evidence of, 246–252
    giant expansion and, 240–241
    heavy element fusing and, 245
    helium flash and, 242–243
    helium fusion in, 242–245
    life expectancy and, 239
    main sequence lower end and, 236–237
    main sequence regarding, 235–239
    main sequence upper end and, 236
    mass loss and, 257
    mass transfer and, 263–264
    misconception, 247
    models and, 233–235
    post-helium flash and, 243–245
    post-main sequence in, 240–246
    red dwarf, 154–155
    star clusters and, 246, 248–249
    star life regarding, 238–239
    variable stars and, 247, 250–252
    white dwarf, 258–259, 262
    ZAMS and, 238
Stellar models, 233–235, **234**
Stellar parallax, **169**–170
Stellar spectra, 130–136
Stellar wind, **224**
Stonehenge, 50, 51
Stony-iron meteorites, **552**, 553

Stony meteorites, **552**, 553–556, 575
Stratospheric Observatory for Infrared
    Astronomy (SOFIA), 107
Stromatolites, **587**, 589
Strong force, **150**
Studying unseen world, 430
S-type asteroids, **564**–565
Subduction zone, 432, **434**
Subsolar point, **466**
Sudbury Neutrino Observatory, 154
Summer solstice, **23**–24
Sun
    age of, 407
    angular diameter and, 39
    annual motion of, 20–21
    atmosphere, 143–148
    chromosphere, 41, 42, 145–146, 147,
      160, 162
    corona, 41, 42, 143, 146–148, 160,
      162–163
    cycles of, 20–25
    Earth seasons and, 21–22, 23–24
    ecliptic and, 21
    energy transport, 152–153
    granulation, 144–145
    helioseismology, 148–149
    hydrogen fusion, 151–152
    interior of, 148–153
    magnetic cycle, 158–159, 160,
      162–163
    misconceptions about, 42
    neutrino counting, 153–154
    nuclear binding energy, 150
    nuclear fusion, 150–154
    observing, 154–155
    photosphere, 143–145, 147
    predicting eclipses and, 43–46
    profile, 144
    rotation, 158
    solar constant and, 161, 164
    solar eclipses and, 37–41
    vibrations, 148
Sun Dagger, 50, 52
Sunset line, 2–3
Sunspots, **143**
    butterfly diagram of, 155, 156
    cycle, 155–157
    Galileo and, 155
    magnetic field and, 158–159
    stars and, 159–160, 161
    Zeeman effect and, 155, 157
Superclusters, **389**
Supergiant, **175**, 176
    expansion and, 240–241
    luminosity classification, 176–178
Supergranules, **145**

Supermassive black holes
    disks/jets and, 362–363
    double-lobed radio sources and,
      358, 361
    in galaxies, 342
    mass regarding, 365
    Sagittarius A*, 319, 321
    time and, 364–366
    triggering eruptions of, 364
Supernova, **268**. *See also* Hypernova
    acceleration regarding, 387
    Earth and, 275–276
    massive star death and, 268–270
    misconception about, 269
    models and, 268–269
    1987, 273–275
    observations of, 272–273
    radiation and, 275
    remnant, 273
    synchrotron radiation and, 272
    types of, 270–271
Supernova remnant, **273**
Surveyor's triangulation method, 168–169
S waves. *See* Shear waves
Synchrotron radiation, **272**
Synodic period, **35**

T

T association, **224**
Taylor, Joseph, 286
T dwarfs, **135**–136
Telescope(s). *See also specific* telescope
    adaptive optics, 108, 112
    buying, 106–107
    computers and, 109, 111
    design, 108, 110–111
    giant, 108–109
    of Herschel, William, 526–527
    high energy astrophysics and, 118–119
    Hubble Space, 117–118
    imaging systems and, 113
    infrared, 107, 118
    interferometry and, 112
    light-gathering power of, 103–104, 105
    light pollution and, 106
    magnifying power, 105
    new-generation, 108–112
    optical, 101–112
    powers of, 103–106
    radio, 114–117
    reflecting, 101–102, 103
    refracting, 101, 102–103, 103–106
    resolving power, 104, 105
    seeing and, 104–105
    space, 117–119
    spectrograph and, 113–114

Temperature, **127**, 128
    chromosphere/corona/photosphere, 147
    Earth, 428
    Jupiter, 496
    luminosity regarding, 173
    Mars, 477
    Mercury, 455
    moon, 443
    Neptune, 540
    Pluto, 545
    Saturn, 511
    sun, 144
    thermostat and, 228–229, 235
    Uranus, 529
    Venus, 465
Temple I, Comet, 569, 570
Temple of Isis, 50
Terminator, **443**–444
Terrestrial planet(s), **401**. *See also* Earth;
    Mars; Mercury; Venus
    atmospheres and, 426–427
    characteristics of, 402–403
    comparative planetology and, 425
    condensation sequence and, 412
    core/mantle/crust/energy flow and, 426
    evolution stages of, 427–428
    guide to, 425–427
    size regarding, 425–426
Tethys, 519
Thales of Miletus, 45–46, 53
Theory, **66**
    big bang, 373–379
    data unification via, 448
    density wave, 315–316
    general relativity, 92–94, 291–292
    GUTs, 385
    misconception about, 66
    neutron star prediction and, 280–281
    nuclear fusion, 215
    solar nebula, 399, 407–408, 412–413
    special relativity, 90–92
    two kinds of, 400
Thermal energy, **127**, 128, 213–214
Thermal pulses, **257**
Thermophiles, **591**–592
Thermostat, pressure/temperature,
    228–229, 235
Thirty Meter Telescope, 108, 109
Tidal heating, **505**–506, 509
Tidally coupled, **443**, 456–457
Tidal tails, 347, **348**
Tides, 87–88
Time. *See also* Space-time
    AGN and, 364–366
    beginning and, 371–372
    football field analogy of, 7

geologic, 589–592
Hubble, 374
look-back, 338–339, 374–375
Time dilation, **293**
Titan, 517–518, 593
Titania, 536
Tombaugh, Clyde, 544
Total lunar eclipse, 33, **36**, 37
Total solar eclipse, **38**, 39, 40–41
Transfer, mass, 263–264
Transit, 417–**418**
Transition, 130, **133**
Travel, space, 595
Triangulation methods, 168–170
Triggering eruptions, 364
Triton, 542–543
Trojan asteroids, **563**
T Tauri, 221, **222**
Tunguska event, 574–575
Turnoff point, 246, **248**
21-cm radiation, **198**–199
2MASS. *See* Two-Micron All Sky Survey
Two-Micron All Sky Survey (2MASS), 109
Two New Sciences (Galilei), 78
Type I (gas tail), 566, **568**
Type II (dust tail), **568**
Type I/Type II supernovae, **271**

U

UFOs. *See* Unidentified Flying Objects
Ultraluminous infrared galaxies, **350**
Ultraviolet, **100**
Umbra, **33**
Umbriel, 537
Unidentified Flying Objects (UFOs), 596.
    See also Intelligent life
Unified model, **363**–364
Uniform circular motion, 53, **53**, 55, 56,
    59–61
Universal mutual gravitation. *See* Mutual
    gravitation
Universe
    acceleration of, 385–386
    age of, 7, 373–374, 382, 388, 391
    antimatter and, 376
    big bang theory of, 373–379
    cosmic background radiation, 375–376,
        390–392
    cosmic redshift and, 380–381
    cosmological principle of, 380
    critical density and, 382–384
    curvature of, 390–392
    dark energy in, 387–388
    dark matter in, 382–383
    edge-center problem, 370–371
    element building and, 376–379

energy/matter equality era and,
    377–378
expanding, 372–373
fate of, 388
field of view measuring, 2–7
geocentric, 54
heliocentric, 58–61, 68–70
inflationary, 384–385
introduction to, 370–373
island, 332
large-scale structure in, 389–390
life in, 595–599
look-back time and, 374–375
misconceptions, 6, 371, 372
models of, 381–384
observable, 372
Olbers's paradox and, 371
photon/particle soup and, 376–377
Ptolemaic, 55, 57
recombination era in, 378–379
reionization era in, 378
time/beginning and, 371–372
Unseen world, studying, 430
Uranus
    atmosphere of, 528–529
    discovery of, 526–528
    history of, 538
    interior of, 529, 531–533
    Jupiter/Saturn compared with, 533,
        535, 538
    layers of, 531
    life regarding, 593
    Mab/Portia and, 533
    magnetic field of, 531–532
    Miranda and, 537–538
    moons of, 533, 536–538
    motion of, 528, 530
    Neptune's discovery regarding, 539
    Oberon/Titania and, 536
    occultation and, 533, 534
    profile of, 529
Ureilite meteorites, 565
Urey, Harold, 587

V

Valley networks, **483**
Van Allen belts, **431**
Variable stars, **247**
    Cepheid/RR Lyrae, 247, 250
    evolution evidence in, 247,
        250–252
    HR diagram regarding, 250–251
    Milky Way measurement and,
        305–306
    period changes in, 251–252
    pulsating, 250

Velocity, **79**. *See also* Escape
    velocity
    circular, 82, 84
    radial, 139
Velocity dispersion method, **341**
Venting, comet, 567, 570
Venus
    atmosphere of, 466–467
    coronae and, 471, 474
    cratering on, 468–469
    Earth compared with, 465, 466, 469,
        475–476
    Galileo and, 69
    as greenhouse, 467, 475–476
    interior of, 475–476
    Ishtar Terra on, 474
    lava channels and, 471
    life regarding, 593
    maps of, 467–468
    Maxwell and, 468
    probes of, 467
    profile of, 465
    rotation of, 412, 466, 475
    shield volcanoes and, 470, 473
    speculation about, 465
    surface of, 467–469
    volcanism on, 470–474
Vernal equinox, **23**
Very Large Array (VLA), 115, 116
Very Large Telescope (VLT), 108, 112
Very Long Baseline Array (VLBA), 115
Vesicular, **450**
Vesta, 559, 561
Violent motion, **77**
Visual binary system, **180**, 181
VLA. *See* Very Large Array
VLBA. *See* Very Long Baseline Array
VLT. *See* Very Large Telescope
Voids, **389**
Volcanoes
    composite/shield, 470, 472
    Earth, 470, 472–473
    of Io, 507–509
    Mars, 470, 473, 482–483
    types of, 470, 472
    Venus, 470–474
von Fraunhofer, Joseph, 123

W

War of the Worlds (Wells), 477
Water, Mars, 483–487
Water hole, **596**
Wavelength, **99**
Wavelength of maximum intensity,
    128–129
Weak force, **150**

Weakly interacting massive particles
  (WIMPs), **383**
Welles, Orson, 477
Wells, H.G., 477
West point, **17**
White dwarf, **175**, 176
  Chandrasekhar limit and, 262
  as compact object, 259
  evolution of, 258–259, 262
  mass regarding, 259, 262
  Sirius B as, 258
  subatomic particles and, 258–259
Widmanstätten patterns, **552**–553
Wien's law, 129
Wild II, Comet, 569, 570
Wilkinson Microwave Anisotropy Probe
  (WMAP), 391–392
Wilson, Robert, 375

WIMPs. *See* Weakly interacting massive
  particles
Wind
  pulsar, 282, 283
  solar, 147, 431–432
  stellar, 224
Winter solstice, **23**–24
WMAP. *See* Wilkinson Microwave Anisotropy Probe
Wright, Thomas, 303

X

X-ray binaries, 293–295
X-ray bursters, **288**
X-ray Observatory, Chandra, 119

Y

Yearlong video example, 589

Young Stellar Objects (YSOs), **220**
  associations of, 224
  birth line and, 220
  Herbig-Haro objects, 221, 223
  jets and, 221, 223–224
  observations of, 221–223
  protostellar disks, 220–221, 223
  star formation and, 220–224
  T Tauri, 221, 222
YSOs. *See* Young Stellar Objects

Z

ZAMS. *See* Zero-age main sequence
Zeeman effect, 155, **157**
Zenith, **17**
Zero-age main sequence (ZAMS), 238
Zodiac, **25**
Zwicky, Fritz, 280